INSTRUCTOR'S MANUAL

College PHYSICS

Fifth Edition

SERWAY • FAUGHN

JERRY S. FAUGHN

CHARLES TEAGUE

HARCOURT COLLEGE PUBLISHERS

Fort Worth Philadelphia San Diego New York Orlando Austin San Antonio

Toronto Montreal London Sydney Tokyo

Portions of this work were published in previous editions.

Printed in the United States of America

ISBN 0-03-022489-6

0 1 2 3 4 5 6 7 8 9 202 12 11 10 9 8 7 6 5 4

PREFACE

This guide has been written to accompany the textbook *College Physics*, Fifth edition, by Raymond A. Serway and Jerry S. Faughn. Included are answers to all the end-of-chapter problems, answers to all even-numbered conceptual questions, and a separate list of answers to even-numbered problems.

We welcome your comments on the accuracy of the solutions as presented here, as well as suggestions for alternative approaches. We strongly encourage you to keep this manual out of the hands of students. The obvious reason is that instructors in many colleges throughout the country use this textbook, and many of them use graded problems as part of the final grade. Additionally, even in those instances when the problems are not used in a direct fashion like this, it is still advantageous for students to struggle with some problems in order to improve their problem-solving skills. Feel free to post answers and solutions to selected questions and problems, but we encourage you to take precautions to preserve the manual as a whole.

This manual is considered to be for the benefit of the instructor, and as a result, we have written the solutions as efficiently as possible. We have often omitted commentary, intermediate steps, and even initial steps that would be beneficial to many students. If you post solutions from this manual, try including your own explanations so that you communicate more effectively with your students. Likewise the conceptual questions have been answered with extreme brevity, without reciting detailed arguments that lead to the answer.

If you would like to modify the solutions to satisfy your own tastes, the manual is available on discs that you can obtain by contacting your sales representative.

Jerry Faughn
Charles Teague

CHAPTER ONE SOLUTIONS

Chapter One Readings

Amend, J.R., Measurement: The Basic Science: Scientific Measurement and Experiment Design, Jones and Bartlett Publishers, Sudbury Mass., 1997

A.V. Astin, "Standards of Measurements," *Scientific American*, June 1968 p. 50.

H. Butterfield, "The Scientific Revolution," *Scientific American*, September 1960, p.173

Carlson, J.E., "Fermi Problems on Gasoline Consumption," *The Physics Teacher*, 35, 308, 1997

J. Friberg, " Numbers and Measures in the Earliest Written Records," *Scientific American*, February 1984, p.110.

G. Goth, "Dimensional Analysis by Computer," *The Physics Teacher*, February 1986, p. 75.

L.M. Lederman, "The value of Fundamental Science," *ScientificAmerican*, November 1984, p. 40.

Romano, J.D., "Supermarket Physics: Estimating Grocery Bills as an Aid in Learning Probabilities and Error Addition," *The Physics Teacher*, 34, 562, 1996

1.1 (a) $[V] = L^3$, $[A] = L^2$, $[h] = L$

$[V] = [A][h]$

$L^3 = L^2L = L^3$. Thus, the equation is dimensionally correct.

(b) $V_{cylinder} = \pi R^2 h = (\pi R^2)h = Ah$, where $A = \pi R^2$

$V_{rectangular\ object} = lwh = (lw)h = Ah$, where $A = lw$.

1.2 v has units of (L/T). a has units of L/T^2 and x has units of L. Thus, the left side of the equation has units of $v^2 = (L/T)^2 = L^2/T^2$, and the right side has units of $ax = (L/T^2)\,L = L^2/T^2$. Therefore, from the standpoint of units alone, the equation might be valid.

1.3 Substituting in dimensions, we have

$$(T) = \sqrt{\frac{(L)}{(L/T^2)}} = \sqrt{T^2} = (T)$$

Thus, the dimensions are consistent.

1.4 (a) Given that $a \propto F/m$, we have $F \propto ma$. Therefore, the units of force are those of ma, $F = M(L/T^2)$.

(b) Newton $= \dfrac{\text{kg m}}{\text{s}^2}$.

1.5 (a) From $x = Bt^2$, we have $B = x/t^2$. Thus, B has units of L/T^2.

(b) $x = A\sin(2\pi ft)$ has units of

L = (A)(pure number).
Thus, A has units of L.

1.6 $c = 2.997924574 \times 10^8$ m/s
(a) Rounded to 3 significant figures: $c = 3.00 \times 10^8$ m/s
(b) Rounded to 5 significant figures: $c = 2.9979 \times 10^8$ m/s
(c) Rounded to 7 significant figures: $c = 2.997925 \times 10^8$ m/s

1.7 (a) 78.9 ± 0.2 has 3 significant figures.
(b) 3.788×10^9 has 4 significant figures.
(c) 2.46×10^{-6} has 3 significant figures.
(d) $0.0032 = 3.2 \times 10^{-3}$ has 2 significant figures.

1.8 (a) The sum is rounded to 797 because 756 in the terms to be added has no positions beyond the decimal.
(b) 3.2 x 3.563 must be rounded to 11 because 3.2 has only two significant figures.
(c) $5.67 \times \pi$ must be rounded to 17.8 because 5.67 has only three significant figures.

1.9 (a) $(2.437 \times 10^4)(6.5211 \times 10^9)/(5.37 \times 10^4) = 2.9594 \times 10^9 = 2.96 \times 10^9$
(b) $(3.14159 \times 10^2)(27.01 \times 10^4)/(1234 \times 10^6) = 6.8764 \times 10^{-2}$
$= 6.876 \times 10^{-2}$

1.10 (a) $c = 2\pi r = 2\pi(3.5 \text{ cm})$ must be rounded to 22 cm. The number 2 and π are considered as known to many significant figures, while 3.5 is known only to two.
(b) $A = \pi r^2 = \pi(4.65 \text{ cm})^2$ must be rounded to the number of significant figures in 4.65, which gives an answer of 67.9 cm^2.

1.11 The distance around is 38.44 m + 19.5 m + 38.44 m + 19.5 m = 115.88 m, but this answer must be rounded to 115.9 m because the distance 19.5 m carries information to only one place past the decimal.

1.12 Adding the two lengths together, we get 228.76 cm. However, 135.3 cm has only one decimal place. Therefore, only one decimal place accuracy is possible in the sum, changing 228.76 cm to 228.8 cm.

1.13 Distance = $(4 \times 10^{16}$ m)(3.281 ft/1 m) = 1×10^{17} ft

1.14 Age of earth = $(1 \times 10^{17}$s)(1 y/3.156×10^7 s) = 3.16×10^9 y.

1.15 $c = (3.00 \times 10^8$ m/s)(3600 s/h)(1 km/10^3 m)(1mi/1.609 km) = $6.71 \text{ X } 10^8$ mi/h

1.16 (a) 1 mi/h = (1 mi/h)(1.609 km/mi) = 1.609 km/h
(b) 55 mi/h = (55 mi/h)(1.609 km per hr/1 mi per hr) = 88.5 km/h
(c) increase = 10 mi/h = (10 mi/h)(1.609 km per hr/1 mi per hr) = 16.1 km/h

1.17 area = 4(area of one wall) = (4)(8.0 ft)(12.0 ft) = 384 ft^2. This is converted to square meters as 384 $\text{ft}^2(1\text{m}/3.281\text{ft})^2 = 36 \text{ m}^2$

1.18 Volume of house = (50.0 ft)(26 ft)(8.0 ft) = 1.04×10^4 ft^3

$= (1.04 \times 10^4\ ft^3)(2.832 \times 10^{-2}\ m^3/ft^3) = 295\ m^3$

$= (2.95 \times 10^2\ m^3)(10^2\ cm/m)^3 = 2.95 \times 10^8\ cm^3$

1.19 weight = (number of blocks)(weight per block)

$= (2 \times 10^6)(2.5\ tons) = 5 \times 10^6\ tons$

or, in lbs

$(5 \times 10^6\ tons)(2 \times 10^3\ lb/ton) = 1 \times 10^{10}\ lb$

in newtons, we have

$(1 \times 10^{10}\ lb)(1\ N/0.2248\ lb) = 4.45 \times 10^{10}\ N$

1.20 Since you have only 16 hours (57,600 s) per day, you can count only $57,600 per day.

So it would take $\dfrac{\$\ 1 \times 10^9}{\$5.76 \times 10^4/day} \approx 1.74 \times 10^4$ days $\approx$ 47.5 y.

Right now, you are at least 18 y old, and so you would finish counting out the money at age 65. It would provide you with a nice retirement, but a very boring life until then. We would not advise it.

1.21 25.0 acre ft =

$(25.0\ acre\ ft)(43{,}560\ ft^2/acre)(12\ in/ft)^3(2.54\ cm/in)^3(1 m/100\ cm)^3$

$= 3.08 \times 10^4\ m^3$

1.22 Volume of pyramid = $\frac{1}{3}$ (base)(height)

$= \frac{1}{3}[(13.0\ acres)(43{,}560\ ft^2/acre)](481\ ft) = 9.08 \times 10^7\ ft^3,$

$= (9.08 \times 10^7\ ft^3)(2.832 \times 10^{-2}\ m^3)/(1\ ft^3) = 2.57 \times 10^6\ m^3.$

1.23 Volume of cube = L^3 = 1 quart (Where L = length of one side of the cube.)

Thus, $L^3 = (1\ quart)\left(\dfrac{1\ gallon}{4\ quarts}\right)\left(\dfrac{3.786\ liters}{1\ gallon}\right)\left(\dfrac{1000\ cm^3}{1\ liter}\right) = 946.5\ cm^3,$

and $L = 9.82$ cm

1.24 We require $(mass)_{al} = (mass)_{iron}$

Thus, $(density)_{al}\left(\frac{4}{3}\pi r^3\right) = (density)_{iron}\left(\frac{4}{3}\pi (2.0\ cm)^3\right)$, or

$r^3 = \left(\dfrac{(density)_{iron}}{(density)_{al}}\right)(2.0\ cm)^3 = \left(\dfrac{7.86\ kg/m^3}{2.70\ kg/m^3}\right)(2.0\ cm)^3 = 23.3\ cm^3$

and $r = 2.86$ cm

1.25 (a) mass = (density)(volume) = $\left(\dfrac{1.0 \times 10^{-3}\ kg}{1.0\ cm^3}\right)(1\ m^3)$

$= (1.0 \times 10^{-3}\ kg/cm^3)(1\ m^3)\left(\dfrac{10^2\ cm}{1\ m}\right)^3 = 1000\ kg$

(b) As rough calculation, treat as if 100% water.

cell: mass = density x volume $= \left(\dfrac{10^3\ kg}{1\ m^3}\right)\dfrac{4}{3}\pi(0.5 \times 10^{-6}\ m)^3 = 5.2 \times 10^{-16}\ kg$

kidney: mass = density x volume = $\left(\frac{10^3\ \text{kg}}{1\ \text{m}^3}\right)\frac{4}{3}\pi\,(4 \times 10^{-2}\ \text{m})^3 = 0.27$ kg

fly: mass = density x vol = (density)($\pi r^2 h$)

$= \left(\frac{10^3\ \text{kg}}{1\ \text{m}^3}\right)\pi\,(10^{-3}\ \text{m})^2(4 \times 10^{-3}\ \text{m}) = 1.3 \times 10^{-5}$ kg

---

1.26 number of pounds = (number of burgers)(weight/burger)
= (5×10^{10} burgers)(0.25 lb/burger) = 1.25×10^{10} lb
number of head of cattle = (weight needed)/(weight per head)
=(1.25×10^{10} lb)/(300 lb/head) = 4.17×10^7 head
Assumptions are 0.25 lb of meat per burger and 300 lb of meat per head of cattle

---

1.27 number of balls needed = (number lost per hitter)(number hitters)(games) = (1/4 ball per hitter)(10 hitters per inning)(9 innings per game)(81 games) = 1800 balls. Assumptions are 1 ball lost for every four hitters, 10 hitters per inning, 9 innings per game, and 81 games per season.

1.28 The number of tuners is found by dividing the number of residents of the city by the number of residents serviced by one tuner. We shall assume 1 tuner per 10,000 residents and a population of 7.5 million. Thus, number of tuners = (7.5×10^6)/(10,000) = 750

1.29 The x coordinate is found as $x = r\cos\theta = (2.5\ \text{m})(\cos 35°) = 2.1$ m
and the y coordinate is $y = r\sin\theta = (2.5\ \text{m})(\sin 35°) = 1.4$ m

---

1.30 The x distance out to the fly is 2 m and the y distance up to the fly is 1 m. Thus, we can use the Pythagorean theorem to find the distance from the origin to the fly as,

distance = $\sqrt{x^2 + y^2} = \sqrt{(2.0\ \text{m})^2 + (1.0\ \text{m})^2} = \sqrt{5.0\ \text{m}^2} = 2.24$ m

---

1.31 The distance from the origin to the fly is r in polar coordinates, and this was found to be 2.24 m in problem 30. The angle θ is the angle between r and the horizontal reference line (the x axis in this case). Thus, the angle can be found as

$\tan\theta = y/x = (1.0\ \text{m})/(2.0\ \text{m}) = 0.5$

Thus, $\theta = 26.6°$. The polar coordinates are r = 2.24 m and θ = 26.6 °.

1.32 The x distance between the two points is 8.0 cm and the y distance between them is 1.0 cm. The distance beween them is found from the Pythagorean theorem.

distance = $\sqrt{x^2 + y^2} = \sqrt{(8.0\ \text{cm})^2 + (1.0\ \text{cm})^2} = \sqrt{65\ \text{cm}^2} = 8.1$ cm.

1.33 (a) The length of the unknown side is

$b = \sqrt{c^2 - a^2} = \sqrt{(9)^2 - (6)^2} = 6.71$ m

(b) $\tan\theta = \frac{6}{6.71} = 0.894$ (c) $\sin\phi = \frac{6.71}{9} = 0.746$

1.34 (a) $\sin\theta = \frac{\text{side opposite}}{\text{hypotenuse}}$ so, side opposite = (sin 30.0°)(3.00 m) = 1.5 m.

(b) $\cos\theta = \dfrac{\text{adjacent side}}{\text{hypotenuse}}$ so, adjacent side = (cos 30.0°)(3.00 m) = 2.6 m.

1.35 (a) The side opposite $\theta = 3$. (b) The side adjacent to $\phi = 3$

(c) $\cos\theta = \dfrac{4}{5}$ (d) $\sin\phi = \dfrac{4}{5}$ (e) $\tan\phi = \dfrac{4}{3}$

1.36 From the Pythagorean theorem, $c = \sqrt{(5.00\text{ m})^2 + (7.00\text{ m})^2} = 8.60\text{ m}$

1.37 $\tan\theta = \dfrac{5}{7}$, so $\theta = 35.5°$

1.38 Assume an average of 1 can per person each week and a population of 250 million.

number cans per yr

= (number cans per person each week)(population)(weeks per yr)

=(1 can per person each week)(2.5×10^8 people)(52 weeks per yr)

= 1.3×10^{10} can/yr

number of tons = (weight per can)(number of cans per yr)

= (0.5 oz per can)(1.3×10^{10} cans per yr) = 2×10^5 tons/yr

Assumes an average weight of 0.5 oz of aluminum per can.

1.39 (a) The volume of Saturn is $V = \frac{4}{3}\pi r^3 = \frac{4}{3}\pi(5.85 \times 10^7\text{ m})^3 = 8.39 \times 10^{23}\text{ m}^3$

and the density is $\dfrac{m}{V} = \dfrac{(5.68 \times 10^{26}\text{ kg})}{(8.39 \times 10^{23}\text{ m}^3)} = 677\text{ kg/m}^3. = 0.677\text{ g/cm}^3$.

(b) The surface area of Saturn is

$A = 4\pi r^2 = 4\pi(5.85 \times 10^7\text{ m})^2 = 4.30 \times 10^{16}\text{ m}^2 = 4.63 \times 10^{17}\text{ ft}^2$

1.40 The constants must have units of $1.5\ \dfrac{\text{million ft}^3}{\text{month}}$ and $0.008\ \dfrac{\text{million ft}^3}{(\text{month})^2}$.

Thus $V = \left(1.5 \times 10^6\ \dfrac{\text{ft}^3}{\text{month}}\right)t + \left(0.008 \times 10^6\ \dfrac{\text{ft}^3}{(\text{month}^2)}\right)t^2$. To convert,

use 1 month = 2.59×10^6 sec, to obtain

$$V = \left(0.579\ \frac{\text{ft}^3}{\text{sec}}\right)t + \left(1.19 \times 10^{-9}\ \frac{\text{ft}^3}{(\text{sec}^2)}\right)t^2$$

1.41 The term s has dimensions of L, a has dimensions of LT^{-2}, and t has dimensions of T. Therefore, the equation, $s = ka^m t^n$ has dimensions of

$L = (LT^{-2})^m(T)^n$ or $L^1T^0 = L^mT^{n-2m}$.

The powers of L and T must be the same on each side of the equation. Therefore,

$L^1 = L^m$ and m = 1.

Likewise, equating terms in T, we see that n - 2m must equal 0. Thus,

n = 2m = 2.

The value of k, a dimensionless constant, cannot be obtained by dimensional analysis.

1.42 (a) For a sphere, $A = 4\pi R^2$. In this case, $R_2 = 2R_1$.

Hence, $A_2/A_1 = (4\pi R_2{}^2)/(4\pi R_1{}^2) = (R_2{}^2)/(R_1{}^2) = (2R_1)^2/(R_1{}^2) = 4.$

(b) For a sphere, $V = 4/3)\pi R^3)$ so $\frac{V_2}{V_1} = ((4/3)\pi R_2{}^3)/((4/3)\pi R_1{}^3)$

$= (R_2{}^3)/(R_1{}^3) = (2R_1)^3/(R_1{}^3) = 8$

1.43 Let the tub measure 1.3 m by 0.5 m by 0.3 m.

(a) It contains water $m = \rho V = (10^3\ \text{kg/m}^3)0.2\ \text{m}^3 = 200$ kg (of the order of 100 kg).

(b) Pennies are now mostly zinc, but consider copper pennies filling 80% of the volume of the tub.

Their mass is $0.80(8.93 \times 10^3\ \text{kg/m}^3)(0.2\ \text{m}^3) = 1400$ kg (of the order of 1000 kg).

1.44 $V = At$. Therefore, $t = \frac{V}{A} = \frac{3.78 \times 10^{-3}\ \text{m}^3}{25.0\ \text{m}^2} = 1.51 \times 10^{-4}$ m

---

1.45 r, a, b, c and s all have units of L. So,

$$\sqrt{\frac{(s - a)(s - b)(s - c)}{s}} = \sqrt{\frac{\text{L} \times \text{L} \times \text{L}}{\text{L}}} = \sqrt{\text{L}^2} = \text{L}$$

1.46 $\left(\frac{\text{kg m}}{\text{s}^2}\right) = \frac{\text{G(kg)}^2}{(\text{m}^2)}$

Cross-multiplying the units of G are found to be $\frac{\text{m}^3}{\text{kg s}^2}$.

1.47 (a) 1 yr = (1 yr)(365.242 days/1yr)(86400 s/1day) = 3.16×10^7 s.

(b) Let us consider a segment of the surface of the moon which has an area of 1.0 m^2 and a depth of 1.0 m. This imaginary box on the moon has a volume of 1.00 m^3. The volume of a meteorite is found as

Vol/meteorite $= \frac{4}{3}\pi r^3 = \frac{4}{3}\pi(0.5 \times 10^{-6}\ \text{m})^3 = 5.24 \times 10^{-19}\ \text{m}^3$. Since this volume of meteorites strikes the 1.0 m^2 area of the moon each second, the time to fill the volume is

time = (volume of box)/(volume of meteorites striking box per second)

time = $(1\ \text{m}^3)/(5.24 \times 10^{-19}\ \text{m}^3/\text{s}) = 1.91 \times 10^{18}\ \text{s} = 6.0 \times 10^{10}$ yr

---

1.48 The volume of oil equals $V = \frac{9.00 \times 10^{-7}\ \text{kg}}{918\ \text{kg/m}^3} = 9.8 \times 10^{-10}\ \text{m}^3$.

If the diameter of a molecule is d, then that same volume must equal $d(\pi r^2)$ = (thickness of slick)(area of oil slick) where $r = 0.418$ m. Thus,

$d = \frac{9.80 \times 10^{-10}\ \text{m}^3}{\pi(0.418\ \text{m})^2} = 1.78 \times 10^{-9}$ m.

1.49 (a) $\frac{\$1000}{\text{s}} \times \frac{60\ \text{s}}{\text{min}} \times \frac{60\ \text{min}}{\text{h}} \times \frac{24\ \text{h}}{\text{day}} \times \frac{365.25\ \text{days}}{\text{y}} = \$3.16 \times 10^{10}$ per year

Therefore, it would take $\frac{\$4 \times 10^{12}}{\$3.16 \times 10^{10}} = 127$ y

(b) The circumference of the Earth at the equator is

$2\pi(6378 \times 10^3) = 4 \times 10^7$ m. The length of one dollar bill is 0.155 m so that the length of 4 trillion bills is 6.2×10^{11} m. Thus, the \$ 4 trillion dollars would encircle the earth

$$\frac{6.2 \times 10^{11} \text{ m}}{4 \times 10^7 \text{ m}} = 15{,}500 \text{ times.}$$

ANSWERS TO CONCEPTUAL QUESTIONS

2. In a typical 30 day month, there are 43,200 minutes. A typical heart beating at 70 beats/min will beat 3×10^6 times in this interval.

4. Let us assume the atoms are solid spheres of diameter 10^{-10} m. Then, the volume of each atom is of the order of 10^{-30} m^3. (More precisely, volume $= \frac{4}{3}\pi r^3 = \frac{1}{6}\pi d^3$.) Therefore, since 1 $cm^3 = 10^{-6}$ m^3, the number of atoms in the solid is on the order of $\frac{10^{-6}}{10^{-30}} = 10^{24}$ atoms. A more precise calculation would require knowledge of the density of the solid and the mass of each atom. However, our estimate agrees with the more precise calculation to within a factor of 10.

6. Realistically, the only lengths you might be able to verify are the length of a football field and the length of a housefly. The only time intervals subject to verification would be the length of a day and the time between normal heartbeats.

8. No. Dimensional analysis cannot reveal the presence of numerical constants in an equation. For example, a freely-falling object, starting from rest, obeys the equation $v^2 = 2ax$. Dimensional analysis would say that the equations $v^2 = 3ax$ or $v^2 = ax$ might be valid.

10. No. The aluminum foil label should have only two significant figures; the Gloss Sheen foil also only two. The Hickory farms label might or might not be correct, depending on whether we count the zero in 340 g.

CHAPTER TWO SOLUTIONS

Chapter Two Readings

Cohen, I.B. "Galileo," *Scientific American,* August 1949, p. 40.

Drake, S "Galileo's Discovery of the Law of Free Fall," *Scientific American,* May 1973, p. 84.

Gingerich, "The Galileo Affair," *Scientific American,* August 1982, p. 132.

Langford, J.J., Galileo, Science and the Church, 3rd ed., The University of Michigan Press, Ann Arbor, Michigan, 1992.

Salow, R., Thornton, J. and Siegel, P., "Is the Yellow Light Long Enough?," *The Physics Teacher,* 31, 80, 1993

Zandy, J.F., "Galileo, Einstein, and the Church," *American Journal of Physics,* 61, 202, 1993

2.1 Distances traveled are

$x_1 = v_1 t_1 = (80.0 \text{ km/h})(0.5 \text{ h}) = 40.0 \text{ km}$

$x_2 = v_2 t_2 = (100.0 \text{ km/h})(0.2 \text{ h}) = 20.0 \text{ km}$

$x_3 = v_3 t_3 = (40.0 \text{ km/h})(0.75 \text{ h}) = 30.0 \text{ km}$

Thus, the total time is 1.7 h, and the total distance traveled is 90.0 km.

(a) $\bar{v} = \frac{x}{t} = \frac{90.0 \text{ km}}{1.7 \text{ h}} = 52.9 \text{ km/h}$

(b) $x = 90.0$ km (see above)

2.2 (a) In the first half of the trip, the average velocity is

$\bar{v} = (x_2 - x_1)/20.0 \text{ s} = +50.0 \text{ m}/20.0 \text{ s} = +2.50 \text{ m/s}$

(b) On the return leg, we have

$\bar{v} = (x_3 - x_2)/22.0 \text{ s} = (0 - 50.0 \text{ m})/22.0 \text{ s} = -2.27 \text{ m/s}$

(c) For the entire trip,

$\bar{v} = (x_3 - x_1)/42.0 \text{ s} = 0/42.0 \text{ s} = 0$

2.3 (a) Boat A requires 1 h to cross the lake and 1 h to return, total time 2h. Boat B requires 2 h to cross the lake at which time the race is over, Boat B being on the other side of the lake or 60 km from the finish .

(b) Average velocity is the displacement of the boat divided by the time required to accomplish the displacement. The winning boat is back where it started, its displacement thus being zero yielding a zero average velocity.

2.4 $t = \frac{x}{v} = \frac{8.4 \times 10^{-2} \text{ m}}{3.5 \times 10^{-6} \text{ m/s}} = 2.4 \times 10^4 \text{ s} = 6.67 \text{ h}$

2.5 $2 \text{ h} + \frac{9 \text{ min}}{60 \text{ min/h}} + \frac{21 \text{ s}}{3600 \text{ s/h}} = 2.156 \text{ h}$

and $26 \text{ miles} + \frac{385 \text{ yd}}{1760 \text{ yd/mile}} = 26.22 \text{ miles}$

Thus, the average speed is 26.22 miles/2.156 h = 12.2 mph.

2.6 (a) $v_{0,1} = (x_1 - x_0)/(\Delta t) = (4.0\text{ m} - 0)/1.0\text{ s} = +4.0\text{ m/s}$

(b) $v_{0,4} = (x_4 - x_0)/\Delta t = (-2.0\text{ m} - 0)/\ 4.0\text{ s} = -\ 0.5\text{ m/s}$

(c) $v_{1,5} = (x_5 - x_1)/\Delta t = (0 - 4.0\text{ m})/4.0\text{ s} = -\ 1.0\text{ m/s}$

(d) $v_{0,5} = (x_5 - x_0)/\Delta t = (0 - 0)/5.0\text{ s} = 0$

2.7 (a) The time for the faster car is 10 miles/70 mph = 0.14 h, or 8.57 min. The time for the slower car is 10 miles/55 mph = 0.18 h or 10.9 min. The difference in time is 2.34 min.

(b) When the faster car has a 15.0 min lead, it is ahead by a distance equal to that traveled by the slower car in a time of 15.0 min. This distance is given by:

$$x = vt = (55.0\text{ mi/h})(15.0\text{ min})\left(\frac{1.00\text{ h}}{60.0\text{ min}}\right) = 13.8\text{ mi.}$$

The faster car pulls ahead of the slower car at a rate of:

$v_{relative} = 70.0\text{ mph} - 55.0\text{ mph} = 15.0\text{ mph}$. Thus, the time required for it to get 13.8 mi ahead is:

$$t = \frac{x}{v_{relative}} = \frac{13.8\text{ mi}}{15.0\text{ mi/h}} = 0.920\text{ h}$$

Finally, the distance the faster car has traveled during the time it is gaining a 13.8 mi lead is given by:

$x = vt = (70.0\text{ mi/h})(0.920\text{ h}) = 64.4\text{ mi.}$

2.8 The distance traveled by the space shuttle in one orbit is 2π(Earth's radius + 200 miles) = $2\pi(3963 + 200) = 26{,}156.9$ miles

and so the required time is $\dfrac{26156.9\text{ miles}}{19800\text{ miles/h}} = 1.32\text{ h}$

2.9 The total time for the trip is $t = t_1 + 22.0\text{ min} = t_1 + 0.367\text{ h}$, where t_1 is the time spent traveling at 89.5 km/h. Thus, the distance traveled is

$$x = \bar{v}\,t = (89.5\text{ km/h})t_1 = (77.8\text{ km/h})(t_1 + 0.367\text{ h})$$

or, $(89.5\text{ km/h})t_1 = (77.8\text{ km/h})t_1 + 28.5\text{ km}$

From which, $t_1 = 2.44\text{ h}$ for a total time of $t = t_1 + 0.367\text{ h} = 2.81\text{ h}$.

Therefore, $x = \bar{v}\,t = (77.8\text{ km/h})(2.81\text{ h}) = 218\text{ km}$

2.10 (a) The speed of the tortoise is $v_t = 0.1\text{ m/s}$, and the speed of the hare is

$v_h = 20 \times 0.1\text{ m/s} = 2.0\text{ m/s}$.

$x_t = x_h + 0.2\text{ m}$

$v_t t = v_h(t - 120\text{ s}) + 0.2\text{ m}$, or

$(0.1\text{ m/s})t = 2.0\text{ m/s}(t - 120\text{ s}) + (0.2\text{ m})$.

From which, $t = 126\text{ s}$.

(b) $x_t = v_t t = (0.1\text{ m/s})(126\text{ s}) = 12.6\text{ m}$

2.11 Let t_t be the maximum time to complete the trip.

$$t_t = \frac{\text{total distance}}{\text{needed average speed}} = \frac{1600\text{ m}}{250\text{ km/h}}\ \frac{1\text{ km/h}}{0.278\text{ m/s}} = 23.02\text{ s.}$$

The time spent to complete the first half, t_1, is

$$t_1 = \frac{\text{half distance}}{v_{1ave}}\ \frac{800\text{ m}}{230\text{ km/h}}\ \frac{1\text{ km/h}}{0.278\text{ m/s}} = 12.51\text{ s.}$$

Thus, the maximum time that can be spent on second half of the trip is

$t_2 = t_t - t_1 = 23.02\text{ s} - 12.51\text{ s} = 10.51\text{ s}$,

and the required average speed on the second half is

$$v_{2ave} = \frac{\text{half distance}}{t_2} = \frac{800 \text{ m}}{10.51 \text{ s}} = 76.12 \text{ m/s} \frac{1 \text{km/h}}{0.278 \text{ m/s}} = 273.8 \text{ km/h}.$$

2.12 The distance traveled by A (the runner traveling at 6.0 mi/h) when they meet is $x_1 = v_A t$, and the distance traveled by B (the runner moving at 5 mi/h) when they meet is $x_2 = v_B t$. We also know that $x_1 + x_2 = 7.0$ mi. From this last equation, we find,

$$(6.0 \text{ mi/h})\, t + (5.0 \text{ mi/h})t = 7.0 \text{ mi},$$

or $(11 \text{ mi/h})t = 7.0$ mi, and $t = \frac{7}{11}$ h .

Thus, the distance traveled by A when they meet is

$x_1 = (6.0 \text{ mi/h})(\frac{7}{11} \text{ h}) = 3.818$ mi, and $x_2 = (5.0 \text{ mi/h})(\frac{7}{11}\text{h}) = 3.182$ mi.

They meet 2/11 mi or 0.18 miles west of the flag pole.

2.13

interval (s)	Δt (s)	Δx (m)	$\bar{v}$ (m/s)
2 to 2.01	0.01	0.014	1.40
2 to 2.2	0.20	0.27	1.35
2 to 2.5	0.50	0.66	1.32
2 to 3.0	1.00	1.26	1.26
2 to 4.0	2.00	2.34	1.17

(a) The average velocity for the complete interval is

$$\bar{v} = \Delta x_t/\Delta t = 2.34 \text{ m}/2.00 \text{ s} = 1.17 \text{ m/s}.$$

(b) The velocity at $t = 2$s is approximately equal to 1.40 m/s.

2.14 (a) A few typical values are

t(s)	x(m)
1.0	5.75
2.0	16.0
3.0	35.3
4.0	68.0
5.0	118.8

(b) We will use a 0.4 s interval centered at $t = 4$ s. We find at $t = 3.8$ s, $x = 60.154$ m and at $t = 4.2$ s, $x = 76.566$ m.

Therefore, $v = \frac{\Delta x}{\Delta t} = \frac{16.412 \text{ m}}{0.4 \text{ s}} = 41.03$ m/s

Using a time interval of 0.2 s, we find the corresponding values to be: at $t = 3.9$ s, $x = 63.9893$ m and at $t = 4.1$ s, $x = 72.1908$ m.

Thus, $v = \frac{\Delta x}{\Delta t} = \frac{8.2015 \text{ m}}{0.2 \text{ s}} = 41.008$ m/s

For a time interval of 0.1 s, the values are:

at $t = 3.95$ s, $x = 65.9724$ m, and at $t = 4.05$ s, $x = 70.0726$ m.

Therefore, $v = \frac{\Delta x}{\Delta t} = \frac{4.1002 \text{ m}}{0.1 \text{ s}} = 41.002$ m/s

(c) At $t = 4$ s, $x = 68$ m. Thus, for the first 4 s, $\bar{v} = \frac{\Delta x}{\Delta t} = \frac{68 \text{ m}}{4 \text{ s}} = 17$ m/s.

This value is much less than the instantaneous velocity at $t = 4$ s.

2.15 (a) $v(t = 0.50 \text{ s}) = [x(t = 1 \text{ s}) - x(t = 0)]/(1.00 \text{ s}) = +4.00 \text{ m}/1.00 \text{ s} = +4.00$ m/s

(b) $v(t = 2\text{s}) = [x(t = 2.5 \text{ s}) - x(t = 1 \text{ s})]/(2.50 \text{ s} - 1.00 \text{ s})$

= (-2.0 m - 4.0 m)/1.5 s
= -6.0 m/1.5 s = -4.0 m/s

(c) $v(t=3\text{ s}) = [x(t = 4\text{ s}) - x(t = 2.5\text{ s})]/(4.0\text{s} - 2.5\text{ s})$
= (-2.0m -(-2.0m))/1.5 s = 0

(d) $v(t = 4.5\text{ s}) = [x(t = 5\text{ s}) - x(t = 4\text{s})]/(5\text{ s} - 4\text{ s})$
= (0 - (-2.0 m))/1.0 s = + 2.0 m/s

2.16 From the definition of acceleration, $\Delta v = a(\Delta t) = (0.80\text{ m/s}^2)(2.0\text{ s}) = 1.6$ m/s. From this, the final velocity is $V_f = 7.0\text{ m/s} + 1.6\text{ m/s} = 8.6\text{ m/s}$

2.17 The average acceleration is found as

$$\bar{a} = \Delta v/\Delta t = (+8.0\text{ m/s} - 5.0\text{ m/s})/(4.0\text{ s}) = 0.75\text{ m/s}^2.$$

2.18 $$\bar{a} = \Delta v/\Delta t = \frac{(-8.0\text{ m/s}) - (10.0\text{ m/s})}{12 \times 10^{-3}\text{ s}} = -1.5 \times 10^3\text{ m/s}^2$$

2.19 $$v_i = 55\frac{\text{mi}}{\text{h}}\frac{(0.447\text{ m/s})}{(1\text{ mi/h})} = 24.58\text{ m/s};$$
and by the same method, $v_f = 26.82$ m/s. Thus, $\Delta v = 2.24$ m/s, and from the definition of acceleration $\Delta t = \Delta v/a = (2.24\text{ m/s})/(0.6\text{ m/s}^2) = 3.73$ s.

2.20 (a) $\bar{a}(0\text{ to }5\text{ s}) = \Delta v/\Delta t = (0 - 0)/5.0\text{ s} = 0$
$\bar{a}(5\text{ s to }15\text{ s}) = (+8.0\text{ m/s} - (-8.0\text{ m/s}))/(10.0\text{ s}) = +1.6\text{ m/s}^2.$
$\bar{a}(0\text{ to }20\text{ s}) = (+8.0\text{ m/s} -(-8.0\text{ m/s}))/20.0\text{ s} = +0.80\text{ m/s}^2.$

(b) At $t = 2$ s, the slope of the tangent line to the curve is 0.
At $t = 10.0$ s, the slope of the tangent line is $+1.6\text{ m/s}^2$.
At $t = 18.0$ s, the slope of the tangent line is 0

2.21 (a) The average acceleration can be found from the curve, and its value will be $\bar{a} = \Delta v/\Delta t = (16\text{ m/s})/\ 2.0\text{ s} = +\ 8.00\text{ m/s}^2$.

(b) The instantaneous acceleration at t = 1.5 s equals the slope of the tangent line to the curve at that time. The line will have a slope of about $+11.0\text{ m/s}^2$.

2.22 From $v^2 = v_0^2 + 2ax$, we have $(10.97 \times 10^3\text{ m/s})^2 = 0 + 2a(220\text{ m})$, so that $a = 2.74 \times 10^5\text{ m/s}^2$ which is 2.79×10^4 times g!

2.23 (a) From the definition of acceleration, we have

$$a = \frac{v - v_0}{t} = \frac{0 - 40\text{ m/s}}{5.0\text{ s}} = -\ 8.0\text{ m/s}^2.$$

(b) From $x = v_0 t + \frac{1}{2}at^2$, we have

$$x = (40\text{ m/s})(5.0\text{ s}) + \frac{1}{2}(-8.0\text{ m/s}^2)(5.0\text{ s})^2 = 100\text{ m}.$$

2.24 (a) $$t = \frac{v - v_0}{a} = \frac{0 - 100\text{ m/s}}{-5\text{ m/s}^2} = 20\text{ s}$$

(b) $$x = \bar{v}\,t = \left(\frac{v + v_0}{2}\right)t = \frac{100\text{ m/s} + 0}{2}20\text{ s} = 1000\text{ m} = 1.0\text{ km}$$

Therefore, the minimum distance to stop exceeds the length of the runway, so it cannot land safely.

2.25 (a) The time it takes the truck to reach 20 m/s is found from $v = v_o + at$, solving for t yields yielding $t = \frac{v - v_o}{a} = \frac{20\ \text{m/s} - 0\ \text{m/s}}{2.0\ \text{m/s}^2} = 10\ \text{s}$

The total time is thus 10 s + 20 s + 5.0 s = 35 s.

(b) The average velocity is the total distance traveled divided by the total time taken. The distance traveled during the first 10 s is $x_1 = \bar{v}\, t = (\frac{0 + 20}{2})(10) = 100\ \text{m}$.

The distance traveled during the next 20 s is

$x_2 = v_o t + \frac{1}{2} at^2 = (20)(20) + 0 = 400$ m, a being 0 for this interval.

The distance traveled in the last 5 s is

$$x_3 = \bar{v}\, t = (\frac{20 + 0}{2})(5.0) = 50\ \text{m}.$$

The total distance $x = x_1 + x_2 + x_3 = 100 + 400 + 50 = 550$ m, and the average velocity is given by

$$\bar{v} = \frac{x}{t} = \frac{550}{35} = 15.7\ \text{m/s}.$$

2.26 (a) With 120 km/h = 33.33 m/s, we have

$$v^2 = v_o^2 + 2ax = (33.33\ \text{m/s})^2 = 0 + 2a(240\ \text{m}).$$

From which, $a = 2.32\ \text{m/s}^2$.

(b) Using $v = v_o + at$, we have $33.33\ \text{m/s} = 0 + (2.32\ \text{m/s}^2)\, t$, or $t = 14.4$ s.

2.27 (a) From $v = v_o + at$, we have

$$t = \frac{v - v_o}{a} = \frac{5.4 \times 10^5\ \text{m/s} - 3.0 \times 10^5\ \text{m/s}}{8.0 \times 10^{14}\ \text{m/s}^2} = 3 \times 10^{-10}\ \text{s}.$$

(b) From $x = v_o t + \frac{1}{2} at^2$

$$x = (3.0 \times 10^5\ \text{m/s})(3 \times 10^{-10}\ \text{s}) + \frac{1}{2}(8.0 \times 10^{14}\ \text{m/s}^2)(3 \times 10^{-10}\ \text{s})^2$$

$$= 1.26 \times 10^{-4}\ \text{m}$$

2.28 Use $v^2 = v_o^2 + 2ax$. We have, with 60 mph = 26.82 m/s,

$0 = (26.82\ \text{m/s})^2 + 2a(100\ \text{m})$, or

$a = -3.60\ \text{m/s}^2$

2.29 (a) From $v^2 = v_o^2 + 2ax$ we have

$$a = \frac{v^2 - v_o^2}{2x} = \frac{(30\ \text{m/s})^2 - (20\ \text{m/s})^2}{2(200\ \text{m})} = +1.25\ \text{m/s}^2$$

(b) From $\Delta x = \bar{v}\, \Delta t$ and $\bar{v} = (v_o + v_f)/2$, we have

$$\Delta t = \frac{(2\ \Delta x)}{(v_o + v_f)} = \frac{(2(200\ \text{m}))}{(20\ \text{m/s} + 30\ \text{m/s})} = 8\ \text{s}.$$

2.30 (a) The time for the lead car to stop is $t = \frac{\Delta v}{a} = \frac{0 - 25\ \text{m/s}}{-2.0\ \text{m/s}^2} = 12.5$ s. The distance it travels in this time is given by

$x_1 = \bar{v}\,t = \frac{25\ \text{m/s} + 0}{2}\ 12.5\ \text{s} = 156\ \text{m}$

(b) The maximum distance the chase car has to stop in is $x_2 = 40 + 156 = 196$ m. The acceleration required for it to stop in this distance is found from $v_2{}^2 = v_{o2}{}^2 + 2a_2x_2$ or $0 = (30)^2 + 2a_2(196)$, which yields $a_2 = -2.30\ \text{m/s}^2$.

(c) The time for the chase car to stop is $t = \frac{\Delta v}{a} = \frac{0\ -\ 30\ \text{m/s}}{-2.3\text{m/s}^2} = 13.1\ \text{s}$

2.31 The change in velocity during the first 15.0 s is $\Delta v = a\,\Delta t$, or $\Delta v = (2.77\ \text{m/s}^2)(15.0\ \text{s}) = 41.55$ m/s. Thus, the constant velocity for the 2.05 min (123 s) interval is 41.55 m/s.

(a) $x = x_1 + x_2 + x_3$

$= [(0 + \frac{1}{2}(2.77\ \text{m/s}^2)(15.0\ \text{s})^2)] + [(41.55\ \text{m/s}\ (123\ \text{s}) + 0)]$

$+ [(41.55\ \text{m/s}\ (4.39\ \text{s}) + \frac{1}{2}(-9.47\ \text{m/s}^2)(4.39\ \text{s})^2)]$

$= 311.6\ \text{m} + 5110.6 + 91.2\ \text{m} = 5513.4\ \text{m}.$

(b) ($\bar{v}_1 = \frac{311.6\ \text{m}}{15.0\ \text{s}} = 20.8\ \text{m/s}$, $\bar{v}_2 = \frac{5110.6\ \text{m}}{123\ \text{s}} = 41.55\ \text{m/s}$,

$\bar{v}_3 = \frac{91.2\ \text{m}}{4.39\ \text{s}} = 20.8\ \text{m/s}$, and $\bar{v}_{total} = \frac{(\Delta x)_{total}}{t_{total}} = \frac{5513.4\ \text{m}}{142.4\ \text{s}} = 38.7\ \text{m/s}.$

2.32 Using the equation $x = v_ot + \frac{1}{2}at^2$ yields $x = 20(40) - 1.0(40)^2/2 = 0$, which is obviously wrong. The error occurs because the equation used is for uniformly accelerated motion, which this is not.
The acceleration is $-1.0\ \text{m/s}^2$ for the first 20 s and 0 for the last 20 s. The distance traveled in the first 20 s is:
$x = v_ot + \frac{1}{2}at^2 = (20)(20) - 1.0(20)^2/2 = 200$ m. During the last 20 s, the train is at rest.
Thus, the total distance traveled in the 40 s interval is 200 m.

2.33 $v_f = 40.0\ \text{mi/h} = 17.9\ \text{m/s}$ and $v_o = 0$

(a) To find the distance traveled, we first find the acceleration as

$a = \frac{v\ -\ v_o}{t} = \frac{17.9\ \text{m/s}\ -\ 0}{12.0\ \text{s}} = 1.49\ \text{m/s}^2$, and

$x = v_ot + \frac{1}{2}at^2 = \frac{1}{2}(1.49\ \text{m/s}^2)(12.0\ \text{s})^2 = 107\ \text{m}.$

(b) The acceleration was found in part (a) as $1.49\ \text{m/s}^2$.

2.34 The velocity when the brakes are applied is

$v_i = v_o + at = 0 + (1.5\ \text{m/s}^2)(5.0\ \text{s}) = 7.5\ \text{m/s}.$

(a) After braking, $v_f = v_i + at = 7.5\ \text{m/s} + (-2.0\ \text{m/s}^2)(3.0\ \text{s}) = 1.5\ \text{m/s}.$

(b) $x = x_1 + x_2 = \bar{v}_1t_1 + \bar{v}_2t_2$

$\bar{v}_1 = \frac{0\ +\ 7.5\ \text{m/s}}{2} = 3.75\ \text{m/s}$, $\bar{v}_2 = \frac{7.5\ \text{m/s}\ +\ 1.5\ \text{m/s}}{2} = 4.5\ \text{m/s}.$

Thus, $x = (3.75\ \text{m/s})(5.0\ \text{s}) + (4.5\ \text{m/s})(3.0\ \text{s}) = 32.3\ \text{m}.$

2.35 The initial velocity of the train is v_i = 82.4 km/h = 22.9 m/s and the final velocity is v_f = 16.4 km/h = 4.56 m/s. We also know that $\Delta x = \bar{v}\,t$, so

$$t = \frac{\Delta x}{\bar{v}} \text{ and } \bar{v} = \frac{v_i + v_f}{2} = 13.73 \text{ m/s.}$$

Therefore, $t = \dfrac{400 \text{ m}}{13.73 \text{ m/s}} = 29.1$ s.

2.36 (a) Take $t = 0$ at the time when the first player starts to chase the second player. At this time, the second player is 36 m in front of the first player. Let us write down $x = v_o t + \frac{1}{2}at^2$ for both players. For the first player, we have $x_1 = v_o t + \frac{1}{2}at^2 = 0 + \frac{1}{2}(4 \text{ m/s}^2)t^2$, (1)

and for the second player, $x_2 = v_o t + \frac{1}{2}at^2 = (12 \text{ m/s})t + 0$ (2)

When the players are side-by-side, $x_1 = x_2 + 36$ m (3)

From Equations (1), (2), and (3), we find $t^2 - 6t - 18 = 0$.

The roots of this equation are $t = -2.2$ s and $t = +8.2$ s. We must choose the 8.2 s answer since the time must be greater than zero.

(b) $\Delta x_1 = v_{o1}t + \frac{1}{2}a_1 t^2 = 0 + \frac{1}{2}(4 \text{ m/s}^2)(8.2 \text{ s})^2 = 134$ m

---

2.37 (a) Use $v^2 = v_o^2 + 2ay$ with $v = 0$. We have $0 = (25.0 \text{ m/s})^2 + 2(-9.80 \text{ m/s}^2)y_m$. This gives the maximum height, y_m, as $y_m = 31.9$ m.

(b) The time to reach the highest point is found from the definition of acceleration as $t = \dfrac{0 - 25.0 \text{ m/s}}{(-9.8 \text{ m/s}^2)} = 2.55$ s

(c) From the symmetry of the motion, the ball takes the same amount of time to reach the ground from its highest point as it does to move from the ground to its highest point. Thus, $t = 2.55$ s.

(d) We can use $v = v_o + at$, with the position of the ball at its highest point as the origin of our coordinate system. Thus, $v_o = 0$, and t is the time for the ball to move from its maximum height to ground level. This was found in part (c) to be 2.55 s. Thus,

$$v = 0 + (-9.80 \text{ m/s}^2)(2.55 \text{ s}) = -25 \text{ m/s.}$$

2.38 Use $y = v_{oy}t + \frac{1}{2}at^2$, or $-76.0 \text{ m} = 0 + \frac{1}{2}(-9.80 \text{ m/s}^2)t^2$. This gives $t = 3.94$ s

---

2.39 (a) After 2.00 s, we find that $v = v_o + gt = -1.50 + (-9.80)2.00 = -21.1$ m/s, so the speed is 21.1 m/s.

(b) Using $x = v_o t + \dfrac{gt^2}{2}$ we have the distance the ball falls in 2.00 s as

$x_b = (-1.50)(2.00) + (-9.80)(2.00)^2/2 = -22.6$ m, and the distance the helicopter moves is $x_c = (-1.50 \text{ m/s})(2.00 \text{ s}) = -3.0$ m.

Therefore, the mailbag is (-22.6 m) - (- 3.0 m) = - 19.6 m below the helicopter after two seconds.

(c) Here we have after 2.00 s,

$v = v_o + gt = +1.50 + (-9.80)(2.00)^2/2 = -18.1$ m/s, or a speed of 18.1 m/s

In this case, the helicopter rises 3.0 m during the 2.00 s interval while the mailbag moves

$$x_b = \bar{v}\, t = \left(\frac{1.50 \text{ m/s} - 18.1 \text{ m/s}}{2}\right)(2.00 \text{ s}) = -16.6 \text{ m from the}$$

release point. Thus, the separation between the two at the end of 2.00 s is

$3.0 \text{ m} - (-16.6 \text{ m}) = 19.6 \text{ m}$

2.40 We shall first find the height of the rocket and its velocity at the instant it runs out of fuel. The height of the rocket at this time is found from

$y = v_0 t + \frac{1}{2}at^2$ as $y_1 = 0 + \frac{1}{2}(29.4 \text{ m/s}^2)(4.00 \text{ s})^2 = 235 \text{ m}$

The velocity at this height is found from $v = v_0 + at$. We have

$v_1 = 0 + (29.4 \text{ m/s}^2)(4.00 \text{ s}) = 117.6 \text{ m/s}$

At this point, the rocket begins to behave as a freely falling body. We shall now find how much higher it rises once its fuel is exhausted by the use of $v^2 = v_0^2 + 2ay$, which yields $0 = (117.6 \text{ m/s})^2 + 2(-9.80 \text{ m/s}^2)h$.

Solving this for the additional height, h gives $h = 706$ m.

Thus, the total height reached is $y_{max} = y_1 + h = 235 \text{ m} + 706 \text{ m} = 941 \text{ m}$.

2.41 (a) Using $a = -g$ and placing the origin at the thrower yields $y = v_0 t - gt^2/2$. When $y = 0$, we get

$[v_0 - gt/2]\, t = 0$ which has two solutions, $t = 0$, and $t = 2v_0/g$.

The $t = 0$ solution corresponds to when the ball is thrown, while the $t = 2v_0/g$ solution corresponds to when the ball is caught. Therefore, the initial velocity must be $v_0 = gt/2 = (9.80)(2.00)/2 = 9.80$ m/s.

(b) Using $v^2 = v_0^2 - 2gy$, we have at the maximum height, $v = 0$, so that

$y_{max} = v_0^2/2g = (9.80)^2/19.6 = 4.90$ m.

2.42 (a) When it reaches the 150 m altitude, its speed is calculated using $v^2 = v_0^2 + 2ay$. This gives $v^2 = (50.0)^2 + 2(2)(150) = 3100 \text{ m}^2/\text{s}^2$, or $v = 55.68$ m/s.

Now, after the engines stop, the rocket experiences free-fall acceleration with an initial speed of 55.68 m/s. The rocket travels a distance x from 150 m to the highest point where x is obtained using $v^2 = v_0^2 + 2gx$. This gives $0 = (55.68)^2 + 2(-9.80)x$, or $x = 158.2$ m.

In total, the maximum altitude of the rocket is 150 + 158.2 = 308 m.

(b) The time for the rocket to reach its highest point can be divided into two times. The first is the time it takes for the rocket to reach 150 m. This is obtained using $v = v_0 + at$, so that $55.68 = 50.0 + 2t$ yielding $t_1 = 2.84$ s. The second piece involves the time it takes for the rocket to climb the additional 158.2 m to its highest point. This time is obtained using $v = v_0 + gt$ and setting v equal to zero yielding $0 = 55.68 - 9.80\, t$, or $t_2 = 5.68$ s as the time from engine turn off to the highest point. The total time is then $t = t_1 + t_2 = 2.84 + 5.68 = 8.52$ s.

(c) We have already determined that 8.52 s is required to reach its highest point. At that time, the rocket begins to fall to the ground. Since it must fall, from rest, 308.2 m under gravity, we have

$308.2 = \frac{gt^2}{2}$ from which $t_3 = 7.93$ s. In total the rocket has been in the air for a time of $t = t_1 + t_2 + t_3 = 2.84 + 5.68\text{ s} + 7.93 = 16.5$ s.

2.43 (a) Choose the origin of the coordinate system at the location of the parachutist. We use $v^2 = v_o^2 + 2ay$, which gives $v^2 = (-10\text{ m/s})^2 + 2(-9.80\text{ m/s}^2)(-50\text{ m})$, from which $v = -32.9$ m/s. The time to reach the ground is found from $v = v_o + at$. This yields

$$t = \frac{v - v_o}{a} = \frac{-32.9\text{ m/s} - (-10\text{ m/s})}{(-9.80\text{ m/s}^2)} = 2.33\text{ s}$$

(b) The velocity was found to be -32.9 m/s in part (a)

2.44 Area A_1 is a rectangle. Thus, $A_1 = hw = v_o t$.
Area A_2 is triangular.

Therefore $A_2 = \frac{1}{2}bh = \frac{1}{2}t(v - v_o)$.

[illegible]otal area under the curve is

$A_2 = v_o t + (v - v_o)t/2$.

[illegible]ment given by the equation is:

[illegible]$t/2$, the same result as above for [illegible]

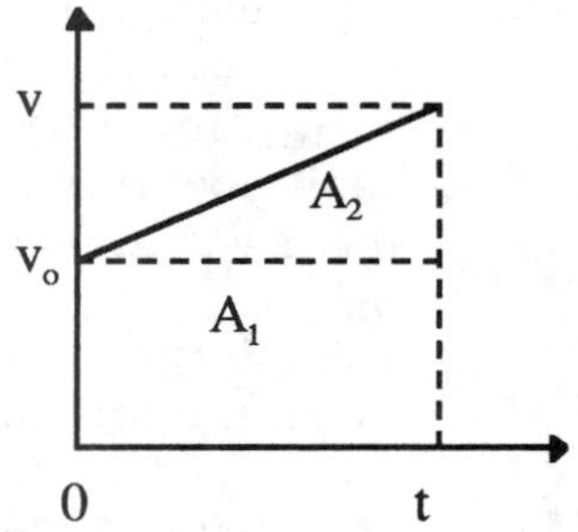

[illegible] (a) The acceleration of the bullet is found from $v^2 = v_o^2 + 2ax$ as

[illegible]$/\text{s})^2 = (400\text{ m/s})^2 + 2a(0.1\text{ m})$. This gives $a = -3.5 \times 10^5$ m/s^2.

(b) The time of contact with the board is found from $v = v_o + at$, or

$$t = \frac{v - v_o}{a} = \frac{300\text{ m/s} - 400\text{ m/s}}{-3.5 \times 10^5\text{ m/s}^2} = 2.86 \times 10^{-4}\text{ s.}$$

2.46 The falling ball moves a distance of (15 m - h) before they meet, where h is the height above the ground at which they pass. Apply $y = v_o t + \frac{1}{2}at^2$ to obtain $-(15\text{ m} - h) = 0 - \frac{1}{2}gt^2$.

This gives $h = 15\text{ m} - \frac{g}{2}t^2$. [1] Applying $y = v_o t + \frac{1}{2}at^2$ to the rising ball gives $h = (25\text{ m/s})t - \frac{1}{2}gt^2$. [2] Equating the expressions for h in [1] and [2] and solving for t gives $t = 0.60$ s.

2.47 [35.0 mi/h = 51.3 ft/s] The distance the car will travel after the brakes are applied may be found from $v^2 = v_o^2 + 2ax$ or $0 = (51.3\text{ ft/s})^2 + 2(-9.00\text{ ft/s}^2)x_a$, so $x_a = 146$ ft. Thus, if the deer is not to be hit, the maximum distance the car can travel before the brakes are applied is given by $x_b = 200\text{ ft} - x_a = 200\text{ ft} - 146\text{ ft} = 54$ft. Before the brakes are applied, the constant speed of the car is 51.3 ft/s and the time required for it to travel 54 ft is:

$t_r = \frac{\Delta x}{v} = \frac{54\text{ ft}}{51.3\text{ ft/s}} = 1.05$ s. Thus, the maximum allowed reaction time is 1.05 s.

2.48 (a) Choosing the balcony as the origin, we have for the first ball

v_{10} = - 14.7 m/s, and for the second ball, v_{20} = + 14.7 m/s. Since the street is at x = - 19.6 m, we have for the first ball,

$-19.6 = -(14.7)t_1 + (-9.80)(t_1)^2/2$, or $4.9(t_1)^2 + (14.7)t_1 - 19.6 = 0$.

This yields t_1 = 1 s or t_1 = - 4 s. We disregard the negative value so that the first ball strikes the ground after 1 s.

For the second ball, we have $-19.6 = (14.7)t_2 + (-9.80)(t_2)^2/2$, or

$4.9(t_2)^2 - (14.7)t_2 - 19.6 = 0$, which gives t_2 = 4 s or t_2 = - 1 s.

As before, we disregard the negative value so that the second ball strikes the ground after 4 s. The difference in time is then 3.00 s.

(b) When the balls strike the ground, their velocities are:

$v_1 = v_{10} + (-g)t_1$ = -14.7 m/s - 9.80 m/s = - 24.5 m/s,

and $v_2 = v_{20} + (-g)t_1$ = +14.7 m/s - (9.80 m/s^2)(4 s) = - 24.5 m/s.

(c) For the first ball, we have $x_1 = (-14.7)(0.8) + (-9.80)(0.8)^2/2 = -14.9$ m.

For the second ball, we have $x_2 = (+14.7)(0.8) + (-9.80)(0.8)^2/2 = 8.6$ m.

So the two balls are $x_2 - x_1$ = 8.6 - (-14.9) = 23.5 m apart.

2.49 We have $v_x = v_{x0} + a_x t = v_{x0}$ - (5.60 m/s^2)(4.20 s)

and $x = \frac{1}{2}(v_{x0} + v_x)t$ becomes 62.4 m = $\frac{1}{2}(v_{x0} + v_x)$4.20 s

So substituting for v_{x0} gives

62.4 m = $\frac{1}{2}$[v_x + (5.6 m/s^2)(4.20 s) + v_x] 4.20 s

gives v_x = 3.10 m/s

2.50 (a) We require $x_s = x_k$ when $t_s = t_k + 1$

$x_s = \frac{1}{2}(3.50 \text{ m/s}^2)(t_k + 1)^2 = \frac{1}{2}(4.90 \text{ m/s}^2)(t_k)^2 = x_k$

t_k = 5.45 s

(b) $x_k = \frac{1}{2}$ (4.90 m/s^2)(5.45 s)^2 = 73.0 m

(c) v_k = (4.90 m/s^2)(5.45 s) = 26.7 m/s

v_s = (3.50 m/s^2)(6.45 s) = 22.6 m/s

2.51 (a) The velocity with which the first stone hits the water is

$v_1^2 = v_0^2 + 2ay$ = (- 2.00 m/s)^2 + 2(-9.80 m/s^2)(-50.0 m), or

v_1 = - 31.37 m/s (31.4 m/s). The time for the first stone to reach the water is then found from $v = v_0 + at$, which gives

-31.37 m/s = - 2.00 m/s - (9.80 m/s^2)t_1, or t_1 = 3.0 s

(b) Since they hit simultaneously, the second stone which is released 1.00 s later, will hit the water after an elapsed time of 2.00 s. Thus,

$y = v_0 t + \frac{1}{2}at^2$ yields - 50.0 m = v_0(2.00 s) + $\frac{1}{2}$(- 9.80 m/s^2)(2.00 s)^2,

or

v_0 = - 15.2 m/s. (15 m/s)

(c) We found the velocity of the first stone in part (a) above. The velocity of the second is found as

$v_2^2 = v_0^2 + 2ay$ = (- 15.2 m/s)^2 + 2(- 9.80 m/s^2)(-50.0 m) , which gives

$v_2 = -34.8$ m/s. (35 m/s)

2.52 Let us first find the speed of the student at the beginning of the final 500 yd dash. For the first 10 min, she had run a distance of one mile (1760 yd) less 500 yd for a total distance of 1260 yd. Thus her average velocity was $\bar{v} = 1260$ yd/600 s, which when converted to m/s is 1.92 m/s. We shall assume that this was her speed at the beginning of the final 500 yd dash. Thus, she must cover 500 yd (457 m) in 2 min (120 s) starting with 1.92 m/s initial velocity. The average velocity that she must have to make the last 500 yd in two minutes is

$\bar{v} = \Delta x/\Delta t = (457 \text{ m})/(120 \text{ s}) = 3.81$ m/s. From $\bar{v} = \dfrac{v_0 + v}{2}$, we find the

required final velocity to be $v = 2\bar{v} - v_0 = 2(3.81 \text{ m/s}) - 1.92 \text{ m/s} = 5.70$ m/s.

The needed acceleration is $a = \dfrac{v - v_0}{t} = \dfrac{5.70 \text{ m/s} - 1.92 \text{ m/s}}{120 \text{ s}} = 0.032 \text{ m/s}^2$.

Thus, her maximum acceleration of 0.15 m/s^2 is more than sufficient.

2.53 (a) Using $d = \dfrac{gt^2}{2}$, we have $t = \sqrt{\dfrac{2d}{g}} = \sqrt{\dfrac{2(23)}{9.80}} = 2.17$ s.

(b) Using $v = v_0 + gt$, we have $v = (9.80)(2.17) = 21.3$ m/s.

(c) It takes the sound to reach the spectator a total time of

$\dfrac{23 \text{ m}}{340 \text{ m/s}} = 0.068$ s. So that in total, we have 2.17 s + 0.068 s = 2.24 s

---

2.54 The initial distance the leader is ahead of the second swimmer equals the distance the leader swims in 0.50 s, which is (4.0 m/s)(0.50 s) = 2.0 m. Thus, the leader has 50 m to go and the second swimmer has 52 m to the end of the pool. The time for the leader to reach the end of the pool is

$$t = \frac{x}{v} = \frac{50 \text{ m}}{4 \text{m/s}} = 12.5 \text{ s.}$$

In this same time, the second swimmer must swim 52 m. The minimum velocity is $v = \dfrac{x}{t} = \dfrac{52 \text{ m}}{12.5 \text{ s}} = 4.16$ m/s

---

2.55 (a) $\Delta x = v\Delta t = (1100 \text{ ft/s})(5.0 \text{ s}) = 5500$ ft

(b) For the airplane, $v = \Delta x/\Delta t = (5500 \text{ ft})/(5.0 + 10)\text{s} = 367$ ft/s.

(c) Light would require a time $\Delta t = 5500 \text{ ft}/9.9 \times 10^8 \text{ ft/s} = 5.56\ \mu\text{s}$ to travel from plane to observer. During this time the plane would travel only a distance of 0.002 ft.

2.56 (a) Let d represent the distance between A and B. Let t_1 be the time for which the walker has the higher speed in 5.00 m/s $= \dfrac{d}{t_1}$. Let t_2

represent the longer time for the return trip in -3.00 m/s $= -\dfrac{d}{t_2}$.

Then the times are $t_1 = \dfrac{d}{5.00 \text{ m/s}}$ and $t_2 = \dfrac{d}{3.00 \text{ m/s}}$. The average speed is:

$$\bar{v} = \frac{\text{Total distance}}{\text{Total time}} = \frac{d + d}{\dfrac{d}{5.00 \text{ m/s}} + \dfrac{d}{3.00 \text{ m/s}}} = \frac{2d}{\dfrac{(8.0 \text{ m/s})d}{15.0 \text{ m}^2/\text{s}^2}} = 3.75 \text{ m/s.}$$

(b) She starts and finishes at point A. With total displacement = 0, the average velocity = 0.

2.57 Let the ball fall 1.5 m. It strikes at a speed given by:

$v_x^2 = v_{xo}^2 + 2ax$ gives $\quad v_x^2 = 0 + 2(-9.80\ \text{m/s}^2)(-1.5\ \text{m})$

$v_x = -5.42\ \text{m/s}$

and its stopping is described by

$v_x^2 = v_{xo}^2 + 2ax$ gives $\quad 0 = (-5.42\ \text{m/s})^2 + 2a_x(-10^{-2}\ \text{m})$

From which $a_x = 1500\ \text{m/s}^2$

2.58 We have $y = -\frac{1}{2}gt^2 + v_o t + y_o$

becoming $\quad 0 = -(4.9\ \text{m/s}^2)t^2 - (8.00\ \text{m/s})t + 30.0\ \text{m}$

Solving the quadratic equation for t and using only the positive value, we have $\quad t = 1.79\ \text{s}$.

2.59 (a) $y = -\frac{1}{2}gt^2 + v_o t + y_o$ gives $\quad y = (5.0)t - 4.9t^2 + 21$.

Setting y = 0 and solving the quadratic, gives $t = 2.64\ \text{s}$.

(b) $v = v_o - gt = -20.9\ \text{m/s}$

(c) $y = v_o t - \frac{1}{2}gt^2 + y_o$ gives $\quad 21 = 5t + 4.9t^2$

From which $t = 1.62\ \text{s}$ and $v = 20.9\ \text{m/s}$ down.

2.60 Time to fall 3 m is found from $y = v_o t - \frac{1}{2}gt^2$

as $\quad -3.00\ \text{m} = 0 - \frac{1}{2}(9.80\ \text{m/s}^2)t^2 \quad t = 0.782\ \text{s}$.

(a) With the horse galloping at 10.0 m/s, the horizontal distance is $vt = 7.82$ m. So, (b) And $t = 0.782$ s.

ANSWERS TO CONCEPTUAL QUESTIONS

2. You can ignore the time for the lightning to reach you because light travels at the speed of 3 x 10^8 m/s, a speed so fast that in our day-to-day activities it is essentially infinite.

4. The average velocity of an object is defined as the displacement of the object divided by the time interval during which the displacement occurred. If the average velocity is zero, the displacement must also be zero.

6. In Figure (a) the first three images show the object moving slightly farther during each time interval. Thus, it has a positive acceleration. Between image three and four, and four and five, it moves much farther indicating a sudden increase in the magnitude of the acceleration. Finally, between image five and six, it slows, with a negative acceleration.
In figure (b) the spacing between each image remains constant, so the object is moving with a constant velocity.
In Figure (c) the object has a positive acceleration.

8. Velocities are equal only if both magnitude and direction are the same. These objects have different directions, so the velocities are not the same.

10 The rule of thumb assumes constant velocity. If the car(s) move with constant acceleration, the velocity would continually be changing. This would mean the distance between the cars would continually have to change for the rule of thumb to be valid, which could require a slowing down, which would imply a change in the value of the acceleration.

12. (a) The car is moving to the east and increasing in speed.
(b) The car is moving to the east but slowing in speed.
(c) The car is moving to the east at constant speed.
(d) The car is moving to the west but slowing in speed.
(e) The car is moving to the west and speeding up.
(f) The car is moving to the west at constant speed.
(g) The car starts from rest and begins to speed up toward the east.
(h) The car starts from rest and begins to speed up toward the west.

14. The balls speed up and slow down at the same rate, but the distances of travel are different in different time intervals. For example, the rising ball starts at a high speed and slows down. This means that it travels a longer distance in, say, the first second than does the slower moving dropped ball. Thus, the balls will meet above the midway point.

16. (a) The ball moves such that the images on the film will always be separated by the same distance.
(b) Starting at the right-most image, the images will be getting closer together as one moves toward the left.
(c) Starting at the right-most image, the images will be getting farther apart as one moves toward the left.
(d) As one moves from left to right, the balls will first get farther apart in each successive image, then closer together when the balls begin to slow down.

CHAPTER THREE SOLUTIONS

Chapter Three Readings

Brancazio, P, "The Trajectory of a Fly Ball," *The Physics Teacher*, January 1985, p. 20.

Brown, R.A., "Maximizing the Range of a Projectile", *The Physics Teacher*, 30, 344, 1992

Drake, S. and MacLachlan, J., "Galileo's Discovery of the Parabolic Trajectory," *Scientific American*, March 1975, p. 102.

Review

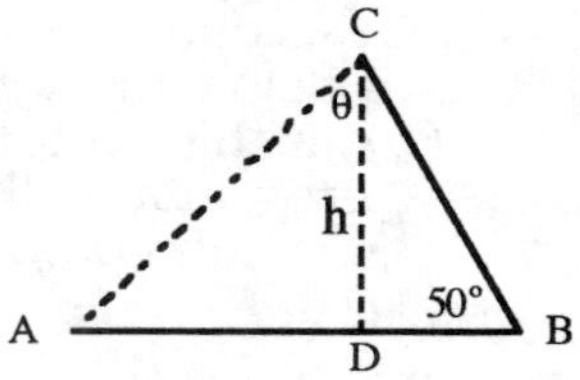

(a) The length of the height of the triangle is given by

$h = 260.8 \sin 50° = 199.8$ ft.

The side DB has length

$DB = 260.8 \cos 50° = 167.6$ ft,

leaving the side

$AD = 311.4 - 167.6 = 143.8$ ft.

The angle $\theta = \tan^{-1}\frac{AD}{h} = \tan^{-1}\frac{143.8}{199.8} = 35.7°$ and

$AC = [(AD)^2 + h^2]^{1/2} = [(143.8)^2 + (199.8)^2]^{1/2} = 246.2$ ft.

The remaining side of the triangle (from C to A) is thus 246.2 ft in a direction 35.7° west of south.

(b) The area of the triangle is given by

$\text{Area} = \frac{1}{2}bh = \frac{1}{2}(311.4)(199.8)$

$= 3.111 \times 10^4 \text{ ft}^2 \left(\frac{1 \text{ acre}}{43560 \text{ ft}^2}\right) = 0.714$ acres.

3.1 Your sketch should be drawn to scale, and should look somewhat like that pictured at the right. The angle from the westward direction, θ, can be measured to be 4.34° north of west, and the distance from your sketch can be converted according to the scale used to be 7.92 m.

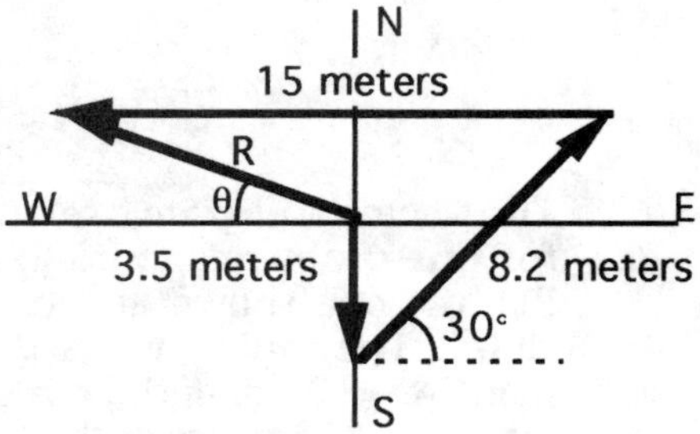

3.2 Your sketch when drawn to scale should look somewhat like the one at the right. The distance R and the angle θ can be measured to give, upon use of your scale factor, the values of R = 421 ft at about 3° below the horizontal.

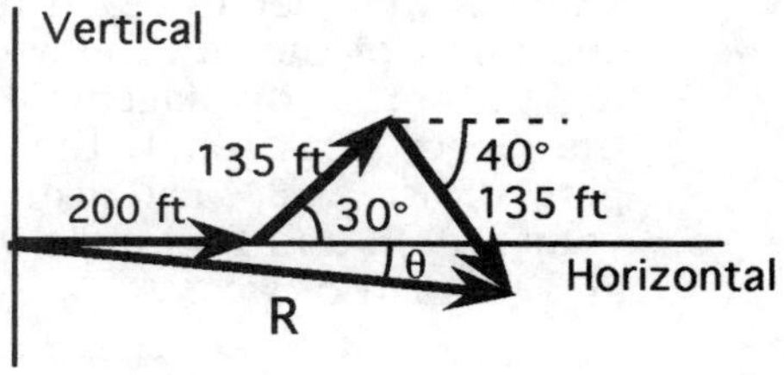

3.3 (a) Drawing these to scale and maintaining their respective directions yields a resultant of 5.2 m at an angle of 60° above the x axis.
(b) Maintain the direction of A, but reverse the direction of B by 180°. The resultant is 3.0 m at an angle of 30° below the x axis.
(c) Maintain the direction of B, but reverse the direction of A. The resultant is 3.0 m at an angle of 150° with respect to the + x axis.
(d) Maintain the direction of A, reverse the direction of B, and multiply its magnitude by two. The resultant is 5.2 m at an angle of 60° below the + x axis.

3.4 (a) Carefully draw, to scale, a vector 3.00 units long along the x direction, and from the tip of this vector, draw another of length 4.00 units in the negative y direction. The resultant is the length, to scale, of the vector drawn from the tail of the first to the tip of the second. This will be a vector 5.00 units long and at an angle of 53° below the x axis.
(b) In this case, the second vector, - B, will be in the + y direction. The resultant will still be 5 units long, but at an angle of 53° above the +x direction.

3.5 The displacement vectors A = 8.00 m westward and B = 13.0 m north can be drawn to scale as at the right. The vector C represents the displacement that the man in the maze must undergo to return to his starting point. The scale used to draw the sketch can be used to find C to be 15.3 m and the angle θ can be measured to be about 58°.

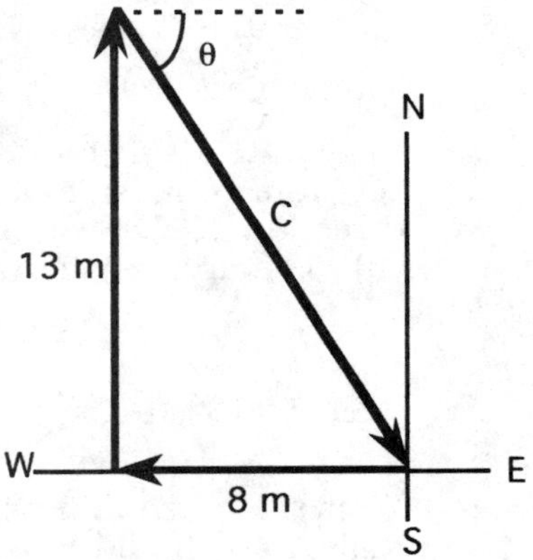

3.6 The vector diagram sketched for this problem should look like the one shown at the right. The initial displacement A = 100 m and the resultant R = 175 m are both known. In order to reach the end point of the run following the initial displacement, the jogger must follow the path shown as B. The distance can be found from the scale used for your sketch and the angle θ measured. The results should be about 83 m at 33° north of west.

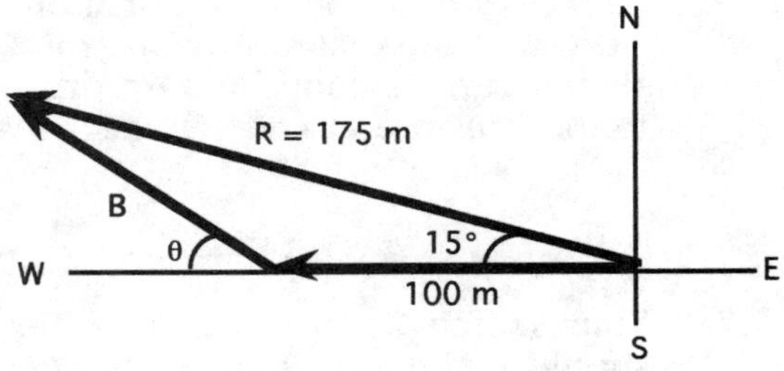

3.7 A total distance of $\sqrt{(6.00)^2 + (5.40)^2} = 8.07$ m with an angle of $\tan^{-1}\frac{5.40}{6.00} = 42.0°$ south of east.

3.8 The person would have to walk
3.10 sin(25.0°) = 1.31 km north, and 3.10 cos(25.0°) = 2.81 km east.

3.9 (a) Her resultant x (east-west) displacement is -3.00 + 0 + 6.00 = 3.00 blocks, while her resultant y (north-south) displacement is 0 + 4.00 + 0 = 4.00 blocks. Her resultant displacement is then 5.00 blocks at 53.1° north of east.
(b) Her total distance is 3.00 + 4.00 + 6.00 = 13.00 blocks.

3.10 Let A be the vector corresponding to the 10.0 yd run, B to the 15.0 yd run, and C to the 50.0 yd pass. Also, we choose a coordinate system with the $+y$ direction downfield, and the $+x$ direction toward the sideline to which the player runs. The components of the vectors are then

$$A_x = 0 \qquad A_y = -10.0 \text{ yd}$$
$$B_x = 15.0 \text{ yds} \qquad B_y = 0$$
$$C_x = 0 \qquad C_y = +50.0 \text{ yds}$$

From these, $R_x = \Sigma F_x = 15.0$ yds, and $R_y = \Sigma F_y = 40.0$ yds, and the Pythagorean theorem gives

$$R = \sqrt{(R_x)^2 + (R_y)^2} = \sqrt{(15.0 \text{ yds})^2 + (40.0 \text{ yds})^2} = 42.7 \text{ yds}$$

3.11 After 3 h moving at 41.0 km/h, the hurricane is 123 km from the island, 61.5 km west and 106.52 km north. It then travels an additional (4.50 - 3.00)(25.0) = 37.5 km north. In total, it has traveled 61.5 km west and 106.52 + 37.5 = 144.02 km north. Therefore, the hurricane is

$$\sqrt{(61.5)^2 + (144.02)^2} = 156.6 \text{ km away from the island.}$$

3.12 The east and north components of the displacement from Dallas (D) to Chicago (C) are the sums of the east and north components of the displacements from Dallas to Atlanta (A) and from Atlanta to Chicago. In equation form

$$d_{DCeast} = d_{DAeast} + d_{ACeast} = 730 \cos 5° - 560 \sin 21° = 727.2 - 200.6 = 526.6 \text{ miles.}$$

$$d_{DCnorth} = d_{DAnorth} + d_{ACnorth} = 730 \sin 5° + 560 \cos 21° = 63.6 + 522.8 = 586.4 \text{ miles.}$$

By the Pythagorean theorem, $d = \sqrt{(d_{DCeast})^2 + (d_{DCnorth})^2} = 788.1$ mi

Then $\tan\theta = \frac{d_{DCnorth}}{d_{DCeast}} = 1.12$ and $\theta = 48.1°$.

Thus, Chicago is 788 miles at 48.1° north of east of Dallas.

3.13 Finding the components of the displacements a, b, and c gives:

$a_x = a\cos(30.0°) = +152$ km,
$a_y = a\sin(30.0°) = +87.5$ km
$b_x = b\cos(110.0°) = -51.3$ km,
$b_y = b\sin(110.0°) = 141$ km
$c_x = c\cos(180°) = -190$ km,
$c_y = c\sin(180°) = 0$

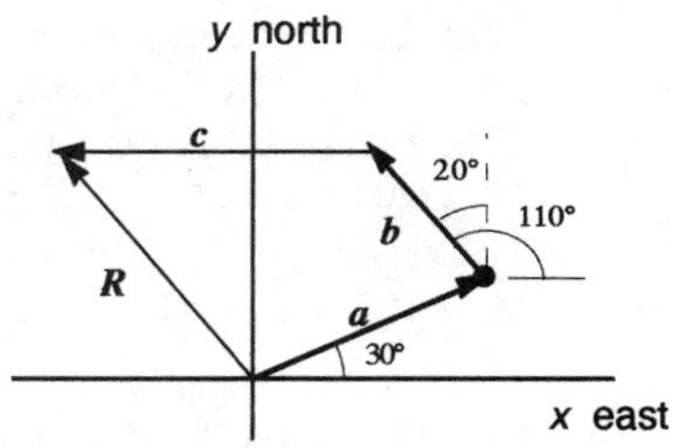

Therefore, the components of the

position vector R are
$R_x = a_x + b_x + c_x = -89.7$ km and $R_y = a_y + b_y + c_y = +228$ km
The magnitude and direction of the resultant are found from
$R = \sqrt{(R_x)^2 + (R_y)^2} = 245$ km and $\tan\theta = \frac{R_y}{R_x} = -2.54$ and $\theta = 111.4°$.
Thus, city C is 245 km at 21.4° west of north from the starting point.

3.14 (a) Let us call F_1 the 120 N force and F_2 the 80 N force. The components of these forces are

$F_{1x} = 60$ N $\quad F_{1y} = 103.9$ N
$F_{2x} = -20.7$ N $\quad F_{2y} = 77.3$ N

The resultant x component is 39.3 N, and the resultant y component is 181.2 N. The resultant is

$$R = \sqrt{(R_x)^2 + (R_y)^2} = 185 \text{ N.}$$

Also, $\tan\theta = \frac{181.2}{39.3} = 4.61$, from which $\theta = 77.8°$

(b) To have a resultant of zero on the mule, the net force above must be cancelled by a force equal in magnitude to it and oppositely directed. Thus, the required force is 185 N at an angle of 257.8°

3.15 We shall use the vector equation, A + B = R, where A is the 150 cm displacement at 120°, R is the resultant displacement and B is the second displacement that we are looking for. The equation above can be solved for B to give B = R - A = R + (-A). The vector R has the following components $R_x = (140 \text{ cm})(\cos 35.0°) = 114.7$ cm,
$R_y = (140 \text{ cm})(\sin 35.0°) = 80.3$ cm.
The vector -A has components $-A_x = 75$ cm, $-A_y = -130$ cm.
Thus, the vector B has the following components
$B_x = R_x + (-A_x) = 190$ cm, and $\quad B_y = R_y + (-A_y) = -49.7$ cm.
From the Pythagorean theorem, B = 196 cm, and $\tan\theta$ gives $\theta = -14.7°$ with respect to the positive x axis.

3.16 $v_{ox} = 100.8$ mi/h = 45.06 m/s and the distance traveled $x = 60.0$ ft = 18.29 m.
The time to reach homeplate is given by $x = v_{ox}t$, which yields
$18.29 \text{ m} = (45.06 \text{ m/s})t$, or $t = 0.406$ s.
In this time interval, the ball has fallen a distance of

$$y = v_{oy}t + \frac{1}{2}at^2 = 0 + \frac{1}{2}(-9.80 \text{ m/s}^2)(0.406 \text{ s})^2 = -0.807 \text{ m} = 2.65 \text{ ft.}$$

3.17 We have $v_{ox} = 5.0$ m/s and $v_{oy} = 0$. The time of flight for Tom is found from $y = v_{oy}t + \frac{1}{2}at^2$. This gives $-1.5 \text{ m} = 0 + \frac{1}{2}(-9.80 \text{ m/s}^2)t^2$, or $t = 0.553$ s.
The distance moved in the x direction during this time is
$x = v_{ox}t = (5.0 \text{ m/s})(0.553 \text{ s}) = 2.8$ m.
The horizontal component of velocity does not change during the flight, so Tom strikes the floor with a horizontal component of velocity of $v_{ox} = 5.0$ m/s. The vertical component of velocity is found as
$v_y = v_{oy} + at = 0 - (9.80 \text{ m/s}^2)(0.553\text{s}) = -5.4$ m/s.

3.18 (a) $v_{ox} = 18.0$ m/s, $v_{oy} = 0$. We find the time of fall as $y = v_{oy}t + \frac{1}{2}at^2$, or

$$-50.0 \text{ m} = \frac{1}{2}(-9.80 \text{ m/s}^2)t^2, \quad \text{which gives } t = 3.19 \text{ s.}$$

(b) At impact, the horizontal component of velocity is $v_x = v_{ox} = 18.0$ m/s, and the vertical component is

$$v_y = v_{oy} + at = 0 + (-9.80 \text{ m/s}^2)(3.19 \text{ s}) = -31.3 \text{ m/s.}$$

The resultant velocity is found from the pythagorean theorem

$$v = \sqrt{(31.3 \text{ m/s})^2 + (18.0 \text{ m/s})^2} = 36.1 \text{ m/s,}$$

at an angle below the horizontal found as

$$\tan\theta = 31.3/18.0 \quad \text{which yields} \quad \theta = 60.1°.$$

3.19 We choose our origin at the initial position of the projectile. After 3 s, it is at ground level, $y = -H$. To find H, we use $y = v_{oy}t + \frac{1}{2}at^2$.

$$-H = (15 \text{ m/s})(\sin 25°)(3 \text{ s}) + \frac{1}{2}(-9.80 \text{ m/s}^2)(3.0 \text{ s})^2 = -25.1 \text{ m, or } H = 25 \text{ m}$$

3.20 First, compute the components of the initial velocity.

$$v_{ox} = v_o\cos 53.0° = 12.0 \text{ m/s}, \quad v_{oy} = v_o\sin 53.0° = 16.0 \text{ m/s.}$$

(a) We can find the time required for the ball to reach the position of the crossbar from $x = v_{ox}t$ as: 36.0 m = (12.0 m/s)(t), or $t = 2.99$ s. At this time the height of the football above the ground is

$$y = v_{oy}t + \frac{1}{2}at^2 = (16.0 \text{ m/s})(3.00\text{s}) + \frac{1}{2}(-9.80 \text{ m/s}^2)(3.00 \text{ s})^2 = 3.90 \text{ m.}$$

Thus, the ball clears the crossbar by 3.90 m - 3.05 m = 0.85m.

(b) The vertical component of the velocity of the ball as it moves over the crossbar is $v_y = v_{oy} + at = 16.0 \text{ m/s} - (9.80 \text{ m/s}^2)(3.00 \text{ s}) = -13.4$ m/s. The negative sign indicates the ball is moving downward.

3.21 (a) First, find the speed of the car when it reaches the edge of the cliff from $v^2 = v_o^2 + 2ax = 0 + 2(4.00 \text{ m/s}^2)(50.0 \text{ m})$, or $v = 20.0$ m/s. Now, consider the projectile phase of the car's motion. We shall first find the vertical velocity with which the car strikes the water as $v_y^2 = v_{oy}^2 + 2ay = ((-20.0 \text{ m/s})\sin 24.0°)^2 + 2(-9.80 \text{ m/s}^2)(-30.0 \text{ m})$, or $v_y = -25.6$ m/s. The time of flight is found from $v_y = v_{oy} + at$ as

$-25.6 \text{ m/s} = (-20.0 \text{ m/s})(\sin 24.0°) + (-9.80 \text{ m/s}^2)t$, which gives $t =$ 1.78 s.

The horizontal motion of the car during this time is

$$x = v_{ox}t = (20.0 \text{ m/s})(\cos 24.0°)(1.78 \text{ s}) = 32.5 \text{ m.}$$

(b) The time of flight of the car has already been found in part (a).

3.22 The components of the initial velocity are $v_{ox} = 40.0 \cos 30.0° = 34.6$ m/s and $v_{oy} = 40.0 \sin 30.0° = 20.0$ m/s

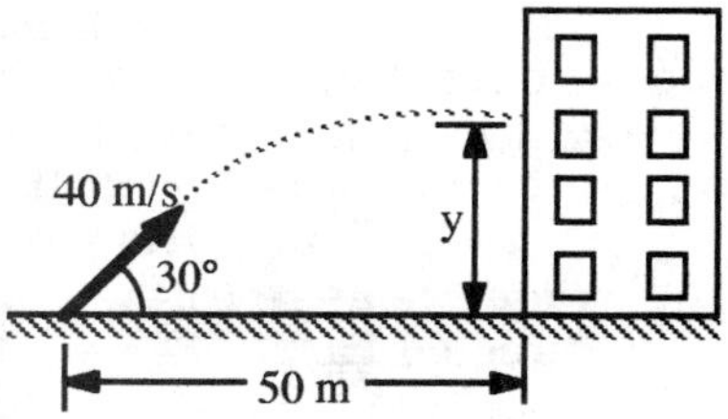

The time for the water to reach the building is given by

$x = v_{ox}\,t$, or 50.0 m = (34.6 m/s) t and $t = 1.44$ s.

Then the height of the water when it reaches the building is given by

$$y = v_{oy}t - \frac{1}{2}gt^2 = 20.0(1.44) - 4.9(1.44)^2$$

= 18.6 m.
The water strikes the building 18.6 meters above ground level.

3.23 (a) The projectile is moving horizontally at the highest point of the trajectory. The y-component of velocity is zero but the x-component is $v_{ox} = v_o\cos\theta_0 = 60\cos 30° = 52.0$ m/s
(b) The x-component of the distance is

$$v_0(\cos\theta_0)t = 60(\cos 30°)\,4 = 208 \text{ m.}$$

The y-component of the distance is

$$v_0(\sin\theta_0)t - \frac{1}{2}gt^2 = 60(\sin 30°)\,4 - 4.9(4)^2 = 41.6 \text{ m.}$$

The distance is given by the Pythagorean theorem to be 212 m.

3.24 The velocity of the plane relative to the ground is the vector sum of the velocity of the plane relative to the air and the velocity of the air relative to the ground, or $\mathbf{v}_{pg} = \mathbf{v}_{pa} + \mathbf{v}_{ag}$.

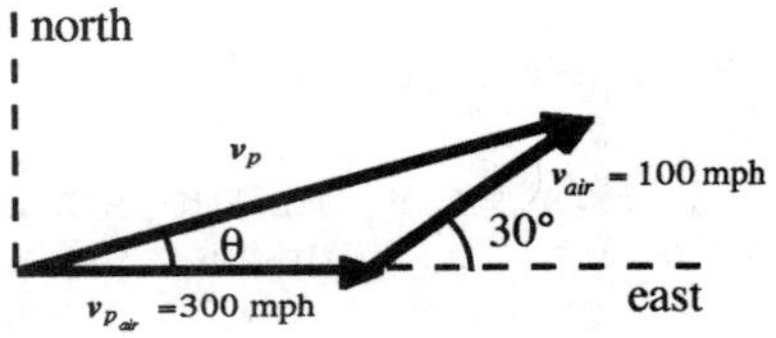

The components of this velocity are
$v_p)_{east} = 300 + 100\cos 30.0° = 387$ mph
and
$v_p)_{north} = 0 + 100\sin 30.0° = 50$ mph
Thus, the magnitude and direction are given by

$$v_p = \sqrt{v^2_{peast} + v^2_{pnorth}} = 390 \text{ mph}$$

and $\tan\theta = \dfrac{v_{pnorth}}{v_{peast}} = 0.129$ and $\theta = 7.4°$

The plane moves at 390 mph at 7.4° north of east relative to the ground.

3.25 We have $\mathbf{v}_{bs}$ = velocity of boat relative to the shore
$\mathbf{v}_{bw}$ = velocity of boat relative to the water,
and $\mathbf{v}_{ws}$ = velocity of water relative to the shore.

$$\mathbf{v}_{bs} = \mathbf{v}_{bw} + \mathbf{v}_{ws}.$$

Take downstream as the positive direction. Then $v_{ws} = 1.5$ m/s for both parts of the trip. Going downstream, $v_{bw} = 10$ m/s.
Therefore, $v_{bs} = 10\text{ m/s} + 1.5\text{ m/s} = 11.5$ m/s, and the time required is

$$t_1 = \frac{300 \text{ m}}{11.5 \text{ m/s}} = 26.1 \text{ s.}$$

Going upstream, $v_{bw} = -10$ m/s. Thus, $v_{bs} = -10\text{ m/s} + 1.5\text{ m/s} = -8.5$ m/s,
and the time is $t_2 = \dfrac{-300 \text{ m}}{-8.5 \text{ m/s}} = 35.3$ s.

The time for the round trip is $t = t_1 + t_2 = 61$ s

3.26 We have $\mathbf{v}_{bw} = 10$ m/s is the velocity of the boat relative to the water, and is a vector directed northward.
$\mathbf{v}_{ws} = 1.50$ m/s, the velocity of the water relative to the shore, and is directed east.
$\mathbf{v}_{bs}$ = the velocity of the boat relative to the shore, and is a vector directed at an angle of θ, relative to the northward direction.

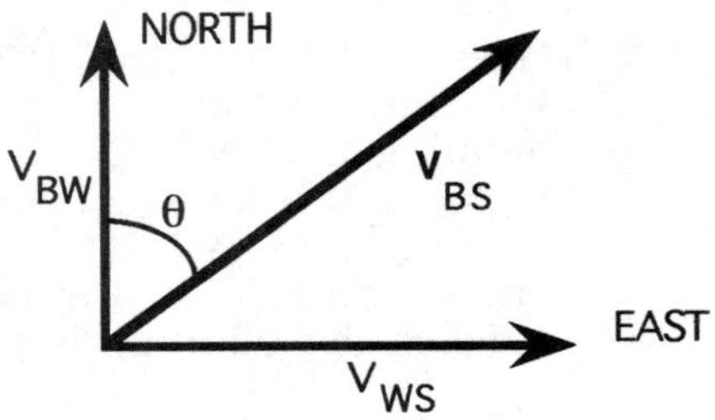

$v_{bs} = v_{bw} + v_{ws}$
Northward component of v_{bs} is $v_{bs}\cos\theta = 10.0$ m/s (1)
Eastward component is $v_{bs}\sin\theta = 1.50$ m/s (2)
Dividing (2) by (1) gives $\tan\theta = 0.15$ and $\theta = 8.53°$.

Then, from (1) $v_{bs} = \frac{10.0 \text{ m/s}}{\cos 8.53} = 10.1$ m/s.

The time to cross the river is $t = \frac{300 \text{ m}}{v_{bs}\cos\theta} = \frac{300 \text{ m}}{10.0 \text{ m/s}} = 30$ s.

The eastward drift = $(v_{bs}\sin\theta)t = (1.50 \text{ m/s})(30 \text{ s}) = 45$ m.

3.27 v_{bw} = the velocity of the boat relative to the water.
v_{ws} = the velocity of the water relative to the shore, and is directed east.
v_{bs} = the velocity of the boat relative to the shore.

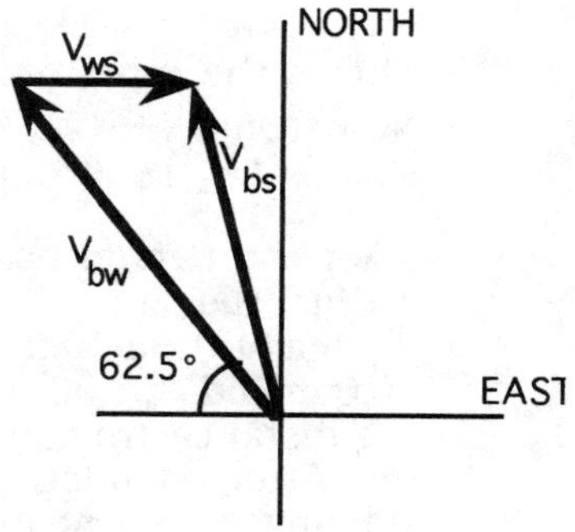

$v_{bs} = v_{bw} + v_{ws}$
The northward components of this equation (where north is across the stream) are

$v_{bs})_N = v_{bw})_N + v_{ws})_N$

$v_{bs})_N = (3.30 \text{ mi/h}) \sin 62.5 + 0 = 2.93$ mi/h.

And, the time to cross the stream is

$t = \frac{0.505 \text{ mi}}{2.93 \text{ mi/h}} = 0.172$ h.

The eastward components of the relative velocity equation (where east is parallel to the current) are:
$v_{bs})_E = v_{bw})_E + v_{ws})_E = -(3.30 \text{ mi/h}) \cos 62.5 + 1.25 \text{ mi/h} = -0.274$ mi/h.
The distance traveled parallel to the shore =
$(v_{bs})_E\, t = (-0.274 \text{ mi/h})(0.172 \text{ h}) = -0.0472 \text{ mi} = -249 \text{ ft} = 249$ ft upstream.

3.28 v_{pa} = the velocity of the plane relative to the air = 200 km/h.
v_{ag} = the velocity of the air relative to the ground = 50.0 km/h (south).
v_{pg} = the velocity of the plane relative to the ground (to be due east).

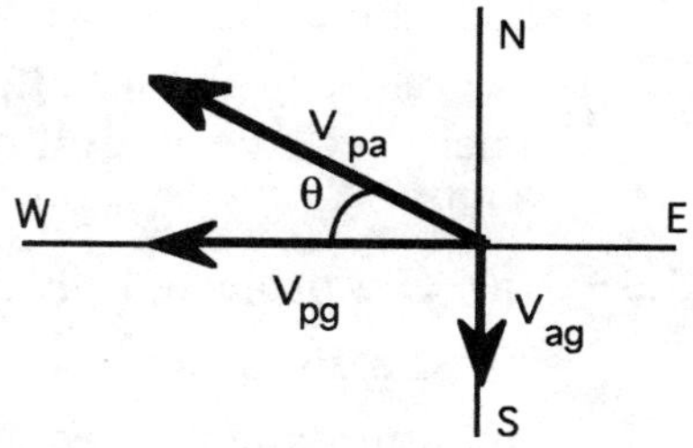

$v_{pg} = v_{pa} + v_{ag}$
For v_{pg} to have zero northward component, we must have

$v_{pa}\sin\theta = v_{ag}$, or $\sin\theta = \frac{50.0 \text{ km/h}}{200 \text{ km/h}} = 0.25$ and $\theta = 14.5°$ Thus, the plane should head at 14.5° north of west. Since v_{pg} has zero northward component, $v_{pg} = v_{pa}\cos\theta = (200 \text{ km/h})\cos 14.5°$.
This gives, $v_{pg} = 194$ km/h, the plane's ground speed.

3.29 The bumpers are initially 100 m = 0.1 km apart. After time t the bumper of the leading car travels $40t$, while the bumper of the chasing car travels $60t$. Since the cars are bumper-to-bumper at time t, we have $0.1 + 40t = 60t$, yielding $t = 0.005$ h = 18 s.

3.30 v_{bc} = the velocity of the ball relative to the car.

v_{be} = the velocity of the ball relative to the earth.

v_{ce} = velocity of the car relative to the earth = 10 m/s.

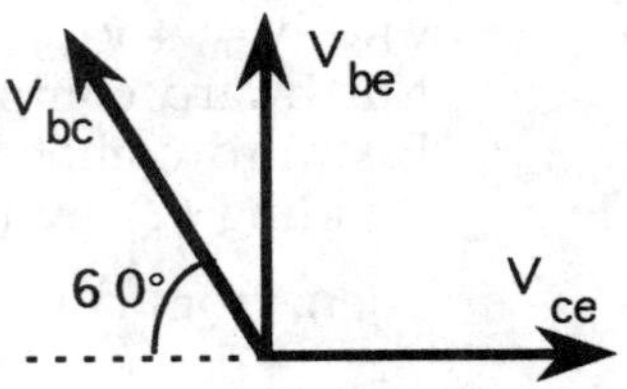

$v_{be} = v_{bc} + v_{ce}$

Since v_{be} has zero horizontal component, we have $0 = -v_{bc}\cos 60.0 + v_{ce}$.

So, $v_{bc} = \dfrac{10.0\text{ m/s}}{0.5} = 20.0$ m/s, and the vertical components

$v_{be} = v_{bc}\sin 60.0 + 0 = (20.0\text{ m/s})(0.866) = 17.3$ m/s.

This is the initial velocity of the ball relative to the earth.

Now from $v_y^2 = v_{oy}^2 + 2ay$, we have $0 = (17.3\text{ m/s})^2 + 2(-9.80\text{ m/s}^2)h$ to give $h = 15.3$ m, the maximum height the ball rises.

3.31 After the person has walked half way around the circular path of 5.00 m radius, the
(a) magnitude of the displacement vector is the diameter of the circle or 10.0 m and
(b) distance traveled is half the circumference or $\pi r = 15.7$ m.
(c) After completing the circular path, the person is back at the starting point and the displacement is zero.

3.32 Since R = A + B, then B = R - A and the components of the second displacement are:

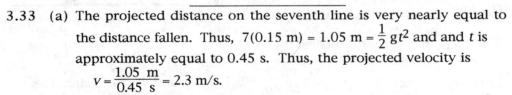

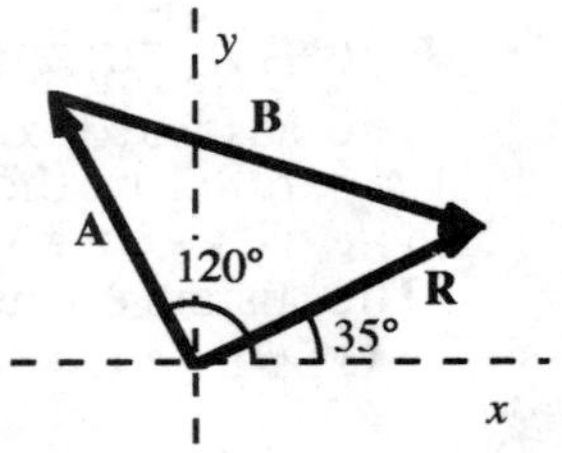

$B_x = R_x - A_x = 140\cos 35.0° - 150\cos 120.0°$
$= +190$ cm,

and $B_y = R_y - A_y$
$= 140\sin 35° - 150\sin 120° = -49.6$cm.

The magnitude is $B = \sqrt{B_x^2 + B_y^2} = 196$ cm,

and the direction is found by $\tan\theta = \dfrac{B_y}{B_x}$

$= -0.26$ so $\theta = -14.7°$

Therefore, the second displacement is 196 cm at 14.7° below the positive x axis.

3.33 (a) The projected distance on the seventh line is very nearly equal to the distance fallen. Thus, $7(0.15\text{ m}) = 1.05\text{ m} = \frac{1}{2}gt^2$ and and t is approximately equal to 0.45 s. Thus, the projected velocity is

$v = \dfrac{1.05\text{ m}}{0.45\text{ s}} = 2.3$ m/s.

(b) All objects fall vertically at the same acceleration, $g = 9.80\text{ m/s}^2$.

3.34 (a) Choosing the edge of the table as the origin of our coordinate system, we have $y = v_{yo}t - gt^2/2$, with $v_{yo} = 0$ so that $y = -gt^2/2$. The ball reaches the floor ($y = -1.00$ m) when

$t^2 = \dfrac{2(-1.00\text{ m})}{-9.80\text{ m/s}^2}$ or $t = 0.452$ s. At this time $x = v_{xo}t = 1.20$ m.

Therefore $v_{xo} = \dfrac{1.20\text{ m}}{0.452\text{ s}} = 2.66$ m/s.

(b) When the ball velocity is directed at 45° below the horizontal, we have $|v_y| = v_x$ or $gt = v_{xo}$, or $t = \frac{v_{xo}}{g} = \frac{2.66}{9.80} = 0.271$ s.
Then $y = -(9.80)(0.271)^2/2 = -0.36$ m.
Therefore, the ball will be 1 - 0.36 = 0.64 m above the floor.

3.35 v_{wc} = the velocity of the water relative to the car.
v_{we} = the velocity of the water relative to the earth.
v_{ce} = the velocity of the car relative to the earth.

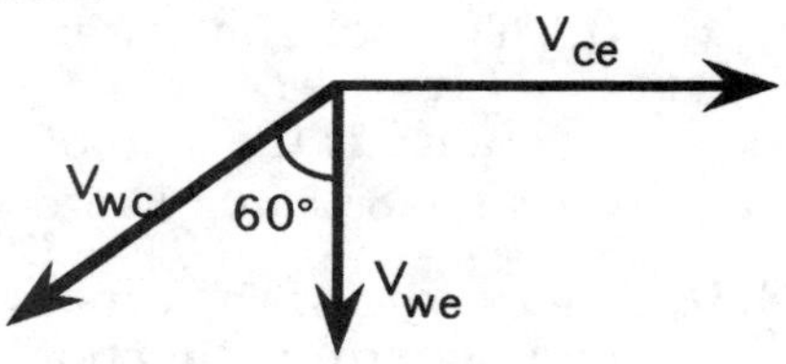

$v_{we} = v_{wc} + v_{ce}$

(a) v_{we} has zero horizontal component.
Thus, $v_{wc}\sin 60° = v_{ce} = 50.0$ km/h,
or $v_{wc} = 57.7$ km/h at 60.0° west of vertical.

(b) Since v_{ce} has zero vertical component,
$v_{we} = v_{wc}\cos 60.0° = (57.7\text{ km/h})(0.5) = 28.9$ km/h downward.

3.36 $AC = v_1 t = (90\text{ km/h})(2.5\text{ h}) = 225$ km
$AD = AC\cos 40 = 172.4$ km, and
$DC = AC\sin 40 = 144.6$ km
BD = AD - A B = 172.4 km - 80.0 km = 92.4 km
From the triangle BCD,
$BC = \sqrt{(BD)^2 + (DC)^2} = \sqrt{(92.4\text{ km})^2 + (144.6\text{ km})^2} = 171.6$ km.
Since car 2 travels this distance in 2.50 h, its constant speed is

$$v_2 = \frac{171.6\text{ km}}{2.50\text{ h}} = 68.6\text{ km/h}$$

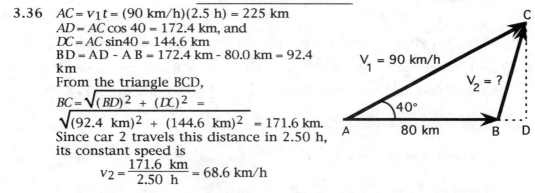

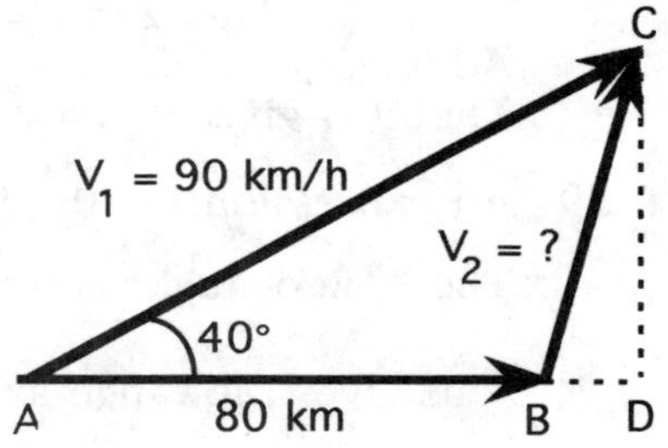

3.37 (a) The distance, s, moved in the first three seconds is given by

$$s = v_0 t + \frac{1}{2}at^2 = (100\text{ m/s})(3.00\text{ s}) + \frac{1}{2}(30\text{ m/s}^2)(3.00\text{ s})^2 = 435\text{ m}.$$

At this time its x location is $x_1 = s\cos 53.0° = 261.8$ m, its vertical height is $h = s\sin 53.0° = 347.4$ m. Its velocity at this time is

$$v = v_0 + at = 100\text{ m/s} + (30.0\text{ m/s}^2)(3.00\text{ s}) = 190\text{ m/s}.$$

This is the initial velocity for the next phase of its motion. Thus, the rocket begins its projectile motion with an x component of velocity of 114.3 m/s and a y component of 151.7 m/s. We find the maximum height during the projectile phase from $v_y = v_{oy} + at$ as
$0 = 151.7\text{ m/s} - (9.80\text{ m/s}^2)t_2$ which gives $t_2 = 15.48$ s as the time to reach the top of its arc after free-fall starts. During this time, it rises a distance h which can be found from $h = v_{oy}t + \frac{1}{2}at_2^2$ as

$$h = (151.7\text{ m/s})(15.48\text{ s}) + \frac{1}{2}(-9.80\text{ m/s}^2)(15.48\text{ s})^2 = 1174.1\text{ m}.$$

Thus, the maximum height reached is

$$H = h + \Delta y = 347.4\text{ m} + 1174.1\text{ m} = 1521.5\text{ m}. \ (1.5 \times 10^3\text{ m})$$

(b) The time to fall a distance H vertically, starting with $v_{oy} = 0$ is found from $y = v_{oy}t + \frac{1}{2}at^2$, or $-1521.5 \text{ m} = 0 + \frac{1}{2}(-9.80 \text{ m/s}^2)\, t_3{}^2$

This gives $t_3 = 17.62$ s, and a total time of free-fall flight of

$t_2 + t_3 = 15.48 \text{ s} + 17.62 \text{ s} = 33.1$ s.

Thus, the total time of flight is $T = 3 \text{ s} + 33.1 \text{ s} = 36.1$ s. (36 s)

(c) The horizontal range during free-fall is

$x = v_{ox}t = (114.3 \text{ m/s})(33.1 \text{ s}) = 3783.3$ m, and the total horizontal range is the sum of the range during powered flight, 261.8 m, plus 3783.3 m. Range = 261.8 m + 3783.3 m = 4045 m (4.00×10^3 m)

3.38 $v_{1w} = -v_{2w}$ (The canoes have the same speed relative to the water, but go in opposite directions.)

(1e = number one relative to the earth)

(1w = number one relative to the water)

(we = water relative to the earth)

$v_{1e} = v_{1w} + v_{we}$, and $v_{2e} = v_{2w} + v_{we}$

We are given that $v_{1e} = 2.9$ m/s and $v_{2e} = -1.2$ m/s.

We have $2.9 \text{ m/s} = -v_{2w} + v_{we}$ (1)

$-1.2 \text{ m/s} = v_{2w} + v_{we}$ (2)

Adding, gives $2v_{we} = 1.7$ m/s, so, $v_{we} = 0.85$ m/s.

Then (1) gives $v_{1w} = 2.05$ m/s, and (2) gives $v_{2w} = -2.05$ m/s.

3.39 An expression for the horizontal range can be found from $x = v_{ox}t$.

The time of flight is found from $y = v_{oy}t + \frac{1}{2}at^2$ with $y = 0$, as $t = \frac{2v_{oy}}{g}$.

This gives the range as $x = v_{ox}\left(\frac{2v_{oy}}{g}\right)$.

On earth this becomes $x_e = v_{ox}\left(\frac{2v_{oy}}{g_e}\right)$, and on the moon, $x_m = v_{ox}\left(\frac{2v_{oy}}{g_m}\right)$.

Dividing x_m by x_e, we have $x_m = \left(\frac{g_e}{g_m}\right)(x_e)$. With $g_m = \frac{1}{6}g_e$, we find

$x_m = 18$ m. For Mars, $g_{mars} = 0.38g_e$, and we find $x_{mars} = 7.9$ m.

3.40 The time to reach the opposite bank is found from $x = v_{ox}t$ as

$$t = \frac{10 \text{ m}}{v_o \cos 15°} \quad (1).$$

Now use $y = v_{oy}t + \frac{1}{2}at^2$ with $y = 0$ at the opposite bank. Thus, this equation reduces to: $0 = v_{oy}t - \frac{1}{2}gt^2$ or $v_{oy} = \frac{gt}{2} = v_o \sin 15°$ (2)

Eliminate t from (2) by use of (1) and solve for v_o to get $v_o = 14$ m/s.

3.41 (a) First, find the time for the coyote to travel the 70 m to the edge of the cliff. $x = v_o t + \frac{1}{2}at^2$ gives $70 \text{ m} = 0 + \frac{1}{2}(15 \text{ m/s}^2)\, t^2$, or $t = 3.06$ s.

The minimum speed of the roadrunner is $v = \frac{x}{t} = \frac{70 \text{ m}}{3.06 \text{ s}} = 23$ m/s.

(b) Find the horizontal velocity of the coyote when he reaches the edge of the cliff.

$v_x = v_o + at = 0 + (15\ m/s^2)(3.06\ s) = 45.8\ m/s.$

Now, find the time to drop 100 m vertically starting with $v_{oy} = 0$.

$$y = v_{oy}t + \frac{1}{2}at^2 \qquad -100\ m = 0 + \frac{1}{2}(-9.80\ m/s^2)\,t^2$$

From which, $t = 4.52$ s. At this time, the horizontal position can be found from $x = v_o t + \frac{1}{2}at^2$ as

$$x = (45.8\ m/s)(4.52\ s) + \frac{1}{2}(15\ m/s^2)(4.52\ s)^2 = 360\ m.$$

3.42 The components of the initial velocity for the shell are $v_o)_{hor} = 1700 \cos 55.0° = 975$ m/s and $v_o)_{vert} = 1700 \sin 55.0° = 1393$m/s .
(a) The time of flight is the time for the shell to return to its original level ($y = 0$), so we use $y = v_{oy}t + \frac{1}{2}at^2$ or $0 = 1393t - 4.9\,t^2$ and find $t = 0$ or $t = 284$ s. The time of flight is therefore 284 s or 4.73 min.
(b) The horizontal distance traveled during this time (i.e., the range) is given by $x = v_o t = 975(284) = 2.77 \times 10^5$ m/s = 277 km.

3.43 (a) The time to reach the fence is found from $x = v_{ox}t$, as

$$t = \frac{130\ m}{v_o \cos 35°} = \frac{158.7}{v_o}.$$

At this time, the ball must be 20 m above its launch position.

$y = v_{oy}t + \frac{1}{2}at^2$ gives

$$20\ m = (v_o \sin\ 35°)\,\frac{158.7}{v_o} - \frac{9.80\ m/s^2}{2}\left(\frac{158.7}{v_o}\right)^2.$$

From which, $v_o = 42$ m/s.

(b) $t = \dfrac{158.7\ m}{41.7} = = 3.8\ s$

(c) $v_x = v_o \cos 35° = (41.7\ m/s)(\cos 35°) = 34\ m/s$

$v_y = v_{oy} + at = (41.7 \sin 35°) - (9.80)(3.81) = -13\ m/s$

$v = \sqrt{(34.2)^2 + (13.4)^2} = 37\ m/s$

3.44 We shall first find the initial velocity of the ball thrown vertically upward. At its maximum height, $v = 0$ and $t = 1.50$ s.

$v = v_o + at$ gives $0 = v_{oy} + (-9.80\ m/s^2)(1.50\ s)$, or $v_{oy} = 14.7$ m/s.

In order for the second ball to reach the same vertical height as the first, the second must have the same initial vertical velocity. Thus, we can find v_o as $\quad v_o = \dfrac{v_{oy}}{\sin 30°} = 29.4$ m/s.

3.45 The time of flight of the ball is found as

$$y = v_{oy}t + \frac{1}{2}at^2 \quad 0 = (20\ m/s)\sin 30°(t) + \frac{1}{2}(-9.80\ m/s^2)\,t^2 \quad \text{or } t = 2.04\ s.$$

The horizontal distance the football moves in this time is

$x = v_{ox}t = (20\ m/s)\cos 30°(2.04\ s) = 35.3\ m.$

Thus, the catcher must run a distance of 35.3 m - 20 m = 15.3 m in the direction the ball was thrown, to catch the ball. He has a time of 2.04 s to run this distance. Thus, the speed is $\quad v = \dfrac{15.3\ m}{2.04\ s} = 7.5$ m/s.

3.46 The horizontal displacement at time t is: $x = (v_0 \cos 45°)t = \frac{v_0 t}{\sqrt{2}}$. Thus, when $x = 10$ m, the time must be $t = \frac{10\sqrt{2}}{v_0}$. At this time, the vertical displacement should be $y = 3.05\text{ m} - 2.00\text{ m} = +1.05\text{ m}$. Therefore, using $y = v_{0y}t + \frac{1}{2}at^2$, we have $1.05 = \frac{v_0}{\sqrt{2}}\frac{10\sqrt{2}}{v_0} + \frac{1}{2}(-9.80\text{ m/s}^2)[\frac{10\sqrt{2}}{v_0}]^2$ yielding $v_0 = 10.4$ m/s

---

3.47 Note that $\tan\theta_0 = h_0/x$ where h_0 is the intial target height and x is the horizontal displacement. For the projectile $y_p = v_0 \sin\theta_0 t - \frac{1}{2}gt^2$, and $x = v_0\cos\theta_0 t$. Combining and eliminating t in first term on right side gives: $y_p = \tan\theta_0 x - \frac{1}{2}gt^2$.

Substituting h_0/x for $\tan\theta_0$ gives: $y_p = h_0 - \frac{1}{2}gt^2$ (1)

For the falling target: $y_t = h_0 - \frac{1}{2}gt^2$ (2)

From (1) and (2) it can be seen that $y_t = y_p$ at all times t.
Thus, the projectile will hit the target.

3.48 (a) For the male anatomy, we have

x-component	y component
$d_{1x} = 0$	$d_{1y} = 104$ cm
$d_{2x} = 46$ cm	$d_{2y} = 19.5$ cm

This gives a resultant component of $d_x = 46$ cm, and a resultant y component $d_y = 123.5$ cm. Therefore,

$d = \sqrt{(46\text{ cm})^2 + (123.5\text{ cm})^2} = 131.8\text{ cm}$; $\tan\theta = 2.68$, or $\theta = 69.6°$.

For the female anatomy, we have

x-component	y component
$d_{1x} = 0$	$d_{1y} = 84$ cm
$d_{2x} = 38$ cm	$d_{2y} = 20.2$ cm

Giving resultant component of $d_x = 38$ cm, and a resultant y component $d_y = 104.2$ cm.

Thus, $d = \sqrt{(38\text{ cm})^2 + (104.2\text{ cm})^2} = 110.9\text{ cm}$; $\theta = \tan^{-1}(2.74) = 70°$.

(b) To normalize, multiply all distances by the appropriate scale factors which are: $s_m = \frac{200\text{ cm}}{180\text{ cm}} = 1.111$ and $s_f = \frac{200\text{ cm}}{168\text{ cm}} = 1.190$.

Multiplying all distances by these scale factors and recomputing the sums, yields

$d_m' = 146.4$ cm and the angle is 69.6°

$d_f' = 132.0$ cm and the angle is 70°.

To compute the vector difference $\Delta d = d_m' - d_f' = d_m' + (-d_f')$, we have

x-component	y component
$d_{mx}' = 51.0$ cm	$d_{my}' = 137.2$ cm
$-d_{fx}' = -45.1$ cm	$-d_{fy}' = -124.0$ cm

For a resultant x component of 5.9 cm, and a resultant y component of 13.2 cm. The Pythagorean theorem yields, $\Delta d = 14.5$ cm,

and $\tan\theta = \frac{13.2 \text{ cm}}{5.9 \text{ cm}} = 2.24$, from which $\theta = 65.9°$

3.49 First, consider the motion that yields maximum range. To achieve maximum range, the projectile should be launched at 45° above the horizontal. In this case, the initial components are:

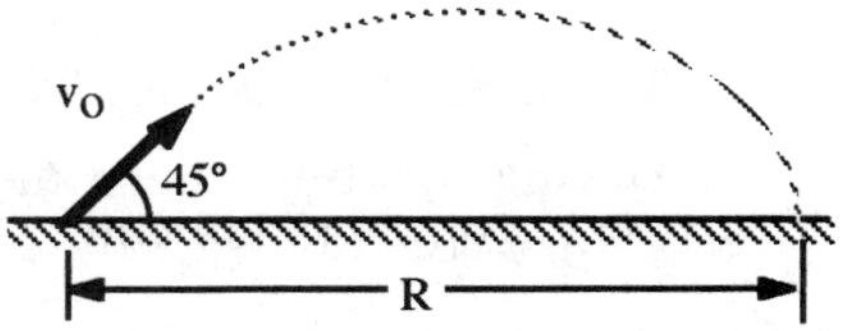

$$v_{ox} = v_{oy} = v_o \cos 45° = v_o \frac{\sqrt{2}}{2} = \frac{v_o}{\sqrt{2}}$$

The time of flight may be found from $v_y = v_{oy} - gt$. When the projectile returns to the original level, $v_y = -v_{oy}$. Thus, we have

$$-v_{oy} = v_{oy} - gt, \text{ or } t = \frac{2v_{oy}}{g}.$$

Then, since $v_{oy} = \frac{v_o}{\sqrt{2}}$, we have $t = \frac{2\frac{v_o}{\sqrt{2}}}{g} = \frac{\sqrt{2}v_o}{g}$

The range, R, is the horizontal distance traveled in this time,

or $R = v_{ox}\, t = \frac{v_o}{\sqrt{2}} \frac{\sqrt{2}v_o}{g} = \frac{v_o^2}{g}$.

That is, the relation between the maximum range and the launch speed of the projectile is $v_o^2 = gR$ (equation 1)

Now, consider throwing the projectile straight upward at speed v_o. The time required for the projectile to reach maximum height may be found from $v_y = v_{oy} - gt$. At maximum height, $v_y = 0$, and $v_{oy} = v_o$,

so $0 = v_o - gt$.

The time to reach maximum altitude is therefore given by $t = \frac{v_o}{g}$. The altitude of the projectile at this time may be found from

$$y = \bar{v}_y\, t = \left(\frac{v_y + v_{oy}}{2}\right)t.$$

This gives the maximum height as $h = \left(\frac{0 + v_o}{2}\right)\left(\frac{v_o}{g}\right)$

Thus, the maximum height is $h = \frac{v_o^2}{2g}$, and from equation 1 above, $h = \frac{R}{2}$.

3.50 (a) At the top of the arc $v_y = 0$, and from $v_y = v_{oy} - gt$, we find the time to reach the top of the arc to be

$t = \frac{v_o \sin\theta_o}{g}$ (1) . The vertical height, h, reached in this time is found from $y = v_{oy}t - \frac{1}{2}gt^2$ as $h = (v_o \sin\theta_o)\,t - \frac{1}{2}gt^2$ (2) .

Substitute into (2) for t from (1), and we find $h = \frac{v_o^2 \sin^2\theta_o}{2g}$.

(b) The total time of flight, T, is twice the time given in (1) above. The horizontal range, R, is found from $x = v_{ox}T$ as

$$R = (v_0\cos\theta)\frac{2v_0\sin\theta}{g}\text{ , or }R = \frac{v_0^2\sin(2\theta)}{g}.$$

3.51 We have $v_{be} = \sqrt{v^2_{br} + v^2_{re}} = 13\text{ km/h}$ and $\theta = \tan^{-1}\frac{5.0}{12} = 22.6°$.

The time to cross the river is $t = \frac{1.5\text{ km}}{v_{br}} = \frac{1.5\text{ km}}{12\text{ km/h}} = 0.125\text{ h} = 7.5\text{ min}$

During this time the boat drifts downstream a distance of

$v_{re}t = (5\text{ km/h})(0.125\text{ h}) = 0.625\text{ km} = 625\text{ m}.$

3.52 We have $v_{wg} = -0.500\text{ m/s}$ = velocity of water relative to the ground,

$v_{sg} = \frac{0.56\text{ m}}{0.800\text{ s}} = 0.7\text{ m/s}$ = velocity of skater relative to the ground, and

$v_{sg} = v_{sw} + v_{wg}$.

(a) (i) $v_{sg} = v_{sw} + v_{wg}$ gives $0.7\text{ m/s} = v_{sw} + (-0.5\text{ m/s})$, or
$v_{sw} = 1.20\text{ m/s}$.

(ii) $v_{sg} = -0.5\text{ m/s}$ (same as the water), so $v_{sg} = v_{sw} + v_{wg}$ gives
$-0.5\text{ m/s} = v_{sw} + (-0.5\text{ m/s})$, or $v_{sw} = 0$.

(b) $d_{sw} = v_{sw}\,t = (1.20\text{ m/s})(0.800\text{ s}) = 0.96\text{ m}$

(c) time to go upstream = 0.800 s

time to drift back downstream $= \frac{0.56\text{ m}}{0.50\text{ m/s}} = 1.12$ s, for a total time of

1.92 s. Therefore, $\bar{v} = \frac{d_{sw}}{\text{time}} = \frac{0.96\text{ m}}{1.92\text{ s}} = 0.5\text{ m/s}$

3.53 We know, $v_{ox} = v_0\cos 45.0 = 17.68\text{ m/s}$, and $v_{oy} = v_0\sin 45.0 = 17.68\text{ m/s}$.

The time to go 50.0 m horizontally is $t = \frac{\Delta x}{v_{ox}} = \frac{50.0\text{ m}}{17.68\text{ m/s}} = 2.83\text{ s}$

and the height at this time is

$y = v_0t + \frac{1}{2}at^2 = (17.68\text{ m/s})(2.83\text{ s}) + \frac{1}{2}(-9.80\text{ m/s}^2)(2.83\text{ s})^2 = 10.8\text{ m}.$

Thus, the net should be placed 10.8 m above the cannon.

3.54 Find initial velocity of dart when shot at rest, horizontally, one meter above the ground. From $y = v_{yo}t + \frac{1}{2}at^2$ we have $t = \left(\frac{-2y}{g}\right)^{1/2}$

and $x = v_{xo}t$ thus $v_{xo} = x/t = x/(-2y/g)^{1/2} = x(g/(-2y))^{1/2} = 5(9.80/2)^{1/2}$,
or $v_{xo} = 11.1\text{ m/s}$.

Find how far the dart will go if it is shot horizontally, one meter above the ground while sliding down the board at 2 m/s:

$y = v_{yo}t + \frac{1}{2}at^2$

$0 = gt^2/2 + v_{yo}t - y = 4.9t^2 + 2(0.707)t - 1$ and thus

$t = (-1.414 + [(1.414)^2 + 4(4.90)]^{1/2})/2(4.90) = 0.32995\text{ s}$

$x = v_{xo}t = [11.07 + 2(0.707)](0.32995) = 4.12\text{ m}$

3.55 (a)(b) Since the shot leaves the gun horizontally, the time it takes to reach the target is $t = \frac{x}{v_o}$. The vertical distance traveled in this time is $y = -\frac{1}{2}gt^2 = -\frac{g}{2}\left(\frac{x}{v_o}\right)^2 = Ax^2$ where $A = -\frac{g}{2v_o^2}$

(c) If $x = 3.00$m, $y = -0.210$ m, then $A = \frac{-0.210}{9.00} = -0.023$.

$$v_o = \sqrt{\frac{g}{2A}} = \sqrt{\frac{9.80}{0.046}} = 14.6 \text{ m/s}$$

3.56 Calling his first direction the x direction, we find the following:
His first displacement is solely in the x direction and equals
$R_{1x} = 10.0$ m.
He then begins to move in the negative y direction for 5.00 m. His displacement is
$R_{2y} = -5.00$ m.
He now turns right by 90.0° once again to walk in the negative x direction. His displacement is:
$R_{3x} = -7.00$ m.

Thus, $R = \sqrt{(3.00)^2 + (5.00)^2} = 5.83$ m

at $\theta = \arctan\frac{5}{3} = 59.0°$ to the right from original direction.

3.57 The first displacement has the following components.
$R_{1x} = 75$ m cos 240° = -37.5 paces, and
$R_{1y} = 75$ m sin 240° = -65.0 paces.
The second displacement gives
$R_{2x} = 125$ m cos 135° = - 88.4 paces, and
$R_{2y} = 125$ m sin 135° = + 88.4 paces.
Finally, the third displacement gives:
$R_{3x} = 100$ m cos 160° = -94.0 paces, and
$R_{3y} = 100$ m sin 160° = + 34.2 paces.
The resultant components are $R_x = -220$ paces and $R_y = 57.6$ paces.

So, $R = \sqrt{(-220 \text{ paces})^2 + (57.6 \text{ paces})^2} = 227$ paces

at $\theta = \arctan\frac{57.6}{220} = 165°$

3.58 The resultant x component of the velocity is
$v_x = 300 + 100\cos 30.0° = 386.6$ mph, and
$v_y = 100\sin 30.0° = 50$ mph.

So, $v = \sqrt{(386.6 \text{ mph})^2 + (50 \text{ mph})^2} = 390$ mph

at $\theta = \arctan\frac{50}{386.6} = 7.37°$ N of E.

3.59 (a) The time of flight of the first snowball is the nonzero root of

$$y = v_{yo}t_1 + \frac{1}{2}at_1^2$$

$$0 = (25 \text{ m/s}) \sin 70°\, t_1 - \frac{1}{2}(9.80 \text{ m/s}^2)\, t_1^2$$

$$t_1 = \frac{2(25\ \text{m/s})\ \sin 70°}{9.80\ \text{m/s}^2} = 4.79\ \text{s.}$$

The distance to your target is

$x = v_{xo}t_1 = (25.0\ \text{m/s})\cos 70.0°(4.79\ \text{s}) = 41.0\ \text{m}$

Now, the second snowball is described as

$$y = v_{yo}t_2 + \frac{1}{2}at_2{}^2$$

$$0 = (25.0\ \text{m/s})\ \sin\theta_2\ t_2 - \frac{1}{2}(9.80\ \text{m/s}^2)\,t_2{}^2$$

$t_2 = (5.10\ \text{s})\sin\theta_2$

$x = v_{xo}t_2 = (25\ \text{m/s})\cos\theta_2(5.10\ \text{s})\sin\theta_2 = (128\ \text{m})\sin\theta_2\cos\theta_2$

$0.321 = \sin\theta_2\cos\theta_2$

Using $\sin 2\theta = 2\sin\theta\cos\theta$

we have $0.321 = \frac{1}{2}\sin 2\theta_2$ and $\quad 2\theta_2 = \arcsin 0.643 \quad \theta_2 = 20.0°$

(b) The second snowball is in the air for time $t_2 = (5.10\ \text{s})\sin\theta_2 = (5.10\ \text{s})\sin 20.0° = 1.75\ \text{s}$, so you throw it after the first by $t_1 - t_2 = 4.79\ \text{s} - 1.75\ \text{s} = 3.05\ \text{s}$.

3.60 For the ball thrown at 45°, the distance traveled before hitting the Earth is $D = \frac{v_0{}^2}{g}$

For the bouncing ball $\quad D = \frac{v_0{}^2\ \sin 2\theta}{g} + \frac{\left(\frac{v_0}{2}\right)^2 \sin 2\theta}{g}$

where θ is the angle it makes with the ground when thrown and when bouncing. We require

$$\frac{v_0{}^2}{g} = \frac{v_0{}^2\ \sin 2\theta}{g} + \frac{\left(\frac{v_0}{2}\right)^2 \sin 2\theta}{g}$$

$\sin 2\theta = \frac{4}{5} \qquad \theta = 26.6°$

The time for flight of any projectile can be found as:

$$y = v_{yo}t + \frac{1}{2}at^2$$

$$0 = v_0\sin\theta_0 t - \frac{1}{2}gt^2$$

If $t = 0$ is the time the ball is thrown, then $\quad t = \frac{2v_0\sin\theta_0}{g}$ is the time at landing. So for the ball thrown at 45°

$$t_{45} = \frac{2v_0\sin 45°}{g}$$

For the bouncing ball,

$$t = t_1 + t_2 = \frac{2v_0\sin 26.6°}{g} + \frac{2(v_0/2)\sin 26.6°}{g} \quad \text{so} \ \frac{t}{t_{45}} = \frac{1.34}{1.41} = 0.949$$

3.61 $\quad y = \tan(\theta_0)\ x - \frac{g}{2v_0{}^2\cos^2(\theta_0)}\,x^2\,.$

Setting $x = d\cos(\phi)$, and $y = d\sin(\phi)$, we have

$$d\sin(\phi) = \tan(\theta_0)\, d\cos(\phi) - \frac{g}{2v_0^2\cos^2(\theta_0)}\,(d\cos(\phi))^2 .$$

Solving for d yields,

$$d = \frac{2v^2{}_0\cos(\theta_0)[\sin(\theta_0)\cos(\phi) \;-\; \sin(\phi)\cos(\theta_0)]}{g\cos^2(\phi)} \text{ , or}$$

$$d = \frac{2v^2{}_0\cos(\theta_0)\;\sin(\theta_0 - \phi)}{g\cos^2(\phi)} .$$

ANSWERS TO CONCEPTUAL QUESTIONS

2. The magnitudes add when **A** and **B** are in the same direction. The resultant will be zero when the two vectors are equal in magnitude and opposite in direction.

4. The minimum sum for two vectors occurs when the two vectors are opposite in direction. If they are unequal, their sum cannot add to zero.

6. The component of a vector can only be equal to or less than the vector itself. It can never be greater than the vector.

8. The components of a vector will be equal in magnitude if the vector lies at a 45° angle with the two axes along which the components lie.

10. They both start from rest in the downward direction and accelerate alike in the vertical direction. Thus, they reach the ground with the same vertical speed. However, the ball thrown horizontally had an initial horizontal component of velocity which is maintained throughout the motion. Thus, the ball thrown horizontally moves with the greater speed.

12. The car can round a turn at a constant *speed* of 90 miles per hour. Its velocity will be changing, however, because it is changing in direction.

14. The balls will be closest at the instant the second ball is projected. The first ball will always be going faster than the second ball. There will be a one second time interval between their collisions with the ground. The two move with the same acceleration in the vertical direction. Thus, changing their horizontal velocity can never make them hit at the same time.

16. Let v_x and v_y represent its original velocity components, (a) $x = v_x\frac{v_y}{g}$ and $y = \frac{v_y{}^2}{2g}$
(b) Its velocity is horizontal and equal to v_x. (c) Its acceleration is vertically downward, $-g$. With air resistance, the answers to (a) and (b) would be smaller. As for (c) the magnitude would be somewhat larger for the acceleration would have a component horizontally backward.

18. The horizontal velocity of the yellow ball does not affect its vertical motion, which is identical to that of the vertical free fall of the red ball.

20. The passenger sees the ball go into the air and come back in the same way he would if he were at rest on the Earth. An observer by the tracks would see the ball follow the path of a projectile. If the train were accelerating, the ball would fall behind the position it would reach in the absence of the acceleration.

CHAPTER FOUR SOLUTIONS

Chapter Four Readings

Brancazio, P., "The Physics of Kicking a Football," *The Physics Teacher,* October 1985, p. 403

Cohen, B.I., "Isaac Newton," *Scientific American,* December 1955, p. 73.

Crane, H.R., "Digital Electronic Balances: Mass or Weight?," *The Physics Teacher,* 29, 142, 1991

McCloskey, M., "Intuitive Physics," *Scientific American,* April 1983, p. 122.

Palmer, F., "Friction," *Scientific American,* February 1051, p. 54.

Zimmerer, R., "The Measurement of Mass," *The Physics Teacher,* September 1983, p. 354

4.1 (a) $F_R = ma = (6.0\text{ kg})(2.0\text{ m/s}^2) = 12\text{ N}$.

(b) $a = \frac{F_R}{m} = \frac{12\text{ N}}{4.0\text{ kg}} = 3.0\text{ m/s}^2$.

4.2 The acceleration given to the football is found from $v = v_0 + at$ as

$$a = \frac{v - v_0}{t} = \frac{10\text{ m/s} - 0}{0.20\text{ s}} = 50\text{ m/s}^2.$$

Then, from Newton's 2nd Law, we find $F = ma = (0.50\text{ kg})(50\text{ m/s}^2) = 25\text{ N}$.

4.3 On earth $w = mg$. If g changes to g', the new weight would be $w' = mg'$.

Therefore, $\frac{w'}{w} = \frac{mg'}{mg} = \frac{g'}{g}$, or $w' = \frac{g'}{g}w$.

On the moon, $g' = \frac{1}{6}g$. Thus, $w' = \frac{1}{6}w = \frac{5}{6}$ lb. This is equivalent to 3.71 N. On Jupiter, $g' = 2.64\,g$. The techniques above give the weight on Jupiter to be 58.7 N. The mass is the same at all three locations. The weight on the earth is 22.2 N, and $\frac{w}{g} = \frac{22.2\text{ N}}{9.80\text{ m/s}^2} = 2.27\text{ kg}$,

---

4.4 $a = \frac{F}{m} = \frac{750000\text{ N}}{1.5 \times 10^7\text{ kg}} = 0.05\text{ m/s}^2$, and

$v = v_0 + at = 0 + (0.05)t$ with $v = 80\text{ km/h} = 22.22\text{ m/s}$ gives

$t = 444.4\text{ s} = 7.4\text{ min}$

4.5 Summing the forces on the plane shown gives

$\Sigma F_x = F - f = 10\text{ N} - f$

$= (0.20\text{ kg})(2.0\text{ m/s}^2)$.

From which

$f = 9.6\text{ N}$

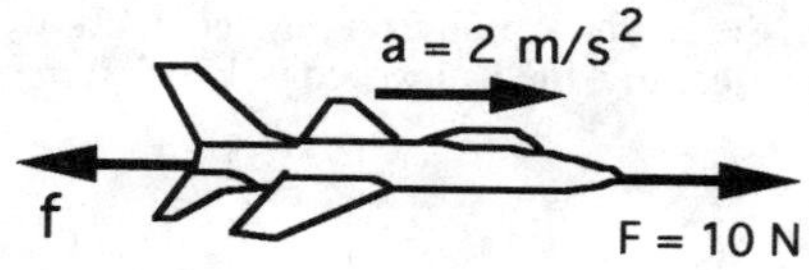

4.6 First, find the acceleration of the bullet from the equations of motion with constant acceleration, as

$$a = \frac{v^2 - v_0^2}{2x} = \frac{(320\ \text{m/s})^2 - 0}{2(0.82\ \text{m})} = 6.24 \times 10^4\ \text{m/s}^2.$$

Then, $F = ma = (5.0 \times 10^{-3}\ \text{kg})(6.24 \times 10^4\ \text{m/s}^2) = 310\ \text{N}$

4.7 (a) From the second law, the acceleration of the boat is

$$a = \frac{F_R}{m} = \frac{2000\ \text{N} - 1800\ \text{N}}{1000\ \text{kg}} = 0.20\ \text{m/s}^2$$

(b) The distance moved is found from

$$x = v_0 t + \frac{1}{2}at^2 = 0 + \frac{1}{2}(0.2\ \text{m/s}^2)(10.0\ \text{s})^2 = 10\ \text{m}.$$

(c) Its velocity is found as $v = v_0 + at = 0 + (0.2\ \text{m/s}^2)(10.0\ \text{s}) = 2\ \text{m/s}$.

4.8 (a) We resolve the forces shown into their components as

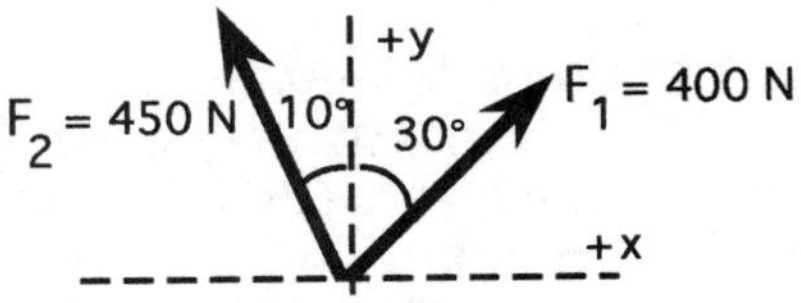

	x comp	y comp
400 N:	200. N	346. N
450 N:	-78.1 N	443. N
F_R:	122 N	789 N

The magnitude of the resultant force is found from the Pythagorean theorem as $F_R = \sqrt{(\Sigma F_x)^2 + (\Sigma F_y)^2} = \sqrt{(122\ \text{N})^2 + (789\ \text{N})^2} = 798\ \text{N}$,

and $\tan\theta = \frac{\Sigma F_y}{\Sigma F_x} = \frac{789}{122} = 6.47$, from which $\theta = 81.2°$. Thus, the resultant force is at an angle of 8.8° to the right of the forward direction.

(b) The acceleration is in the same direction as F_R and is given by

$$a = F_R/m = 798\ \text{N}/\ 3000\ \text{kg} = 0.266\ \text{m/s}^2.$$

4.9 The resultant of the two forces is found from the Pythagorean theorem as $F_R = \sqrt{(390\ \text{N})^2 + (180\ \text{N})^2} = 430\ \text{N}$, and $\tan\theta = \frac{390\ \text{N}}{180\ \text{N}} = 2.166$,

or $\theta = 65.2°$. Thus, $a = \frac{F_R}{m} = \frac{430\ \text{N}}{270\ \text{kg}} = 1.59\ \text{m/s}^2$ at 65.2° north of east.

4.10 Using $v^2 = v_0^2 - 2gh$ with $v_0 = 0$, we find that at the moment the ball hits the ground, its velocity v_1 is $v_1 = \sqrt{(-2)(-9.80)(30)} = 24.25\ \text{m/s}$ in the downward direction. If the ball rebounds to a height of 20 m, then its velocity v_2 as it leaves the ground is

$v_2 = \sqrt{(-2)(-9.80)(20)} = 19.80\ \text{m/s}$ in the upward direction. The average acceleration between when the ball hits the ground and when it leaves the ground is then

$$a = \frac{v_2 - v_1}{\Delta t} = \frac{(19.8) - (-24.25)}{0.002\ \text{s}} = 22025\ \text{m/s}^2\ \text{upward}.$$

Therefore, the average force is

$$F = ma = (0.50\ \text{kg})(22025\ \text{m/s}^2) = 1.10 \times 10^4\ \text{N upward}.$$

4.11 First, use $\Sigma F_y = 0$:

$T_2 \sin 37.0° - 600\text{ N} = 0$

From which, $T_2 = 997$ N.

Now, use $\Sigma F_x = 0$:

$T_2 \cos 37.0° - T_1 = 0$

Since $T_2 = 997$ N, we find $T_1 = 796$ N.

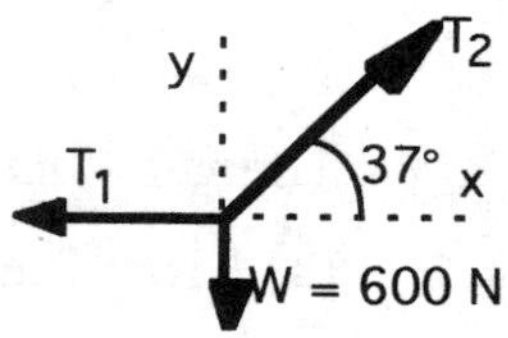

4.12 Use $\Sigma F_x = 0$ as

$T_1 \cos 40° - T_2 \cos 40° = 0$, or $T_1 = T_2$

From $\Sigma F_y = 0$, we have

$T_1 \sin 40° + T_2 \sin 40° - 100\text{ N} = 0$

Thus, $T_1 = T_2 = 77.8$ N.

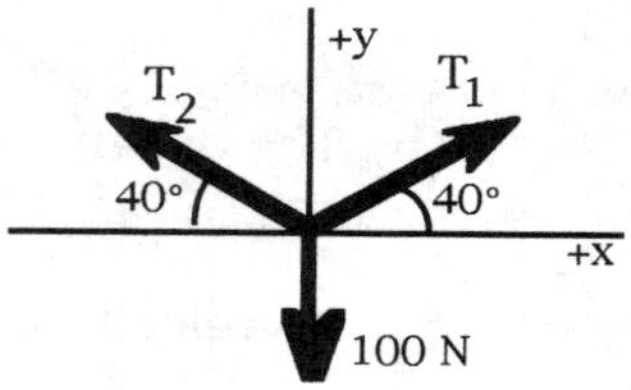

4.13 From $\Sigma F_x = 0$, we have

$T_1 \cos 30° - T_2 \cos 60° = 0$

Thus, $T_1 = 0.577\, T_2$ (1)

From $\Sigma F_y = 0$,

$T_1 \sin 30° + T_2 \sin 60° - 150\text{ N} = 0$ (2)

Solving (1) and (2) simultaneously,

$T_2 = 130$ N and $T_1 = 75$ N

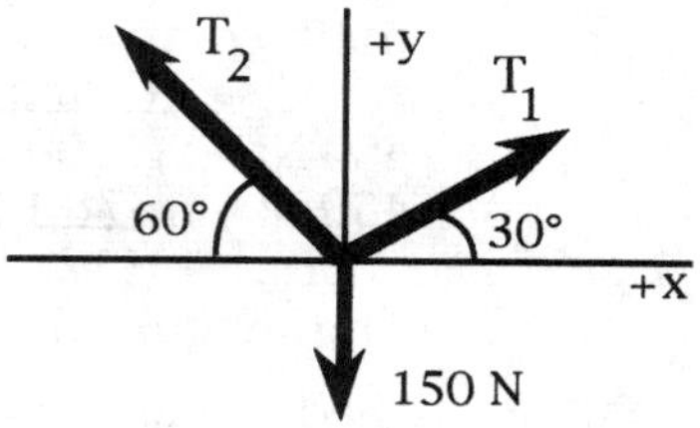

4.14 From $\Sigma F_x = 0$, we have

$W_2 \cos\alpha - (110\text{ N}) \cos 40° = 0$ (1)

From $\Sigma F_y = 0$, we have

$W_2 \sin\alpha + (110\text{ N}) \sin 40° - 220\text{ N} = 0$ (2)

Dividing (2) by (1) yields

$\tan\alpha = \dfrac{149.3}{84.26} = 1.772$, or $\alpha = 60.55°$.

Then, from either (1) or (2), $W_2 = 171.4$ N.

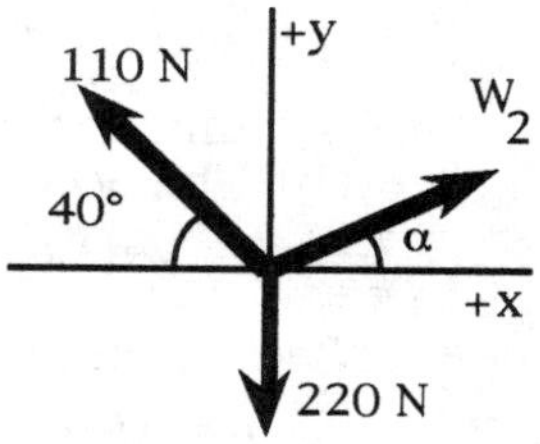

4.15 (a) A study of the forces on the block that are parallel to the incline reveals that

$\Sigma F_x = F\cos\theta - mg\sin\theta = 0$, so

$F = (2.0\text{ kg})(9.80)\dfrac{\sin 60°}{\cos 60°} = 33.9\text{ N. (34 N)}$

(b) A study of the forces on the block that are perpendicular to the incline shows that

$\Sigma F_y = N - F\sin\theta - mg\cos\theta = 0$, so that

$N = F\sin\theta + mg\cos\theta = (33.9\text{ N})\sin 60° + (2.0\text{ kg})(9.80\text{ m/s}^2)\cos 60° = 39\text{ N}.$

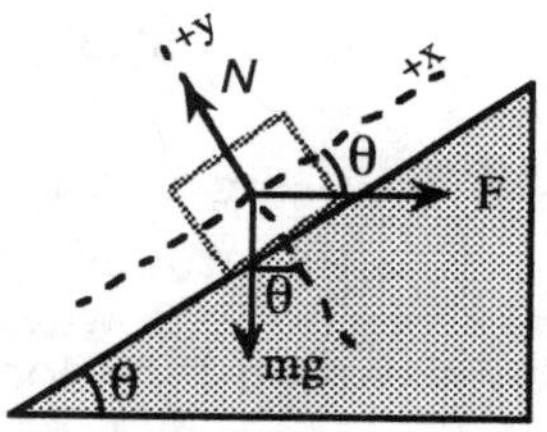

4.16 The total force in the forward direction is $2(600)\cos(30.0°) = 1039.2$ N
If the boat moves with constant velocity, then the total force acting on the boat must be zero. Since the total force acting perpendicular to the boat is already zero, the resistive force on the boat must have magnitude 1039.2 N and must point in the backward direction.

4.17 The forces on the bucket are the tension in the rope and the weight, 49 N, of the bucket. We call the positive direction upward, and use the second law.

$\Sigma F_y = ma_y$

$T - 49\text{ N} = (5.0\text{ kg})(3.0\text{ m/s}^2)$

$T = 64\text{ N}.$

4.18 (a) From the second law, we find the acceleration as

$$a = \frac{F}{m} = \frac{10\text{ N}}{30\text{ kg}} = 0.333\text{ m/s}^2.$$

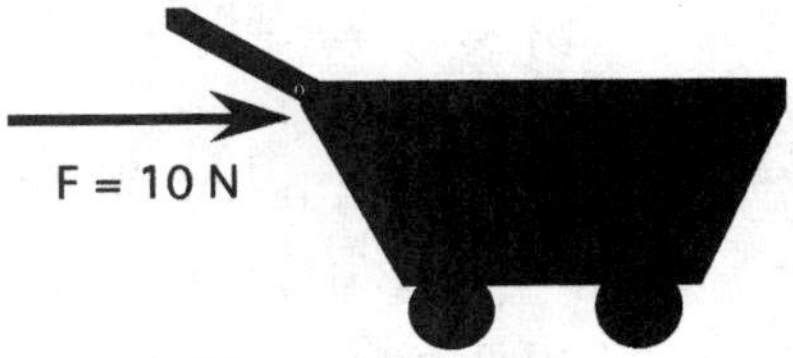

To find the distance moved, we use

$$x = v_0t + \frac{1}{2}at^2 = 0 + \frac{1}{2}(0.333\text{ m/s}^2)(3.0\text{ s})^2 =$$

1.5 m

(b) If the shopper places her 30 N (3.06 kg) child in the cart, the new acceleration will be $a = \frac{F}{m_{total}} = \frac{10\text{ N}}{33.06\text{ kg}} = 0.302\text{ m/s}^2$, and the new distance traveled in 3.0 s will be $x' = 0 + \frac{1}{2}(0.302\text{ m/s}^2)(3.0\text{ s})^2 = 1.4\text{ m}.$

4.19 (a) The average acceleration is given by

$$\bar{a} = \Delta v/\Delta t = (v_f - v_i)/\Delta t = (5.00\text{ m/s} - 20.0\text{ m/s})/4.000\text{ s} = -3.75\text{ m/s}^2.$$

The average force is found from the second law as

$$\bar{F} = m\bar{a} = (2.000 \times 10^3\text{ kg})(3.75\text{ m/s}^2) = 7500\text{ N}$$

(b) The distance traveled is:

$$x = \bar{v}\,t = \frac{(5.00\text{ m/s} + 20.0\text{ m/s})}{2}(4.000\text{ s}) = 50.0\text{ m}.$$

4.20 Letting $m_1 = 10.0$ kg and $m_2 = 5.00$ kg, we have

$m_1a = m_1g - T.$

$m_2a = T - m_2g\sin\theta.$

Adding these gives

$(m_1 + m_2)a = m_1g - m_2g\sin\theta.$

Thus, $a = \left(\frac{m_1 - m_2\sin\theta}{m_1 + m_2}\right)g$, or

$$a = \left(\frac{10.0 - (5.00)\sin 40°}{15}\right)9.80 = 4.43\text{ m/s}^2.$$

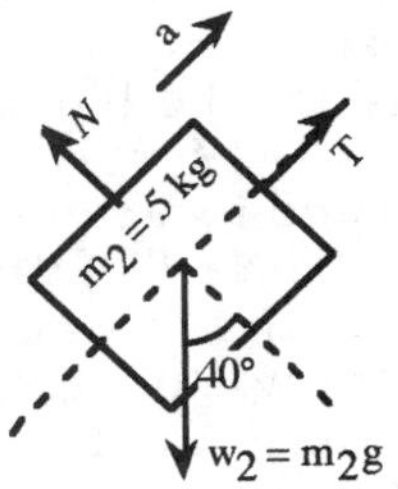

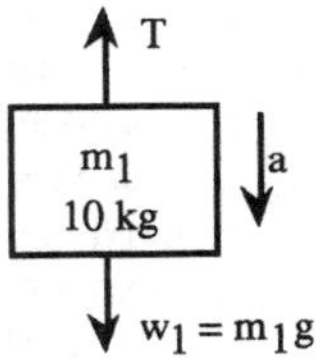

Using this value of a gives: $T = m_1(g - a) = 10.0(9.80 - 4.43) = 53.7$ N.

4.21 (a) The resultant external force acting on this system having a total mass of 6.0 kg is 42 N directed horizontally toward the right. Thus, the acceleration produced is $a = \frac{F}{m} = \frac{42\text{ N}}{6.0\text{ kg}} = 7.0\text{ m/s}^2.$

The acceleration of the system is 7.0 m/s^2 horizontally toward the right.

(b) Draw a free body diagram of the 3.0 kg object and apply Newton's second law to the horizontal forces acting on this object. This gives

$\Sigma F_x = ma_x$ or 42 N - T = (3.0 kg)(7.0 m/s^2), and therefore T = 21 N.
(c) The force accelerating the 2.0 kg object is the force exerted on it by the 1.0 kg object. Therefore, this force is given by:
F = ma = (2.0 kg)(7.0 m/s^2), or
F = 14 N directed horizontally toward the right.

4.22 v_0 = 90.0 km/h = 25.0 m/s, and $a = \frac{F}{m} = \frac{-1.87 \text{ x } 10^6 \text{ N}}{5.22 \text{ x } 10^6 \text{ kg}} = -0.358 \text{ m/s}^2$.
(a) $v = v_0 + at$ gives: v = 25.0 m/s + (-0.358 m/s^2) (30.0 s) = 14.3 m/s.
(b) $x = \bar{v}\, t = \left(\frac{25.0 \text{ m/s} + 14.3 \text{ m/s}}{2}\right)$ (30.0 s) = 589 m.

4.23 The acceleration of the mass down the incline is given by
$x = v_0 t + \frac{1}{2}at^2$, or 0.8 m = 0 + $\frac{1}{2}a(0.50 \text{ s})^2$.
This gives a = 6.4 m/s^2.
Thus, the force down the incline is $F = ma$ = (2.0 kg)(6.4 m/s^2) = 13 N.

4.24 Choosing our x axis along the incline with the positive direction up the incline, we have:
$\Sigma F_x = ma_x = T - w \sin 18.5° = (40.0 \text{ kg})a_x$,
which gives $a_x = \frac{140 \text{ N} - 124.4 \text{ N}}{40.0 \text{ kg}} = 0.390 \text{ m/s}^2$.
Since we have constant acceleration, we find (using $v^2 = v_0^2 + 2ax$):
$v^2 = 0 + 2(0.39 \text{ m/s}^2)(80 \text{ m})$, or v = 7.90 m/s.

4.25 First consider the block moving along the horizontal. The only force in the direction of movement is T. Thus
$\Sigma F_x = ma$ gives
T = (5.00 kg)a. (1)
Next consider the block which moves vertically. The forces on it are the tension T and its weight, 98 N. Thus,
$\Sigma F_y = ma$ = 98 N - T = (10.0 kg)a. (2)

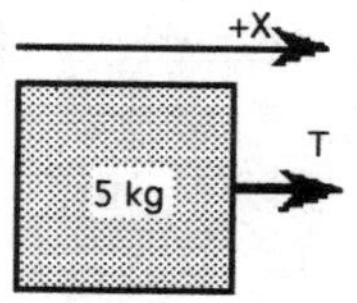

(a)

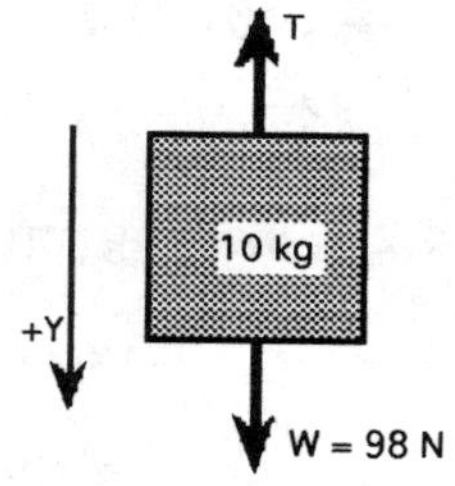

(b)

Note that both blocks must have the same magnitude of acceleration. Equations (1) and (2) can be solved simultaneously to give.
a = 6.53 m/s^2, and T = 32.7 N

4.26 First, consider forces on the upper block. They are T_1, the tension in the cable connecting the block to the ceiling of the elevator, T_2, the tension connecting the blocks, and the weight of the block, 98 N.
$\Sigma F_y = ma_y$ gives:
T_1 - T_2 -98 N = (10.0 kg)(2.00 m/s^2). (1)
The forces on the lower block are T_2 and its weight, 98 N. $\Sigma F_y = ma_y$ gives
T_2 - 98 N = (10.0 kg)(2.00 m/s^2). (2)

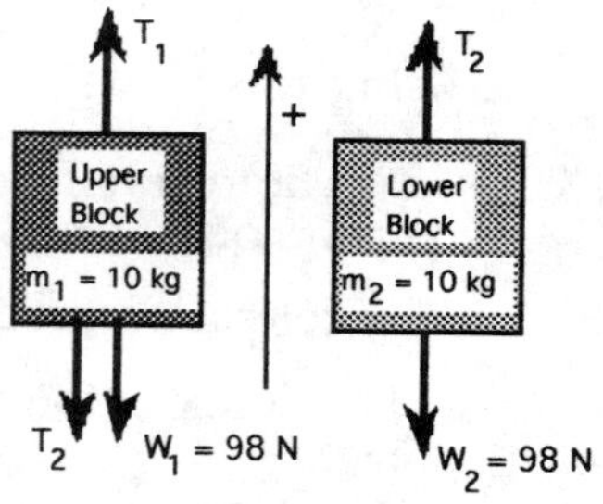

From (2), we find: $T_2 = 118$ N, and using this in (1), we find $T_1 = 236$ N.

4.27

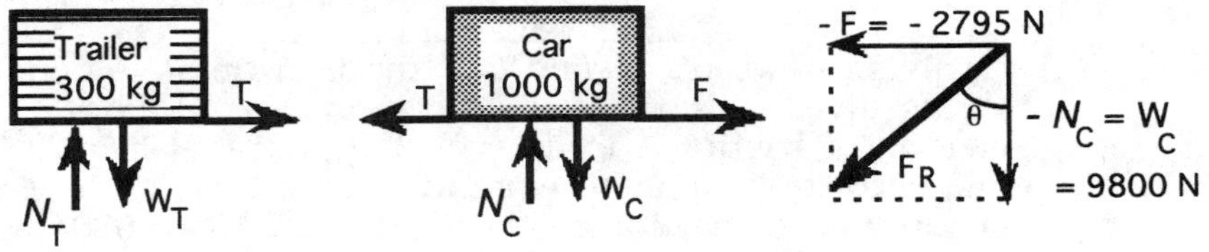

Apply the 2nd law to the trailer to get: $T = (300\text{ kg})(2.15\text{ m/s}^2) = 645$ N.
For the car: $F - T = 1000\text{ kg}(2.15\text{ m/s}^2)$, which gives: $F = 2795$ N.
(a) The net force on the car = $F - T = m_{car}a = 2150$ N (directed forward).
(b) From above, we know that $T = 645$ N in forward direction.
(c) The force exerted on the trailer by the car is - $T = 645$ N (rearward).
(d) The force exerted on the road by the car is the resultant of the reaction force $-F$ and the weight of the car as show above. This force is found to be $F_R = 10{,}190$ N at $\theta = 15.9°$ to the left of the vertical.

4.28 First, consider the 3.00 kg rising mass. The forces on it are the tension, T, and its weight, 29.4 N. With the upward direction as positive, the second law becomes

$T - 29.4\text{ N} = (3.00\text{ kg})a.$ (1)

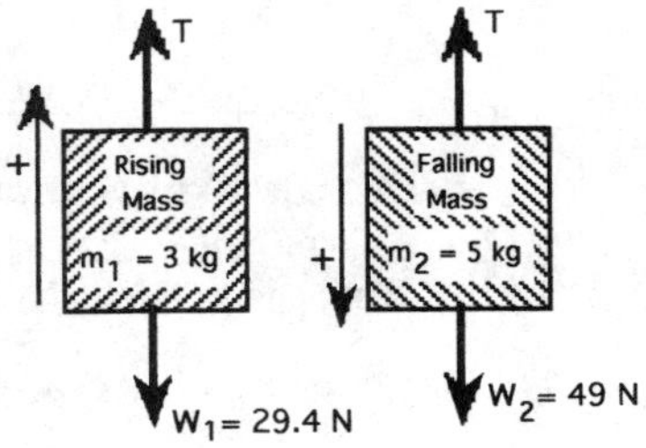

The forces on the falling 5.00 kg mass are its weight and T, and its acceleration is the same as that of the rising mass. Calling the positive direction down for this mass, gives

$49\text{ N} - T = (5.00\text{ kg})a.$ (2)

Equations (1) and (2) can be solved simultaneously to give
(a) the tension as $T = 36.8$ N,
(b) and the acceleration as $a = 2.45\text{ m/s}^2$.
(c) Consider the 3.00 kg mass. We have

$$y = v_0t + \frac{1}{2}at^2 = 0 + \frac{1}{2}(2.45\text{ m/s}^2)(1.00\text{ s})^2 = 1.23\text{ m.}$$

4.29 (a) To bring the block to the verge of motion, we exert a force of 75 N, but from the first law, we know: $\Sigma F_x = 0$, which gives

$75\text{ N} - f = 0$, or $f = 75$ N where f is the force of friction.

We know, since motion is imminent, that $f = \mu_s N$ where μ_s is the coefficient of static friction and N is the normal force. For our case, $N = mg$. Thus, $f = \mu_s mg$, and $\mu_s = \dfrac{f}{mg} = \dfrac{75\text{ N}}{196\text{ N}} = 0.38$.

(b) When there is motion, the analysis is virtually the same as that above. We find: $\mu_k = \dfrac{60\text{ N}}{196\text{ N}} = 0.31$.

4.30 (a) The static friction force on M_1 can have a maximum value of

$f = \mu_s N = \mu_s mg = 0.5(10)9.80 = 49$ N.

This is more than the weight of M_2 (39.2 N). Hence, the system does not move. $a = 0$

(b) Once in motion the friction force on M_1 becomes

$f = \mu_k N = \mu_k mg = 0.3(10)9.80 = 29.4$ N.

This is less than the gravitational force of 39.2 N on M_2.

$F_{net} = m_{total}a$ then yields $a = \dfrac{F_{net}}{m_{total}} = \dfrac{(39.2 - 29.4)}{(10 + 4)} = 0.70 \text{ m/s}^2$

4.31 (a) Applying Newton's second law, the horizontal components of the forces give $F\cos 20° - f = 0$,
yielding a frictional force $f = 300 \cos 20.0° = 282$ N.
The vertical component equation is: $N - F \sin 20° - W = 0$,
yielding a normal force $N = 300 \sin 20.0° + 1000 = 1103$ N.
The coefficient of friction is then $\mu_k = \dfrac{f}{N} = \dfrac{282}{1103} = 0.256$

(b) The vertical equation becomes $F\sin 20.0° + N - w = 0$, yielding a normal force $N = w - F\sin 20.0° = 897$ N.
The friction force now becomes $f = \mu_k N = 0.256(897) = 230$ N.
The horizontal component equation is $F\cos 20.0° - f = ma = \dfrac{w}{g}a$. The resulting acceleration is

$$a = \frac{(F\cos 20.0° - f)g}{w} = \frac{(300\cos 20° - 230)9.80}{1000} = 0.509 \text{ m/s}^2$$

4.32 (a) $a = \dfrac{v_f - v_0}{t} = \dfrac{6.00 \text{ m/s} - 12.0 \text{ m/s}}{5 \text{ s}} = -1.20 \text{ m/s}^2$.
We also know that $N = mg$. Now apply the second law:
$-f = m(-1.20 \text{ m/s}^2)$ or $f = m(1.20 \text{ m/s}^2)$. (1)
But, also, $f = \mu_k N = \mu_k mg$. From (1) above, we have

$$\mu_k mg = m(1.20 \text{ m/s}^2) \text{, so } \mu_k = \frac{1.20 \text{ m/s}^2}{9.80 \text{ m/s}^2} = 0.122.$$

(c) $x = \bar{v}\, t = \left(\dfrac{v_0 + v_f}{2}\right) t = \left(\dfrac{12.0 \text{ m/s} + 6.00 \text{ m/s}}{2}\right)(5.00 \text{ s}) = 45.0$ m.

4.33 The Normal force acting on the crate is given by $N = F + mg\cos\theta$. The net force tending to move the crate down the incline is $mg\sin\theta - f_s$, where f_s is the force of static friction between the crate and the incline. If the crate is in equilibrium, then $mg\sin\theta - f_s = 0$, so that $f_s = mg\sin\theta$. But, we also know

$f_s \le \mu_s$ (normal force) $= \mu_s (F + mg\cos\theta)$.

Therefore, we may write

$mg\sin\theta \le \mu_s (F + mg\cos\theta)$, or

$$F \ge \frac{mg\sin\theta}{\mu_s} - mg\cos\theta = \left(\frac{\sin\theta}{\mu_s} - \cos\theta\right) mg.$$

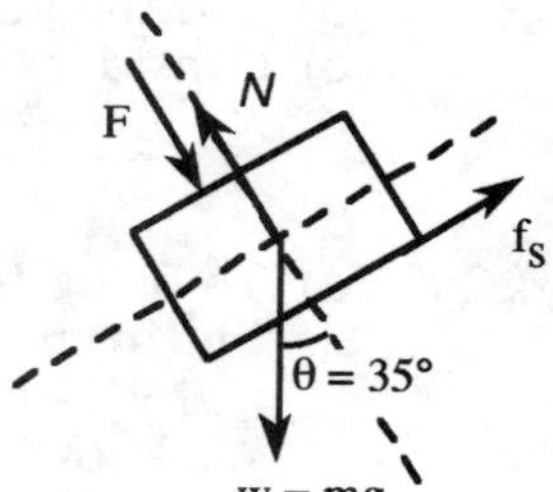

From which, $F \ge \left(\dfrac{\sin 35°}{0.300} - \cos 35°\right)(3.00)(9.80) = 32.1$ N.

4.34 In the vertical direction, we have
$N - 300 \text{ N} - (400 \text{ N})\sin 35.2° = 0$
from which, $N = 530.6$ N.
Therefore, $f = \mu_k N = (0.57)(530.6 \text{ N}) = 302.4$ N.
Then, from the second law, applied along the horizontal direction, we have
$(400 \text{ N}) \cos 35.2° - 302.4 \text{ N} = (30.6 \text{ kg})a_x$

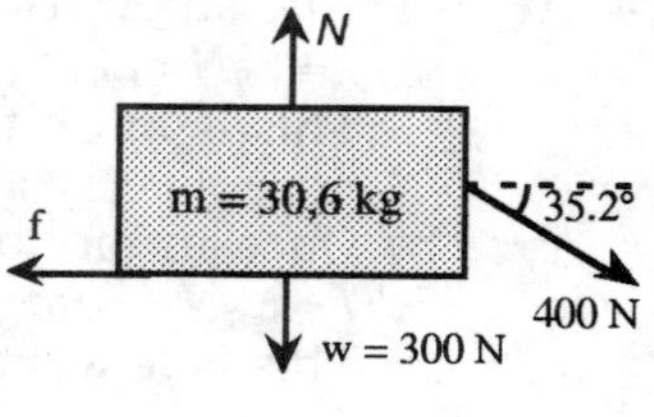

from which $a_x = 0.80 \text{ m/s}^2$.

Then, from $x = v_{0x}t + \frac{1}{2} a_x t^2$, we have $4 \text{ m} = 0 + \frac{1}{2}(0.8 \text{ m/s}^2) t^2$,

which gives $t = 3.16$ s.

4.35 (a) The object will fall so that $ma = mg - bv$, where the downward direction is taken as positive.

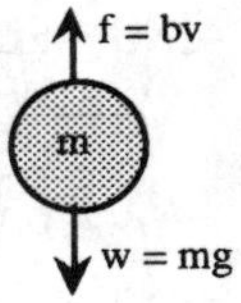

Therefore, $a = \frac{(mg - bv)}{m}$ equilibrium is reached ($a = 0$) when $v = v_{terminal} = mg/b = (50)(9.80)/15 = 32.7$ m/s.

(b) If the initial velocity is less than 32.7 m/s, then $a_0 \geq 0$ and 32.7 m/s is the largest velocity obtained by the object. On the other hand, if the initial velocity is <u>greater</u> than 32.7 m/s, then $a_0 \leq 0$ and 32.7 m/s is the <u>smallest</u> velocity obtained by the object. Note also that if the initial velocity is 32.7 m/s, then $a_0 = 0$ and the object continues falling with a constant speed of 32.7 m/s.

4.36 (a) Find the normal force N on the 25.0 kg box:

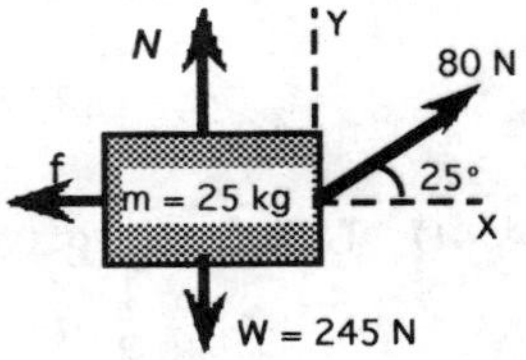

$\Sigma F_y = 0 = N + (80.0 \text{ N}) \sin 25.0° - 245 \text{ N}$,

or $N = 211$ N.

Now find the friction force, f, as

$f = \mu_k N = 0.300(211 \text{ N}) = 63.3$ N.

From the second law, we have $\Sigma F_x = ma$, or

$(80.0 \text{ N})\cos 25.0° - 63.3 \text{ N} = (25.0 \text{ kg})a$

or $a = 0.366 \text{ m/s}^2$.

(b) When the box is on the incline, $\Sigma F_y = 0$ gives

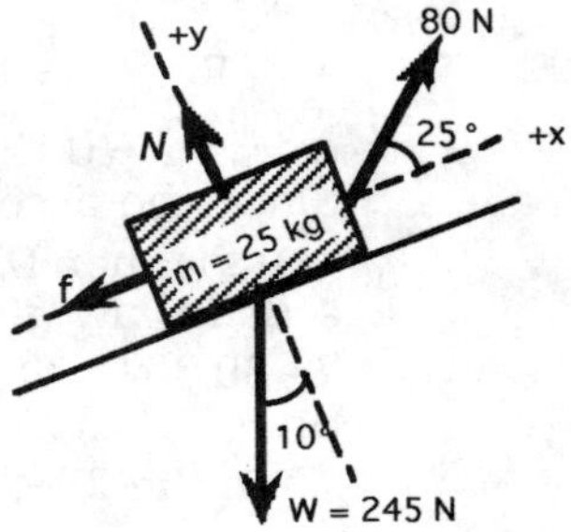

$N + (80.0 \text{ N})\sin 25.0° - (245 \text{ N})\cos 10.0°$, or

$N = 207$ N, and the friction force is

$f = \mu_k N = 0.300(207 \text{ N}) = 62.1$ N.

The net force parallel to the incline is

$\Sigma F_x = F\cos 25° - w\sin 10.0° - f = -32.1$ N.

Then $a_x = \frac{\Sigma F_x}{m} = \frac{-32.1}{25.0} = -1.29 \text{ m/s}^2$

down the incline.

4.37 The acceleration of the system is found from

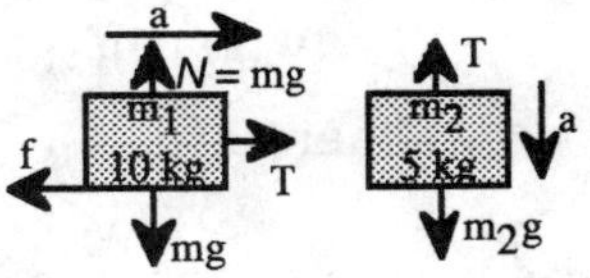

$y = v_0 t + \frac{1}{2} at^2$, or $1.00 = 0 + \frac{1}{2} a(1.20)^2$

which gives $a = 1.39 \text{ m/s}^2$.

Using the free body diagram of m_2, the second law gives $5.00(9.80) - T = 5(1.39)$, or $T = 42.1$ N.

Then applying the second law to the horizontal forces on m_1,

$42.1 - f = 10.0(1.39)$, or $f = 28.2$ N.

Since $N = m_1 g = 98.0$ N, we have $\mu_k = \frac{f}{N} = \frac{28.2}{98.0} = 0.288$.

4.38 (a) The force of friction is found as $f = \mu_k N = \mu_k mg$.

Now, choose the positive direction of the x axis in the direction of motion and apply the second law. We have:

$-f = ma_x$, or $a_x = -f/m = \mu_k g$.

Use $v^2 = v_0^2 + 2ax$, with $v = 0$, $v_0 = 50.0$ km/h $= 13.9$ m/s. We have

$0 = (13.9\ \text{m/s})^2 + 2(-\mu_k g)x$, or $\quad x = \frac{(13.9\ \text{m/s})^2}{2\mu_k g}$. (1)

With $\mu_k = 0.100$, this gives a value for x of $x = 98.6$ m

(b) With $\mu_k = 0.600$, (1) above gives $x = 16.4$ m

4.39 First, let us find the normal force acting on the box by use of $\Sigma F_y = 0$. We have $N - w\cos 30.0° = 0$, or $N = mg\cos 30.0°$.

Now apply Newton's 2nd law to the motion parallel to the ramp.

$\Sigma F_x = mg\sin 30° - f = ma_x$.

But, $f = \mu_k N = \mu_k mg\cos 30.0°$.

Thus, the 2nd law becomes

$mg\sin 30.0° - \mu_k mg\cos 30.0° = ma_x$, or

$$\mu_k = \frac{\sin 30.0°}{\cos 30.0°} - \frac{a_x}{g\cos 30.0°}$$

$$= \tan 30.0° - \frac{a_x}{g\cos 30.0°}$$

$$= 0.577 - \frac{1.20\ \text{m/s}^2}{(9.80\ \text{m/s}^2)(0.866)} = 0.436.$$

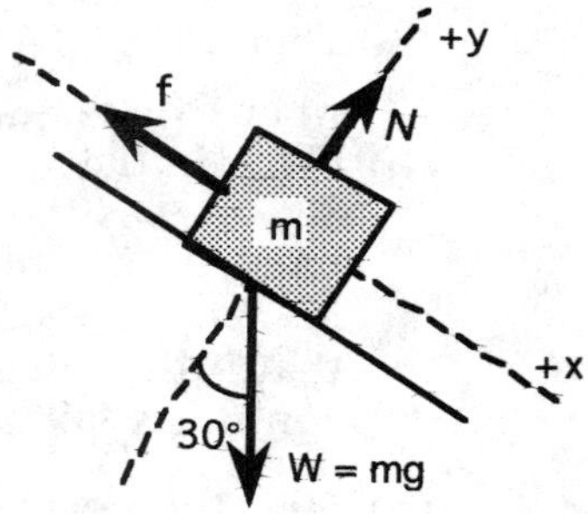

4.40 Using the given distance and time,

$x = v_0 t + \frac{1}{2}at^2$ gives

$1.00\ \text{m} = 0 + \frac{1}{2}a(16.00\ \text{s}^2)$,

or $\quad a = 0.125\ \text{m/s}^2$. (a)

Since the acceleration of the 4.00 kg mass is then $0.125\ \text{m/s}^2$, Newton's second law gives

$T - 39.2\ \text{N} = (4.00\ \text{kg})(0.125\ \text{m/s}^2)$

or $\quad T = 39.7$ N. (b)

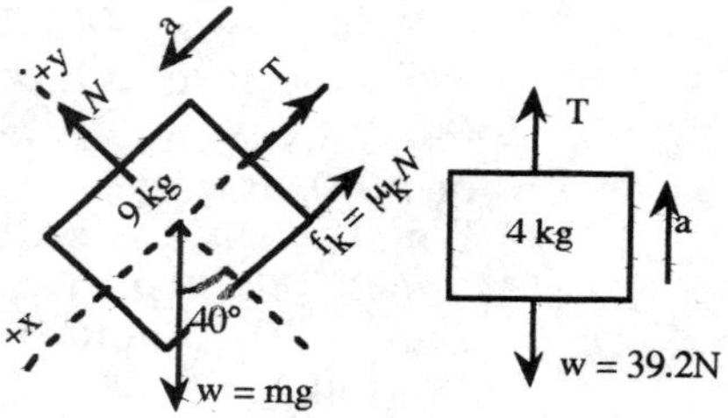

Then the 2nd law for the 9.00 kg mass gives: $\Sigma F_y = ma_y = 0$,

or $N = w\cos 40.0° = (9.00\ \text{kg})(9.80\ \text{m/s}^2)\cos 40.0° = 67.6$ N,

and $\Sigma F_x = ma_x$, or $\quad mg\sin 40.0° - T - f = (9.00\ \text{kg})a$, which yields

$f = (9.00\ \text{kg})(9.80\ \text{m/s}^2)\sin 40.0° - 39.7\ \text{N} - (9.00\ \text{kg})(0.125\ \text{m/s}^2) = 15.9$ N.

Therefore, $\quad \mu = \frac{f}{N} = \frac{15.9\ \text{N}}{67.6\ \text{N}} = 0.235.$ (c)

4.41 First, apply the 2nd law to the 12.0 kg block: $118\ \text{N} - T = (12.0\ \text{kg})a$ (1)

For the 7.00 kg block, we have

$N = w\cos 37.0° = 54.8$ N, and

$f = \mu_k N = 0.25(54.8\ \text{N}) = 13.7$ N

Apply the second law to the 7.00 kg block. We have:

$T - f - (68.6\ \text{N})\sin 37° = (7.00\ \text{kg})a$. (2)

Solving (1) and (2) simultaneously gives: $\quad a = 3.32\ \text{m/s}^2$.

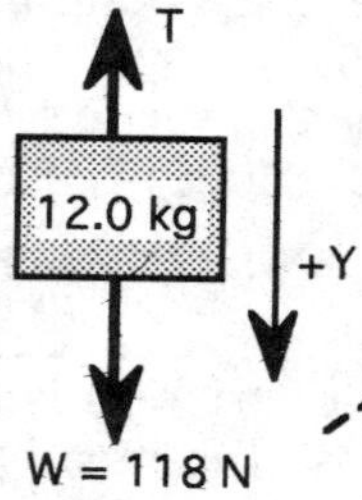

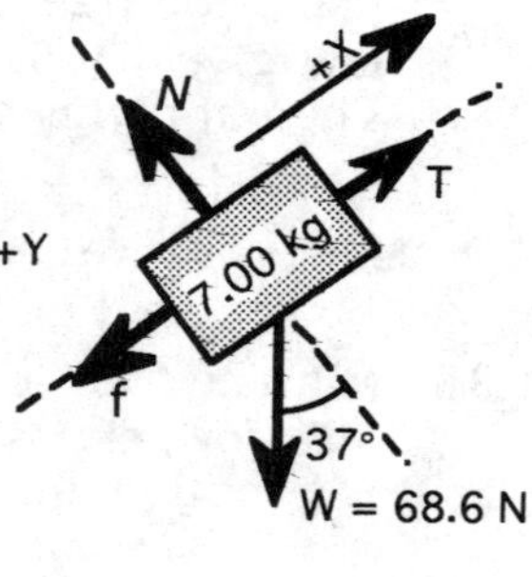

4.42 When the minimum force F is used, the block tends to slide down the incline and the friction force, f_s, is directed up the incline. While the block is still in equilibriium, we have

$\Sigma F_x = F\cos 60° + f_s - W\sin 60.0° = 0,$ (1)

and

$\Sigma F_y = N - F\sin 60.0° - W\cos 60.0° = 0.$ (2)

For minimum F (impending motion),

$f_s = \mu_s N = 0.300\ N.$ (3)

Equation (2) gives $N = 0.866F + 9.80$ N. (4)

Equation (3) becomes: $f_s = 0.260\ F + 2.94$ N.

Then (1) gives: $0.50F + 0.26F + 2.94\text{ N} - 17.0\text{ N} = 0$, yielding $F = 18.5$ N. (a)

Finally, equation (4) gives $N = 25.8$ N. (b)

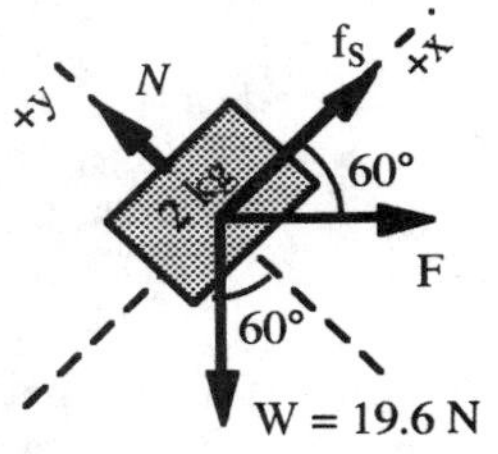

4.43

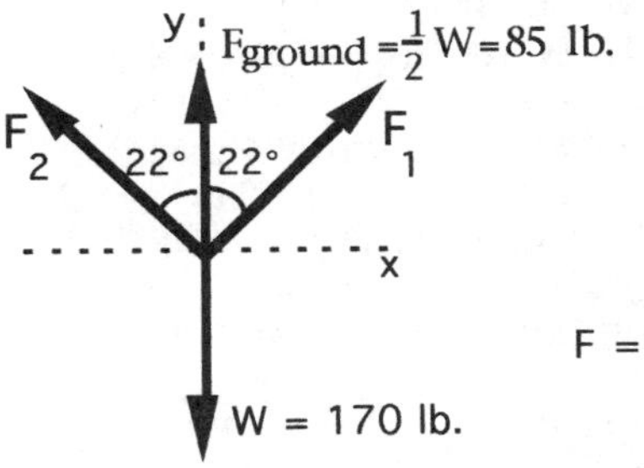

Free-Body Diagram of Person

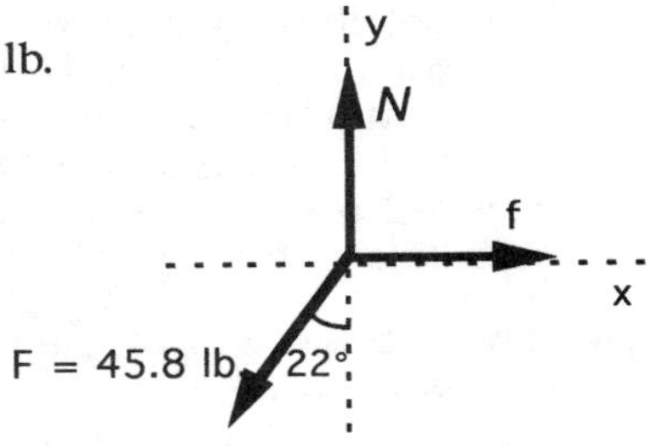

Free-Body Diagram of Crutch Tip

From the free-body diagram of the person, find the compression force acting along the line of each crutch.

$\Sigma F_x = 0$ gives $F_1 \sin 22.0° - F_2 \sin 22.0° = 0$, or $F_1 = F_2 = F.$

Then $\Sigma F_y = 0$ gives $2F\cos 22.0° - 85.0\text{ lb} = 0$. From which, $F = 45.8$ lb.

Now consider a crutch tip as shown.

$\Sigma F_x = 0$ becomes $f - (45.8\text{ lb})\sin 22.0° = 0$, or $f = 17.2$ lb.

$\Sigma F_y = 0$ becomes $N - (45.8\text{ lb})\cos 22.0° = 0$, or $N = 42.5$ lb.

Assuming the crutch tip is on the verge of slipping, the minimum possible coefficient of friction is $\mu_s = \dfrac{f}{N} = \dfrac{17.2\text{ lb}}{42.5\text{ lb}} = 0.404.$

4.44 (a) First, draw a free-body diagram, (Fig. 1) of the top block. Since $a_y = 0$, $N_1 = 19.6$ N and therefore, $f_k = \mu_k N_1 = (0.300)(19.6) = 5.88$ N.

$\Sigma F_x = ma_T$ gives $10.0\text{ N} - 5.88\text{ N} = (2.00\text{ kg})a_T,$

or $a_T = 2.06\text{ m/s}^2.$ (for top block)

Now draw a free-body diagram (Fig. 2) of the bottom block and observe that

$\Sigma F_x = Ma_B$ gives $f = 5.88\text{ N} = (8.00\text{ kg})a_B,$

or $a_B = 0.735\text{ m/s}^2.$ (for the bottom block)

In time t, the distance each block moves (starting from rest) is

$d_T = \frac{1}{2}a_T t^2 = (1.03\text{ m/s}^2)\,t^2$, and

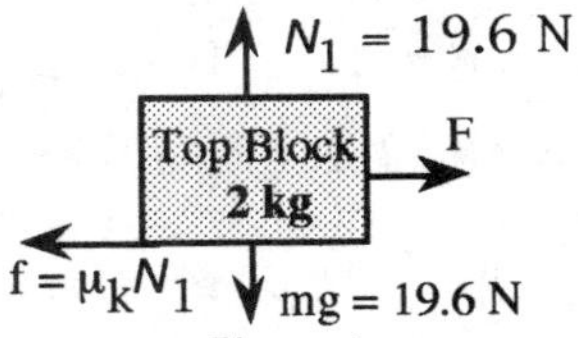

Figure 1

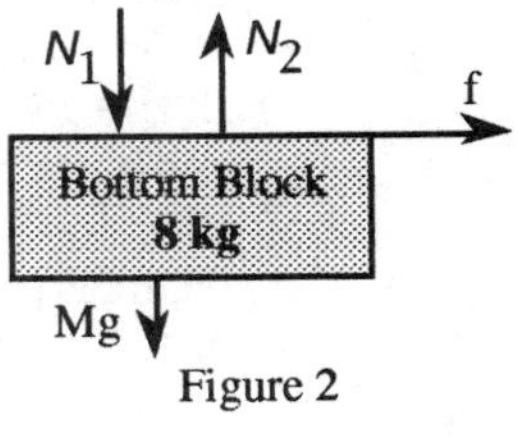

Figure 2

$$d_B = \frac{1}{2}a_B t^2 = (0.368\ \text{m/s}^2)\,t^2.$$

For the top block to reach the right edge of the bottom block, it is necessary that

$d_T = d_B + L$, or (See Fig. 3.)

$(1.03\ \text{m/s}^2)\,t^2 = (0.368\ \text{m/s}^2)\,t^2 + 3.00\ \text{m}$

which gives: $t = 2.13\ \text{s}$

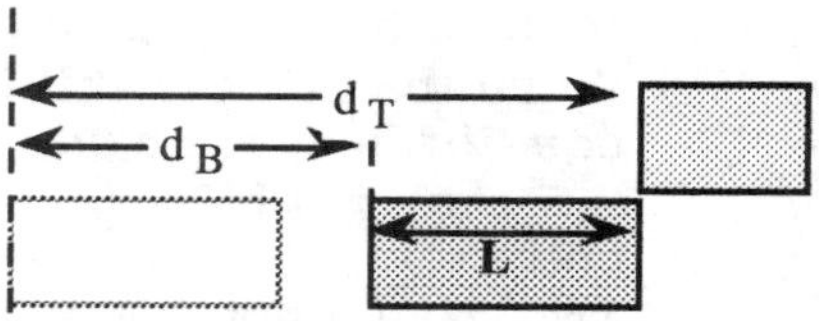

Figure 3

(b) From above,

$$d_B = \frac{1}{2}a_B t^2 = (0.368\ \text{m/s}^2)(2.13\ \text{s})^2 = 1.67\ \text{m}.$$

4.45 The resultant x component of the two forces exerted on the traffic light by the cables is 0, since $(60.0\ \text{N})\cos 45° - (60.0\ \text{N})\cos 45.0° = 0$.
The resultant y component is:

$(60.0\ \text{N})\sin 45.0° + (60.0\ \text{N})\sin 45° = 84.9\ \text{N}$

The resultant force is, thus, 84.9 N vertically upward. The forces on the traffic light are the 84.9 vertical force exerted by the cables and the weight. The resultant of these two must equal zero, from the first law. Thus, $w = 84.9\ \text{N}$

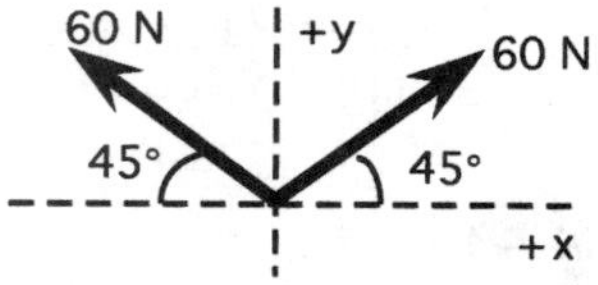

4.46 The acceleration of the ball is found as

$v^2 = v_0^2 + 2ax$

$(20.0\ \text{m/s})^2 = 0 + 2a(1.50\ \text{m})$

From which, $a = 133.3\ \text{m/s}^2$.

The resultant force on the ball is the upward force, F, exerted by the thrower, less the weight of the ball, 1.47 N, downward. The second law becomes

$F - 1.47\ \text{N} = (.150\ \text{kg})(133.3\ \text{m/s}^2)$

$F = 21.5\ \text{N}$.

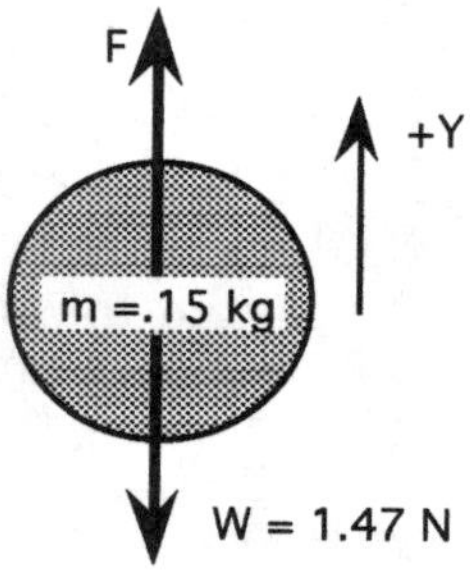

4.47 On the level surface the normal force, N, equals 600 N, and the force of friction is $f = \mu_k N = (0.05)(600\ \text{N}) = 30\ \text{N}$.
The 600 N weight is equivalent to a mass of 61.2 kg, and from the second law, the acceleration is $a = f/m = (-30\ \text{N})/(61.2\ \text{kg}) = -0.49\ \text{m/s}^2$.
The distance traveled before coming to rest is found from $v^2 = v_0^2 + 2ax$, or $0 = (7\ \text{m/s})^2 + 2(-0.49\ \text{m/s}^2)x$. From which: $x = 50\ \text{m}$.

4.48 (a) Consider the weight on the table. Apply $\Sigma F_y = 0$, as

$N - w_1 = 0$ (where N is the normal force). (1)

From $\Sigma F_x = 0$, we have: $T - f = 0$. (2)

For the hanging weight, $\Sigma F_y = 0$ becomes: $w_2 - T = 0$. (3)

With $w_1 = 100\ \text{N}$ and $w_2 = 50.0\ \text{N}$, Equation (3) gives

$T = w_2 = 50.0\ \text{N}$. Then, from eq. (2), we find $f = 50.0\ \text{N}$.

(b) If the system is on the verge of slipping, $f = \mu_s N$.
With $f = 50.0\ \text{N}$ and $N = 100\ \text{N}$ from Equation (1), we find $\mu_s = 0.500$.

(c) If $\mu_k = 0.250$, then $f = (0.250)(100\ \text{N}) = 25.0\ \text{N}$, and from Equation (2) $T = 25.0\ \text{N}$.
Finally, from Equation (3), $w_2 = T = 25.0\ \text{N}$.

4.49 (a) The friction force between the box and the truck bed causes the box to move with the truck.

(b) The maximum value of the acceleration the truck can have before the box slides can be found by finding the maximum value of the static friction force on the box. This is: $f_{max} = \mu_s N = \mu_s mg$.
Thus, from Newton's Second Law,

$$a_{max} = f_{max}/m = \mu_s g = 0.300(9.80 \text{ m/s}^2) = 2.94 \text{ m/s}^2.$$

4.50 Let $F = 85.0$ N, $m = 4.00$ kg, $\theta = 55.0°$, and $a = 6.00 \text{ m/s}^2$.
From the forces perpendicular to the ceiling, we have $F\sin\theta - mg - N = 0$, so that $N = F\sin\theta - mg$.
The forces parallel to the ceiling yield $F\cos\theta - f_k = ma$.
But $f_k = \mu_k N$, so that $F\cos\theta - \mu_k [F\sin\theta - mg] = ma$,

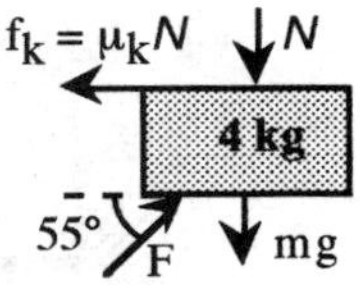

$$\text{or } \mu_k = \frac{F\cos\theta - ma}{F\sin\theta - mg} = \frac{(85.0)\cos 55.0° - (4.00)(6.00)}{(85.0)\sin 55.0° - (4.00)(9.80)} = 0.81.$$

4.51 (a) Let μ_1 be the coefficient of kinetic friction between the aluminum block and the steel wedge (which is 0.47 from the table in the chapter), and let μ_2 be the coefficient of kinetic friction between the copper block and the steel wedge (which is 0.36 from the table). Looking first at m_1, we have $m_1 a = T - \mu_1 m_1 g$.

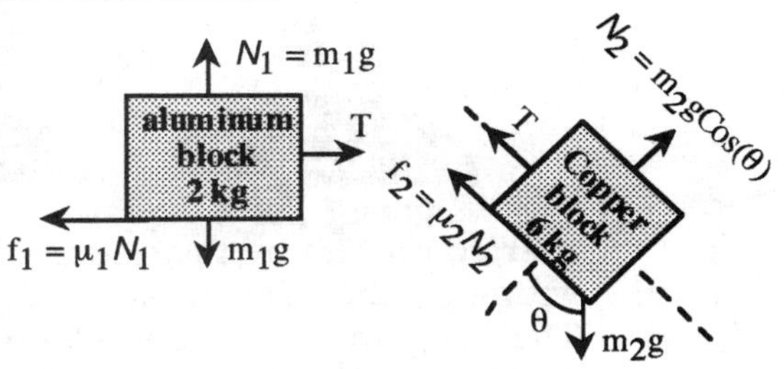

Looking at mass m_2, we have $m_2 a = m_2 g\sin\theta - \mu_2 m_2 g\cos\theta - T$.
Adding these equations: $(m_1 + m_2)a = m_2 g \sin\theta - \mu_2 m_2 g\cos\theta - \mu_1 m_1 g$.

Therefore, we have $a = \left(\dfrac{m_2(\sin\theta - \mu_2\cos\theta) - \mu_1 m_1}{m_1 + m_2}\right)g$,

so that

$$a = \left(\frac{6.00(\sin 30.0° - (0.360)\cos 30.0°) - (0.470)(2.00)}{8.00}\right) 9.80$$

$$= 0.232 \text{ m/s}^2.$$

(b) Using $T = m_1(a + \mu_1 g)$, we have $T = 2(0.232 + (0.470)(9.80)) = 9.68$ N

4.52 (a) Let $m_1 = 5.00$ kg, $m_2 = 4.00$ kg, and $m_3 = 3.00$ kg. T_1 is the tension in the string between m_1 and m_2, and T_2 is the tension in the string between m_2 and m_3. Then we may write for m_1: $m_1 a = T_1 - m_1 g$
while for m_2 we have: $m_2 a = T_2 + m_2 g - T_1$,
and for m_3 we have $m_3 a = m_3 g - T_2$.
Adding these equations yields $(m_1 + m_2 + m_3)a = (-m_1 + m_2 + m_3)g$,

so that $a = \dfrac{-m_1 + m_2 + m_3}{m_1 + m_2 + m_3} g = 1.63 \text{ m/s}^2$.

(b) From above $T_1 = m_1(a + g) = 57.2$ N, and $T_2 = m_3(g - a), = 24.5$ N.

4.53 (a) $x = v_0 t + \frac{1}{2}at^2$ gives: $2.00 \text{ m} = 0 + \frac{1}{2}a_x(1.50 \text{ s})^2$, or $a_x = 1.78 \text{ m/s}^2$.

(b) and (c) Newtons second law along the incline gives:
$(29.4 \text{ N})\sin 30.0° - f = (3.00 \text{ kg})(1.78 \text{ m/s}^2)$, or $f = 9.37$ N.

Perpendicular to the plane, we have equilibrium, so
$N = (29.4\text{ N})\cos 30.0° = 25.5\text{ N}.$

Then $f = \mu_k N$, or $\qquad \mu_k = \frac{f}{N} = \frac{9.37\text{ N}}{25.5\text{ N}} = 0.368.$

(d) Finally $v^2 = v_0^2 + 2ax$ becomes $v^2 = 0 + 2(1.78\text{ m/s}^2)(2.00\text{ m})$,
from which $\quad v = 2.67\text{ m/s}.$

4.54 (a) Force diagrams for penguin and sled are shown. The primed forces are reaction forces for the corresponding unprimed forces.

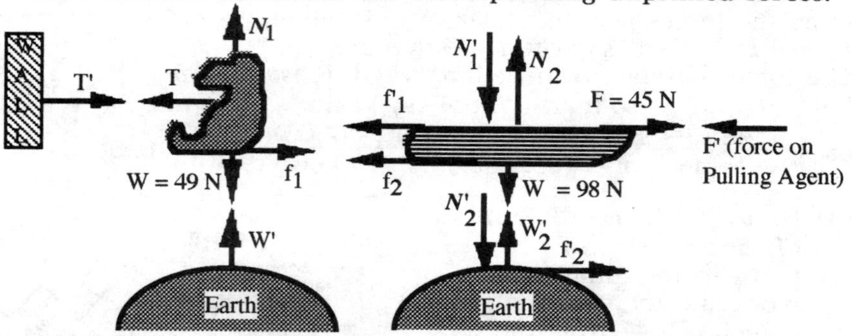

(b) The weight of the penguin is 49 N, and hence the normal force exerted on him by the sled, N_1, is also 49 N. Thus, the friction force acting on the penguin is: $\quad f_1 = \mu_k N_1 = 0.2(49\text{ N}) = 9.8\text{ N}.$
The penguin does not accelerate. Thus, the tension in the cord attached to the wall and the friction force must be equal: $\quad T = 9.8\text{ N}$

(c) The normal force exerted on the sled plus penguin is the weight of the penguin (49 N) plus the weight of the sled (98 N). Thus, the net normal force, N_2 equals 147 N, and the friction force between sled and ground is: $\quad f_2 = \mu_k N_2 = 0.2(147\text{ N}) = 29.4\text{ N}.$
Applying the second law to the sled along the horizontal direction gives: $\quad 45\text{ N} - 9.80\text{ N} - 29.4\text{ N} = (10.0\text{ kg})a, \qquad$ or $a = 0.58\text{ m/s}^2.$

4.55 (a) Apply the 2nd law to the 10 kg block:
$T = (10\text{ kg})a, \qquad (1)$
and for the 20 kg block:
$50\text{ N} - T = (20\text{ kg})a. \qquad (2)$
Solving (1) and (2) simultaneously:
$T = 17\text{ N},$
and $\quad a = 1.7\text{ m/s}^2.$

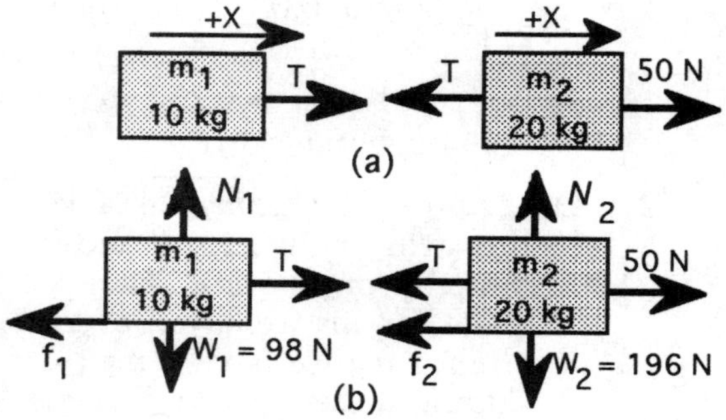

(b) The friction force on the 10 kg block is:
$f_1 = \mu_k N = 0.1(98\text{ N}) = 9.8\text{ N}.$
On the 20 kg block, we have $f_2 = 0.1(196\text{ N}) = 19.6\text{ N}.$
Thus, the second law for the 10 kg block is $\quad T - 9.8\text{ N} = (10\text{ kg})a, \quad (3)$
and for the 20 kg block $\quad 50\text{ N} - T - 19.6\text{ N} = (20\text{ kg})a. \quad (4)$
Solving (3) and (4) together, we have: $T = 17\text{ N}$, $a = 0.69\text{ m/s}^2.$

4.56 (a)

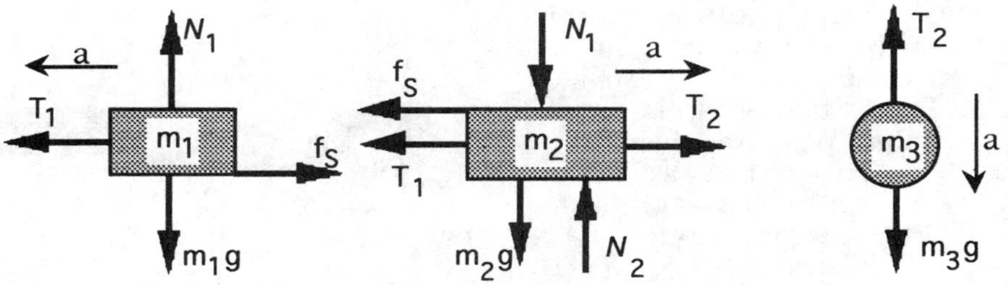

(b) and (c) $\Sigma F_x = ma_x$, therefore (for the mass m_1)

$T_1 - \mu m_1 g = m_1 a$, or $T_1 - (0.30)(2.0)(9.8) = 2.0a$. (1)

Similarly, for m_2:

$T_2 - T_1 - \mu m_1 g = m_2 a$, or

$T_2 - T_1 - 2.0(9.8)(0.30) = 3.0a$. (2)

$\Sigma F_y = ma_y$ for the mass m_3 gives:

$m_3 g - T_2 = m_3 a$, or $T_2 = 98 - 10.0a$. (3)

Solving (1), (2), and (3) gives: $T_1 = 17$ N, $T_2 = 41$ N, and $a = 5.8$ m/s^2.

4.57 Let us call the forces exerted by each of the men F_1 and F_2. Thus, when pulling in the same direction, Newton's second law becomes

$F_1 + F_2 = (200\text{ kg})(1.52\text{ m/s}^2)$, or

$F_1 + F_2 = 304$ N. (1)

When pulling in opposite directions, $F_1 - F_2 = (200\text{ kg})(-0.518\text{ m/s}^2)$, or

$F_1 - F_2 = -103.6$ N (2)

Solving simultaneously, we find: $F_1 = 100$ N, and $F_2 = 204$ N.

4.58 In the vertical direction, we have

$T\cos 4.0° - mg = 0$, or

$T\cos 4.0° = 29.4$ N

Thus, $T = 29.5$ N.

In the horizontal direction, the second law becomes:

$T\sin 4.0° = (3.0\text{ kg})a$.

Since $T = 29.5$ N, we have

$a = 0.69$ m/s^2.

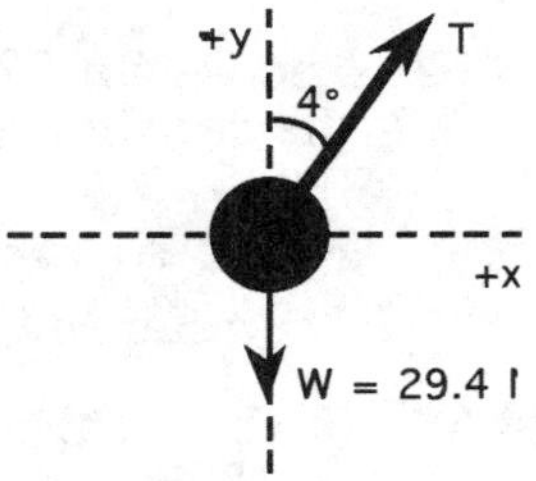

4.59 The magnitudes of the accelerations are the same for all three blocks. Applying Newton's second law to the 10.0 kg block gives

$10.0(9.80) - T_1 = 10.0a$

Since we are given that $a = 2.00$ m/s^2, this yields $T_1 = 78.0$ N.

Applying the second law to the 5.00 kg block gives:

$T_1 - T_2 - \mu_k(49.0) = 5.00a$.

or, $T_2 = 78.0 - 5.00(2.00) - 49.0\mu_k$

which simplifies to $T_2 = 68.0 - 49.0\mu_k$ (1)

Applying the second law to the 3.00 kg block gives:

$T_2 - f - W\sin 25.0° = ma$

or $T_2 - \mu_k(29.4\cos 25.0°) - 29.4\sin 25.0° = 3.00(2.00)$

which reduces to $T_2 - 26.6\mu_k = 18.4$ (2)

Solving (1) and (2) simultaneously gives:

$T_2 = 35.9$ N, and $\mu_k = 0.66$. Also, from above, $T_1 = 78.0$ N.

4.60 From Fig. (a), the normal force on the penguin is $N = 70.0\text{ N}$,
and the second law applied to the penguin gives

$f = (7.14\text{ kg})a$, or

$a = f/(7.14\text{ kg})$.

At pending motion, $f = \mu_s N$, or

$f = 0.700(70.0\text{ N}) = 49.0\text{ N}$.

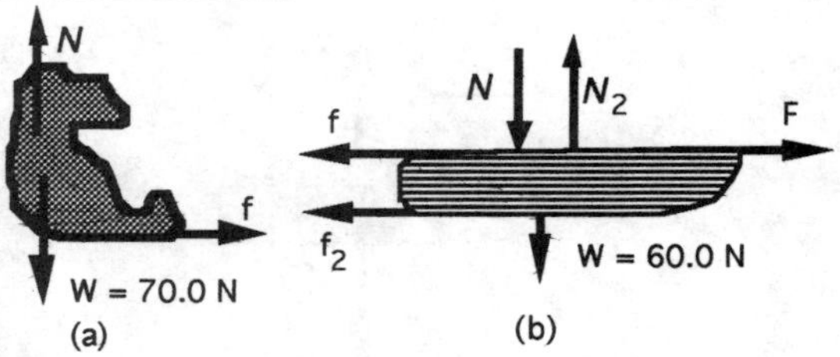

Thus, $a_{max} = \dfrac{f_{max}}{7.14\text{ kg}} = 49.0\text{ N}/7.14\text{ kg} = 6.86\text{ m/s}^2$.

From the free-body diagram of the sled [Fig. (b) above],

$N_2 = 70.0\text{ N} + 60.0\text{ N} = 130\text{ N}$.

Thus, the force of friction between sled and snow is:

$f_2 = \mu_k N_2 = 0.100(130\text{ N}) = 13.0\text{ N}$.

Applying the second law to the sled gives

$F - f - f_2 = (6.12\text{ kg})a$, or $\qquad F = f + 13.0\text{ N} + (6.12\text{ kg})a$.

F has its maximum value when f and a have their maximum values.

Thus, $F_{max} = 49.0\text{ N} + 13.0\text{ N} + (6.12\text{ kg})(6.86\text{ m/s}^2) = 104\text{ N}$

4.61 Letting m be the mass of the person, the total downward force acting on the person is $mg - 100 = (80)(9.80) - 100 = 684\text{ N}$. From Newton's 2nd law the constant acceleration of the person is

$a_y = \dfrac{684\text{ N}}{80\text{ kg}} = 8.55\text{ m/s}^2$ downward.

Then $v_y^2 = v_{oy}^2 + 2a_y(\Delta y) = 0 + 2(8.55)(30)$ gives $\qquad v_y = 23\text{ m/s}$.

4.62 The weight 8820 N is equivalent to a mass of 900 kg. The acceleration of the car while it stops can be found as follows.

$v^2 = v_o^2 + 2ax$ becomes $0 = (35\text{ m/s})^2 + 2a(1000\text{ m})$, and this gives $a = -0.6125\text{ m/s}^2$.

The retarding force on the car is $F = ma = (900\text{ kg})(-0.6125\text{ m/s}^2) = -550\text{ N}$.

4.63 In the vertical direction, we have

$(8000\text{ N})\sin 65° - w = 0$, so $\qquad w = 7250\text{ N}$.

$m = \dfrac{w}{g} = \dfrac{7250\text{ N}}{9.80\text{ m/s}^2} = 739.8\text{ kg}$.

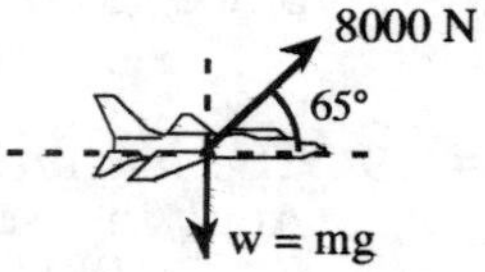

Along the horizontal, the second law becomes,

$(8000\text{ N})\cos 65° = (739.8\text{ kg})a_x$, so $a_x = 4.57\text{ m/s}^2$.

4.64 $mg\sin\theta = m(5.00\text{ m/s}^2) \qquad \theta = 30.7°$

$mg\cos\theta = T \qquad T = 0.843\text{ N}$

4.65 The forces on the center board are shown at the right. In the horizontal direction, we see that $N_1 = N_2 = N$. Therefore, $f_1 = \mu_s N_1$ and $f_2 = \mu_s N_2$. So, $f_1 = f_2 = f$.
In the vertical direction, we have $\Sigma F_y = 0$, which gives $2f - 95.5\text{ N} = 0$.
Thus, $f = 47.75$ N, and $N = \frac{f}{\mu_s} = \frac{47.75\text{ N}}{0.663} = 72.0$ N.

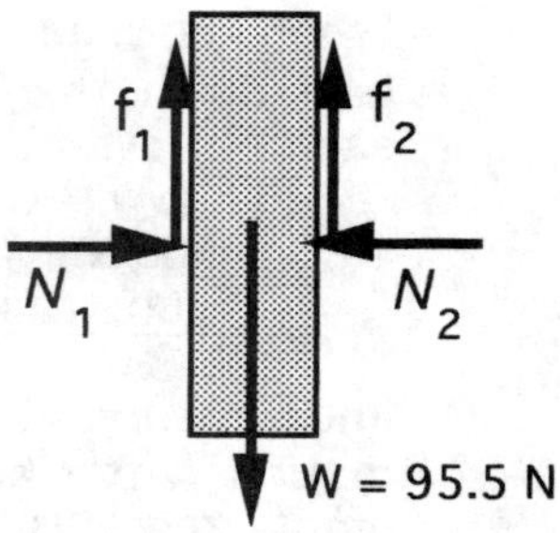

4.66 First, we will compute the needed accelerations:
(1) Before it starts to move: $a_y = 0$.
(2) During the first 0.8 s: $a_y = \frac{v_y - v_{0y}}{t} = \frac{1.2\text{ m/s} - 0}{0.80\text{ s}} = 1.5\text{ m/s}^2$.
(3) While moving at constant velocity: $a_y = 0$.
(4) During the last 1.5 s: $a_y = \frac{v_y - v_{0y}}{t} = \frac{0 - 1.2\text{ m/s}}{1.5\text{ s}} = -0.8\text{ m/s}^2$.
Newton's second law is: $T - 706\text{ N} = (72\text{ kg})a_y$, or
$T = 710\text{ N} + (72\text{ kg})a_y$.
(a) When $a_y = 0$, $T = 710$ N.
(b) When $a_y = 1.5\text{ m/s}^2$, $T = 820$ N.
(c) When $a_y = 0$, $T = 710$ N.
(d) When $a_y = -0.8\text{ m/s}^2$, $T = 650$ N.

4.67 Let M = mass of keg $= \frac{300\text{ N}}{g} = 30.6$ kg.
Then mass of Bob $= \frac{900\text{ N}}{g} = 3M$, and
mass of Kathy = mass of nails = $2M$.
Also, the time to move 10 m from rest is given by $10\text{ m} = 0 + \frac{1}{2}at^2$, or

$$t = \sqrt{\frac{20\text{ m}}{a}}. \quad (1)$$

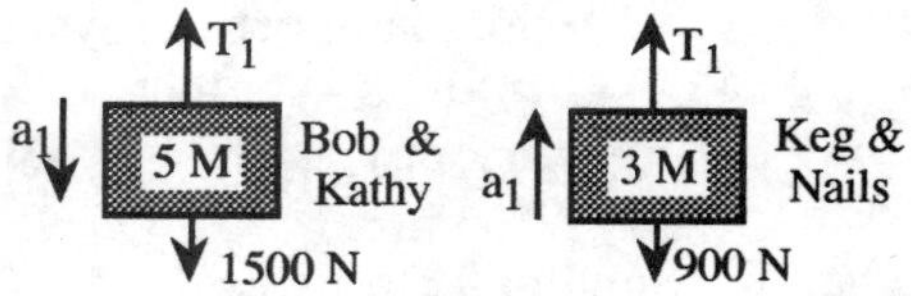

Figure 1

For downward trip of Bob and Kathy:
Apply Newton's 2nd law to each object shown in Figure 1 to get:
$1500\text{ N} - T_1 = (5M)a_1$, and $T_1 - 900\text{ N} = (3M)a_1$, which yield
$a_1 = \frac{600\text{ N}}{8M} = \frac{600\text{ N}}{244.8\text{ kg}} = 2.45\text{ m/s}^2$, and equation (1) gives
$t_1 = 2.86$ s as the time for this part of the trip.

After Bob lets go and Kathy starts toward the top, the 2nd law applied to each object shown in Figure 2 gives:
$T_2 - 600\text{ N} = (2M)a_2$, and
$900\text{ N} - T_2 = (3M)a_2$,

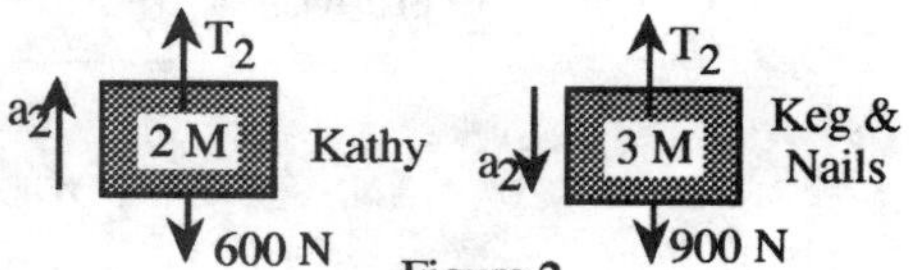

Figure 2

which gives $a_2 = \frac{300\text{ N}}{5M} = \frac{300\text{ N}}{153\text{ kg}} = 1.96\text{ m/s}^2$. Then equation (1) yields
$t_2 = 3.19$ s as the time for this part.

When the nails spill and Kathy starts back down, the 2nd law applied to each object in Figure 3 yields:

$600\text{ N} - T_3 = (2M)a_3$, and

$T_3 - 300\text{ N} = Ma_3$, giving

$$a_3 = \frac{300\text{ N}}{3M} = \frac{100\text{ N}}{30.6\text{ kg}} = 3.27\text{ m/s}^2,$$

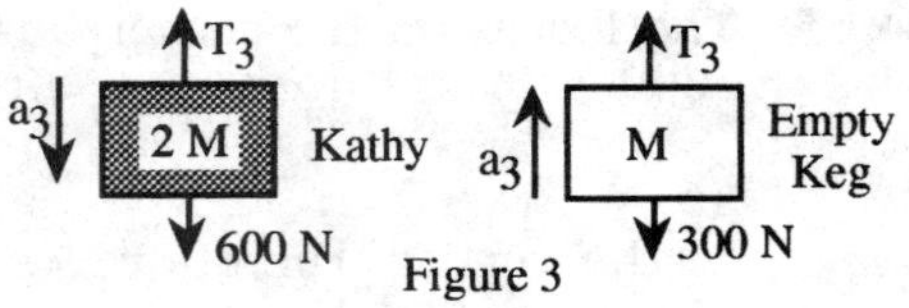

Figure 3

and equation (1) yields $t_3 = 2.47$ s as the time for this part of the motion. After Kathy lets go, the tension in the rope is zero, and the empty keg falls freely (a = g) to the ground. The time for this part is

$$t_4 = \sqrt{\frac{20\text{ m}}{9.80\text{ m/s}^2}} = 1.43\text{ s}.$$

The total time for the entire accident is $t_1 + t_2 + t_3 + t_4 = 9.95$ s.

4.68 We have $T_1\sin\theta_1 + T_2\sin\theta_2 = w$ (1)

$T_1\cos\theta_1 = T_2\cos\theta_2$ (2)

(a) Eliminate T_2 and solve for T_1.

$$\frac{T_1(\sin\theta_1\cos\theta_2 + \cos\theta_1\sin\theta_2)}{\cos\theta_2} = w$$

Solution follows from trig identity.

(b) Substitution yields, $T_1 = 514$ N, and $T_2 = 558$ N, and $T_3 = w = 325$ N

4.69 (a) First consider Pat and the chair as the system. Note that the two ropes support the system and $T = 250$ N in each rope.

Applying $\Sigma F = ma$

$2T - 480 = ma$ where $m = \frac{480}{9.80} = 49.0$ kg

Solving for a gives $a = \frac{(500 - 480)}{49} = 0.408\text{ m/s}^2$.

(b) ΣF (on Pat) $= N + T - 320 = ma$ where $m = \frac{320}{9.80} = 32.7$ kg

$N = ma + 320 - T = 32.7(0.408) + 320 - 250 = 83.3$ N.

4.70 Let R represent the horizontal force of air resistance.

(a) $\Sigma F_x = ma_x$ becomes $T\sin 40.0° - R = 0$

$\Sigma F_y = ma_y$ becomes $T\cos 40.0° - w = 0$

Then $T = \frac{mg}{\cos 40°} = \frac{6080\text{ N}}{\cos 40.0°} = 7930$ N

$R = 7930\sin 40.0° = 5100$ N

ANSWERS TO CONCEPTUAL QUESTIONS

2. There may be many forces acting on the object, but there cannot be a net force if it is at rest.

4. w = mg and g decreases with altitude. Thus, to get a good buy, purchase it in Denver. If if were sold by mass, it would not matter where you bought it.

6. If it has a large mass, it will take a large force to alter its motion even when floating in space. Thus, to avoid injuring herself, she should push it gently toward the storage compartment.

8. The net force acting on the object decreases as the resistive force increases. Eventually, the resistive force becomes equal to the weight of the object, and the net force goes to zero. In this condition, the object stops accelerating, and the velocity of the rock stops increasing and stays constant. The rock has reached its terminal velocity.

10. As the barbell goes through the bottom of a cycle, the lifter exerts upward force on it, and the scale reads the larger upward force the floor exerts on them together. Around the top of the weight's motion, the scale reads less than average. If the iron is moving upward, the lifter can declare she has thrown it, just by letting go of it for a moment. Thus, the case is included in the previous answer.

12. Any object will increase in speed any time there is a net force on it. Thus, there must be a net force to produce a changing speed. A changing acceleration can be produced by a constant force acting on an object that has a decreasing mass. This is happening to the rocket as it burns fuel.

14. The truck's skidding distance can be shown to be $x = \frac{v_0^2}{2\mu g}$ where μ is the coefficient of sliding friction and v_0 is the initial velocity of the truck. This equation demonstrates that the mass of the truck does not affect the skidding distance, but halving the velocity will decrease the skidding distance by one-fourth.

16. Because the mass of the truck is decreasing, the acceleration will increase.

18. Consider a boy sitting on a chair in the back of a truck when the truck begins to move forward. If the boy is to move along with the truck, the force in the direction of motion to speed him up is the force of friction between the chair and his pants. This force will be in the direction of motion of the truck and the boy.

CHAPTER FIVE SOLUTIONS

Chapter Five Readings

Davis, G.R., "Energy for Planet Earth," *Scientific American*, September 1990, p. 54.

Dyson, F.J., "Energy in the Universe," *Scientific American*, September 1971, p. 50.

"Energy and Power," *Scientific American*, September 1971.

Hubbard, H.M., "The Real Cost of Energy," *Scientific American*, April 1991, p. 36.

Leff, H.S. and Mallinkrodt, A.J., "Stopping Objects with Zero External Work: Mechanics Meets Thermodynamics," *American Journal of Physics*, 61, 121, 1993

Mallinckrodt, A.J. and Leff, H.S., "All About Work," *American Journal of Physics*, 60, 356, 1992

Waring, G., "Energy and the Automobile," *The Physics Teacher*, 18, 1980, p. 494.

Review (a) Using energy concepts: Choose final level of the object as zero PE level. $(KE+PE)_{\text{initial}} + W_{nc} = (KE+PE)_{\text{final}}$ with $y_i = 4.0 \sin 30° = 2.0$ m and $y_f = 0$

$$\frac{1}{2} mv_i^2 + mgy_i + (Fs - fs) = \frac{1}{2} mv_f^2 + mgy_f$$

$$0 + 10(9.80)2.0 + (80(4.0) - 20(4.0)) = \frac{1}{2} (10)\, v^2 + 0$$

which yields $v_f = 9.3$ m/s

(b) Applying Newton's second law to the motion parallel to the incline: $F_{net} = ma$ gives $F + mg\sin\theta - f = ma$,

or $80 + 10(9.80)\sin 30° - 20 = 10a$

This yields $a = 10.9$ m/s^2. Then the final velocity is found by $v^2 = v_o^2 + 2as = 0 + 2(10.9)4.0$, which yields $v = 9.3$ m/s

---

5.1 If the weights are to move at constant velocity, the net force on them must be zero. Thus, the lifting force is equal to 350 N, and the work done against gravity is

$W = (F\cos\theta)s = (350 \text{ N})(\cos 0°)(2.00 \text{ m}) = 700$ J

5.2 $w = mg = (20.0 \text{ kg})(9.80 \text{ m/s}^2)$ and 196 N = the applied force to lift the bucket at constant speed.

$W = (F\cos\theta)s = 6.00 \times 10^3 \text{ J} = Fs = (196 \text{ N})\, s$

yielding, $s = 30.6$ m.

5.3 $W = (F\cos\theta)s = (5000 \text{ N})(\cos 0°)(3000 \text{ m}) = 1.5 \times 10^7$ J

5.4 The component of force along the direction of motion is

$F\cos\theta = (35 \text{ N})\cos 25° = 31.7$ N. The work done by this force is

$W = (F\cos\theta)s = (31.7 \text{ N})(50 \text{ m}) = 1.6 \times 10^3$ J.

5.5 (a) The force of gravity is given by $mg = 5.0(9.80) = 49$ N and is directed downwards. The angle between the force of gravity and the direction of motion is $\theta = 90° - 30° = 60°$, and so the work done by gravity is given as $W_g = 49(2.5)\cos 60° = 61$ J.
(b) The normal force exerted on the block by the incline is
$N = mg\cos 30° = 42.4$ N,
so the friction force is $f_k = \mu_k N = 0.436(42.4\text{ N}) = 18.5$ N. This force is directed opposite to the displacement (i.e. $\theta = 180°$). Therefore the work it does is
$W_f = f_k s\cos\theta = (18.5\text{ N})(2.5\text{ m})(\cos 180°)$, giving $W_f = -46$ J.
(c) Since the normal force is perpendicular to the displacement, the work done by the normal force is zero.

5.6 $F_x = 16.0\cos 25° = 14.5$ N,
$F_y = 16.0\sin 25° = 6.76$ N
$W = (2.50)(9.80) = 24.5$ N
$\Sigma F_y = N - W - F_y = 0$
gives $N = 31.3$ N
(a) $W_F = (16.0\cos 25°)(2.20) = 31.9$ J
(b) $W_N = (31.3\cos 90°)(2.20) = 0$
(c) $W_{gravity} = (24.5\cos 90°)(2.2) = 0$
(d) $W_{net} = W_F + W_N + W_{gravity} = 31.9$ J

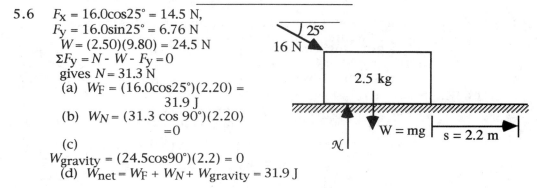

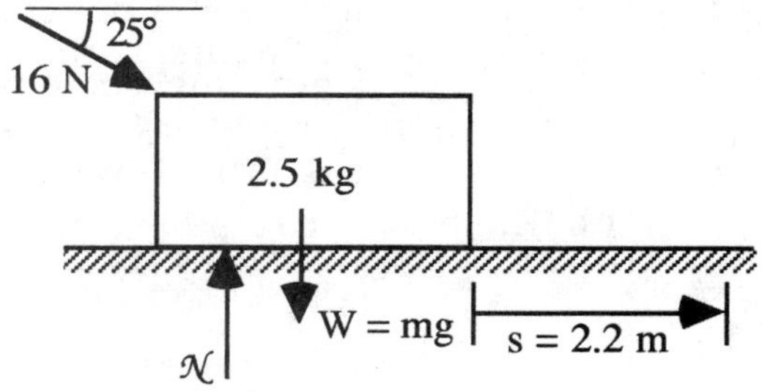

5.7 (a) The work-energy theorem, $W = \Delta KE$, gives
$$5000\text{ J} = \frac{1}{2}(2500\text{ kg})v_f^2 - 0,\text{ or}\quad v_f = 2\text{ m/s}.$$
(b) $W = (F\cos\theta)s = F(25.0\text{ m}) = 5000$ J, so $F = 200$ N.

5.8 Using $KE = \frac{1}{2}mv^2$, we have $\frac{1}{2}(7.00)(3.00)^2 = \frac{1}{2}(0.00245)v^2$, so $v = 160$ m/s.

5.9 (a) We use the work-energy theorem to find the work.
$$W = \Delta KE = \frac{1}{2}mv_f^2 - \frac{1}{2}mv_o^2 = 0 - \frac{1}{2}(70.0\text{ kg})(4.0\text{ m/s})^2 = -560\text{ J}.$$
(b) $W = (F\cos\theta)s = (f\cos 180°)s = -fs$.
But, the frictional force f is found as,
$f = \mu_k N = (0.70)(70.0\text{ kg})(9.80\text{ m/s}^2) = 480$ N.
Thus, $W = -fs = -(480\text{ N})s = -560$ J, which gives, $s = 1.2$ m.

5.10 (a) $KE_A = \frac{1}{2}mv_A^2 = \frac{1}{2}(0.60\text{ kg})(2.0\text{ m/s})^2 = 1.2$ J.
(b) $KE_B = \frac{1}{2}mv_B^2 = 7.5\text{ J} = \frac{1}{2}(0.60\text{ kg})v_B^2$. Thus, $v_B = 5.0$ m/s.
(c) Work $= \Delta KE = KE_B - KE_A = 7.5\text{ J} - 1.2\text{ J} = 6.3$ J.

5.11 The net upward force is $F_{net} = 2(355\text{ N}) - 700\text{ N} = 10$ N. The final speed can then be calculated from the work energy theorem as
$$\text{Net work} = \Delta KE = \frac{1}{2}mv_f^2 - \frac{1}{2}mv_i^2,\text{ or,}$$

$(10\text{ N})(0.25\text{ m}) = \frac{1}{2}(71.4\text{ kg})v_f^2 - 0$, which gives $v_f = 0.265$ m/s.

5.12 At the top of the arc, $v_y = 0$, and $v_x = v_{ox} = 40\cos 30.0° = 34.64$ m/s. Therefore $v^2 = v^2_x + v^2_y = (34.64\text{ m/s})^2$, and

$$KE = \frac{1}{2}mv^2 = \frac{1}{2}(0.150)(34.64)^2 = 90.0\text{ J}.$$

5.13 (a) The final kinetic energy of the bullet is

$$KE_f = \frac{1}{2}mv^2 = \frac{1}{2}(2.0\times10^{-3}\text{ kg})(3.00\times10^2\text{ m/s})^2 = 90\text{ J}.$$

(b) We know that $W = \Delta KE = 90\text{ J} - 0 = 90$ J, and that

$W = (\bar{F}\cos\theta)s = (\bar{F})(\cos 0°)(0.50\text{ m}) = 90$ J. Thus, $\bar{F} = 180$ N.

5.14 We have equilibrium in a direction perpendicular to the incline. Thus, from $\Sigma F_y = 0$, we find the normal force to be

$N = w\cos 20° = (98\text{ N})(0.94) = 92.1$ N, therefore

$f = \mu_k N = (0.4)(92.1\text{ N}) = 36.8$ N.

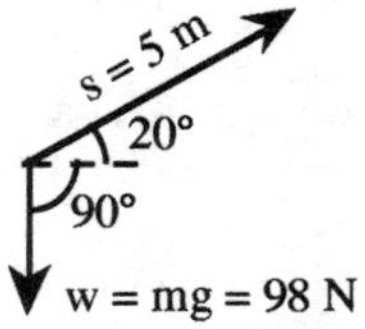

(a) $W_{grav} = ws\cos 110° = (98\text{ N})(5.00\text{ m})(-0.342) = -168$ J.

(b) $W(\text{applied force}) = Fs = (100\text{ N})(5.00\text{ m}) = 500$ J

(c) $\Delta KE = W_{net} = W_{grav} + W_{applied\ force} + W_{friction}$, or

$\Delta KE = -168\text{ J} + 500\text{ J} + (36.8)(5.00\text{ m})\cos 180° = 148$ J.

(d) $\Delta KE = \frac{1}{2}mv_f^2 - \frac{1}{2}mv_i^2 = \frac{1}{2}(10.0\text{ kg})v_f^2 - \frac{1}{2}(10.0\text{ kg})(1.50\text{ m/s})^2$

$= 148$ J,

so $v_f = 5.64$ m/s.

5.15 The work energy theorem is $W_{net} = KE_f - KE_i$. The net work done on the car is the work done by the motor less the work done against friction. We have, $W_{net} = (10^3\text{ N})(20\text{ m}) - (950\text{ N})(20\text{ m}) = 1000$ J.

We are given that $KE_i = 0$. Thus, $KE_f = 1000\text{ J} = \frac{1}{2}(2000\text{ kg})v^2$.

From which, $v = 1.0$ m/s.

5.16 The initial kinetic energy of the sled is $KE_i = \frac{1}{2}(10\text{ kg})(2.0\text{ m/s})^2 = 20$ J, and the force of friction is, $f = \mu_k N = (0.1)(98\text{ N}) = 9.8$ N.

$W = fs(\cos 180°) = KE_f - KE_i$, or

$(9.8\text{ N})s(-1) = 0 - 20$ J, from which, $s = 2.0$ m.

5.17 (a) With our choice for the zero level for potential energy at point B, $PE_B = 0$. At point A, the potential energy is given by $PE_A = mgy$ where y is the vertical height above the zero level. With $d = 50$ m, this height is found as:

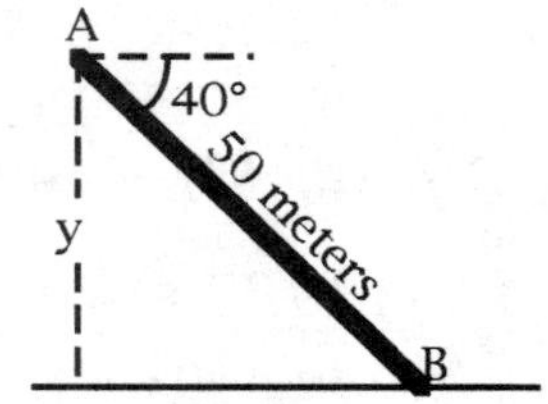

$y = (50\text{ m})\sin 40.0° = 32.14$ m. Thus,

$PE_A = 1000\text{ kg}(9.80\text{ m/s}^2)32.14\text{ m} = 3.15\times10^5$ J.

The difference in potential energy between points A and B is

$PE_A - PE_B = 3.15\times10^5\text{ J} - 0 = 3.15\times10^5$ J.

(b) With our choice of the zero level at point A, we have $PE_A = 0$. The potential energy at B is given by $PE_B = mgy$ where, y is the vertical distance of point B below point A. In part (a) we found the magnitude of this distance to be 32.14 m. Because this distance is now below the zero reference level, it is a negative number. Thus,

$PE_B = (1000\ \text{kg})(9.80\ \text{m/s}^2)(-\ 32.14\ \text{m}) = -\ 3.15 \times 10^5\ \text{J}$, and

$\Delta PE = PE_A - PE_B = 0 - (-3.15 \times 10^5\ \text{J}) = 3.15 \times 10^5\ \text{J}$.

5.18 (a) Relative to the ceiling, $y = -1$ m.

Thus, $PE = mgy = (2.00\ \text{kg})(9.80\ \text{m/s}^2)(-1.00\ \text{m}) = -19.6\ \text{J}$

(b) Relative to the floor, $y = 2.00$ m, so

$PE = mgy = (2.00\ \text{kg})(9.80\ \text{m/s}^2)(2.00\ \text{m}) = 39.2\ \text{J}$

(c) Relative to the height of the ball, $y = 0$, and $PE = 0$.

5.19 Choosing the gravitational potential energy to be zero at the bottom of the swing, the total energy ($E = KE + PE_g$) of the pendulum at the top of the swing is,

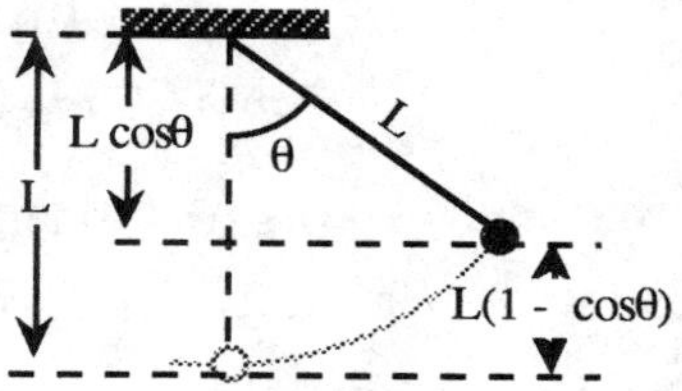

$E_{top} = 0 + mg(L - L\cos\theta) = mgL\ (1 - \cos\theta)$.

At the bottom of the swing, we have

$E_{bottom} = 0 + \frac{1}{2}mv^2 = \frac{1}{2}mv^2$.

Using conservation of energy, $\frac{1}{2}mv^2 = mgL\ (1 - \cos\theta)$, or

$v = \sqrt{2gL\ (1 - \cos\theta)} = \sqrt{2(9.80)(2.0)(1 - \cos 25°)} = 1.9\ \text{m/s}$.

5.20 Let m be the mass of the ball, R be the radius of the circle, F be the 30 N force. The work-energy theorem yields (choosing $y = 0$ at the bottom of the circle) $mg(2R) + \frac{1}{2}mv_{top}^2 + \text{pitcher's work} = \frac{1}{2}mv_{bottom}^2$, or

$2mgR + \frac{1}{2}mv_{top}^2 + F(\pi R) = \frac{1}{2}mv_{bottom}^2$, so that

$v_{bottom} = \sqrt{4gR + v_{top}^2 + \frac{2\pi FR}{m}} = \sqrt{4(9.80)(0.6) + (15)^2 + \frac{2\pi(30)(0.6)}{0.25}}$

or $v_{bottom} = 26.5\ \text{m/s}$.

5.21 (a) We take the zero level of potential energy at the lowest point of the arc. When the string is held horizontal initially, the initial position is 2 m above the zero level. Thus, $PE = mgy = wy = (40\ \text{N})(2\ \text{m}) = 80\ \text{J}$.

(b) From the sketch, we see that at an angle of 30° the ball is (2.0 m)(1 - cos30°) above the lowest point of the arc. Thus, $PE = (40\ \text{N})(2.0\ \text{m})(1 - \cos 30°) = 11\ \text{J}$.

(c) The zero level has been selected at the lowest point the arc. Therefore, $PE = 0$ at this point.

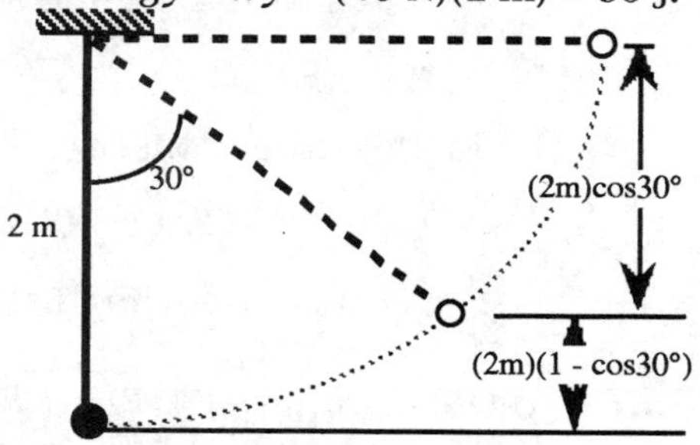

5.22 Using conservation of energy, we have

$\frac{1}{2}(50)(10)^2 = \frac{1}{2}(50)(1.0)^2 + (50)(9.80)H$, so that $H = 5.1$ m.

5.23 There are no non-conservative forces that do any work. As a result, we use conservation of mechanical energy, with the zero level for potential energy selected at the base of the hill. Also, note that $v_i = 0$, and we shall call the initial vertical height of the sled h.

$$\frac{1}{2}mv_i^2 + mgy_i = \frac{1}{2}mv_f^2 + mgy_f, \text{ or } \quad 0 + mgh = \frac{1}{2}m(3.00 \text{ m/s})^2 + 0.$$

The mass cancels, and we solve for h to find $h = 0.459$ m.

5.24 (a) We take the zero level for potential energy at the level of point B, and use $\frac{1}{2}mv_i^2 + mgy_i = \frac{1}{2}mv_f^2 + mgy_f$ to obtain

$$0 + (0.400 \text{ kg})g(5.00 \text{ m}) = \frac{1}{2}(0.400 \text{ kg})v_B^2 + 0.$$ From this, $v_B = 9.90$ m/s.

(b) At point C,with the starting point at A, we again use

$$\frac{1}{2}mv_i^2 + mgy_i = \frac{1}{2}mv_f^2 + mgy_f$$ and obtain

$$0 + (0.400 \text{ kg})g(5.00 \text{ m}) = \frac{1}{2}(0.400 \text{ kg})v_C^2 + (0.400 \text{ kg})g(2.00 \text{ m}),$$

giving $v_C = 7.67$ m/s.

5.25 (a) Choose the zero level for potential energy at point B, and we have

$PE_A = mgh = (0.2 \text{ kg})(9.80 \text{ m/s}^2)(0.30 \text{ m}) = 0.588$ J.

(b) From conservation of mechanical energy,

$\Delta KE = \Delta U = 0.588$ J and since $KE_i = 0$, $KE_f = 0.588$ J.

(c) From $KE_f = \frac{1}{2}mv^2$, we have $0.588 \text{ J} = \frac{1}{2}(0.2 \text{ kg})v^2$, and $v = 2.42$ m/s.

(d) At point C, $PE_C = mgh_C = (0.2 \text{ kg})(9.80 \text{ m/s}^2)(0.20 \text{ m}) = 0.392$ J, and

$KE = 0.588 \text{ J} - 0.392 \text{ J} = 0.196$ J.

5.26 (a) We choose the zero level for potential energy at the bottom of the arc. The initial height of Tarzan above this level is shown in the sketch to be

$(30\text{m})(1 - \cos 37°) = 6.04$ m.

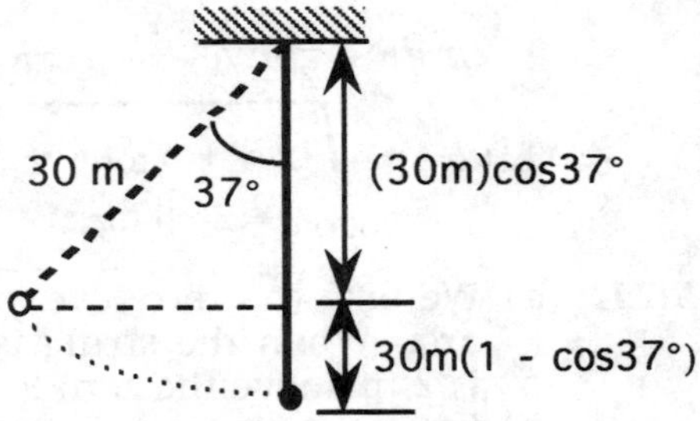

We use conservation of mechanical energy.

$$\frac{1}{2}mv_i^2 + mgy_i = \frac{1}{2}mv_f^2 + mgy_f$$

$$0 + mg(6.04 \text{ m}) = \frac{1}{2}mv^2 + 0.$$ From which, $v = 10.9$ m/s.

(b) In this case, conservation of mechanical energy becomes

$$\frac{1}{2}mv_i^2 + mgy_i = \frac{1}{2}mv_f^2 + mgy_f, \text{ or}$$

$$\frac{1}{2}m(4.00 \text{ m/s})^2 + mg(6.04 \text{ m}) = \frac{1}{2}mv^2 + 0,$$ which gives $v = 11.6$ m/s.

5.27 (a) $(PE + KE)_{\text{initial}} = (PE + KE)_{\text{final}}$

$$M_1gy_{1i} + M_2gy_{2i} + M_3gy_{3i} + KE_{1i} + KE_{2i} + KE_{3i} = M_1gy_{1f} + M_2gy_{2f} + M_3gy_{3f} + KE_{1f} + KE_{2f} + KE_{3f}$$

$$0 = (5.0(4) + 10.0(0) + 15.0(-4))9.80 + \frac{1}{2}(5.0 + 10.0 + 15.0)v^2$$

which yields $v = 5.11$ m/s

5.28 (a) Letting m the the mass of the projectile, k be the spring constant, d be 0.120 m, and H = 20.0 m, we have, using conservation of energy

$$\frac{1}{2}kd^2 = mgH, \text{ or } k = \frac{2mgH}{d^2} = \frac{2(0.02)(9.80)(20.0)}{(0.120)^2} = 544 \text{ N/m.}$$

(b) Here we have $\frac{1}{2}kd^2 = mgd + \frac{1}{2}mv^2$, so that

$$v = \sqrt{\frac{kd^2}{m} - 2gd} = \sqrt{\frac{(544.4)(0.120)^2}{0.020} - 2(9.80)(0.120)} = 19.7 \text{ m/s.}$$

5.29 At maximum height, $v_y = 0$ and $v_x = v_{xo}$. Thus, $v_f = v_{xo} = 40\cos 60° = 20$ m/s
Conservation of energy gives:

$$(PE + KE)_{\text{initial}} = (PE + KE)_{\text{final}}$$

$$\frac{1}{2}mv_i^2 + mgy_i = \frac{1}{2}mv_{xo}^2 + mgy_f$$

$$\frac{1}{2}mv_i^2 - \frac{1}{2}mv_{xo}^2 = mg(y_f - y_i) = mgh$$

$$h = (v_i^2 - v_{xo}^2)/2g = (40^2 - 20^2)/2(9.80) = 61.2 \text{ m}$$

5.30 From conservation of energy, $(PE_g)_f = (PE_s)_i$, or

$$(0.250 \text{ kg})(9.80 \text{ m/s}^2)h = (1/2)(5000 \text{ N/m})(0.100 \text{ m})^2.$$

This gives a maximum height: $h = 10.2$ m.

5.31 (a) Choose the zero level for potential energy at the level of B. Between A and B, we can use $\frac{1}{2}mv_i^2 + mgy_i = \frac{1}{2}mv_f^2 + mgy_f$ which becomes

$$0 + (0.400 \text{ kg})g(5.00 \text{ m}) = \frac{1}{2}(0.400 \text{ kg})v_B^2 + 0, \text{ yielding } v_B = 9.90 \text{ m/s.}$$

(b) We choose the starting point at B, the zero level at B, and the end point at C. $W_{nc} = \frac{1}{2}mv_f^2 - \frac{1}{2}mv_i^2 + mgy_f - mgy_i$ giving

$$W_{nc} = 0 - \frac{1}{2}(0.400 \text{ kg})(9.90 \text{ m/s})^2 + (0.400 \text{ kg})g(2.00 \text{ m}) - 0, \text{ or}$$

$W_{nc} = -11.8$ J. Thus, 11.8 J of energy is "lost" overcoming friction.

5.32 Let m equal the mass of the box, L be the length of the incline, θ be the angle of the incline, and μ_k be the coefficient of kinetic friction between box and incline. The initial energy of the box is KE_1, while the final energy is $KE_2 + mgL\sin\theta$. Using the work-energy theorem, we have $KE_2 + mgL\sin\theta = KE_1 - \mu_k mgL\cos\theta + FL$, so that

$$\Delta KE = KE_2 - KE_1 = FL - mgL(\sin\theta + \mu_k\cos\theta)$$

$$= (100)(20.0) - (80.0)(20.0)(\sin 30° + 0.22\cos 30°) = 895 \text{ J.}$$

5.33 We shall take the zero level of potential energy to be at the lowest level reached by the diver under the water.

$$W_{nc} = \frac{1}{2}mv_f^2 - \frac{1}{2}mv_i^2 + mgy_f - mgy_i$$

$$\bar{F}(5.0 \text{ m})\cos 180° = 0 - 0 + 0 - (70 \text{ kg})g(15 \text{ m}), \text{ or}$$

$$\bar{F} = 2.1 \times 10^3 \text{ N.}$$

5.34 $W_{nc} = W_{thrust} + W_{resistance} = \Delta KE.$

$= F_{thrust}s - F_{resistance}s = \frac{1}{2}mv_f^2 - \frac{1}{2}mv_i^2,$

$= (7.5 \times 10^4 - 4.0 \times 10^4)(500) = \frac{1}{2}(1.5 \times 10^4)(v_f^2 - (60)^2)$, or $v_f = 77$ m/s.

5.35 The initial vertical height of the car above the zero reference level at the base of the hill is $y_i = (5.0 \text{ m})\sin 20° = 1.71$ m.
The energy lost through friction is

$W_{nc} = -fs = -(4000 \text{ N})(5.0 \text{ m}) = -2 \times 10^4$ J.

We now use,

$$W_{nc} = \frac{1}{2}mv_f^2 - \frac{1}{2}mv_i^2 + mgy_f - mgy_i$$

$-2 \times 10^4 \text{ J} = \frac{1}{2}(2100 \text{ kg})v^2 - 0 + 0 - (2100 \text{ kg})g(1.71 \text{ m})$, or $v = 3.8$ m/s.

5.36 (a) The initial vertical height of the child above the zero level for gravitational energy at the bottom of the arc is

$(2.00 \text{ m})(1 - \cos 30°) = 0.268$ m.

In the absence of friction, we use conservation of mechanical energy as $\frac{1}{2}mv_i^2 + mgy_i = \frac{1}{2}mv_f^2 + mgy_f$, or

$0 + mg(0.268 \text{ m}) = \frac{1}{2}mv^2 + 0.$ This gives, $v = 2.29$ m/s.

(b) In the presence of friction, we use

$$W_{nc} = \frac{1}{2}mv_f^2 - \frac{1}{2}mv_i^2 + mgy_f - mgy_i.$$

$$W_{nc} = \frac{1}{2}(25.0 \text{ kg})(2.00 \text{ m/s})^2 - 0 + 0 - (25.0 \text{ kg})g(0.268 \text{ m}) = -15.6 \text{ J}.$$

5.37 (a) Let $L = 3$ m be the length of the ramp, and $m = 10$ kg be the mass of the block, and $\theta = 30°$ be the angle of the incline. Also let μ_k be the coefficient of kinetic friction between block and floor and D = 5 m. We may start with conservation of energy along the ramp and write, $mgL\sin\theta + 0 = \frac{1}{2}mv_{bottom}^2$, so that

$v_{bottom} = \sqrt{2gL\sin\theta} = \sqrt{2(9.80)(3)\ \sin 30} = 5.42$ m/s.

(b) Using energy considerations, we have $0 - mgL\sin\theta = -\mu_k mgD$ so that $\mu_k = \frac{L}{D}\sin\theta = \frac{3.00}{5.00}\sin 30° = 0.3.$

(c) All the initial potential energy is lost due to friction, which is

$mgy_i = mgL\sin\theta = (10.0)(9.80)(3.00)\sin 30° = 147$ J.

5.38 $(PE + KE)_{initial} = W_{nc} + (PE + KE)_{final}$

$$M_1gy_{1i} + M_2gy_{2i} + M_3gy_{3i} + KE_{1i} + KE_{2i} + KE_{3i} = W_{nc} + M_1gy_{1f} + M_2gy_{2f} + M_3gy_{3f} + KE_{1f} + KE_{2f} + KE_{3f}$$

$$0 = 30(4) + (5.0(4.0) + 10.0(0) + 15.0(-4.0))9.80 + \frac{1}{2}(5.0 + 10.0 + 15.0)v^2$$

which gives $v = 4.26$ m/s

5.39 We shall take the zero level for PE at the base of the hill. The skier starts at a vertical height above this level of

$h_o = (200 \text{ m})\sin 10.5° = 36.45$ m.

While on the hill, the normal force is $N_1 = w\cos 10.5° = mg\cos 10.5°$, and while on the level ground, $N_2 = w = mg$.

$W_{nc} = \frac{1}{2}mv_f^2 - \frac{1}{2}mv_i^2 + mgy_f - mgy_i$, or

$-f_1\,(200\text{ m}) - f_2\,(x) = 0 - 0 + 0 - mgh_o$

$-\mu_k N_1(200\text{ m}) - \mu_k N_2(x) = -mgh_o$

$-(0.0750)mg\cos 10.5°(200\text{ m}) - (0.075)mg(x) = -mg(36.45\text{ m})$, giving

$x = 289$ m.

5.40 The normal force, N, acting on the sled is found from $\Sigma F_y = 0$.

$N - (20\text{ kg})g\cos 20° = 0$, which gives $N = 184$ N.

The friction force is therefore $f = \mu_k N = 0.20(184\text{ N}) = 36.8$ N, and the work done by the force of friction as the sled moves a distance s up the hill is $W_{nc} = -fs = -(36.8\text{ N})s$.

Now use: $W_{nc} = \frac{1}{2}mv_f^2 - \frac{1}{2}mv_i^2 + mgy_f - mgy_i$, or

$$-(36.8\text{ N})s = 0 - \frac{1}{2}(20\text{ kg})(4.0\text{ m/s})^2 + (20\text{ kg})g(s)\sin 20° - 0.$$

In the last term, $y_f = s(\sin 20°)$ is the final vertical height of the sled above the zero reference level at the bottom of the hill.

Solving for s we find $s = 1.5$ m.

5.41 (a) $W_{nc} = \Delta KE + \Delta PE$, but $\Delta KE = 0$ because the speed is constant. The skier rises a vertical distance of (60 m)sin30° = 30 m. Thus,

$$W_{nc} = (70\text{ kg})g(30\text{ m}) = 2.06 \times 10^4\text{ J}.$$

(b) The time to travel 60 m at a constant speed of 2.0 m/s is 30 s. Thus,

$$P_{input} = \frac{W}{\Delta t} = \frac{2.06 \times 10^4\text{ J}}{30\text{ s}} = 686\text{ W} = 0.919\text{ hp}.$$

5.42 (a) The work done by the student is

$W = \Delta PE = mg(\Delta y) = (50.0\text{ kg})g(5.00\text{ m}) = 2.45 \times 10^3$ J.

The time to do this work if she is to match the power output of a 200 W lightbulb is: $\Delta t = W/\bar{P} = 2.45 \times 10^3\text{ J}/200\text{ W} = 12.25$ s.

Thus, the average velocity is $\bar{v} = 5.00\text{m}/12.25\text{ s} = 0.408$ m/s.

(b) The work done has already been found in part (a).

5.43 $P = \frac{energy\ spent}{\Delta t} = \frac{(\Delta m)gh}{\Delta t} = (1.2 \times 10^6)(9.80)(50)$

$= 5.88 \times 10^8\text{ W} = 590$ MW.

5.44 (a) We use the work-kinetic energy theorem as

$W = \Delta KE = \frac{1}{2}mv^2 - \frac{1}{2}mv_0^2$, so in this case,

$W = \frac{1}{2}mv^2 - 0 = \frac{1}{2}(1500\text{ kg})(10.0\text{ m/s})^2 = 7.50 \times 10^4$ J.

(b) The average power is given by

$\bar{P} = W/\Delta t = 7.5 \times 10^4\text{ J}/3.00\text{ s} = 2.5 \times 10^4\text{ W} = 33.5$ hp.

(c) $a = \frac{\Delta v}{\Delta t} = \frac{10\text{ m/s} - 0}{3.00\text{ s}} = 3.33\text{ m/s}^2$. Thus, $F = ma$ becomes

$F = (1500\text{ kg})(3.33\text{ m/s}^2) = 5000$ N.

at $t = 2.00$ s, $v = v_0 + at$ gives $v = 0 + (3.33\text{ m/s}^2)(2.00\text{ s}) = 6.66$ m/s, so

$P_{instantaneous} = Fv = (5000\text{ N})(6.66\text{ m/s}) = 3.33 \times 10^4\text{ W} = 44.7\text{ hp}.$

5.45 (a) Let us first find the net work done on the car by use of

$$W_{net} = \frac{1}{2} mv^2 - \frac{1}{2} mv_0^2 = \frac{1}{2}(1500\text{ kg})(18\text{ m/s})^2 - 0 = 2.43 \times 10^5\text{ J}.$$

The net work, W_{net}, is the work done by the engine, W_E, minus the work done by friction, W_f. Thus, the work done by the engine is

$W_E = W_{net} + W_f = 2.43 \times 10^5\text{ J} + (400\text{ N})d$, where d is the distance traveled by the car in 12 s. The power input by the engine is

$\bar{P} = W_E/12\text{ s} = (2.43 \times 10^5\text{ J}/12\text{ s}) + (400\text{ N})(d/12\text{ s})$, but ($d/12$ s) is the average velocity during this interval, which is 9 m/s.

Thus, $\bar{P} = 2.39 \times 10^4\text{ W} = 32\text{ hp}.$

(b) The constant acceleration of the car during the 12 seconds is

$a = \Delta v/\Delta t = (18\text{ m/s})/12\text{ s} = 1.5\text{ m/s}^2$, and the net force is given by F = ma as $F_E - f = ma$ where F_E is the forward thrust by the engine.

Therefore, $F_E = f + ma = 400\text{ N} + (1500\text{ kg})(1.5\text{ m/s}^2) = 2650\text{ N}$, and the instantaneous power at 12 s (when $v = 18$ m/s) is

$P_i = Fv = (2650\text{ N})(18\text{ m/s}) = 4.77 \times 10^4\text{ W} = 63.9\text{ hp}.$

5.46 (a) The distance moved upward in the first 3 s is

$$\Delta y = \bar{v}\, t = \left(\frac{0 + 1.75\text{ m/s}}{2}\right)(3.00\text{ s}) = 2.625\text{ m}.$$

$$W_{nc} = \frac{1}{2} mv_f^2 - \frac{1}{2} mv_i^2 + mgy_f - mgy_i = \frac{1}{2} mv_f^2 - \frac{1}{2} mv_i^2 + mg(\Delta y), \text{ or}$$

$$W_{nc} = \frac{1}{2}(650\text{ kg})(1.75\text{ m/s})^2 - 0 + (650\text{ kg})g(2.625\text{ m}) = 1.772 \times 10^4\text{ J}.$$

Also, $W_{nc} = \bar{P}\, t$, so $\bar{P} = \frac{W_{nc}}{t} = \frac{1.772 \times 10^4\text{ J}}{3.00\text{ s}} = 5910\text{ W} = 7.92\text{ hp}.$

(b) When moving upward at constant speed ($v = 1.75$ m/s), the applied force equals the weight = $(650\text{ kg})(9.80\text{ m/s}^2) = 6370\text{ N}$.

Therefore, $P = Fv = (6370\text{ N})(1.75\text{ m/s}) = 11{,}200\text{ W} = 14.9\text{ hp}.$

5.47 Let ΔN be the number of steps taken in time Δt. We determine the number of steps per unit time by

$$\text{Power} = \frac{\text{work done}}{\Delta t} = \frac{(\text{work per step per unit mass})(\text{mass})(\#\text{ steps})}{\Delta t}$$

or $70\text{ J/s} = 0.60 \frac{\text{J}}{\text{kg step}}(60\text{ kg})\frac{\Delta N}{\Delta t}$, or $\frac{\Delta N}{\Delta t} = 1.94\text{ steps/s}.$

$$v = \frac{\Delta x}{\Delta t} = \frac{\Delta N}{\Delta t}\left(\frac{\text{length}}{\text{step}}\right) = (1.94\text{ step/s})(1.5\text{ m/step}) = 2.9\text{ m/s}.$$

5.48 Let us assume that the friction force between the car and the road surface is constant and the same in both cases. The work required to stop the car is equal to its initial kinetic energy. If the speed is doubled as in this example, the work required is quadrupled. Since the work done is equal to force times the distance traveled, the car will travel four times as far when the speed is doubled, so the estimated distance it skids is 140 m. The kinetic energy of the car is changed into internal energy associated with the tires, brake pads, and road as they heat up.

5.49 The mass of the cart is 10.0 kg, and we use $W_{net} = \Delta KE = \frac{1}{2} m v_f^2 - \frac{1}{2} m v_0^2$,

or $(40.0\ N)(12.0\ m) = (1/2)(10.0\ kg) v_f^2 - 0$, giving $v_f = 9.80\ m/s$.

5.50 (a) Using conservation of energy, $\frac{1}{2} m v_i^2 + mgy_i = \frac{1}{2} m v_f^2 + mgy_f$, or

$$0 + (75\ kg)g(1.0\ m) = \frac{1}{2}(75\ kg) v_f^2 + 0. \quad \text{Thus,} \quad v_f = 4.43\ m/s.$$

(b) $W_{nc} = -Fs = -F(5.0 \times 10^{-3}\ m)$ where F is the force exerted on the man by the floor. From the work-energy theorem,

$$W_{nc} = \frac{1}{2} m v_f^2 - \frac{1}{2} m v_i^2 + mgy_f - mgy_i, \text{ which becomes}$$

$$-F(5.0 \times 10^{-3}\ m) = 0 - \frac{1}{2}(75\ kg)(4.43\ m/s)^2 + 0 - (75\ kg)g(5.0 \times 10^{-3}\ m).$$

Thus, $F = 1.47 \times 10^5\ N$

5.51 The initial energy of the system is $E_i = \frac{1}{2} k x_i^2 = \frac{1}{2}(8.0)(0.05)^2 = 0.01\ J$.
The mechanical energy lost due to friction in the barrel is
$|W_{nc}| = fs = (0.032)(0.15) = 0.0048\ J$, so that the sphere has
$E = E_i - |W_{nc}| = 0.01 - 0.0048 = 0.0052\ J$ of energy leaving the barrel.
Setting this equal to the kinetic energy of the sphere gives
$\frac{1}{2}(0.0053) v^2 = 0.0052\ J$, so that $v = 1.4\ m/s$.

5.52 (a) The initial energy of the system is $E_i = (5)(9.80)(4) = 196\ J$.
When the two masses pass each other the total energy is

$$E_{pass} = KE + PE = \frac{1}{2}(5.00)v^2 + \frac{1}{2}(3.00)v^2 + 5.00(9.80)(2.00) + (3.00)(9.80)(2.00),$$

or $E_{pass} = 4v^2 + 156.8$ since the masses move with the same speed and are 2.00 m above the floor when they pass each other. Using conservation of energy, we have $E_{pass} = E_i$, or

$4.00v^2 + 156.8 = 196$, which gives $v = 3.13\ m/s$.

(b) Here, we have $E_{floor} = \frac{1}{2}(5.00)\ v^2 + \frac{1}{2}(3.00)v^2 + 3.00(9.80)(4.00)$

$= 4.00v^2 + 117.6$,

and $E_{floor} = E_i$, or $4.00v^2 + 117.6 = 196\ J$, giving $v = 4.43\ m/s$.

(c) When the string goes slack, the total energy of the 3.00 kg mass is

$E_3 = \frac{1}{2} 3.00(4.43)^2 + 3.00(9.80)(4.00) = 147\ J$. At its highest point,

all of this is gravitational potential energy, so that
$(3.00\ kg)(9.80\ m/s^2)D = 147\ J$, which yields $D = 5.00\ m$. Therefore, the 3.00 kg will travel 1.00 m higher than it was when the 5.00 kg touched the floor.

5.53 On the incline $N = w\cos 37° = 391\ N$, and $f = \mu_k N = (0.25)(391\ N) = 97.8\ N$.
Now, we apply Newton's second law to the block on the incline in a direction along the incline

$T - 97.8\ N - (490\ N)\sin 37° = (50\ kg)a$, or

$T = 392.7\ N + (50\ kg)a$. (1)

Now consider the hanging block, with the positive direction selected as downward. $\Sigma F_y = 980\text{ N} - T = (100\text{ kg})a$. (2)

Solving (1) and (2) simultaneously, $T = 588.5$ N.

From the work energy theorem,

$(\Delta KE)_A$ = net work done on A by all forces
$= Ts\cos 0° + Ns\cos 90° + fs\cos 180° + ws\cos 127°$
$=(588.5\text{ N})(20\text{ m}) - (97.8\text{ N})(20\text{ m}) + (490\text{ N})(20\text{ m})(-0.602)$
$= 3.9 \times 10^3$ J.

5.54 Using the work-energy theorem, we have $\frac{1}{2}kd^2 = \mu_k mgD$, so

$\frac{1}{2}(100)(0.1)^2 = \mu_k(2.00)(9.80)(0.250)$, giving $\mu_k = 0.102$.

5.55 (a) Use $W = \frac{1}{2}mv_f^2 - \frac{1}{2}mv_0^2$ with W the work done on the baseball by the hand. (This is the negative of the work done on the hand by the baseball.) $W = -Fs = -F(.020\text{ m}) = 0 - (1/2)(0.15\text{ kg})(25\text{ m/s})^2$, or $F = 2.3 \times 10^3$ N. From the third law this is also the magnitude of the force on the hand.

(b) The steps are identical to those above, except $s = 0.10$ m. The result is $F = 470$ N

5.56 (a) Let $m = 2000$ kg be the mass of the car, W_E be the work done by the engine, and $f = -500$ N be the air resistance force. Assuming constant acceleration, we may say $v = v_0 + at$ with $v_0 = 0$, or $20 = a(15)$, giving $a = 1.33\text{ m/s}^2$. Then we use Newton's force law, so that $F + f = ma$, where F is the forward thrust produced by the engine. Therefore, $F - 500 = (2000)(1.33)$, or $F = 3166.67$ N. Finally, the average velocity of the car during the 15 s time interval is $\bar{v} = \frac{v_f + v_0}{2} = \frac{0 + 20}{2} = 10$ m/s, and so that the average power is:

$P_{ave} = Fv_{ave} = (3166.67)(10) = 31700$ W, or 42 hp.

(b) The forward thrust of the engine is constant at 3166.67 N throughout the motion. Therefore, at $t = 15$ s, we have

$P = Fv|_{t = 15s} = (3166.67\text{ N})(20\text{ m/s}) = 63000$ W or 85 hp.

5.57 (a) Using conservation of energy, we have $MgH_1 = \frac{1}{2}Mv_2^2 + MgH_2$ so that

$v_2 = \sqrt{2g(H_1 - H_2)}$
$= \sqrt{2(9.80)(50.0 - 10.0)}$
or $v_2 = 28$ m/s.

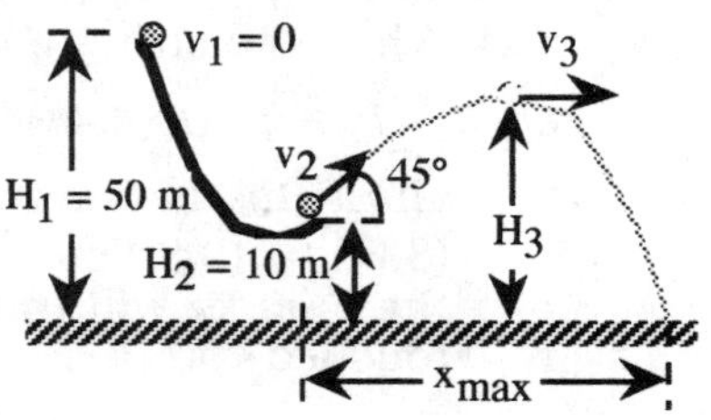

(b) Recognizing that $v_{3y} = 0$ (top of arc), conservation of energy gives

$MgH_3 + \frac{1}{2}M(v_{3x})^2 = \frac{1}{2}Mv_1^2 + MgH_1$. Since $v_{3x} = v_{2x} = 28.0\cos(45°) =$ 19.8 m/s, this yields

$$H_3 = H_1 - \frac{(v_{3x})^2}{2g} = 50 - \frac{(19.8)^2}{2(9.80)} = 30 \text{ meters.}$$

(c) Letting the origin of an xy coordinate system be located at the base of the track below where the ski jumper leaves the track, we have

$x = 28(\cos 45)t = 19.8\ t,$ and $y = 10 + 28(\sin 45)\ t - 4.9\ t^2.$

Setting $y = 0$ (ground level) gives $4.9t^2 - 19.8t - 10 = 0$ which has a positive solution of $t = 4.495$ s. At this time,

$x = x_{max} = 19.8(4.495) = 89$ m.

5.58 (a) When the mass is held in equilibrium by the spring, the spring force F_s is equal to the component of weight down the incline (see Figure 1). Thus, $kx = Mg\sin\theta$ which gives

$$k = \frac{(2.0\ \text{kg})(9.80\ \text{m/s}^2)}{0.10\ \text{m}} \sin 30° = 98\ \text{N/m}.$$

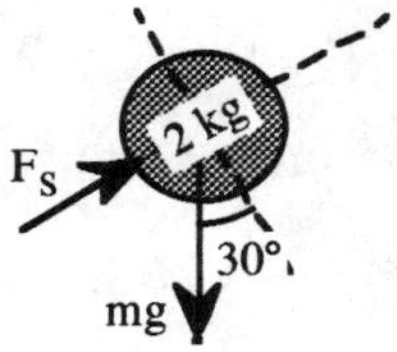

Figure 1

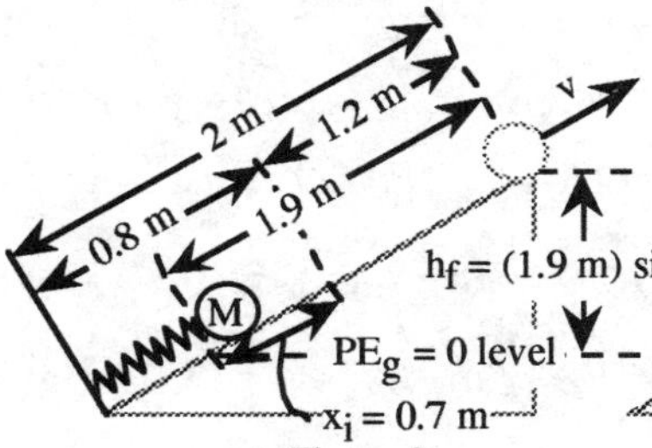

Figure 2

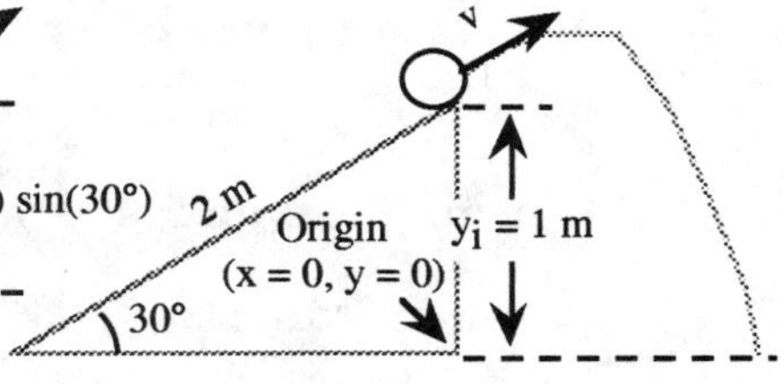

Figure 3

(b) We need the speed of the mass as it leaves the incline. Using conservation of energy with $PE_g = 0$ at the initial level of the mass (see Figure 2), we write $\frac{1}{2}Mv_f^2 + Mgh_f + 0 = 0 + 0 + \frac{1}{2}kx_i^2.$

This gives,

$$v_f^2 = \frac{(98\ \text{N/m})}{(2.0\ \text{kg})}(0.70\ \text{m})^2 - 2.0(9.8\ \text{m})(1.9\ \text{m})(0.5) = 5.39\ \text{m}^2,$$

or $v = 2.32$ m/s.

For the projectile part of the trip, the components of the initial velocity are: $v_{ox} = v\cos 30° = 2.0$ m/s, and $v_{oy} = v\sin 30° = 1.16$ m/s. With the origin at the base of the incline (see Figure 3),

$$\Delta y = y - 1.00\ \text{m} = v_{oy}t - \frac{1}{2}gt^2 = (1.16\ \text{m/s})t - (4.9\ \text{m/s}^2)t^2.$$

Setting $y = 0$ (floor level) and solving for t gives a positive solution of $t = 0.585$ s. At this time $x = v_{ox}t = (2.0\ \text{m/s})(0.585\ \text{s}) = 1.2$ m

---

5.59 (a) Letting m be the mass of the block and μ_k be the coefficient of kinetic friction between block and wall, we have, since the block moves with constant speed,

$\Sigma F_y = F\sin\theta - \mu_k N - mg = 0,$ and $\Sigma F_x = F\cos\theta - N = 0.$

Thus, $N = F\cos\theta$ and $F\sin\theta - \mu_k F\cos\theta = mg,$ or

$$F = \frac{mg}{\sin\theta - \mu_k\cos\theta} = \frac{(5)(9.80)}{\sin 30° - (0.3)\cos 30°} = 204\ \text{N}.$$

Then, $W_F = (F\sin\theta)L = (204)\sin 30°(3) = 310$ J.

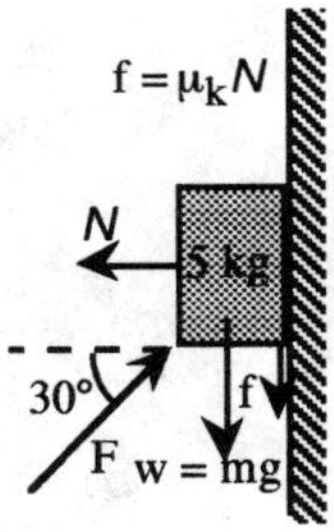

(b) Here we have

$W_g = mgL\cos 180° = -(5.0)(9.80)(3.0) = -150$ J.

(c) Since N is perpendicular to the displacement, we have $W_N = 0$ J.

(d) The increase in gravitational potential energy $= mgL = 150$ J.

5.60 (a) The putty is in equilibrium when it comes to rest so $\Sigma F_y = 0$. Thus, $+kx_{max} - Mg = 0$,

or $x_{max} = Mg/k = \dfrac{(0.300\ \text{kg})(9.80\ \text{m/s}^2)}{19.6\ \text{N/m}} = 0.15$ m.

(b) Here we use conservation of energy, assuming zero gravitational potential energy where the mass first contacts the spring, and write

$0 + (Mg)x_f + \frac{1}{2}kx_f^2 = 0 + Mgy_i + 0$ (with upward as positive).

This gives, $x_f^2 + (0.300\ \text{kg})x_f - (0.15\ \text{m}^2) = 0$, which has one negative solution: $x_f = -0.57$ m, so the spring is <u>compressed</u> 0.57 m.

5.61 (a) Neglecting air resistance $R = \dfrac{v_0^2 \sin 2\theta}{g}$ (See Chapter 3.)

The max. range occurs when $\sin 2\theta = 1$ ($\theta = 45°$), so $v_0^2 = gR_{max}$.

Thus, $KE_i = \frac{1}{2}mv_0^2 = \frac{1}{2}mgR_{max}$. Now consider each of the objects in turn.

javelin: $KE_i = \frac{1}{2}mgR_{max} = \frac{1}{2}(0.80\ \text{kg})g(89\ \text{m}) = 349$ J.

discus: $KE_i = \frac{1}{2}mgR_{max} = \frac{1}{2}(2.0\ \text{kg})g(69\ \text{m}) = 676$ J.

shot: $KE_i = \frac{1}{2}mgR_{max} = \frac{1}{2}(7.2\ \text{kg})g(21\ \text{m}) = 741$ J.

(b) We use $W = \Delta KE$, with the initial velocity of the object equal to zero. The force, F, is applied over an assumed distance of 2.0 m while it is in the thrower's hand. We see, $W = Fs = F(2.0\ \text{m}) = \Delta KE$, or $F = \Delta KE/(2.0\ \text{m})$.

javelin: $F = (349\ \text{J})/(2.0\ \text{m}) = 175$ N.
discus: $F = (676\ \text{J})/(2.0\ \text{m}) = 338$ N.
shot: $F = (741\ \text{J})/(2.0\ \text{m}) = 371$ N.

(c) Yes, if the muscles of the body are capable of exerting a force of 371 N on an object (and giving it a kinetic energy of 741 J), one would expect the javelin to leave the hand with a speed of 43 m/s and to reach a range of 189 m. Since this predicted range is much larger than the range found in practice, air resistance must exert a considerable influence.

5.62 (a) Let $m = 5.00$ kg be the mass of the block, and $D = 0.250$ m be the length of AB. Also, let $L_1 = 0.15$ m be the initial compression of the left spring. The initial energy of the system is $\frac{1}{2}200(0.15)^2 = 2.25$ J. Using the work-energy theorem, we may write

$\frac{1}{2}kL_1^2 - \mu_k mgD = \frac{1}{2}kR_1^2$ where R_1 is the first compression of the spring on the right. Therefore, $R_1 = \sqrt{L_1^2 - 2\mu_k mgD/k}$, or

$R_1 = \sqrt{(0.15)^2 - (2)(0.08)(5.00)(9.80)(0.25)/200} = 0.113$ m.

(b) First, we note that $\mu_k mgD = 0.080(5.00)(9.80)(0.25) = 0.98$ J of energy is lost due to friction every time the length AB is transversed. When the block is against the spring on the right, it has 2.25 - 0.98 = 1.27 J of energy left. Hence, it can transverse AB for a second time, losing another 0.98 J of energy, leaving it with 0.29 J. Thus, it compresses the spring on the left by

$\sqrt{(2(0.29)/200)} = 0.054$ m. At this point, the block has only 0.29 J of energy so that it cannot transverse AB for a third time. Instead, it only travels a distance d where

$\mu_k mgd = 0.29$, so that $d = 0.074$ m, and so the block comes to rest at $d = 0.074$ m to the right of point A.

5.63 (a) The potential energy associated with the wind force is $+Fx$, where x is the horizontal distance traveled, with x positive when swinging into the wind and negative when swinging in the direction the wind is blowing. The initial energy of Jane is, (using the pivot point of the swing as the point of zero gravitational energy),

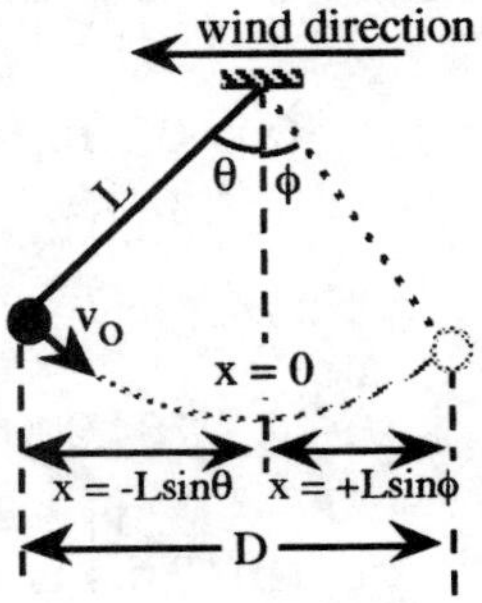

$E_i = (KE + PE_g + PE_{wind})_i = \frac{1}{2}mv^2_0 - mgL\cos\theta - FL\sin\theta$

where m is her mass. At the end of her swing, her energy is

$E_f = (KE + PE_g + PE_{wind})_i = 0 - mgL\cos\phi + FL\sin\phi$, so conservation of energy ($E_i = E_f$) gives

$\frac{1}{2}mv^2_0 - mgL\cos\theta - FL\sin\theta = -mgL\cos\phi + FL\sin\phi$,

This leads to $v_0 = \sqrt{2gL(\cos\theta - \cos\phi) + 2\frac{FL}{m}(\sin\theta + \sin\phi)}$.

But $D = L\sin\phi + L\sin\theta$, so that $\sin\phi = \frac{D}{L} - \sin\theta = \frac{50}{40} - \sin 50° = 0.484$

which gives $\phi = 28.94°$. Using this, we have $v_0 = 6.15$ m/s.

(b) Here (again using conservation of energy)we have,

$-MgL\cos\phi + FL\sin\phi + \frac{1}{2}Mv^2 = -MgL\cos\theta - FL\sin\theta$,

where M is the combined mass of Jane and Tarzan.

Therefore, $v = \sqrt{2gL(\cos\phi - \cos\theta) - 2\frac{FL}{M}(\sin\theta + \sin\phi)}$ which gives

$v = 9.87$ m/s as the minimum speed needed.

5.64 $\frac{1}{2}(1.20 \text{ N/cm})(0.050 \text{ m})^2$

$= (0.100 \text{ kg})(9.80 \text{ m/s}^2)(0.05 \text{ m}) \sin 10° + \frac{1}{2}(0.100 \text{ kg})v^2$

$0.15 \text{ J} = 0.00851 \text{ J} + (0.05 \text{ kg})\, v^2$

$v = 1.68$ m/s

5.65 $P\Delta t = W = \Delta KE = \frac{(\Delta m)v^2}{2}$

The density is

$\rho = \frac{\Delta m}{\text{vol}} = \frac{\Delta m}{A\Delta x}$

Substituting this into the first equation and solving for P, since

$\frac{\Delta x}{\Delta t} = v$

For a constant speed, we get

$$P = \frac{\rho A v^3}{2}$$

Also, since $P = Fv$, $F = \frac{\rho A v^2}{2}$

5.66 Consider the entire motion,

$KE_i + PE_i + W_{nc} = KE_f + PE_f$

(a) $0 + mgy_i + f_1 d_1 \cos 180° + f_2 d_2 \cos 180° = \frac{1}{2} mv^2 + 0$

$80.0\text{ kg}(9.80\text{ m/s}^2)1000\text{ m} - 50.0\text{ N}(800\text{ m}) - 3600\text{ N}(200\text{ m})$

$= \frac{1}{2}(80\ kg)v_f^2$

$784{,}000\text{ J} - 40{,}000\text{ J} - 720{,}000\text{ J} = \frac{1}{2}(80.0\ kg)v_f^2$

$v_f = 24.5\text{ m/s}$

(b) This is too fast for safety.

(c) Now in the same work-energy equation d_2 is unknown and $d_1 = 1000\text{ m} - d_2$

$784{,}000\text{ J} - 50\text{ N}(1000\text{ m} - d_2) - 3600\text{ N}d_2 = \frac{1}{2}\ (80.0\ kg)(5.00\text{ m/s})^2$

From which, $d_2 = 206\text{ m.}$

(d) Really the air drag will depend on the skydiver's speed. It will be larger than her 784 N weight only after the chute is opened. It will be nearly equal to 784 N before she opens the chute and again before she touches down, whenever she moves near terminal speed.

5.67 (a) $E = \frac{1}{2}kx_1^2 - mgx_1 = \frac{1}{2}(2.50 \times 10^4)(0.1)^2 + 25.0\text{ kg}(9.80\text{ m/s}^2)(-0.100\text{ m}) =$ 100 J

(b) $mg(x_2 + x_1) = 125$

From which $x_2 = 0.410\text{ m}$

(c) At $x = 0$

$\frac{1}{2}mv_0^2 - mg(0 - x_1) = 125$

$v_0 = 2.84\text{ m/s}$

(d) KE and v are at a maximum when $a = 0$, $\Sigma F = 0$ when spring force up = weight down.

$(2.50 \times 10^4\text{ N/m})x_d = (25.0\text{ kg})(9.80\text{ m/s}^2)$

$x_d = -9.80\text{ mm}$

(e) $100.5\text{ J} = \frac{1}{2}(2.50 \times 10^4)(-9.8 \times 10^{-3})^2 + (25.0)(9.80)(-9.8 \times 10^{-3}) + \frac{1}{2}$ $25.0v_e^2$

From which, $v_{max} = 2.85\text{ m/s}$

5.68 The nonconservative work due to friction must equal the change in the kinetic energy plus the change in the potential energy. Therefore,

$-\mu mgx\cos\theta = \Delta KE + \frac{1}{2}kx^2 - mgx\sin\theta$

and because $v_i = v_f = 0$, $\Delta KE = 0$.

Thus,

$$-\mu(2.00)(9.80)(\cos 37°)(0.200) = \frac{100(0.2)^2}{2} - 2.00(9.80)(\sin 37)(0.200)$$

and we find $\mu = 0.115$. Note that in the above we had a gain in elastic potential energy for the spring and a loss in gravitational potential energy. The net loss in mechanical energy is equal to the energy lost due to friction.

5.69 Choose $y = 0$ at the river. Then $y_i = 36$ m, $y_f = 4$ m, the jumper falls 32.0m, and the cord stretches 7.0 m. Between bridge and bottom,

$$mgy_i = mgy_f + \frac{1}{2}kx_f^2$$

$$(700 \text{ N})(36.0 \text{ m}) = (700 \text{ N})(4.0 \text{ m}) + \frac{1}{2}k(7.0 \text{ m})^2$$

$$k = 914 \text{ N/m}$$

5.70 (a) On the upward swing of the mass, conservation of energy gives

$$\frac{1}{2}mv_0^2 = mgL(1 - \cos\theta)$$

$$v_0 = \sqrt{2gL(1 - \cos\theta)}$$

(b) $v_0 = \sqrt{2(9.8 \text{ m/s}^2)(1.20 \text{ m})(1 - \cos 35°)} = 2.06 \text{ m/s}$

ANSWERS TO CONCEPTUAL QUESTIONS

2. (a) The chicken does positive work on the ground. (b) No work is done. (c) The crane does positive work on the bucket. (d) The force of gravity does negative work on the bucket. (e) The leg muscles do positive work on the individual.

4. (a) Kinetic energy is always positive. Mass and speed squared are both positive. (b) Gravitational potential energy can be negative when the object is below, closer to the Earth, the chosen zero level.

6. (a) Kinetic energy is proportional to the speed squared. Doubling the speed makes the object's kinetic energy four times larger. (b) If the total work done on an object in some process is zero, its speed must be the same at the final point as it was at the initial point.

8. The total energy of the bowling ball is conserved. Because the ball initially has gravitational potential energy *mgh* and no kinetic energy, it will again have zero kinetic energy when it returns to its original position. Air resistance and friction at the support will cause the ball to come back to a point slightly below its initial position. On the other hand, if anyone gives a forward push to the ball anywhere along its path, the demonstrator will have to duck.

10. The effects are the same except for such features as having to overcome air resistance outside. The person must lift his body slightly with each step on the tilted treadmill. Thus, the effect is that of running uphill.

12. As the person runs she gains kinetic energy and this adds to the gravitational potential energy she has at the top of her jump, thus increasing her height. Also, stored elastic potential energy in the pole is converted to gravitational potential energy at the top of the leap.

14. The kinetic energy is converted to internal energy in the form of heat in the brake pads of the car, the roadway, and the tires.

16. The kinetic energy is a maximum at the instant the ball is released. The gravitational potential energy is a maximum at the top of the flight path.

CHAPTER SIX SOLUTIONS

Chapter Six Readings

Ordway, F., "Principles of Rocket Engines," *Sky and Telescope*, 14, 1954, p. 48.

Resh, R.E., "Air Bags," *Scientific American*, v. 274 (June '96), p 116.

6.1 $KE = \frac{1}{2}mv^2 = \frac{1}{2}\frac{(mv)^2}{m} = \frac{1}{2}\frac{p^2}{m}$

6.2 Use $p = mv$:

(a) $p = (1.67 \times 10^{-27}$ kg$)(5.00 \times 10^6$ m/s$) = 8.35 \times 10^{-21}$ kg m/s
(b) $p = (1.50 \times 10^{-2}$ kg$)(3.00 \times 10^2$ m/s$) = 4.50$ kg m/s
(c) $p = (75.0$ kg$)(10.0$ m/s$) = 750$ kg m/s
(d) $p = (5.98 \times 10^{24}$ kg$)(2.98 \times 10^4$ m/s$) = 1.78 \times 10^{29}$ kg m/s

---

6.3 (a) Since the ball was thrown straight upward, it is at rest momentarily ($v = 0$) at its maximum height. Therefore, $p = 0$.

(b) The maximum height is found from $v^2 = v_0^2 + 2ay$ with $v = 0$.
$0 = (15 \text{ m/s})^2 - 2(9.80 \text{ m/s}^2)h_{max}$. Thus, $h_{max} = 11.5$ m.
We need the velocity at $\frac{h_{max}}{2} = 5.75$ m, thus $v^2 = v_0^2 + 2ay$ gives
$v^2 = (15 \text{ m/s})^2 - 2(9.80 \text{ m/s}^2)(5.75 \text{ m})$, or $v = 10.6$ m/s.
Therefore, $p = (0.10 \text{ kg})(10.6 \text{ m/s}) = 1.1$ kg m/s.

6.4 (a) The momentum of the bullet is $(0.003)(1500) = 4.5$ kg m/s. The momentum of the baseball is $p = (0.145)v$, where v is the speed of the baseball. Therefore, if the two momenta are equal, we must have $(0.145)v = 4.5$, so $v = 31.0$ m/s.

(b) The kinetic energy of the bullet is $\frac{1}{2}(0.003)(1500)^2 = 3375$ J,
while the kinetic energy of the baseball is $\frac{1}{2}(0.145)(31.0)^2 = 69.7$ J.
The bullet has the larger kinetic energy by a factor of 48.4.

6.5 Use, $F\Delta t = \Delta p = mv_f - mv_i$.
$F(0.30 \text{ s}) = 0 - (1500 \text{ kg})(15 \text{ m/s})$
$F = -7.5 \times 10^4$ N (the negative sign indicates the direction of the force is opposite to that of the car's original motion.

6.6 Impulse $= \bar{F}t = \Delta p = m(\Delta v)$.
Thus, Impulse $= (70.0 \text{ kg})(5.20 \text{ m/s} - 0) = 364$ kg m/s
and
$\bar{F} = \frac{\text{Impulse}}{t} = \frac{364 \text{ kg m/s}}{0.832 \text{ s}} = 438 \text{ kg m/s}^2$, or $\bar{F} = 438$ N.

6.7 (a) First, find the impulse delivered to the ball.
$F\Delta t = \Delta p = mv_f - mv_i = 0 - (0.500 \text{ kg})(15.0 \text{ m/s}) = -7.5$ kg m/s.

(b) $F\Delta t = -7.5$ kg m/s, and $\Delta t = 0.020$ s, so

$$F = \frac{-7.5 \text{ kg m/s}}{0.020 \text{ s}} = -375 \text{ N}.$$

The force on the ball is 375 N in the direction opposite to the original direction of motion of the ball. The force on the receiver is also 375 N but in the direction the ball was moving.

6.8 (a) The impulse equals the area under the F versus t graph. This area is the sum of the area of the rectangle plus the area of the triangle. Thus,

$$\text{Impulse} = (3.0 \text{ s})(2.0 \text{ N}) + \frac{1}{2}(2.0 \text{ s})(2.0 \text{ N}) = 8.0 \text{ N s}.$$

(b) $F\Delta t = \Delta p = mv_f - mv_i$.
$8.0 \text{ N s} = (1.5 \text{ kg})v_f - 0$
$v_f = 5.3 \text{ m/s}$.

(c) $F\Delta t = \Delta p = mv_f - mv_i$.
$8.0 \text{ Ns} = (1.5 \text{ kg})v_f - (1.5 \text{ kg})(-2.0 \text{ m/s})$
$v_f = 3.3 \text{ m/s}$.

6.9 Impulse = area under curve = (two triangular areas each of altitude 4 N and base 2 s) + (one rectangular area of width 1 s and height of 4 N.)

(a) Thus, $\text{Impulse} = 2(\frac{1}{2}(2.0 \text{ s})(4.0 \text{ N})) + (1.0 \text{ s})(4.0 \text{ N}) = 12 \text{ N s}$.

(b) $\Delta p = \text{impulse} = mv_f - mv_i. = 12 \text{ N s}$,
or $(2.00 \text{ kg})v_f - (2.00 \text{ kg})(0) = 12 \text{ N s}$,
so $v_f = 6.0 \text{ m/s}$.

(c) if $v_0 = -2.00 \text{ m/s}$, then $(2.00 \text{ kg})v_f - (2.00 \text{ kg})(-2.0 \text{ m/s}) = 12 \text{ N s}$, and $v_f = 4 \text{ m/s}$.

6.10 (a) The impulse is the area under the curve between 0 and 3.0 s.
This is: $\text{Impulse} = (4.0 \text{ N})(3.0 \text{ s}) = 12.0 \text{ N s}$.

(b) The area under the curve between 0 and 5.0 s is:
$\text{Impulse} = (4.0 \text{ N})(3.0 \text{ s}) + (-2.0 \text{ N})(2.0 \text{ s}) = 8.00 \text{ N s}$.

(c) Use, $F\Delta t = \Delta p = mv_f - mv_i$.
at 3.0 s: $12 \text{ N s} = (1.5 \text{ kg})v - 0$, or $v = 8.0 \text{ m/s}$.
at 5.0 s: $8.0 \text{ N s} = (1.5 \text{ kg})v - 0$, or $v = 5.3 \text{ m/s}$.

6.11 (a) $\frac{\Delta x}{\bar{v}} = \frac{1.20 \text{ m}}{12.5 \text{ m/s}} = 0.096 \text{ s}$

(b) $\bar{F} = \frac{\Delta p}{\Delta t} = \frac{m(\Delta v)}{\Delta t} = \frac{1400(25.0)}{0.096} = 3.65 \times 10^5 \text{ N}$

(c) $\bar{a} = \frac{\bar{F}}{m} = \frac{3.65 \times 10^5 \text{ N}}{1400 \text{ kg}} = 260 \text{ m/s}^2 \left(\frac{1 \text{ g}}{9.80 \text{ m/s}^2}\right) = 26.5 \text{ g's}$

6.12 (a) From $F\Delta t = \Delta p = mv_f - mv_i$,
we have $(3.0 \text{ N})(1.5 \text{ s}) = (0.50 \text{ kg})v - 0$, or
$v = 9.0 \text{ m/s}$.

(b) Again use $F\Delta t = \Delta p = mv_f - mv_i$.
$(-4.0 \text{ N})(3.0 \text{ s}) = (0.50 \text{ kg})v - (0.50 \text{ kg})(9.0 \text{ m/s})$, or
$v = -15 \text{ m/s}$.

6.13 (a) Use $F\Delta t = \Delta p = mv_f - mv_i = (0.15 \text{ kg})[(-22 \text{ m/s}) - (20 \text{ m/s})]$, or

$F\Delta t$ = -6.3 kg m/s. The negative sign indicates that the impulse is in the direction opposite to the initial velocity.

(b) F = (impulse)/Δt = -(6.3 kg m/s)/2.0 x 10^{-3} s) = -3.2 x 10^3 N

6.14 Only the component of the ball's velocity perpendicular to the wall will change. This velocity component before hitting the wall is (10.0)sin60° = 8.66 m/s. After hitting the wall, this component is -8.66 m/s, because the rebound angle is also 60°. The change in momentum during contact with the wall is therefore

Δp = (3.0)(8.66) - (3.00)(-8.66) = 51.96 kg m/s.

The average force on ball is then $F = \frac{\Delta p}{\Delta t}$ = 51.96/0.200 = 260 N directed away from the wall.

6.15 From conservation of momentum (after = before), we find the velocity of the man: (74.5 kg)v_{man} +(1.20 kg)(5.00 m/s) = 0, or

v_{man} = -8.05 x 10^{-2} m/s (direction is southward)

The time to travel 5.00 m to shore is t = 5.00 m/8.05 x 10^{-2} m/s = 62 s.

6.16 Before the collision, we have the total momentum being

(0.20)(55) + 0 = 11 kg m/s.

After the collision, we have for total momentum

(0.20)(40) + (0.046)v = 8 + 0.046v.

Conservation of momentum gives

8.0 + 0.046v = 11, which yields v = 65 m/s.

6.17 (a) From conservation of momentum, we have, choosing the direction of the bullet's motion as positive, $m_R v_R + m_b v_b = 0$, which gives

$$v_R = -\frac{m_b}{m_R} v_b = -\frac{5.0 \text{ x } 10^{-3}}{3.06} 300 \text{ m/s} = -0.49 \text{ m/s}.$$

(b) The mass of the man plus rifle is 74.5 kg. We use the same approach as in (a), to find $v = -\frac{5.0 \text{ x } 10^{-3}}{74.5}(300 \text{ m/s}) = -2.0 \text{ x } 10^{-2}$ m/s.

6.18 (a) Let v_g and v_p be the velocity of the girl and the plank relative to the ice surface. Then we may say that $v_g - v_p$ is the velocity of the girl relative to the plank, so that $v_g - v_p = 1.50$. (1)

But also we must have $m_g v_g + m_p v_p = 0$, since total momentum of the girl-plank system is zero relative to the ice surface. Therefore

$45.0 v_g + 150 v_p = 0$, or $v_p = -0.300\ v_g$. (2)

Putting this into the equation (1) above gives

$v_g - (-0.300\ v_g) = 1.50$, or v_g = 1.15 m/s.

(b) Then, using (2) above: v_p = -0.300(1.15) = -0.346 m/s.

6.19 Consider the thrower first, with velocity after the throw of v_t

momentum after = momentum before

(65.0 kg)v_t + (0.045 kg)(30.0 m/s) = (65.045 kg)(2.50 m/s), or

v_t = 2.48 m/s.

Now, consider the (catcher + ball), with velocity of v_c after the catch:

(60.045 kg)v_c = (0.045 kg)(30.0 m/s) + (60 kg)(0), or v_c = 2.25 x 10^{-2} m/s.

6.20 (a) Total momentum must be conserved for the earth-ball system. Initially, this total is zero. The speed of the ball before impact with the ground is given by $(7.00)(9.80)(3.00) = \frac{1}{2}(7.00)v^2$, or

$v = 7.7$ m/s (downward). Therefore, taking upward as positive, conservation of momentum gives $M_e V_e + m_b v = 0 + 0$ (Since both ball and Earth were initially at rest.)

Thus, $V_e = \frac{m_b}{M_e} v = \frac{-7.0 \text{ kg}}{5.98 \times 10^{24} \text{ kg}}(-7.7 \text{ m/s}) = 9.0 \times 10^{-24}$ m/s.

Note that we have ignored the fact that the ball really travels a distance slightly smaller than 7 m because the Earth comes up to meet the ball. However, the small velocity of the Earth indicates that our assumption is justified.

(b) The velocity of the Earth is so small that its motion can be ignored when dealing with the motion of terrestrial objects.

6.21 $(p_{total})_{before} = (p_{total})_{after}$,
or $(p_{ball})_{before} + (p_{pin})_{before} = (p_{ball})_{after} + (p_{pin})_{after}$
$(7.00 \text{ kg})(v_{ball})_{before} + 0 = (7.00 \text{ kg})(+1.80 \text{ m/s}) + (2.00 \text{ kg})(3.00 \text{ m/s})$
This gives $(v_{ball})_{before} = 2.66$ m/s.

6.22 $p_{after} = p_{before}$ gives $(3.00 \text{ kg} + M)\frac{v}{3} = (3.00 \text{ kg})v$.
Cancel v and solve for M; $M = 6.00$ kg.

6.23 (a) $p_{after} = p_{before}$ becomes $(3M)v = M(3.00 \text{ m/s}) + (2M)(1.20 \text{ m/s})$, where M is the common mass of the cars, and v is the velocity of the combination after the collision. This gives $v = 1.80$ m/s.

(b) $KE_{before} = \frac{1}{2}(2.00 \times 10^4 \text{ kg})(3.00 \text{ m/s})^2 + \frac{1}{2}(4.00 \times 10^4 \text{ kg})(1.20 \text{ m/s})^2$
$= 1.19 \times 10^5$ J.

$KE_{after} = \frac{1}{2}(60000 \text{ kg})(1.80 \text{ m/s})^2 = 9.72 \times 10^4$ J.

Thus, the kinetic energy lost = 2.16×10^4 J.

6.24 Let us apply conservation of energy to the block from the time just after the bullet has passed through until it reaches its maximum height in order to find its speed V just after the collision.

$$\frac{1}{2}mv_i^2 + mgy_i = \frac{1}{2}mv_f^2 + mgy_f$$

$$\frac{1}{2}(1.50 \text{ kg})V^2 + 0 = 0 + (1.50 \text{ kg})g(0.12 \text{ m})$$

$V = 1.53$ m/s.

Now use conservation of momentum from before until just after the collision in order to find the initial speed of the bullet, v_o,

$(7.00 \times 10^{-3} \text{ kg})(v_o) = (1.50 \text{ kg})(1.53 \text{ m/s}) + (7.00 \times 10^{-3} \text{ kg})(200 \text{ m/s})$,
from which

$$v_o = 528 \text{ m/s}.$$

6.25 We equate momentum before to momentum just after, to get
$(3.0 \times 10^{-2} \text{ kg})(200 \text{ m/s}) = (1.8 \times 10^{-1} \text{ kg})V$.

V is the velocity of the bullet-baseball combination immediately after the collision, and its value is found to be, $V = 33.33$ m/s.
The problem now becomes that of finding the height, H, reached by a projectile launched straight upward at 33.33 m/s. $v^2 = v_0^2 + 2ay$, gives $0 = (33.33 \text{ m/s})^2 + 2(-9.80 \text{ m/s}^2)H$, ($v = 0$ at the top), so $H = 57$ m.

6.26 First, we will find the horizontal speed, v_{ox}, of the block and embedded bullet just after impact. At this instant, the block-bullet combination has become a projectile, so we find the time to reach the floor by use of:

$$y = v_{oy}t + \frac{1}{2}at^2,$$

which becomes

$$-1.00 \text{ m} = 0 + \frac{1}{2}(-9.80 \text{ m/s}^2)t^2,$$

giving $t = 0.452$ s.

Thus, the initial horizontal velocity can be found as:

$$v_{ox} = \frac{x}{t} = 2.00 \text{ m}/0.452 \text{ s} = 4.43 \text{ m/s}.$$

Now use conservation of momentum for the collision, with v_b = speed of incoming bullet:

$$(8.00 \times 10^{-3} \text{ kg})v_b = (258 \times 10^{-3} \text{ kg})(4.43 \text{ m/s}), \text{ so}$$

$v_b = 142.9$ m/s. (about 320 mph)

6.27 First, using conservation of energy to find the speed of the block and embedded bullet just after impact:

$$\frac{1}{2}(m + M)V^2 = \frac{1}{2}kd^2,$$

or

$$V = \sqrt{\frac{kd^2}{m + M}} = \sqrt{\frac{(150 \text{ N/m})(0.80 \text{ m})^2}{(0.0120 + 0.100) \text{ kg}}} = 29.3 \text{ m/s}$$

Now, use conservation of momentum to find the speed of the bullet before impact:

$$(m + M)V = mv,$$

or

$$v = \frac{m + M}{m}V = \frac{0.112 \text{ kg}}{0.0120 \text{ kg}}(29.3 \text{ m/s}) = 273 \text{ m/s}$$

6.28 (a) Using conservation of momentum, $(P_{total})_{before} = (P_{total})_{after}$, gives

$$(4.0 \text{ kg})(5.0 \text{ m/s}) + (10 \text{ kg})(3.0 \text{ m/s}) + (3.0 \text{ kg})(-4.0 \text{ m/s}) = [(4.0 + 10 + 3.0)\text{kg}]v,$$

where v is the speed of the three mass system after collision.
Therefore, $v = +2.2$ m/s, or 2.2 m/s toward the right.

(b) No. For example, if the 10 kg and 3.0 kg mass were to stick together first, they would move with a speed given by solving
$(13 \text{ kg})v_1 = (10 \text{ kg})(3.0 \text{ m/s}) + (3.0 \text{ kg})(-4.0 \text{ m/s})$, so $v_1 = 1.38$ m/s.
Then when this 13 kg combined mass collides with the 4.0 kg mass, we have $(17 \text{ kg})v = (4.0 \text{ kg})(5.0 \text{ m/s}) + (13 \text{ kg})(1.38 \text{ m/s})$, so that $v = 2.2$ m/s, just like part (a)

6.29 (a) From conservation of momentum,

$$(5.00 \text{ g})(20.0 \text{ cm/s}) = (5.00 \text{ g})v_{1f} + (10.0 \text{ g})v_{2f}. \quad (1)$$

Also for an elastic, head-on, collision, we have
$v_{1i} + v_{1f} = v_{2i} + v_{2f}$, which becomes

$20.0\text{ cm/s} + v_{1f} = v_{2f}$. (2)

Solve (1) and (2) simultaneously:

$v_{1f} = -6.67\text{ cm/s}$, and $v_{2f} = 13.3\text{ cm/s}$.

(b) $KE_{before} = \frac{1}{2}(5.00 \times 10^{-3}\text{ kg})(20.0 \times 10^{-2}\text{ m/s})^2 = 10^{-4}\text{ J}$,

$KE_{second\ object} = \frac{1}{2}(10.0 \times 10^{-3}\text{ kg})(13.3 \times 10^{-2})^2 = 8.89 \times 10^{-5}\text{ J}$, so

$\frac{KE_{second\ object}}{KE_{before}} = 0.88$.

6.30 $m_1v_{1i} + m_2v_{2i} = m_1v_{1f} + m_2v_{2f}$.

$(10.0\text{ g})(20.0\text{ cm/s}) + (15.0\text{ g})(-30.0\text{ cm/s}) = (10.0\text{ g})v_{1f} + (15.0\text{ g})v_{2f}$, (1)

and $v_{1i} + v_{1f} = v_{2i} + v_{2f}$, which becomes

$20.0\text{ cm/s} + v_{1f} = -30.0\text{ cm/s} + v_{2f}$. (2)

Solve (1) and (2) simultaneously: $v_{1f} = -40.0\text{ cm/s}$; $v_{2f} = 10.0\text{ cm/s}$.

6.31 Momentum conservation gives: $m_1v_{1i} + m_2v_{2i} = m_1v_{1f} + m_2v_{2f}$, or

$(25.0\text{ g})(20.0\text{ cm/s}) + (10.0\text{ g})(15.0\text{ cm/s}) = (25.0\text{ g})v_{1f} + (10.0\text{ g})v_{2f}$. (1)

For head-on elastic collisions, we know that $v_{1i} + v_{1f} = v_{2i} + v_{2f}$.

Thus, $20.0\text{ cm/s} + v_{1f} = 15.0\text{ cm/s} + v_{2f}$. (2)

Solving (1) and (2) yields $v_{1f} = 17.1\text{ cm/s}$, and $v_{2f} = 22.1\text{ cm/s}$.

6.32 First, consider conservation of momentum,

$m_1v_{1i} + m_2v_{2i} = m_1v_{1f} + m_2v_{2f}$.

Both balls have the same mass, so this equation becomes

$v_{1i} + v_{2i} = v_{1f} + v_{2f}$. (1)

For an elastic head-on collision, we also have

$v_{1i} - v_{2i} = -(v_{1f} - v_{2f})$

Let us solve this equation for v_{1f}.

$v_{1f} = v_{2f} + v_{2i} - v_{1i}$ (2)

Use (2) to eliminate v_{1f} from (1). The result is

$v_{2f} = v_{1i}$ (3)

Now, eliminate v_{2f} from (1) by use of (3). We find

$v_{1f} = v_{2i}$ (4)

Thus, equations (3) and (4) show us that, under the conditions of equal mass, objects striking one another in a head-on elastic collision, the two objects exchange velocities. Thus, we may write the results of the various collisions as

(a) $v_{1f} = 0$, $v_{2f} = 1.50\text{ m/s}$

(b) $v_{1f} = -1.00\text{ m/s}$, $v_{2f} = 1.50\text{ m/s}$

(c) $v_{1f} = 1.00\text{ m/s}$, $v_{2f} = 1.50\text{ m/s}$

6.33 (a) First, we conserve momentum in the x direction (the direction of travel of the fullback):

$(90\text{ kg})(5.0\text{ m/s}) + 0 = (185\text{ kg})V\cos\theta$

where θ is the angle between the direction of the final velocity V and the x axis. We find: $V\cos\theta = 2.43\text{ m/s}$ (1)

Now consider conservation of momentum in the y direction (the direction of travel of the opponent.

$(95\text{ kg})(3.0\text{ m/s}) + 0 = (185\text{ kg})(V\sin\theta)$

which gives, $V\sin\theta = 1.54\text{ m/s}$ (2)

Divide equation (2) by (1):

$\tan\theta = 1.54/2.43 = 0.633$, from which $\theta = 32.3°$.
Then, either (1) or (2) gives: $V = 2.9$ m/s.

(b) $KE(\text{before}) = \frac{1}{2}(90\text{ kg})(5.0\text{ m/s})^2 + \frac{1}{2}(95\text{ kg})(3.0\text{ m/s})^2 = 1.55 \times 10^3$ J

$KE(\text{after}) = \frac{1}{2}(185\text{ kg})(2.88\text{ m/s})^2 = 7.67 \times 10^2$ J

Thus, the kinetic energy lost (to 2 sig. figures) is 780 J.

6.34 (a) Use east and north as the positive directions. Momentum conservation in the x (east-west) direction gives:

$(p_{after})_x = (p_{before})_x$, or

$(8.00\text{ kg})(0) + (10.0\text{ kg})v_{2x} = (8.00\text{ kg})(15.0\text{ m/s}) + (10.0\text{ kg})(0)$.

This gives: $v_{2x} = 12$ m/s.

Momentum conservation in the y (north-south) direction is

$(p_{after})_y = (p_{before})_y$, or

$(8.00\text{ kg})(-4.00\text{ m/s}) + (10.0\text{ kg})v_{2y} = (8.00\text{ kg})(0) + (10.0\text{ kg})(0)$.

This gives: $v_{2y} = 3.2$ m/s.

Thus, after collision, the velocity of the 10 kg mass is

$v_{2y} = \sqrt{(v_{2x}^2 + v_{2y}^2)} = 12.42$ m/s

at $\theta = \tan^{-1}\frac{v_{2y}}{v_{2x}} = \tan^{-1}(0.267) = 14.9°$ north of east.

(b) The kinetic energy before the collision is

$KE_i = \frac{1}{2}(8.00\text{ kg})(15.0\text{ m/s})^2 + \frac{1}{2}(10.0)(0)^2 = 900$ J.

The kinetic energy after the collision is

$KE_f = \frac{1}{2}(8.00\text{ kg})(-4.00\text{ m/s})^2 + \frac{1}{2}(10.0)(12.42\text{ m/s})^2 = 835.3$ J.

Therefore $KE_f - KE_i = -64.8$ J, so that 7.2% of the original total kinetic energy is lost in the collision.

6.35 We use a coordinate system with the positive direction of the x axis toward the east and positive y toward the north. We set the initial speed of the 3000 kg car as v_o, and use conservation of momentum. First, we consider the y direction:

$(3000\text{ kg})v_o = (5000\text{ kg})(5.22\text{ m/s})\sin 40°$, giving $v_o = 5.59$ m/s.

A similar calculation for the x direction shows the initial velocity of the 2000 kg car to be 10 m/s eastward.

6.36 (a) Let the puck which is initially at rest be m_2, and let ϕ be the angle the velocity of this puck makes with the x axis after collision. Then,

$p_{xi} = p_{xf} \Rightarrow \quad m_1v_{1i} = m_1v_{1f}\cos\theta + m_2v_{2f}\cos\phi$, and

$p_{yi} = p_{yf} \Rightarrow \quad 0 = m_1v_{1f}\sin\theta - m_2v_{2f}\sin\phi$. These become:

$(0.20\text{ kg})(2.0\text{ m/s}) = (0.20\text{ kg})(1.0\text{ m/s})\cos 53° + (0.30\text{ kg})v_{2f}\cos\phi$ (1)

and $0 = (0.20\text{ kg})(1.0\text{ m/s})\sin 53° - (0.30\text{ kg})v_{2f}\sin\phi$. (2)

From these equations, we find:

$\phi = \tan^{-1}(0.571) = 29.7°$, and $v_{2f} = 1.1$ m/s.

(b) Then, $\frac{\Delta KE}{KE_i} = \frac{(KE_f - KE_i)}{KE_i} = -0.32$ or 32% lost.

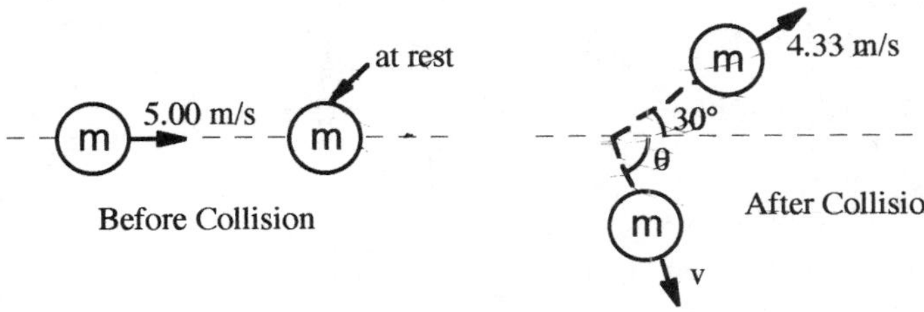

6.37 (a) $(p_x)_{after} = (p_x)_{before}$,
$m(4.33\cos 30°) + m(v\cos\theta) = m(5.00) + 0$
which yields $v\cos\theta = 1.25$ (equation 1)
$(p_y)_{after} = (p_y)_{before}$
$m(4.33\sin 30°) - m(v\sin\theta) = 0 + 0$
or $v\sin\theta = 2.17$. (equation 2)
Solving equations 1 and 2 simulataneously:

$$\tan\theta = \frac{2.17}{1.25} = 1.732, \text{ or } \theta = 60°.$$

Also, $v^2(\cos^2\theta + \sin^2\theta) = (1.25)^2 + (2.17)^2 = 6.27$,
yielding $v = 2.5$ m/s.
Thus, the velocity of the second ball afterwards is 2.50 m/s at 60° from the original line of motion, as shown.

(b) $KE_{before} = \frac{1}{2} m(5.00)^2 + 0 = m(12.5)$,

and $KE_{after} = \frac{1}{2} m(4.33)^2 + \frac{1}{2} m(2.5)^2 = m(12.5)$.

Thus, the collision is elastic.

6.38 Impulse = area under curve between $t = 0$ and $t = 3.0$ s.

$$\bar{F}(\Delta t) = \text{triangle} + \text{rectangle} = \frac{1}{2}(2.0\text{ s})(4\text{ N}) + (1.0\text{ s})(4.0\text{ N}) = 8.0\text{ N s}$$

Thus, $\bar{F} = \dfrac{\text{impulse}}{\Delta t} = \dfrac{8.0\text{ N s}}{3.0\text{ s}} = 2.67\text{ N}$

6.39 Impulse $= F\Delta t = \Delta p = mv_f - mv_i$.
$= 0.400\text{ kg}(-22.0\text{ m/s} - 15.0\text{ m/s}) = -14.8\text{ kg m/s}$.
Thus, an impulse of 14.8 kg m/s in the direction of the final velocity of the ball.

6.40 No external force acts on the system (astronaut plus wrench), so the total momentum is constant. We have final momentum = initial momentum = 0, or $m_{wrench}v_{wrench} + m_{astronaut}v_{astronaut} = 0$.

Thus $v_{astronaut} = -\dfrac{m_{wrench}v_{wrench}}{m_{astronaut}} = -\dfrac{(0.500\text{ kg})(20.0\text{ m/s})}{80.0\text{ kg}} = -0.125\text{ m/s}$

or, the astronaut drifts toward the ship at 0.125 m/s. At this speed, the time to travel to the ship is

$$t = \frac{30.0\text{ m}}{0.125\text{ m/s}} = 240\text{ s} = 4\text{ minutes}.$$

6.41 We use: $m_1v_{1i} + m_2v_{2i} = m_1v_{1f} + m_2v_{2f}$, (1)
and $v_{1i} - v_{2i} = -(v_{1f} - v_{2f})$. (2)
With $v_{2i} = 0$, (1) and (2) can be solved simultaneously to show that

$$v_{2f} = \frac{2m_1}{m_1 + m_2} v_{1i}, \quad \text{and} \quad v_{1f} = \frac{m_1 - m_2}{m_1 + m_2} v_{1i}.$$

(a) If $m_1 = 2.0$ g, $m_2 = 1.0$ g, and $v_{1i} = 8.0$ m/s: $v_{2f} = \frac{32}{3}$ m/s,

and $v_{1f} = \frac{8}{3}$ m/s.

(b) If $m_1 = 2.0$ g, $m_2 = 10$ g, and $v_{1i} = 8.0$ m/s: $v_{2f} = \frac{8}{3}$ m/s

and $v_{1f} = \frac{-16}{3}$ m/s.

(c) In case (a) $KE_{final} = \frac{1}{2} m_1 v_{1f}^2 = \frac{1}{2}(2.0 \times 10^{-3} \text{ kg})(\frac{8}{3} \text{ m/s})^2$

$= 7.11 \times 10^{-3}$ J.

In case (b) $KE_{final} = \frac{1}{2} m_1 v_{1f}^2 = \frac{1}{2}(2.0 \times 10^{-3} \text{ kg})(\frac{16}{3} \text{ m/s})^2 = 2.8 \times 10^{-2}$ J.

Since the incident kinetic energy is the same in case (a) and case (b), it is clear that the incident particle loses more KE in case (a).

6.42 Using conservation of momentum gives:

$$(m + M)V = mv_0 + M(0), \text{ or } \quad V = \frac{m}{m+M} v_0 \qquad (1)$$

where V is the speed of the (pendulum+bullet) combination immediately after the collision, and v_0 is the speed of the bullet. M is the pendulum mass, and m is the bullet's mass.

We have: $\frac{KE_f}{KE_i} = \frac{(m + M)V^2}{mv_0^2}$. Eliminate V by use of (1) in the preceding equation to find:

$$\frac{KE_f}{KE_i} = \frac{m}{m + M} = \frac{8.00 \times 10^{-3} \text{ kg}}{8.00 \times 10^{-3} \text{ kg} + 2.00 \text{ kg}} = 3.98 \times 10^{-3}, \text{ or } 0.398\ \%.$$

6.43 We shall first use conservation of energy to find the speed of the bead just before it strikes the ball. The zero level of potential energy is at the level of point B. We have, $(1/2)mv_i^2 + mgy_i = (1/2)mv_f^2 + mgy_f$, or

$0 + (0.400 \text{ kg})(g)(1.50 \text{ m}) = \frac{1}{2}(0.400 \text{ kg})v_{1i}^2 + 0$, giving $\quad v_{1i} = 5.42$ m/s.

We now treat the collision to find the speed of the ball immediately after the collision. Momentum conservation gives:

$$(0.400 \text{ kg})(5.42 \text{ m/s}) + 0 = (0.400 \text{ kg})v_{1f} + (0.600 \text{ kg})v_{2f} \qquad (1)$$

For an elastic collision, $v_{1f} + v_{1i} = v_{2f} + v_{2i}$,

or $$v_{1f} + 5.42 = v_{2f} + 0. \qquad (2)$$

Solve (1) and (2) simultaneously to find, $\quad v_{2f} = 4.34$ m/s.

Apply conservation of energy to the 0.6 kg ball after impact to find:

$$\frac{1}{2}(0.600 \text{ kg})(4.34 \text{ m/s})^2 + 0 = 0 + (0.600 \text{ kg})(g)H, \quad \text{or} \quad H = 0.96 \text{ m}.$$

6.44 We will first find the speed as he enters the water. We select the origin of the coordinate system at the initial position of the diver.

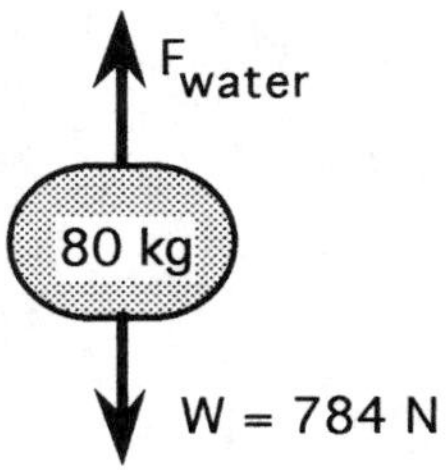

$v^2 = v_0^2 + 2ax$ gives, $v^2 = 0 + 2(-9.80 \text{ m/s}^2)(-3.00 \text{ m})$, or
$v = -7.67$ m/s.
Now consider the deceleration period. From the impulse-momentum theorem, we have
$F\Delta t = \Delta p = mv_f - mv_i$, so
$F(2.0 \text{ s}) = 0 - (80 \text{ kg})(-7.67 \text{ m/s})$, giving $F = 3.07 \times 10^2$ N.
This is the net force acting on the man. But
$F = F_{water} - mg = F_{water} - 784 \text{ N} = 307 \text{ N}$
Thus, $F_{water} = 1.1 \times 10^3$ N.

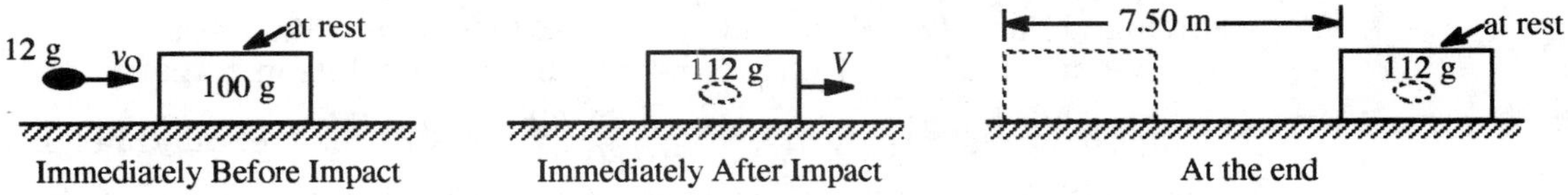

6.45 Using conservation of energy from immediately after to the end gives:
$KE)_{after} = KE)_{end}$ + (work done against friction),

or, $\frac{1}{2}(M + m)V^2 = 0 + fd = (\mu N)d$

$\frac{1}{2}(0.112 \text{ kg})V^2 = (0.650)\,((0.112 \text{ kg})(9.80 \text{ m/s}^2))(7.50 \text{ m})$,

from which, $V = 9.77$ m/s.
Then, using conservation of momentum from immediately before to immediately after impact gives:
$(0.012 \text{ kg})v_0 + (0.100 \text{ kg})(0) = (0.112 \text{ kg})(9.77 \text{ m/s})$,
or $v_0 = 91.2$ m/s.

6.46 (a) Let v_{1i} and v_{2i} be the speeds of m_1 and m_2 just before the collision. Then conservation of energy gives:

$v_{1i} = -v_{2i} = \sqrt{2gh} = \sqrt{2(9.80 \text{ m/s}^2)5.00 \text{ m}} = 9.90$ m/s.

(b) From Conservation of momentum:
$2.00v_{1f} + 4.00v_{2f} = 2.00(9.9 \text{ m/s}) + 4.00(-9.90 \text{ m/s})$,
or $2.00v_{1f} + 4.00v_{2f} = -19.8$ m/s.
(1)
For an elastic head-on collision,
$v_{1f} + v_{1i} = v_{2f} + v_{2i}$,
giving $v_{1f} + 9.90 \text{ m/s} = v_{2f} - 9.90 \text{ m/s}$,
or, $v_{1f} + 19.80 \text{ m/s} = v_{2f}$ (2)

Solving (1) and (2) simultaneously gives
$v_{1f} = -16.5$ m/s, and $v_{2f} = 3.30$ m/s

(c) Applying conservation of energy to each block after the collision

gives: $h_{1f} = \frac{(v_{1f})^2}{2g} = \frac{(-16.5 \text{ m/s})^2}{19.6 \text{ m/s}^2} = 13.9$ m

and $h_{2f} = \frac{(v_{2f})^2}{2g} = \frac{(3.30 \text{ m/s})^2}{19.6 \text{ m/s}^2} = 0.56$ m

---

6.47 (a) Let $m_1 = 0.500$ kg and $m_2 = 1.00$ kg. Before the collision the speed of m_2 is zero, whereas the speed of m_1 is obtained using the conservation of energy,

$$(0.500)(9.80)(2.50) = \frac{1}{2}(0.500)v^2, \text{ so } \quad v = 7.00 \text{ m/s.}$$

Apply conservation of momentum from just before to just after the collision: $m_1 v_{1f} + m_2 v_{2f} = m_1 v_{1i} + m_2 v_{2i}$ becomes

$$(0.500)v_{1f} + (1)v_{2f} = (0.500)(7.00),$$

yielding $v_{1f} + 2v_{2f} = 7.00.$ (1)

For an elastic, head-on collision, $v_{1f} - v_{2f} = -(v_{1i} - v_{2i})$,

which gives $v_{1f} - v_{2f} = -7.00.$ (2)

Solving (1) and (2) yields $v_{1f} = -2.33$ m/s, $v_{2f} = 4.67$ m/s.

(b) Apply conservation of energy to m_1 after the collision to get

$$m_1 g h = \frac{1}{2} m_1 v^2{}_{1f}, \text{ or } h = \frac{(-2.33 \text{ m/s})^2}{2(9.80)} = 0.277 \text{ m. (rebound height)}$$

(c) This block has an initial speed of 4.67 m/s horizontally when it flies off the table as a projectile. Treating the intersection of the table with the floor as the origin for an xy coordinate system, we have

$$y - 2 = 0 - \frac{1}{2}gt^2, \text{ and } x = 4.67\,t. \text{ Thus (at } y = 0\text{), } t = \sqrt{\frac{4}{9.80}} = 0.639 \text{ s,}$$

and $x = (4.67)(0.639) = 2.98$ m when this block lands on the floor.

(d) After the 0.500 kg mass comes back down the incline, it flies off the table with a horizontal velocity of 2.33 m/s. Using the same origin as above, we may write $t = 0.639$ s (as above) at floor level, and

$x = (2.33)(0.639) = 1.49$ m when it lands on the floor.

6.48 Applying conservation of mechanical energy from just after the collision until the end of the swing is reached, we have

$$\frac{1}{2}(M + m)V^2 = (M + m)gh$$

where M is the mass of the pendulum, m the mass of the bullet, h the vertical height through which the pendulum swings, and V is the velocity of the (pendulum plus bullet) immediately after the collision.

The equation above reduces to $V = \sqrt{2gh}$. (1)

Now apply conservation of momentum from just before to just after the collision. We have: $m v_0 = (M + m)V$ (2)

where v_0 is the speed of the bullet just prior to collision.

We now solve (1) and (2) simultaneously to find the following equation for v_0.

$$v_0 = \frac{(M + m)}{m}\sqrt{2gh}$$

$$= \frac{(2.5 \text{ kg} + 8.0 \times 10^{-3} \text{ kg})}{8.0 \times 10^{-3} \text{ kg}}\sqrt{2g(6.0 \times 10^{-2} \text{ m})} = 3.40 \times 10^2 \text{ m/s}$$

6.49 (a) The initial momentum of the system is zero, which remains constant throughout the motion. Therefore, when m_1 leaves the wedge, we must have

$$m_2 v_{wedge} + m_1 v_{block} = 0, \text{ or}$$

$(3.00 \text{ kg}) v_{wedge} + (0.500 \text{ kg})(+ 4.00 \frac{\text{m}}{\text{s}}) = 0$, so

$v_{wedge} = -0.670$ m/s.

(b) Using conservation of energy as the block slides down the smooth (frictionless) wedge, we have

$$[KE_{block} + PE_{block}]_i + [KE_{wedge}]_i = [KE_{block} + PE_{block}]_f + [KE_{wedge}]_f$$

or $[0 + m_1 g h] + 0 = [\frac{1}{2} m_1 (4.00)^2 + 0] + \frac{1}{2} m_2 (-0.670)^2$, which

gives $h = 0.953$ m.

6.50 (a) Let M be the mass of each cart. Then, if v_0 is the initial velocity of the red cart, applying conservation of momentum to the collision gives $Mv_b + Mv_r = Mv_0$, or $v_b + v_r = v_0$ (1)
where v_b and v_r are the velocities of the blue and red carts after collision. In an elastic, head-on collision, we have
$v_{1f} - v_{2f} = -(v_{1i} - v_{2i})$, or (in this case), $v_r - v_b = -v_0$. (2)
Solving (1) and (2) together to get $v_r = 0$, and $v_b = v_0 = 3.0$ m/s.

(b) Using conservation of energy for the cart-spring system, we have

$$\frac{1}{2} M v_b^2 = \frac{1}{2} k d^2, \text{ so } \quad d = \sqrt{\frac{M}{k}}\, v_b = \sqrt{\frac{0.25}{50}}\,(3.0) = 0.21 \text{ m.}$$

6.51 (a) First, use conservation of energy to find the recoil speed of the combined mass m_3 and the embedded shot m_2:

$$KE_f + PE_{sf} = KE_i + PE_{s\,i},$$

or $0 + \frac{1}{2}(4500 \text{ N/m})(0.500 \text{ m})^2 = \frac{1}{2}(8000 \text{ kg}) V^2$.

This gives $V = -0.375$ m/s (positive taken to be toward right).
Now, use conservation of momentum to find the speed of the shot, m_2, just before impact: $m_2 v_2 + 0 = (m_2 + m_3) V$, or
$v_2 = (8000 \text{ kg})(-0.375 \text{ m/s})/(10.0 \text{ kg})$, yielding $v_2 = -300$ m/s.

(b) Before the cannon goes off the (cannon + shot) system has a total momentum of zero. Therefore, immediately after the cannon goes off, the total momentum of this system must still be zero. Thus,

$$m_1 v_1 + m_2 v_2 = 0. \quad \text{Therefore,} \quad v_1 = \frac{m_2}{m_1} v_2 = \frac{10.0}{800}(-300) = 3.75 \text{ m/s.}$$

(c) The change in kinetic energy of the cannon is

$$KE_f - KE_i = 0 - \frac{1}{2} m_1 v_1^2, \text{ which equals the work done by friction.}$$

Thus, $-(1/2) m_1 v_1^2 = -\mu_k m_1 g x$, where x is the distance the cannon travels beyond point A before coming to rest. Therefore,

$$x = \frac{v_1^2}{2\mu_k g} = \frac{(3.75)^2}{2(0.60)(9.80)} = 1.2 \text{ m.}$$

6.52 After falling from rest at a height of 60.0 m, the velocity of the water will be given by: $v^2 = v_0^2 + 2gh = 0 + 2(9.80)(60.0) = 1176$,
so $v = 34.3$ m/s.
The force exerted by the water hitting the bucket is

$$F_{bucket} = -F_{water} = -\frac{\Delta p_{water}}{\Delta t} = -\frac{0 - (0.25 \text{ kg})(34.3 \text{ m/s})}{1.00 \text{ s}} = 8.6 \text{ N.}$$

The weight of the water in the bucket is $(0.25 \text{ kg/s})(3.00 \text{ s})(9.80 \text{ m/s}^2) = 7.35$ N, and the weight of the bucket itself is

$(0.75\ \text{kg})(9.80\ \text{m/s}^2) = 7.35\ \text{N}$
In total, at $t = 3.00$ s, the scale will read $8.6 + 7.35 + 7.35 = 23$ N

6.53 First, determine the recoil speed, v_0, of the base of the swing immediately after the bird takes off. From conservation of momentum, we have $(52.0\ \text{g})(2.00\ \text{m/s}) + (153\ \text{g})(-v_0) = 0$, and $v_0 = 0.68$ m/s. Now, apply conservation of energy to the rising swing.

$KE_f + PE_f = KE_i + PE_i$, or $0 + mgh = \frac{1}{2}mv_0^2 + 0$, which gives

$$h = \frac{v_0^2}{2g} = \frac{(0.680\ \text{m/s})^2}{2(9.80\ \text{m/s}^2)} = 2.36 \times 10^{-2}\ \text{m} = 2.36\ \text{cm}.$$

6.54 Before the collision, the total momentum of both cars is
$P_{before} = (2000)(10.0) + (3000)(0) = 20000$ kg m/s.
After the collision, the cars stick together having a total mass of 5000 kg. Therefore the momentum after the collision is $P_{after} = 5000\ v$. Conservation of momentum gives: $5000\ v = 20000$, so the speed of the combined two car system is $v = 4.00$ m/s. As a result, the kinetic energy of the two car system just after the collision is

$KE_{after} = \frac{1}{2}(5000)(4.00)^2 = 40{,}000$ J. When the two car system comes to a stop after moving 2.00 m, the change in kinetic energy must equal the work due to friction. Therefore we have

$0 - 40{,}000 = -\mu_k(5000)(9.80)(2.00)$, so that $\mu_k = 0.410$.

6.55 Energy is conserved for the bob between bottom and top of swing:

$$\frac{1}{2}Mv_b^2 = Mg2(l)$$

From which $v_b = 2\sqrt{gl}$
Momentum is conserved in the collision as

$$mv = m\frac{v}{2} + M(2)\sqrt{gl}$$

From which $v = \frac{4M}{m}\sqrt{gl}$

6.56 Conservation of the x-component of momentum gives

$$-mv_0 + 3mv_0 = 3mv_{2x}$$

Likewise, the y-component of momentum gives

$$0 = -mv_{1y} + 3mv_{2y}$$

By conservation of energy, we have

$$\frac{1}{2}mv_0^2 + \frac{1}{2}3mv_0^2 = \frac{1}{2}mv_{1y}^2 + \frac{1}{2}3m(v_{2x}^2 + v_{2y}^2)$$

We have $v_{2x} = \frac{2v_0}{3}$ and $v_{1y} = 3v_{2y}$
So, the energy equation becomes

$$4v_0^2 = 9v_{2y}^2 + \frac{4}{3}v_0^2 + 3v_{2y}^2$$

From which $v_{2y} = \frac{\sqrt{2}}{3}v_0$

(a) The mass m has final speed

$$v_{1y} = 3v_{2y} = \sqrt{2}\ v_0$$

and mass $3m$ moves at

$$\sqrt{v_{2x}^2 + v_{2y}^2} = \sqrt{\frac{4}{9}v_0^2 + \frac{2}{9}v_0^2} = \sqrt{\frac{2}{3}}\,v_0$$

(b) $\theta = \arctan\frac{v_{2y}}{v_{2x}} = \arctan\ \frac{\sqrt{2}}{3}v_0\frac{3}{2v_0} = 35.3°$

6.57 I have mass 85 kg and can jump to a height of about 25 cm. Thus, I leave ground with speed given by

$v_f^2 - v_0^2 = 2ay$

$0 - v_0^2 = 2(-9.80\text{ m/s}^2)(0.25\text{ m})$

From which $v_0 = 2.2$ m/s

Total momentum is conserved as I push the Earth down and myself up:

$0 = (-5.98 \times 10^{24}\text{ kg})v_e + (85\text{ kg})2.2\text{ m/s}$

This gives a value for the velocity of the earth of about 10^{-23} m/s

---

6.58 (a) Use $p_{after} = p_{before}$. This gives $m_1v_{1f} + m_2v_{2f} = m_1v_0$ (1)

Where m_1 is the mass of the neutron and v_{1f} is its final speed, and m_2 and v_{2f} refer to the carbon atom.

For a head-on elastic collision, we use: $v_{1i} - v_{2i} = -(v_{1f} - v_{2f})$,

Which gives: $v_0 = -(v_{1f} - v_{2f})$. (2)

Use $m_2 = 12m_1$ in equations (1) and (2) and solve them simultaneously to give $v_{1f} = -\frac{11}{13}v_0$, and $v_{2f} = \frac{2}{13}v_0$.

Now, $KE(\text{neutron initial}) = \frac{1}{2}m_1v_0^2$

and the kinetic energy of the carbon nucleus after the collision is

$$KE(\text{carbon after}) = \frac{1}{2}(12\,m_1)\left(\frac{2}{13}\right)^2 v_0^2.$$

The ratio of $KE(\text{carbon after})$ to $KE(\text{neutron initial}) = \frac{48}{169} = 0.28$

(b) If $KE(\text{neutron before}) = 1.6 \times 10^{-13}$ J, and with $\frac{KE(\text{carbon})}{KE(\text{neutron})} = 0.284$,

we have $KE(\text{carbon}) = 4.54 \times 10^{-14}$ J.

The remaining energy $1.6 \times 10^{-13}\text{ J} - 4.54 \times 10^{-14}\text{ J} = 1.2 \times 10^{-13}$ J remains with the neutron.

6.59 Consider first conservation of momentum in the x direction.

$mv_0 = mv_2\cos\theta + mv_1\cos 30°$ (note that masses cancel) (1)

where v_1 is the speed of the cue ball after the collision, v_2 that of the target, θ is the angle between the final velocity of the target and the x axis, and v_0 the initial speed of the cue ball. Now, consider conservation of momentum in the y direction:

$0 = mv_1\sin 30° - mv_2\sin\theta$ (note the masses again cancel) (2)

Since this is an elastic collision, kinetic energy is conserved. We have

$\frac{1}{2}mv_0^2 = \frac{1}{2}mv_1^2 + \frac{1}{2}mv_2^2$ (3)

To solve (1), (2), and (3) simultaneously, rearrange (1) and (2) so the terms involving θ are isolated on the left sides, then square (1) and (2) and add them. After some reduction, the resulting equation is

$v_2^2 = v_0^2 - (2v_0\cos 30°)v_1 + v_1^2$ (4)

Now substitute (4) into (3) to eliminate v_2. The result is

$$v_1 = v_0 \cos 30° \qquad (5)$$

But we are given that $v_0 = 4.0$ m/s. Thus (5) yields $v_1 = 3.46$ m/s.
Then from (4), we find $v_2 = 2.00$ m/s.
Finally, we find from (2) that $\sin\theta = 0.866$, or $\theta = 60.0°$.

6.60 The deceleration of the first block is $a = -\frac{f_k}{M} = -\mu g$. Therefore, just before collision, M has a speed $v = \sqrt{v_0^2 - 2\mu g d}$
Using conservation of momentum from just before to just after collision, we have

$$Mv + 0 = Mv_1 + 2Mv_2 \qquad (1)$$

where v_1 and v_2 are the speeds of the two blocks just after collision.
Also, since this is an elastic, head-on collision: $v_{1f} - v_{2f} = -(v_{1i} - v_{2i})$, or in this case,

$$v_1 - v_2 = -v \qquad (2)$$

Solving these equations gives

$$v_2 = \frac{2}{3}v = \sqrt{\frac{4}{9}v_0^2 - \frac{8}{9}\mu g d}. \qquad (3)$$

The second block has the same deceleration as the first. It comes to rest when its velocity is 0, and therefore it will move a distance D given by $0 - v_2^2 = -2\mu g D$. Substituting Eq. (3) for v_2 into this expression, we find

$$D = \frac{2v_0^2}{9\mu g} - \frac{4d}{9}$$

as the distance the second block slides.

CONCEPTUAL ANSWERS CHAPTER SIX

2. No. Only in a precise head-on collision with equal and opposite momentum can both balls wind up at rest. Yes. In the second case, assuming equal masses for each ball, if Ball 2, originally at rest, is struck squarely by Ball 1, then Ball 2 takes off with the velocity of Ball 1. Then Ball 1 is at rest.

4. The skater gains the most momentum by catching and then throwing the frisbee.

6. Kinetic energy can be written as $p^2/2m$. Thus, even through the particles have the same kinetic energies their momenta may be different due to a difference in mass.

8. The resulting collision is intermediate between an elastic and a completely inelastic collision. Some energy of motion is transformed as the pieces buckle, crumple, and heat up during the collision. Also, a small amount is lost as sound.
The most kinetic energy is lost in a head-on collision, so the expectation of damage to the passengers is greatest.

10. The smaller object loses the most kinetic energy in the collision.

12. The superhero is at rest before the toss and the net momentum of the system is zero. When he tosses the piano, say toward the right, something must get an equal amount of momentum to the left to keep the momentum at zero. This something recoiling to the left must be Superman. He cannot stay at rest.

14. The passenger must undergo a certain momentum change in the collision. This means that a certain impulse must be exerted on the passenger by the steering wheel, the window, an air bag, or something. By increasing the time during which this momentum change occurs, the resulting force on the passenger can be decreased.

16. A certain impulse is required to stop the egg. But, if the time during which the momentum change of the egg occurs is increased, the resulting force on the egg is reduced. The time is increased as the sheet billows out as the egg is brought to a stop. The force is reduced low enough so that the egg will not break.

CHAPTER SEVEN SOLUTIONS

Chapter Seven Readings

Beams, J., "Ultra-High-Speed Rotation," *Scientific American,* April 1961, p. 134.

Cohen, I.B., "Newton's Discovery of Gravity," *Scientific American,* March 1981, p. 166.

Pipkin, F., "Gravity Up in the Air," *The Sciences,* July/August 1984, p. 24.

Powell, C.S., "Star Dreck," *Scientific American,* v. 274 (Jan. '96) p22.

Ruthen, R., "Catching the Wave," *Scientific American,* V. 266 (Mar. '92) p90-99.

Spetz, G., "Detection of Gravity Waves," *The Physics Teacher,* May 1984, p. 282.

Turner, E.L., "Gravitational Lenses," *Scientific American,* July 1988, p. 54.

Review (a) Newton's Universal Gravitation Law may be written as

$$F = \frac{Gm_1m_2}{r^2} = m_1\frac{Gm_2}{r^2}.$$

If F is the gravitational force (weight) a mass m_1 located on the surface of a planet experiences, then m_2 is the mass of the planet and r, the distance separating m_1 and m_2 is the radius of the planet R. Comparing the above expression to weight = m_1g, we see that the acceleration due to gravity at the surface of the planet is given by

$$g = \frac{Gm_2}{R^2}$$

For Mars, $m_2 = 6.42 \times 10^{23}$ kg, and $R = 3.37 \times 10^6$ m.

Therefore, $g_{Mars} = (6.673 \times 10^{-11}) \dfrac{6.42 \times 10^{23}}{(3.37 \times 10^6)^2} = 3.77 \text{ m/s}^2$.

(b) Using $y = v_0t + \frac{1}{2}at^2$ with $v_{0y} = 0$, and $a_y = g_{Mars}$, we find

$$t = \sqrt{\frac{2y}{g_{Mars}}} = \sqrt{\frac{2(20.0 \text{ m})}{3.77 \text{ m/s}^2}} = 3.26 \text{ s}.$$

7.1 (a) $\theta = \frac{s}{r} = \frac{60\ 000 \text{ mi}}{1.0 \text{ ft}} = (\frac{60\ 000 \text{ mi}}{1.0 \text{ ft}})(\frac{5280 \text{ ft}}{1.0 \text{ mi}}) = 3.2 \times 10^8$ rad.

(b) $\theta = 3.2 \times 10^8 \text{ rad} = 3.2 \times 10^8 \text{ rad}(\frac{1 \text{ rev}}{2\pi \text{ rad}}) = 5.0 \times 10^7$ rev.

7.2 Distance traveled = $s = r\theta$, where θ is in radians.

For 30°, $\theta = 30°(\frac{\pi \text{ rad}}{180°}) = 0.524$ rad,

so $s = (4.1 \text{ m})(0.524 \text{ rad} = 2.2$ m.

For $\theta = 30$ radians, $s = (4.1 \text{ m})(30 \text{ rad}) = 120$ m

For $\theta = 30$ rev., $\theta = (30 \text{ rev})(\frac{2\pi \text{ rad}}{\text{rev}}) = 60\pi$ rad,

and $s = (4.1 \text{ m})(60\pi \text{ rad}) = 770$ m.

CHAPTER SEVEN SOLUTIONS

7.3 (a) $\omega = (33 \text{ rev/min})(2\pi \text{ rad/rev})(1 \text{ min}/60 \text{ s}) = 3.5 \text{ rad/s}$.
(b) $\theta = \omega t = (3.5 \text{ rad/s})(1.5 \text{ s}) = 5.2 \text{ rad}$.

7.4 The earth moves through 2π rad in one year (3.156×10^7 s). Thus,

$$\omega = \frac{2\pi \text{ rad}}{3.156 \times 10^7 \text{s}} = 1.99 \times 10^{-7} \frac{\text{rad}}{\text{s}}.$$

Alternatively, the earth moves through 360° in one year (365.242 days).

Thus, $$\omega = \frac{360°}{365.2 \text{ days}} = 0.986 \frac{\text{deg}}{\text{day}}.$$

7.5 Use $\omega = \omega_0 + \alpha t$, with $\omega = 0.20 \text{ rev/s} = 1.256 \text{ rad/s}$.
$1.256 \text{ rad/s} = 0 + \alpha(30 \text{ s})$, or $\alpha = 4.2 \times 10^{-2} \text{ rad/s}^2$.

7.6 $\theta = 4.7 \text{ rev} = 29.5$ radians, there is a constant angular acceleration. Thus,
$\theta = \omega_0 t + \frac{1}{2}\alpha t^2$ yields $29.5 \text{ rad} = 0 + \frac{1}{2}\alpha(1.2 \text{ s})^2$, or $\alpha = 41 \text{ rad/s}^2$.

7.7 In this problem, $\omega^2 = \omega_0{}^2 + 2\alpha\theta$ becomes,
$(2.2 \text{ rad/s})^2 = (0.60 \text{ rad/s})^2 + 2(0.70 \text{ rad/s}^2)\theta$, so $\theta = 3.2 \text{ rad}$.

7.8 $\omega_f = 2.51 \times 10^4 \text{ rev/min} = 2.63 \times 10^3 \text{ rad/s}$

(a) $$\alpha = \frac{\omega_f - \omega_0}{t} = \frac{2.63 \times 10^3 \text{ rad/s} - 0}{3.20 \text{ s}} = 8.22 \times 10^2 \text{ rad/s}^2.$$

(b) $$\theta = \omega_0 t + \frac{1}{2}\alpha t^2 = 0 + \frac{1}{2}(8.22 \times 10^2 \text{ rad/s}^2)(3.20 \text{ s})^2 = 4.21 \times 10^3 \text{ rad}$$

7.9 $\omega_0 = 100 \text{ rev/min} = 10.47 \text{ rad/s}$

(a) $$t = \frac{\omega - \omega_0}{\alpha} = \frac{0 - 10.47 \text{ rad/s}}{-2.00 \text{ rad/s}^2} = 5.24 \text{ s}.$$

(b) $$\theta = \bar{\omega} t = \frac{\omega + \omega_0}{2} t = \frac{0 + 10.47 \text{ rad/s}}{2}(5.24 \text{ s}) = 27.4 \text{ rad}.$$

7.10 $\omega_f = 5 \text{ rev/s} = 10\pi \text{ rad/s}$. We will break the motion into two stages: (1) an acceleration period and (2) a deceleration period. While speeding up,

$$\theta_1 = \bar{\omega} t = \frac{0 + 10\pi \text{ rad/s}}{2}(8.0 \text{ s}) = 125.7 \text{ rad}.$$ While slowing down,

$$\theta_2 = \bar{\omega} t = \frac{10\pi \text{ rad/s} + 0}{2}(12.0 \text{ s}) = 188.5 \text{ rad}.$$

So, $\theta_{total} = \theta_1 + \theta_2 = 314.2 \text{ rad} = 50 \text{ rev}$.

7.11 $$\bar{\omega} = \frac{\theta}{t} = \frac{(37.0 \text{ rev})(2\pi \text{ rad/1rev})}{3.00 \text{ s}} = 77.5 \text{ rad/s}.$$

But also, $$\bar{\omega} = \frac{\omega + \omega_0}{2} = \frac{98.0 \text{ rad/s} + \omega_0}{2} = 77.5 \text{ rad/s}.$$

Thus, $\omega_0 = 57.0 \text{ rad/s}$.

Then, $$\alpha = \frac{\omega - \omega_0}{t} = \frac{98.0 \text{ rad/s} - 57.0 \text{ rad/s}}{3 \text{ s}} = 13.7 \text{ rad/s}^2.$$

7.12 (a) Using $\theta = \frac{1}{2}\alpha t^2$, we have $$\alpha = \frac{2\theta}{t^2} = \frac{2(40 \text{ rev})(2\pi\text{rad/rev})}{(60 \text{ s})^2} = 0.14 \text{ rad/s}^2.$$

(b) $\omega = \omega_0 + \alpha t = 0 + (0.14)(60) = 8.4 \text{ rad/s}$.

7.13 $\theta = \dfrac{\omega^2 - \omega_0{}^2}{2\alpha} = \dfrac{0 - (18.0 \text{ rad/s})^2}{2(-1.90 \text{ rad/s}^2)} = 85.3 \text{ rad.}$

$s = r\theta$ and $r = \frac{1}{2}$ diameter $= 1.20$ cm,

so $s = (1.20 \text{ cm})(85.3 \text{ rad}) = 102 \text{ cm} = 1.02$ m.

7.14 $s = v_0 t + \frac{1}{2} at^2 = (17.0 \text{ m/s})(5.00 \text{ s}) + \frac{1}{2}(2.00 \text{ m/s}^2)(5.00 \text{ s})^2 = 110$ m.

$s = r\theta$, and $r = 48 \text{ cm} = 0.480$ m

Thus, $\theta = \dfrac{s}{r} = \dfrac{110 \text{ m}}{0.480 \text{ m}} = 229.2 \text{ rad} = 36.5$ rev.

7.15 (a) $\omega_0 = \dfrac{33 \times 2\pi}{60 \text{ s}} = 1.1\,\pi$ rad/s. Using $\omega = \omega_0 + \alpha t$, we have

$0 = 1.1\,\pi + \alpha(20)$, yielding $\alpha = -0.17 \text{ rad/s}^2$.

(b) Using $\theta = \omega_0 t + \frac{1}{2}\alpha t^2$, we have $\theta = (1.1\,\pi)(20) + \frac{1}{2}(-0.17)(20)^2$, or

$\theta = 34.6 \text{ rad} = 5.5$ revolutions.

(c) Using $v_t = r\omega$, we get $v_t = (0.14)(1.1\,\pi) = 0.48$ m/s.

7.16 The rotational velocity of the earth is

$\omega = 2\pi \dfrac{\text{rad}}{\text{day}} \dfrac{1 \text{ day}}{86400 \text{ s}} = 7.27 \times 10^{-5}$ rad/s, and

the radius of the earth is $r = 6.38 \times 10^6$ m.

(a) $a_r = r\omega^2 = (6.38 \times 10^6 \text{ m})(7.27 \times 10^{-5} \text{ rad/s})^2 = 3.37 \times 10^{-2} \text{ m/s}^2$.

(b) $a_r = r\omega^2 = 0$ since $r = 0$ (The north pole is on the rotation axis.)

7.17 The radius is 2.5 mi = 4.02×10^3 m.

$a_r = r\omega^2$ becomes $9.80 \text{ m/s}^2 = (4.02 \times 10^3 \text{ m})\omega^2$, so $\omega = 5.0 \times 10^{-2}$ rad/s.

7.18 $a_{centripetal} = \dfrac{v^2}{r} = \dfrac{(60 \text{ mph}(1.47 \text{ ft/s/1 mph}))^2}{1.0 \text{ ft}} = 7.8 \times 10^3 \text{ ft/s}^2$ directed toward the center of the tire.

7.19 (a) The final angular velocity is 78 rev/min = 8.17 rad/s, and the radius of the disk is equal to 5.0 in = 1.27×10^{-1} m.

$\alpha = \Delta\omega/\Delta t = \dfrac{(8.17 \text{ rad/s})}{(3.0 \text{ s})} = 2.72 \text{ rad/s}^2$, and $a_t = r\alpha = 3.45 \times 10^{-1} \text{ m/s}^2$.

(b) $v_t = r\omega = (1.27 \times 10^{-1} \text{ m})(8.17 \text{ rad/s}) = 1.04$ m/s.

(c) At $t = 1.00$ s, $a_t = 3.45 \times 10^{-1} \text{ m/s}^2$. From $\omega = \omega_0 + \alpha t$, we find $\omega = 2.72$ rad/s at $t = 1.00$ s.

Thus, $a_r = \dfrac{v_t{}^2}{r} = r\omega^2 = (0.127 \text{ m})(2.72 \text{ rad/s})^2 = 0.940 \text{ m/s}^2$.

$a_{total} = \sqrt{(a_t)^2 + (a_r)^2} = 1.00 \text{ m/s}^2$, and $\tan\theta = a_t/a_r = .367$, or $\theta = 20°$

7.20 (a) When $a_c = a_t$, we have $a_c = \dfrac{v_t{}^2}{r} = 0.500 \text{ m/s}^2$

or $v_t{}^2 = (0.500 \text{ m/s}^2)(400 \text{ m})$, giving $v_t = 14.14$ m/s.

(b) Since $v_t{}^2 = v^2{}_{ot} + 2a_t s$ when $v_t = 14.14$ m/s, we see that

$$s = \frac{v_t^2 - 0}{2a_t} = \frac{(14.14\ \text{m/s})^2}{2(0.500\ \text{m/s}^2)}, \text{ or } \quad s = 200 \text{ m.}$$

(c) $v_t = v_{ot} + a_t t$ gives $\quad 14.14\ \text{m/s} = 0 + (0.500\ \text{m/s}^2)\,t$, or $\quad t = 28.3$ s.

7.21 Let m be the mass of a red corpuscle and let r be the radius of the centrifuge. We are given

$$F_c = 4.0 \times 10^{-11}\ \text{N} = \frac{mv^2}{r} = mr\omega^2, \text{ so}$$

$$\omega = \sqrt{\frac{F_c}{mr}} = \sqrt{\frac{4.00 \times 10^{-11}}{(3.00 \times 10^{-16})(0.15)}} = 942.8\ \text{rad/s} = 150\ \text{rev/s.}$$

7.22 The friction force must supply the force producing the centripetal acceleration.

Thus, we must have $f = F_c$, where $f = \mu mg$, and $F_c = \dfrac{mv^2}{r}$.

Therefore, $\mu mg = \dfrac{mv^2}{r}$. The mass cancels, and we have

$v^2 = \mu rg = 0.70(20\ \text{m})(9.80\ \text{m/s}^2)$, from which, $\quad v = 12$ m/s.

7.23 (a) $a_r = r\omega^2 = (2.00\ \text{m})(3.00\ \text{rad/s})^2 = 18.0\ \text{m/s}^2$.

(b) $F = ma_r = (50.0\ \text{kg})(18.0\ \text{m/s}^2) = 900$ N

(c) We know the centripetal acceleration is caused by the force of friction. Therefore, $f = 900$ N. Also, the normal force, N, is equal to 490 N.

Thus, $\mu = f/N = 900\ \text{N}/490\ \text{N} = 1.84$. A coefficient of friction greater than one is unreasonable. Thus, she is not going to be able to stay on the ride.

7.24 (a) The radial acceleration must not exceed $7g = 7(9.80\ \text{m/s}^2) = 68.6\ \text{m/s}^2$.

Thus, from $a_r = \dfrac{v_t^2}{r}$, we have $r = (100\ \text{m/s})^2/68.6\ \text{m/s}^2 = 1.46 \times 10^2$ m.

(b) $F = ma_r = m(7g) = 7(mg) = 7$(pilot's weight)

$= 7(80.0\ \text{kg})(9.80\ \dfrac{\text{m}}{\text{s}^2}) = 5488$ N.

7.25 (a) From $\Sigma F_y = 0$, we have

$N\cos\theta = mg \qquad (1)$

where N is the normal force exerted on the car by the ramp.

Now, use $F_{\text{radial inward}} = ma_r$:

$N\sin\theta = mv^2/r \qquad (2)$

Divide (2) by (1) $\qquad \tan\theta = v^2/rg$

(b) $\tan\theta = (13.4\ \text{m/s})^2/(50.0\ \text{m})(9.80\ \text{m/s}^2)$

$\tan\theta = 0.366$, so $\qquad \theta = 20.1°$.

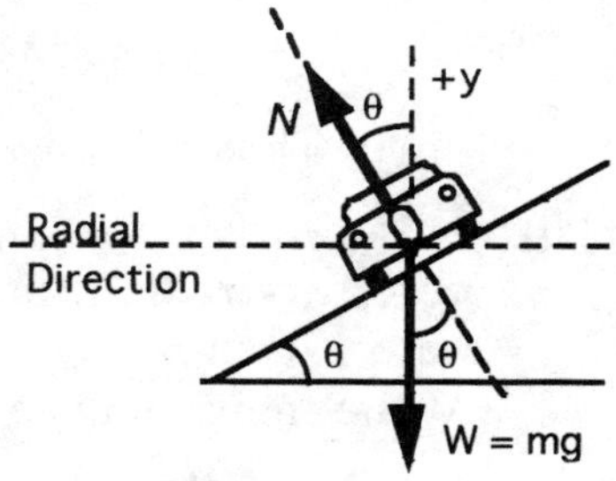

7.26 (a) Since the 1 kg mass is in equilibrium, we have for the tension in the string, $T = mg = (1.0)(9.80) = 9.8$ N.

(b) Since the centripetal acceration of the puck is produced by the tension in the string, we have $\quad F_c = T = 9.8$ N.

(c) Using $F_c = \frac{m_{puck} v^2}{r}$, we have $v = \sqrt{\frac{F_c r}{m_{puck}}} = \sqrt{\frac{9.80(1.0)}{0.25}} = 6.3$ m/s.

7.27 As he passes through the bottom of his swing, the force that the vine must supply is equal to (1) his weight plus (2) the needed radial force.

From Newton's second law, we have $T - mg = m\frac{v^2}{r}$, or

$$T = mg + m\frac{v^2}{r} = (85 \text{ kg})(9.80 \text{ m/s}^2) + (85 \text{ kg})\frac{(8 \text{ m/s})^2}{10 \text{ m}} = 1.4 \times 10^3 \text{ N}.$$

Since 1400 N > 1000 N, the vine will break.

7.28 (a) First we calculate ω using

$\omega = (4.0 \text{ rev/min})(2\pi \text{ rad/rev})(1 \text{ min}/60 \text{ s}) = 0.42$ rad/s.

Next we use $a_c = r\omega^2 = (9)(0.42)^2 = 1.58 \text{ m/s}^2$.

(b) At the lowest point, we have $F - mg = ma_c$, so

$F = (40.0 \text{ kg})(9.80 + 1.58)\text{m/s}^2 = 455$ N.

(c) At the highest point, we have $-F + mg = ma_c$, giving

$F = (40.0 \text{ kg})(9.80 - 1.58) \text{ m/s}^2 = 329$ N.

(d) At a point halfway up, we have a vertical component of the force which equals to the child's weight (392 N) pointing upward and a component pointing toward the center having magnitude

$F_c = ma_c = 63.2$ N.

In total the seat exerts a force

$F_R = \sqrt{((392)^2 + (63.2)^2)} = 397$ N, in a direction of

$\theta = \tan^{-1}\frac{63.2}{392} = 9.16°$ from the vertical.

7.29 (a) At A the forces on the car are the normal force, N, and its weight.

We have $F_c = \frac{mv^2}{r} = N - mg$, or $N = mg + \frac{mv^2}{r}$, which gives

$$N = (500 \text{ kg})(9.80 \text{ m/s}^2) + \frac{(500 \text{ kg})(20.0 \text{ m/s})^2}{10.0 \text{ m}} = 2.49 \times 10^4 \text{ N}.$$

(b) At B we have, $F_c = \frac{mv^2}{r} = mg - N$, or $N = m(g - \frac{v^2}{r})$.

For the vehicle to remain on the track, it is necessary to have

$N \geq 0$ which means $g \geq \frac{v^2}{r}$ or $v \leq \sqrt{rg}$.

Thus, $v_{max} = v \leq \sqrt{rg} = \sqrt{(15.0 \text{ m})(9.80 \text{ m/s}^2)} = 12.1$ m/s

---

7.30 At the top of the vertical circle, the speed must be great enough so the necessary radial force is equal to or greater than the weight, mg, of the water. That is: $F_c \geq mg$, so $mv^2/r \geq mg$, or $v^2 \geq rg$.

At the minimum speed, we have $v^2_{min} = rg$, or

$v_{min} = \sqrt{rg} = \sqrt{(1.00 \text{ m})(9.80 \text{ m/s}^2)} = 3.13$ m/s.

7.31 At the half-way point the spaceship is 1.92×10^8 m from both bodies.

The force exerted on the ship by the Earth is $F_1 = \frac{Gm_1 m_2}{r^2}$, or

$$F_1 = \frac{(6.67 \times 10^{-11}\ \text{Nm}^2/\text{kg}^2)(3.00 \times 10^4\ \text{kg})(5.98 \times 10^{24}\ \text{kg})}{(1.92 \times 10^8\ \text{m})^2} = 325\ \text{N}.$$

The force exerted on the ship by the moon is $F_2 = \frac{Gm_1m_2}{r^2}$, or

$$F_2 = \frac{(6.67 \times 10^{-11}\ \text{Nm}^2/\text{kg}^2)(3.00 \times 10^4\ \text{kg})(7.36 \times 10^{22}\ \text{kg})}{(1.92 \times 10^8\ \text{m})^2} = 4.00\ \text{N}$$

Thus, the resultant force is (325 N - 4.00 N) = 321 N directed toward the earth.

7.32 (a) The Sun-Earth distance is 1.496×10^{11} m, and the Earth-Moon distance is 3.84×10^8, so the distance from the Sun to the Moon during a solar eclipse is $1.496 \times 10^{11}\ \text{m} - 3.84 \times 10^8 = 1.49216 \times 10^{11}$ m. The mass of the Sun, Earth, and Moon are $m_S = 1.991 \times 10^{30}$ kg, $m_E = 5.98 \times 10^{24}$ kg, and $m_M = 7.36 \times 10^{22}$ kg. We have

$$F_{SM} = \frac{Gm_1m_2}{r^2} = \frac{(6.67 \times 10^{-11}\ \text{Nm}^2/\text{kg}^2)(1.991 \times 10^{30})(7.36 \times 10^{22})}{(1.49216 \times 10^{11})^2}$$

$F_{SM} = 4.39 \times 10^{20}$ N.

(b) $$F_{EM} = \frac{(6.67 \times 10^{-11}\text{Nm}^2/\text{kg}^2)(5.98 \times 10^{24})(7.36 \times 10^{22})}{(3.84 \times 10^8)^2}$$

$= 1.99 \times 10^{20}$ N.

(c) $$F_{SE} = \frac{(6.67 \times 10^{-11}\text{Nm}^2/\text{kg}^2)(1.991 \times 10^{30})(5.98 \times 10^{24})}{(1.496 \times 10^{11})^2}$$

$= 3.55 \times 10^{22}$ N.

7.33 The force exerted on the 2 kg mass by the 3 kg mass is in the positive y direction and given by:

$$F_1 = \frac{Gm_1m_2}{r^2} = \frac{(6.67 \times 10^{-11}\ \text{Nm}^2/\text{kg}^2)(3.0\ \text{kg})(2.0\ \text{kg})}{(2.0\ \text{m})^2} = 1.00 \times 10^{-10}\ \text{N}.$$

The force exerted on the 2.0 kg mass by the 4.0 kg mass is in the positive x direction, and is

$$F_2 = \frac{Gm_1m_2}{r^2} = \frac{(6.67 \times 10^{-11}\ \text{Nm}^2/\text{kg}^2)(4.0\ \text{kg})(2.0\ \text{kg})}{(4.0\ \text{m})^2} = 3.34 \times 10^{-11}\ \text{N}.$$

The resultant F is found from the Pythagorean theorem to be

$F_R = 1.1 \times 10^{-10}$ N. Also, $\theta = \tan^{-1}\left(\frac{F_1}{F_2}\right) = 72°$.

7.34 At the equilibrium position, the magnitude of the force exerted by the earth on the object is equal to the magnitude of the force exerted by the sun on the object. Thus,

$$\frac{GM_Em}{(1.50 \times 10^{11} - r)^2} = \frac{GM_Sm}{r^2}, \text{ giving}$$

$$\frac{r^2}{(1.50 \times 10^{11} - r)^2} = \frac{M_S}{M_E} = \frac{1.991 \times 10^{30}}{5.98 \times 10^{24}} = 3.33 \times 10^5$$

Taking the square root of both sides gives

$$\frac{r}{(1.50 \times 10^{11} - r)} = 577, \text{ which gives} \qquad r = 1.50 \times 10^{11}\ \text{m}.$$

7.35 Assume that the Moon moves around the center of the Earth, and

$F_C = F_G$ gives $\quad \dfrac{mv^2}{r} = \dfrac{GmM_E}{r^2}$, or $\quad M_E = \dfrac{rv^2}{G}$.

$$v = \frac{\text{distance traveled}}{\text{time required}} = \frac{2\pi r}{\text{period}} = \frac{2\pi(3.84 \times 10^8 \text{ m})}{27.32 \text{ days}(86{,}400 \text{ s/day})} = 1022 \text{ m/s}.$$

Thus, $M_E = \dfrac{(3.84 \times 10^8 \text{ m})(1022 \text{ m/s})^2}{6.67 \times 10^{-11} \text{ Nm}^2/\text{kg}^2} = 6.01 \times 10^{24}$ kg.

The estimate is slightly high because the Moon actually orbits the center of mass of the Earth-Moon system, not the center of the Earth.

7.36 (a) Using $\dfrac{GmM}{r^2} = \dfrac{mv^2}{r}$, where M is the mass of the Earth and m is the mass of the satellite, we get:

$$r = \frac{GM}{v^2} = \frac{(6.67 \times 10^{-11})(5.98 \times 10^{24})}{(5000)^2} = 1.59 \times 10^7 \text{ m}.$$

The radius of the Earth is 6.37×10^6 m, so

$h = 1.59 \times 10^7 - 6.37 \times 10^6 = 9.58 \times 10^6$ m is the satellite's altitude.

(b) Here we use: $T = \dfrac{\text{circumference of orbit}}{\text{speed of satellite}} = \dfrac{2\pi r}{v} = \dfrac{2\pi(1.59 \times 10^7)}{5000}$

which gives, $T = 20{,}000 \text{ s} = 5.55$ h.

7.37 (a) We have $F = \dfrac{mv^2}{r} = \dfrac{GM_Em}{r^2}$. With $r = 2R_E$,

$$v^2 = \frac{GM_E}{r} = \frac{(6.67 \times 10^{-11} \text{ Nm}^2/\text{kg}^2)(5.98 \times 10^{24} \text{ kg})}{(1.28 \times 10^7 \text{ m})}.$$

This gives, $v = 5.58 \times 10^3$ m/s.

(b) The period is given by

$$T = \frac{2\pi r}{v} = \frac{2\pi(1.28 \times 10^7 \text{ m})}{5.58 \times 10^3 \text{ m/s}} = 1.44 \times 10^4 \text{ s} = 239 \text{ min} \approx 4 \text{ h}.$$

(c) $F_2 = \dfrac{Gm_1m_2}{r^2} = \dfrac{(6.67 \times 10^{-11} \text{ Nm}^2/\text{kg}^2)(5.98 \times 10^{24} \text{ kg})(600 \text{ kg})}{(1.28 \times 10^7 \text{ m})^2}$, or

$F_2 = 1.47 \times 10^3$ N.

7.38 (a) $F_C = ma_C = F_G$. Therefore, $\quad ma_C = \dfrac{GmM_{moon}}{r^2}$, and

$$a_C = \frac{GM_{moon}}{r^2} = \frac{(6.67 \times 10^{-11} \text{Nm}^2/\text{kg}^2)(7.36 \times 10^{22} \text{ kg})}{(1.74 \times 10^6 \text{ m})^2} = 1.62 \text{ m/s}^2.$$

(b) $a_C = \dfrac{v^2}{r}$, so $v^2 = a_Cr = (1.62 \text{ m/s}^2)(1.74 \times 10^6 \text{ m})$ yields

$v = 1.68 \times 10^3$ m/s.

(c) The time to orbit $= \dfrac{\text{distance around}}{\text{speed}} = \dfrac{2\pi r}{v}$, so

$$t = \frac{2\pi(1.74 \times 10^6 \text{ m})}{1.68 \times 10^3 \text{ m/s}} = 6.51 \times 10^3 \text{ s} = 108 \text{ min} = 1.81 \text{ h}.$$

7.39 (a) $PE = -\dfrac{GM_Em}{r} = \dfrac{(6.67 \times 10^{-11} \text{ Nm}^2/\text{kg}^2)(5.98 \times 10^{24} \text{ kg})(100 \text{ kg})}{(8.38 \times 10^6 \text{ m})}$

$= -4.76 \times 10^9$ J

(b) $F = \frac{GM_E m}{r^2} = \frac{(6.67 \times 10^{-11}\ \text{Nm}^2/\text{kg}^2)(5.98 \times 10^{24}\ \text{kg})(100\ \text{kg})}{(8.38 \times 10^6\ \text{m})^2}$

$= 5.68 \times 10^2$ N

7.40 (a) The escape speed from the moon is

$v = \sqrt{\frac{2GM}{R}}$ For the moon, $M = 7.36 \times 10^{22}$ kg and $R = 1.74 \times 10^6$ m.

$v = 2.38 \times 10^3$ m/s (5300 mph)

(b) The steps are the same for mercury, with $M = 3.18 \times 10^{23}$ kg and $R = 2.43 \times 10^6$ m. $v = 4.18 \times 10^3$ m/s (9350 mph)

(c) For Jupiter, $M = 1.90 \times 10^{27}$ kg, $R = 6.99 \times 10^7$ m and v is found to be 6.02×10^4 m/s (about 135,000 mph).

7.41 $F_C = F_G$ gives $\frac{mv^2}{r} = \frac{GmM_E}{r^2}$, which reduces to $v = \sqrt{\frac{GM_E}{r}}$

and period $= \frac{2\pi r}{v} = 2\pi r\sqrt{\frac{r}{GM_E}}$,

$r = R_E + 200$ km $= 6380$ km $+ 200$ km $= 6580$ km Thus,

period $= 2\pi(6.58 \times 10^6\ \text{m})\sqrt{\frac{(6.58 \times 10^6\ \text{m})}{(6.67 \times 10^{-11}\ \text{Nm}^2/\text{kg}^2)(5.98 \times 10^{24}\ \text{kg})}}$

$= 5310$ s $= 88.5$ min $= 1.48$ h

(b) $v = \sqrt{\frac{GM_E}{r}} = \sqrt{\frac{(6.67 \times 10^{-11}\ \text{Nm}^2/\text{kg}^2)(5.98 \times 10^{24}\ \text{kg})}{(6.58 \times 10^6\ \text{m})}}$

$= 7.79 \times 10^3$ m/s $= 7.79$ km/s

(c) $KE_f + PE_f = KE_i + PE_i$ + energy input, gives

input $= \frac{1}{2}mv_f^2 - \frac{1}{2}mv_i^2 + \left(\frac{-GM_E m}{r_f}\right) - \left(\frac{-GM_E m}{r_i}\right)$ (1)

$r_i = R_E = 6.38 \times 10^6$ m, $\quad v_i = \frac{2\pi R_E}{24\ \text{h}} = 4.64 \times 10^2$ m/s

Substituting the appropriate values into (1), yields minimum energy input $= 6.43 \times 10^9$ J, This assumes that the launch is from the equator.

7.42 (a) Use $\theta = \omega_0 t + \frac{1}{2}\alpha t^2$.

$\theta = (3.00\ \text{rad/s})(2.00\ \text{s}) + \frac{1}{2}(1.50\ \text{rad/s}^2)(2.00\ \text{s})^2$

$\theta = 9$ rad $= 516°$ or $\theta = 516° - 360° = 156°$

(b) The angular velocity at 2.00 s is

$\omega = \omega_0 + \alpha t$

$\omega = 3.00\ \text{rad/s} + (1.50\ \text{rad/s}^2)(2.00\ \text{s}) = 6$ rad/s.

7.43 (a) The force F_1 exerted on the 4 kg mass by the 2 kg mass at the origin is directed to the left and so is the force F_2 exerted on the 4 kg mass by the 3 kg mass. Thus, the resultant force is to the left and is equal to the sum of F_1 and F_2. (See Figure 1 below.)

$F_{net} = F_1 + F_2$

$= \frac{6.67 \times 10^{-11}\ \text{Nm}^2/\text{kg}^2(2.0)(4.0)}{(4.0\ \text{m})^2} + \frac{6.67 \times 10^{-11}\ \text{Nm}^2/\text{kg}^2(3.0)(4.0)}{(2.0\ \text{m})^2}$

$= 2.3 \times 10^{-10}$ N in -x direction.

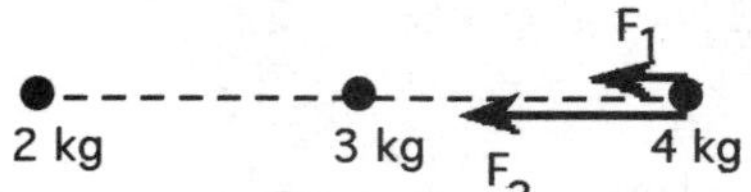

Figure 1

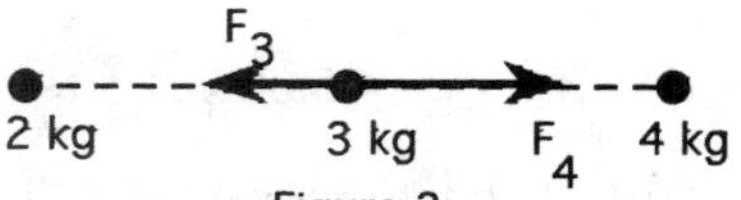

Figure 2

(b) The force exerted on the 3 kg mass by the 2 kg mass is to the left and the force exerted by the 4 kg mass is to the right. (See Figure 2 above.) The net force is

$$F_{net} = \frac{6.67 \times 10^{-11}\ \text{Nm}^2/\text{kg}^2(3.0)(4.0)}{(2.0\ \text{m})^2} - \frac{6.67 \times 10^{-11}\ \text{Nm}^2/\text{kg}^2(3.0)(2.0)}{(2.0\ \text{m})^2}$$

$= 1.0 \times 10^{-10}$ N (in +x direction).

7.44 $\omega = 0.500\ \text{rev/s} = \pi\ \text{rad/s}$.

(a) $v_t = r\omega = (0.80\ \text{m})(\pi\ \text{rad/s}) = 2.51\ \text{m/s}$.

(b) $a_r = r\omega^2 = v_t^2/r = (2.51\ \text{m/s})^2/0.80\ \text{m} = 7.90\ \text{m/s}^2$.

(c) $F = \frac{mv^2}{r}$ If the maximum value of T is 100 N, then we have

$$100\ \text{N} = \frac{(5.00\ \text{kg})v^2}{0.80\ \text{m}}.$$

From which, $v = 4.00$ m/s.

7.45 $F_C = F_G$ gives $\frac{mv^2}{R} = \frac{GmM}{R^2}$, or $M = \frac{Rv^2}{G}$.

$$v = \frac{\text{distance traveled}}{\text{time}} = \frac{2\pi R}{\text{period}} = \frac{2\pi(4.22 \times 10^8\ \text{m})}{(1.77\ \text{days})(86{,}400\ \text{s/day})}, \text{ or}$$

$v = 1.733 \times 10^4$ m/s.

Thus, $M = \frac{(4.22 \times 10^8\ \text{m})(1.733 \times 10^4\ \text{m/s})^2}{6.67 \times 10^{-11}\ \text{Nm}^2/\text{kg}^2} = 1.90 \times 10^{27}$ kg.

7.46 (a) $\omega = (1200\ \text{rev/min})(1\ \text{min}/60\ \text{s})(2\pi\ \text{rad/rev}) = 126\ \text{rad/s}$.

(b) $v_t = r\omega = (2.00 \times 10^{-2}\ \text{m})(126\ \text{rad/s}) = 2.51\ \text{m/s}$.

(c) $a_r = r\omega^2 = 947\ \text{m/s}^2$.

(d) $\theta = \omega t = (125.6\ \text{rad/s})(2.00\ \text{s}) = 251\ \text{rad}$, and
$s = r\theta = (6.00 \times 10^{-2}\ \text{m})(251\ \text{rad}) = 15.1\ \text{m}$.

7.47 The distance of the satellite from the center of the earth is $r = R_E + h$, where R_E is the radius of the earth and h is the height of the satellite above the earth. We find $r = 6.62 \times 10^6$ m. The required force is supplied by gravitation. Thus, $\frac{mv^2}{r} = \frac{GmM_E}{r^2}$, or $v^2 = \frac{GM_E}{r}$.

With $M_E = 5.98 \times 10^{24}$ kg, we have:

(a) $v = 7.77 \times 10^3$ m/s.

(b) $T = \frac{2\pi r}{v} = \frac{2\pi(6.62 \times 10^6\ \text{m})}{7.77 \times 10^3\ \text{m/s}} = 5.36 \times 10^3\ \text{s} = 89.3\ \text{min}$.

7.48 (a) The required angular velocity is

$$\omega = 2\pi \frac{\text{rad}}{\text{day}} \frac{1\ \text{day}}{86400\ \text{s}} = 7.272 \times 10^{-5} \frac{\text{rad}}{\text{s}}$$

The gravitational force exerted on the satellite by the Earth must supply force that causes the centripetal acceleration.

Thus, $F_c = mr\omega^2 = \frac{GM_E m}{r^2}$,

giving $r^3 = \frac{GM_E}{\omega^2} = \frac{(6.67 \times 10^{-11} \text{ N m}^2/\text{kg}^2)(5.98 \times 10^{24} \text{ kg})}{(7.272 \times 10^{-5} \text{ rad/s})^2}$

or $r = 4.23 \times 10^7$ m.

(b) The radius of the Earth is 6.37×10^6 m so that the altitude of the satellite is $4.23 \times 10^7 \text{ m} - 6.37 \times 10^6 \text{ m} = 3.59 \times 10^7 \text{ m} = 22{,}294$ miles.

7.49 (a) The forces acting on the car at the top of its circular arc are the normal force, N, and the weight. We have $F = \frac{mv^2}{r} = mg - N$, or

$N = mg - \frac{mv^2}{r}$. (1)

(b) When the normal force goes to zero, we have, from (1)
$v^2 = rg = (30.0 \text{ m})g$. From which,
$v = 17.1$ m/s

7.50 (a) At the bottom of the swing, $T - mg = \frac{mv^2}{L}$, or

$T = mg + \frac{mv^2{}_b}{L} = (0.400)(9.80) + \frac{(0.400)(3.00)^2}{0.800} = 8.42$ N.

(b) From conservation of energy, we may write
(PE_g)at top of swing $= KE)$at bottom , or
$mgL(1 - \cos\theta_{max}) = \frac{1}{2} mv^2{}_{bottom}$, giving

$\cos\theta_{max} = 1 - \frac{v^2{}_{bottom}}{2gL} = 1 - \frac{(3.00 \text{ m/s})^2}{2(9.80 \text{ m/s}^2)(0.800 \text{ m})} = 0.426.$

Thus, $\theta_{max} = 64.8°$.

(c) At $\theta = \theta_{max}$, the pendulum is at rest, so the radial force
$F_c = \frac{mv^2}{L} = T - Mg\cos\theta_{max} = 0.$
Thus, $T = Mg\cos\theta_{max} = (0.400 \text{ kg})(9.80 \text{ m/s}^2)\cos 64.8° = 1.67$ N.

7.51 (a) We have the expression for the gravity on a body as $g = \frac{GM}{R^2}$. We write this equation down twice, once for the star and once for the earth and divide the two. The result is

$\frac{g_{star}}{g_{earth}} = \frac{M_s}{M_e}\left(\frac{R_e}{R_s}\right)^2 = \frac{2.99 \times 10^{30}}{5.98 \times 10^{24}}\left(\frac{6.38 \times 10^6}{10^4}\right)^2$

which gives a value of g on the star of 1.99×10^{12} m/s^2.

(b) $w = mg = (0.120 \text{ kg})(1.99 \times 10^{12} \text{ m/s}^2) = 2.38 \times 10^{11}$ N

(c) $PE = mgh = (70.0 \text{ kg})(1.99 \times 10^{12} \text{ m/s}^2)(10^{-2} \text{ m}) = 1.39 \times 10^{12}$ J

7.52 (a) Consider a person at the equator standing on a pair of scales. There are two forces on him W, his true weight, and the upward force exerted on him by the scale, W', which we shall call his apparent

weight since it, by Newton's third law, is what the scale will read.
We have $W - W' = \frac{mv^2}{r}$, or $W' = W - \frac{mv^2}{r}$ so, $W > W'$.

(b) At the poles $v = 0$, and $W' = W = mg = (75.0\text{ kg})(9.80\text{ m/s}^2) = 735\text{ N}$.
At the equator $W' = 735\text{ N} - (75.0\text{ kg})(0.034\text{ m/s}^2) = 732.5\text{ N}$.

7.53 We know $f = \mu_s N$ where f must equal mg to support the rider. The normal force must supply the needed centripetal force, thus $N = m\omega^2 r$.

Therefore, $\mu_s = \frac{g}{\omega^2 r} = \frac{(9.80\text{ m/s}^2)}{(5.00\text{ rad/s})^2(3.00\text{ m})} = 0.131.$

7.54 (a) At the beginning of the motion, $v = 0$, and from $F_c = \frac{mv^2}{r}$, we see that F_c, the required force toward the center of the circle is also zero. Thus, $T = 0$.

(b) Use conservation of mechanical energy to find an expression for v, the velocity of the stuntman at any point along the arc of his swing:
$\frac{1}{2}mv_i^2 + mgy_i = \frac{1}{2}mv_f^2 + mgy_f$ gives $0 + mgR = \frac{1}{2}mv^2 + mgy$.

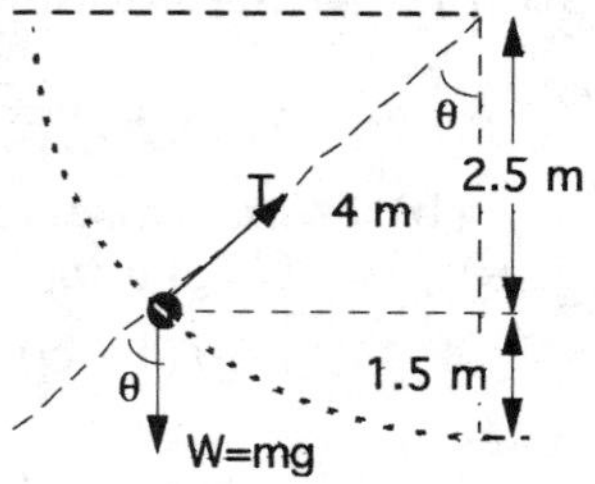

Thus, $v^2 = 2g(R - y)$, (1)
where R is the radius of the path, and y is the vertical distance above the zero reference level (chosen at the bottom of the arc).
When $y = 1.5$ m,
$v^2 = 2g(4.0\text{ m} - 1.5\text{ m}) = 49\text{ m}^2/\text{s}^2$.
The necessary force is
$$F_c = \frac{mv^2}{R} = \frac{(70\text{ kg})(49\text{ m}^2/\text{s}^2)}{4.0\text{ m}} = 858\text{ N}.$$
But F_c is given by $T - mg\cos\theta = 858$ N,
where $\cos\theta = 2.5\text{ m}/4\text{ m} = .625$ ($\theta = 51.3°$).
Therefore, $T = 858\text{ N} + (70\text{ kg})g(\cos 51.3°) = 1.3 \times 10^3\text{ N}$.

(c) At the bottom of the arc ($y = 0$), equation (1) gives $v^2 = 78.4\text{ m}^2/\text{s}^2$.
Thus, the necessary force is
$$F_c = \frac{mv^2}{r} = (70\text{ kg})(78.4\text{ m}^2/\text{s}^2)/4.0\text{ m} = 1372\text{ N}.$$
Also, the force producing the centripetal acceleration at the bottom of the arc is $F_c = T - mg$,
so $T = F_c + mg = 1372\text{ N} + (70\text{ kg})g = 2.1 \times 10^3\text{ N}$.

7.55 (a) A study of the forces acting on the ball gives
$T\sin\theta = \frac{mv^2}{r}$ (1) and $T\cos\theta = mg$ (2)
with $r = L\sin\theta$. Dividing one equation by the other gives $\frac{\sin\theta}{\cos\theta} = \frac{v^2}{gL\sin\theta}$ (3)

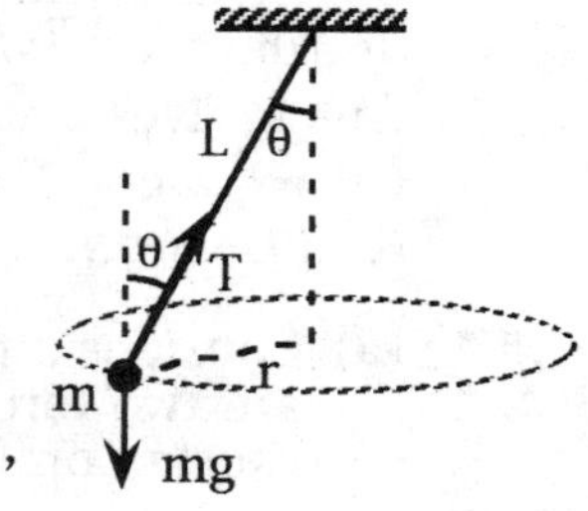

so, $v = \sqrt{\frac{gL\sin^2\theta}{\cos\theta}} = \sqrt{\frac{(9.80)(1.5)\sin^2 30°}{\cos 30°}}$,
$v = 2.1$ m/s.

(b) Going back to equation (3), we have $\frac{\sin^2\theta}{\cos\theta} = \frac{v^2}{gL} = \frac{1 - \cos^2\theta}{\cos\theta}$, so

$\cos^2\theta + \frac{v^2}{gL}\cos\theta - 1 = 0$. Putting in the values for v, g, and L, yields
$\cos^2\theta + 1.088\cos\theta - 1 = 0$, giving $\cos\theta = 0.594$, or $\cos\theta = -1.68$.
We disregard the second solution since $\cos\theta \geq -1$ for all angles.
Therefore, we have only the first solution yielding $\theta = 54°$.

(c) Using Equation (2) above, we have $\cos\theta = \frac{mg}{T} = \frac{(0.5)(9.80)}{9.8} = 0.5$,
from which $\theta = 60°$. Putting this into equation (3) yields,

$$v = \sqrt{\frac{gL\sin^2\theta}{\cos\theta}} = \sqrt{\frac{(9.80)(1.5)\sin^2 60°}{\cos 60°}} = 4.7 \text{ m/s}.$$

7.56 The speed of the skier after dropping distance h is found using conservation of energy as

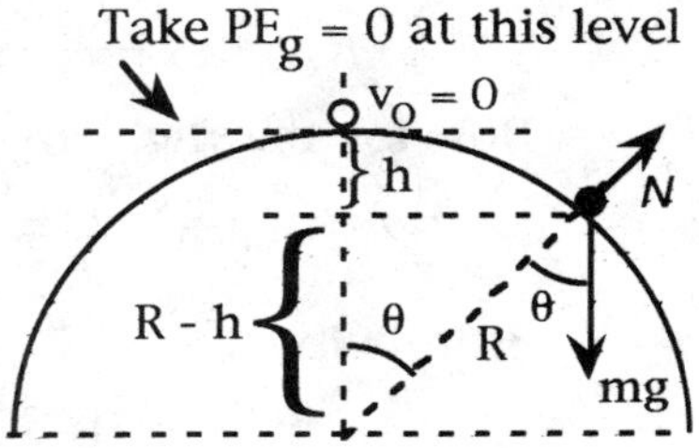

$$\frac{1}{2}mv^2 - mgh = 0 + 0, \text{ or } \qquad v^2 = 2gh.$$

The radial force acting on the skier is given by

$$F_c = \frac{mv^2}{R} = mg\cos\theta - N = mg(1 - \frac{h}{R}) - N.$$

Substituting for v^2 gives $2mg\frac{h}{R} = mg(1 - \frac{h}{R}) - N$.

The skier leaves the hill when $N = 0$ which occurs when

$$2\frac{h}{R} = 1 - \frac{h}{R}, \text{ yielding } \quad h = \frac{R}{3}.$$

7.57 Using Kepler's Third law $T^2 = ka^3$, we have

$$(75.6)^2 = \left(\frac{0.57 + x}{2}\right)^3$$

The farthest distance $x = 2(75.6)^{2/3} - 0.57 = 35.2$ A.U. (near the orbit of Pluto)

7.58 $\Sigma F = ma$ gives $G\frac{m_{planet}M_{star}}{r^2} = \frac{m_{planet}v^2}{r}$

$$G\frac{M_{star}}{r} = v^2 = r^2\omega^2$$

$$GM_{star} = r_x{}^3\omega_x{}^2 = r_y{}^3\omega_y{}^2$$

$$\omega_y = \omega_x\left(\frac{r_x}{r_y}\right)^{3/2}$$

$$\omega_y = \left(\frac{90°}{5y}\right)3^{3/2} = \frac{468°}{5y}$$

So planet Y has turned through 1.30 revolutions.

7.59 (a) $F = G\frac{m_1m_2}{r^2} = 6.67 \times 10^{-11}\frac{(100 \times 1.99 \times 10^{30} \text{ kg})(10^3 \text{ kg})}{(10000 \text{ m} + 50.0 \text{ m})^2} = 1.31 \times 10^{17}$ N

This will give the ship an average acceleration of

$$\frac{1.31 \times 10^{17}\ \text{N}}{10^{3}\ \text{kg}} = 1.31 \times 10^{14}\ \text{m/s}^2$$

(b) $\Delta F = G\frac{m_1 m_2}{r_f^2} - G\frac{m_1 m_2}{r_b^2}$,

so $\frac{\Delta F}{m_2} = \frac{G m_1 (r_b^2 - r_f^2)}{r_f^2 r_b^2}$

$$= \frac{6.67 \times 10^{-11}[(10100\ \text{m})^2 - (10000\ \text{m})^2](100 \times 1.99 \times 10^{30}\ \text{kg})}{(10100\ \text{m})^2(10000\ \text{m})^2}$$

$= 2.62 \times 10^{12}$ N/kg

7.60 We interpret "lunar escape speed" to be the escape speed from the surface of a stationary moon alone in the universe:

$$\frac{1}{2} m v_{esc}^2 = G\frac{M_m m}{R_m} \quad \text{so} \quad v_{esc} = \sqrt{\frac{2GM_m}{R_m}} \quad \text{and} \quad v_{launch} = 2\sqrt{\frac{2GM_m}{R_m}}$$

Now for the flight from Moon to Earth, conservation of energy gives

$$\frac{1}{2} m v_{launch}^2 - G\frac{mM_m}{R_m} - G\frac{mM_e}{R_{el}} = \frac{1}{2} m v_{impact}^2 - G\frac{mM_m}{r_{m2}} - G\frac{mM_e}{R_e}$$

From which, $v_{impact} = (2G(\frac{3M_m}{R_m} + \frac{M_m}{r_{m2}} + \frac{M_e}{R_e} - \frac{M_e}{R_e})^{1/2}$

$$=(2G(\frac{3 \times 7.36 \times 10^{22}\ \text{kg}}{1.74 \times 10^{6}\ \text{m}} + \frac{7.36 \times 10^{22}\ \text{kg}}{3.84 \times 10^{8}\ \text{m}} + \frac{5.98 \times 10^{24}\ \text{kg}}{6.37 \times 10^{6}\ \text{m}} - \frac{5.98 \times 10^{24}\ \text{kg}}{3.84 \times 10^{8}\ \text{m}})^{1/2}$$

$= 11.8$ km/s

7.61 $\frac{1}{2} m_o v_{esc}^2 = G\frac{m_p m_o}{r_p}$ $\quad v_{esc} = \sqrt{\frac{2Gm_p}{r_p}}$ with $m_p = \rho\frac{4}{3}\pi r_p^3$ we have

$$v_{esc} = \sqrt{\frac{2G\rho\frac{4}{3}\pi r_p^3}{r_p}} = \sqrt{\frac{8\pi G\rho}{3}}\ r_p$$

So, the escape velocity is proportional to r_p

7.62 For the block to just make it through the top of the loop, the needed force at point C must equal the block's weight, or

$$\frac{Mv_C^2}{R} = Mg \qquad \text{giving} \qquad v_C = \sqrt{Rg}.$$

Using conservation of energy, from when the block starts from rest until it reaches point C, gives

$(PE_s)_i$ = (energy spent against friction along AB) + $(KE)_C + (PE)_C$

or $\quad \frac{1}{2} kd^2 = \mu_k M g L_{AB} + \frac{1}{2} Mv_C^2 + Mg(2R)$.

Thus, $d^2 = \frac{2M}{k}[\mu_k g L_{AB} + \frac{1}{2} v_C^2 + 2gR] = \frac{2Mg}{k}[\mu_k L_{AB} + 2.5R]$

$$= \frac{(2)(0.50\ \text{kg})(9.80\ \text{m/s}^2)}{78.4\ \text{N/m}^2}[(0.30)(2.5\ \text{m}) + 2.5(1.5\ \text{m})] = 0.563\ \text{m}^2.$$

Therefore, $d = 0.75$ m is the minimum compression needed.

7.63 (a) The initial total energy of the block is $E_i = \frac{1}{2}mv^2{}_0 + mg(2R)$.

At point A, the total energy is $E_A = \frac{1}{2}mv^2{}_A + mg(R)$ and, since

$E_i = E_A$ we have $\frac{1}{2}mv^2{}_0 + mg(2R) = \frac{1}{2}mv^2{}_A + mg(R)$.

This gives, $v_A = v^2{}_0 + 2gR = (4)^2 + 2(9.80)(1.5)$, so $v_A = 6.7$ m/s.
The force of the block is given as

$$n_A = \frac{mv^2{}_A}{R} = \frac{mv^2{}_0}{R} + 2mg = \frac{(0.50)(4.0)^2}{1.5} + 2(0.5)(9.80) = 15.1 \text{ N}.$$

At point B, we have $E_B = \frac{1}{2}mv^2{}_B = E_A = \frac{1}{2}mv^2{}_0 + 2mg(R)$

so $v^2{}_B = v^2{}_0 + 4gR = (4)^2 + 4(9.80)(1.5) = 8.6$ m/s.

The force from the track on the block is $n_B = \frac{mv^2{}_B}{R} + mg$.

Thus, $$n_B = \frac{m(v^2{}_0 + 4gR)}{R} + mg = \frac{mv^2{}_0}{R} + 5mg, \text{ or}$$

$$n_B = \frac{(0.5)(4)^2}{1.5} + 5(0.5)(9.80) = 29.8 \text{ N}.$$

(b) Let E_C be the energy of the block at point C.

Then $E_C - E_B = -\mu_k(mg)L$. But also $E_C = \frac{mv^2{}_C}{2} + mg(2R)$, so

$$\frac{mv^2{}_C}{2} + mg(2R) = \frac{1}{2}mv^2{}_B - \mu_k(mg)L = \frac{1}{2}mv^2{}_0 + 2mgR - \mu_k(mg)L.$$

Thus, $v^2{}_C = v^2{}_0 - 2\mu_k gL$. Next, we observe that $n_C + mg = \frac{mv^2{}_C}{R}$,

so $$n_C = \frac{m(v^2{}_0 - 2\mu_k gL)}{R} - mg = \frac{mv^2{}_0}{R} - \left(\frac{2\mu_k L}{R} + 1\right)mg.$$

If the block just barely makes it to point C, we must have $n_C = 0$ so

$$\frac{mv^2{}_0}{R} - \left(\frac{2\mu_k L}{R} + 1\right)mg = 0, \text{ or } \quad \frac{2\mu_k L}{R} = \frac{v^2{}_0}{gR} - 1$$

from which $$\mu_k = \frac{v^2{}_0}{2gL} - \frac{R}{2L} = \frac{(4)^2}{2(9.80)(0.4)} - \frac{1.5}{2(0.4)} = 0.166.$$

7.64 (a) At A we must have $mg = \frac{mv_A{}^2}{R}$, or $v_A{}^2 = gR$ in order for the coaster to remain on the track. By energy conservation, we have

$\Delta PE + \Delta KE = 0$, or $-\frac{mgh}{3} + \frac{m(v_A{}^2 - v_0{}^2)}{2} = 0$.

Substituting for v_A and solving we find $v_0 = \sqrt{g(R - \frac{2h}{3})}$.

(b) If the coaster just makes it to point B, then $v_B = 0$.

By conservation of energy $[0 - \frac{mv_0{}^2}{2}] + mg(h' - h) = 0$.

Substituting for v_0 gives $h' = \frac{R}{2} + \frac{2h}{3}$.

7.65 If the car is about to slip down the plane,

$$+mg\sin\theta - f = \frac{mv^2}{R}\cos\theta, \text{ where } f = \mu[mg\cos\theta + \frac{mv^2}{R}\sin\theta]$$

From the above, we find $v_{min} = [Rg(\tan\theta - \mu)/(1 + \mu\tan\theta)]^{1/2}$.

$v_{min} = [(100)(9.80)(\tan 10° - 0.1)/(1.00 + 0.100\tan 10°)]^{1/2} = 8.57$ m/s

If the car is ready to slip up the plane, then $+mg\sin\theta + f = \frac{mv^2}{R}\cos\theta$.

and $v_{max} = [Rg(\tan\theta + \mu)/(1 - \mu\tan\theta)]^{1/2}$.

$v_{max} = [(100)(9.80)(\tan 10° + 0.100)/(1 - 0.100\tan 10°)]^{1/2} = 16.6$ m/s.

ANSWERS TO CONCEPTUAL QUESTIONS

2. The need for a large force toward the center of the circular path on objects near the equator will cause the earth to bulge at the equator. A force toward the center of the circular path is not needed at the poles, so the radius in this direction will be smaller than at the equator.

4. The speedometer will be inaccurate. The speedometer measures the number of revolutions per second of the tires.

6. The car cannot round a turn at constant velocity because constant velocity means the direction of the velocity is not changing. The statement is possible if the word velocity is replaced by the word speed.

8. The astronaut is accelerating toward the Earth at the same rate as is the spaceship. Thus, if the astronaut drops a wrench, it will float in space next to him. Likewise, he will float in space next to a desk or with reference to the spaceship. Thus, he believes himself to be weightless.

10. Consider one end of a string connected to a balance and the other end connected to an object, of true weight w. The tension T in the string will be measured by the balance and will be construed as the apparent weight. We have $w - T = ma_c$. This gives, $T = w - ma_c$. Thus, the apparent weight is less than the actual weight by the term ma_c. At the poles the centripetal acceleration is zero. Thus, $T = w$. However, at the equator the term containing the centripetal acceleration is nonzero, and the apparent weight is less than the true weight.

12. If the acceleration is constant in magnitude and perpendicular to the velocity, the object is moving in a circular path at constant speed. If the acceleration is parallel to the velocity, the object is either speeding up, v and a in same direction, or slowing down, v and a in opposite directions.

14. The most massive particles will require the largest force to make them move in a circular path. This means the heaviest particles will migrate to the bottom of the container where its bottom will produce a force on the particles of magnitude great enough to cause the motion in a circular path. Thus, the old adage cream comes to the top applies.

16. Kepler's second law says that equal areas are swept out in equal times by a line drawn from the Sun to the planet. For this to be so, the planet must move fastest when it is closest to the Sun. This, surprisingly, occurs during the winter.

18. If it were at an angle of 90°, there would be no way for the string to exert an upward component, overcoming the weight, to keep the yo-yo in equilibrium in the vertical direction. It cannot swing at this angle.

CHAPTER EIGHT SOLUTIONS

Chapter Eight Readings

Borgwald, J.M. and Schreiner, S., "Classroom Analysis of Rotating Space Vehicles in 2001: A Space Odyssey", The Physics Teacher, 31, 406, 1993

Brody, H., "The Moment of Inertia of a Tennis Racket," *The Physics Teacher*, April 1985, p. 213.

Frohlich, C., "The Physics of Somersaulting and Twisting," *Scientific American*, March 1980, p. 154.

Griffing, D.F., *The Dynamics of Sports: Why That's the Way the Ball Bounces*, Mohican Publishing Co., 1982

Kreifeldt, J.G. and Chuang, M., "Moment of Inertia: Psychophysical Study of an Overlooked Sensation," *Science*, 1979, p. 588.

Laws, K, "The Physics of Dance," *Physics Today*, February 1985, p. 25.

Post, R.F. and Post, S.F., "Flywheels," Scientific American, December 1973, p. 17.

Review (a) Using the law of gravitation, one gets

$$\frac{GM_e m}{d^2} = \frac{GM_m m}{(d_c - d)^2},$$ where d is the distance from the center of the earth to the point of gravitational equilibrium. Substitution and cancellation gives

$$\frac{81}{d^2} = \frac{1}{(d_c - d)^2}.$$

Taking the square root, $9(d_c - d) = d$,

or $d = (9/10)\,d_c = 0.9(3.84 \times 10^5 \text{ km})$ (about 215,000 mi).

(b) The center of mass is found from $M_e d = M_m(d_c - d)$, where d is the distance from the center of the earth to the center of mass of the earth-moon system.

Substitution yields $81d = (d_c - d)$, or $d = \frac{d_c}{82} = 4.68 \times 10^3$ km.

The location of the center of mass is 4.68×10^3 km (about 2900 miles) from the center of the earth. This places it about 1000 miles below the surface of the earth.

8.1 In order to exert the minimum force, the force must be applied perpendicular to the wrench. With the pivot at the nut, we have

$$\tau = Fd$$

or $40.0 \text{ N·m} = F(0.300 \text{ m})$.

So, $F = 133$ N

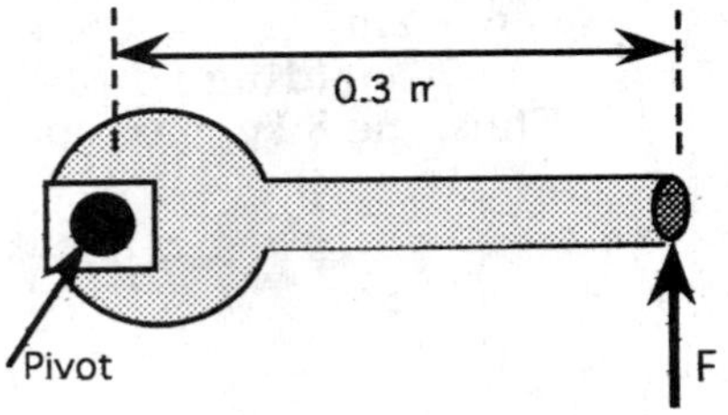

8.2 The lever arm is

$d = (1.20 \times 10^{-2} \text{ m})\cos 48° = 8.03 \times 10^{-3}$ m, and the torque is:

$\tau = Fd = (80.0\ \text{N})(8.03 \times 10^{-3}\ \text{m}) = 0.642\ \text{N m (CCW)}.$

8.3 We have $\tau = (F)(\text{lever arm}) = (Mg)(L\sin\theta)$, or
$$\tau = (3.0\ \text{kg})(9.80\ \text{m/s}^2)(2.0\ \text{m})\sin 5° = 5.1\ \text{N·m}.$$

8.4 Resolve the 100 N force into components perpendicular to and parallel to the rod, as
$F_{par} = (100\ \text{N})\cos 57° = 54.5$ N, and
$F_{perp} = (100\ \text{N})\sin 57° = 83.9$ N.

Torque of $F_{par} = 0$ since its line of action passes through the pivot point. Torque of F_{perp} is
$\tau = (83.9\ \text{N})(2.00\ \text{m}) = 168$ N m, (CW).

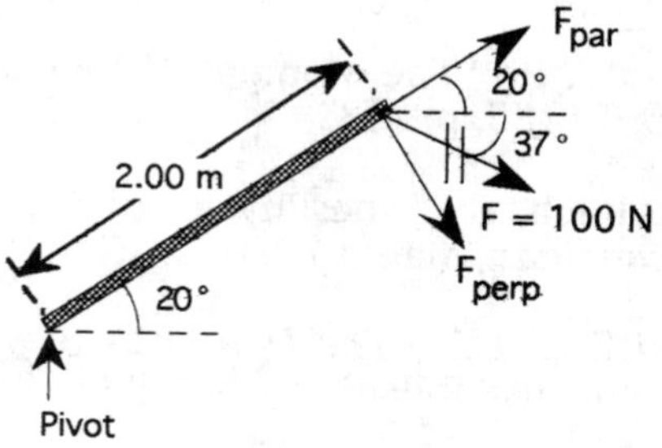

8.5 (a) We have $\tau_o = (2)(25)\cos 30° - (4)(10)\sin 20° = 29.6$ N m (CCW).
(b) We have $\tau_c = (2)(30)\sin 45° - (2)(10)\sin 20° = 35.6$ N m (CW).

8.6 $$y_{cg} = \frac{\Sigma m_i y_i}{\Sigma m_i}$$
$$= \frac{2.00\ \text{kg}(+3.00\ \text{m}) + 3.00\ \text{kg}(+2.50\ \text{m}) + 2.50\ \text{kg}(0) + 4.00\ \text{kg}(-0.50\ \text{m})}{2.00\ \text{kg} + 3.00\ \text{kg} + 2.50\ \text{kg} + 4.00\ \text{kg}}$$
$= 1.00$ m.

8.7 $$x_{cg} = \frac{\Sigma m_i x_i}{\Sigma m_i}$$
$$= \frac{16.0\ \text{kg}(0\ \text{m}) + 1.00\ \text{kg}(0.100\ \text{nm}\cos 53°) + 1.00\ \text{kg}(0.100\ \text{nm}\cos 53°)}{16.0\ \text{kg} + 1.00\ \text{kg} + 1.00\ \text{kg}}$$
$= 6.69 \times 10^{-3}$ nm.
$$y_{cg} = \frac{\Sigma m_i y_i}{\Sigma m_i}$$
$$= \frac{16\ \text{kg}(0\ \text{m}) + 1\ \text{kg}(0.100\ \text{nm}\sin 53°) + 1\ \text{kg}(-0.100\ \text{nm}\sin 53°)}{16\ \text{kg} + 1\ \text{kg} + 1\ \text{kg}}$$
$= 0$.

8.8 $$x_{cg} = \frac{\Sigma m_i x_i}{\Sigma m_i} = \frac{5(0) + 3(0) + 4(3) + 8(x)}{5 + 3 + 4 + 8}$$
yielding $8x + 12 = 0$, or $x = -1.5$ m.
$$y_{cg} = \frac{\Sigma m_i y_i}{\Sigma m_i} = \frac{5(0) + 3(4) + 4(0) + 8(y)}{5 + 3 + 4 + 8},$$
yielding $8y + 12 = 0$, or $y = -1.5$ m
Thus, the 8 kg mass should be placed at (-1.5 m,-1.5 m).

8.9 Start by breaking the object into two parts, a rectangle, A_1, 4 ft x 4 ft, with center of gravity (2ft,2ft) and a rectangle, A_2, 4 ft x 2 ft, with center of gravity (6 ft,1 ft) as shown in the diagram. The x coordinate of the center of gravity is given by

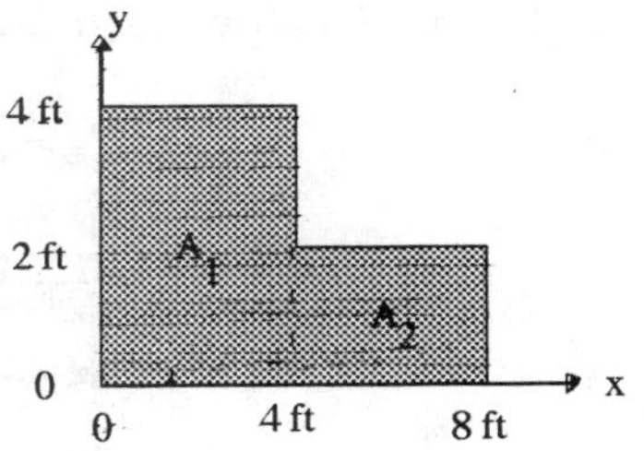

$$x_{cg} = \frac{(m_1x_1 + m_2x_2)}{(m_1 + m_2)} = \frac{(A_1\sigma x_1 + A_2\sigma x_2)}{(A_1\sigma + A_2\sigma)}$$

where σ is the mass per unit area for the plywood. Canceling this density and computing the areas, we have

$$x_{cg} = \frac{16.0 \text{ ft}^2(2.00 \text{ ft}) + 8.00 \text{ ft}^2(6.00 \text{ ft})}{16.0 \text{ ft}^2 + 8.00 \text{ ft}^2} = 3.33 \text{ ft}$$

Similarly,

$$y_{cg} = \frac{16.0 \text{ ft}^2(2.00 \text{ ft}) + 8.00 \text{ ft}^2(1.00 \text{ ft})}{16.0 \text{ ft}^2 + 8.00 \text{ ft}^2} = 3.33 \text{ ft} = 1.67 \text{ ft}$$

8.10 The fact that the meter stick balances alone at the 49.7 mark means that its center of gravity is located at this point and its entire mass may be considered to be located there. After the 50.0 gram mass is attached at the 10.0 cm mark, the center of gravity of the combination is located at the 39.2 mark since that is where the combination balances. Therefore, we have for the combination

$$x_{cg} = \frac{(m_1x_1 + m_2x_2)}{(m_1 + m_2)} = \frac{m_{stick}(49.7 \text{ cm}) + (50.0 \text{ g})(10.0 \text{ cm})}{m_{stick} + 50.0 \text{ g}}$$
$$= 39.2 \text{ cm},$$

which reduces to $49.7m_{stick} + 500 \text{ g} = 39.2m_{stick} + 1960\text{g}$

yielding $m_{stick} = 139$ g.

8.11 Total torque about the elbow gives

$-(0.330 \text{ m})(2.00 \text{ kg})(9.80 \text{ m/s}^2) + F_B\cos 75°(0.080 \text{ m}) = 0,$

or $F_B = 312$ N.

8.12 Taking torques about the left end of the scaffold, we have

$T_1(0) - (700 \text{ N})(1 \text{ m}) - (200 \text{ N})(1.50 \text{ m}) + T_2(3.00 \text{ m}) = 0.$

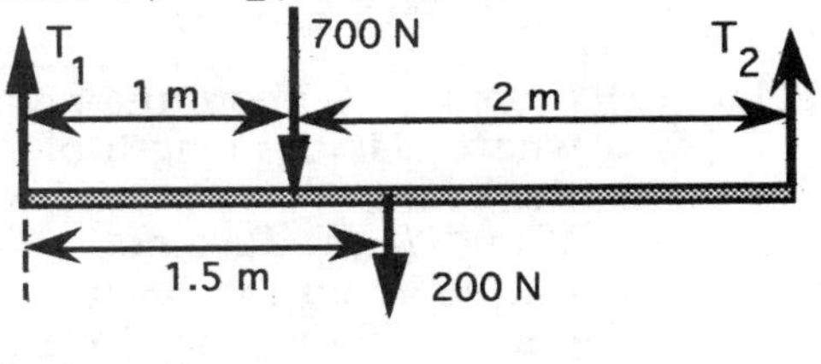

From which, $T_2 = 333$ N.

Then, from $\Sigma F_y = 0$, we have

$T_1 + T_2 - 700 \text{ N} - 200 \text{ N} = 0.$

Since $T_2 = 333$ N, we find

$T_1 = 567$ N.

8.13 Choosing the pivot point at the point O shown, $\Sigma\tau = 0$ becomes

$(50 \text{ N})(7.5 \text{ cm}) + T(0) - R(3.5 \text{ cm}) = 0.$

Thus, $R = 107$ N.

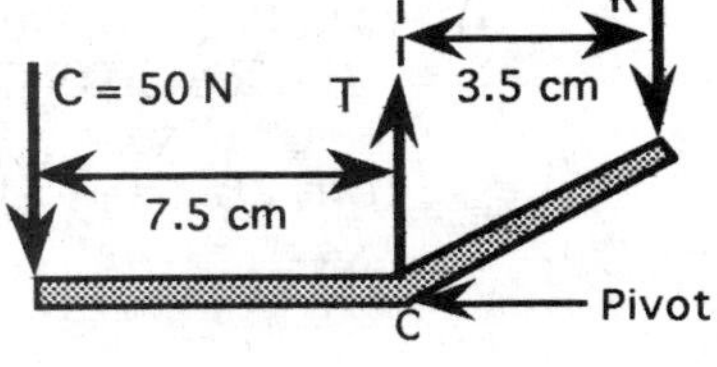

Now, apply $\Sigma F_y = 0$ to obtain

$-50 \text{ N} + T - 107 \text{ N} = 0$

and $T = 157$ N.

8.14 (a) See the diagram below:

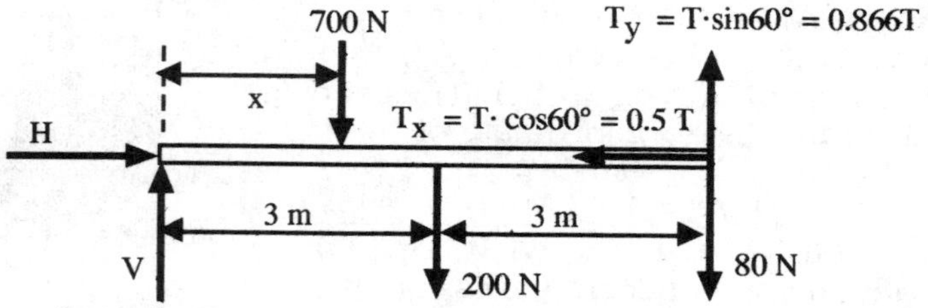

(b) If $x = 1$ m, then

$\Sigma\tau_{\text{left end}}$ = (-700 N)(1.00 m) - (200 N)(3.00 m) - (80.0 N)(6.00 m) + (0.866T)(6.00 m). Equating this to zero gives: $T = 343$ N.

From $\Sigma F_x = 0$, $H = 0.500\ T = 171$ N.

From $\Sigma F_y = 0$, $V = 980$ N - $0.866T = 683$ n.

(c) If $T = 900$ N

$\Sigma\tau_{\text{left end}}$ = (-700 N)(x) - (200 N)(3.00 m) - (80.0 N)(6.00 m) + (779.4 N)(6.00 m).

Equating this to zero and solving for x gives: $x = 5.14$ m.

8.15 We call the tension in the cord at the left end of the sign, T_1 and the tension in the cord near the middle of the sign, T_2, and we choose our pivot point at

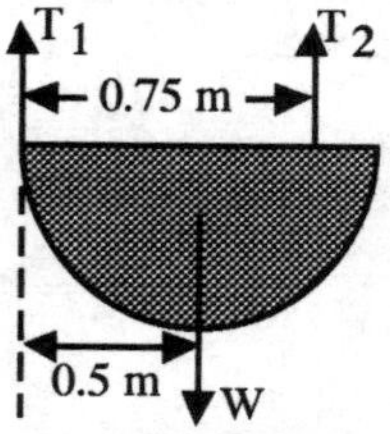

the point where T_1 is attached.

$\Sigma\tau_{\text{pivot}} = 0 = (-W)(0.5 \text{ m}) + T_2(0.75 \text{ m}) = 0$, so, $T_2 = \frac{2}{3} W$

From $\Sigma F_y = 0$, $T_1 + T_2 - W = 0$.

Substituting the expression for T_2 and solving, we find

$T_1 = \frac{1}{3} W$.

8.16 (a) From $\Sigma\tau = 0$ about the pivot shown, we have $(T\sin 30°)d - (200 \text{ N})d = 0$ where d is the length of the beam. The forces H, V, and T_x produce no torque about the pivot point. Solving for T, We find: $T = 400$ N.

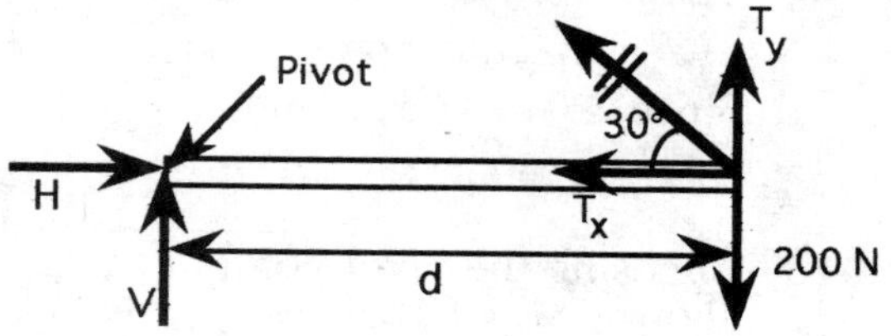

(b) From $\Sigma F_x = 0$, we have

$H - T\cos 30.0° = 0$.

$T = 400$ N, so $H = 346$ N (to right).

From $\Sigma F_y = 0$, $V + T\sin 30.0° - 200 \text{ N} = 0$, which yields $V = 0$.

8.17 (a) The free body diagram of the horizontal rod is shown to the right. Summing the torques about the left end of the rod yields

$-W_{rod}(3.00\text{ m}) - W_{sign}(4.00\text{ m}) + (T\sin 60°)(6.00\text{ m}) = 0,$

giving

$(0.866\ T)(6.00\text{ m})$
$= (100\text{ N})(3.00\text{ m}) + (500\text{ N})(4.00\text{ m}),$

or $T = 443$ N.

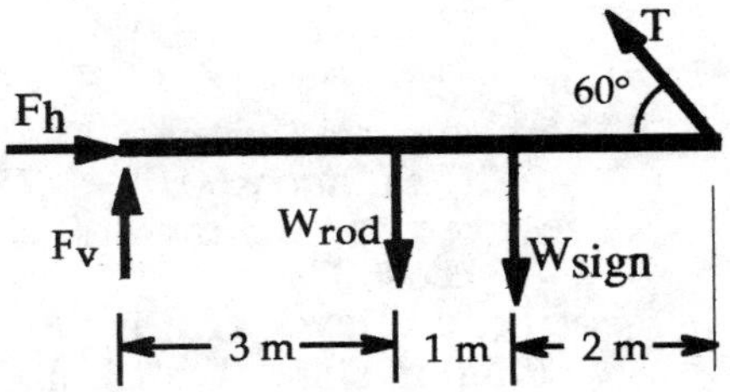

(b) Summing the force components in the horizontal direction yields

$F_h - T\cos 60° = 0$, or $F_h = 443 \cos 60° = 222$ N.

Summing force components in the vertical direction yields

$F_v + T\sin 60° - W_{rod} - W_{sign} = 0$, or $F_v = 216$ N

8.18

F_t = Tension force in Deltoid Muscle,

F_s = Force exerted on arm by shoulder joint

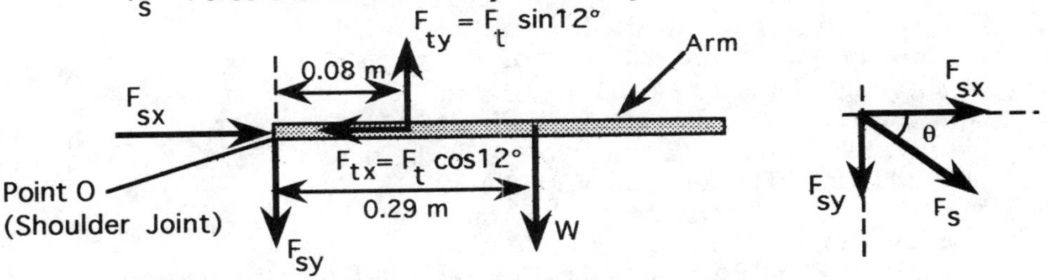

$\Sigma\tau_O = F_t\sin 12°(0.080\text{ m}) - (41.5\text{ N})(0.29\text{ m}) = 0.$

From which $F_t = 724$ N (Tension in deltoid muscle)

$\Sigma F_y = 0$ gives $\quad -F_{sy} + F_t\sin 12° - 41.5\text{ N} = 0$, yielding, $\quad F_{sy} = 109$ N.

$\Sigma F_x = 0$ gives $\quad F_{sx} = F_t\cos 12°$ and $F_{sx} = 708$ N.

Therefore, $\quad F_s = \sqrt{(F_{sx})^2 + (F_{sy})^2} = 716$ N,

and $\quad \tan\theta = \dfrac{F_{sy}}{F_{sx}} = 0.1539$, or $\quad \theta = 8.75°$.

8.19 We choose the pivot point at the left end, and use $\Sigma\tau = 0$.

$-(700\text{ N})(0.500\text{ m}) - (294\text{ N})(1.00\text{ m}) + (T_1\sin 40°)(2.00\text{ m}) = 0$, which yields

$T_1 = 501$ N.

Now use $\Sigma F_x = 0$.

$T_1\cos 40° - T_3 = 0.$

With $T_1 = 501$ N, this gives

$T_3 = 384$ N.

Finally, $\Sigma F_y = 0$ gives

$T_2 + T_1\sin 40° - 994\text{ N} = 0.$

From which, $T_2 = 672$ N.

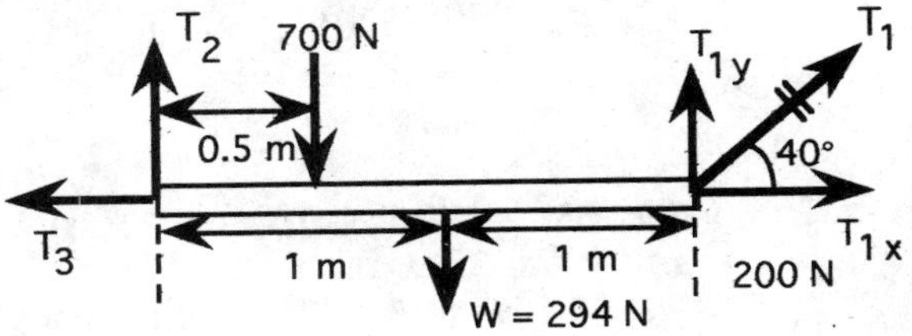

8.20 Use $\Sigma F_y = 0$: F_1 - 500 N - 800 N = 0,
or F_1 = 1300 N. (1)
Now, apply $\Sigma F_x = 0$: $f - F_2 = 0$, or $f = F_2$. (2)
The lever arm for the 500 N force is
(7.50 m)cos60.0° = 3.75 m
The lever arm for the 800 N force is
$d$cos60° = d/2 .
For F_2, the lever arm is
(15.0 m)sin60.0° = 13 m.

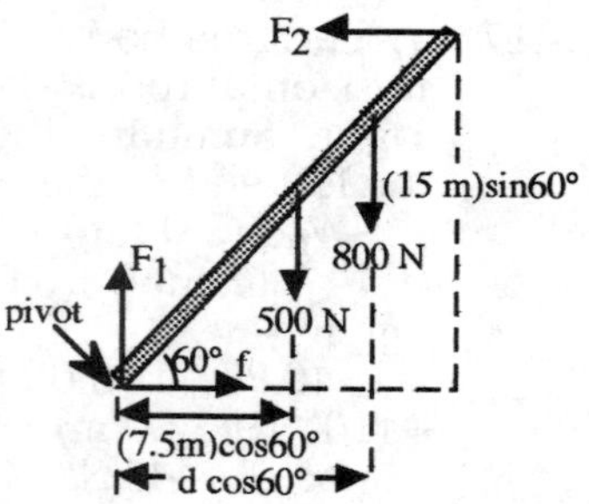

Using $\Sigma\tau = 0$ with pivot pt. at base of the ladder, -(500 N)(3.75 m) - (800 N)(d/2) + F_2(13.0 m) = 0 (3)
(a) When d = 4.0 m, Equation (3) gives: F_2 = 267 N
Equation (2) then gives f = 267 N, and F_1 = 1300 N from above.
(b) If d = 9.0 m: Equation (3) gives F_2 = 421 N,
Equation (2) yields f = 421 N,
and Equation (1) gives F_1 = 1300 N.
If the ladder is ready to slip, $\mu_s = f/F_1$ = (421 N)/1300 N = 0.324.

8.21 Use $\Sigma F_y = 0$: F_1 - 200 N - 800 N = 0.
Thus, F_1 = 1000 N.
The friction force, f, at the base of the ladder is $f = \mu_s F_1$ when the ladder is on the verge of slipping. Thus, f = 0.6(1000 N) = 600 N.
Now use $\Sigma F_x = 0$: $f - F_2 = 0$, or $F_2 = f$ = 600 N.
Finally, use $\Sigma\tau = 0$ with the pivot pt. at the base of the ladder. The lever arm for the 200 N force is (4.0 m)cos50°) = 2.57 m.
The lever arm for the 800 N force is
$d$cos50° = 0.643d, where d is the distance from the base of the ladder up to the position of the person. Finally, the lever arm for the force F_2 is (8 m) sin50° = 6.13 m. We have:
-(200 N)(2.57 m) - (800 N)(.643d) +(600 N)(6.13 m) = 0
giving, d = 6.2 m.

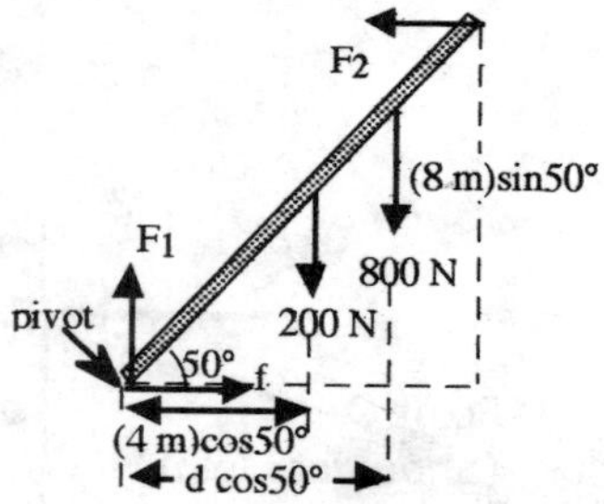

8.22 Observing that the cable is perpendicular to the boom and summing the torques about the lower end of the boom gives:

$$-(1200\text{ N})\left(\frac{L}{2}\cos 65°\right) + T\left(\frac{3L}{4}\right) - (2000\text{ N})(L\cos 65°) = 0$$

or T = 1465 N.

Then, from $\Sigma F_x = 0$,
$H = T\cos 25°$ = 1328 N (toward the right),
and from $\Sigma F_y = 0$,
V = 3200 N - $T\sin 25°$ = 2581 N (upward).

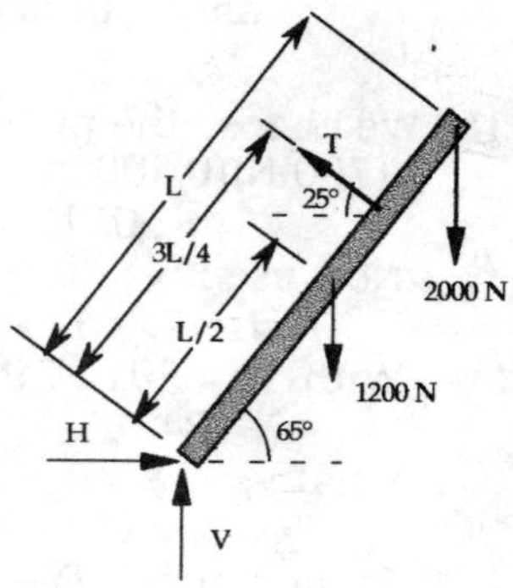

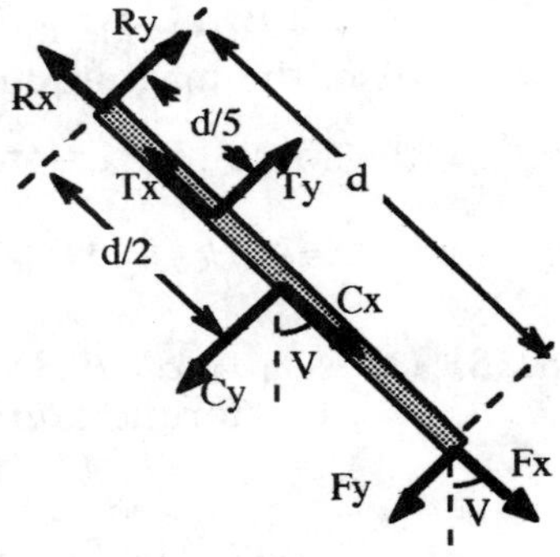

8.23 Let us first resolve all forces into components parallel to and perpendicular to the leg, as shown. Use $\Sigma\tau = 0$ about the pivot indicated.

$T_y(d/5) - C_y(d/2) - F_y(d) = 0$, where d is the length of the lower leg.

$C_y = C\sin V = (30.0\text{ N})\sin 40.0° = 19.3\text{ N}$, and

$F_y = F\sin V = (12.5\text{ N})\sin 40.0° = 8.03\text{ N}$.

Thus, $T_y = 88.5\text{ N}$, but $T_y = T\sin 25°$.

So, $T = 209\text{ N}$.

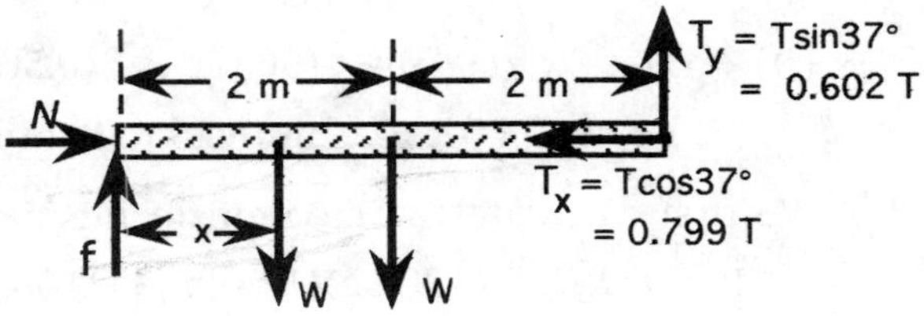

8.24 The free body diagram is shown. For a maximum value of x, the rod is on the verge of slipping, so

$f = \mu_k N = 0.50\ N$.

Now, use $\Sigma F_x = 0$

$N = T_x = T\cos 37°$, so

$N = 0.799\ T$.

Therefore, $f = 0.50\ N. = 0.399\ T$.

From $\Sigma F_y = 0$, $f + T_y - 2W = 0$,

or $0.399\ T + 0.602\ T = 2W$

which reduces to $T = 2W$.

Taking torques about the left end, we have

$-W\cdot x - W(2.0\text{ m}) + T(\sin 37°)(4.0\text{ m}) = 0$, which gives $x = 2.8\text{ m}$.

8.25 $I = \Sigma m_i r_i^2$

(a) First, apply the above equation about the x axis. We have,

$I_x = (3.00\text{ kg})(9.00\text{ m}^2) + (2.00\text{ kg})(9.00\text{ m}^2) + (2.00\text{ kg})(9.00\text{ m}^2) + (4.00\text{ kg})(9.00\text{ m}^2) = 99.0\text{ kgm}^2$.

(b) About the y axis, we have

$I_y = (3.00\text{kg})(4.00\text{m}^2) + (2.00\text{ kg})(4.00\text{ m}^2) + (2.00\text{ kg})(4.00\text{ m}^2) + (4.00\text{ kg})(4.00\text{ m}^2) = 44.0\text{ kgm}^2$.

(c) The distance, r, (from an axis through O and perpendicular to the page) out to each of the masses is found from the pythagorean theorem: $r = \sqrt{(2.00\text{ m})^2 + (3.00\text{ m})^2} = \sqrt{13.00\text{ m}^2}$,

and the moment of inertia is

$I_O = (3.00\text{ kg})(r^2) + (2.00\text{ kg})(r^2) + (2.00\text{ kg})(r^2) + (4.00\text{ kg})(r^2)$, or

$= (11.00\text{ kg})(13.00\text{ m}^2) = 143\text{ kg m}^2$.

8.26 We use $\tau = I\alpha$.

$\tau_x = I_x\alpha = (99.0\text{ kg m}^2)(1.50\text{ rad/s}^2) = 149\text{ N m}$

$\tau_y = I_y\alpha = (44.0\text{ kg m}^2)(1.50\text{ rad/s}^2) = 66.0\text{ N m}$

$\tau_O = I_O\alpha = (143\text{ kg m}^2)(1.50\text{ rad/s}^2) = 215\text{ N m}$

8.27 $\omega_O = 50\text{ rev/min} = 5.24\text{ rad/s}$

$$\alpha = \frac{\omega - \omega_O}{t} = \frac{0 - 5.24\text{ rad/s}}{6.00\text{ s}} = -0.873\text{ rad/s}^2$$

$\tau = I\alpha = (12.5 \text{ kg m}^2)(-0.873 \text{ rad/s}^2) = -10.9 \text{ N·m}$

Also, the magnitude of the torque is given by $fr = 10.9$ N·m, where f is the force of friction. Therefore, $f = \dfrac{10.9 \text{ N·m}}{0.50 \text{ m}} = 21.8$ N, and

$f = \mu_k N$ yields $\mu_k = \dfrac{f}{N} = \dfrac{21.8 \text{ N}}{70 \text{ N}} = 0.31.$

8.28 (a) $\tau_{net} = I\alpha = (6.8 \times 10^{-4} \text{ kg m}^2)(66 \text{ rad/s}^2) = 4.49 \times 10^{-2} \text{ kg m}^2.$

The torque exerted by the fish = Fr, so the net torque is

$\tau_{net} = Fr - 1.3 \text{ Nm} = 4.49 \times 10^{-2} \text{ kg m}^2.$

From which, $F = \dfrac{1.345 \text{ Nm}}{4.0 \times 10^{-2} \text{ m}} = 34$ N.

(b) $\theta = \omega_0 t + \frac{1}{2}\alpha t^2 = 0 + \frac{1}{2}(66 \text{ rad/s}^2)(0.50 \text{ s})^2 = 8.25$ rad, and

$s = r\theta = (4.0 \times 10^{-2} \text{ m})(8.25 \text{ rad}) = 0.33 \text{ m} = 33 \text{ cm}.$

8.29 We first calculate the moment of inertia as

$I = \frac{1}{2}MR^2 = \frac{1}{2}(150 \text{ kg})(1.50 \text{ m})^2 = 168.8 \text{ kg m}^2.$

Then we note that $\omega_f = 0.500$ rev/s = π rad/s, and calculate α as,

$\omega = \omega_0 + \alpha t$ or π rad/s = 0 + α (2.00 s). Thus, $\alpha = \pi/2 \text{ rad/s}^2.$

Then $\tau = I\alpha$ becomes $Fr = I\alpha$, or $F = \dfrac{I\alpha}{r} = \dfrac{(169 \text{ kg m}^2)(\pi/2 \text{ rad/s}^2)}{1.5 \text{ m}} = 177$ N.

8.30 The resultant torque is given by

$(120 \text{ N})(0.81 \text{ m}) - (100 \text{ N})(0.81 \text{ m}) = 16.2 \text{ N m}$

The moment of inertia is: $I = \frac{1}{2}mr^2 = \frac{1}{2}(2.1 \text{ kg})(0.81 \text{ m})^2 = 0.689 \text{ kg m}^2.$

Then, $\tau = I\alpha$ gives $\alpha = \dfrac{\tau}{I} = \dfrac{16.2 \text{ Nm}}{0.689 \text{ kg m}^2} = 24 \text{ rad/s}^2.$

8.31 The moment of inertia of the pulley is

$I = \frac{1}{2}MR^2 = \frac{1}{2}(5.00 \text{ kg})(0.600 \text{ m})^2 = 0.900 \text{ kg m}^2.$

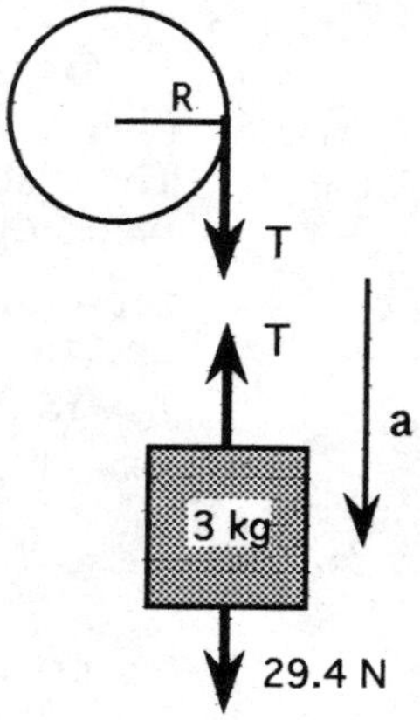

First we apply Newton's second law to the falling bucket of mass 3.00 kg (weight 29.4 N). We have

$29.4 \text{ N} - T = (3.00 \text{ kg})a.$ (1)

Now apply $\tau = I\alpha$ to the pulley. We have

$TR = I\alpha = I\left(\dfrac{a}{R}\right).$

Thus, $T = \dfrac{I\ a}{R^2} = \dfrac{0.900 \text{ kg m}^2}{(.600 \text{ m})^2}\ a.$ (2)

We can solve (1) and (2) simultaneously to find a. We find,

(a) $a = 5.35 \text{ m/s}^2$ downward.

(b) To find how far it drops, we use $y = v_0 t + \frac{1}{2}at^2.$

$y = 0 + \frac{1}{2}(5.35 \text{ m/s}^2)(4.00 \text{ s})^2 = 42.8 \text{ m}$

(c) $\alpha = \frac{a}{R} = \frac{5.35\ \text{m/s}^2}{0.600\ \text{m}} = 8.91\ \text{rad/s}^2.$

8.32 The initial angular velocity of the wheels is zero, and the final angular velocity is $\omega_f = \frac{v}{r} = \frac{50.0\ \text{m/s}}{1.25\ \text{m}} = 40.0\ \text{rad/s}.$

Thus, $\alpha = \frac{\omega_f - \omega_0}{t} = \frac{40.0\ \text{rad/s} - 0}{0.48\ \text{s}} = 83.3\ \text{rad/s}^2.$

$\tau_{\text{center of a wheel}} = fr$, so $\tau = I\alpha$ gives

$$f = \frac{I\alpha}{r} = \frac{(110\ \text{kg m}^2)(83.3\ \text{rad/s}^2)}{1.25\ \text{m}} = 7.33 \times 10^3\ \text{N, and}$$

$$\mu_k = \frac{f}{N} = \frac{7.33 \times 10^3\ \text{N}}{1.40 \times 10^4\ \text{N}} = 0.524.$$

8.33 The moment of inertia of the spool is:

$$I = \frac{1}{2}Mr^2 = \frac{1}{2}(0.500\ \text{kg})(0.500\ \text{m})^2$$
$$= 6.25 \times 10^{-2}\ \text{kg m}^2.$$

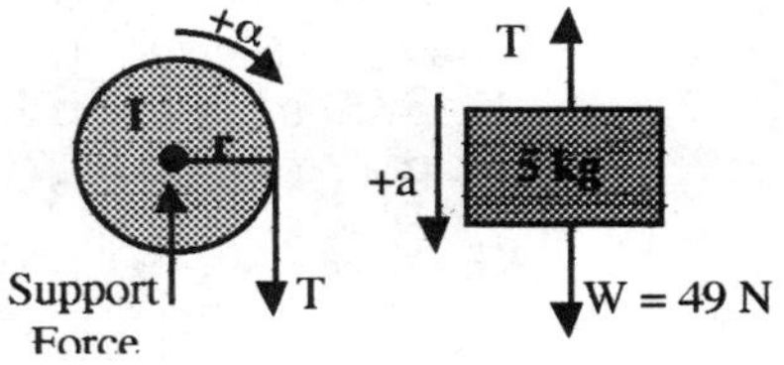

Applying Newton's second law to the hanging mass, we obtain (taking down as positive),

$$\Sigma F_y = 49\ \text{N} - T = (5.00\ \text{kg})a. \qquad (1)$$

Applying Newton's second law to the rotating spool gives

$$\Sigma\tau_{\text{center}} = Tr = I\alpha, \text{ or } T = \frac{I\alpha}{r} = \frac{6.25 \times 10^{-2}\ \text{kg m}^2}{0.500\ \text{m}}\alpha = (0.125\ \text{kg m})\alpha \quad (2)$$

Since the string does not slip on the spool, $a = r\alpha$, and equation (2) becomes, $T = (0.125\ \text{kg m})(\frac{a}{0.500\ \text{m}}) = (0.25\ \text{kg})a.$

Therefore, equation (1), yields

$$49\ \text{N} - (0.25\ \text{kg})a = (5.00\ \text{kg})a, \text{ or } \quad a = \frac{49\ \text{N}}{5.25\ \text{kg}} = 9.33\ \text{m/s}^2.$$

When the mass has dropped 4.00 meters, the angle through which the spool has rotated is $\theta = \frac{s}{r} = \frac{4.00\ \text{m}}{0.500\ \text{m}} = 8.0\ \text{rad}$

and the angular acceleration is $\alpha = \frac{a}{r} = \frac{9.33\ \text{m/s}^2}{0.500\ \text{m}} = 18.7\ \text{rad/s}^2$

Therefore, $\omega^2 = \omega_0^2 + 2\alpha\theta = 0 + 2(18.7\ \text{rad/s}^2)(8.0\ \text{rad})$, yielding $\omega = 17.3\ \text{rad/s}$.

8.34 (a) Newton's second law for the cylinder is

$$mg - T = ma. \qquad (1)$$

(b) $\tau = I\alpha$ becomes: $Tr = \frac{1}{2}mr^2\alpha. \qquad (2)$

(c) Solve (2) for T and substitute $\alpha = a/r$. We find:

$$T = \frac{mr^2a}{2r^2} = \frac{ma}{2}. \qquad (3)$$

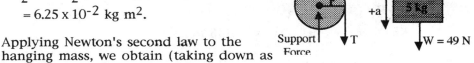

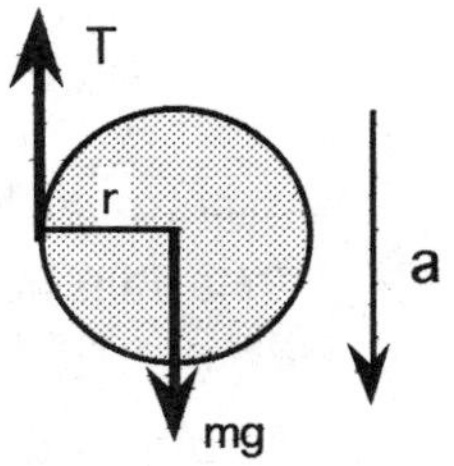

Finally, substitute (3) into (1) to find,

$$mg - \frac{ma}{2} = ma \text{ which gives} \qquad a = \frac{2}{3}g.$$

8.35 (a) $KE_{trans} = \frac{1}{2} mv^2 = \frac{1}{2}(10.0 \text{ kg})(10.0 \text{ m/s})^2 = 500 \text{ J}.$

(b) $KE_{rot} = \frac{1}{2} I\omega^2 = \frac{1}{2}\left(\frac{1}{2} mr^2\right)\left(\frac{v^2}{r^2}\right) = \frac{1}{4}(10.0 \text{ kg})(10.0 \text{ m/s})^2 = 250 \text{ J}.$

(c) $KE_{total} = KE_{trans} + KE_{rot} = 750 \text{ J}.$

8.36 Using $W = \Delta KE = KE_f - KE_i = \frac{1}{2} I\omega^2 - 0,$

we get $I = \frac{2W}{\omega^2} = \frac{2(3000 \text{ J})}{(200 \text{ rad/s})^2} = 0.150 \text{ kg m}^2.$

8.37 The moment of inertia of the cylinder is

$I = \frac{1}{2} mr^2 = \frac{1}{2}(81.6 \text{ kg})(1.50 \text{ m})^2 = 91.8 \text{ kg m}^2$, and

the angular acceleration of the merry-go-round is found as

$\alpha = \tau/I = (F\,r)/I = (50.0 \text{ N})(1.50 \text{ m})/(91.8 \text{ kg m}^2) = 0.817 \text{ rad/s}^2.$

At $t = 3.00$ s, we find the angular velocity, $\omega = \omega_0 + \alpha t$, to be

$\omega = 0 + (0.817 \text{ rad/s}^2)(3.00 \text{ s}) = 2.45 \text{ rad/s}$, and

$KE = \frac{1}{2} I\omega^2 = \frac{1}{2}(91.8 \text{ kg m}^2)(2.45 \text{ rad/s})^2 = 276 \text{ J}.$

8.38 (a) The angular velocity of the flywheel is 5000 rev/min = 524 rad/s, and its moment of inertia is,

$I = \frac{1}{2} mr^2 = \frac{1}{2}(500 \text{ kg})(2.00 \text{ m})^2 = 10^3 \text{ kg m}^2.$

Therefore, the stored energy is

$KE = \frac{1}{2} I\omega^2 = \frac{1}{2}(10^3 \text{ kg m}^2)(524 \text{ rad/s})^2 = 1.37 \times 10^8 \text{ J}.$

(b) A 10.0 hp motor is equivalent to 7460 W. Therefore, if energy is used at the rate of 7460 J/s, the stored energy will last for

$t = E/P = 1.37 \times 10^8 \text{ J}/7.46 \times 10^3 \text{ J/s} = 1.84 \times 10^4 \text{ s} = 5.11 \text{ h}.$

8.39 Work done $= Fs = (5.57 \text{ N})(0.80 \text{ m}) = 4.46 \text{ J}$, and

Work $= \Delta KE = \frac{1}{2} I\omega_f^2 - \frac{1}{2} I\omega_0^2 = \frac{1}{2} I\omega_f^2.$ ($\omega_0 = 0$ since top starts from rest.)

Thus, $4.46 \text{ J} = \frac{1}{2}(4.00 \times 10^{-4} \text{ kg m}^2)\omega_f^2$ and from this, $\omega_f = 149$ rad/s.

8.40 We will use conservation of energy in the form

$$\frac{1}{2} Mv_i^2 + \frac{1}{2} I\omega_i^2 + Mgy_i = \frac{1}{2} Mv_f^2 + \frac{1}{2} I\omega_f^2 + Mgy_f$$

$$0 + 0 + Mg(6.0 \text{ m})\sin 37^\circ = \frac{1}{2} M(0.20 \text{ m})^2\omega_f^2 + \left(\frac{1}{2}\right)\frac{2}{5} M(0.20)^2\omega_f^2 + 0$$

where we have used $v_f = r\omega_f$ and $I = \frac{2}{5} MR^2$.

The mass cancels from the equation, and we find the angular velocity to be $\omega_f = 36$ rad/s.

8.41 Using conservation of energy

$$\frac{1}{2} Mv_f^2 + \frac{1}{2} I\omega_f^2 + 0 = 0 + Mgy_i$$

where the zero of potential energy has been taken at the final position of the hanging mass.

Since $I = \frac{1}{2}Mr^2 = \frac{1}{2}(0.500\text{ kg})(0.500)^2 = 6.25 \times 10^{-2}\text{ kg m}^2$

and $v_f = r\,\omega_f = (0.500\text{ m})\omega_f$

this becomes

$$\frac{1}{2}(5.00\text{ kg})(0.250\text{ m}^2)\omega_f^2 + \frac{1}{2}(6.25 \times 10^{-2}\text{ kg m}^2)\omega_f^2$$

$$= (5.00\text{ kg})(9.80\text{ m/s}^2)(4.00\text{ m})$$

which yields $(0.656\text{ kg m}^2)\omega_f^2 = 196\text{ J}$.

Solving for ω_f, we get $\omega_f = 17.3\text{ rad/s}$

8.42 (a) The angular velocity of the earth on its axis is $\omega = 2\pi\text{ rad/day} = 7.27 \times 10^{-5}\text{ rad/s}$. We assume the earth is a uniform sphere of radius R and calculate its moment of inertia as

$$I = \frac{2}{5}mR^2 = \frac{2}{5}(5.98 \times 10^{24}\text{ kg})(6.38 \times 10^6\text{ m})^2 = 9.74 \times 10^{37}\text{ kg m}^2.$$

The angular momentum is found as

$$L = I\omega = (9.74 \times 10^{37}\text{ kg m}^2)(7.27 \times 10^{-5}\text{ rad/s}) = 7.08 \times 10^{33}\text{ J s}.$$

(b) For the orbiting earth, $\omega = 2\pi\text{ rad/yr} = 1.99 \times 10^{-7}\text{ rad/s}$, and the angular momentum is given by

$$L = I\omega = mr^2\omega = (5.98 \times 10^{24}\text{ kg})(1.49 \times 10^{11}\text{ m})^2(1.99 \times 10^{-7}\text{ rad/s}),$$

$$L = 2.66 \times 10^{40}\text{ J s}.$$

8.43 Since both particles move around the axis in the same direction, their contributions to the total angular momentum and the total angular momentum of the system is:

$$L_{total} = L_1 + L_2 = I_1\omega_1 + I_2\omega_2 = (m_1r_1^2)\omega_1 + (m_2r_2^2)\omega_2.$$

Also, $\omega_1 = \omega_2 = \frac{v}{r} = \frac{5.00\text{ m/s}}{0.500\text{ m}} = 10.0\text{ rad/s}$.

Thus,

$$L_{total} = (4.00\text{ kg})(0.500\text{ m})^2(10.0\text{ rad/s}) + (3.00\text{ kg})(0.500\text{ m})^2(10.0\text{ rad/s})$$

or $L_{total} = 17.5\text{ kg m}^2\text{/s} = 17.5\text{ J s}$ (counterclockwise)

8.44 Using conservation of angular momentum, we have

$L_{apogee} = L_{perihelion}$, or $(mr_a^2)\omega_a = (mr_p^2)\omega_p$. Thus,

$$(mr_a^2)\frac{v_a}{r_a} = (mr_p^2)\frac{v_p}{r_p}, \text{ giving}$$

$r_av_a = r_pv_p$, or $v_a = \frac{r_p}{r_a}v_p = \frac{0.59\text{ AU}}{35\text{ AU}}(54\text{ km/s}) = 0.91\text{ km/s}$.

8.45 The initial moment of inertia of the system is: $I_i = \Sigma m_ir_i^2 = (4M)(1\text{ m})^2$. The moment of inertia of the system after the spokes are shortened is

$$I_f = \Sigma m_fr_f^2 = (4M)(0.50\text{ m})^2.$$

We conserve angular momentum as:

$$\omega_f = \frac{I_i}{I_f}\omega_i = (4)(2.0\text{ rev/s}) = 8.0\text{ rev/s}.$$

8.46 Let M and m be the mass of the cylinder and putty, respectively, and let R be the radius of the cylinder. Then the total angular momentum before the putty hits the cylinder is

$$L_{before} = I_0\omega_0 = \frac{MR^2}{2}\omega_0$$

$$= \frac{(10.0\ \text{kg})(1.00\ \text{m})^2(7.00\ \text{rad/s})}{2} = 35.00\ \text{kg m}^2/\text{s}.$$

After the putty hits the cylinder, we have

$$L_{after} = I_f\omega = (I_0 + mr^2)\omega = \left(\frac{MR^2}{2} + mr^2\right)\omega$$

$$= \left(\frac{(10.0\ \text{kg})(1.00\ \text{m})^2}{2} + (0.250\ \text{kg})(.900\ \text{m})^2\right)\omega = (5.20\ \text{kg m}^2)(\omega).$$

Using $L_{before} = L_{after}$, we have $(5.20\ \text{kg m}^2)\omega = 35.00\ \text{kg m}^2/\text{s}$, so $\omega = 6.73$ rad/s.

8.47 The total angular momentum is given by

$$I_{total} = I_{weights} + I_{student} = 2(mr^2) + (3.0\ \text{kg m}^2)$$

Before: $r = 1$ m. Thus, $I_i = 2(3.0\ \text{kg})(1.0\ \text{m})^2 + (3.0\ \text{kg m}^2) = 9.0\ \text{kg m}^2$.

After: $r = 0.30$ m. Thus, $I_f = 2(3.0\ \text{kg})(0.30\ \text{m})^2 + (3.0\ \text{kg m}^2) = 3.54\ \text{kg m}^2$.

We now use conservation of angular momentum $I_f\omega_f = I_i\omega_i$, or

(a) $\omega_f = \frac{I_i}{I_f}\omega_i = \frac{9}{3.54}(0.75\ \text{rad/s}) = 1.9$ rad/s.

(b) $KE_i = \frac{1}{2}I_i\omega_i^2 = \frac{1}{2}(9.0\ \text{kg m}^2)(0.75\ \text{rad/s})^2 = 2.5$ J,

$KE_f = \frac{1}{2}I_f\omega_f^2 = \frac{1}{2}(3.54\ \text{kg m}^2)(1.91\ \text{rad/s})^2 = 6.4$ J.

8.48 $I_0 = mr_0^2 = (0.120\ \text{kg})(0.400\ \text{m})^2 = 1.92 \times 10^{-2}\ \text{kg m}^2$

$r_f = r_0 - 15.0\ \text{cm} = 40.0\ \text{cm} - 15.0\ \text{cm} = 0.25$ m. Thus,

$I_f = mr_f^2 = (0.120\ \text{kg})(0.25\ \text{m})^2 = 7.50 \times 10^{-3}\ \text{kg m}^2$, and

$\omega_0 = \frac{v_0}{r_0} = \frac{0.800\ \text{m/s}}{0.400\ \text{m}} = 2.00$ rad/s. Now, use conservation of angular momentum: $\omega_f = \frac{I_0}{I_f}\omega_0 = \frac{1.92 \times 10^{-2}\ \text{kg m}^2}{7.50 \times 10^{-3}\ \text{kg m}^2}(2.00\ \text{rad/s}) = 5.12$ rad/s.

The work done $= \Delta KE = \frac{1}{2}I_f\omega_f^2 - \frac{1}{2}I_0\omega_0^2$. Substituting the appropriate values found earlier, we have: work done $= 5.99 \times 10^{-2}$ J.

8.49 (a) The moment of inertia of the system is given by

$$I = I_{man} + I_{wheel} = mr^2 + \frac{1}{2}MR^2 = (80\ \text{kg})r^2 + \frac{1}{2}(25\ \text{kg})(2.0\ \text{m})^2.$$

When the man is at a distance of $r = 2.0$ m from the axis, the equation above gives $I_i = 370\ \text{kg m}^2$, and when the man moves to a point 1.0 m from the center ($r = 1.0$ m), the moment of inertia becomes,

$I_f = 130\ \text{kg m}^2$. The initial angular velocity of the system is $\omega_i = 0.20$ rev/s $= 1.26$ rad/s, and we find the final angular velocity via conservation of angular momentum, as

$$\omega_f = \frac{I_i}{I_f}\,\omega_i = \frac{370}{130}\,(1.26 \text{ rad/s}) = 3.6 \text{ rad/s}.$$

(b) The change in kinetic energy is $KE_f - KE_i = \frac{1}{2} I_f \omega_f^2 - \frac{1}{2} I_i \omega_i^2$, or

$$\Delta KE = \frac{1}{2}(130 \text{ kg m}^2)(3.58 \text{ rad/s})^2 - \frac{1}{2}(370 \text{ kg m}^2)(1.26 \text{ rad/s})^2 = 540 \text{ J}.$$

This difference results from work done by the man on the system as he walks inward.

8.50 (a) From conservation of angular momentum: $(I_1 + I_2)\omega = I_1\omega_0$, or

$$\omega = \frac{I_1}{I_1 + I_2}\,\omega_0.$$

(b) $K_f = \frac{1}{2}(I_1 + I_2)\omega^2$, and $\quad K_i = \frac{1}{2} I_1 \omega_0^2$,

so $\dfrac{K_f}{K_i}$ = (after some algebra) = $\dfrac{I_1}{I_1 + I_2}$ which is less than 1.

8.51 (a) To determine M, we use the fact that the total vertical force must be zero, so $19.6 - (0.1)(9.80) - (0.700)(9.80) - M(9.80) = 0$, and $M = 1.20$ kg.

(b) To determine where it should be placed, we use the fact that the total torque must be zero. Choosing the zero end of the stick as the pivot point, we have

$$(-0.700 \text{ kg})(9.80 \text{ m/s}^2)(0.0500 \text{ m}) + (19.6 \text{ N})(0.400 \text{ m}) - (0.100 \text{ kg})(9.80 \text{ m/s}^2)(0.500 \text{ m}) - (1.20 \text{ kg})(9.80 \text{ m/s}^2)d = 0.$$

Thus, $d = 0.596$ m from the zero end, or M should be hung at the 59.6 cm mark.

8.52 (a) $KE = \frac{1}{2} I\omega^2 = \frac{1}{2}\frac{(I\omega)^2}{I} = \frac{1}{2}\frac{L^2}{I}$

8.53 The free body diagram is shown at the right.

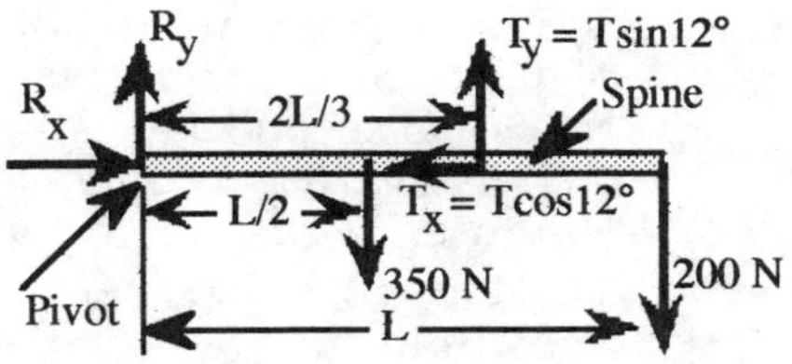

$\Sigma\tau = 0$, yields

$$-\frac{L}{2}(350 \text{ N}) + (T\sin 12°)\left(\frac{2L}{3}\right) - (200 \text{ N})L = 0.$$

From which, $T = 2.70 \times 10^3$ N.

Compression force along spine = R_x.

$\Sigma F_x = 0$, which gives $R_x = T_x = T\cos 12° = 2.65 \times 10^3$ N.

8.54 (a) From Newton's second law, we have $mg\sin 37° - T = ma$, which gives

$$(12.0 \text{ kg})(9.80 \text{ m/s}^2)\sin 37° - T = (12.0 \text{ kg})(2.00 \text{ m/s}^2),$$

or $T = 46.8$ N.

(b) The angular acceleration of the wheel is:

$$\alpha = \frac{a}{r} = \frac{2.00 \text{ m/s}^2}{0.100 \text{ m}} = 20.00 \text{ rad/s}^2.$$ From $\tau = I\alpha$, we have:

$$I = \frac{\tau}{\alpha} = \frac{Tr}{\alpha} = \frac{(46.8 \text{ N})(0.100 \text{ m})}{20.00 \text{ rad/s}} = 0.234 \text{ kg m}^2.$$

(c) $\omega = \omega_0 + \alpha t$ becomes: $\omega = 0 + (20.00 \text{ rad/s}^2)(2.00 \text{ s}) = 40.0$ rad/s.

8.55 Since the ladder is about to slip,
$f = (f_s)_{max} = \mu_s N$ at each contact point.
Because the ladder is still (barely) in equilibrium: $\Sigma F_x = 0$, which gives

$f_1 - N_2 = 0$, or $N_2 = 0.500 N_1$ (1)

$\Sigma F_y = 0$ becomes

$N_1 - W + f_2 = 0$, or $N_1 + 0.500 N_2 = W$.

Using (1) from above, this result reduces to

$N_1 = 0.8\ W$ (2)

Then (1) becomes $N_2 = 0.4\ W$ (3)

Summing torques about the lower end gives

$$-W\frac{L}{2}\cos\theta + N_2 L\sin\theta + f_2 L\cos\theta = 0,$$

or, using (2) and (3)

$$-W\frac{L}{2}\cos\theta + (0.4W)L\sin\theta + 0.500(0.4\ W)L\cos\theta = 0,$$

This can be written as

$-0.3\cos\theta + 0.4\sin\theta = 0$, or $\tan\theta = 0.75$ and $\theta = 36.9°$.

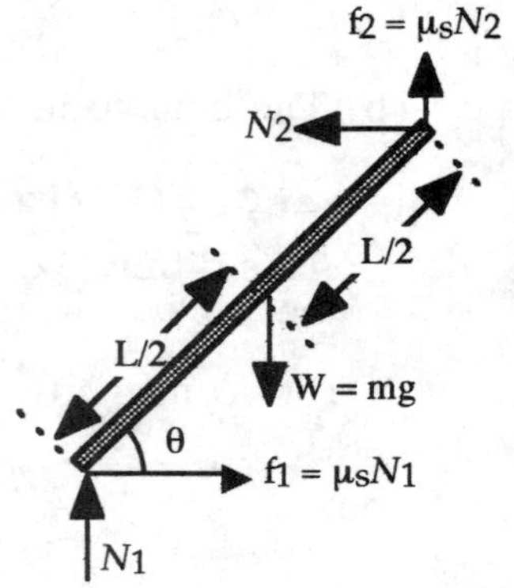

8.56 Use the lower left hand corner as the pivot point, and apply $\Sigma\tau = 0$.

$$-(10.0\text{ N})(.150\text{ m}) - (T_1\cos 50°)(.150\text{ m}) + (T_1\sin 50°)(0.30\text{ m}) = 0$$

Which gives, $T_1 = 11.2$ N.

Now use $\Sigma F_x = 0$:

$-F + (11.2)\cos 50° = 0$, and $F = 7.23$ N.

Finally, $\Sigma F_y = 0$ yields

$T_2 - 10.0\text{ N} + (11.2\text{ N})\sin 50° = 0$

so, $T_2 = 1.39$ N.

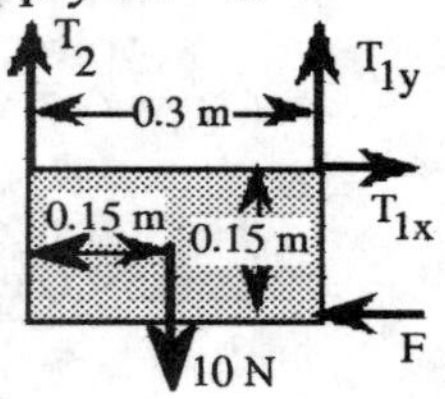

8.57 The forces on a rolling object on an incline of slope angle θ are the force of friction, f, the normal force, N, and its weight, mg. We apply Newton's second law with the x axis along the plane, to find,

$mg\sin\theta - f = ma$. (1)

Now use, $\tau = I\alpha$, or $fr = I\alpha = I(a/r)$.

Therefore, $f = (I/r^2)a$. (2)

Substitute into (1) for the frictional force f from (2) and solve the resulting equation for a.

$$a = \frac{g\sin\theta}{\left(1 + \frac{I}{mr^2}\right)}.$$

This is the linear acceleration of the center of mass of the rolling object. For a solid sphere, $I = \frac{2}{5}mr^2$ or $(I/mr^2) = \frac{2}{5}$. From this, we see that $a = g\sin\theta/1.4$.

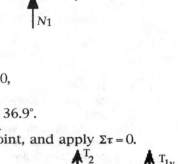

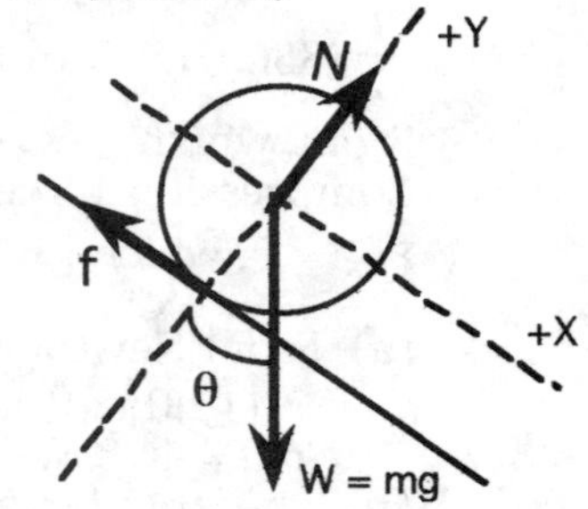

Using the same approach for a solid cylinder, $\frac{I}{mr^2} = \frac{1}{2}$, and $a = g\sin\theta/1.5$

Finally, for a hollow ring, $(I/mr^2) = 1$, and $a = g\sin\theta/2$.

Thus, we find $a_{sphere} > a_{cylinder} > a_{ring}$, so the sphere wins and the ring comes in last.

8.58 Since no horizontal forces act on the child-boat system, the center of gravity of this system remains stationary as the child moves in the boat.

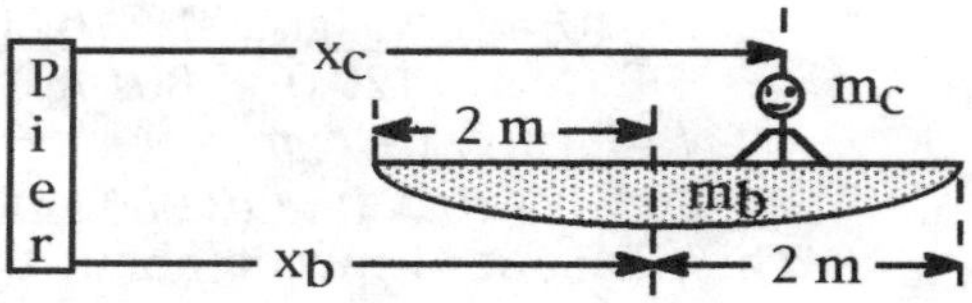

Thus $\dfrac{(m_c x_c + m_b x_b)}{(m_c + m_b)} =$ constant, and since the masses do not change $m_c x_c + m_b x_b$ = constant.

We are given: $m_c = 40.0$ kg $m_b = 70.0$ kg . Initially, $x_c = 3.00$ m and $x_b = 5.00$ m.

Therefore, at any time

$(40.0 \text{ kg})x_c + (70.0 \text{ kg})x_b = (40.0 \text{ kg})(3.00 \text{ m}) + (70.0 \text{ kg})(5.00 \text{ m})$
$= 470 \text{ kg m}$ (1)

When the child reaches the right end of the boat, $x_b = x_c - 2.00$ m.

Thus, equation (1) gives $40.0x_c + 70.0(x_c - 2.00 \text{ m}) = 470$ m, which yields $x_c = 5.55$ m. The maximum distance from the pier that the child can reach is therefore $x_{total} = x_c + 1.00 \text{ m} = 6.55$ m. This leaves him 0.45 m from the turtle.

8.59 (a) and (b)

First, we write down the second law for the 2.0 kg mass.

$T_1 - 19.6 \text{ N} = (2.0 \text{ kg})a.$ (1)

Now, we write the second law for the 5.0 kg mass.

$49 \text{ N} - T_2 = (5.0 \text{ kg})a.$ (2)

Finally, $\tau = I\alpha$ for the pulley becomes

$(T_2 - T_1)(0.50 \text{ m}) = (5.0 \text{ kg m}^2)(a/0.5 \text{ m})$

or $T_2 - T_1 = (20 \text{ kg})a.$ (3)

Equations (1), (2), and (3) can be solved simultaneously to give

$a = 1.1 \text{ m/s}^2$, $T_1 = 22$ N, and $T_2 = 44$ N.

8.60 (a) and (b)

First, we write down Newton's second law for the 3 kg mass.

$T_2 = (3.00 \text{ kg})a.$ (1)

The second law for the 4.00 kg mass is

$39.2 \text{ N} - T_1 = (4.00 \text{ kg})a.$ (2)

Now apply $\tau = I\alpha$ to the pulley (axis of rotation at its center)

$(T_1 - T_2)r = (0.500 \text{ kg m}^2)(a/r)$, or

$T_1 - T_2 = (5.56 \text{ kg})a.$ (3)

Equations (1), (2) and (3) can be solved simultaneously to give:

$a = 3.12 \text{ m/s}^2$, $T_1 = 26.7$ N, and $T_2 = 9.36$ N.

8.61 (a) $\tau = rF = (30.0 \text{ m})(0.800 \text{ N}) = 24.0 \text{ N m}$

(b) $\alpha = \dfrac{\tau}{I} = \dfrac{rF}{mr^2} = \dfrac{24.0}{(0.75)(30.0)^2} = 0.0356 \text{ rad/s}^2$

(c) $a_T = \alpha r = (0.0356)(30.0) = 1.07 \text{ m/s}^2$

8.62 When they touch, the center of mass is distant from the center of the larger puck by

$$y = \frac{(0 + 80.0\ g(4.00 + 6.00)cm)}{(120.0 + 80.0)g} = 4.00\ cm$$

(a) $L = r_1 m_1 v_1 + r_2 m_2 v_2$

$= 0 + (0.060\ m)(0.080\ kg)(1.50\ m/s) = 7.20 \times 10^{-3}\ kg\ m^2/s$

The moment of inertia about the center of mass is

$$I = \frac{1}{2}m_1 r_1^2 + m_1 d_1^2 + \frac{1}{2}m_2 r_2^2 + m_2 d_2^2$$

$$I = \frac{1}{2}(0.12\ kg)(0.06\ m)^2 + (0.12\ kg)(0.04\ m)^2$$

$$+ \frac{1}{2}(0.08\ kg)(0.04\ m)^2 + (0.08\ kg)(0.06\ m)^2 = 7.6 \times 10^{-4}\ kg\ m^2$$

(b) Angular momentum is conserved:

$$\omega = \frac{L}{I} = \frac{7.20 \times 10^{-3}\ kg\ m^2/s}{7.6 \times 10^{-4}\ kg\ m^2} = 9.47\ rad/s$$

8.63 (a) $L = 2(5.0\ m)(75.0\ kg)(5.00\ m/s) = 3750\ kg\ m^2/s$

(b) $KE_1 = 2(\frac{1}{2})(75.0\ kg)(5.00\ m/s)^2 = 1.88\ kJ$

(c) Angular momentum is conserved $L = 3750\ kg\ m^2/s$

(d) By conservation of angular momentum,

$3750 = 2(2.5)(75.0)(v)$

$v = 10.0\ m/s$

(e) $KE_2 = 2(\frac{1}{2})(75.0\ kg)(10.00\ m/s)^2 = 7500\ J$

(f) $W = K_2 - K_1 = 5.62\ kJ$

8.64 (a) $L_1 = 2(\frac{d}{2})(M)(v) = dMv$

(b) $KE = 2(\frac{1}{2})Mv^2 = Mv^2$

(c) $L_2 = L_1 = dMv$

(d) $L_2 = 2(\frac{d}{4})(M)(v_2)$

so, $v_2 = 2v$

(e) $KE_2 = 2(\frac{1}{2}Mv_2^2) = Mv_2^2 = 4Mv^2$

(f) $W = KE_2 - KE_2 = 3Mv^2$

8.65 Using the fact that the scaffold is in translational equilibrium, we have

$\Sigma F_y = T_L - 750\ N - 345\ N - 500\ N - 1000\ N + T_R = 0$, or

$T_L + T_R = 2595\ N$ (1)

where T_L and T_R are the tensions in the left and right cables, respectively. Since the scaffold is also in rotational equilibrium, we may write,

$\Sigma\tau_{left\ end} = -(750\ N)(1.00\ m) - (345\ N)(1.50\ m) - (500\ N)(2.00\ m)$

$- (1000\ N)(2.50\ m) + (T_R)(3.00\ m) = 0,$

or $T_R = 1589\ N$. Then equation (1) gives $T_L = 1006\ N$.

8.66 The free body diagram is shown at the right. The resultant torque about the center of the pulley is

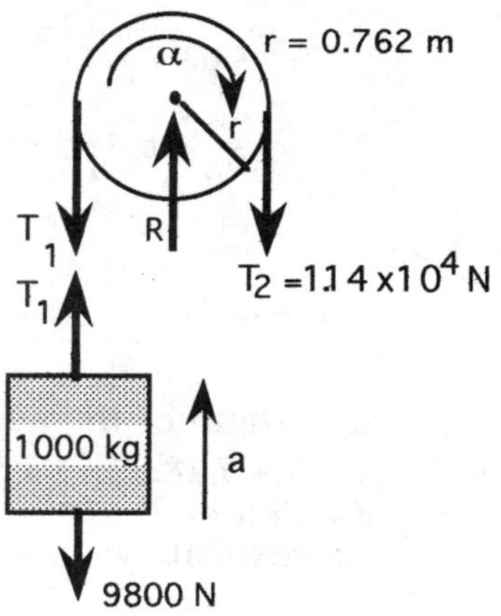

$(1.14 \times 10^4 \text{ N})r - T_1 r = (79.8 \text{ kg m}^2)\alpha$ (1)

From Newton's second law, applied in the vertical direction, we have

$T_1 - 9800 \text{ N} = (1000 \text{ kg})a$ (2)

Since there is no slipping, we also have
$a = r\alpha = (0.762 \text{ m})\alpha.$ (3)
Solving (1), (2), and (3) simultaneously, we find $a = 1.41 \text{ m/s}^2.$

8.67 (a) The table turns opposite to the way the woman walks, so its angular momentum cancels that of the woman. From conservation of angular momentum, we have $L_f = L_i = 0$, so
$L_f = I_W\omega_W + I_{table}\omega_{table} = 0$, and

$$\omega_{table} = -\frac{I_W}{I_{table}}\omega_{woman} = -\frac{m_W r^2}{I_{table}} \times \frac{v_{woman}}{r}, \text{ or}$$

$$\omega_{table} = -\frac{(60 \text{ kg})(2.0 \text{ m})^2}{500 \text{ kg m}^2} \times \frac{1.5 \text{ m/s}}{2.0 \text{ m}} = -0.36 \text{ rad/s. } (0.36 \text{ rad/s CCW})$$

(b) work done $= \Delta KE = KE_f - 0 = \frac{1}{2} m_{woman} v^2_{woman} + \frac{1}{2} I\omega^2_{table}$

$$= \frac{1}{2}(60 \text{ kg})(1.5 \text{ m/s})^2 + \frac{1}{2}(500 \text{ kg m}^2)(0.36 \text{ rad/s})^2 = 99.9 \text{ J.}$$

8.68 First compute some needed constants:
mass of people $= m_p = (5.5 \times 10^9)(70 \text{ kg}) = 3.85 \times 10^{11}$ kg
$I_{(\text{due to people})} = I_p = m_p R^2_E = (3.85 \times 10^{11} \text{ kg})(6.37 \times 10^6 \text{ m})^2 = 1.56 \times 10^{25} \text{ kg m}^2$.
I for Earth alone:

$$I_E = \frac{2}{5} M_E R^2_E = \frac{2}{5}(5.98 \times 10^{24} \text{ kg})(6.37 \times 10^6 \text{ m})^2 = 9.71 \times 10^{37} \text{ kg m}^2.$$

Original angular speed of Earth: $\omega_0 = \frac{2\pi \text{ rad}}{1 \text{ day}}\frac{1 \text{ day}}{86400 \text{ s}} = 7.27 \times 10^{-5}$ rad/s.

The original angular momentum of the system (Earth plus people) is

$$L_0 = I_E\omega_0 + I_p\omega_0 = (I_E + I_p)\omega_0$$

The tangential speed of a point on the equator of the Earth is $v = R_E\omega$ so when the people start running, their tangential speed is
$v' = v + 2.5 \text{ m/s} = R_E\omega + 2.5$ m/s, and their angular speed is

$$\omega' = \frac{v'}{R_E} = \omega + \frac{2.5 \text{ m/s}}{R_E},$$ where ω is the new angular speed of the Earth.

The angular momentum of the system is now given by

$$L_f = L_{earth} + L_{people} = I_E\omega + I_p\omega' = I_E\omega + I_p\left(\omega + \frac{2.5 \text{ m/s}}{R_E}\right), \text{or}$$

$$L_f = (I_E + I_p)\omega + \frac{I_p}{R_E}(2.5 \text{ m/s}).$$

Conserving angular momentum($L_f = L_0$) gives:

$\omega = \omega_0 - \frac{I_p}{R_E(I_E + I_p)}(2.5 \text{ m/s})$, or $\frac{\omega}{\omega_0} = 1 - \frac{(2.5 \text{ m/s})I_p}{\omega_0 R_E(I_E + I_p)}$.

$\frac{\omega}{\omega_0} = 1 - \frac{(2.5)(1.56 \times 10^{25})}{(7.27 \times 10^{-5})(6.37 \times 10^{6})(9.71 \times 10^{37} + 1.56 \times 10^{25})}$,

$\frac{\omega}{\omega_0} = 1 - 8.67 \times 10^{-16}$. Thus, the ratio of the length of the new day to the old day is $\frac{T}{T_0} = \frac{2\pi}{\omega}\frac{\omega_0}{2\pi} = \frac{1}{\frac{\omega}{\omega_0}} = \frac{1}{1 - 8.67 \times 10^{-16}} \approx 1 + 8.67 \times 10^{-16}$, and

the length of the new day is $T \approx T_0(1 + 8.67 \times 10^{-16})$
$T = T_0 + T_0(8.67 \times 10^{-16}) = 24 \text{ h} + (86{,}400 \text{ s})(8.67 \times 10^{-16})$, or
$T \approx 24 \text{ h} + 7.5 \times 10^{-11}$ s. Therefore, the day is lengthened by approximately 7.5×10^{-11} s.

8.69 Let us first consider conservation of energy, with the zero level for potential energy at the base of the ramp. We have

$\frac{1}{2}mv_i^2 + \frac{1}{2}I\omega_i^2 + mgy_i = \frac{1}{2}mv_f^2 + \frac{1}{2}I\omega_f^2 + mgy_f$, or

$\frac{1}{2}mv_i^2 + \frac{1}{2}I\omega_i^2 + 0 = 0 + 0 + (mg)(s)\sin 20°$, where s is the distance the hoop rolls up the ramp. For a hoop, $I = mr^2$. Thus,

$I\omega_i^2 = mr^2\omega_i^2 = m(r\omega_i)^2 = mv_i^2$.

Therefore, our equation for conservation of energy becomes

$\frac{1}{2}mv_i^2 + \frac{1}{2}mv_i^2 = (mg)(s)\sin 20°$, or, solving for s, we have

$s = v_i^2/g\sin 20°$. Since $v_i = r\omega_i = (3.0 \text{ m})(3.0 \text{ rad/s}) = 9.0$ m/s, we find

$s = (9.0 \text{ m/s})^2/(9.80 \text{ m/s}^2)\sin 20° = 24$ m.

8.70 (a) and (b)

For the cylinder; $\Sigma\tau = (2T)R = \frac{1}{2}MR^2\frac{a}{R}$, (1)

where a is the acceleration of the falling masses.

For each of the falling masses:

$\Sigma F = mg - T = ma$. (2)

Combining Equations (1) and (2), we find:

$T = \frac{Mmg}{M + 4m}$, and $a = \frac{4mg}{(M + 4m)}$.

8.71 $f_1 = N_2 = \mu N_1$

where f_1 is the friction force on the cylinder exerted by the floor wall. This force is to the right. N_2 is the normal force exerted on the cylinder by the vertical wall. This force is horizontal and to the left. The force N_1 is the upward normal force exerted on the cylinder by the floor.

$f_2 = \mu N_2$

f_2 is the friction force exerted on the ball by the vertical wall. It is directed vertically upward.

$F = f_1 + f_2$

As F grows so do f_1 and f_2.

Therefore, since $\mu = \frac{1}{2}$, $f_1 = \frac{N_1}{2}$ and $f_2 = \frac{N_2}{2} = \frac{N_1}{4}$

$$F + N_1 + \frac{N_1}{4} = w \qquad (1)$$

and $$F = \frac{N_1}{2} + \frac{N_1}{4} = \frac{3}{4}N_1 \qquad (2)$$

$$F + \frac{5}{4}N_1 = w$$

$$F + \frac{5}{4}\left(\frac{4}{3}F\right) = w$$

$$\frac{8}{3}F = w$$

$$F = \frac{3}{8}w$$

8.72 For the board just starting to move

$$\Sigma\tau = I\alpha$$

$$mg\frac{l}{2}\cos\theta = \frac{1}{3}ml^2\alpha$$

$$\alpha = \frac{3}{2}\left(\frac{g}{l}\right)\cos\theta$$

The tangential acceleration of the end is

$$a_t = \alpha l = \frac{3}{2}g\cos\theta$$

Its vertical component is $a_y = a_t\cos\theta = \frac{3}{2}g\cos^2\theta$

If this is greater than g, the board will pull ahead of the ball in falling:

(a) $\frac{3}{2}g\cos^2\theta \geq g$

$$\cos^2\theta \geq \frac{2}{3}$$

So, $\theta \leq 35.3°$

(b) To be underneath the release point of the ball,

$$r_c = l\cos\theta = \frac{l\cos^2\theta}{\cos\theta} = \frac{2l}{3\cos\theta}$$

ANSWERS TO CONCEPTUAL QUESTIONS

2. The lever arm of a particular force is found with respect to some reference point. Thus, an origin for calculating torques must be specified. However, for an object in equilibrium, the calculation of the torque is independent of the location of the origin.

4. Drawing her legs up against her chest reduces her moment of inertia. Because angular momentum is conserved, a decrease in moment of inertia is accompanied by an increase in angular velocity. Thus, she rotates faster. To come out of the flip, she must increase her moment of inertia. This can be accomplished by extending her arms and/or legs.

6. The object of the game in walking a tightrope is to keep the center of gravity of the walker directly above the rope. If the body becomes slightly overbalanced such as to slip off to the right, a small movement of the pole to the left will help to restore balance.

8. You can use conservation of energy to find the velocity of the objects at the bottom of the incline. You will find that the solid sphere moves fastest, and the hollow cylinder moves the slowest. Thus, the sphere wins the race and the hollow cylinder finishes last.

10. The velocity of a sphere at the bottom of an incline of height h is given by $v = \sqrt{\frac{10gh}{7}}$
Thus, the velocity of the spheres depend solely on the height at which they start and not their mass or radius. Thus, the spheres finish in a tie.

12. The basic premise of this question is correct. The tendency is for the body of the airplane to turn counterclockwise. However, it is prevented from doing so by the force of the air on the wings of the plane.

14. (a) Consider two people pushing with equal magnitude forces in opposite directions and at opposite ends of a table. The net force will be zero, yet the net torque is not zero.
(b) Consider a falling body. The net force acting on it is its weight, yet the net torque about the center of gravity is zero.

16. As the cat falls, angular momentum must be conserved. Thus, if the upper half of the body twists in one direction, something must get an equal angular momentum in the opposite direction. Rotating the lower half of the body in the opposite direction satisfies the law of conservation of angular momentum.

CHAPTER NINE SOLUTIONS

Chapter Nine Readings

Denton, E., "The Buoyancy of Marine Animals," *Scientific American*, July 1960, p. 118.

Gilman, J.J., "Fracture in Solids," *Scientific American*, February 1960, p. 94.

Smith, N., "Bernoulli and Newton in Fluid Mechanics," *The Physics Teacher*, 10, 1972, p. 451.

Morrison, P., "Under Pressure", *Scientific American*, v. 274 (June '96) p. 113.

9.1 Stress $= \frac{F}{A}$, where $F = 0.3(\text{weight}) = 0.3(480\text{ N}) = 144\text{ N}$,
and $A = \pi r^2 = \pi(0.50 \times 10^{-2}\text{ m})^2 = 7.85 \times 10^{-5}\text{ m}^2$. Thus,

$$\text{Stress} = \frac{144\text{ N}}{7.85 \times 10^{-5}\text{ m}^2} = 1.8 \times 10^6\text{ Pa}$$

9.2 Using $Y = \frac{FL_o}{A(\Delta L)}$, we get $A = \frac{FL_o}{Y(\Delta L)} = \pi(d/2)^2$.

So, $$d = \sqrt{\frac{4mgL_o}{\pi Y(\Delta L)}} = \sqrt{\frac{4(380\text{ kg})(9.80\text{ m/s}^2)(18.0\text{ m})}{\pi(2 \times 10^{11}\text{ Pa})(0.009\text{ m})}} = 6.89\text{ mm}.$$

9.3 Using $Y = \frac{FL_o}{A(\Delta L)}$ with $A = \pi(d/2)^2$ and $F = mg$, we get

$$Y = \frac{mgL_o}{\pi(d/2)^2\Delta L} = \frac{4(90\text{ kg})(9.80\text{ m/s}^2)(50\text{ m})}{\pi(0.01\text{ m})^2(1.6\text{ m})} = 3.5 \times 10^8\text{ Pa}.$$

9.4 The maximum stress $= F/A_{min} = 5.0 \times 10^8$ Pa.
Therefore, $A_{min} = (70\text{ kg})(9.80\text{ m/s}^2)/5.0 \times 10^8\text{ Pa} = 1.37 \times 10^{-6}\text{ m}^2$.
But, $A_{min} = \frac{\pi d^2}{4}$, from which, $d_{min} = 1.3$ mm.

9.5 We assume a length for the femur of 0.50 m. The amount of compression ΔL is given by:

$$\Delta L = \frac{L(\text{stress})}{Y} = \frac{(5.0 \times 10^{-1}\text{ m})(160 \times 10^6\text{ Pa})}{14.5 \times 10^9\text{ Pa}} = 5.52 \times 10^{-3}\text{ m} = 5.5\text{ mm}.$$

9.6 We know that the shear modulus is given by

$$S = \frac{\text{shear stress}}{\text{shear strain}} = \frac{\text{stress}}{(\Delta x/h)}$$

or, $$\text{Stress} = S\left(\frac{\Delta x}{h}\right) = (1.5 \times 10^{10}\text{ Pa})\left(\frac{5.0\text{ m}}{10^4\text{ m}}\right) = 7.5 \times 10^6\text{ Pa}.$$

9.7 From the defining equation for the shear modulus, we find Δx as

$$\Delta x = \frac{h(F/A)}{S} = \frac{(5.0 \times 10^{-3} \text{ m})(20 \text{ N})/(14 \times 10^{-4} \text{ m}^2)}{3.0 \times 10^6 \text{ Pa}} = 2.4 \times 10^{-5} \text{ m}.$$

or $x = 2.4 \times 10^{-2}$ mm.

9.8 (a) When at rest, the tension in the cable is equal to the weight of the 800 kg mass, 7840 N. Thus, from the definition of Young's modulus, we find the amount the cable is stretched:

$$\Delta L = \frac{(F/A)\ L}{Y} = \frac{\left((7840 \text{ N})/(4.00 \times 10^{-4} \text{ m}^2)\right)(25.0 \text{ m})}{(20 \times 10^{10} \text{ Pa})} = 2.45 \times 10^{-3} \text{ m},$$

or $\Delta L = 2.45$ mm.

(b) We write down Newton's second law for the block when it is accelerating upward.

$T - mg = ma$, or $T = m(g + a)$. (1)

When a = 3 m/s^2, we find: $T = 1.02 \times 10^4$ N, so

$$\Delta L_{new} = \frac{F\ L}{Y\ A} = \frac{(1.02 \times 10^4 \text{ N})(25.0 \text{ m})}{(20 \times 10^{10} \text{ Pa})(4.00 \times 10^{-4} \text{ m}^2)} = 3.20 \times 10^{-3} \text{ m} = 3.20 \text{ mm}$$

Therefore, the increase in elongation is:

$\Delta L_{new} - \Delta L = 3.20 \text{ mm} - 2.45 \text{ mm} = 0.75 \text{ mm}.$

(c) If the stress (F/A) is not to exceed 2.2×10^8 Pa, the maximum force allowed is: $F = T = (2.2 \times 10^8 \text{ Pa})(4.00 \times 10^{-4} \text{ m}^2) = 8.8 \times 10^4$ N.

From (1) we find the largest mass to be:

$$m = \frac{T}{a + g} = \frac{8.8 \times 10^4 \text{ N}}{(3.00 + 9.80)\text{m/s}^2} = 6.9 \times 10^3 \text{ kg}.$$

9.9 Applying Newton's second law to the dancer gives:

$N - mg = ma$

where N is the normal force the floor exerts on the dancer and a is the upward acceleration (if any) the dancer is given. Thus,

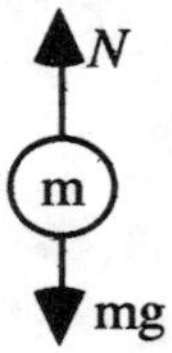

$N = m(g + a)$

is the force exerted on the dancer by the floor.

(a) In this case, $a = 0$ and $N = mg = 490$ N.

Therefore, $P = \frac{F}{A} = \frac{490 \text{ N}}{26.0 \times 10^{-4} \text{ m}^2} = 1.88 \times 10^5$ Pa.

(b) Here, $a = +4.00$ m/s^2. Thus, $N = m(g + a) = 690$ N, or $P = 2.65 \times 10^5$ Pa.

9.10 Let W be its weight. Then each tire supports $W/4$, so that $P = \frac{F}{A} = \frac{W}{4A}$,

yielding: $W = 4AP = 4(0.024 \text{ m}^2)(2.0 \times 10^5 \text{ N/m}^2) = 1.9 \times 10^4$ N.

9.11 The area of one of the legs is $A = \pi r^2 = \pi(10^{-2} \text{ m})^2 = \pi \times 10^{-4} \text{ m}^2$.

The force exerted by one leg on the floor is

$$F = \frac{1}{2}(\text{weight of man} + \text{weight of chair}) = \frac{1}{2}(75 \text{ kg})(9.80 \text{ m/s}^2) = 368 \text{ N}.$$

Thus, $P = F/A = 368 \text{ N}/(\pi \times 10^{-4})\text{m}^2 = 1.2 \times 10^6$ Pa.

9.12 Let H be the height of the pillar, and let A be its cross-sectional area. Then, the pressure at the base is:

$$P = \frac{mg}{A} = \frac{\rho(AH)g}{A} = (\rho g)H = (\text{weight per unit volume})H = (5.0 \times 10^4 \text{ N})\text{H}$$

With a maximum pressure of $P_{max} = 1.7 \times 10^7$ Pa, the maximum height is

$$H_{max} = \frac{P_{max}}{5.0 \times 10^4 \text{ N/m}^3} = \frac{1.7 \times 10^7 \text{ Pa}}{5.0 \times 10^4 \text{ N/m}^3} = 3.4 \times 10^2 \text{ m.}$$

9.13 $P_g = P - P_{atm} = \rho g h = (10^3 \text{ kg/m}^3)(9.80 \text{ m/s}^2)(1200 \text{ ft})(1\text{m}/3.281 \text{ ft})$, or
$P_g = 3.58 \times 10^6$ Pa.

9.14 The gauge pressure of the fluid at the level of the needle must equal the gauge pressure in the artery.

$P_{gauge} = \rho g h = 1.33 \times 10^4$ Pa, so

$$h = \frac{1.33 \times 10^4 \text{ Pa}}{(1.02 \times 10^3 \text{ kg/m}^3)(9.80 \text{ m/s}^2)} = 1.33 \text{ m}$$

9.15 We use $P = P_0 + \rho g h$, where $\rho = 806$ km/m^3 for ethyl alcohol, and
$P_0 = 1.10 \text{ atm} = 1.114 \times 10^5$ Pa.
Thus,
$P = 1.114 \times 10^5 \text{ Pa} + (806 \text{ kg/m}^3)(9.80 \text{ m/s}^2)(4.0 \text{ m}) = 1.43 \times 10^5$ Pa, or
$P = 1.4$ atm.

9.16 The pressure at the upper surface of each liquid is given by

$P = P_{atm} - \rho_w g h_w = P_{atm} - \rho g h$. Therefore, $\rho = \left(\frac{h_w}{h}\right)\rho_w$.

9.17 We first find the absolute pressure at the interface between oil and water: $P_t = P_{atm} + \rho g h$, or

$P_t = 1.013 \times 10^5 \text{ Pa} + (7.00 \times 10^2 \text{ kg/m}^3)(9.80 \text{ m/s}^2)(0.300 \text{ m}) = 1.03 \times 10^5$ Pa.

This is the pressure at the top of the water. To find the absolute pressure at the bottom, we use: $P = P_t + \rho g h$, or

$P = 1.03 \times 10^5 \text{ Pa} + (1.00 \times 10^3 \text{ kg/m}^3)(9.80 \text{ m/s}^2)(0.200 \text{ m}) = 1.05 \times 10^5$ Pa.

9.18 First, use Pascal's principle, $\frac{F_2}{A_2} = \frac{F_1}{A_1}$, to find the piston 1 will exert on the handle:

$$F_1 = \frac{A_1}{A_2} F_2 = \frac{\frac{\pi d_1^2}{4}}{\frac{\pi d_2^2}{4}} F_2 = \frac{(0.25 \text{ in})^2}{(1.5 \text{ in})^2} (500 \text{ lb})$$
$$= 13.9 \text{lb}$$

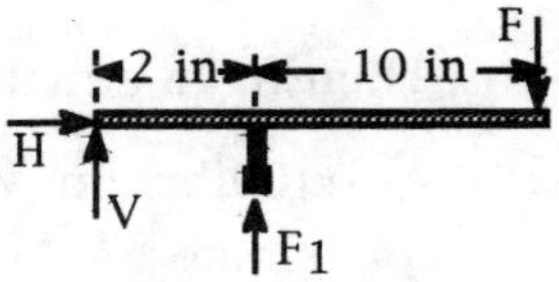

Free-Body diagram of handle

Now, consider torques on the jack handle with the pivot point at the left end.

$\Sigma\tau = 0 = (13.9 \text{ lb})(2 \text{ in}) - F(12 \text{ in}) = 0$,

or $F = 2.31$ lb.

9.19 $\frac{F_2}{A_2} = \frac{F_1}{A_1}$ Pascal's principle becomes:

$$F_{brake} = \frac{A_{brake\ cylinder}}{A_{master\ cylinder}} (F_{pedal}) = \frac{1.75 \text{ cm}^2}{6.4 \text{ cm}^2} (44 \text{ N}) = 12.0 \text{ N}$$

This is the normal force exerted on the brake shoe. The frictional force is: $f = \mu N = 0.50(12.0\text{ N}) = 6.0\text{ N}$, and the torque is
$\tau = f \cdot r_{tire} = (6.0\text{ N})(0.34\text{ m}) = 2.0\text{ N m}$.

9.20 Since the frog floats, the buoyant force = the weight of the frog. Also, the weight of the displaced fluid = weight of the frog, so
$\rho_{fluid} V g = m_{frog} g$, or,

$$m_{frog} = \rho_{fluid} V = (1.35 \times 10^3\text{ kg/m}^3)\left(\frac{1}{2}\right)\left(\frac{4\pi(6.00 \times 10^{-2}\text{ m})^3}{3.00}\right).$$

Hence, $m_{frog} = 0.611\text{ kg}$.

9.21 The weight of the truck, W, is equal to the weight of the additional water displaced when the truck drives onto the boat. This is:
$W = \rho_w(\Delta V)g = (10^3\text{ kg/m}^3)(4.00\text{m})(6.00\text{ m})(0.0400\text{ m})(9.80\text{ m/s}^2) = 9.41 \times 10^3\text{ N}$.

9.22 The buoyant force, B, on the iceberg must be equal to its weight, w, in order for it to float. Thus: $B = w$.
But, the buoyant force is equal to the weight of the water displaced. Therefore, $\rho_w V_{uw} g = \rho_{ice} V_{total} g$ where V_{uw} is the volume of the iceberg under water and V_{total} is the total volume of the berg.

We have, $\dfrac{V_{uw}}{V_{total}} = \dfrac{\rho_{ice}}{\rho_w} = \dfrac{920}{1030} = 0.89$.

Therefore, 89% of the volume is submerged and 11% is exposed.

9.23 The balloon is in equilibrium under the action of three forces, F_b, the buoyant force on the balloon, w, its weight, and T, the tension in the string. We have: $\Sigma F_y = 0 \Rightarrow$ $T = F_b - w$. (1)

F_b = weight of displaced air = $\rho_{air} V g$, or

$F_b = (1.29\text{ kg/m}^3)(9.80\text{ m/s}^2)\frac{4}{3}\pi(0.500\text{ m})^3 = 6.62\text{ N}$.

w = weight of empty balloon + weight of enclosed helium, or

$w = (0.012\text{ kg})(9.80\text{ m/s}^2) + (0.181\text{ kg/m}^3)\frac{4}{3}\pi(0.500\text{ m})^3\ (9.80\text{ m/s}^2)$

$= 1.05\text{ N}$

Then from equation (1), $T = 6.62\text{ N} - 1.05\text{ N} = 5.57\text{ N}$.

9.24 At equilibrium, we must have $\Sigma F_y = B - F_{spring} - W = 0$, or
$F_{spring} = k(\Delta L) = B - W$, where B is the buoyant force, $k(\Delta L)$ is the downward spring force, and W is the weight of the block of wood.
But, $W = mg = (5.00\text{ kg})(9.80\text{ m/s}^2) = 49.0\text{ N}$ and

$$B = (\rho_w V)g = \left(\rho_w\left(\frac{m_{wood}}{\rho_{wood}}\right)\right)g = \left(1000\left(\frac{5.00\text{ kg}}{650}\right)\right)(9.80\text{ m/s}^2) = 75.4\text{ N}$$

Therefore, $F_{spring} = k(\Delta L) = B - W = 75.4\text{ N} - 49.0\text{ N} = (160\text{ N/m})(\Delta L)$,

which yields $\Delta L = \dfrac{26.4\text{ N}}{160\text{ N/m}} = 0.165\text{ m} = 16.5\text{ cm}$

9.25 (a) The forces on the object are the tension, T, in the string connecting it to a balance, The weight of the object, w, and the buoyant force on it, B. Because the object is in equilibrium when immersed in the alcohol, we have $\Sigma F_y = 0$, which gives,
$T + B = w$, or $200\text{ N} + B = 300\text{ N}$. Thus, $B = 100\text{ N}$.

We also know that the buoyant force is equal to the weight of the displaced alcohol. So, $B = \rho_{alcohol} V_{alcohol} g$.
But, $V_{alcohol}$ is equal to the volume of the object because the object is completely submerged. Thus,

$$V_{object} = \frac{B}{\rho_{alcohol} g} = \frac{100 \text{ N}}{(700 \text{ kg/m}^3)(9.80 \text{ m/s}^2)} = 1.46 \times 10^{-2} \text{ m}^3.$$

(b) The mass of the 300 N object is 30.6 kg, and now that we know its volume, its density can be found as

$$\rho = \frac{m}{V} = 2.10 \times 10^3 \text{ kg/m}^3.$$

9.26 (a) The forces acting on the object when suspended in water are the tension in the string, T_1, the weight of the object, and the buoyant force, B_w. At equilibrium, we have

$$B_w = w - T_1 = 300 \text{ N} - 265 \text{ N} = 35 \text{ N}.$$

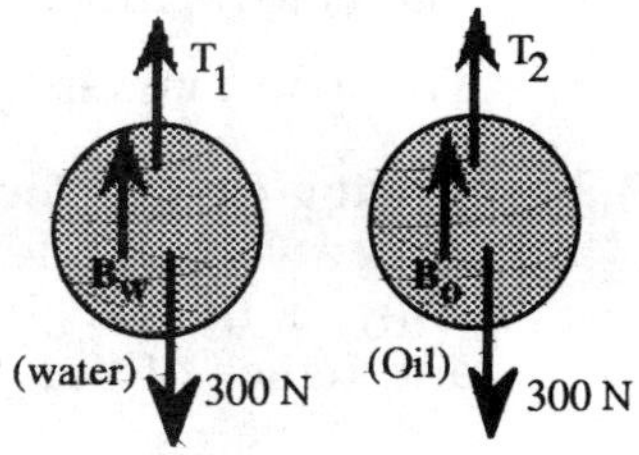

Also, $B_w = \rho_w V g$. Therefore,

$$V = \frac{35 \text{ N}}{(10^3 \text{ kg/m}^3)(9.80 \text{ m/s}^2)} = 3.57 \times 10^{-3} \text{ m}^3.$$

The mass of the 300 N object is 30.6 kg, and the volume V found above is the volume of water displaced which is also the volume of the object. Thus, the density of the object is:

$$\rho_{object} = m_{object}/V = 30.6 \text{ kg}/3.57 \times 10^{-3} \text{ m}^3 = 8.57 \times 10^3 \text{ kg/m}^3.$$

(b) When submerged in the oil, the forces on the object are T_2, the tension in the string, the weight of the object, w, and the buoyant force of the oil, B_o. For equilibrium, we have $T_2 + B_o = w$, or $B_o = w - T_2 = 300 \text{ N} - 275 \text{ N} = 25 \text{ N}$. However, the buoyant force exerted by the oil is also equal to the weight of the oil displaced. The volume of the oil displaced is equal to the volume of the object. Thus, the density of the oil is

$$\rho_{oil} = \frac{m_{oil}}{V} = \frac{w_{oil}}{gV} = \frac{25 \text{ N}}{(9.80 \text{ m/s}^2)(3.57 \times 10^{-3} \text{ m}^3)} = 714 \text{ kg/m}^3.$$

9.27 Applying Newton's second law:
$\Sigma F_y = B - W_{total} = B - (m_{shell} + m)g = (m_{shell} + m)a$
Therefore,

$$a = \frac{B}{(m_{shell} + m)} - g. \qquad (1)$$

The volume is $V = \frac{4}{3}\pi r^3 = \frac{4}{3}\pi(0.10 \text{ m})^3 = 4.19 \times 10^{-3} \text{ m}^3$. Thus,

B = (weight of displaced water) $= \rho_{water} V g$
$= (1000 \text{ kg/m}^3)(4.19 \times 10^{-3} \text{ m}^3)(9.80 \text{ m/s}^2) = 41.1 \text{ N}$,

and $m = \rho V = (806 \text{ kg/m}^3)(4.19 \times 10^{-3} \text{ m}^3) = 3.38 \text{ kg}$.

Equation (1) for the acceleration then gives:

$$a = \frac{41.1 \text{ N}}{(0.400 \text{ kg} + 3.38 \text{ kg})} - 9.80 \text{ m/s}^2 = 1.07 \text{ m/s}^2$$

9.28 When the system floats, $F_B = w$, or the weight of the displaced water equals the weight of the object. Therefore, $\rho_w(\pi r^2 z)g = 1.96 \text{ N}$, where $(\pi r^2)z$ = volume of displaced water. The depth of the bottom end is thus,

$$z = \frac{1.96\ \text{N}}{(10^3\ \text{kg/m}^3)\pi(2.00 \times 10^{-2}\ \text{m})^2(9.80\ \text{m/s}^2)} = 0.159\ \text{m} = 15.9\ \text{cm}.$$

9.29 When the mattress is totally submerged, the buoyant force exerted by the water (and hence the total weight that can be supported) is:

$$F_m = \rho_w V g = (10^3\ \text{kg/m}^3)(2.0\ \text{m})(0.50\ \text{m})(0.08\ \text{m})(9.80\ \text{m/s}^2) = 784\ \text{N}$$

The total mass supported is the sum of the mass of the mattress and the mass of the load, or $M = m_{\text{mattress}} + m = \frac{784\ \text{N}}{9.80\ \text{m/s}^2} = 80\ \text{kg}.$

The load mass is therefore: $m = M - m_{\text{mattress}} = 80\ \text{kg} - 2.0\ \text{kg} = 78\ \text{kg}.$

9.30 Looking first at the top scale and the iron block, we have: $T_1 + B = W_{\text{iron}}$, where T_1 is the tension in the spring scale, B is the buoyant force and W_{iron} is the weight of the iron block. The volume, V, of the iron block, and hence of the displaced oil, is:

$$V = \frac{m_{\text{iron}}}{\rho_{\text{iron}}} = \frac{2.00\ \text{kg}}{7860\ \text{kg/m}^3} = 2.54 \times 10^{-4}\ \text{m}^3.$$

Then $B = \rho_{\text{oil}} V g = (916\ \text{kg/m}^3)(2.54 \times 10^{-4}\ \text{m}^3)()9.80\ \text{m/s}^2) = 2.28\ \text{N}.$

Therefore,

$$T_1 = W_{\text{iron}} - B = 19.6\ \text{N} - 2.28\text{N} = 17.3\ \text{N}.$$

Next we look at the bottom scale which reads T_2. (i.e., exerts an upward force T_2 on the system) Consider the external vertical forces acting on the beaker-oil-iron combination.

$\Sigma F_y = 0$ gives $\quad T_1 + T_2 - w_{\text{beaker}} - w_{\text{oil}} - w_{\text{iron}} = 0$, or

$T_2 = (m_{\text{beaker}} + m_{\text{oil}} + m_{\text{iron}})g - T_1 = (5.00\ \text{kg})(9.80\ \text{m/s}^2) - 17.3\ \text{N}.$

Thus, $\quad T_2 = 31.7\ \text{N}$ is the lower scale reading.

9.31 The volume rate of flow $= \frac{\text{Volume}}{\text{time}} = vA$, where A is the cross-sectional area of the pipe and v is the average velocity of the water in the pipe. Therefore, the average velocity is

$$v = \frac{\text{Volume}}{At} = \frac{20.0\ \text{gal}}{(1.00\ \text{in}^2)(30.0\ \text{s})}\left(\frac{231\ \text{in}^3}{1\ \text{gal}}\right) = 154\ \text{in/s}$$

9.32 The cross-sectional area of the 2.0 cm diameter hose is $A = \pi \times 10^{-4}\ \text{m}^2$, and the flow rate is: $Av = (\pi \times 10^{-4}\ \text{m}^2)(1.5\ \text{m/s}) = 1.5\pi \times 10^{-4}\ \text{m}^3/\text{s}$.
The volume to be filled is $(1.5\ \text{m})(0.6\ \text{m})(0.4\ \text{m}) = 3.6 \times 10^{-1}\ \text{m}^3$.
The time required to fill the trough is:

$$\text{time} = \frac{\text{volume}}{\text{flow rate}} = \frac{3.6 \times 10^{-1}\ \text{m}^3}{1.5\ \pi \times 10^{-4}\ \text{m}^3/\text{s}} = 7.6 \times 10^2\ \text{s} = 13\ \text{min}$$

9.33 (a) Flow Rate $= Av = (2.0\ \text{cm}^2)(40\ \text{cm/s}) = 80\ \text{cm}^3/\text{s}$.
However, since blood has a mass of 1 g/cm^3, this is equivalent to a mass flow rate of 80 g/s.

(b) From the equation of continuity, we have:

$$v_2 = \frac{A_1 v_1}{A_2} = \frac{2}{3000}(40\ \text{cm/s}) = 2.7 \times 10^{-2}\ \text{cm/s}.$$

9.34 We select point 1 just above the wing and point 2 just below it. As a result, the difference in vertical heights between these two points is negligible, and Bernoulli's equation reduces to

$$P_2 - P_1 = \frac{1}{2}\rho(v_1^2 - v_2^2) = \frac{1}{2}(1.29\text{ kg/m}^3)[(300\text{ m/s})^2 - (280\text{ m/s})^2]\text{ , or}$$

$P_2 - P_1 = 7480$ Pa. The net upward force is therefore

$$F = (P_2 - P_1)A = (7480\text{ Pa})(20.0\text{ m}^2) = 1.50 \times 10^5\text{ N upward.}$$

9.35 (a) We find the flow velocity in the second section from the continuity equation: $v_2 = \frac{A_1 v_1}{A_2} = \frac{10}{2.5} v_1 = 4(2.75\text{ m/s}) = 11.0\text{ m/s}$.

(b) Choosing the zero level for y along the common center line of the pipes, we have:

$$P_1 + \frac{1}{2}\rho v_1^2 = P_2 + \frac{1}{2}\rho v_2^2\text{, or }\quad P_2 = P_1 + \frac{1}{2}\rho(v_1^2 - v_2^2)\text{, giving}$$

$$P_2 = (1.20 \times 10^5\text{ Pa}) + \frac{1}{2}(1650\text{ kg/m}^3)[(2.75\text{ m/s})^2 - (11.0\text{ m/s})^2]\text{, and}$$

$$P_2 = 2.64 \times 10^4\text{ Pa.}$$

9.36 $P_{1gauge} = P_1 - P_{atm} = \frac{F}{A_1} = \frac{2.00\text{ N}}{2.50 \times 10^{-5}\text{ m}^2} = 8.00 \times 10^4$ Pa.

We write Bernoulli's equation as:

$$\frac{1}{2}\rho v_2^2 = (P_1 - P_2) + \frac{1}{2}\rho v_1^2 + \rho g(y_1 - y_2).$$

The last term goes to zero because the syringe is in a horizontal position. Also, we realize that $P_1 - P_2 = P_1 - P_{atm} = P_{1gauge} = 8.00 \times 10^4$ Pa. Finally, we assume $v_1 = 0$ in comparison to the speed inside the needle. Thus, with these substitutions, we find $v_2 = 12.6$ m/s.

9.37 $\Delta P = P_2 - P_1 = \frac{1}{2}\rho(v_1^2 - v_2^2)$ (ignoring differences in height), so

$$\Delta P = \frac{1}{2}(1.29\text{ kg/m}^3)\left(((0.15\text{ m/s})^2 - (0.30\text{ m/s})^2)\right) = -4.4 \times 10^{-2}\text{ Pa}$$

9.38 First, consider the path from the standpoint of projectile motion to find the speed at which the water emerges from the tank. The time to drop one meter with an intial vertical velocity of zero is:

$$y = v_{oy}t + \frac{1}{2}at^2 \Rightarrow 1.00\text{ m} = 0 + \frac{1}{2}(9.80\text{ m/s}^2)t^2\text{, or}\quad t = 0.452\text{ s,}$$

and from the horizontal motion: $v_x = v_0 = \frac{\Delta x}{t} = \frac{0.600\text{ m}}{0.452\text{ s}} = 1.33$ m/s.

We now use Bernoulli's equation, with point 1 at the top of the tank and point 2 at the level of the hole. With $P_1 = P_2 = P_{atm}$ and v_1 approximately equal to zero, we have: $\frac{1}{2}\rho v_2^2 = \rho g(y_1 - y_2) = \rho g h$, giving

$$h = \frac{v_o^2}{2g} = \frac{(1.33\text{ m/s})^2}{2(9.80\text{ m/s}^2)} = 9.00 \times 10^{-2}\text{ m} = 9.00\text{ cm.}$$

9.39 (a) We choose point 1 at the surface of the tank and point 2 at the hole. Both of these points are at atmospheric pressure, so the pressure cancels from Bernoulli's equation. We also assume that v_1 is negligibly small. Finally, we choose the zero level for y at the level of the hole. Under these conditions, we have:

$$v_2 = \sqrt{2gy} = \sqrt{2g(16.0\ \text{m})} = 17.7\ \text{m/s}.$$

(b) The area of the hole is found from the flow rate as:

$$A = \frac{\text{flow rate}}{v_2} = \frac{4.17 \times 10^{-5}\ \text{m}^3/\text{s}}{17.7\ \text{m/s}} = 2.35 \times 10^{-6}\ \text{m}^2.$$

From which the diameter is easily found to be 1.73 mm.

9.40 First, find the velocity inside the larger portions:

$$v_1 = \left(\frac{\text{flow rate}}{A_1}\right) = \left(\frac{1.80 \times 10^{-4}\ \text{m}^3/\text{s}}{4.91 \times 10^{-4}\ \text{m}^2}\right) = 0.367\ \text{m/s}.$$

The absolute pressure in the large section (to left) is

$$P_1 = P_{atm} + \rho g h_1 = P_{atm} + (1000\ \text{kg/m}^3)(9.80\ \text{m/s}^2)(0.10\ \text{m})$$
$$= P_{atm} + 980\ \text{Pa}.$$

In the absolute pressure in the constriction is:

$$P_2 = P_{atm} + (1000\ \text{kg/m}^3)(9.80\ \text{m/s}^2)(0.050\ \text{m}) = P_{atm} + 490\ \text{Pa}.$$

Now use Bernoulli's equation:

$$v_2^2 = v_1^2 + \frac{2}{\rho}(P_1 - P_2) = (0.367\ \text{m/s})^2 + \frac{2(490\ \text{Pa})}{1000\ \text{kg/m}^2}$$

where we have chosen $y = 0$ at the level of the centerline of the pipe. This yields $v_2 = 1.06$ m/s, and from the flow rate, we find:

$$A_2 = \left(\frac{\text{flow rate}}{v_2}\right) = \frac{1.80 \times 10^{-4}\ \text{m}^3/\text{s}}{1.06\ \text{m/s}} = 1.71 \times 10^{-4}\ \text{m}^2 = \frac{\pi d_2^2}{4},$$

from which $d_2 = 1.5 \times 10^{-2}\ \text{m} = 1.5\ \text{cm}$.

9.41 (a) The flow rate, Av, as given may be expressed as follows:

25 liters/30 s = 0.833 liters/s = 833 cm^3/s.

The area of the faucet tap is π cm^2, so we can find the velocity as

$$v_2 = \frac{\text{flow rate}}{A_2} = \frac{833\ \text{cm}^3/\text{s}}{\pi\ \text{cm}^2} = 265\ \text{cm/s} = 2.65\ \text{m/s}.$$

(b) Similarly, the velocity in the main pipe is:

$$v_1 = \frac{\text{flow rate}}{A_1} = \frac{833\ \text{cm}^3/\text{s}}{\pi(3.0\ \text{cm})^2} = 29.5\ \text{cm/s} = 0.295\ \text{m/s}.$$

Now, we use Bernoulli's equation with point 1 to be in the main pipe and point 2 to be at the faucet tap:

$$P_1 - P_2 = \frac{1}{2}\rho(v_2^2 - v_1^2) + \rho g(y_2 - y_1),\ \text{which gives}$$

$$P_1 - P_2 = \frac{1}{2}(10^3\ \text{kg/m}^3)[(2.65\ \text{m/s})^2 - (0.295\ \text{m/s})^2] + (10^3\ \text{kg/m}^3)(9.80\ \text{m/s}^2)(2.00\ \text{m}),\ \text{or}$$

$$P_{gauge} = P_1 - P_2 = 2.3 \times 10^4\ \text{Pa}.$$

9.42 (a) Using Bernoulli's equation with point 1 at the top of the tank and point 2 at the exit from the tube, we have:

$$P_1 + \frac{1}{2}\rho v_1^2 + \rho g y_1 = P_2 + \frac{1}{2}\rho v_2^2 + \rho g y_2,\ \text{where}\ P_1 = P_2 = P_{atm}.$$

For a large tank v_1 is approximately equal to zero, and $y_1 - y_2 = h$. This gives $v_2 = \sqrt{2gh}$.

(b) Use Bernoulli's equation with point 1 at the top of the tank and point 2 at the highest point in the tube:

$$P_1 + \frac{1}{2}\rho v_1^2 + \rho g y_1 = P_2 + \frac{1}{2}\rho v_2^2 + \rho g y_2, \text{ where } P_1 = P_{atm}.$$

When the siphon ceases to work, the fluid will be at rest at point 2, or $v_2 = v_1 = 0$, and $y_2 - y_1 = y_{max}$, so $P_{atm} = P + \rho g y_{max}$.

The minimum value of P is 0. Therefore, $y_{max} = \frac{P_{atm}}{\rho g}$.

9.43 Because there are two edges (the inside and outside of the ring) we have,

$$\gamma = \frac{F}{L_{total}} = \frac{F}{2(\text{circumference})} = \frac{F}{4\pi r} = \frac{1.61 \times 10^{-2} \text{ N}}{2.20 \times 10^{-1} \text{ N}} = 7.32 \times 10^{-2} \text{ N/m}$$

9.44 The tension in the string attaching the sheet to the balance is equal to the sum of the vertical component of the surface force plus the weight of the sheet. This is a two sided surface, so the surface force is F = $\gamma 2L$. Since $L = 3.0 \times 10^{-2}$ m, the vertical component of this force is:

$$F_v = \gamma 2L\cos\theta = (6 \times 10^{-2} \text{ m})\gamma\cos\theta.$$

When $\theta = 0°$, the tension measures 0.4 N and we have:

$$T = F_v + w \quad \text{becoming} \quad 0.40 \text{ N} = +(6 \times 10^{-2} \text{ m})\gamma + w. \qquad (1)$$

When $\theta = 180°$, $T = 0.39$ N, and we have

$$T = F_v + w \quad \text{becoming} \quad 0.39 \text{ N} = -(6 \times 10^{-2} \text{ m})\gamma + w. \qquad (2)$$

Solving equations (1) and (2) simultaneously gives $\gamma = 8.3 \times 10^{-2}$ N/m.

9.45 The height the blood can rise is given by

$$h = \frac{2\gamma\cos\theta}{\rho g r} = \frac{2(5.8 \times 10^{-2} \text{ N/m})}{(1050 \text{ kg/m}^3)(9.80 \text{ m/s}^2)(2.0 \times 10^{-6} \text{ m})} = 5.6 \text{ m}$$

9.46 The vertical component of the surface force is equal to the weight of water inside the capillary tube: $F_v = w$, or

$\gamma L\cos\theta = \gamma(2\pi r)\cos\theta = w = \rho(\pi r^2)hg$, where h is the height of the water in the tube. We solve the above for the surface tension.

$$\gamma = \frac{\rho r h g}{2\cos\theta} = \frac{(1080 \text{ kg/m}^3)(5.0 \times 10^{-4} \text{ m})(2.1 \times 10^{-2} \text{ m})(9.80 \text{ m/s}^2)}{2}$$

which yields $\gamma = 5.6 \times 10^{-2}$ N/m

9.47 We have

$$h = 5 \times 10^{-2} \text{ m} = \frac{2\gamma\cos\theta}{\rho g r} = \frac{2(8.80 \times 10^{-2} \text{ N/m})}{(1035 \text{ kg/m}^3)(9.80 \text{ m/s}^2)r}$$

From which, we find r = 3. 47 x 10^{-4} m, or a diameter of 0.694 mm.

9.48 From the definition of the coefficient of viscosity, we have

$$F = \frac{\eta A v}{L} = \frac{(1.79 \times 10^{-3} \text{ Ns/m}^2)(0.80 \text{ m})(1.2 \text{ m})(0.5 \text{ m/s})}{10^{-4} \text{ m}} = 8.6 \text{ N}$$

9.49 From the definition of the coefficient of viscosity, we have

$$F = \frac{\eta A v}{L} = \frac{(1500 \times 10^{-3} \text{ Ns/m}^2)(4.00 \times 10^{-4} \text{ m}^2)(0.30 \text{ m/s})}{1.50 \times 10^{-3} \text{ m}} = 0.12 \text{ N}$$

9.50 From Poiseuille's law: $P_1 - P_2 = \frac{(\text{flow rate})8\eta L}{\pi R^4}$

$$P_1 - P_2 = \frac{(8.6 \times 10^{-5}\ \text{m}^3/\text{s})8(0.12\ \text{Ns/m}^2)(50\ \text{m})}{\pi(5.0 \times 10^{-3}\ \text{m})^4}$$

$= 2.1 \times 10^6$ Pa $= 20.7$ atm.

Also, since $P_2 = 1.0$ atm, this is also the gauge pressure at the inlet point of the pipe.

9.51 Flow rate $= \frac{(\Delta P)\pi R^4}{8L\eta} = \frac{(400\ \text{Pa})\pi(2.6 \times 10^{-3}\ \text{m})^4}{8(2.7 \times 10^{-3}\ \text{Pa s})(8.4 \times 10^{-2}\ \text{m})}$

$= 3.16 \times 10^{-5}\ \text{m}^3/\text{s}$

Then $v = \frac{\text{flow rate}}{\text{area}} = \frac{3.16 \times 10^{-5}\ \text{m}^3/\text{s}}{\pi(2.6 \times 10^{-3}\ \text{m})^2} = 1.5\ \text{m/s}$

9.52 From Poiseuille's law: $\Delta P = \frac{(\text{flow rate})8L\eta}{\pi R^4}$.

For water, 1 g/s = 1 cm^3/s = 10^{-6} m^3/s. Therefore,

$$\Delta P = \frac{(10^{-6}\ \text{m}^3/\text{s})8(0.03\ \text{m})(1.0 \times 10^{-3}\ \text{N s/m}^2)}{\pi(1.5 \times 10^{-4}\ \text{m})^4} = 1.5 \times 10^5\ \text{Pa}$$

9.53 The required flow rate $= \frac{500\ \text{cm}^3}{1800\ \text{s}} = 2.78 \times 10^{-1}\ \text{cm}^3/\text{s} = 2.78 \times 10^{-7}\ \text{m}^3/\text{s}$

If the solution is elevated 1 m, the pressure differential across the needle is $\Delta P = \rho g y = (1000\ \text{kg/m}^3)(9.80\ \text{m/s}^2)(1.0\ \text{m}) = 9800$ Pa

We find the radius via Poiseuille's law. $R^4 = \frac{8L\eta(\text{flow rate})}{\pi \Delta P}$, or

$$R^4 = \frac{8(2.5 \times 10^{-2}\ \text{m})(1.0 \times 10^{-3}\ \text{N s/m}^2)(2.78 \times 10^{-7}\ \text{m}^3/\text{s})}{\pi(9800\ \text{Pa})}$$

From which $R = 2.06 \times 10^{-4}$ m = 0.206 mm, or diameter = 0.41 mm.

9.54 The Reynold's number is

$$RN = \frac{\rho v d}{\eta} = \frac{(1050\ \text{kg/m}^3)(0.55\ \text{m/s})(2.0 \times 10^{-2}\ \text{m})}{2.7 \times 10^{-3}\ \text{N s/m}^2} = 4.3 \times 10^3.$$

In this region ($RN > 3000$), the flow is turbulent.

9.55 From the definition of the Reynolds's number,

$$v_{max} = \frac{(RN_{max})\eta}{\rho d} = \frac{(2000)(10^{-3}\ \text{Ns/m}^2)}{(10^3\ \text{kg/m}^3)(2.5 \times 10^{-2}\ \text{m})} = 8.0 \times 10^{-2}\ \frac{\text{m}}{\text{s}} = 8.0\ \frac{\text{cm}}{\text{s}}$$

9.56 Fick's law enables us to find the difference in concentration as

$$\Delta C = \frac{(\text{diffusion rate})L}{DA} = \frac{(5.33 \times 10^{-15}\ \text{kg/s})(0.10\ \text{m})}{(5.0 \times 10^{-10}\ \text{m}^2/\text{s})(6.0 \times 10^{-4}\ \text{m}^2)}$$

$= 1.8 \times 10^{-3}\ \text{kg/m}^3$

9.57 We use Fick's law to find the diffusion coefficient.

$$D = \frac{\text{diffusion rate}}{A\left(\frac{\Delta C}{L}\right)} = \frac{5.7 \times 10^{-15}\ \text{kg/s}}{(2.0 \times 10^{-4}\ \text{m}^2)(3.0 \times 10^{-2}\ \text{kg/m}^4)}$$

$$= 9.5 \times 10^{-10}\ \text{m}^2/\text{s}$$

9.58 From Stoke's law, $F = 6\pi\eta r v$. Therefore,

$$\eta = \frac{F}{6\pi r v} = \frac{3.0 \times 10^{-13}\ \text{N}}{6\pi(2.5 \times 10^{-6}\ \text{m})(4.5 \times 10^{-4}\ \text{m/s})} = 1.4 \times 10^{-5}\ \text{N s/m}^2$$

9.59 We use $v_t = \frac{2r^2 g}{9\eta}(\rho - \rho_f)$

or $(\rho - \rho_f) = \frac{9\eta v_t}{2r^2 g} = \frac{9(1.0 \times 10^{-3}\ \text{N s/m}^2)(1.10 \times 10^{-2}\ \text{m/s})}{2(5.0 \times 10^{-4})^2(9.80\ \text{m/s}^2)} = 20.2\ \text{kg/m}^3.$

Thus, $\rho = \rho_f + 20.2\ \text{kg/m}^3 = 1000\ \text{kg/m}^3 + 20.2\ \text{kg/m}^3 = 1.02 \times 10^3\ \text{kg/m}^3$

9.60 If at the end of one hour a particle is still in suspension, then its terminal velocity must be less than 5.0 cm/h = 1.39×10^{-5} m/s. Thus, we use $v_t = \frac{2r^2 g}{9\eta}(\rho - \rho_f)$ to find

$$r^2 = \frac{9\eta v_t}{2g(\rho - \rho_f)} = \frac{9(1.00 \times 10^{-3}\ \text{N s/m}^2)(1.39 \times 10^{-5}\ \text{m/s})}{2(9.80\ \text{m/s}^2)(800\ \text{kg/m}^3)}$$

and $r = 2.82 \times 10^{-6}$ m = 2.82 microns is the size of the largest particles that can still remain in suspension.

9.61 $A_1 = \frac{A_2 v_2}{v_1}$, where $A_2 = 1.96 \times 10^{-5}\ \text{m}^2$ = area of aorta.

Then A_1 = total capillary cross-section needed.

$$A_1 = \frac{(1.96 \times 10^{-5}\ \text{m}^2)(1.0\ \text{m/s})}{10^{-2}\ \text{m/s}} = 1.96 \times 10^{-3}\ \text{m}^2$$

But, A_1 = (number of capillaries)$A_{\text{single capillary}}$, and

$A_{\text{single capillary}} = 7.85 \times 10^{-11}\ \text{m}^2$.

Thus, number of capillaries = $\frac{1.96 \times 10^{-3}\ \text{m}^2}{7.85 \times 10^{-11}\ \text{m}^2} = 2.5 \times 10^7$ = 25 million.

9.62 (a) The speed at the narrow section is found from the equation of continuity:

$$v_2 = \frac{A_1 v_1}{A_2} = \frac{d_1^2}{d_2^2} v_1 = 16\, v_1 = 16.00\ \text{m/s}.$$

(b) We choose the zero level for y at the common center line of the horizontal pipes, and solve the resulting form of Bernoulli's equation for the pressure at the narrow section, point 2.

$$P_2 = P_1 + \frac{1}{2}\rho(v_1^2 - v_2^2)$$

$$= (3.00 \times 10^5\ \text{Pa}) + \frac{1}{2}(1000\ \text{kg/m}^3)((1.00\ \text{m/s})^2 - (16.00\ \text{m/s})^2)$$

$$= 1.73 \times 10^5\ \text{Pa}$$

9.63 When the sinker alone is submerged, the forces on the system are T_1, the tension in the string attached to the block, w_B, the weight of the block, w_S, the weight of the sinker, and B_S, the buoyant force on the sinker. Since equilibrium exists, we have

$$T_1 = w_B + w_S - B_S. \qquad (1)$$

When both are submerged, the forces on the system are T_2, the tension in the string attached to the block, the weight of the block, the buoyant force on the block, B_B, and the buoyant force on the sinker. From the first condition for equilibrium, we have

$$T_2 = w_B + w_S - B_B - B_S. \qquad (2)$$

Subtract (2) from (1) to give: $T_1 - T_2 = B_B$.

Thus, the buoyant force on the block is: $B_B = 200\text{ N} - 140\text{ N} = 60.0\text{ N}$.

However, the buoyant force on the block is equal to the weight of water displaced by the block: $B_B = 60\text{ N} = \rho_w V_{block} g$.

Thus, $V_{block} = \dfrac{60.0\text{ N}}{(1000\text{ kg/m}^3)(9.80\text{ m/s}^2)} = 6.12 \times 10^{-3}\text{ m}^3$.

The mass of the 50 N block is 5.10 kg. So, its density is

$$\rho = \frac{m}{V} = \frac{5.10\text{ kg}}{6.12 \times 10^{-3}\text{ m}^3} = 833\text{ kg/m}^3.$$

9.64 The forces on the balloon while in flight are B_a, the buoyant force of the air, w_{He}, the weight of the helium, w_B, the weight of the balloon, and w_L, the weight of the load. These quantities are found as follows, $B_a = \rho_a V_{balloon} g$, $w_{He} = \rho_{He} V_{balloon} g$, $w_B = (600\text{ kg})g$, and $w_L = (4000\text{ kg})g$.

When floating in equilibrium, we have: $B_a = w_{He} + w_B + w_L$, or

$$\rho_a V_{balloon} g = \rho_{He} V_{balloon} g + (600\text{ kg})g + (4000\text{ kg})g.$$

The density of Helium is 0.179 kg/m^3 and the density of air is 1.29 kg/m^3. Thus, we can solve for the volume of the balloon to find

$$V_{balloon} = 4.14 \times 10^3\text{ m}^3.$$

9.65 When the balloon comes into equilibrium, we must have

$$\Sigma F_y = B - w_{balloon} - w_{He} - w_{string} = 0$$

where w_{string} is the weight of the string above the ground, and B is the buoyant force. Thus, $w_{string} = B - w_{balloon} - w_{He}$. (1)

The mass per unit length of the string is:

$$\lambda = \frac{m}{L} = \frac{0.05\text{ kg}}{2.0\text{ m}} = 2.5 \times 10^{-2}\text{ kg/m}.$$

Thus, $w_{string} = \lambda h g = (0.025\text{ kg/m})(9.80\text{ m/s}^2)h$; $B = \rho_{air} V g = 3.39\text{ N}$; $w_{balloon} = m_{balloon} g = 2.45\text{ N}$; and $w_{He} = \rho_{He} V g = 0.470\text{ N}$.

Equation (1) above then becomes:

$$h = \frac{3.39\text{ N} - 2.45\text{ N} - 0.470\text{ N}}{(2.5 \times 10^{-2}\text{ kg/m})(9.80\text{ m/s}^2)} = \frac{0.470\text{ N}}{0.245\text{ kg/s}^2} = 1.9\text{ m}$$

9.66 Let us find the tension to stretch the wire by 0.1 mm.

The area $= A = \dfrac{\pi d^2}{4} = 3.80 \times 10^{-8}\text{ m}^2$. Thus, the force is

$$F = \frac{YA(\Delta L)}{L_0} = \frac{(18 \times 10^{10}\text{ Pa})(3.80 \times 10^{-8}\text{ m}^2)(10^{-4}\text{ m})}{3.1 \times 10^{-2}\text{ m}} = 22\text{ N}.$$

We have an equilibrium situation, so

$\Sigma F_x = 0$ becomes $F\cos 30° - F\cos 30° = 0$,

$\Sigma F_y = 0$ becomes $2F\sin30° = 2(22.1\text{ N})\sin30° = 22\text{ N}$ directed down the page in the textbook figure.

9.67 Solve by work-energy methods taking where the object is released from rest 10 m above the surface as the initial state and where the object comes to rest distance d below the surface of the water as the final state. The work-energy equation becomes:

$$W_{nc} = (KE_f - KE_i) + (PE_f - PE_i) = (0 - 0) + (mgy_f - mgy_i).$$

If we neglect friction effects and energy loss upon impact, the only non-conservative force doing work is the buoyant force, which acts as a retarding force after the object is in the water. Thus,

$$W_{nc} = -F_b d = -(\rho_{water} V_o g)\, d.$$

Here V_o is the volume of the object. Also, $m = \rho_o V_o$ where ρ_o is the density of the object. Choosing the zero of gravitional potential energy at the water surface, the work-energy equation becomes:

$$-(\rho_{water} V_o\, g)\, d = (\rho_o V_o)\, g[(-d) - 10\text{ m}].$$ This reduces to

$$d = (\rho_o / \rho_{water})(d + 10\text{ m}).$$ With $\rho_o/\rho_{water} = 0.60$, this last equation yields $d = 15\text{ m}$.

9.68 When the bar of soap, of cross-sectional area A, is in water only, the forces on it are the buoyant force of the water and its weight, w. Because it is floating, we know $B_w = w$. The buoyant force, B_w, is

$$B_w = \rho_w(A)(1.5 \times 10^{-2}\text{ m})g = w$$

From this equation, we find

$$\frac{w}{Ag} = \rho_w(1.5 \times 10^{-2}\text{ m}) \quad (1)$$

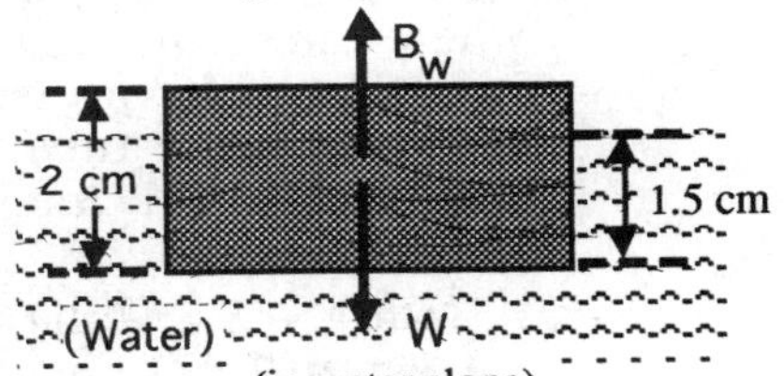

When the bar is floating in both water and oil, the forces on it are the buoyant force of the oil, the buoyant force of the water, and its weight. We have

$$B_o + B_w = w. \quad (2)$$

Let us call x the height of the bar that is in oil. Thus, the portion of the height of the bar which is in water is $(2 \times 10^{-2}\text{ m} - x)$. Equation (2) becomes

$$\rho_o(A)(x)g + \rho_w A(2.0 \times 10^{-2}\text{ m} - x)g = w$$

or, $$\rho_o x + \rho_w(2.0 \times 10^{-2}\text{ m} - x) = \frac{w}{Ag}.$$

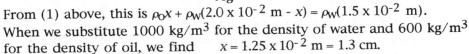

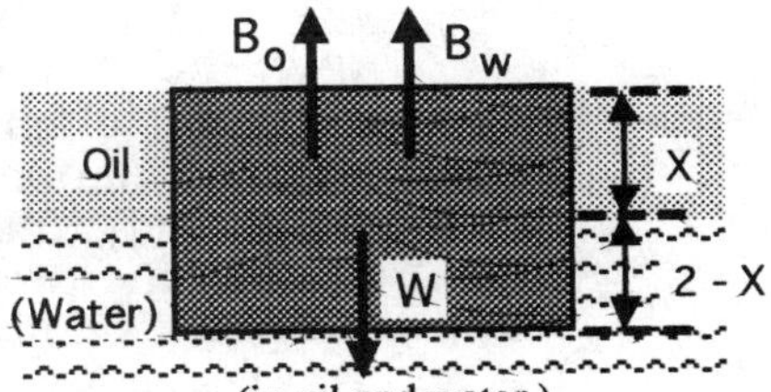

From (1) above, this is $\rho_o x + \rho_w(2.0 \times 10^{-2}\text{ m} - x) = \rho_w(1.5 \times 10^{-2}\text{ m})$.
When we substitute 1000 kg/m^3 for the density of water and 600 kg/m^3 for the density of oil, we find $x = 1.25 \times 10^{-2}\text{ m} = 1.3\text{ cm}$.

9.69 Let s stand for the edge of the cube, h for the depth of immersion, ρ_{ice} stand for the density of the ice, ρ_w stand for the density of water, and ρ_a stand for density of the alcohol.

(a) According to Archimedes' principle, at equilibrium we have

$$\rho_{ice} g s^3 = \rho_w g h s^2$$

giving $$h = s\frac{\rho_{ice}}{\rho_w}$$

With $\rho_{ice} = 0.917 \times 10^3\text{ kg/m}^3$, $\rho_w = 1.00 \times 10^3\text{ kg/m}^3$, and $s = 20\text{ mm}$ we get $h = 20(0.917) = 18.34\text{ mm}$

(b) We assume that the top of the cube is still above the alcohol surface. Letting h_a stand for the thickness of the alcohol layer, we have

$$\rho_a g s^2 h_a + \rho_w g s^2 h_w = \rho_{ice} g s^3$$

giving $$h_w = \frac{\rho_{ice}}{\rho_w} s - \frac{\rho_a}{\rho_w} h_a$$

With $\rho_a = 0.806 \times 10^3$ kg/m^3, and $h_a = 5$ mm we obtain

$$h_w = 18.34 - (0.806)(5) = 14.31 \text{ mm}$$

(c) Here $h_w' = s - h_a'$, so Archimedes' principle gives

$$\rho_a g s^2 h_a' + \rho_w g s^2 (s - h_a') = \rho_{ice} s^3$$

Leading to $\rho_a h_a' + \rho_w (s - h_a') = \rho_{ice} s$

From which, $$h_a' = \frac{s(\rho_w - \rho_{ice})}{(\rho_w - \rho_a)} = 20 \frac{1.000 - 0.917}{1.000 - 0.806} = 8.557 \text{ mm}$$

9.70 (a) $P = \frac{\Delta E}{\Delta t} = \frac{\Delta mgh}{\Delta t} = \frac{\Delta m}{\Delta t} gh = Rgh$

(b) $P_{EL} = 0.85(8.50 \times 10^5)(9.80)(87) = 616$ MW

9.71 (a) Consider the pressure at points A and B (at the same level in the two tubes).

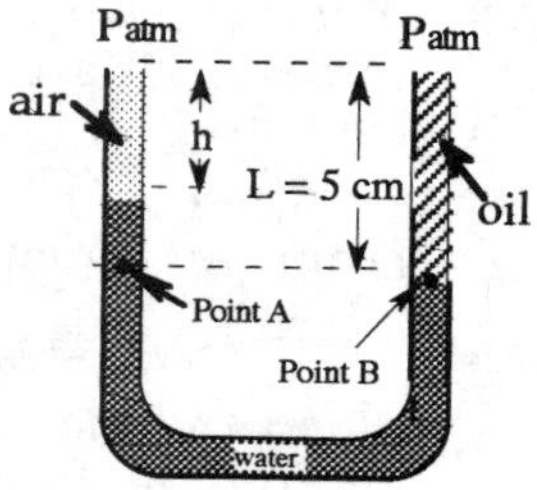

Using the left tube:

$P_A = P_{atm} + \rho_a g h + \rho_w g (L - h)$,

where the second term is due to the variation of air pressure with altitude.

Using the right tube: $P_B = P_{atm} + \rho_o g L$.

But Pascal's principle says that $P_A = P_B$.

Therefore,

$$P_{atm} + \rho_o g L = P_{atm} + \rho_a g h + \rho_w g (L - h), \quad \text{or}$$

$$(\rho_w - \rho_a) h = (\rho_w - \rho_o) L, \quad \text{giving}$$

$$h = \left(\frac{\rho_w - \rho_o}{\rho_w - \rho_a}\right) L = \left(\frac{1000 - 750}{1000 - 1.29}\right)(5.00 \text{ cm}) = 1.25 \text{ cm}.$$

(b) Consider the diagram at the right showing the situation when the air flow over the left tube equalizes the fluid levels in the two tubes. First, apply Bernoulli's equation to points A and B ($y_A = y_B$, $v_A = v$, and $v_B = 0$). This gives:

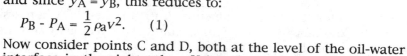

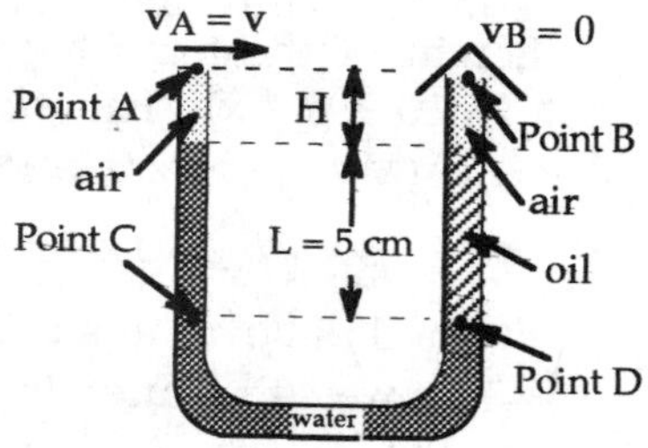

$$P_A + \frac{1}{2}\rho_a v^2 + \rho_a g y_A = P_B + \frac{1}{2}\rho_a (0)^2 + \rho_a g y_B$$

and since $y_A = y_B$, this reduces to:

$$P_B - P_A = \frac{1}{2}\rho_a v^2. \quad (1)$$

Now consider points C and D, both at the level of the oil-water interface in the right tube. Using the variation of pressure with depth in static fluids, we have:

$$P_C = P_A + \rho_a g H + \rho_w g L, \text{ and } \quad P_D = P_B + \rho_a g H + \rho_o g L.$$

But Pascal's principle says that $P_C = P_D$. Equating these two gives:

$$P_B + \rho_a g H + \rho_o g L = P_A + \rho_a g H + \rho_w g L, \text{ or}$$

$$P_B - P_A = (\rho_w - \rho_o) g L. \quad (2)$$

Substitute equation (1) for $P_B - P_A$ into (2) to obtain

$\frac{1}{2}\rho_a v^2 = (\rho_w - \rho_o) g L$, or

$$v = \sqrt{\frac{2gL(\rho_w - \rho_o)}{\rho_a}} = \sqrt{2(9.80\ \text{m/s}^2)(0.05\ \text{m})\left(\frac{1000 - 750}{1.29}\right)} = 13.8\ \text{m/s}.$$

9.72 Consider the diagram and apply Bernoulli's equation to points A and B, taking $y = 0$ at the level of point B, and recognizing that v_A is approximately zero. This gives:

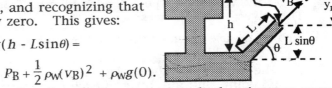

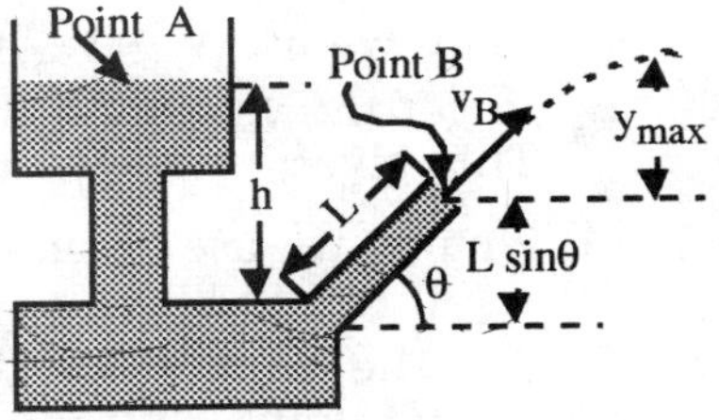

$$P_A + \frac{1}{2}\rho_w(0)^2 + \rho_w g(h - L\sin\theta) = P_B + \frac{1}{2}\rho_w(v_B)^2 + \rho_w g(0).$$

Now, recognize that $P_A = P_B = P_{atmosphere}$ since both points are open to the atmosphere (neglecting variation of atmospheric pressure with altitude). Thus, we obtain

$$v_B = \sqrt{2g(h - L\sin\theta)} = \sqrt{2(9.80\ \text{m/s}^2)(10.0\text{m} - (2.00\ \text{m})\sin 30°)} = 13.3\ \text{m/s}.$$

Now the problem reduces to one of projectile motion.

$v_{oy} = v_B \sin 30° = 6.64$ m/s. Then $v^2_y = v^2_{oy} + 2a(\Delta y)$ gives at the top of the arc (where $y = y_{max}$ and $v_y = 0$)

$0 = (6.64\ \text{m/s})^2 + 2(-9.80\ \text{m/s}^2)(y_{max} - 0)$, or

$y_{max} = 2.3$ m (above the level where the water emerges)

9.73 The pressure on the ball is given by: $P = P_{atm} + \rho_w g h$ so the change in pressure on the ball when it is on the surface of the ocean to when it is at the bottom of the ocean is $\Delta P = \rho_w g h$.

In addition, from the definition of bulk modulus, this increase in pressure will change the volume of the ball as follows:

$\Delta V = \frac{-V\Delta P}{B}$, where B is the bulk Modulus. This change in volume can be written as $\Delta V = V_f - V_i = \frac{4}{3}\pi r_f^3 - \frac{4}{3}\pi r_i^3 = \frac{4}{3}\pi(r_f^3 - r_i^3)$. Equating the expressions for ΔV gives $\frac{4}{3}\pi(r_f^3 - r_i^3) = \frac{4}{3}\pi r_i^3 \frac{\Delta P}{B}$,

or $r_f^3 = r_i^3(1 - \frac{\Delta P}{B})$. Thus, the final radius of the ball is

$$r_f = r_i\left(1 - \frac{\Delta P}{B}\right)^{1/3}$$

The decrease in diameter of the ball is $\Delta D = 2(r_i - r_f)$

$$\text{or } \Delta D = 2r_i\left(1 - \left(1 - \frac{\Delta P}{B}\right)^{1/3}\right) = D_i\left(1 - \left(1 - \frac{\Delta P}{B}\right)^{1/3}\right)$$

$$= (3.00\ \text{m})\left(1 - \left(1 - \frac{1.01 \text{ X } 10^8\ \text{PA}}{14 \text{ X } 10^{10}\ \text{PA}}\right)^{1/3}\right) = 7.2 \text{ X } 10^{-4}\ \text{m} = 0.72\ \text{mm}$$

9.74 Let $V = \frac{4}{3}\pi r^3$ be the volume of the ball, D the depth of the water, m the mass of the ball. Then while the ball is under the water

$(m + m_{air})a = B - (m + m_{air})g$, or

$$(m + \rho_{air}V)a = \rho_{water}Vg - (m + \rho_{air}V)g, \text{ so } a = \frac{(\rho_{water} - \rho_{air})V - m}{m + \rho_{air}V}g.$$

$$a = \left(\frac{(1000 - 1.29)(\text{kg/m}^3)\ \frac{4}{3}\pi(0.10\text{ m})^3 - 1.0\text{ kg}}{1.0\text{ kg} + 1.29\ (\text{kg/m}^3)\ \frac{4}{3}\pi(0.10)^3}\right)(9.80\text{ m/s}^2) = 31.0\text{ m/s}^2.$$

Then we use $v^2 = v^2{}_0 + 2a(\Delta y) = 0 + 2\left(31.0\text{ m/s}^2(2.0\text{ m})\right) = 124.1\text{ m}^2/\text{s}^2$, to get the velocity of the ball as it emerges from the pool.
This gives: $v = 11.1$ m/s.
Finally, we use $\frac{1}{2}(m + m_{air})v^2 = (m + m_{air})gh$ to get $h = 6.3$ m.

9.75 (a) The pressure on the surface of the two hemispheres is constant at all points and the force on each element of surface area is directed along the radius of the hemispheres. The applied force along the axis must balance the force on the "effective" area which is the projection of the actual surface onto a plane perpendicular to the x axis, $A = \pi R^2$. Therefore,

$$F = (P_{atm} - P)\pi R^2.$$

(b) For the values given

$$F = (P_{atm} - 0.10P_{atm})\pi(0.30\text{ m})^2 = 0.254P_{atm} = 2.6 \times 10^4\text{ N}$$

9.76 We call the position of the lower hole point 1 and the position of the higher hole point 2. Both of these points are at atmospheric pressure. From our earlier study of projectile motion, the range is given by

$$R = v_1t_1 = v_2t_2. \qquad (1)$$

An expression for the time for the water to reach the floor can also be found through the projectile motion equations. We have

$y = v_{oy}t + \frac{1}{2}at^2 = 0 + \frac{1}{2}gt^2$, or $t = \sqrt{\frac{2}{g}h}$ where h is the height through which the projectile falls before it reaches ground level. Thus, we have the time for the water from the upper hole to reach the floor to be:

$t_2 = \sqrt{\frac{2}{g}(0.120\text{ m})}$, and the time for the water from the lower hole as

$t_1 = \sqrt{\frac{2}{g}(0.0500\text{ m})}$.

Substitute these two values for the times into (1) above to give

$$v_1{}^2 = 2.4v_2{}^2. \qquad (2)$$

Since the pressure cancels from Bernoulli's equation, it reduces to

$$(v_1{}^2 - v_2{}^2) = 2g(y_2 - y_1). \qquad (3)$$

Given: $y_2 = 0.120$ m, $y_1 = 0.0500$ m. Then, with the use of (2) and (3) we find

$$v_2 = 0.99\text{ m/s}.$$

Let us now consider Bernoulli's Equation once again, with a point 3 at the top of the tank and point 2 still at the position of the top hole. Both these points are at atmospheric pressure, and the velocity of fall of water at the top of the tank is negligibly small. We find:

$$\rho g y_3 = \frac{1}{2}\rho v_2^2 + \rho g y_2, \text{ or} \qquad \rho g(y_3 - y_2) = \rho g h = \frac{1}{2}\rho v_2^2.$$

From which, $h = \frac{v_2^2}{2g} = \frac{(0.99 \text{ m/s})^2}{2(9.80 \text{ m/s}^2)} = 5 \times 10^{-2} \text{ m} = 5.0 \text{ cm}.$

Thus, the water surface is 5.0 cm above the top hole or 17.0 cm above the bottom of the tank.

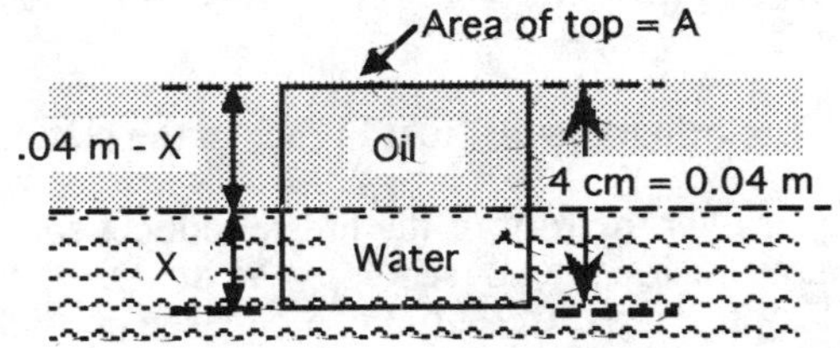

9.77 [Refer to the above diagram for this problem.]
Since the Block floats, Total buoyant force = weight of block, or
$F_{B(oil)} + F_{B(water)}$ = weight of block. This becomes:

$$\rho_{oil}\left(A(4.00 \times 10^{-2} \text{ m} - x)\right)g + \rho_{water}(Ax)g = \rho_{block}\left(A(4.00 \times 10^{-2} \text{ m})\right)g$$

where $A(4.00 \times 10^{-2} \text{ m} - x)$ = volume of oil displaced, and Ax = volume of water displaced. Canceling A, and substituting into the equation above, we have:

$$(930 \text{ kg/m}^3)(4.00 \times 10^{-2} \text{ m} - x) + (1000 \text{ kg/m}^3)x = (960 \text{ kg/m}^3)(4.00 \times 10^{-2} \text{ m})$$

Solving for x: $x = 1.71 \times 10^{-2} \text{ m} = 1.71 \text{ cm}.$

9.78 To have the object float fully submerged in the fluid, its average density must be the same as that of the fluid. Therefore, we must add ethanol to water until the density of the mixture is 900 kg/m^3. If m = mass of mixture, m_e = mass of ethanol, and m_w = mass of water, we obtain:

$$m = m_e + m_w. \qquad (1)$$

For the volumes: $V = V_e + V_w$. (2)

Equation (1) becomes: $\rho V = \rho_e V_e + \rho_w V_w$ and with the use of equation (2), this reduces to $\frac{\rho}{\rho_w}(V_e + V_w) = \frac{\rho_e}{\rho_w}(V_e) + V_w$, or

$$0.9(V_e + V_w) = (0.806)(V_e) + V_w$$

which yields: $V_e = 1.064V_w = (1.064)(500 \text{ cc}) = 532 \text{ cm}^3$.

ANSWERS TO CONCEPTUAL QUESTIONS

2. Both must have the same strength. The force on the back of each dam is the average pressure of the water times the area of the dam. If both reservoirs are equally deep, the force is the same.

4. The external pressure on the chest cavity makes it difficult to take a breath while under water. Thus, a snorkel will not work in deep water.

6. The buoyant force depends on the amount of air displaced by the objects. Since they have the same dimensions, the buoyant force will be the same on each.

8. The larger the density of a fluid, the higher does an object float in it. Thus, an object will float lower in low density alcohol.

10. The water level on the side of the glass stays the same. The floating ice cube displaces its own weight of liquid water, and so does the liquid water into which it melts.

12. A breeze from any direction speeds up to go over the mound, and the air pressure drops at this opening. Air then flows through the burrow from the lower to the upper entrance.

14. No. The somewhat lighter barge will float higher in the water.

16. The rapidly moving air over the roof of the house reduces the downward pressure on it. However, the stagnant air inside the house keeps the pressure the same as it was in the absence of the storm. This pressure differential can be large enough to push off the roof. Opening windows helps to equalize the pressure inside and out, providing minimal protection in a storm.

CHAPTER TEN SOLUTIONS

Chapter Ten Readings

Berry, R.S., "When the Melting and Freezing Points are not the Same," *Scientific American*, August 1990, p.68.

Greenslade, T.B., "The Maximum Density of Water," *The Physics Teacher*, November 1985, p. 474.

Hall, M.B., "Robert Boyle," *Scientific American*, August 1967, p. 84.

Jones, F., "Fahrenheit and Celsius, A History," *Physics Today*, 18, 1980, p. 594.

Otani, R. and Siegel, P., "Determining Absolute Zero in the Kitchen Sink", The Physics Teacher, 29, 316, 1991.

Romer, R.H., "Temperature Scales: Celsius, Fahrenheit, Kelvin, Reaumur, and Romer," *The Physics Teacher*, October 1982, p. 450.

Ruthern, R., "Illuminating Zero", Scientific American, v. 268 (Apr. '93) p32-33.

Wilson, R.E., "Standards of Temperature," *Physics Today*, January 1953, p. 10.

10.1 (a) $T_F = 1.8T_C + 32 = 1.8(-273.15) + 32 = -459.67°$

(b) $T_C = \frac{5}{9}(T_F - 32) = \frac{5}{9}(98.6 - 32) = 37°\text{ C}$,

(c) $T_F = 1.8T_C + 32 = 1.8(T_K - 273.15) + 32 = -279.7°\text{ F}$.

10.2 $T_C = \frac{5}{9}(T_F - 32) = \frac{5}{9}(136 - 32) = 57.8°\text{ C}$,

and $T_C = \frac{5}{9}(T_F - 32) = \frac{5}{9}(-127 - 32) = -88.3°\text{ C}$.

10.3 (a) To convert from Celsius to Fahrenheit, we use

$$T_F = \frac{9}{5}T_C + 32 = \frac{9}{5}(-252.87\text{ °C}) + 32 = -423\text{°F}$$

and to convert to Kelvin, we use

$$T_K = T_C + 273 = -253\text{°C} + 273 = 20\text{ K}.$$

(b) We use an approach here that is identical to that used in (a).

$$T_F = 68\text{°F} \quad \text{and} \quad T_K = 293\text{ K}$$

10.4 Let us use $T_C = \frac{5}{9}(T_F - 32)$ with $T_F = -40\text{°C}$. $T_C = \frac{5}{9}(-40 - 32) = -40\text{°C}$.

10.5 Since we have a linear graph, we know that the pressure is related to the temperature as $P = A + BT$, where A and B are constants. To find A and B, we use the given data:

$$0.900\text{ atm} = A + (-80.0\text{°C})B \qquad (1)$$
$$1.635\text{ atm} = A + (78.0\text{°C})B \qquad (2)$$

Solving (1) and (2) simultaneously, we find:

$A = 1.272$ atm, and $B = 4.652 \times 10^{-3}$ atm/°C.

Therefore, $P = 1.272 \text{ atm} + (4.652 \times 10^{-3} \text{ atm/°C})T$.

(a) At absolute zero: $P = 0 = 1.272 \text{ atm} + (4.652 \times 10^{-3} \text{ atm/°C})T$, which gives $T = -273.5°C$.

(b) At the freezing point of water: $P = 1.272 \text{ atm} + 0 = 1.272 \text{ atm}$, and at the boiling point:

$$P = 1.272 \text{ atm} + (4.652 \times 10^{-3} \text{ atm/°C})(100°C) = 1.737 \text{ atm}.$$

10.6 When volume is constant, we have a linear relation between pressure and temperature. That is, at temperature T, the pressure is given by, $P = A + BT$, where A and B are constants. To find A and B, we use the given data:

$$0.700 \text{ atm} = A + (100°C)B \quad (1)$$
$$0.512 \text{ atm} = A + 0 \quad (2)$$

Thus, from (2): $A = 0.512 \text{ atm}$.

Then from (1): $B = 1.88 \times 10^{-3} \text{ atm/°C}$.

Therefore, $P = 0.512 \text{ atm} + (1.88 \times 10^{-3} \text{ atm/°C})T$.

(a) When $P = 0.0400$ atm, we have

$0.04 \text{ atm} = 0.512 \text{ atm} + (1.88 \times 10^{-3} \text{ atm/°C})T$, yielding $T = -251°C$.

(b) When $T = 450°C$,

$$P = 0.512 \text{ atm} + (1.88 \times 10^{-3} \text{ atm/°C})(450°C) = 1.358 \text{ atm}.$$

10.7 Apply $T_F = \frac{9}{5} T_C + 32$ to two different temperatures, which we will call 1 and 2. We have:

$$T_{F1} = \frac{9}{5} T_{C1} + 32, \quad (1)$$

and

$$T_{F2} = \frac{9}{5} T_{C2} + 32. \quad (2)$$

Subtract (1) from (2) to obtain: $T_{F2} - T_{F1} = \frac{9}{5}(T_{C2} - T_{C1})$

or, $\Delta T_F = \frac{9}{5} \Delta T_C$.

10.8 Use $L = L_0(1 + \alpha(T - T_0))$:

$L_{-20} = L_0 + \alpha L_0(-20.0°C) - L_0 T_0$, and $L_{35} = L_0 + \alpha L_0(35.0°C) - L_0 T_0$.

$\Delta L = L_{35} - L_{-20} = \alpha L_0(55°C)$,

or $\Delta L = (11 \times 10^{-6} \text{ /°C})(518 \text{ m})(55°C) = 0.313 \text{ m} = 31 \text{ cm}$.

10.9 $\Delta L = \alpha L_0 \Delta T = (1.42 \times 10^{-5} \text{ °C}^{-1})(2.168 \text{ cm})(85°C) = 2.62 \times 10^{-3} \text{ m}$.

Thus, $L = L_0 + \Delta L = 2.168 \text{ cm} + .00262 \text{ cm} = 2.171 \text{ cm}$.

10.10 (a) The change in length is

$\Delta L = \alpha L_0 \Delta T = (19 \times 10^{-6} \text{ °C}^{-1})(1.3000 \text{ m})(-20.0°C) = -4.94 \times 10^{-4} \text{ m}$

Thus, the final length of the pendulum is: $L_f = 1.2995$ m.

(b) From the expression for the period, $T = 2\pi\sqrt{\frac{L}{g}}$, we see that as the length decreases the period decreases. Thus, the clock runs fast.

10.11 We shall choose the radius as our linear dimension.

$L = L_0[1 + \alpha(T - T_0)]$

$2.21 \text{ cm} = 2.20 \text{ cm}[1 + (130 \times 10^{-6} \text{ C}^{-1})\Delta T]$, giving $\Delta T = 35°C$.

Therefore, $T = 55°C$.

10.12 $\Delta V = \beta V_0 \Delta T = 3\alpha V_0 \Delta T =$,

$$\text{so } \Delta T = \frac{\Delta V}{3\alpha V_0} = \frac{100 \text{ x } 10^{-6} \text{ m}^3}{3(24 \text{ x } 10^{-6} \text{ m}^3(°\text{C})^{-1})(\text{m}^3)} = 1.39° \text{ C}.$$

10.13 (a) We must raise the diameter (a linear dimension) of the sleeve to match the diameter of the shaft, and it is necessary to increase the diameter of the sleeve by $\Delta L = 1.6 \text{ x } 10^{-2}$ cm.

$\Delta L = \alpha L_0 \Delta T$

$1.6 \text{ x } 10^{-2}$ cm= $(19 \text{ x } 10^{-6}\ °\text{C}^{-1})(3.196 \text{ cm})(\Delta T)$

We find, $\Delta T = 263.5$C°.

(b) We must cool the shaft to contract its diameter from 3.212 cm down to 3.196 cm, a change of $-1.6 \text{ x } 10^{-2}$ cm.

$\Delta L = \alpha L_0 \Delta T$

$-1.6 \text{ x } 10^{-2}$ cm= $(19 \text{ x } 10^{-6}\ °\text{C}^{-1})(3.212 \text{ cm})(\Delta T)$, or $\Delta T = -262.2$ C°.

10.14 Let us consider a solid which has a volume given by $V_0 = A_0 L_0$ at T_0. At a temperature T, the volume is $V = AL$. Let us consider the area first. We have, $\Delta A = A - A_0 = 2\alpha A_0 \Delta T$. Therefore, $A = (1 + 2\alpha\Delta T)A_0$.
Similarly, the new linear dimension is: $L = (1 + \alpha\Delta T)L_0$.

So, $V = AL = (1 + 2\alpha\Delta T)A_0(1 + \alpha\Delta T)L_0 = A_0 L_0(1 + \alpha\Delta T + 2\alpha\Delta T + 2\alpha^2\Delta T)$.

The term involving α^2 is negligibly small in comparison to the other terms in the parenthesis of the last equation. Thus,

$V = AL = A_0 L_0(1 + 3\alpha\Delta T)$, or $V = V_0(1 + 3\alpha\Delta T) = V_0 + 3\alpha V_0 \Delta T$.

Thus, $\Delta V = V - V_0 = \beta V_0 \Delta T$ (where $\beta = 3\alpha$).

10.15 (a) $L = L_0[1 + \alpha(T - T_0)]$,

or 5.050 cm = 5.000 cm$[1 + (24 \text{ x } 10^{-6}\ °\text{C}^{-1})\Delta T]$.

From which, $\Delta T = 417$C°, and $T = 437$°C.

(b) We must get $L_{al} = L_{brass}$ for some ΔT, or

$L_{oal}(1 + \alpha_{al}\Delta T) = L_{obrass}(1 + \alpha_{brass}\Delta T)$

5.000 cm$[1 + (24 \text{ x } 10^{-6}\ °\text{C}^{-1})\Delta T]$ = 5.050 cm$[1 + (19 \text{ x } 10^{-6}\ °\text{C}^{-1})\Delta T]$.

Solving for ΔT gives $\Delta T = 2079$ C°, so $T = 2099$°C.

This will not work because aluminum melts at 660°C

10.16 Let us first find the length of the aluminum column at 29.4 °C.

$\Delta L_c = L_c - L_{oc} = \alpha L_{oc}\Delta T$, or

$L_c = (1 + \alpha\Delta T)L_{oc} = [1 + (24 \text{ x } 10^{-6}\text{C}^{-1})(8.2\ °\text{C})]18.7 \text{ m} = 18.704$ m.

We must now find what length of tape (at 21.2 °C when the scale markings were painted on) will be 18.704 m long at 29.4 °C.

$L_t = (1 + \alpha\Delta T)L_{ot}$, or

$$L_{ot} = \frac{L_t}{(1 + \alpha\Delta T)} = \frac{18.704 \text{ m}}{(1 + (11 \text{ x } 10^{-6} \text{ C}^{-1})(8.2\ °\text{C}))} = 18.702 \text{ m}.$$

Thus, the steel tape will read the length of the aluminum column to be 18.702 m at a temperature of 29.4 °C.

10.17 Let us find the elongation of the circumference when heated.

$\Delta L = \alpha L_0 \Delta T = (17.3 \text{ x } 10^{-6}\ °\text{C}^{-1})(3.142 \text{ x } 10^{-2} \text{ m})(43\ °\text{C}) = 2.34 \text{ x } 10^{-5}$ m.

When the band cools but is not allowed to contract, the tension in the band must be sufficient to stretch it by an amount ΔL.

$$\text{Stress} = Y\text{ strain} = Y\frac{\Delta L}{L_o} = (18 \times 10^{10}\text{ Pa})\frac{2.34 \times 10^{-5}\text{ m}}{3.142 \times 10^{-2}\text{ m}} = 1.34 \times 10^{8}\text{ Pa.}$$

But Stress $= \frac{F}{A}$ and A = width X thickness.

Thus, $A = (4.0 \times 10^{-3}\text{ m})(5.0 \times 10^{-4}\text{ m}) = 20 \times 10^{-7}$ m, and

$F = (20 \times 10^{-7}\text{ m}^2)(1.34 \times 10^{8}\text{ Pa}) = 270$ N.

10.18 $V_o = 45$ liters $= 45 \times 10^{-3}\text{ m}^3$. When the gasoline warms to 35°C, its new volume can be found from: $\Delta V = \beta V_o \Delta T$.

This is the volume which must overflow.

$\Delta V = (9.6 \times 10^{-4}\text{C}^{-1})(45 \times 10^{-3}\text{ m}^3)(25°\text{C})$, or

$\Delta V = 1.08 \times 10^{-3}$ m = 1.1 liters (about 0.29 gallons).

10.19 The change in Celsius temperature of the gasoline as it leaves the truck and enters the storage tank is: $\Delta T_F = \frac{9}{5}\Delta T_C$, or $-36\text{ °F} = \frac{9}{5}\Delta T_C$.

Thus, $\Delta T_C = -20$ °C. We are given that the final volume of gasoline, V_f, is 1000 gal, and we are to find the volume, V_o, when it was on the truck at 90 °F:

$$\frac{\Delta V}{V_o} = \frac{V_f - V_o}{V_o} = \beta\Delta T = (9.6 \times 10^{-4}\text{C}^{-1})(-20\text{ °C}) = -1.92 \times 10^{-2},$$

giving $V_f = 0.9808 V_o$. From which, $V_o = \frac{1000\text{ gal}}{0.9808} = 1020$ gallons.

10.20 $$8.315\frac{\text{J}}{\text{mol K}} = 8.315\left(\frac{\text{J}}{\text{mol K}}\right)\left(\frac{1\text{ N m}}{1\text{ J}}\right)\left(\frac{10^3\text{ L}}{1\text{ m}^3}\right)\left(\frac{1\text{ atm}}{1.013 \times 10^5\text{ N/m}^2}\right)$$

$$= 8.208 \times 10^{-2}\frac{\text{L atm}}{\text{mol K}}$$

10.21 (a) With constant volume, $\frac{P_f V_f}{T_f} = \frac{P_i V_i}{T_i}$ becomes

$$T_f = \frac{T_i P_f}{P_i} = \frac{(300\text{ K})3P_i}{P_i} = 900\text{ K} = 627\text{ °C}.$$

(b) $\frac{P_f V_f}{T_f} = \frac{P_i V_i}{T_i}$ gives, $\frac{2P_i 2V_i}{T_f} = \frac{P_i V_i}{300\text{ K}}$, or $T_f = 1200\text{ K} = 927\text{°C}$.

10.22 (a) $$n = \frac{PV}{RT} = \frac{(9.0\text{ atm})(1.013 \times 10^5\text{ Pa/atm})(8.0 \times 10^{-3}\text{ m}^3)}{(8.31\text{ Nm/mol K})(293\text{ K})} = 3.0\text{ moles}$$

(b) $N = nN_a = (3.0\text{ mol})(6.02 \times 10^{23}\frac{\text{molecules}}{\text{mol}}) = 1.8 \times 10^{24}$ molecules.

10.23 (a) From $PV = nRT$, we have

$$n = \frac{PV}{RT} = \frac{(1.013 \times 10^5\text{ Pa})(10^{-6}\text{ m}^3)}{(8.31\text{ J/mol K})(293\text{ K})} = 4.16 \times 10^{-5}\text{ mol.} \quad (1)$$

Thus, the number of molecules ($N = nN_A$) is

$$N = (4.16 \times 10^{-5}\text{ mol})(6.02 \times 10^{23}\frac{\text{molecules}}{\text{mole}}) = 2.5 \times 10^{19}\text{ molecules.}$$

(b) Since V, R, and T are all constants, (1) above shows that the ratio of n to P is a constant. Thus, $\frac{n_f}{n_i} = \frac{P_f}{P_i}$, or

$$n_f = (4.16 \times 10^{-5}\ \text{mol})\frac{10^{-11}\ \text{Pa}}{1.013 \times 10^{5}\ \text{Pa}} = 4.1 \times 10^{-21}\ \text{mol.}$$

10.24 We may use of the ideal gas equation expressed as $\frac{P_f V_f}{T_f} = \frac{P_i V_i}{T_i}$.

Substitute $P_f = \frac{P_i}{2}$ and $T_f = \frac{3}{4} T_i$ to obtain, $\frac{V_f}{V_i} = \frac{3}{2}$.

10.25 $\frac{P_f V_f}{T_f} = \frac{P_i V_i}{T_i}$, which becomes

$$\frac{(0.800 \times 10^5\ \text{Pa})(0.700\ \text{m}^3)}{T_f} = \frac{(0.200 \times 10^5\ \text{Pa})(1.50\ \text{m}^3)}{300\ \text{K}}.$$

From which, $T_f = 560\ \text{K} = 287\ ^\circ\text{C}$.

10.26 $P_f = \frac{n_f R T_f}{V_f}$ and, $P_0 = \frac{n_0 R T_0}{V_0}$, so $\frac{P_f}{P_0} = \frac{n_f T_f V_0}{n_0 T_0 V_f}$.

But $V_0 = V_f$ and $n_f = \frac{1}{2} n_0$. Therefore, $\frac{P_f}{P_0} = \frac{1}{2}\left(\frac{T_f}{T_0}\right) = \frac{1}{2}\left(\frac{338}{288}\right) = 0.587$.

$P_f = 5.87$ atm, since $P_0 = 10.0$ atm.

10.27 Applying the ideal gas law to both the initial and final states of the oxygen in the tank gives: $P_i V_i = n_i R T_i$, (1)

and $P_f V_f = n_f R T_f$ (2)

Dividing (2) by (1), remembering that $V_f = V_i$ and $T_f = T_i$, gives:

$$n_f = n_i \left(\frac{P_f}{P_i}\right) = (0.40\ \text{mol})\frac{25\ \text{atm}}{40\ \text{atm}} = 0.25\ \text{mol.}$$

Thus, the quantity of oxygen withdrawn must be
0.4 mol - 0.25 mol = 0.15 mol.
Since, for oxygen (O_2), 1 mol = 32 g, the mass of oxygen withdrawn is found to be: $m = (0.15\ \text{mol})\frac{32\ \text{g}}{1\ \text{mol}} = 4.8\ \text{g}$

10.28 Let us use $V = \frac{4}{3}\pi r^3$ as the volume of the balloon, and the ideal gas law in the form: $\frac{P_f V_f}{T_f} = \frac{P_i V_i}{T_i}$ to give, $r_i^3 = \frac{300\ \text{K}}{200\ \text{K}}\frac{.030\ \text{atm}}{1\ \text{atm}}(20\ \text{m})^3$.

This yields $r_i = 7.1$ m.

10.29 $V_i = (\pi r^2) h_i = \pi(1.50\ \text{m})^2(4.00\ \text{m}) = 28.3\ \text{m}^3$ (original volume of gas inside) At 220 m down:

$P = P_{atm} + \rho g h = 1.013 \times 10^5\ \text{Pa} + (1025\ \text{kg/m}^3)(9.80\ \text{m/s}^2)(220\ \text{m})$, or

$P = 2.311 \times 10^6$ Pa.

$$V_f = V_i \frac{P_i T_f}{P_f T_i} = 28.3\ \text{m}^3 \frac{(1.013 \times 10^5\ \text{Pa})}{(2.311 \times 10^6\ \text{Pa})}\frac{(278)}{(298)} = 1.16\ \text{m}^3$$

Also, $V_f =$ (area)$h' = \pi(1.50\ \text{m})^2 h'$. Which gives:

$h' = 0.164$ m = 16.4 cm = height of the remaining air space

Thus, the water has risen a distance of $h - h' = 4.000\ \text{m} - 0.164\ \text{m} = 3.84$ m inside the hull.

10.30 We first find the pressure of the air in the bubble when at a depth of 100 m by use of $P = P_{atm} + \rho g h$:

$$P = 1.013 \times 10^5 \text{ Pa} + (1000 \text{ kg/m}^3)(9.80 \text{ m/s}^2)(100 \text{ m}) = 1.08 \times 10^6 \text{ Pa}.$$

We now use: $\frac{P_f V_f}{T_f} = \frac{P_i V_i}{T_i}$. However, at constant temperature, this becomes: $P_f V_f = P_i V_i$, or, $(1.013 \times 10^5 \text{ Pa}) V_f = (1.08 \times 10^6 \text{ Pa})(1.50 \text{ cm}^3)$, and $V_f = 16.0 \text{ cm}^3$.

10.31 $PV = nRT = \left(\frac{m}{M}\right) RT$ where m is the mass of the gas present and M is the molecular weight of this type gas. Thus, $\rho = \frac{m}{V} = \frac{PM}{RT}$.

When pressure is constant, this gives: $\frac{\rho_f}{\rho_i} = \frac{T_i}{T_f}$ = or $\rho_f = \rho_i \left(\frac{T_i}{T_f}\right)$.

We have $\rho_f = \rho_i \left(\frac{T_i}{T_f}\right) = 0.179 \text{ kg/m}^3 \left(\frac{273 \text{ K}}{373 \text{ K}}\right) = 0.131 \text{ kg/m}^3$

10.32 We first find the pressure exerted by the gas on the wall of the container.

$$P = \frac{NkT}{V} = \frac{3N_a kT}{V} = \frac{3RT}{V} = \frac{3(8.31 \text{ N m/mol K})(293 \text{ K})}{8.00 \times 10^{-3} \text{ m}^3} = 9.13 \times 10^5 \text{ Pa}.$$

Thus, the force on one of the walls of the cubical container is

$$F = PA = (9.13 \times 10^5 \text{ Pa})(4.00 \times 10^{-2} \text{ m}^2) = 3.65 \times 10^4 \text{ N}.$$

10.33 The average kinetic energy $= \frac{3}{2} kT$ regardless of the gas.

Thus, $\langle KE \rangle = \frac{3}{2} kT = \frac{3}{2} (1.38 \times 10^{-23} \text{ J/K})(300 \text{ K}) = 6.21 \times 10^{-21} \text{ J}$.

10.34 (a) The total random kinetic energy in one mole is the average kinetic energy of one atom times the number of atoms, Avogadro's number.

$$KE = N_A \frac{3}{2} kT = (6.02 \times 10^{23} \text{ atoms}) \frac{3}{2} (1.38 \times 10^{-23} \text{ J/K})(300 \text{ K}) = 3740 \text{ J}.$$

(b) One mol of hydrogen (H_2) has a mass of 2.00×10^{-3} kg, so

$KE = 3740 \text{ J} = \frac{1}{2} (2.00 \times 10^{-3} \text{ kg}) v^2$, giving $v = 1930 \text{ m/s}$.

10.35 One mole of helium has Avogadro's number of molecules and contains a mass of 4.00 g. Let us call m the mass of one atom, and we have

$N_a m = 4.00$ g/mol, or $m = \frac{4.00 \text{ g/mol}}{6.02 \times 10^{23} \text{ molecules/mol}}$, giving

$m = 6.64 \times 10^{-24}$ g/molecule $= 6.64 \times 10^{-27}$ kg/molecule.

Helium gas has one atom per molecule so this is also the mass per atom.

10.36 From the ideal gas equation,

$$P = \frac{nRT}{V} = \frac{(3.00 \text{ mol})(8.31 \text{ J/mol K})(300 \text{ K})}{2.24 \times 10^{-2} \text{ m}^3} = 3.34 \times 10^5 \text{ Pa}.$$

10.37 $(KE)_{\text{molecule}} = \frac{1}{2} mv^2_{\text{vrms}} = \frac{3}{2} kT$, so $v^2_{\text{vrms}} = \frac{3kT}{m}$.

The mass of a hydrogen molecule is

$$m = \frac{\text{mass of 1 mol}}{N_A} = \frac{2.00 \times 10^{-3}\ \text{kg/mol}}{6.02 \times 10^{23}\ \text{molecules/mol}}$$

$= 3.32 \times 10^{-27}$ kg/molecule.

Similarly, for CO_2, $m = 7.31 \times 10^{-26}$ kg/molecule.

$$v^2_{\text{hydrogen}} = \frac{3kT}{m} = \frac{3(1.38 \times 10^{-23}\ \text{J/mol K})(240\ \text{K})}{3.32 \times 10^{-27}\ \text{kg/molecule}}, \text{ yielding}$$

$v_{\text{hydrogen}} = 1.73 \times 10^3$ m/s = 1.73 km/s.

For CO_2 molecules,

$$v^2_{\text{carbon dioxide}} = \frac{3kT}{m} = \frac{3(1.38 \times 10^{-23}\ \text{J/mol K})(240\ \text{K})}{7.31 \times 10^{-26}\ \text{kg/molecule}}, \text{ and}$$

$v_{\text{carbon dioxide}} = 369$ m/s = 0.369 km/s.

$$\frac{v_{\text{escape}}}{6} = \frac{10.3\ \text{km/s}}{6} = 1.71\ \text{km/s}.$$

Thus, hydrogen will escape, but carbon dioxide will not. The predominant component in the atmosphere of Venus is carbon dioxide and hydrogen is present only in combination with other elements.

10.38 (a) $\langle KE \rangle = \frac{3}{2} kT = \frac{3}{2}(1.38 \times 10^{-23}\ \text{J/K})(423\ \text{K})$

$= 8.76 \times 10^{-21}$ J/molecule.

(b) $\langle KE \rangle = \frac{1}{2} mv^2_{\text{rms}} = 8.76 \times 10^{-21}$ J,

so $v_{\text{rms}} = \sqrt{\frac{1.75 \times 10^{-20}\ \text{J}}{m}}$. (1)

For helium:

$$m = \frac{4.00\ \text{gm/mol}}{6.02 \times 10^{23}\ \text{molecules/mol}} = 6.64 \times 10^{-24}\ \text{gm/molecule, or}$$

$m = 6.64 \times 10^{-27}$ kg/molecule.

Similarly for argon:

$$m = \frac{39.9\ \text{gm/mol}}{6.02 \times 10^{23}\ \text{molecules/mol}} = 6.63 \times 10^{-23}\ \text{gm/molecule, and}$$

$m = 6.63 \times 10^{-26}$ kg/molecule.

Thus equation (1) above gives: $v_{\text{rms}} = 1.62 \times 10^3$ m/s (for helium)

and, $v_{\text{rms}} = 5.14 \times 10^2$ m/s (for argon).

10.39 For one of these elastic head-on collisions, the change in momentum of one molecule of mass m is: $\Delta mv = mv_f - mv_i = mv - (-mv) = 2mv$.

Therefore, the total impulse imparted to the chest in 1 minute (60 s) is:

$$\text{Impulse} = (2mv)N = 2\left(8.0 \times 10^{-3}\ \frac{\text{kg}}{\text{bullet}}\right)(400\ \frac{\text{m}}{\text{s}})(150\ \text{bullets}) = 960\ \text{J·s}.$$

Thus, $\bar{F} = \frac{\text{Impulse}}{\text{time}} = \frac{960\ \text{N s}}{60\ \text{s}} = 16\ \text{N}$

10.40 For one of these elastic head-on collisions, the change in momentum of one molecule of mass m is: $\Delta mv = mv_f - mv_i = mv - (-mv) = 2mv$.

The total impulse delivered to the wall in one second is

$\bar{F}(1.0\text{ s}) = 2mvN$, where N is the number of molecules hitting the wall in the 1 second interval. Therefore,

$$\bar{F} = \frac{(2 \times 4.68 \times 10^{-26}\text{ kg} \times 300\text{ m/s})(5 \times 10^{23})}{1.0\text{ s}} = 14.0\text{ N, and}$$

$$P = \frac{\bar{F}}{A} = \frac{14.0\text{ N}}{8.0 \times 10^{-4}\text{ m}^2} = 1.8 \times 10^4\text{ Pa.}$$

10.41 We must first find the temperature of the gas from the ideal gas law.

$$T = \frac{PV}{nR} = \frac{(8.10 \times 10^5\text{ Pa})(5.0 \times 10^{-3}\text{ m}^3)}{(2.0\text{ mol})(8.31\text{ J/mol K})} = 244\text{ K. Thus,}$$

$$\langle KE \rangle = \frac{3}{2}kT = \frac{3}{2}(1.38 \times 10^{-23}\text{ J/mol K})(244\text{ K}) = 5.1 \times 10^{-21}\text{ J/molecule.}$$

10.42 (a) $\Delta L_{\text{Length}} = \alpha L_0 \Delta T = (9 \times 10^{-6}\text{ °C}^{-1})(20\text{ cm})(75\text{ °C}) = 1.4 \times 10^{-2}\text{ cm.}$

(b) $\Delta D_{\text{Diameter}} = \alpha D_0 \Delta T = (9 \times 10^{-6}\text{ °C}^{-1})(1.0\text{ cm})(75\text{ °C}) = 6.8 \times 10^{-4}\text{ cm.}$

(c) $\Delta V = 3\alpha V_0 \Delta T = 3(9 \times 10^{-6}\text{ °C}^{-1})(15.7\text{ cm}^3)(75\text{ °C}) = 3.2 \times 10^{-2}\text{ cm}^3.$

10.43 We will first find the pressure that existed at the bottom of the lake by finding the pressure that would be required to compress the trapped gas to the extent indicated by the marking indicator. If the cross-sectional area of the container is A,

$$P_f = P_i \frac{V_i}{V_f} = (1\text{ atm})\frac{(1.5\text{ m})(A)}{(0.4\text{ m})(A)} = 3.75\text{ atm}$$

But, $P_f = P_{atm} + \rho g h$, so $P_f - P_{atm} = 3.75\text{ atm} - 1.00\text{ atm} = 2.75\text{ atm.}$

Therefore, $$h = \frac{2.75\text{ atm}}{\rho g} = \frac{2.75(1.013 \times 10^5\text{ Pa})}{(1000\text{ kg/m}^3)(9.80\text{ m/s}^2)} = 28\text{ m}$$

10.44 $V_0 = 10\text{ gallons}\left(\frac{3.8 \times 10^{-3}\text{ m}^3}{\text{gallon}}\right) = 0.038\text{ m}^3.$

The change in volume between 20°C and 0°C of ten gallons of gas is

$$\Delta V = \beta V_0 \Delta T = (9.6 \times 10^{-4}\text{ C}^{-1})(0.038\text{ m}^3)(20\text{ °C}) = 7.3 \times 10^{-4}\text{ m}^3.$$

This is equivalent to a mass of $m = \rho \Delta V = (730\text{ kg/m}^3)(7.3 \times 10^{-4}\text{ m}^3)$, or $m = 0.53$ kg is the extra mass obtained.

10.45 In equilibrium, $P_{gas} = \frac{mg}{A} + P_{atm} = \frac{49\text{ N}}{0.050\text{ m}^2} + 1.013 \times 10^5\text{ Pa}$ which gives: $P_{gas} = 1.023 \times 10^5\text{ Pa.}$

From the ideal gas law, the volume occupied by the gas is:

$$V = \frac{nRT}{P_{gas}} = \frac{(3.00\text{ mol})(8.31\text{ J/mol K})(500\text{ K})}{1.023 \times 10^5\text{ Pa}} = 0.122\text{ m}^3.$$

The height of the cylindrical gas chamber is therefore

$$h = \frac{V}{A} = \frac{0.122\text{ m}^3}{0.050\text{ m}^2} = 2.4\text{ m.}$$

10.46 (a) The volume of the liquid increases as $\Delta V_{liq} = V_0 \beta \Delta T$. The volume of the flask increases as $\Delta V_g = V_0(3\alpha)\Delta T$. Therefore, the overflow in the capillary is: $V_c = V_0 \Delta T(\beta - 3\alpha)$; and in the capillary $V_c = A\Delta h$.

Therefore, $$\Delta h = \frac{V_0 \Delta T(\beta - 3\alpha)}{A}.$$

(b) For a mercury thermometer $\beta(Hg) = 1.82 \times 10^{-4}$ °C^{-1}, and for glass, $3\alpha = 3 \times 9 \times 10^{-6}$ °C^{-1}. Thus, $\beta - 3\alpha$ is approximately equal to β and we may safely ignore the expansion of the shell.

10.47 We have: $d_{oc} = 0.99 d_{op}$ (1)
The diameter is a linear dimension. Thus, we use $L = (1 + \alpha \Delta T) L_0$, with the ultimate goal of finding the temperature at which the final diameter of the piston and cylinder are equal ($d_{fc} = d_{fp}$).
Thus, $(1 + \alpha_c \Delta T) d_{oc} = (1 + \alpha_p \Delta T) d_{op}$. (2)
Using (1) in (2), we have: $(1 + \alpha_c \Delta T)(0.99) = (1 + \alpha_p \Delta T)$, or

$$\Delta T = \frac{0.01}{0.99\alpha_c - \alpha_p} = \frac{0.01 \text{ °C}}{(0.99)(24 \times 10^{-6}) - 11 \times 10^{-6}} = 784 \text{ °C}.$$

Therefore, $T_f = T_0 + \Delta T = 784$ °C + 20 °C = 804 °C.

10.48 Since $\Delta L = L_0 \alpha \Delta T$, the tape has expanded by
$\Delta L = (1.1 \text{ m})(11 \times 10^{-6} \text{ °C}^{-1})(5.0 \text{ °C}) = 0.060$ mm, so it reads the height of the child to be shorter by 0.060 mm, assuming of course, that the child's height does not change due to the increase in temperature.

10.49 (a) We assume that the change in the volume is negligible and find the final temperature of the air in the tire from the ideal gas law.
$(P_{absolute})_f = 3.20$ atm and $(P_{absolute})_i = 2.80$ atm.

Thus, with constant volume: $T_f = \frac{P_f}{P_i} T_i = \frac{3.20 \text{ atm}}{2.80 \text{ atm}}(300 \text{ K}) = 343$ K

(b) We use the ideal gas law to find the final number of moles of gas present in terms of the initial quantity. After the release has occurred, both the volume and pressure of the air in the tire are the same as in the initial state, only the quantity and temperature have changed. Therefore, $P_f V_f = n_f R T_f$ and $P_i V_i = n_i R T_i$.

Dividing yields $n_f = n_i \frac{T_i}{T_f} = n_i \frac{300 \text{ K}}{343 \text{ K}} = 0.875 n_i$. Thus, the amount released must be $\Delta n = n_i - n_f = 0.125 n_i$, or 12.5 % of the original mass of air in the tire.

10.50 Because gas can flow from one container to the other, the pressure must be the same in the two containers at all times. Let us call the flask that is raised to 100 °C container 1, and the container that is maintained at 0 °C is container 2. We also know that the total number of moles in the two containers combined remains a constant. Thus,

$$n_{1f} + n_{2f} = n_{1i} + n_{2i} \quad (1)$$

But, $n = \frac{PV}{RT}$. The volume remains constant, so (1) becomes

$$P_f\left(\frac{1}{T_{1f}} + \frac{1}{T_{2f}}\right) = P_i\left(\frac{1}{T_{1i}} + \frac{1}{T_{2i}}\right).$$

We know that $T_{1f} = 373$ K, $T_{2f} = 273$ K, $T_{1i} = T_{2i} = 273$ K, and $P_i = 1$ atm.
Thus, we find: $P_f = 1.15 \text{ atm} = 1.17 \times 10^5$ Pa.

10.51 For $\Delta L = L_s - L_c$ to be constant, the rods must expand by equal amounts:

$$\alpha_c L_c \Delta T = \alpha_s L_s \Delta T \quad \text{so} \quad L_s = \frac{\alpha_c L_c}{\alpha_s} \quad \text{and} \quad \Delta L = \frac{\alpha_c L_c}{\alpha_s} - L_c$$

Therefore $L_C = \frac{\Delta L \alpha_C}{(\alpha_C - \alpha_S)} = \frac{5.00 \text{ cm}(11 \times 10^{-6} /\text{C}°)}{(17 \times 10^{-6} /\text{C}° - 11 \times 10^{-6} /\text{C}°)} = 9.17 \text{ cm}$

and $L_S = \frac{\Delta L \alpha_C}{(\alpha_C - \alpha_S)} = 5 \text{ cm}(\frac{17}{6}) = 14.17 \text{ cm}$

10.52 $P = \frac{nRT}{V} = \left(\frac{9.00 \text{ g}}{18.0 \text{ g/mol}}\right)\left(\frac{8.315 \text{ J}}{\text{mol K}}\right)\left(\frac{773 \text{ K}}{2.00 \times 10^{-3} \text{ m}^3}\right) = 1.61 \text{ MPa} = 15.9 \text{ atm}$

10.53 (a) $\frac{PV}{T} = \frac{P'V'}{T}$ $\quad V' = V + \text{A}h \quad P' = P + \frac{kh}{\text{A}}$

$(P + \frac{kh}{\text{A}})(V + \text{A}h) = PV\frac{T}{T}$

$((1.013 \times 10^5 \text{ N/m}^2) + (2.0 \times 10^5 \text{ N/m}^2)\text{h})(5.00 \times 10^{-3} \text{ m}^3 + (0.0100 \text{ m}^2)\text{h})$

$= (1.013 \times 10^5 \text{ N/m}^2)(5.00 \times 10^{-3} \text{ m}^3)\frac{523 \text{ K}}{293 \text{ K}}$

or $\quad 2000h^2 + 2013h - 397 = 0$

which gives $\quad h = 0.169 \text{ m}$

(b) $P' = P + \frac{kh}{\text{A}} = 1.013 \times 10^5 \text{ N/m}^2 + \frac{2.0 \times 10^3 \text{ N/m}(0.169)}{0.01 \text{ m}^3} = 1.35 \times 10^5 \text{ Pa}$

10.54 (a) $\Delta L = \alpha L_0 \Delta T = (12 \times 10^{-6} \text{C}^{-1})(250 \text{ m})(20 \text{ °C}) = 0.060 \text{ m}$

(b) We know that $\frac{\text{stress}}{\text{strain}} = Y$, where Y is Young's modulus. Thus,

stress = Y(strain), but strain = $\frac{\Delta L}{L_0}$ We also know that $\Delta L = \alpha L_0 \Delta T$, so

strain = $\alpha \Delta T$, and $\quad$ stress = $\alpha Y \Delta T$.

(c) We have

stress = $\alpha Y \Delta T = (12 \times 10^{-6} \text{C}^{-1})(2.0 \times 10^{10} \text{ Pa})(20 \text{ °C}) = 4.8 \times 10^6$ Pa.

This is well within the safe limit of 2×10^7 Pa. The bridge will not crumble.

10.55 $P_i = (0.95)(1 \text{ atm}) = 9.62 \times 10^4$ Pa

$P_h = P_0 + \rho gh = 1.013 \times 10^5 \text{ Pa} + (10^3 \text{ kg/m}^3)(9.80 \text{ m/s}^2)(10 \text{ m})$, or

$P_h = 1.99 \times 10^5$ Pa is the absolute pressure at 10 m down in the water.

Therefore, $P_f = 0.95P_h = 1.89 \times 10^5$ Pa.

We assume that the temperature of the gas remains at body temperature throughout.

Thus, $V_f = V_i \frac{P_i}{P_f} = (0.820 \text{ liters}) \frac{9.62 \times 10^4 \text{ Pa}}{1.89 \times 10^5 \text{ Pa}} = 0.417$ liters.

10.56 $PV = nRT$, and $n = \frac{m}{M}$ (where M is the molar mass)

Therefore, $PV = \frac{mRT}{M}$, from which: $\frac{m}{V} = \frac{PM}{RT} = \rho$.

10.57 Note that at temperature T the mercury just fills the spherical bulb of the thermometer. At temperature $T + \Delta T$, the mercury has expanded into the cylindrical stem of the thermometer. If the expansion of the glass is neglected, the increase in the volume of the mercury equals the volume of mercury now in the stem. This is a cylindrical volume of cross-sectional area A and height Δh, so $\Delta V = A(\Delta h)$. The original volume of mercury equals the volume of the spherical bulb, or $V_0 = \frac{4}{3}\pi R^3$ where R is the radius of the bulb.

After the change in temperature, the new volume of the mercury is given by $V = V_0[1+\beta(\Delta T)]$, where $\beta = 1.82 \times 10^{-4}\ (°C)^{-1}$ is the coefficient of volume expansion for mercury. The change in volume is thus $\Delta V = V - V_0 = \beta V_0(\Delta T)$. Therefore, the height the mercury has risen in the stem is $\Delta h = \frac{\Delta V}{A} = \frac{\beta V_0(\Delta T)}{A}$.

The diameter of the stem is $d = 5.0 \times 10^{-3}$ cm and the radius of the bulb is $R = \frac{0.30 \text{ cm}}{2} = 0.15$ cm. Hence, when the temperature increases 25°C, the distance the mercury rises in the stem is 3.3 cm

10.58 (a) $L_1 = r_1\theta = L_0(1 + \alpha_1\Delta T)$ $\quad L_2 = r_2\theta = L_0(1 + \alpha_2\Delta T)$

$$\Delta r = r_2 - r_1 = \frac{L_0(\alpha_2 - \alpha_1)\Delta T}{\theta}$$

Therefore, $\theta = L_0(\alpha_2 - \alpha_1)\frac{\Delta T}{r_2 - r_1}$

(b) From the above, we see that θ approaches 0 as ΔT approaches 0 or as $(\alpha_2 - \alpha_1)$ approaches zero.
(c) It bends the other way.

ANSWERS TO CONCEPTUAL QUESTIONS

2. The temperature of the copper drops and the water temperature rises until each temperature is the same. This is thermal equilibrium.

4. The temperature of the bearing can be increased until its diameter becomes large enough to slip over the axle.

6. The lower temperature will make the power line decrease in length. This increases the tension in the line to the point that it is near breaking.

8. At high temperature and pressure, the steam inside exerts large forces on the pot and cover. Strong latches hold them together, but they would explode apart if you tried to open the hot cooker.

10. The ideal gas law applied in the form $\frac{PV}{T}$ = constant assumes the number of molecules does not change.

12. There should be slightly more of the lighter, more rapidly moving nitrogen molecules at higher altitudes.

14. Cylinder A will be at three times the pressure of cylinder B.

16. The pressure of the liquid surrounding the bubble decreases, allowing the trapped gas inside the bubble to expand.

18. Velocity is a vector quantity, so direction must be considered. If there are the same number of particles moving to the right along the x direction as there are to the left along the $-x$ direction, say, the x component of velocity will be zero.

20. At the same temperature, the lighter gas will have molecules with the faster rms speed. Helium moves faster.

CHAPTER ELEVEN SOLUTIONS

Chapter Eleven Readings

Allen, P.B., "Conduction of Heat," *The Physics Teacher*, December 1983, p. 582.

Barr, E., "James Prescott Joule and the Quiet Revolution," *The Physics Teacher*, April 1969, p. 199.

Berry, R.S., "When the Melting and Freezing Points are not the Same," *Scientific American*, August 1990, p.68

Bohren, C.F., What Light Through Yonder Window Breaks?, John Wiley & Sons, New York, 1991.

Chalmers, B., "How Water Freezes," Scientific American, February 1959, p. 144.

Dyson, J., "What is Heat?" *Scientific American*, September 1954, p. 58.

Kelley, J., "Heat, Cold, and Clothing," *Scientific American*, February 1956, p. 194.

Velarde, M.G., "Convection," *Scientific American*, January 1989, p. 92.

Wilson, M., "Count Rumford," *Scientific American*, October 1960, p. 158.

Review The change in temperature of the rod is

$$\Delta T = \frac{Q}{mc} = \frac{10^4 \text{ J}}{(0.350 \text{ kg})(900 \text{ J/kg °C})} = 31.7\text{ °C},$$

and the new length of the rod is:

$$L = L_0(1 + \alpha\Delta T) = 20.000\text{ cm}(1 + (24\times10^{-6}\text{ °C}^{-1})(11.7\text{°C})) = 20.01\text{ cm}.$$

11.1 The amount of energy equivalent to a climb up a rope of length h is $Q = \Delta PE = mgh$. Since 1"food calorie" = 10^3 calorie = 4186 Joules,

$$Q = mgh = (50.0\text{ kg})(9.80\text{ m/s}^2)(10.0\text{ m})\left(\frac{1\text{ Cal}}{4186\text{ J}}\right) = 1.17\text{ Calorie}.$$

11.2 $Q = 500\text{ Cal} = 500(4184)\text{ J} = 2.09\times10^6\text{ J}$. From $Q = \Delta PE = mgh$, we find

$$h = \frac{Q}{mg} = \frac{2.09\times10^6\text{ J}}{(75.0\text{ kg})(9.80\text{ m/s}^2)} = 2.84\times10^3\text{ m}.$$

11.3 $Q = mc\Delta T = (0.100\text{ kg})(129\text{ J/kg°C})(80.0\text{°C}) = 1032\text{ J}$

11.4 From $Q = mc\Delta T$, we find: $\Delta T = \frac{Q}{mc} = \frac{1200\text{ J}}{(0.050\text{ kg})(387\text{ J/kg°C})} = 62\text{ °C}$.
Thus, the final temperature is $T = 25\text{°C} + 62\text{°C} = 87\text{°C}$

11.5 The kinetic energy of the bullet is

$$KE = \frac{1}{2}mv^2 = \frac{1}{2}(5.00\times10^{-3}\text{ kg})(3.00\times10^2\text{ m/s})^2 = 225\text{ J}.$$

If half of this goes into heat, $Q = \frac{225\ \text{J}}{2} = 112.5$ J, and

$$\Delta T = \frac{Q}{mc} = \frac{112.5\ \text{J}}{(5.00 \times 10^{-3}\ \text{kg})(128\ \text{J/kg°C})} = 176\ °\text{C}.$$

11.6 $Q = 400$ cal $= 1674$ J, so $\Delta T = \frac{Q}{mc} = \frac{1674\ \text{J}}{(5.00 \times 10^{-2}\ \text{kg})(230\ \text{J/kg°C})} = 146°\text{C}$,

and $T_f = 166°\text{C}$.

11.7 Consider a 1.00 kg mass of water:

$$Q = \Delta PE = mgh = (1.00\ \text{kg})(9.80\ \text{m/s}^2)(50.0\ \text{m}) = 490\ \text{J}$$

Also, $\Delta T = \frac{Q}{mc} = \frac{490\ \text{J}}{(1.00\ \text{kg})(4.186 \times 10^3\ \text{J/kg°C})} = 0.117\ °\text{C}$.

So, $T_f = 10.1\ \text{C°}$.

11.8 (a) We use $Q = mc\Delta T = (0.85)\frac{1}{2}mv^2$, or

$$\Delta T = \frac{0.85v^2}{2c} = \frac{0.85(3.0\ \text{m/s})^2}{2(387\ \text{J/kg°C})} = 9.9 \times 10^{-3}\text{°C}.$$

(b) The remaining energy is absorbed by the horizontal surface on which the block slides.

11.9 Let us find the heat extracted from the system in one minute.

$$Q = m_{cup}c_{cup}\Delta T + m_{water}c_{water}\Delta T, \text{ or}$$

$$Q = [(0.20\ \text{kg})(900\ \text{J/kg°C}) + (0.80\ \text{kg})(4186\ \text{J/kg°C})](1.5°\text{C}) = 5293\ \text{J}.$$

If this much heat is removed each minute, the rate of removal of heat is

$$P = \frac{Q}{\Delta t} = \frac{5293\ \text{J}}{60\ \text{s}} = 88.2\ \text{J/s} = 88\ \text{W}.$$

11.10 First, convert the change in temperature, ΔT, from Fahrenheit to Celsius:

$$T_{C1} = \frac{5}{9}(T_{F1} - 32), \text{ and } T_{C2} = \frac{5}{9}(T_{F2} - 32).$$

Thus, $\Delta T_C = T_{C2} - T_{C1} = \frac{5}{9}\Delta T_F$, and if $\Delta T_F = 1°$, then $\Delta T_C = \frac{5}{9}$ °C.

Now, use $Q = mc\Delta T$ and the fact that 1 lbm = 0.4536 kg to evaluate the Btu:

1 Btu = (1 lbm)(4186 J/kg °C)(1 ° F) = (0.4536 kg)(4186 J/kg °C)($\frac{5}{9}$ °C)

which yields 1 Btu = 1055 J.

11.11 The heat needed to raise the temperature of the water to 25°C is:

$$Q_{needed} = (0.500\ \text{kg})(4186\ \text{J/kg°C})(5.00°\text{C}) = 1.05 \times 10^4\ \text{J}.$$

The heat received from each pellet is:

$$Q_{pellet} = (10^{-3}\ \text{kg})(128\ \text{J/kg°C})(175°\text{C}) = 22.4\ \text{J/pellet}$$

Thus, the number of pellets needed is:

$$n = \frac{Q_{needed}}{Q_{pellet}} = \frac{1.05 \times 10^4\ \text{J}}{22.4\ \text{J/pellet}} = 467\ \text{pellets}.$$

11.12 Our heat loss = heat gain equation becomes: $m_{iron}c_{iron}\Delta T_{iron} = m_{water}c_w\Delta T_w$

or, $(0.40\ \text{kg})(448\ \text{J/kg°C})(500°\text{C} - T) = (20\ \text{kg})(4186\ \text{J/kg°C})(T - 22°\text{C})$.

From which, we find: $T = 23°C$.

11.13 (heat gain = heat loss) becomes: $m_{water}c_w\Delta T_w = m_{gold}c_g\Delta T_g$.
Thus, $m_{water}(4186 \text{ J/kg°C})(25.0°C) = (3.00 \text{ kg})(129 \text{ J/kg°C})(50.0°C)$, or
$m_{water} = 0.185 \text{ kg} = 185 \text{ g}$.

11.14 (heat gain = heat loss) becomes:
$m_{cup}c_c\Delta T_c + m_w c_w\Delta T_w + m_{stirrer}c_s\Delta T_s = m_{Ag}c_{Ag}\Delta T_{Ag}$, or
$m_{cup}(900 \text{ J/kg°C})(5.0°C) + (0.225 \text{ kg})(4186 \text{ J/kg°C})(5.0°C)$
$+ (0.04 \text{ kg})(387 \text{ J/kg°C})(5°C) = (0.4 \text{ kg})(234 \text{ J/kg°C})(55°C)$.
We find: $m_{cup} = 80 \times 10^{-3} \text{ kg} = 80 \text{ g}$.

11.15 $\Delta Q_{system} = 0$, since the system does not exchange heat with the environment.
$\Delta Q_{system} = (0.200 \text{ kg})(4186 \text{ J/kg°C})(T_f - 10°C)$
$+ (0.300 \text{ kg})(900 \text{ J/kg°C})(T_f - 10°C)$
$+ (0.100 \text{ kg})(4186 \text{ J/kg°C})(T_f - 100°C) = 0$
Which gives $T_f = 35°C$.

11.16 $\Delta Q_{system} = 0$, since the system does not exchange heat with the environment.
$\Delta Q_{system} = (0.1 \text{ kg})(900 \text{J/kg°C})(20°C - 10°C)$
$+ (0.25 \text{ kg})(4186 \text{ J/kg°C})(20°C - 10°C)$
$+ (0.05 \text{ kg})(387 \text{ J/kg°C})(20°C - 80°C) + (0.07 \text{ kg})(c_2)(20°C - 100°C)$.
Which gives $c_2 = 1.8 \times 10^3 \text{ J/kg°C} = 0.44 \text{ cal/g°C}$.

11.17 $500°F = 260°C$, $100°F = 37.8°C$, and $75°F = 23.9°C$.
(heat gain = heat loss) becomes:
$m_{iron}c_{iron}\Delta T_{iron} = m_{water}c_{water}\Delta T_{water}$
$m_{iron}(448 \text{ J/kg°C})(260°C - 37.8°C) = m_{water}(4186 \text{ J/kg°C})(37.8°C - 23.9°C)$
$\frac{m_{water}}{m_{iron}} = 1.7$ Thus, 1.7 kg of water is required for every kg of iron cooled.

11.18 First, we assume that both the water and aluminum will gain heat while the copper loses heat.
$m_w c_w\Delta T_w + m_{al}c_{al}\Delta T_{al} = m_{cu}c_{cu}\Delta T_{cu}$
$0.250(4186)(T - 20.0) + 0.400(900)(T - 26.0) = 0.100(387)(100 - T)$
yielding $T = 23.6°C$, showing our assumption that the aluminum would gain heat to have been incorrect.
Alternately, one could have assumed that the water would gain heat while the copper and aluminum would lose heat. Then the calculation would have been:
$m_w c_w\Delta T_w = m_{al}c_{al}\Delta T_{al} + m_{cu}c_{cu}\Delta T_{cu}$
$0.250(4186)(T - 20.0) = 0.400(900)(26.0 - T) + 0.100(387)(100 - T)$
which also yields $T = 23.6°C$.

11.19 heat loss = heat gain
$m_{cu}c_{cu}\Delta T_{cu} = m_{al}c_{al}\Delta T_{al} + m_w c_w\Delta T_w + m_{steel}c_{steel}\Delta T_{steel}$,
but $\Delta T_w = \Delta T_{steel} = 0$.
$(0.200 \text{ kg})(387 \text{ J/kg°C})(85°C - 25°C) = m_{al}(900 \text{ J/kg°C})(25°C - 5°C)$
$m_{al} = 0.26 \text{ kg} = 260 \text{ g}$

11.20 Q= (heat to melt) + (heat to warm melted ice to 100°C)
+ (heat to vaporize 5.0 g)

$Q = (5.0 \times 10^{-2}\ \text{kg})(3.33 \times 10^5\ \text{J/kg}) + (5.0 \times 10^{-2}\ \text{kg})(4186\ \text{J/kg°C})(100°\text{C}) + (5.0 \times 10^{-3}\ \text{kg})(2.26 \times 10^6\ \text{J/kg}) = 4.9 \times 10^4\ \text{J}$

11.21 heat gain = heat loss

(heat to melt ice) + (Heat to warm melted ice to T_f) = (loss of heat by 1 kg of water)

$(0.100\ \text{kg})(3.33 \times 10^5\ \text{J/kg}) + (0.100\ \text{kg})(4186\ \text{J/kg°C})(T_f) = (1.00\ \text{kg})(4186\ \text{J/kg°C})(80.0 - T_f)$

$T_f = 65.5°\text{C}$ (66°C)

11.22 The heat needed is the sum of the following terms.

Q_{needed} = (heat to reach melting point) + (heat to melt) + (heat to reach boiling point) + (heat to vaporize) + (heat to reach 110°c).

Thus, we have

$$Q_{needed} = 0.04\ \text{kg}\left[2090 \frac{\text{J}}{\text{kg°C}}(10°\text{C}) + (3.33 \times 10^5 \frac{\text{J}}{\text{kg}}) + (4186 \frac{\text{J}}{\text{kg°C}})(100°\text{C}) + 2.26 \times 10^6 \frac{\text{J}}{\text{kg}} + (2010 \frac{\text{J}}{\text{kg°C}})(10°\text{C})\right],$$

or $Q_{needed} = 1.2 \times 10^5\ \text{J}$.

11.23 heat loss = heat gain

(heat to cool steam to 100°C) + (heat to condense steam) + (heat to cool condensed steam to 50°C) = (heat gain by cool water) + (heat gain by cup)

$m_s[(2010\ \text{J/kg})(20°\text{C}) + 2.26 \times 10^6\ \text{J/kg} + (4186\ \text{J/kg°C})(50°\text{C})] = (.35\ \text{kg})(4186\ \text{J/kg°C})(30°\text{C}) + (.30\ \text{kg})(900\ \text{J/kg°C})(30°\text{C})$

From which, $m_s = 21\ \text{g}$.

11.24 The equilibrium temperature is 100°C since the temperature of the water ceases to rise when it starts boiling away.

heat gain = heat loss

$m_{steam}L_v + m_{water}c_{water}\Delta T_{water} = m_{Hg}c_{Hg}\Delta T_{Hg}$

$m_s(2.26 \times 10^6\ \text{J/kg}) + (0.05\ \text{kg})(4186\ \text{J/kg})(20°\text{C}) = (1.94\ \text{kg})(138\ \text{J/kg})(100°\text{C})$

yielding $m_s = 10^{-2}\ \text{kg} = 10\ \text{g}$.

11.25 The energy required to melt 1.0 kg of snow is

$Q = (1.0\ \text{kg})(3.33 \times 10^5\ \text{J}) = 3.33 \times 10^5\ \text{J}$.

The friction force is: $f = \mu N = \mu mg = (0.20)(75\ \text{kg})(9.80\ \text{m/s}^2) = 147\ \text{N}$.

Therefore, the work done is: $W = fs = (147\ \text{N})S$.

Thus, $(147\ \text{N})S = 3.33 \times 10^5\ \text{J}$, and $S = 2.3 \times 10^3\ \text{m}$.

11.26 heat loss = heat gain

(loss as water cools to T_f) = (heat to melt ice)
+ (heat to warm melted ice to T_f)

$(.65\ \text{kg})(4186\ \text{J/kg°C})(25°\text{C} - T_f) = (0.1\ \text{kg})(3.33 \times 10^5\ \text{J/kg}) + (0.10\ \text{kg})(4186\ \text{J/kg°C})(T_f)$

$T_f = 11°\text{C}$

11.27 Heat to raise ice to 0°C = ΔQ_1.

$\Delta Q_1 = m_{ice}c_{ice}(\Delta T)_{ice} = (40\text{ g})(0.5\text{ cal/g°C})(78\text{ °C}) = 1560\text{ cal}$

The heat the cup and water can lose before they reach 0°C = ΔQ_2.

$\Delta Q_2 = m_{cu}c_{cu}(\Delta T)_{cu} + m_w c_w(\Delta T)_w$

$= (0.08\text{ kg})(387\ \frac{\text{J}}{\text{kg°C}})(25\text{°C}) + (0.56\text{ kg})(4186\ \frac{\text{J}}{\text{kg°C}})(25\text{°C}) = 14{,}185\text{ cal}$

We see that $\Delta Q_2 > \Delta Q_1$ so the ice will reach 0°C and at least start to melt. The heat to melt the ice is ΔQ_3:

$\Delta Q_3 = m_{ice}(L_f)_{ice} = (0.04\text{ kg})(3.33\times 10^5\text{ J/kg})(1\text{cal}/4.186\text{ J}) = 3192\text{ cal}$

$\Delta Q_2 > \Delta Q_1 + \Delta Q_3$. Thus, all the ice melts and the final temperature is greater than 0°C. Let us find the final temperature T_f.

$\Delta Q_{system} = \Delta Q_{water} + \Delta Q_{cup} + \Delta Q_{raise\ ice\ to\ 0°} + \Delta Q_{melt\ ice} + \Delta Q_{warm\ melted\ ice} = 0$

$\Delta Q_{system} = (.56\text{ kg})(4186\ \frac{\text{J}}{\text{kg°C}})(T_f - 25\text{°C}) + (.08\text{ kg})(387\ \frac{\text{J}}{\text{kg°C}})(T_f - 25\text{°C}) + (0.04\text{ kg})(2090\text{ J/kg°C})(78\text{°C}) + (0.04\text{ kg})(3.33\times 10^5\text{ J/kg}) + (0.04\text{ kg})(4186\text{ J/kg°C})(T_f - 0\text{°C}) = 0$

From which, $T_f = 15.6\text{°C}$ (16°C)

11.28 (a)Heat to cool system to 0°C = $\Delta Q_1 = m_{cup}c_{al}(\Delta T)_{cup} + m_{water}c_{water}(\Delta T)_{water}$

$= (.10\text{ kg})(900\text{ J/kg°C})(30\text{°C}) + (0.18\text{ kg})(4186\text{ J/kg°C})(30\text{°C}) = 25{,}304\text{ J}$

The amount of ice, at 0°C, which must melt to absorb this much heat is:

$$m_{ice} = \frac{\Delta Q_1}{L_f} = \frac{25304\text{ J}}{3.33\times 10^5\text{ J/kg}} = 7.60\times 10^{-2}\text{ kg} = 76\text{ g}$$

Therefore, if 100 g of ice is used, not all of the ice will melt, $T_f = 0\text{°C}$ with 24 g of ice left over.

(b) If 50 g of ice is used, all the ice melts and $T_f > 0\text{°C}$. Let's find T_f.

$\Delta Q_{system} = m_{ice}L_f + m_{ice}c_{water}(T_f - 0\text{°C}) + m_{water}c_{water}(T_f - 30\text{°C}) + m_{cup}c_{al}(T_f - 30\text{°C}) = 0$

$= (0.05\text{ kg})(3.33\times 10^5\ \frac{\text{J}}{\text{kg}}) + (.05\text{ kg})(4186\ \frac{\text{J}}{\text{kg°C}})T_f$

$+ (0.18\text{ kg})(4186\ \frac{\text{J}}{\text{kg°C}})(T_f - 30\text{°C}) + (0.1\text{ kg})(900\ \frac{\text{J}}{\text{kg°C}})(T_f - 30\text{°C}) = 0$

This yields: $T_f = 8.2\text{°C}$.

11.29 (a)Q_1 = heat to melt all the ice

$= (50\times 10^{-3}\text{ kg})(3.33\times 10^5\text{ J/kg}) = 1.67\times 10^4\text{ J}$

Q_2 = (heat to raise temp of melted ice to 100°C)

$= (50\times 10^{-3}\text{ kg})(4186\text{ J/kg°C})(100\text{°C}) = 2.09\times 10^4\text{ J}$.

Thus, the total heat to melt ice and raise temp to 100°C = 3.76×10^4 J

Q_3 = heat available as steam condenses

$= (10\times 10^{-3}\text{ kg})(2.26\times 10^6\text{ J/kg})$,

or $Q_3 = 2.26\times 10^4$ J. Thus, we see that $Q_3 > Q_1$, but $Q_3 < Q_1 + Q_2$. Therefore, all the ice melts but $T_f < 100\text{°C}$. Let us now find T_f.

heat gain = heat loss

$(0.05\text{ kg})(3.33\times 10^5\text{ J/kg}) + (0.05\text{ kg})(4186\text{ J/kg°C})(T_f - 0\text{°C}) =$

$(0.01\text{ kg})(2.26 \times 10^6\text{ J/kg}) + (0.01\text{ kg})(4186\text{ J/kg°C})(100°\text{C} - T_f)$

From which, $T_f = 40°\text{C}$.

(b) Q_1 = heat to melt all ice = 1.67×10^4 J (see part (a))

Q_2 = heat given up as steam condenses $= (10^{-3}\text{ kg})(2.26 \times 10^6 \frac{\text{J}}{\text{kg}})$

$= 2.26 \times 10^3$ J

Q_3 = (heat given up as condensed steam cools to 0°C)

$= (10^{-3}\text{ kg})(4186\text{ J/kg°C})(100°\text{C}) = 418$ J

Note that $Q_2 + Q_3 < Q_1$ Therefore, the final temperature will be 0°C with some ice remaining. Let us find the mass of ice which must melt to condense the steam and cool the condensate to 0°C.

$mL_f = Q_2 + Q_3 = 2678$ J

Thus, $m = \frac{2678\text{ J}}{3.33 \times 10^5\text{ J/kg}} = 8.0 \times 10^{-3}\text{ kg} = 8.0\text{ g}$.

11.30 (a) $H = \frac{\Delta Q}{\Delta t} = \frac{kA\Delta T}{L} = \frac{(397\text{ J/s m°C})(15 \times 10^{-4}\text{ m}^2)(30°\text{C})}{0.080\text{ m}} = 220\text{ J/s}$

(b) The steps are identical here as in (a) except $k = 0.0234$ J/s m°C.

The result is: $H = 1.3 \times 10^{-2}$ J/s.

(c) $k = 0.10$ J/s m°C, and $H = 5.6 \times 10^{-2}$ J/s.

11.31(a) $H = \frac{\Delta Q}{\Delta t} = \frac{kA\Delta T}{L} = \frac{(0.8 \frac{\text{J}}{\text{s m°C}})(0.16\text{ m}^2)(11.1°\text{C})}{3.0 \times 10^{-3}\text{ m}} = 470 \frac{\text{J}}{\text{s}}$ (into house)

(b) $H = \frac{\Delta Q}{\Delta t} = \frac{kA\Delta T}{L} = \frac{(0.8 \frac{\text{J}}{\text{s m°C}})(0.16\text{ m}^2)(38.9°\text{C})}{3.0 \times 10^{-3}\text{ m}} = 1.7 \times 10^3 \frac{\text{J}}{\text{s}}$ (to outdoors)

11.32 $R_{total} = \Sigma R_i$

$= R_{\text{outside air film}} + R_{\text{shingles}} + R_{\text{sheating}} + R_{\text{cellulose}} + R_{\text{dry wall}} + R_{\text{inside air film}}$.

$= (0.17 + 0.87 + 1.32 + 3(3.7) + 0.45 + 0.17)\text{ft}^2\text{ F° h/BTU} = 14\text{ ft}^2\text{ F° h/BTU}$

11.33 For the Thermopane:

$$H = \frac{\Delta Q}{\Delta t} = \frac{A(\Delta T)}{\left(\Sigma \frac{L_i}{k_i}\right)}$$

$$= \frac{(1.0\text{ m}^2)(23.0°\text{C} - 0°\text{C})}{\frac{5.0 \times 10^{-3}\text{ m}}{0.8\text{ J/sm°C}} + \frac{10^{-2}\text{ m}}{0.0234\text{ J/sm°C}} + \frac{5.0 \times 10^{-3}\text{ m}}{0.8\text{ J/sm°C}}} = 52\text{ J/s}.$$

For the single pane:

$$H = \frac{\Delta Q}{\Delta t} = \frac{kA\Delta T}{L} = \frac{(0.8\text{ J/s m°C})(1\text{ m}^2)(23°\text{C})}{1 \times 10^{-2}\text{ m}} = 1.84 \times 10^3\text{ J/s}.$$

11.34 $A = A_{\text{end walls}} + A_{\text{ends of attic}} + A_{\text{side walls}} + A_{\text{roof}}$

$A = 2(8.00\text{ m} \times 5.00\text{ m}) + 2(2.00 \times \frac{1}{2} \times (4.00\text{ m}) \times (4.00\text{ m})\tan 37°)$

$$+ 2(10.0\,\text{m}) \times 5.00\,\text{m}) + 2(10\,\text{m} \times \frac{4\text{m}}{\cos 37°})$$

$A = 304\,\text{m}^2$.

$$H = \frac{\Delta Q}{\Delta t} = \frac{kA\Delta T}{L} = \frac{(4.8 \times 10^{-4}\ \text{kW/ m°C})(304\ \text{m}^2)(25°\text{C})}{0.21\ \text{m}}$$

$$= 17.4\,\text{kW} = 4.15\,\frac{\text{kcal}}{\text{s}}$$

Thus, the heat lost per day = (4.15 kcal/s)(86,400 s) = 3.59×10^5 kcal/day.

The gas needed to replace this loss = $\frac{3.59 \times 10^5\ \text{kcal/day}}{9300\ \text{kcal/m}^3} = 39\,\text{m}^3/\text{day}$.

11.35 Let us call the copper rod object 1 and the aluminum rod object 2. At equilibrium, the flow rate through each must be the same. We have

$$\frac{k_2 A_2 \Delta T}{L_2} = \frac{k_1 A_1 \Delta T}{L_1}.$$

Since the cross-sectional areas of the rods are the same and the temperature difference across the rods are also equal, we have

$$\frac{k_2}{L_2} = \frac{k_1}{L_1}, \text{ or } \frac{238\ \text{J/s m°C}}{L_2} = \frac{397\ \text{J/s m°C}}{0.15\ \text{m}}.$$

From which, we find $L_2 = 9.0 \times 10^{-2}\,\text{m} = 9.0\,\text{cm}$.

11.36 The heat needed to melt 5.0 kg of ice = mL_f = (5.0 kg)(3.33×10^5 J/kg)

$= 1.67 \times 10^6$ J

Thus, the required flow rate during the 8.0 h (2.88×10^4 s) period is:

$$\frac{\Delta Q}{\Delta t} = \frac{1.67 \times 10^6\ \text{J}}{2.88 \times 10^4\ \text{s}} = 57.8\ \text{J/s}.$$

Then, $\frac{\Delta Q}{\Delta t} = \frac{kA\Delta T}{L}$ becomes: $57.8\ \text{J/s} = \frac{k(0.8\ \text{m}^2)(20°\text{C})}{2.0 \times 10^{-2}\ \text{m}}$,

and we find $k = 7.2 \times 10^{-2}$ J/s m°C.

11.37 The area of the sphere is $A = 4\pi r^2 = 4\pi(0.060\,\text{m})^2 = 4.52 \times 10^{-2}\,\text{m}^2$.

$P_{net} = \sigma Ae(T^4 - T_o^4)$, and for a perfect radiator, $e = 1$. Thus,

$P_{net} = = (5.67 \times 10^{-8}\ \text{W/m}^2\text{K}^4)(4.52 \times 10^{-2}\ \text{m}^2)((473\ \text{K})^4 - (295\ \text{K})^4)$

$= 110\,\text{W}$.

11.38 From $P_{net} = \sigma Ae(T^4 - T_o^4)$:

For two identical objects, we have the ratio of the power emitted by the hotter to that from the colder is

$$\frac{P_h}{P_c} = \frac{(1200\ \text{K})^4 - (273\ \text{K})^4}{(1100\ \text{K})^4 - (273\ \text{K})^4} = \frac{2.07 \times 10^{12}}{1.46 \times 10^{12}} = 1.4$$

11.39 We use $P_{net} = \sigma Ae(T^4 - T_o^4)$:

$25\ \text{W} = (5.67 \times 10^{-8}\ \text{W/m}^2\text{K}^4)(2.5 \times 10^{-5}\ \text{m}^2)(0.25)(T^4 - (295\ \text{K})^4)$

From which, $T = 2.9 \times 10^3\ \text{K} = 2.6 \times 10^3\ °\text{C}$.

11.40 The power radiated by an object is given by $P = \sigma AeT^4$, where T is the absolute temperature. The power output from Star X (at 6000 K) is therefore

$P_X = \sigma A_X(1)(6000)^4$, and the power output of Star Y (at 12000 K) is

$P_y = \sigma A_y (1)(12000)^4$,
Since the two stars have the same size, $A_x = A_y$ and the ratio of the total power outputs (luminosities) is:

$$\frac{P_y}{P_x} = \frac{T_y{}^4}{T_x{}^4} = \left(\frac{12000\text{ K}}{6000\text{ K}}\right)^4 = (2)^4 = 16.$$

11.41 The area of the bottom of the kettle is $\pi \times 10^{-2}$ m^2, and the temperature difference across the bottom is 2°C. The rate of heat transfer is

$$H = \frac{\Delta Q}{\Delta t} = \frac{kA\Delta T}{L} = \frac{(397\text{ J/s m°C})(\pi \times 10^{-2}\text{ m}^2)(2.00\text{°C})}{2.00 \times 10^{-3}\text{ m}} = 1.25 \times 10^4\text{J/s}.$$

11.42 To raise the temperature of water to 100°C, we need an amount of heat equal to: $Q = (0.250\text{ kg})(4186\text{ J/kg°C})(77\text{°C}) = 8.06 \times 10^4$ J.
The collection rate is $(550\text{ W/m}^2)(1.00\text{ m}^2) = 550\text{ W} = 550\text{ J/s}$.
Therefore, the time required is: $t = 8.06 \times 10^4\text{ J}/(550\text{ J/s}) = 147\text{ s} = 2.44$ min.

11.43 heat gain = heat loss:

$$m_b c_b(T_f - 20\text{°C}) = m_w c_w(90\text{°C} - T_f) \qquad (1)$$

The mass of the bullet, m_b, is 5.0 g, the mass of the water is 100 g, and the specific heat of water is 4186 J/kg°C. We substitute these into (1) and solve for T_f in terms of the specific heat of the bullet, c_b. We find:

$$T_f = \frac{c_b(20\text{°C}) + 7.53 \times 10^6\text{ J/kg}}{(c_b + 8.37 \times 10^4\text{ J/kg°C})}.$$

For the silver bullet, $c_b = 234$ J/kg°C, and $T_f = 89.8$°C.
For the copper bullet, $c_b = 387$ J/kg°C, and $T_f = 89.7$°C. The copper bullet wins.

11.44 $Q = mc(\Delta T) = (50.0\text{ kg})(380\text{ J/kg°C})(20\text{°C}) = 3.80 \times 10^5\text{ J} = 9.08 \times 10^4$ cal.

11.45 heat loss = heat gain
(heat lost by lead)
= (heat to melt ice) + (heat to raise melted ice to final temp)
+ (heat to raise water to final temp) + (heat to raise temp of cup)

$$m(128\,\tfrac{\text{J}}{\text{kg°C}})(86\text{°C}) = (0.04\text{ kg})(3.33 \times 10^5\,\tfrac{\text{J}}{\text{kg}})$$
$$+ (0.04\text{ kg})(4186\,\tfrac{\text{J}}{\text{kg°C}})(12\text{°C})$$
$$+ (.200\text{ kg})(4186\,\tfrac{\text{J}}{\text{kg°C}})(12\text{°C}) + (0.1\text{kg})(387\,\tfrac{\text{J}}{\text{kg°C}})(12\text{°C})$$

From which, $m = 2.4$ kg.

11.46 The mass of water to be heated is:

$$m = (50.0\text{ gal})\left(\frac{3.786\text{ L}}{1\text{ gal}}\right)\left(\frac{10^{-3}\text{ m}^3}{1\text{ L}}\right)(10^3\text{ kg/m})^3 = 189.3\text{ kg}$$

The total heat energy required to raise the temperature of the water to 60° C is:

$$Q = mc\Delta T = (189.3\text{ kg})(4186\text{ J/kg °C})(60.0\text{°C} - 20.0\text{°C}) = 3.17 \times 10^7\text{ J}.$$

The time required can be determined from the power input as:

$t = \frac{\text{energy needed}}{\text{power input}} = \frac{3.17 \times 10^7}{4.80 \times 10^3 \text{ J/s}} = 6.6 \times 10^3 \left(\frac{1 \text{ H}}{3600 \text{ s}}\right) = 1.83 \text{ h}.$

11.47 Temperature remains constant for the first 50 min (3000 s) as the ice is melting. The energy required to melt m kg of ice in 50 min with a constant power input P is:

$Q_1 = P\Delta t = P(3000 \text{ s}) = m(3.33 \times 10^5 \text{ J/kg})$, or $P = \frac{m(3.33 \times 10^5 \text{ J/kg})}{3000 \text{ s}}$.

During the last 10 min, the heat is used to raise the temperature of $(m + 10 \text{ kg})$ of water by 2°C. We have:

$Q_2 = P\Delta t = P(600 \text{ s}) = (m + 10 \text{ kg})(4186 \text{ J/kg°C})(2°\text{C})$,

or $P = \frac{(m + 10 \text{ kg})(4186 \text{ J/kg°C})(2°\text{C})}{600 \text{ s}}$. But the Power input is the same in both cases,

so $\frac{m(3.33 \times 10^5 \text{ J/kg})}{3000 \text{ s}} = \frac{(m + 10 \text{ kg})(4186 \text{ J/kg°C})(2°\text{C})}{600 \text{ s}}$

which yields: m = 1.4 kg

11.48 (heat gain = heat loss) becomes:

$(0.400 \text{ kg})(4186 \text{ J/kg°C})(T_f - 27°\text{C}) + (0.300 \text{ kg})(837 \text{ J/kg°C})(T_f - 27°\text{C})$
$= (0.200 \text{ kg})(387 \text{J/kg°C})(90°\text{C} - T_f)$.

From which, $T_f = 29.4°\text{C}$.

11.49 The power incident on the solar collector is

$P_i = IA = (600 \text{ W/m}^2)\pi(0.25 \text{ m})^2 = 117.8 \text{ W}$.

For a 50% reflector, the collected power is $P_c = 58.9$ W. The total energy required to increase the temperature of the water to the boiling point and to evaporate it is

$Q = mc\Delta T + mL_v = (1.0 \text{ kg})[(4186 \text{ J/kg°C})(80°\text{C}) + (2.26 \times 10^6 \text{ J/kg})]$

or $Q = 2.59 \times 10^6$ J.

The time required is $\Delta t = \frac{Q}{P_c} = \frac{2.59 \times 10^6 \text{ J}}{58.9 \text{ J/s}} = 4.41 \times 10^4 \text{ s} = 12 \text{ h}.$

11.50 The heat added to the air in one hour is:

$Q = 10(200 \text{ J/s})(3600 \text{ s}) = 7.2 \times 10^6$ J.

The mass of the air in the room is:

$m = \rho V = (6 \text{ m})(15.0 \text{ m})(3.0 \text{ m})(1.3 \text{ kg/m}^3) = 351$ kg.

Thus, the change in temperature of the room is:

$\Delta T = \frac{Q}{mc} = \frac{7.2 \times 10^6 \text{ J}}{(351 \text{ kg})(837 \text{ J/kg°C})} = 24.5°\text{C}.$

Therefore, the final temperature is 45°C.

11.51 (a) Let us call rod 1 the aluminum rod, and rod 2 is the iron rod. At equilibrium, the rate of heat transfer through the rods are equal.

Thus, we have: $\frac{k_2 A_2 \Delta T_2}{L_2} = \frac{k_1 A_1 \Delta T_1}{L_1}$.

Since $L_1 = L_2$ and $A_1 = A_2$, this becomes: $\Delta T_1 = \frac{k_2}{k_1}\Delta T_2$,

Let us call the temperature at the interface T. Thus, we have

$100°\text{C} - T = \frac{79.5}{238}(T - 0°\text{C})$, or $T = 75°\text{C}$.

(b) We find, $\frac{\Delta Q}{\Delta t} = \frac{k_2 A_2 \Delta T_2}{L_2}$

$$= \frac{(79.5\ \text{J/s m°C})(5 \times 10^{-4}\ \text{m}^2)(75\text{°C})}{0.15\ \text{m}} = 19.9\ \text{J/s}$$

Therefore, if $\Delta t = 30$ min = 1800 s, we have: $\Delta Q = 3.6 \times 10^4$ J

11.52 The heat required to vaporize 0.500 kg of water at 100 °C is:

$Q = (0.500\ \text{kg})(2.26 \times 10^6\ \text{J/kg}) = 1.13 \times 10^6\ \text{J}$

Thus, the rate of heat transfer is: $\frac{\Delta Q}{\Delta t} = \frac{1.13 \times 10^6\ \text{J}}{60\ \text{s}} = 1.88 \times 10^4$ J/s.

From $\frac{\Delta Q}{\Delta t} = \frac{kA\Delta T}{L}$,

we have $\Delta T = \frac{\Delta Q}{\Delta t}\left(\frac{L}{kA}\right) = \left(1.88 \times 10^4\ \frac{\text{J}}{\text{s}}\right)\frac{5.00 \times 10^{-3}\ \text{m}}{(238\ \text{J/s m°C})\pi(.120\ \text{m})^2}$

or $\Delta T = 8.75$ °C. Thus, $T = 108.75$ °C = 109°C.

11.53 The rate energy is received = $(300\ \text{W/m}^2)(12.0\ \text{m}^2) = 3600\ \text{W} = 3600$ J/s.

Thus, at equilibrium, it must be radiating away 3600 J/s.

$P_{net} = \sigma A e(T^4 - T_o^4)$

$3600\ \text{W} = (5.67 \times 10^{-8}\ \text{W/m}^2\text{K}^4)(12\ \text{m}^2)(1)[T^4 - (253\ \text{K})^4]$

Which yields, $T = 311$ K = 38°C.

11.54 (a) With $Q = mc\Delta T$ and $m = \rho V$, the rate of addition of heat is found as:

$Q = \rho V c \Delta T$, or the amount of heat ΔQ added to a volume ΔV is

$\Delta Q = \rho \Delta V c \Delta T$,

and from this the heat added in a time Δt is $\frac{\Delta Q}{\Delta t} = \rho c \Delta T\left(\frac{\Delta V}{\Delta t}\right)$.

(b) From part (a):

$$c = \frac{\frac{\Delta Q}{\Delta t}}{\rho \Delta T\left(\frac{\Delta V}{\Delta t}\right)} = \frac{(40\ \text{J/s})(1\ \text{cal}/4.186\ \text{J})}{(0.72\ \text{g/cm}^3)(5.8\text{°C})(3.5\ \text{cm}^3\text{/s})} = 0.65\ \text{cal/g °C}.$$

11.55 The masses of all the liquids to be mixed are equal in this problem, so m will cancel from the calorimetry equations.

Let us consider case 1 in which liquids 1 and 2 are mixed:

heat gain = heat loss ⇒ $c_1(7\ \text{°C}) = c_2(3\ \text{°C})$,

or $c_2 = \frac{7}{3} c_1$. (1)

Now consider case 2 in which liquids 2 and 3 are mixed:

heat gain = heat loss ⇒ $c_2(8\ \text{°C}) = c_3(2\ \text{°C})$,

or $c_3 = 4c_2$. (2)

Eliminate c_2 between (1) and (2), and we find: $c_3 = \frac{28}{3} c_1$. (3)

Finally, consider case 3 in which liquids 1 and 3 are mixed.

heat gain = heat loss ⇒

$c_1(T_f - 10\ \text{°C}) = c_3(30\ \text{°C} - T_f)$ (4)

Use (3) to eliminate the specific heats from equation (4), and solve the resulting equation for T_f: $T_f = 28$ °C.

11.56 $m = (4.00 \times 10^{11}\ \text{m}^3)(1000\ \text{kg/m}^3)$

(a) $\Delta Q = mc\Delta T = Pt = (4.00 \times 10^{14}\ m^3)(4186\ J/kg°C)(1.0°C)$
$= 1.68 \times 10^{18}\ J = Pt$

(b) $t = \dfrac{1.68 \times 10^{18}\ J}{10^9\ J/s} = 1.68 \times 10^9\ s = 53.1\ y$

11.57 (a) $(f)mgh = mc\Delta T$

$\dfrac{(0.600)(3.00 \times 10^{-3}\ kg)(9.80\ m/s^2)(50.0\ m)}{4.186\ J/cal} = (3.00\ g)(0.0924$
$cal/gC°)\Delta T$

so $\Delta T = 0.760$ °C for a temperature of 25.8°C

(b) No. Both the change in potential energy and the heat absorbed are proportional to the mass; hence, the mass cancels in the energy relation.

11.58 The bullet will not melt all the ice, so its final temperature is 0°C. Then

$$\left(\frac{1}{2}mv^2 + mc\Delta T\right)_{bullet} = m_w L$$

where m_w is the mass of the melted water.

$$m_w = \frac{0.5(3.00 \times 10^{-3}\ kg)(240\ m/s)^2 + (3.00 \times 10^{-3}\ kg)(128\ J/kg\ C°)(30.0\ C°)}{3.33 \times 10^5\ J/kg}$$
$= 0.294\ g$

11.59 In the steady state condition $H_{Au} = H_{Ag}$ so that

$$k_{Au}A_{Au}\left(\frac{\Delta T}{\Delta x}\right)_{Au} = k_{Ag}A_{Ag}\left(\frac{\Delta T}{\Delta x}\right)_{Ag}$$

In this case $A_{Au} = A_{Ag}$, $\Delta x_{Au} = \Delta x_{Ag}$, $\Delta T_{Au} = (80 - T)$ and $\Delta T_{Ag} = (T - 30)$

where T is the temperature of the junction. Therefore

$k_{Au}(80.0 - T) = k_{Ag}(T - 30.0)$ and $T = 51.2$ °C

11.60 $\dfrac{Q}{t} = kA\dfrac{\Delta T}{L} = P$

$$k = \frac{PL}{A\Delta T} = \frac{(10.0\ W)(0.040\ m)}{(1.20\ m^2)(15.0\ °C)} = 2.22 \times 10^{-2}\ W/m\ C°$$

11.61 The rate of heat loss by sweating = 0.9(300 W) = 270 W = 270 J/s. Thus, the heat dissipated in 1 h = $\left(270\ \dfrac{J}{s}\right)\left(\dfrac{1\ cal}{4.186\ J}\right)\left(\dfrac{3600\ s}{1\ h}\right)$

$= 2.32 \times 10^5\ \dfrac{cal}{h} = 232\ \dfrac{kcal}{h}$.

Therefore, the amount of water at 37°C which must evaporate to absorb this much heat is, $\dfrac{232\ kcal/h}{575\ kcal/kg} = 0.404\ kg$.

There is a water loss of 400 $\dfrac{cm^3}{h}$.

11.62 (a) $P = Fv = (50\ N)(40\ m/s) = 2.0 \times 10^3\ W$

(b) The frictional work done on each object in 10 s is:

$W = Pt = (1000\ J/s)(10\ s) = 10{,}000\ J$, and from $Q = mc\Delta T$, we have

$$\Delta T = \frac{Q}{mc} = \frac{10000\ J}{(5\ kg)(448\ J/kg°C)} = 4.5°C.$$

11.63 (a) The kinetic energy of the car is:

$$KE_{car} = \frac{1}{2}mv^2 = \frac{1}{2}(1500 \text{ kg})(25 \text{ m/s})^2 = 4.69 \times 10^5 \text{ J}.$$

The melting point of aluminum is 660°C. Thus, the heat required to raise the temperature of the brakes from 20°C to the melting point is:

$$Q = mc\Delta T = (60000 \text{ g})(0.9 \text{ J/g C°})(640 \text{ C°}) = 3.46 \times 10^7 \text{ J}.$$

Therefore, the number of stop would be $\dfrac{3.46 \times 10^7 \text{ J}}{4.69 \times 10^5 \text{ J}} = 74$ stops.

(b) This calculation assumes no heat loss to the surroundings, and that all the heat generated in one stops still remains with the brakes until the next application of the brakes.

11.64 During any time interval the heat energy lost by the rod equals the heat energy gained by the helium. Therefore,

$$(mL)_{He} = (mc\Delta T)_{Al}, \text{ or } \quad (\rho VL)_{He} = (\rho Vc\Delta T)_{Al}, \text{ so}$$

$$V_{He} = \frac{(\rho Vc\Delta T)_{Al}}{(\rho L)_{He}} = \frac{(2.7 \text{ g/cm}^3)(100 \text{ cm}^3)(0.21 \text{ cal/g°C})(295.8\text{°C})}{(0.125 \text{ g/cm}^3)(4.99 \text{ cal/g})}$$

$$= 2.69 \times 10^4 \text{ cm}^3 = 27 \text{ liters}$$

CONCEPTUAL ANSWERS

2. In winter the produce is protected from freezing. The specific heat of the Earth is so high that soil freezes only to a depth of a few inches in temperate regions. Throughout the year the temperature will stay nearly constant day and night. Factors to be considered are the insulating properties of the soil, the absence of a path for heat to be radiated away from or to the vegetables, and the hindrance of the formation of convection currents in the small, enclosed space.

4. The high heat capacity of the barrel and water and its high heat of fusion mean that a large amount of heat would have to leak out of the cellar before the water and produce froze solid. Evaporation of the water keeps the relative humidity high to protect foodstuffs from drying out.

6. Yes, if you know the specific heat of zinc and copper, you can determine the relative fraction of each by heating a known weight of pennies to a specific initial temperature, say 100° C, then dump them into a known quantity of water, at say 20° C. The final temperature T will reveal the metal content.

$$m_{pennies}[xc_{cu} + (1 - x)c_{zn}](100° \text{ C} - T) = M_{water}c_{water}(T - 20° \text{ C})$$

Since all quantities are known, except x, the fraction of the penny that is copper will be found by putting in the experimental numbers $m_{pennies}$, M_{water}, T(final) and c_{zn} and c_{cu}.

8. The thin material of the balloon allows heat to be conducted through it rapidly. If the substance inside the balloon is then able to move the heat away from the balloon surface, the balloon will not burst. The water is much better able to do this than is the air because the water has a much higher thermal conductivity (and a higher specific heat as well). Convection currents set up in the water also carry heat away more efficiently than does the air.

10. The black car absorbs more of the incoming energy from the Sun than does the white car, making it more likely to cook the egg.

12. Keep them dry. The air pockets in the pad conduct heat slowly. Wet pads absorb some heat energy in warming up themselves, but the pot would still be hot and the water would quickly conduct and convect a lot of heat right to you.

14. Write 1000 kg(4186 J/kg C°)(1 C°) = V(1.3 kg/m^3)(1000 J/kg C°)(1 C°), to find $V = 3.2 \times 10^3$ m^3.

CHAPTER TWELVE SOLUTIONS

Chapter Twelve Readings

Atkins, P.W., "The Second Law," Scientific American Library, W. H. Freeman and Co., New York, 1984

Bryant, L., "Rudolf Diesel and His Rational Engine," *Scientific American*, August 1969, p. 108.

Cole, D.E., "The Wankel Engine," *Scientific American*, August 1972, p. 14.

Dannen, G., "The Einstein-Szilard Refrigerators," *Scientific American*, v. 276 (Jan. '97) p90.

Dicus, D.A. Letaw, J., Teplitz, D., and Teplitz, V., "The Future of the Universe," *Scientific American*, March 1983, p. 90.

Haber-Schaim, U., "The Role of the Second Law of Thermodynamics in Energy Education," *The Physics Teacher*, January 1983, p. 17.

Wilson, S., "Sadi Carnot," *Scientific American*, August 1981, p. 134.

Review (a) The work done on the projectile by the expanding gas is equal to the area under the process curve, or

$$W = (\text{area of rectangle}) + (\text{area of triangle})$$

$$= P_f(V_f - V_o) + \frac{1}{2}(P_o - P_f)(V_f - V_o) = \frac{(P_f + P_o)}{2}(V_f - V_o)$$

$$= (6.0 \times 10^5\ \text{Pa})(32 \times 10^{-6}\ \text{m}^3) = 19.2\ \text{J}.$$

Using the work-energy theorem, $\Delta KE = W$, we obtain:

$$\frac{1}{2}(40.0 \times 10^{-3}\ \text{kg})v^2 - 0 = 19.2\ \text{J, yielding } v = 31\ \text{m/s}.$$

(b) The air in front of the projectile exerts a retarding force,

$$F_{retard} = P_{air}A,$$

on the projectile. Here, A is the cross-sectional area of the launch tube. The energy spent by the projectile overcoming this retarding force is $W_{spent} = F_{retard}L = P_{air}(AL)$, where L is the length of the launch tube. Thus,

$$W_{spent} = P_{air}(V_f - V_o) = (1.0 \times 10^5\ \text{Pa})(32 \times 10^{-6}\ \text{m}^3) = 3.2\ \text{J}.$$

The requested fraction is then, $\dfrac{W_{spent}}{W} = \dfrac{3.2\ \text{J}}{19.2\ \text{J}} = \dfrac{1}{6}$.

12.1 From the discussion of kinetic theory in Chapter 10, the average kinetic energy per molecule is

$$\langle KE \rangle_{molecule} = \frac{3}{2}kT = \frac{3}{2}\left(\frac{R}{N_A}\right)T.$$

For a monatomic gas containing N noninteracting molecules, the total energy associated with random molecular motions is:

$$U = N\langle KE \rangle_{molecule} = \frac{3}{2}\left(\frac{N}{N_A}\right)RT = \frac{3}{2}nRT.$$

Since $PV = nRT$ for an ideal gas, the internal energy of a monatomic ideal gas is found to be given by:

$U = \frac{3}{2} PV.$

12.2 $W = P\Delta V = PA\Delta L = (2.00 \times 10^5 \text{ Pa})\frac{\pi}{4}(16.0 \times 10^{-2} \text{ m})^2(0.200 \text{ m}) = 804 \text{ J}$

12.3 We call N the number of molecules, and the average kinetic energy per molecule is represented by $\langle KE \rangle$. The total energy of our system is

$$U = N\langle KE\rangle = (3N_a)\frac{3}{2}kT = \frac{9}{2}RT \text{ (where we have used } N_a k = R).$$

Thus, $U = \frac{9}{2}(8.31 \text{ J/mol·K})(303 \text{ K}) = 1.1 \times 10^4 \text{ J}.$

Alternately, we could use the result of Problem 1:

$$U = \frac{3}{2}PV = \frac{3}{2}nRT = \frac{3}{2}(3.0)RT = \frac{9}{2}RT \text{ as above.}$$

12.4 The sketch for the cycle is shown at the right. Let us now find the net work done during the process: During the expansion from a to b we have

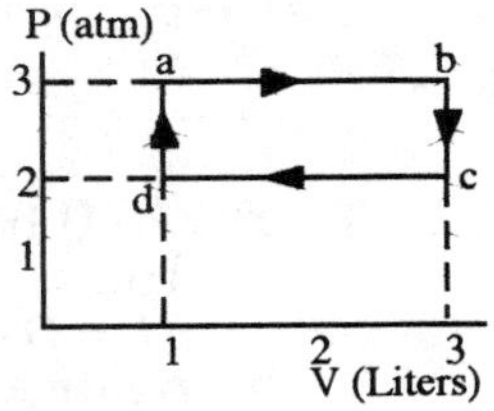

$W_{ab} = P_a(V_b - V_a) = 3(1.013 \times 10^5 \text{ Pa})(0.002 \text{ m}^3) = 610 \text{ J}.$

$W_{bc} = 0$ because $\Delta V_{bc} = 0$

$W_{cd} = P_c(V_d - V_c) = 2(1.013 \times 10^5 \text{ Pa})(-2 \times 10^{-3} \text{ m}^3)$, or

$W_{cd} = -410$ J. $W(\text{d to a}) = 0$ volume remains constant

Thus, the net work is: $W_{abcda} = 610 \text{ J} - 410 \text{ J} = 200 \text{ J}.$

(Note: the net work could also be obtained by computing the area enclosed within one cycle on the PV diagram.)

12.5 (a) $W_{IAF} = W_{IA} + W_{AF}$ (The notation IAF means the work done from I to A to F.) The term $W_{AF} = 0$ because the volume is a constant during this part of the process. Thus,

$$W_{IAF} = W_{IA} = P_I(V_A - V_I) = (4.05 \times 10^5 \text{ Pa})(2.00 \times 10^{-3} \text{ m}^3) = 810 \text{ J}.$$

(b) Along path IF, we find the work by finding the area under the PV curve. This consists of a triangular area plus a rectangular area.

$$W_{IF} = \frac{1}{2}(0.002 \text{ m}^3)(3.04 \times 10^5 \text{ Pa}) + (1.013 \times 10^5 \text{ Pa})(0.002 \text{ m}^3) = 507 \text{ J}.$$

(c) $W_{IBF} = W_{IB} + W_{BF}$. The term W_{IB} equals zero because the volume remains a constant during this part of the process. So,

$$W_{IBF} = W_{BF} = (1.013 \times 10^5 \text{ Pa})(2.00 \times 10^{-3} \text{ m}^3) = 203 \text{ J}.$$

12.6 The sketches for (a) and (b) are shown below.

(a)

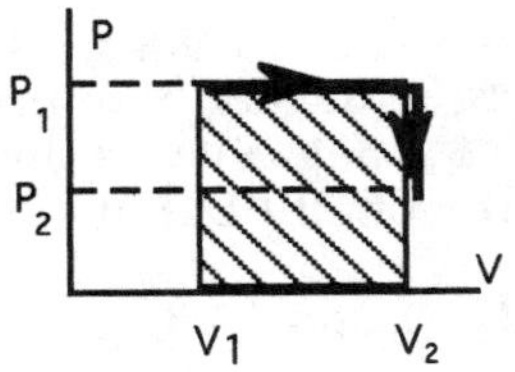

(b)

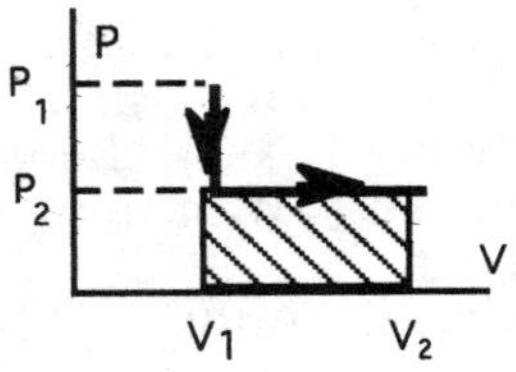

(c) There is more work done in process (a). We recognize this from the figures because there is more area under the PV curve in (a). Physically, more work is done because of the higher pressure during the expansion part of the process.

12.7 $P = 1.5\text{ atm} = 1.52 \times 10^5$ Pa

(a) $W = P\Delta V$, and $\Delta V = 4.0\text{ m}^3$, so $W = (1.52 \times 10^5\text{ Pa})(4.0\text{ m}^3) = 6.1 \times 10^5$ J.

(b) $\Delta V = -3.0\text{ m}^3$, giving $W = (1.52 \times 10^5\text{ Pa})(-3.0\text{ m}^3) = -4.6 \times 10^5$ J.

12.8 In a constant pressure process, the work done is $W = P\Delta V$.

For an ideal gas $PV = nRT$, and $V = \frac{nRT}{P}$, so $\Delta V = V_f - V_i = \frac{nR}{P}(T_f - T_i)$.

This gives, $W = P\Delta V = nR\Delta T = (0.200\text{ mol})(8.31\text{ J/K mol})(280\text{ K}) = 465\text{ J}$

12.9 (a) We use the ideal gas law as: $\frac{P_i V_i}{T_i} = \frac{P_f V_f}{T_f}$.

After canceling P and solving for the final temperature, we have

$$T_f = T_i\left(\frac{V_f}{V_i}\right) = T_i\left(\frac{4V_i}{V_i}\right) = 4(273.15\text{ K}) = 1093\text{ K}.$$

(b) $W = P\Delta V = nR\Delta T = nR(T_f - T_i) = (1\text{ mol})\left(8.31\ \frac{\text{J}}{\text{mol K}}\right)(1093\text{ K} - 273\text{ K})$

or $W = 6.81$ kJ.

12.10 (a) $W = 0$ because the volume remains constant.

The system gives off heat. Thus, $Q < 0$.

$\Delta U = Q - W$ and since $W = 0$, we have $\Delta U = Q$ Therefore, $\Delta U < 0$.

(b) Again, $W = 0$ because the volume remains constant.

$Q > 0$ because the water receives heat.

Again, $\Delta U = Q$ so $\Delta U > 0$.

12.11 The work done by the gas during this process is the area under the process curve on a P-V diagram. This is given by:

W = (area of rectangle) + (area of triangle)

$$= P_0(2V_0 - V_0) + \frac{1}{2}(2V_0 - V_0)(2P_0 - P_0) = 1.5P_0V_0.$$

Using the result of problem 1, the change in the internal energy of this monatomic ideal gas is:

$$\Delta U = U_f - U_i = \frac{3}{2}(2P_0)(2V_0) - \frac{3}{2}(P_0)(V_0) = 4.5\,P_0V_0.$$

Then, the first law of thermodynamics gives: $Q = \Delta U + W = 6P_0V_0$.

12.12 Using the result of problem 1, the change in internal energy is seen to be

$$\Delta U = U_f - U_i = \frac{3}{2}P_fV_f - \frac{3}{2}P_iV_i = \frac{3}{2}(2P_0)(V_0) - \frac{3}{2}(P_o)(2V_o) = 0$$

Then, the first law of thermodynamics gives $0 = Q - W$, or $Q = W$.
Since this is a compression process, work is done on the gas by the surroundings. That is, the gas does a negative amount of work or $W < 0$.
Finally, since $Q = W$ in this case, we conclude that $Q < 0$, or the gas must give off heat.

In summary, we find: $\Delta U = 0$, $Q < 0$, and $W < 0$.

12.13 (a) $W = P\Delta V = [0.3(1.013 \times 10^5\text{ Pa})](3.00 \times 10^{-3}\text{ m}^3 - 8.00 \times 10^{-3}\text{ m}^3)$
$= -152$ J.

(b) $\Delta U = Q - W$ We are given that $Q = -400$ J. Thus,
$\Delta U = -400\text{ J} - (-152\text{ J}) = -248$ J.

12.14 (a) W = area under the PV curve.

$W_{IF} = \frac{1}{2}(0.00200\ m^3)(3.04 \times 10^5\ Pa) + (1.013 \times 10^5\ Pa)(0.002\ m^3)$

$= 507\ J.$

$\Delta U_{IF} = Q_{IF} - W_{IF} = 418\ J - 507\ J = -89\ J$

(b) $W_{IAF} = W_{IA} + 0 = P_I(V_A - V_I) = (4.05 \times 10^5\ Pa)(2.00 \times 10^{-3}\ m^3) = 810\ J.$

ΔU is the same as above. Thus,

$Q_{IAF} = \Delta U + W_{IAF} = -89.0\ J + 810\ J = 721\ J.$

12.15 $\Delta U_{cycle} = Q_{cycle} - W_{cycle} = 0$ (for any complete cycle)

$Q_{cycle} = W_{cycle}$ = area enclosed in PV diagram = $\frac{1}{2}(4\ m^3)(6 \times 10^3\ Pa)$

or, $Q_{cycle} = 12 \times 10^3\ J = 12\ kJ.$

If the cycle is reversed, then $Q_{cycle} = -12\ kJ$

12.16 (a) $W = P\Delta V = (1.013 \times 10^5\ Pa)(3.342 \times 10^{-3}\ m^3) = 338\ J.$

(b) The heat added is: $Q = mL_v = (2 \times 10^{-3}\ kg)(2.26 \times 10^6\ J/kg) = 4520\ J.$

(c) $\Delta U = Q - W = 4520\ J - 338\ J = 4182\ J.$

12.17(a) $\Delta V = A\Delta L = (0.150\ m^2)(-0.20\ m) = -3.0 \times 10^{-2}\ m^3.$

Thus, $W = P\Delta V = (6.0 \times 10^3\ Pa)(-3.0 \times 10^{-2}\ m^3) = -180\ J.$

(b) $Q = \Delta U + W = -8.0\ J - 180J = -188\ J$ (188 J of heat energy are removed from the gas.)

12.18 $W_{BC} = 0$ (constant volume), $W_{CA} < 0\ (\Delta V < 0)$, $W_{AB} > 0\ (\Delta V > 0)$

$\Delta U = Q - W$ gives $\Delta U_{BC} = Q_{BC} - W_{BC} < 0$ (because $Q_{BC} < 0$, $W_{BC} = 0$).

$\Delta U_{cycle} = \Delta U_{AB} + \Delta U_{BC} + \Delta U_{CA} = 0$

Thus, $\Delta U_{AB} > 0$ since both ΔU_{BC} and ΔU_{CA} are negative.

$\Delta U_{CA} = Q_{CA} - W_{CA}$ becomes $Q_{CA} = \Delta U_{CA} + W_{CA} < 0$ since both ΔU_{CA} and W_{CA} are negative.

Also, $Q_{AB} = \Delta U_{AB} + W_{AB} > 0$ since $\Delta U_{AB} > 0$ and $W_{AB} > 0$.

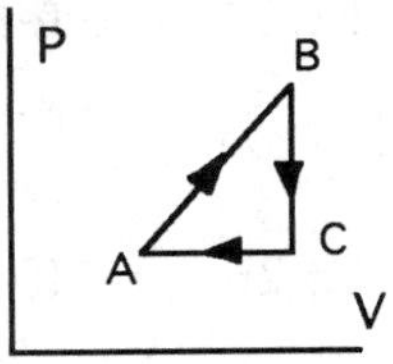

In summary, $Q_{AB} > 0$, $Q_{BC} < 0$, $Q_{CA} < 0$. $W_{AB} > 0$, $W_{BC} = 0$, $W_{CA} < 0$.

$\Delta U_{AB} > 0$, $\Delta U_{BC} < 0$, and $\Delta U_{CA} < 0$

12.19 (a) $W = P\Delta V = (1.013 \times 10^5\ Pa)[(1.09 - 1.00) \times 10^{-6}\ m^3] = +9.12 \times 10^{-3}\ J$

(b) $Q = -mL_f = -(10^{-3}\ kg)(3.33 \times 10^5\ J/kg) = -333\ J.$

$\Delta U = Q - W = -333\ J - 9.12 \times 10^{-3}\ J = -333\ J.$

12.20 (a) The original volume of the aluminum is:

$V = \frac{m}{\rho} = \frac{5.0\ kg}{2.7 \times 10^3\ kg/m^3} = 1.85 \times 10^{-3}\ m^3.$

The change in volume is:

$\Delta V = \beta V_0(\Delta T) = 3(24.0 \times 10^{-6}\ {}^\circ C^{-1})(1.85 \times 10^{-3}\ m^3)(70.0\ {}^\circ C) = 9.32 \times 10^{-6}\ m^3$

The work done is: $W = P\Delta V = (1.013 \times 10^5\ Pa)(9.32 \times 10^{-6}\ m^3) = 0.95\ J$

(b) $Q = mc\Delta T = (5.0\ kg)(900\ J/kg\ {}^\circ C)(70\ {}^\circ C) = 3.2 \times 10^5\ J$

(c) $\Delta U = Q - W \cong Q = 3.2 \times 10^5\ J$

12.21 (a) $W = P\Delta V$ = area under PV curve.

$W_{IAF} = (1.50 \text{ atm})(0.800 - 0.300)$ liters, or

$$W_{IAF} = 1.50(1.013 \times 10^5 \text{ Pa})(0.500 \times 10^{-3} \text{ m}^3) = 76.0 \text{ J}.$$

$W_{IBF} = (2.00 \text{ atm})(0.800 - 0.300)$ liters, or

$$W_{IBF} = 2(1.013 \times 10^5 \text{ Pa})(0.500 \times 10^{-3} \text{ m}^3) = 101 \text{ J}.$$

$$W_{IF} = W_{IAF} + \frac{1}{4}(1.013 \times 10^5 \text{ Pa})(0.500 \times 10^{-3} \text{ m}^3) = 88.7 \text{ J}.$$

(b) We are given that $\Delta U = (180 \text{ J} - 91 \text{ J}) = 89.0 \text{ J}$.
Thus, $Q = \Delta U + W = 89.0 \text{ J} + W$, giving $Q_{AF} = 89.0 \text{ J} + 76.0 \text{ J} = 165 \text{ J}$, $Q_{BF} = 89 \text{ J} + 101 \text{ J} = 190 \text{ J}$, and $Q_F = 89 \text{ J} + 88.7 \text{ J} = 178 \text{ J}$.

12.22 The maximum efficiency equals the Carnot efficiency.

$$\text{Eff}_c = \frac{T_h - T_c}{T_h} = 1 - \frac{T_c}{T_h} = 1 - \frac{293}{573} = 0.488 \text{ (or } 48.8\,\%)$$

12.23 $\text{eff} = 1 - \frac{Q_c}{Q_h} = 0.300$, which gives, $Q_c = 0.700 Q_h$.

(a) Therefore, $Q_c = 0.700(800 \text{ J}) = 560 \text{ J}$

(b) For a Carnot Cycle, $\text{eff} = 1 - \frac{T_c}{T_h} = 0.300$, from which
$T_c = 0.700 T_h = 0.7(500 \text{ K}) = 350 \text{ K}$.

12.24 We use $\text{Eff}_c = 1 - \frac{T_c}{T_h}$ as, $0.300 = 1 - \frac{573 \text{ K}}{T_h}$.
From which, $T_h = 819 \text{ K} = 546\text{ °C}$.

12.25 The temperatures of the reservoirs are 300 °F = 422 K, and
150°F = 65.6°C = 338.7 K. $\text{Eff}_c\ 1 - \frac{T_c}{T_h} = 1 - \frac{338.7}{422} = 0.197$ (or 19.7 %)

12.26 (a) $\text{Eff} = \frac{W}{Q_h} = \frac{200 \text{ J}}{Q_h} = 0.300$. Thus, $Q_h = \frac{200 \text{ J}}{0.300} = 667 \text{ J}$.

(b) $W = Q_h - Q_c$. Therefore, $Q_c = Q_h - W = 667 \text{ J} - 200 \text{ J} = 467 \text{ J}$.

12.27 (a) $W = Q_h - Q_c = 1700 \text{ J} - 1200 \text{ J} = 500 \text{ J}$. $\text{Eff} = \frac{W}{Q_h} = \frac{500 \text{ J}}{1700 \text{ J}} = 0.294$.

(b) The work done in each cycle has been found to be 500 J in part (a).

(c) $P = \frac{W}{\Delta t} = \frac{500 \text{ J}}{0.300 \text{ s}} = 1.67 \times 10^3 \text{ W}$.

12.28 (a) $\text{Eff} = \frac{W}{Q_h} = \frac{Q_h - Q_c}{Q_h} = 1 - \frac{Q_c}{Q_h} = 0.250$.

With $Q_c = 8000$ J, we have $Q_h = 1.07 \times 10^4$ J.

(b) $W = Q_h - Q_c = 2.7 \times 10^3$ J, and from $P = \frac{W}{\Delta t}$, we have

$$\Delta t = \frac{W}{P} = \frac{2.7 \times 10^3 \text{ J}}{5000 \text{ J/s}} = 0.53 \text{ s}.$$

12.29 We have $W = Q_h - Q_c = 200 \text{ J}$, and $\text{Eff} = \frac{W}{Q_h} = \frac{200 \text{ J}}{500 \text{ J}} = 0.4$.

If $\text{Eff} = 0.6\text{Eff}_c$, then $\text{Eff}_c = \frac{0.4}{0.6} = 0.667$.

But, $\text{Eff}_c = 1 - \frac{T_c}{T_h} = 0.667$, thus, $\frac{T_c}{T_h} = 0.333 = \frac{1}{3}$.

12.30 We have, $\text{Eff}_c = 1 - \frac{T_c}{T_h} = 1 - \frac{353}{623} = 0.433$, and $\text{Eff} = \frac{W}{Q_h}$.

Thus, $W = Q_h(\text{Eff}) = 21{,}000\ \text{J}(0.433) = 9.10 \times 10^3$ J.

(a) $P = \frac{W}{t} = \frac{9.10 \times 10^3\ \text{J}}{1.00\ \text{s}} = 9.10 \times 10^3\ \text{W} = 9.10\ \text{kW}$.

(b) $Q_c = Q_h - W = 21000\ \text{J} - 9100\ \text{J} = 1.19 \times 10^4$ J.

The heat expelled in each cycle (which lasts for one second) is $Q_c = 1.19 \times 10^4$ J.

12.31 Work done each second = 1000 MJ = 10^9 J.

$\text{Eff} = \frac{W}{Q_h} = 0.33$, so $Q_h = \frac{W}{.33} = \frac{10^9\ \text{J}}{.33} = 3.0 \times 10^9$ J

But, also $W = Q_h - Q_c$, so $Q_c = Q_h - W = 3.0 \times 10^9\ \text{J} - 10^9\ \text{J} = 2.0 \times 10^9$ J.

Therefore, 2.0 x 10^9 J of heat must be absorbed each second by 10^6 kg of river water.

$$\Delta T = \frac{Q}{mc} = \frac{2.0 \times 10^9\ \text{J}}{(10^6\ \text{J})(4186\ \text{J/kg°C})} = 0.48°\text{C}.$$

12.32 (a) The change in entropy of the water is:

$$\Delta S = \frac{Q}{T} = -\frac{mL_f}{T} = \frac{(1.00\ \text{kg})(-3.33 \times 10^5\ \text{J})}{273\ \text{K}} = -1.22 \times 10^3\ \text{J/K}.$$

(b) The entropy change of the freezer is +1.22 x 10^3 J/K.

12.33 $Q = mL_v = (1.0\ \text{kg})(2.26 \times 10^6\ \text{J/kg}) = 2.26 \times 10^6$ J

$$\Delta S = \frac{Q}{T} = \frac{2.26 \times 10^6\ \text{J}}{373\ \text{K}} = 6.1 \times 10^3\ \text{J/K}$$

12.34 The heat generated equals the potential energy given up by the log.

$Q = mgh = (70.0\ \text{kg})(9.80\ \text{m/s}^2)(25.0\ \text{m}) = 1.72 \times 10^4$ J.

Thus, $\Delta S = \frac{Q}{T} = \frac{1.72 \times 10^4\ \text{J}}{300\ \text{K}} = 57.2$ J/K.

12.35 The heat generated is equal to the kinetic energy lost.

$$Q = (2)(\tfrac{1}{2}mv^2) = (2000\ \text{kg})(20\ \text{m/s})^2 = 8.00 \times 10^5\ \text{J}.$$

So, $\Delta S = \frac{Q}{T} = \frac{8.00 \times 10^5\ \text{J}}{296\ \text{K}} = 2.70 \times 10^3$ J/K.

12.36 (a)

Result	Possible Combinations	Total
all red	RRR	1
2R,1G	RRG,RGR,GRR	3
1R,2G	RGG,GRG,GGR	3
all green	GGG	1

(b) .

Result	Possible Combinations	Total
all red	RRRRR	1

4R,1G	RRRRG,RRRGR,RRGRR,RGRRR,GRRRR	5
3R,2G	RRRGG,RRGRG,RGRRG,GRRRG,RRGGR, RGRGR,GRRGR,RGGRR,GRGRR,GGRRR	10
2R,3G	GGGRR,GGRGR,GRGGR,RGGGR,GGRRG, GRGRG,RGGRG,GRRGG,RGRGG,RRGGG	10
1R,4G	RGGGG,GRGGG,GGRGG,GGGRG,GGGGR	5
all green	GGGGG	1

12.37 (a) The table is shown below. On the basis of the table, the most probable result of a toss is 2 heads and 2 tails.

(b) The most ordered state is the least likely state. Thus, on the basis of the table this is either all heads or all tails.

(c) The most disordered is the most likely state. Thus, this is 2 heads and 2 tails.

Result	Possible Combinations	Total
all heads	HHHH	1
3H,1T	THHH,HTHH,HHTH,HHHT	4
2H,2T	TTHH,THTH,THHT,HTTH,HTHT,HHTT	6
1H,3T	HTTT,THTT,TTHT,TTTH	4
all tails	TTTT	1

12.38 (a) Since there is only one ace of spades out of 52 total cards, the probability is 1/52.

(b) Since there are four aces out of 52 total cards, the probability is 4/52 = 1/13.

(c) Since there are 13 spades out of 52 total cards, the probability is 13/52 = 1/4.

12.39 The maximum efficiency is that of a Carnot engine given by

$$\text{Eff}_c = 1 - \frac{T_c}{T_h} = 1 - \frac{100 \text{ K}}{200 \text{ K}} = 0.5 = 50\% \text{ efficiency.}$$

The claim of 60% efficiency is invalid.

12.40 (a) $\text{Eff}_{max} = 1 - \frac{T_c}{T_h} = 1 - \frac{278}{293} = 5.1 \times 10^{-2}$ (or 5.1 %).

(b) $P = \frac{W}{\Delta t} = 75 \times 10^6$ J/s. Therefore,

$$W = (75 \times 10^6 \text{ J/s})(3600 \text{ s/h}) = 2.7 \times 10^{11} \text{ J/h.}$$

From, $\text{Eff} = \frac{W}{Q_h}$ we find:

$$(Q_h)_{min} = \frac{W}{\text{Eff}_{max}} = \frac{2.70 \times 10^{11} \text{ J/h}}{5.1 \times 10^{-2}} = 5.3 \times 10^{12} \text{ J/h.}$$

12.41 (a) Using $\Delta S = \frac{Q_{input}}{T}$, we have $\Delta S_h = \frac{-Q_h}{T_h}$.

(b) Using $\Delta S = \frac{Q_{input}}{T}$, we have $\Delta S_c = \frac{Q_c}{T_C}$.

(c) Here, $\Delta S_e = \frac{Q_{input}}{T_{input}} - \frac{Q_{output}}{T_{output}} = \frac{Q_h}{T_h} - \frac{Q_c}{T_C}$.

(d) Here, $\Delta S_{isolated} = \Delta S_h + \Delta S_e + \Delta S_c = -\frac{Q_h}{T_h} + \left(\frac{Q_h}{T_h} - \frac{Q_c}{T_C}\right) + \frac{Q_c}{T_C} = 0$

12.42 Entropy change of the hot reservoir: $\Delta S_H = -\frac{Q_H}{T_H} = -\frac{8000\ \text{J}}{500\ \text{K}} = -16.0\,\frac{\text{J}}{\text{K}}$

Entropy change of the cold reservoir: $\Delta S_C = \frac{Q_C}{T_C} = \frac{8000\ \text{J}}{300\ \text{K}} = 26.7\,\frac{\text{J}}{\text{K}}$

and the net entropy change of the system during this irreversible process is: $\Delta S_{total} = 26.7\ \text{J/K} - 16.0\ \text{J/K} = +10.7\ \text{J/K} > 0.$

12.43 The heat discarded is 70% of the input energy for the plant. Thus, the energy going in to the river each second is:

$$\frac{Q}{t} = 0.7(25 \times 10^8\ \text{W}) = 17.5 \times 10^8\ \text{J/s}.$$

Also $\frac{Q}{t} = \left(\frac{m}{t}\right) c\Delta T$, or $\Delta T = \frac{Q/t}{(m/t)c} = \frac{17.5 \times 10^8\ \text{J/s}}{\left(\frac{9.0 \times 10^6\ \text{kg}}{60\ \text{s}}\right)\left(4186\ \frac{\text{J}}{\text{kg}\ ^\circ\text{C}}\right)} = 2.8\ ^\circ\text{C}.$

12.44 The density of water is $\rho = 1000\ \text{kg/m}^3$.
Therefore, 5000 m^3 of water corresponds to a mass of:

$m = (5000\ \text{m}^3)(1000\ \text{kg/m}^3) = 5.0 \times 10^6\ \text{kg}.$

When this mass falls 50 m, its change in potential energy is:

$\Delta PE = -(5.0 \times 10^6)(9.80)(50) = 2.45 \times 10^9\ \text{J}.$

In other words, gravity does 2.45×10^9 J of work on the water every second. Assuming that the internal energy of the water does not change in the process, we may write (using $\Delta U = Q - W$):

$Q = W = 2.45 \times 10^9\ \text{J}$, so

$\Delta S = \frac{Q}{T} = \frac{2.45 \times 10^9\ \text{J}}{(20 + 273.15)\text{K}} = 8.4 \times 10^6\ \text{J/K}$ as the increase in entropy each second.

12.45 [Prove by contradiction]
Assume a quantity of heat, Q flows from the cold object at T_C to the hot object at $T_h > T_C$ (i.e., $Q_C = -Q$ and $Q_h = +Q$)

Then: $\Delta S_C = -\frac{Q}{T_C}$ and $\Delta S_h = \frac{Q}{T_h}$, and the total entropy change of the system is: $\Delta S_T = \Delta S_C + \Delta S_h = -\frac{Q}{T_C} + \frac{Q}{T_h} = Q\left(\frac{T_C - T_h}{T_C T_h}\right).$

The second law requires $\Delta S_T \geq 0$. Thus, we must have $Q(T_C - T_h) > 0$. But, since $(T_C - T_h) < 0$, it is necessary that $Q < 0$. Therefore, $Q_C = -Q > 0$ while $Q_h = Q < 0$, or the heat actually flows from the hot object to the cold object. Thus, Q_C must be positive resulting in a heat flow to the cold object, contary to the original assumption.

12.46 (a) $\Delta U_{1,3} = Q_{123} - W_{123} = 418\ \text{J} - 167\ \text{J} = +251\ \text{J}$

(b) Use $\Delta U_{1,3} = Q_{143} - W_{143}$, with $\Delta U_{1,3} = +251\ \text{J}$.
Thus, $251\ \text{J} = Q_{143} - 63.0\ \text{J}$, or $Q_{143} = +314\ \text{J}$.

(c) $W_{12341} = W_{123} - W_{143} = 167\ \text{J} - 63.0\ \text{J} = +104\ \text{J}$

(d) $W_{14321} = W_{143} - W_{123} = 63.0\ \text{J} - 167\ \text{J} = -104\ \text{J}$

(e) The internal energy change is zero in both cases because both are cyclic processes.

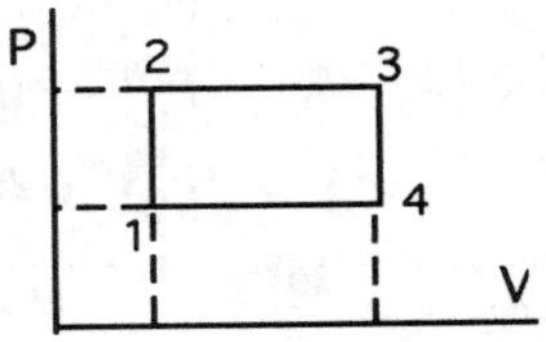

12.47 (a) The area under the path AB gives the work done by the gas for this process:

W_{AB} = (area of rectangle) + (area of triangle)

$= (40.0 \times 10^{-3}\ m^3)(1.013 \times 10^5\ Pa) + \frac{1}{2}(40.0 \times 10^{-3}\ m^3)(4.052 \times 10^5\ Pa) = 1.22 \times 10^4\ J$

Since this is an expansion process, the gas does positive work: $W_{AB} > 0$.

(b) Again, the area under the path in the P-V diagram gives the work. Since this is a compression, the gas does negative work or this represents a work input.

$W_{BC} = -(\text{area of rectangle}) = -(40.0 \times 10^{-3}\ m^3)(1.013 \times 10^5\ Pa) = -4.05 \times 10^3\ J.$

(c) Since this is a cyclic process, $(\Delta U)_{cycle} = 0$. Therefore, the first law of thermodynamics gives: $0 = Q_{net} - W_{net}$, or

$Q_{net} = W_{net} = W_{AB} + W_{BC} + W_{CA} = 1.22 \times 10^4\ J - 4.05 \times 10^3\ J + 0 = 8.15 \times 10^3\ J.$

12.48 (a) The change in length of the rod is:

$\Delta L = \alpha L_0(\Delta T) = (11 \times 10^{-6}\ °C^{-1})(2.0\ m)(20\ °C) = 4.4 \times 10^{-4}\ m.$

The rod exerts a retarding force equal the weight of the load. Thus, $F = 5.88 \times 10^4$ N, so $W = -F(\Delta L) = -(5.88 \times 10^4\ N)(4.4 \times 10^{-4}\ m) = -26\ J.$

(b) $Q = mc\Delta T = (10^2\ kg)(448\ J/kg\ °C)(20\ °C) = 9.0 \times 10^5\ J.$

(c) $\Delta U = Q - W = 8.96 \times 10^5\ J - (-26\ J) = 9.0 \times 10^5\ J.$

12.49 Consider a 1 s time interval. Then, $W = +1500\ kJ = 1.5 \times 10^6\ J.$

We have, $\text{Eff} = \frac{W}{Q_h} = 0.25$. Thus, $Q_h = \frac{W}{0.25} = \frac{1.5 \times 10^6\ J}{0.25} = 6.0 \times 10^6\ J$

and, $Q_c = Q_h - W = 6.0 \times 10^6\ J - 1.5 \times 10^6\ J = 4.5 \times 10^6\ J$

(Q_c = the heat to be absorbed by the coolant water each second.)

The coolant flow is 60 liters/s = $6 \times 10^{-2}\ m^3/s$. Thus, the mass flow is

$\text{mass/s} = (6.0 \times 10^{-2}\ m^3/s)(1000\ kg/m^3) = 60\ kg/s.$

Therefore, we see that the 60 kg of water must absorb 4.5×10^6 J.

From, $Q = mc\Delta T$: $\Delta T = \frac{Q}{mc} = \frac{4.5 \times 10^6\ J}{(60\ kg)(4186\ J/kg°C)} = 18\ °C.$

12.50 (a) The net work done in the entire cycle = area enclosed within the cycle on a PV diagram. Thus,

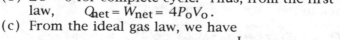

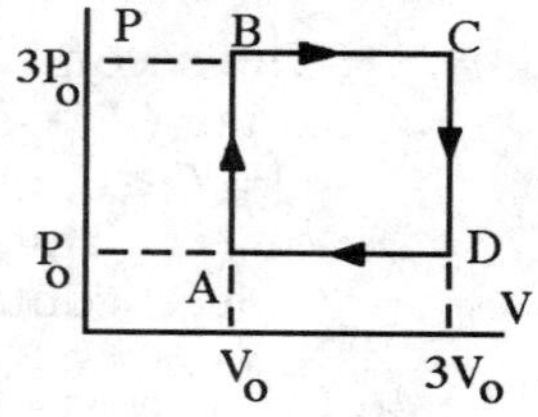

$W_{net} = (3P_0 - P_0)(3V_0 - V_0) = 4P_0V_0.$

(b) $\Delta U = 0$ for complete cycle. Thus, from the first law, $Q_{net} = W_{net} = 4P_0V_0.$

(c) From the ideal gas law, we have

$P_0V_0 = nRT_0 = (1.00\ mol)(8.31\ \frac{J}{mol\ K})(273\ K)$, or

$P_0V_0 = 2.27 \times 10^3\ J.$

Thus, $W_{net} = 4P_0V_0 = 4(2.27 \times 10^3\ J) = 9.07 \times 10^3\ J.$

12.51 (a) $W = P\Delta V$

$= (6.00 \times 10^6\ Pa)(2 - 1)\ m^3 + (4.00 \times 10^6\ Pa)(3 - 2)\ m^3$

$$+ (2.00 \times 10^6 \text{ Pa})(4 - 3) \text{ m}^3$$
$$= 12.0 \text{ MJ}$$

(b) -12.0 MJ

12.52 The work output is $W = \frac{1}{2} m_{train}(5.00 \text{ m/s})^2$.

We are told $\text{Eff} = \frac{W}{Q_h}$

$$0.200 = \frac{1}{2} m_{train}(5.00 \text{ m/s})^2 / Q_h \qquad (1)$$

and $\text{Eff}_c = 1 - \frac{300 \text{ K}}{T_h} = \frac{1}{2} m_{train}(6.5 \text{ m/s})^2 / Q_h \quad (2)$

Solving (1) and (2) for T_h gives $T_h = 453 \text{ K}$

12.53 $\Delta S = \frac{Q_2}{T_2} - \frac{Q_1}{T_1} = \left(\frac{1000}{290} - \frac{1000}{5700}\right) \text{ J/K} = 3.27 \text{ J/K}$

12.54 The work is done on the wire, so $W = -F(\Delta L)$.
But, $F = (\text{stress})(A)$, and $\Delta L = (\text{strain})L$, so
$W = -(\text{stress})(A)(\text{strain})L = -(\text{stress})(\text{strain})V$

12.55 (a) The change in volume of the aluminum is:
$\Delta V = \beta V_0(\Delta T) = (3)(24 \times 10^{-6}\ ^\circ\text{C}^{-1})(3.7 \times 10^{-4} \text{ m}^3)(18\ ^\circ\text{C}) = 4.8 \times 10^{-7} \text{ m}^3$
Thus, $W = P\Delta V = (1.013 \times 10^5 \text{ Pa})(4.8 \times 10^{-7} \text{ m}^3) = 4.9 \times 10^{-2} \text{ J}$.
(b) $Q = mc\Delta T = (1.0 \text{ kg})(900 \text{ J/kg }^\circ\text{C})(18\ ^\circ\text{C}) = 1.6 \times 10^4 \text{ J}$.
(c) $\Delta U = Q - W = 1.6 \times 10^4 \text{ J} - 4.9 \times 10^{-2} \text{ J} = 1.6 \text{X} 10^4 \text{ J}$.

12.56 Q_c = heat to melt 15 g of Hg = $mL_f = (0.015 \text{ kg})(1.18 \times 10^4 \text{ J/kg}) = 177 \text{ J}$.
Q_h = heat removed to freeze 1 g of aluminum = mL_f, or
$Q_h = (10^{-3} \text{ kg})(3.97 \times 10^5 \text{ J/kg}) = 397 \text{ J}$, $\quad W = Q_h - Q_c = 220 \text{ J}$.
(a) $\text{Eff} = \frac{W}{Q_h} = \frac{220 \text{ J}}{397 \text{ J}} = 0.554$, or 55.4%.
(b) $\text{Eff (Carnot)} = \left(\frac{T_h}{T_h - T_c}\right) = \frac{933 \text{ K} - 234.1 \text{ K}}{933 \text{ K}} = 0.749 = 74.9\%$.

12.57 (a) $Q = mc\Delta T = (1 \text{ mol})(20.79 \text{ J/mol K})(120 \text{ K}) = 2.49 \times 10^3 \text{ J}$
(b) $\Delta U = N_a\langle KE\rangle_f - N_a\langle KE\rangle_i = N_a[\frac{3}{2}kT_f - \frac{3}{2}kT_i] = \frac{3}{2}(N_a k)(T_f - T_i)$
$$= \frac{3}{2}R(T_f - T_i) = \frac{3}{2}(8.31 \text{ J/mol K})(120 \text{ K}) = 1.50 \times 10^3 \text{ J}.$$
(c) $W = Q - \Delta U = 2.49 \times 10^3 \text{ J} - 1.50 \times 10^3 \text{ J} = 990 \text{ J}$.

12.58 (a) Let us first find the temperature at point C by use of the ideal gas law: $\frac{P_c V_c}{T_c} = \frac{P_0 V_0}{T_0}$

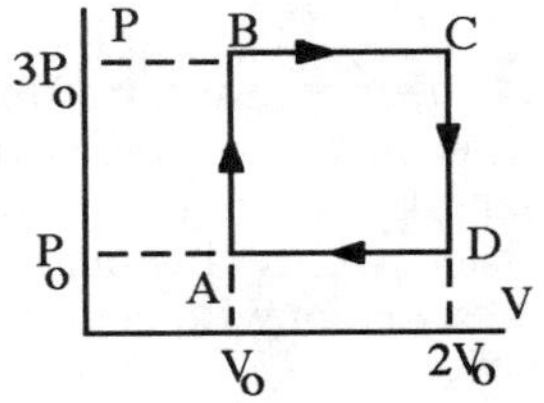

Thus, $T_c = T_0 \frac{P_c V_c}{P_0 V_0} = 6\ T_0$.
Now, find the work done along path ABC. This work is equal to the area under the PV curve.
$W_{ABC} = (3P_0)(2V_0 - V_0) = 3P_0 V_0$.

But, for one mole of gas, the ideal gas law says: $P_0V_0 = RT_0$.
Thus, $W_{ABC} = 3\,RT_0$.
The internal energy of one mole of an ideal gas is found as

$$U = N\langle KE\rangle = N_a(\frac{3}{2}kT) = \frac{3}{2}RT.$$

Thus, $\Delta U_{ABC} = \frac{3}{2}RT_C - \frac{3}{2}RT_0 = \frac{3}{2}R(6T_0) - \frac{3}{2}RT_0 = \frac{15}{2}RT_0.$
Now, from the first law, we find the heat entering the system as

$$Q_{ABC} = \Delta U + W = \frac{15}{2}RT_0 + 3RT_0 = \frac{21}{2}RT_0.$$

(b) Using an approach similar to that used in (a), we find
$W_{CDA} = P_0(V_0 - 2V_0) = -P_0V_0 = -RT_0$, and

$$Q_{ABC} = \Delta U + W = U_A - U_C + W_{CDA} = \frac{3}{2}RT_0 - \frac{3}{2}R(6T_0) - RT_0 = -\frac{17}{2}RT_0$$

Thus, the heat leaving the system is $\frac{17}{2}RT_0$.

(c) $\text{Eff} = \frac{W_{net}}{Q_{input}} = \frac{3RT_0 - RT_0}{\frac{21}{2}RT_0} = \frac{4}{21}$ (approximately 19%).

(d) $\text{Eff}_{max} = 1 - \frac{T_A}{T_C} = 1 - \frac{T_0}{6T_0} = \frac{5}{6}$ (about 83.3 %).

12.59 (a) $\frac{W}{t} = 1.5 \times 10^8$ J/s, $Q = mL = \frac{W}{0.15t}\Delta t$ and $L = 7.8 \times 10^6$ cal/kg.

$$m = \frac{W}{0.15t}\frac{\Delta t}{L} = \frac{(1.5 \times 10^8 \text{ J/s})(86{,}400 \text{ s/day})}{(0.15)(7.8 \times 10^6 \text{ cal/kg})(4.184 \text{ J/cal})},\text{ or}$$

$$m = 2.65 \times 10^6 \text{ kg/day} = 2.7 \times 10^3 \frac{\text{metric tons}}{\text{day}}.$$

(b) $\text{Cost} = \frac{\$8}{\text{metric ton}}\left(2.65 \times 10^3 \frac{\text{metric tons}}{\text{day}}\right)\left(\frac{365 \text{ days}}{\text{y}}\right) = \frac{\$7.7 \times 10^6}{\text{year}}$

(c) Heat discharge rate to the water: $\text{Eff} = \frac{W}{Q_h} = \frac{W}{(W + Q_c)} = \frac{W/t}{W/t + Q_c/t}$

so, $\frac{Q_c}{t} = \frac{W}{t}\left(\frac{1}{\text{Eff}} - 1\right) = \left(1.5 \times 10^8 \frac{\text{J}}{\text{s}}\right)\left(\frac{1}{0.15} - 1\right) = 8.5 \times 10^8 \frac{\text{J}}{\text{s}} = 2.03 \times 10^8 \frac{\text{cal}}{\text{s}}$

Now require $\frac{Q_c}{t} = \frac{mc\Delta T}{t}$ and find:

$$\frac{m}{t} = \frac{1}{c\Delta T}\frac{Q_c}{t} = \frac{2.03 \times 10^8 \text{ cal/s}}{(1 \text{ cal/g C°})5 \text{ C°}} = 4 \times 10^7 \text{ g/s} = 4.0 \times 10^4 \text{ kg/s}.$$

CONCEPTUAL QUESTION ANSWERS

2. Her claim must be rejected. The second law forbids 100% efficiency.

4. Temperature = A measure of molecular motion. Heat = energy in the process of being transferred between objects by random molecular collisions. Thermal energy = an object's energy of random molecular motion and molecular interaction. Internal energy = thermal energy plus chemical energy, strain potential energy, and an object's other energy not associated with center of mass motion or location.

6. A higher steam temperature means that more energy can be extracted from the steam. For a constant temperature heat sink at T_c and steam at T_h, the efficiency of the power plant goes as $\frac{T_h - T_c}{T_h} = 1 - \frac{T_c}{T_h}$ and is maximized for high T_h.

8. $\text{Eff} = \frac{\Delta T}{T_h} = \frac{80}{373} \approx 22\%$ (Assumes atmospheric temperature of 20° C.)

10. Loss of energy to heating the gasoline and the air in which it burns.

12. An analogy due to Carnot is instructive: A waterfall continuously converts mechanical energy into thermal energy. It continuously creates entropy as the organized motion of the falling water turns into disorganized molecular motion. We humans put turbines into the waterfall, diverting some of the energy stream to our use. Water flows spontaneously from high to low elevation and heat flows spontaneously from high to low temperature. Into the great flow of solar radiation from Sun to Earth, living things put themselves. They live on energy flow. A basking snake diverts high-temperature heat through itself temporarily, before the energy is inevitably lost to low-temperature heat radiated into outer space. A tree builds organized cellulose molecules and we build libraries and babies who look like their grandmothers, all out of a thin diverted stream in the universal flow of energy crashing down to disorder. We do not violate the second law, for we build local reductions in the entropy of one thing within the inexorable increase in the total entropy of the Universe. Your roommate's exercise puts heat into the room.

14. Even at essentially constant temperature, heat must flow out of the solidifying sugar into the surroundings, to raise the entropy of the environment. The water molecules become less ordered as they leave the liquid in the container to mix into the whole atmosphere.

16. A slice of hot pizza cools off. Road friction brings a skidding car to a stop. A cup falls to the floor and shatters. Any process is irreversible if it looks funny or frightening when shown in a videotape running backward. The free flight of a projectile is nearly reversible.

CHAPTER THIRTEEN SOLUTIONS

Chapter Thirteen Readings

Bascom, W., "Ocean Waves," *Scientific American*, August 1959, p. 74.

Bascom, W., Waves and Beaches: The Dynamics of the Ocean Surface, New York, Doubleday Anchor Books, 1980.

Einstein, A., and Infeld, L., "The Evolution of Physics, New York, Simon and Schuster, 1961.

Gilbert, B, and Glanz, P., "Springs Distorted and Combined," *The Physics Teacher*, October 1983, p. 430.

Kelby, S.D, and Middleton, R.P, "The Vibrations of Hand Bells," *Physics Education*, Vol. 15, 1980, p. 320.

Oliver, J., "Long Earthquake Waves," *Scientific American*, March 1959, p. 14.

Rossing, T.D. "The Physics of Kettledrums," *Scientific American*, November 1982, p. 172.

Yam, P., "Sound Systems: using the ocean's noise to image undersea objects", *Scientific American*, v. 267 (July '92) p30.

13.1 (a) The force on the mass is: $F = kx = (160\ \text{N/m})(0.15\ \text{m}) = 24\ \text{N}$.
(b) From Newton's second law, the acceleration is

$$a = \frac{F}{m} = \frac{24\ \text{N}}{0.40\ \text{kg}} = 60\ \text{m/s}^2.$$

13.2 (a) The spring constant is given by: $k = \frac{mg}{x} = \frac{50\ \text{N}}{5.0 \times 10^{-2}\ \text{m}} = 1000\ \text{N/m}$,
and the force required to stretch the spring 11 cm (0.11 m) is

$$F = kx = (1000\ \text{N/m})(0.11\ \text{m}) = 110\ \text{N}.$$

(b) The graph will be a straight line passing through the origin and having a slope of 1.0×10^3 N/m.

13.3 (a) Since the collision is perfectly elastic the ball will rebound to the height of 4.00 m and then repeat the motion over and over again.
(b) To determine the period, we use: $x = \frac{1}{2}gt^2$. The time for the ball to hit the ground is $t = \sqrt{\frac{2x}{g}} = \sqrt{\frac{2(4.00\ \text{m})}{9.80\ \text{m/s}^2}} = 0.909\ \text{s}$
This equals one-half the period, so $T = 2(0.909\ \text{s}) = 1.81\ \text{s}$
(c) No. The net force acting on the mass is a constant given by $F = -mg$ (except when it is contact with the ground), which is not in the form of Hooke's law.

13.4 (a) The motion is periodic since the motion repeats over and over with the ball going back and forth between the walls, with no energy lost in the process. Half of the period of the motion is the time for the ball to travel between the walls, which is $\frac{12.0\ \text{m}}{3.00\ \text{m/s}} = 4.0\ \text{s}$, so that the complete period is T = 8.0 s.

(b) The motion is not simple harmonic since the force acting on the ball is not of the form $F = -kx$. In fact, here $F = 0$ everywhere except when the ball is in contact with the walls.

13.5 (a) Using $F = kx$, we have: $k = \frac{30\ \text{N}}{0.01\ \text{m}} = 3000\ \text{N/m}$.

Then, $PE = \frac{kx^2}{2} = \frac{(3000\ \text{N/m})(0.20\ \text{m})^2}{2} = 60\ \text{J}$.

(b) Using conservation of energy, $\frac{mv^2}{2} = \frac{kx^2}{2} = 60\ \text{J}$, so

$$v = \sqrt{\frac{2(60\ \text{J})}{0.05\ \text{kg}}} = 49\ \text{m/s}$$

13.6 (a) $F = kx$, so $k = \frac{F}{x} = \frac{230\ \text{N}}{0.400\ \text{m}} = 575\ \text{N/m}$.

(b) $PE = \frac{1}{2}kx^2 = \frac{1}{2}(575\ \text{N/m})(0.400\ \text{m})^2 = 46\ \text{J}$.

13.7 Using conservation of energy, we have: $\frac{1}{2}kx^2 = mgh$

From which, $k = \frac{2mgh}{x^2} = \frac{2(0.100\ \text{kg})(9.80\ \text{m/s}^2)(0.600\ \text{m})}{(0.02\ \text{m})^2} = 2940\ \text{N/m}$.

13.8 (a) At $x = x_1$, we have $E_1 = KE + PE_s + PE_g = 0 + \frac{(kx_1)^2}{2} + mgx_1$, or

$$E_1 = \frac{(2.50\ \text{x}\ 10^4\ \text{N/m})(-0.100\ \text{m})^2}{2} + (25.0\ \text{kg})(9.80\ \frac{\text{m}}{\text{s}^2})(-0.100\ \text{m}) = 101\ \text{J}.$$

(b) At $x = x_2$, the spring is neither compressed nor stretched. Thus we have $E_2 = KE + PE_s + PE_g = 0 + 0 + mgx_2 = E_1 = 100.5\ \text{J}$, or

$$(25.0\ \text{kg})(9.80\ \frac{\text{m}}{\text{s}^2})(x_2) = 101\ \text{J},\ \text{yielding}\ x_2 = 0.412\ \text{m} = 41.2\ \text{cm}$$

(c) Using $E = KE + PE_s + PE_g = \frac{mv^2}{2} + 0 + 0 = E_1 = 101\ \text{J}$, gives (at $x = 0$)

$(12.5\ \text{kg})v^2 = 101\ \text{J}$, or $v = 2.84\ \text{m/s}$.

(d) Applying Newton's second law gives: $\Sigma F_y = kx_1 - mg = ma$, so

$$a = \frac{kx_1}{m} - g = \frac{(2.50\ \text{x}\ 10^4\ \text{N/m})(0.100\ \text{m})}{25.0\ \text{kg}} - 9.80\ \text{m/s}^2 = 90.2\ \text{m/s}^2.$$

13.9 In the presence of non-conservative forces, we use:

$$W_{nc} = \frac{1}{2}mv_f^2 - \frac{1}{2}mv_i^2 + mgy_f - mgy_i + \frac{1}{2}kx_f^2 - \frac{1}{2}kx_i^2,\ \text{or}$$

$$(20\ \text{N})(0.30\ \text{m}) = \frac{1}{2}(1.5\ \text{kg})v_f^2 - 0 + 0 - 0 + \frac{1}{2}(19.6\ \text{N/m})(0.30\ \text{m})^2 - 0.$$

This gives: $v_f = 2.6\ \text{m/s}$.

13.10 Apply conservation of momentum to the collision:

$$(10.0 \times 10^{-3}\ \text{kg})(300\ \text{m/s}) = (2.00\ \text{kg} + 10 \times 10^{-3}\ \text{kg})V.$$

The velocity of the (block + bullet) just after collision is $V = 1.49$ m/s. We now apply conservation of mechanical energy from just after the collision until the spring is fully compressed. This gives,

$$\frac{1}{2}kx_f^2 = \frac{1}{2}(m + M)V^2,$$

or $x_f^2 = \dfrac{(m + M)V^2}{k} = \dfrac{(2.01\ \text{kg})(1.49\ \text{m/s})^2}{19.6\ \text{N/m}} = 0.228\,\text{m}^2.$

which yields $\quad x_f = 4.78 \times 10^{-1}\,\text{m} = 47.8$ cm.

13.11 (a) In the absence of friction, conservation of mechanical energy becomes: $\quad \frac{1}{2}mv_f^2 = \frac{1}{2}kx_i^2$, or

$\frac{1}{2}(1.5\ \text{kg})v_f^2 = \frac{1}{2}(2000\ \text{N/m})(3.0 \times 10^{-3}\ \text{m})^2$, which gives

$v_f = 1.10 \times 10^{-1}$ m/s = 11 cm/s.

(b) In the presence of non-conservative forces, we use

$$W_{nc} = \frac{1}{2}mv_f^2 - \frac{1}{2}mv_i^2 + mgy_f - mgy_i + \frac{1}{2}kx_f^2 - \frac{1}{2}kx_i^2.$$

If f = 2.0 N, then $W_{nc} = -fs = -(2.0\ \text{N})(3.0 \times 10^{-3}\ \text{m}) = -6.0 \times 10^{-3}$ J.

We have,

$$-6.0 \times 10^{-3}\ \text{J} = \frac{1}{2}(1.5\ \text{kg})v_f^2 - 0 + 0 - 0 + 0 - \frac{1}{2}(2000\ \text{N/m})(3.0 \times 10^{-3}\ \text{m})^2,$$

and $\quad v_f = 6.32 \times 10^{-2}$ m/s = 6.3 cm/s.

(c) If $v_f = 0$, then $W_{nc} = \frac{1}{2}mv_f^2 - \frac{1}{2}mv_i^2 + mgy_f - mgy_i + \frac{1}{2}kx_f^2 - \frac{1}{2}kx_i^2$ becomes:

$$-f(3.0 \times 10^{-3}\ \text{m}) = 0 - 0 + 0 - 0 + 0 - \frac{1}{2}(2000\ \text{N/m})(3.0 \times 10^{-3}\ \text{m})^2$$

giving, $f = 3.0$ N.

13.12 (a) From conservation of energy,

$$KE + PE = E = \text{constant}$$

At $x = A$, $v = 0$, so $KE = 0$, $PE = \frac{1}{2}kA^2$, and $E = 0 + \frac{1}{2}kA^2 = \frac{1}{2}kA^2$

At $x = \frac{A}{2}$, $PE = \frac{1}{2}k(\frac{A^2}{4}) = \frac{1}{4}E$, and $KE + \frac{1}{4}E = E$, so $KE = \frac{3}{4}E$.

(b) If $KE = PE$, then $PE + PE = E$, or $\quad PE = \frac{1}{2}E$.

Thus, $\quad \frac{1}{2}kx^2 = \frac{1}{2}(\frac{1}{2}kA^2)$, and $x = \dfrac{A}{\sqrt{2}}$.

13.13 We use $v = \sqrt{\frac{k}{m}(A^2 - x^2)}$. Squaring gives: $v^2 = \frac{k}{m}(A^2 - x^2)$, yielding

$$v^2 = \frac{19.6\ \text{N/m}}{0.40\ \text{kg}}[(4.0 \times 10^{-2}\ \text{m})^2 - x^2] = 49\ \text{s}^{-2}[1.6 \times 10^{-3}\ \text{m}^2 - x^2].$$

(1)

(a) If $x = 0$, (1) gives: $v = 0.28$ m/s = 28 cm/s (as the maximum velocity)

(b) If $x = -1.5 \times 10^{-2}$ m, (1) gives $v = 0.26$ m/s = 26 cm/s.

(c) if $x = 1.5 \times 10^{-2}$ m, (1) gives $v = 0.26$ m/s = 26 cm/s.

(d) One-half the maximum velocity is 0.14 m/s. (See part (a).) We use this for v in (1) and solve for x to find: $\quad x = 3.5$ cm.

CHAPTER THIRTEEN SOLUTIONS

13.14 (a) $E = \frac{1}{2}kA^2 = \frac{1}{2}(250\text{ N/m})(3.5 \times 10^{-2}\text{ m})^2 = 0.15\text{ J}$

(b) $v = \sqrt{\frac{k}{m}(A^2 - x^2)}$ becomes, with $v = v_{max}$ at $x = 0$, or

$$v_{max} = \sqrt{\frac{k}{m}}A = \sqrt{\frac{250\text{ N/m}}{0.50\text{ kg}}}(3.5 \times 10^{-2}\text{ m}) = 0.78\text{ m/s}.$$

(c) From $F = kx = ma$, we have $a = \frac{k}{m}x$. Thus, $a = a_{max}$ at $x = x_{max} = A$

or, $a_{max} = \frac{k}{m}A = \frac{250\text{ N/m}}{0.50\text{ kg}}(3.5 \times 10^{-2}\text{ m}) = 18\text{ m/s}^2.$

13.15 The maximum velocity occurs when $x = 0$ and is given by

$v = \sqrt{\frac{k}{m}}A$. From this, $0.400\text{ m/s} = \sqrt{\frac{16.0\text{ N/m}}{m}}(0.200\text{ m})$, giving

$m = 4.00\text{ kg}$, and the weight is: $w = mg = (4.00\text{ kg})(9.80\text{ m/s}^2) = 39.2\text{ N}.$

13.16 $v = \sqrt{\frac{k}{m}(A^2 - x^2)} = \sqrt{\frac{10.0\text{ N/m}}{0.0500\text{ kg}}\left((0.250\text{ m})^2 - (0.125\text{ m})^2\right)} = 3.06\text{ m/s}$

13.17 (a) $v = \frac{2\pi r}{T} = \frac{2\pi(0.200\text{ m})}{2.00\text{ s}} = 0.628\text{ m/s}$

(b) $f = \frac{1}{T} = \frac{1}{2.00\text{ s}} = 0.50\text{ Hz}$

(c) $\omega = 2\pi f = 2\pi(0.50\text{ s}^{-1}) = 3.14\text{ rad/s}$

13.18 From the figure it is clear that $x = A\cos(\omega t)$, where A is the radius of the circle and ωt is the angle made by the rotating wheel as measured from the horizontal.

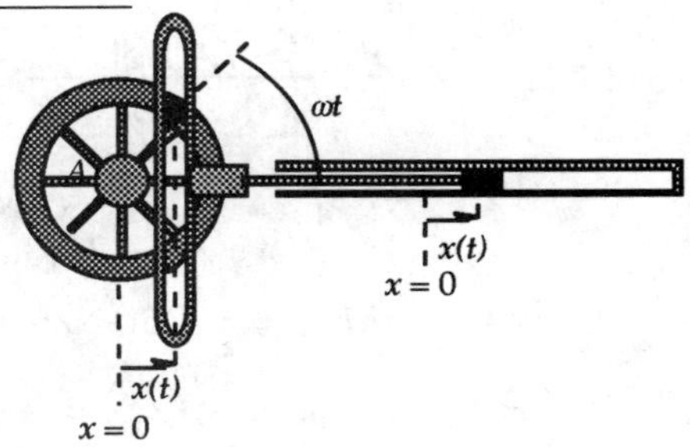

13.19 (a) From, $T = 2\pi\sqrt{\frac{m}{k}}$, we have $k = \frac{4\pi^2 m}{T^2} = \frac{4\pi^2(0.200\text{ kg})}{(0.250\text{ s})^2} = 126\text{ N/m}.$

(b) From $E = \frac{1}{2}kA^2$, $A = \sqrt{\frac{2E}{k}} = \sqrt{\frac{2(2.00\text{ J})}{126\text{ N/m}}} = 0.178\text{ m} = 17.8\text{ cm}.$

13.20 From $f = \frac{1}{T} = \frac{1}{2\pi}\sqrt{\frac{k}{m}}$, we find:

$$k = 4\pi^2 f^2 m = 4\pi^2(5.00\text{ Hz})^2(4.00 \times 10^{-3}\text{ kg}) = 3.95\text{ N/m}.$$

13.21 $k = \frac{F}{x} = \frac{(0.01\text{ kg})(9.80\text{ m/s}^2)}{3.90 \times 10^{-2}\text{ m}} = 2.51\text{ N/m}$, and

$$T = 2\pi\sqrt{\frac{m}{k}} = 2\pi\sqrt{\frac{0.025\text{ kg}}{2.51\text{ N/m}}} = 0.627\text{ s}.$$

13.22 We find the spring constant from: $mg = kx$, or
$(320\text{ kg})(9.80\text{ m/s}^2) = k(8.0 \times 10^{-3}\text{ m})$. Thus, $k = 3.92 \times 10^5$ N/m.

Then, $f = \frac{1}{2\pi}\sqrt{\frac{k}{m}} = \frac{1}{2\pi}\sqrt{\frac{3.92 \times 10^5\text{ N/m}}{2.0 \times 10^3\text{ kg}}} = 2.2$ Hz.

13.23 (a) We have: $x = (0.30\text{ m})\cos \pi t/3$. (1)
At $t = 0$, $x = (0.30\text{ m})\cos 0 = 0.30$ m.
At $t = 0.60$ s: $x = (0.30\text{ m})\cos\left(\frac{\pi}{3}\frac{\text{rad}}{\text{s}}\ 0.60\text{ s}\right) = (0.30\text{ m})\cos(0.628\text{ rad})$,
or $x = 0.24$ m.
(b) The general form for oscillatory motion is: $x = A\cos 2\pi ft$. (2)
Thus, by comparing (1) to (2), we see that $A = 0.30$ m.
(c) Using comparison as in (b), we see that: $2\pi f = \pi/3$, and $f = 1/6$ Hz.
(d) $T = \frac{1}{f} = 6.0$ s

13.24 (a) Here, $A = 3.00$ m, $\omega = \sqrt{\frac{k}{m}} = \sqrt{\frac{5.00\text{ N/m}}{2.00\text{ kg}}} = 1.58$ rad/s, so
$x = A\cos(\omega t) = (3.00\text{ m})\cos[(1.58\text{ rad/s})t]$.
Since $F = -kx$, $F = -kA\cos(\omega t) = -(15.0\text{ N})\cos[(1.58\text{ rad/s})t]$.
At $t = 3.5$: $F = -(15.0\text{ N})\cos(5.53\text{ rad}) = -11.0$ N, or F = 11.0 N to the left.
(b) The period is: $T = \frac{2\pi}{\omega} = \frac{2\pi}{1.58\text{ rad/s}} = 3.97$ s,
so in 3.50 s, it has made n = $\frac{3.50\text{ s}}{3.98\text{ s}} = 0.88$ oscillations

---

13.25 (a) $k = \frac{F}{x} = \frac{7.50\text{ N}}{3.00 \times 10^{-2}\text{ m}} = 250$ N/m.
(b) $T = 2\pi\sqrt{\frac{m}{k}} = 2\pi\sqrt{\frac{0.500\text{ kg}}{250\text{ N/m}}} = 0.281$ s, and $f = \frac{1}{T} = 3.56$ Hz. Thus,
$\omega = 2\pi f = 2\pi(3.56\text{ Hz}) = 22.4$ rad/s.
(c) $E = \frac{1}{2}kA^2 = \frac{1}{2}(250\text{ N/m})(5.00 \times 10^{-2}\text{ m})^2 = 0.313$ J.
(d) $E = \text{const} = \frac{1}{2}mv_0^2 + \frac{1}{2}kx_0^2 = \frac{1}{2}kA^2$. When $v_0 = 0$: $A = x_0 = 5.00$ cm.
(e) $v_{max} = \omega A = (22.4\text{ rad/s})(0.050\text{ m}) = 1.12$ m/s,
$a_{max} = \omega^2 A = (22.4\text{ rad/s})^2(0.050\text{ m}) = 25.0\text{ m/s}^2$
(f) $x = A\cos\omega t = (5.00\text{ cm})\cos[(22.4\text{ rad/s})(0.50\text{ s})] = 1.01$ cm.

13.26 We have: $v = \pm\,\omega\sqrt{A^2 - x^2} = \pm\,\omega\sqrt{A^2 - A^2\cos^2(\omega t)} = \pm\,A\omega\sqrt{1 - \cos^2(\omega t)}$
or $v = \pm\,A\omega\sqrt{\sin^2(\omega t)} = \pm\,A\omega\sin(\omega t)$.
From $a = -\omega^2 x$: $a = -\omega^2 A\cos(\omega t)$.

13.27 $T = 2\pi\sqrt{\frac{L}{g}} = 2\pi\sqrt{\frac{2.00\text{ m}}{9.80\text{ m/s}^2}} = 2.84$ s, so $f = \frac{1}{T} = 0.352$ Hz.
The number of oscillations in 5.00 min is:
$N = (f)(t) = (0.352\text{ Hz})(5.00\text{ min})(60.0\text{ s/min}) = 105.7$, or
105 complete oscillations in 5.00 min.

13.28 Using $T = 2\pi\sqrt{\frac{L}{g}}$, we get $L = \frac{gT^2}{4\pi^2} = \frac{(9.80\ \text{m/s}^2)(9.40\ \text{s})^2}{4\pi^2} = 21.9\ \text{m}.$

13.29 (a) The colder temperature will cause the pendulum to contract. Thus, the period will decrease causing the clock to run faster.

(b) First determine, the length of the pendulum when it is at 20 °C.

$T_0 = 2\pi\sqrt{\frac{L_0}{g}}$, so $\quad L_0 = \frac{gT^2{}_0}{4\pi^2} = \frac{(9.80\ \text{m/s}^2)(1.00\ \text{s})^2}{4\pi^2} = 0.24824\ \text{m}.$

When the temperature changes to -5.0°C, the length of the pendulum will be:

$L = L_0(1 + \alpha(\Delta T)) = (0.24824\ \text{m})[1 + (24 \times 10^{-6}\ {}^\circ\text{C}^{-1})(-25.0^\circ\text{C})] = 0.24809.$

The clock runs faster by a factor of

$\frac{T_0}{T} = \sqrt{\frac{L_0}{L}} = \sqrt{\frac{0.24824}{0.24809}} = 1.0003.$

Thus, in one hour (3600 s) it will gain, (1.0003 - 1)(3600 s) = 1.08 s.

13.30 (a) The period of the clock's pendulum on the Earth is

$T_{Earth} = 2\pi\sqrt{\frac{L}{g}}$, while its period on the Moon is $T_{Moon} = 2\pi\sqrt{\frac{L}{g'}}$.

The ratio of the period on the Moon to that on Earth is:

$\frac{T_{Moon}}{T_{Earth}} = \sqrt{\frac{g}{g'}} = \sqrt{6.01} = 2.452$. The clock's pendulum takes longer to complete one oscillation. Therefore, the clock will run slowly on the Moon.

(b) From the above equation, the clock on the Moon runs slower than the same clock on the Earth by a factor of 2.452. Thus, in 24 hours (Earth time), the clock on the Moon will have advanced an amount given by $\frac{24\ \text{h}}{2.452} = 9.788$ h, and will read 9:47:17 A.M.

13.31 (a) The period of a pendulum is given by $T = 2\pi\sqrt{\frac{L}{g}}$, so $L = \frac{gT^2}{4\pi^2}$.

On Earth, a 1-s pendulum has length $L = \frac{(9.80)(1.0)^2}{4\pi^2} = 0.248\ \text{m} = 25\ \text{cm}.$

On Mars, a 1-s pendulum has length $L = \frac{(3.7)(1.0)^2}{4\pi^2} = 0.0937\ \text{m} = 9.4\ \text{cm}.$

(b) The period of a mass on a spring is given by $T = 2\pi\sqrt{\frac{m}{k}}$.

The mass for a 1-s oscillator is

$m = \frac{kT^2}{4\pi^2} = \frac{(10\ \text{N/m})(1.0\ \text{s})^2}{4\pi^2} = 0.253\ \text{kg} = 0.25\ \text{kg}$

This same mass works for both the Earth and Mars.

13.32(a) The amplitude is the displacement of either a crest or a trough from the equilibrium position (center horizontal line). By inspection, $A = 9$ cm.

(b) The wavelength is the horizontal spacing from one crest to the next. This is twice the spacing between a crest and a trough. By inspection, $\lambda = 20$ cm.

(c) $T = \frac{1}{f} = \frac{1}{25\ \text{Hz}} = 0.04\ \text{s}.$

(d) $v = \lambda f = (20\ \text{cm})(25\ \text{Hz}) = 500\ \text{cm/s} = 5.0\ \text{m/s}.$

13.33 From $\lambda = \frac{v}{f}$, we get: $\lambda = \frac{340\ \text{m/s}}{60000\ \text{s}^{-1}} = 5.67\ \text{mm}.$

13.34 (a) $T = \frac{1}{f} = \frac{1}{88.0 \times 10^6\ \text{Hz}} = 1.14 \times 10^{-8}\ \text{s}.$

(b) $\lambda = \frac{v}{f} = \frac{3.00 \times 10^8\ \text{m/s}}{88.0 \times 10^6\ \text{Hz}} = 3.41\ \text{m}.$

13.35 $f = \frac{8}{12.0\ \text{s}} = 0.667\ \text{Hz}$, and $v = \lambda f = (1.20\ \text{m})(0.667\ \text{Hz}) = 0.80\ \text{m/s}$

13.36 $\lambda_{long} = \frac{v}{f} = \frac{343\ \text{m/s}}{28\ \text{Hz}} = 12.3\ \text{m},$ $\lambda_{short} = \frac{v}{f} = \frac{343\ \text{m/s}}{4200\ \text{Hz}} = 0.082\ \text{m}$

13.37 $f = \frac{40.0\ \text{vib}}{30.0\ \text{s}} = 1.333\ \text{Hz},$ $v = \frac{425\ \text{cm}}{10.0\ \text{s}} = 42.5\ \text{cm/s} = 0.425\ \text{m/s}$

$\lambda = \frac{v}{f} = \frac{0.425\ \text{m/s}}{1.333\ \text{Hz}} = 0.319\ \text{m} = 31.9\ \text{cm}$

13.38 (a) When the boat is stationary in the water, the speed of the wave relative to the boat is $v = f\lambda$. The frequency observed for the wave is then:

$f = \frac{v}{\lambda} = \frac{4.0\ \text{m/s}}{20\ \text{m}} = 0.20\ \text{Hz}.$

(b) When the boat is moving toward the oncoming crests, the speed of the boat relative to the wave is

$v_{boat,wave} = v_{boat,water} + v_{wave,water} = 1 + 4 = 5\ \text{m/s}$

The time required for the boat to travel the 20 m between successive crests is therefore: $T = \frac{\lambda}{v_{boatwave}} = \frac{20\ \text{m}}{5\text{m/s}} = 4\ \text{s}.$

The observed frequency is thus: $f = \frac{1}{T} = 0.25\ \text{Hz}.$

13.39 The speed of the wave is: $v = d/t = 20.0\ \text{m}/0.800\ \text{s} = 25.0\ \text{m/s}.$

We now use, $v = \sqrt{\frac{F}{\mu}}$. We have $\mu = \frac{0.35\ \text{kg}}{1.00\ \text{m}} = 0.35\ \text{kg/m}.$

Thus, $F = v^2\mu = (25.0\ \text{m/s})^2(0.35\ \text{kg/m}) = 219\ \text{N}.$

13.40 (a) The mass per unit length is: $\mu = \frac{0.0600\ \text{kg}}{5.00\ \text{m}} = 1.20 \times 10^{-2}\ \text{kg/m}.$

The required tension is: $F = v^2\mu = (50.0\ \text{m/s})^2(1.20 \times 10^{-2}\ \text{kg/m}) = 30.0\ \text{N}.$

(b) $v = \sqrt{\frac{F}{\mu}} = \sqrt{\frac{8.00\ \text{N}}{1.20 \times 10^{-2}\ \text{kg/m}}} = 25.8\ \text{m/s}.$

13.41 We have $\mu_2 = \frac{m_2}{L_2} = \frac{\frac{m_1}{2}}{L_1} = \frac{1}{2}\frac{m_1}{L_1} = \frac{\mu_2}{2}$, and $F_1 = F_2$.

$$v_2 = \sqrt{\frac{F_2}{\mu_2}} = \sqrt{\frac{2F_1}{\mu_1}} = \sqrt{2}\, v_1 = \sqrt{2}\,(5.00\ \text{m/s}) = 7.07\ \text{m/s}.$$

13.42 (a) The tension in the string is $F = (3.00\ \text{kg})(9.80\ \text{m/s}^2) = 29.4\ \text{N}$.

$$\mu = \frac{F}{v^2} = \frac{29.4\ \text{N}}{(24.0\ \text{m/s})^2} = 5.10 \times 10^{-2}\ \text{kg/m}.$$

(b) If $m = 2.0$ kg, then $F = 19.6$ N, and

$$v = \sqrt{\frac{F}{\mu}} = \sqrt{\frac{19.6\ \text{N}}{5.10 \times 10^{-2}\ \text{kg/m}}} = 19.6\ \text{m/s}. \quad (20\ \text{m/s})$$

13.43 The wave speed is related to tension by $v = \sqrt{\frac{F}{\mu}}$. The required tension for a given speed is: $F = \mu v^2$. Thus, $F_1 = \mu {v_1}^2$ and $F_2 = \mu {v_2}^2$. We know that the mass per unit length of the string is the same in both instances. Therefore, $\frac{F_2}{F_1} = \frac{{v_2}^2}{{v_1}^2}$

or $F_2 = F_1 \frac{{v_2}^2}{{v_1}^2} = (6.00\ \text{N})\left(\frac{30.0\ \text{m/s}}{20.0\ \text{m/s}}\right)^2 = 13.5\ \text{N}.$

13.44 (a) If the end is fixed, there is inversion of the pulse upon reflection. Thus, when they meet, they cancel and the amplitude is zero.

(b) If the end is free there is no inversion on reflection. When they meet the amplitude is $2A = 2(0.15\ \text{m}) = 0.30$ m.

13.45 (a) The maximum occurs when the two waves interfere constructively. Then the amplitudes add for a resultant amplitude of $A = 0.50$ m.

(b) The minimum occurs when the waves interfere destructively. In this case, the individual amplitudes subtract, and we have a resultant of $A = 0.10$ m.

13.46 (a) We compare $x = (0.25\ \text{m})\cos(0.4\pi t)$ to the general equation of motion, $x = A\cos(2\pi f t)$, to find $A = 0.25$ m.

(b) By comparison of the two equations as in (a), we find $2\pi f = 0.4\pi$.

Also, we know that $\omega = 2\pi f = \sqrt{\frac{k}{m}} = 0.4\pi$, or $\frac{k}{m} = (0.4\pi)^2$.

From which: $k = (0.4\pi)^2(0.30\ \text{kg}) = 0.47\ \text{N/m}$.

(c) At $t = 0.30$ s, the position is: $x = (0.25\ \text{m})\cos(0.4\pi 0.3)$, or $x = (0.25)\cos(0.377\ \text{rad}) = (0.25\ \text{m})(0.93) = 0.23$ m.

(d) $v = -\sqrt{\frac{k}{m}(A^2 - x^2)} = -(0.4\pi)\sqrt{(0.25\ \text{m})^2 - (0.23)^2} = -0.12\ \text{m/s}.$

The negative sign is used above because the object is moving toward the equilibrium position (in the negative direction).

13.47 $W = \Delta PE = \frac{1}{2}kx^2 - \frac{1}{2}k{x_0}^2 = \frac{1}{2}(30.0\ \text{N/m})[(0.300\ \text{m})^2 - (0.200\ \text{m})^2] = 0.75\ \text{J}$

13.48 From conservation of mechanical energy, we have $mgh = \frac{1}{2}kx^2$, or

$(0.500\ \text{kg})(9.80\ \text{m/s}^2)(2.00\ \text{m}) = \frac{1}{2}(20.0\ \text{N/m})x^2$.

From which, $x = 0.99$ m.

13.49 (a) Let us choose $y = 0$ at the initial height of the mass and use conservation of mechanical energy:

$$\frac{1}{2}mv_f^2 + mgy_f + \frac{1}{2}kx_f^2 = \frac{1}{2}mv_i^2 + mgy_i + \frac{1}{2}kx_i^2, \text{ or}$$

$$0 - mgh + \frac{1}{2}kh^2 = 0 + 0 + 0,$$

or $k = \frac{2mg}{h} = \frac{2(3.00\text{ kg})(9.80\text{ m/s}^2)}{0.100\text{ m}} = 588\,\frac{\text{N}}{\text{m}}$.

(b) We use conservation of mechanical energy again, as

$$\frac{1}{2}mv_f^2 + mgy_f + \frac{1}{2}kx_f^2 = \frac{1}{2}mv_i^2 + mgy_i + \frac{1}{2}kx_i^2, \text{ which becomes}$$

$$\frac{1}{2}(3.00\text{ kg})v_f^2 - (3.00\text{ kg})(9.80\text{ m/s}^2)(0.0500\text{ m}) + \frac{1}{2}(588\text{ N/m})(0.050\text{ m})^2 = 0,$$

and $v_f = 0.7$ m/s.

13.50 (a) Since no nonconservative forces act on the block after the bullet leaves it, we can use conservation of mechanical energy. The kinetic energy of the block immediately after impact equals the energy in the spring at maximum compression. Thus,

$$\frac{1}{2}(1.00\text{ kg})v_1^2 = \frac{1}{2}(900\text{ N/m})(0.0500\text{ m})^2, \text{ yielding } v_1 = 1.50\text{ m/s}.$$

Also, since no external forces act on the block-bullet system during collision, momentum is conserved:

$$(0.005\text{ kg})(400\text{ m/s}) = (0.005\text{ kg})v_2 + (1.00\text{ kg})v_1,$$

where v_2 and v_1 are the speed of the bullet and the speed of the block after collision. Then, the momentum equation from above gives: $v_2 = 100$ m/s.

(b) The energy lost in the collision is the bullet's initial energy minus the sum of its final energy and the energy imparted to the block. Therefore,

$$E_{loss} = E_{initial} - E_{final} = \frac{1}{2}(0.005\text{ kg})\left(400\ \frac{\text{m}}{\text{s}}\right)^2 - \left[\frac{1}{2}(0.005\text{ kg})\left(100\ \frac{\text{m}}{\text{s}}\right)^2 + \frac{1}{2}(1.00\text{ kg})\left(1.5\ \frac{\text{m}}{\text{s}}\right)^2\right] = 374\text{ J}$$

13.51 Since no nonconservative forces act, mechanical energy is conserved. Choose the zero of gravitational potential energy to coincide with the initial configuration (when the 30 kg mass is 40 cm above the floor).

Then, $KE_i = 0$, $(PE_g)_i = 0$, $(PE_s)_i = \frac{1}{2}(200\text{ N/m})(0.20\text{ m})^2 = 4.00$ J,

and $(PE_s)_f = 0$ . . .

Then conservation of energy gives:

$$KE_f + (PE_g)_f + (PE_s)_f = KE_i + (PE_g)_i + (PE_s)_i$$

$$\frac{1}{2}(m_1 + m_2)v_f^2 + (m_2 g x \sin\theta - m_1 g x) + 0 = 0 + 0 + 4.00\text{ J, or}$$

$$\frac{1}{2}(25\text{ kg} + 30\text{ kg})v_f^2 + (25\text{ kg})(9.80\text{ m/s}^2)(0.2\text{ m})\sin 40° - (30\text{ kg})(9.80\text{ m/s}^2)(0.2\text{ m}) = 4.00\text{ J}$$

Solving for v_f, we find: $v_f = 1.1$ m/s.

13.52 (a) The muzzle velocity is found from conservation of energy.
$\frac{1}{2}mv^2 = \frac{1}{2}kx^2$, or $\frac{1}{2}(10^{-3}\text{ kg})v^2 = \frac{1}{2}(9.80\text{ N/m})(0.200\text{ m})^2$, giving
$v = 19.8$ m/s.

(b) From the equations for projectile motion, we find the time to reach the floor: $y = v_{oy}t + \frac{1}{2}at^2$, or $-1.00\text{ m} = 0 + \frac{1}{2}(-9.80\text{ m/s}^2)t^2$, which gives $t = 0.452$ s. The range is therefore:
$R = v_{ox}t = (19.8\text{ m/s})(0.452\text{ s}) = 8.94\text{ m}$.

13.53 First, find the work done by the nonconservative friction force, choosing the zero of gravitational potential energy to coincide with the initial configuration:

$$W_{nc} = (KE + PE_g + PE_s)_f - (KE + PE_g + PE_s)_i$$
$$= [0 - (2.0\text{ kg})(9.80\text{ m/s}^2)(0.20\text{ m})\sin 37° + \frac{1}{2}(100\text{ N/m})(0.20\text{ m})^2]$$
$$- (0 + 0 + 0) = -0.359\text{ J}.$$

But $W_{nc} = -fs = -[\mu(mg\cos 37°0]\ s = -\mu(15.65\text{ N})(0.20\text{ m}) = -\mu(3.13\text{ J})$,

Thus, $-\mu(3.13\text{ J}) = -0.359$ J, or $\mu = 0.11$

13.54 Consider the motion of the firefighter during the three intervals: (1) before, (2) during, and (3) after collision with the platform.

(a) While falling a height of 5.00 m, his speed changes from $v_0 = 0$ to v_1. We can use conservation of energy to find the velocity at the initial position of the platform, which also is taken to be the zero level for gravitational potential energy. We have

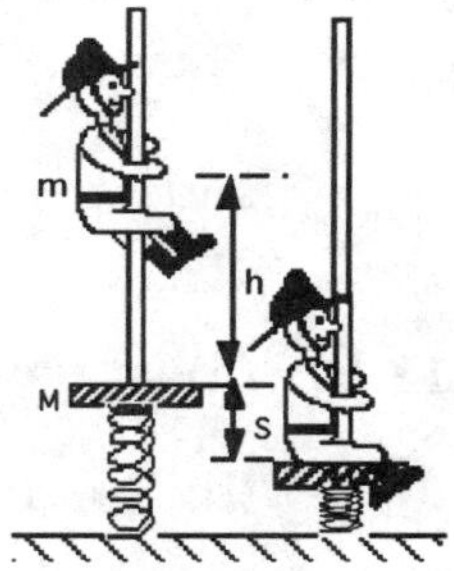

$$-fh = \frac{1}{2}mv_1^2 - mgh, \text{ or } v_1 = \sqrt{2\frac{(-fh + mgh)}{m}}$$

or $v_1 = \sqrt{2\frac{(-300)(5.00)}{60.0} + 2\ (9.80)(5.00)} = 6.93\frac{\text{m}}{\text{s}}$.

(b) During the inelastic collision, momentum is conserved. If v_2 is the speed of the firefighter and platform just after impact, we have:
$mv_1 = (m + M)v_2$, or $v_2 = \frac{60.0}{80.0}(6.93\frac{\text{m}}{\text{s}}) = 5.2\frac{\text{m}}{\text{s}}$. After the collision,we again use conservation of energy (with the distances labeled in the figure and keeping $PE = 0$ at the original platform level):

$$fs = 0 + (m + M)g(-s) + \frac{1}{2}ks^2 - \frac{1}{2}(m + M)v_2^2$$

This results in a quadratic equation in s: $1250s^2 - 484s - 1081 = 0$

Using the quadratic formula and choosing the positive root gives
$s = 1.14$ m.

13.55 (a) Using conservation of energy:
$\frac{1}{2}(m_1 + m_2)v^2 = \frac{1}{2}kA^2$, or $\frac{1}{2}(16.0\text{ kg})v^2 = \frac{1}{2}(100\text{ N/m})(0.20\text{ m})^2$,

which yields $v = 0.50$ m. This is the speed of m_1 and m_2 at the equilibrium point. Beyond this point, the mass m_2 moves with the constant speed of 0.50 m/s while mass m_1 starts to slow down due to the restoring force of the spring.

(b) The energy of the m_1-spring system at equilibrium is:

$$E = \frac{1}{2}m_1v^2 + \frac{1}{2}kx^2 = \frac{1}{2}(9.0\text{ kg})(0.50\text{ m/s})^2 + 0 = 1.125\text{ J.}$$

When m_1 comes to rest and the spring is extended by the new amplitude A', $E = 0 + \frac{1}{2}kA'^2$, $= 0 + \frac{1}{2}(100\text{ N/m})A'^2 = 1.125\text{ J}$

giving $A' = 0.15$ m.

The period of the m_1-spring system is : $T = 2\pi\sqrt{\frac{m_1}{k}} = 1.885$ s, and

it takes $\frac{T}{4} = 0.471$ s after it passes the equilibrium point for the spring to become fully stretched the first time. The distance separating m_1 and m_2 at this is:

$$D = v\left(\frac{T}{4}\right) - A' = (0.50\text{ m/s})(0.471\text{ s}) - 0.15\text{ m} = 0.086\text{ m} = 8.6\text{ cm.}$$

13.56 $F = Mg$ is the tension

$$v = \sqrt{\frac{F}{\mu}} = \sqrt{\frac{Mg}{m/L}} = \sqrt{\frac{MgL}{m}} = \frac{L}{t}\text{ is the wave speed.}$$

Then $$\frac{MgL}{m} = \frac{L^2}{t^2}$$

and $$g = \frac{Lm}{Mt^2} = \frac{1.60\text{ m}(4.00\times 10^{-3}\text{ kg})}{3.00\text{ kg}(3.61\times 10^{-3}\text{ s})^2} = 1.64\text{ m/s}^2$$

13.57 (a) $\omega_0 = \sqrt{\frac{k}{m}} = 15.8$ rad/s

(b) $F_s - mg = ma = m\left(\frac{g}{3}\right)$

$$F_s = \frac{4}{3}mg = 26.1\text{ N}$$

$$x_s = \frac{F_s}{k} = 5.23\text{ cm}$$

13.58 (a) $\Sigma F_y = -2F\sin\theta$ where $\theta = \tan^{-1}\frac{y}{L}$

For a small displacement $\sin\theta \approx \tan\theta \approx = \frac{y}{L}$

and $\Sigma F_y = \frac{-2Fy}{L}$

(b) For a spring system, $\Sigma F = -kx$ becomes $k = -\frac{2F}{L}$

Therefore, $\omega = \sqrt{\frac{k}{m}} = \sqrt{\frac{2F}{mL}}$

13.59 A study of the forces on the balloon shows that the tangential restoring force is given as:

$F_x = -B\sin\theta + mg\sin\theta = -(B - mg)\sin\theta$. But: $B = \rho_{air} Vg$, and $m = \rho_{He} V$. Also, $\sin\theta \approx \theta$ (for small θ), so

$F_x \approx -(\rho_{air} Vg - \rho_{He} Vg)\theta = -(\rho_{air} - \rho_{He}) Vg\theta$.

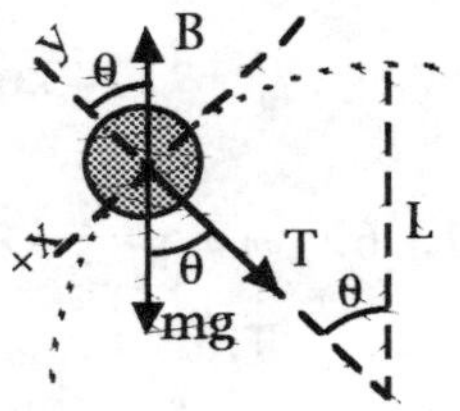

But $\theta = \frac{s}{L}$, and

$$F_x = -(\rho_{air} - \rho_{He}) Vg \frac{s}{L} = -ks, \text{ with } k = (\rho_{air} - \rho_{He}) \frac{Vg}{L}$$

.

Then $T = 2\pi\sqrt{\frac{m}{k}} = 2\pi\sqrt{\frac{\rho_{He} V}{(\rho_{air} - \rho_{He}) \frac{Vg}{L}}} = 2\pi\sqrt{\frac{\rho_{He} L}{(\rho_{air} - \rho_{He}) g}}$, giving

$$T = 2\pi\sqrt{\frac{(0.18)(3.00 \text{ m})}{(1.29 - 0.18)(9.80 \text{ m/s}^2)}} = 1.4 \text{ s}.$$

13.60 (a) The longitudinal wave travels a shorter distance and is moving faster, so it will arrive at point B first.

(b) The wave that travels through the Earth must travel a distance of $2R\sin 30.0° = 2(6.37 \times 10^6 \text{ m})\sin 30.0° = 6.37 \times 10^6$ m at a speed of 7800 m/s. It, therefore, takes $\frac{6.37 \times 10^6 \text{ m}}{7800 \text{ m/s}} = 817$ s.

The wave that travels along the Earth's surface must travel a distance of $S = R\theta = R(\frac{\pi}{3} \text{ rad}) = 6.67 \times 10^6$ m at a speed of 4500 m/s.

It therefore takes $\frac{6.67 \times 10^6}{4500} = 1482$ s.

The time difference is 665 s = 11.1 min.

13.61 First, observe from the geometry of the situation that

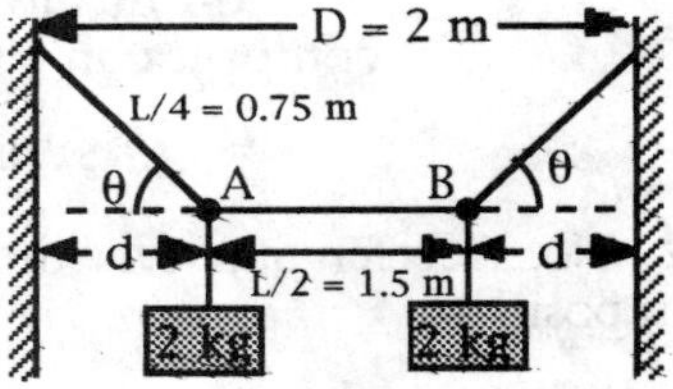

$2d + \frac{L}{2} = D$,

or $d = \frac{D}{2} - \frac{L}{4} = 1.00 \text{ m} - 0.75 \text{ m} = 0.25$ m.

Thus, $\cos\theta = \frac{0.25 \text{ m}}{0.75 \text{ m}} = \frac{1}{3}$, and $\theta = 70.53°$.

Now, consider a free body diagram of point A:

$\Sigma F_x = 0$ becomes $T = T_2\cos\theta$, and

$\Sigma F_y = 0$ becomes $19.6\ N = T_2\sin\theta$.

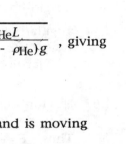

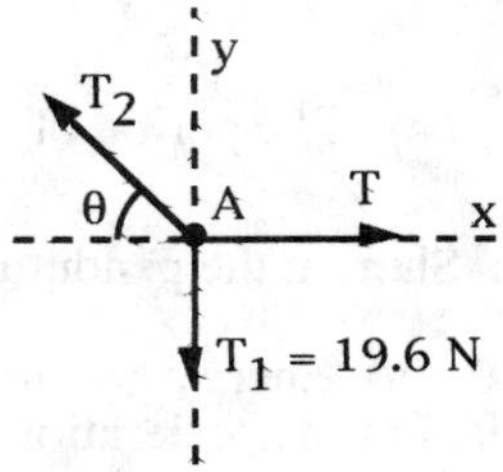

Dividing the second of these equations by the first gives: $\frac{19.6 \text{ N}}{T} = \tan\theta$, or $T = \frac{19.6 \text{ N}}{\tan 70.53°} = 6.93$ N.

The linear density of the string is:

$\mu = \frac{m}{L} = \frac{0.010 \text{ kg}}{3.00 \text{ m}} = 3.33 \times 10^{-3}$ kg/m, so the speed of transverse waves in the string between points A and B is

$$v = \sqrt{\frac{T}{\mu}} = \sqrt{\frac{6.93 \text{ N}}{3.33 \times 10^{-3} \text{ kg/m}}} = 45.6 \text{ m/s}.$$

The time for the pulse to travel 1.5 m from A to B is:

$$t = \frac{1.50\ \text{m}}{45.6\ \text{m/s}} = 0.0329\ \text{s} = 32.9\ \text{ms}.$$

13.62 $\omega = \sqrt{\frac{k}{m}} = \sqrt{\frac{4.70 \times 10^{-4}\ \text{N/m}}{3.00 \times 10^{-4}\ \text{kg}}} = 1.252\ \text{rad/s}$, and $v_{max} = \omega A$.

Thus, $v_{max} = (1.252\ \text{rad/s})(2.00 \times 10^{-3}\ \text{m}) = 2.50 \times 10^{-3}\ \text{m/s} = 2.50\ \text{mm/s}$. This is the maximum velocity of the wingtip 3 mm from the fulcrum. To get the maximum velocity of the outer tip of the wing, treat the wing as a rigid body rotating about the fulcrum. All parts have the same angular velocity, so $\frac{v}{r} = \omega$ leads to: $\frac{v_{\text{far tip}}}{r_{\text{far tip}}} = \frac{v_{\text{near tip}}}{r_{\text{near tip}}}$, or

$$v_{\text{far tip}} = 15.0\ \text{mm}\,\frac{2.50\ \text{mm/s}}{3.0\ \text{mm}} = 12.5\ \text{mm/s} = 1.3\ \text{cm/s}.$$

13.63 Newton's law of gravity is: $F = -\frac{GMm}{r^2} = -\frac{Gm}{r^2}\left(\frac{4}{3}\pi r^3\right)\rho$.

Thus, $F = -\left(\frac{4}{3}\pi\rho Gm\right)r$, which is of Hooke's law form with $k = \frac{4}{3}\pi\rho Gm$.

13.64 (a) From the work-energy theorem, we have

$$W = \frac{1}{2}mv^2 - \frac{1}{2}mv_o^2,$$

or $W = \frac{1}{2}(8.00\ \text{kg})[(3.00\ \text{m/s})^2 - (4.00\ \text{m/s})^2] = -28.0\ \text{J}$.

(b) The distance moved against friction is s, and $f = \mu N = \mu mg$.

Thus, $W = -\mu mgs$, which gives $s = \frac{28.0\ \text{J}}{(0.4)(8.00\ \text{kg})(9.80\ \text{m/s}^2)} = 0.893\ \text{m}$

But s is twice the distance the spring was compressed during the in-and-out motion of the block. Therefore, the distance of compression = 0.446 m

---

ANSWERS TO CONCEPTUAL QUESTIONS

2. No. Acceleration is maximum at maximum displacement and zero at equilibrium (x = 0) position.

4. Friction. This includes both air-resistance and damping within the spring.

6. No. The period of vibration is $2\pi\sqrt{\frac{L}{g}}$ and g is less at high altitude.

8. Shorten the pendulum to decrease the period between ticks.

10. (a) Energy gets four times larger. (b) Maximum speed gets two times larger. (c) Maximum acceleration is doubled. (d) Period is unaffected.

12. You can attach one end to a wall while holding the other end in your hand. To create a longitudinal wave oscillate the spring back and forth along the direction of the stretched spring. To create a transverse wave, shake the string perpendicular to the direction in which the spring is stretched.

14. If the tension remains the same, the speed of a wave on the string does not change. This means, from $v = f\lambda$, that if the frequency is doubled, the wavelength must decrease by a factor of two.

16. The speed of a wave on a string is given by $v = \sqrt{\frac{F}{\mu}}$. This says the speed is independent of the frequency of the wave. Thus, doubling the frequency leaves the speed unaffected.

18. From $v = \sqrt{\frac{F}{\mu}}$ we see that increasing the tension by a factor of four doubles the wave speed.

20. We assume here for simplicity that the Earth's orbit is circular. The motion is not simple harmonic because the resultant force acting on the Earth is not dependent on the displacement. Also, the speed of the Earth is a constant with time, not varying with x as in simple harmonic motion.

CHAPTER FOURTEEN SOLUTIONS

Chapter Fourteen Readings

Baranek, L.N., "Noise," *Scientific American*, December 1966, p. 66.

Borg, E. and Counter, S.A., "The Middle-Ear Muscles," *Scientific American*, August 1989, p. 74.

Boulez, P. and Gerzso, A., "Computers in Music," *Scientific American*, April 1988, p. 44.

Deutsch, D., "Paradoxes of Musical Pitch," *Scientific American*, v. 267 (Aug. '92) p88.

Fletcher, N.H. and Thwaites, S., "The Physics of Organ Pipes," Scientific American, January 1983, p. 94.

Hutchins, C.M., "The Acoustics of Violin Plates," *Scientific American*, October 1981, p. 170.

Kelby S.D. and Middleton, R.P., "The Vibrations of Hand Bells," *Physics Education*, Vol 15, 1980, p. 320.

Monforte, J., "The Digital Reproduction of Sound," Scientific American, December 1984, p. 78.

Rossing, R., The Science of Sound, 2nd ed., Addison-Wesley, Reading 1990

Shadle, C., "Experiments on the Acoustics of Whistling," The Physics Teacher, March 1983, p. 148.

Sundberg, J., "The Acoustics of the Singing Voice," *Scientific American*, March 1977, p. 82.

Suslick, K.S., "The Chemical Effects of Ultrasound," *Scientific American*, February 1989, p. 80.

Von Bekesy, G., *"The Ear,"* Scientific American, August 1957, p. 66.

14.1 The speed of sound in seawater at 25 °C is 1530 m/s.
Therefore, the time for the sound to reach the sea floor and return is:

$$t = 2d/v = 2(150\text{ m})/1530\text{ m/s} = 0.20\text{ s}.$$

14.2 The speed of the sound wave is $v = \lambda f = (0.500\text{ m}) \times (700\text{ Hz}) = 350\text{ m/s}$.

Therefore, $v = 350\text{ m/s} = (331\text{ m/s})\sqrt{1 + \frac{T}{273}}$, from which $T = 32.2°\text{C}$.

14.3 The speed of sound at 27 °C is: $v = (331\text{ m/s})\sqrt{1 + \frac{27}{273}} = 347\frac{\text{m}}{\text{s}}$.

Thus, the wavelengths are: $\lambda_{20\text{ Hz}} = \frac{v}{f} = \frac{347\text{ m/s}}{20.0\text{ Hz}} = 17.3\text{ m}$, and

$$\lambda_{20,000\ \text{Hz}} = \frac{v}{f} = \frac{347\ \text{m/s}}{2.0 \times 10^4\ \text{Hz}} = 1.7 \times 10^{-2}\ \text{m}.$$

14.4 $v = (331\ \text{m/s})\sqrt{1 + \frac{22}{273}} = 344\,\frac{\text{m}}{\text{s}}$.

If d is the distance to the object, the total distance traveled by the sound (there and back) is $2d$. Thus,

$2d = vt = (344\ \text{m/s})(3.00\ \text{s}) = 1032\ \text{m}$, or $d = 516\ \text{m}$.

14.5 $\lambda = \frac{v}{f} = \frac{1.0 \times 10^4\ \text{m/s}}{2.0 \times 10^{10}\ \text{Hz}} = 5.0 \times 10^{-7}\ \text{m}$.

14.6 Let t_1 be the time for the stone to hit the water, and let t_2 be the time for the sound to travel up the well.

Then $d = \frac{1}{2}gt_1^2 = vt_2$, and $t_1 + t_2 = 2.00\ \text{s}$ (the total time).

Therefore, $t_2 = \frac{d}{v} = \frac{gt_1^2}{2v} = 2.00 - t_1$, or $\frac{gt_1^2}{2v} + t_1 - 2.00 = 0$ (1)

But, $v = (331\ \text{m/s})\sqrt{1 + \frac{10.0}{273}} = 337\,\frac{\text{m}}{\text{s}}$, and equation (1) becomes:

$\frac{(9.80\ \text{m/s}^2)}{2(337\ \text{m/s})}t_1^2 + t_1 - 2.00\ \text{s} = 0$, or $(1.454 \times 10^{-2})t_1^2 + t_1 - 2.00\ \text{s} = 0$,

which yields: $t_1 = 1.945\ \text{s}$.

Then $d = \frac{1}{2}gt_1^2 = \frac{(9.80\ \text{m/s})^2(1.945\ \text{s})^2}{2} = 18.5\ \text{m}$.

14.7 (a) $P = IA = I(5.0 \times 10^{-5}\ \text{m}^2)$. At the threshold of hearing, $I = 10^{-12}$ W/m^2. Thus, $P = (10^{-12}\ \text{W/m}^2)(5.0 \times 10^{-5}\ \text{m}^2) = 5.0 \times 10^{-17}\ \text{W}$.

(b) At the threshold of pain, $I = 1\ \text{W/m}^2$.

$P = (1.0\ \text{W/m}^2)(5.0 \times 10^{-5}\ \text{m}^2) = 5.0 \times 10^{-5}\ \text{W}$.

14.8 Given: $\beta = 10\ \text{dB} = 10\log\left(\frac{I}{I_0}\right)$ which yields: $I = 10I_0 = 10^{-11}\ \text{W/m}^2$.

But $I = \frac{P}{4\pi r^2}$, from which $r = \sqrt{\frac{P}{4\pi I}} = \sqrt{\frac{0.050\ \text{W}}{4\pi \times 10^{-11}\ \text{W/m}^2}}$, or

$r = 1.99 \times 10^4\ \text{m} = 20\ \text{km}$.

14.9 We are given $\beta_2 = 85\ \text{dB}$, and $\beta_1 = 70\ \text{dB}$.

Also, $\beta_2 = 10\log\left(\frac{I_2}{I_0}\right)$, and $\beta_1 = 10\log\left(\frac{I_1}{I_0}\right)$. so

$\beta_2 - \beta_1 = 10\log\left(\frac{I_2}{I_1}\right) = 15\ \text{dB}$, or $\log\left(\frac{I_2}{I_1}\right) = 1.5$. Hence $\left(\frac{I_2}{I_1}\right) = 10^{1.5} = 31.6$,

or $I_{\text{Full Orchestra}} = (32)I_{\text{Single Violin}}$.

14.10 At 80 dB, the intensity is $I = 10^{-4}\ \text{W/m}^2$. At 90 dB, $I = 10^{-3}\ \text{W/m}^2$. Therefore, to reach 90 dB from 80 dB would require a sound intensity 10 times the level of one machine. Thus, 10 machines would be required to produce this level.

14.11 We are given that $I_2 = 2I_1$.

Therefore, $\beta_2 - \beta_1 = 10\log\left(\frac{I_2}{I_0}\right) - 10\log\left(\frac{I_1}{I_0}\right) = 10\log\left(\frac{\frac{I_2}{I_0}}{\frac{I_1}{I_0}}\right) = 10\log\left(\frac{I_2}{I_1}\right)$

or $\beta_2 - \beta_1 = 10\log(2) = 3.01$ dB.

14.12(a) $I = \frac{P}{4\pi r^2} = \frac{100\ \text{W}}{4\pi(10.0\ \text{m})^2} = 7.96 \times 10^{-2}\ \text{W/m}^2$.

(b) $\beta = 10\log\left(\frac{7.96 \times 10^{-2}}{10^{-12}}\right) = 10\log(7.96 \times 10^{10}) = 109$ dB

(c) If $\beta = 120$ dB (the threshold of pain), $I = 1\ \text{W/m}^2$, and from $I = \frac{P}{4\pi r^2}$,

and we find: $r^2 = \frac{P}{4\pi I} = \frac{100\ \text{W}}{4\pi(1\text{W/m}^2)} = 7.96\ \text{m}^2$, giving: $r = 2.82$ m.

14.13 (a) From the definition of the decibel level, $\beta = 10\log\left(\frac{I}{I_0}\right)$, we have

$50 = 10\log\left(\frac{I}{10^{-12}}\right)$, giving $I = 10^{-7}\ \text{W/m}^2$ as the intensity at a distance of 10 km from the horn. The power radiated by the horn is therefore:

$P = 4\pi r^2 I = 4\pi(10^4)^2(10^{-7}) = 126$ W.

(b) At 50 m from the horn, the intensity will be given by

$I = \frac{P}{4\pi r^2} = \frac{126}{4\pi(50)^2} = 4.0 \times 10^{-3}\ \text{W/m}^2$. The decibel level at this distance is $\beta = 10\log\left(\frac{4.0 \times 10^{-3}}{10^{-12}}\right) = 96$ dB.

14.14 $\beta = 10\log\left(\frac{I}{I_0}\right) = 70\ \text{dB} = 10\log\left(\frac{I}{10^{-12}\ \text{W/m}^2}\right)$,

from which: $I = 10^{-5}\ \text{W/m}^2$.

Now use, $P = IA = I(4\pi r^2) = (10^{-5}\ \text{W/m}^2)(4\pi(5.0\ \text{m})^2) = 3.1 \times 10^{-3}$ W.

14.15 At A, B, and C,

$I_A = \frac{\text{const}}{r_A{}^2}$, $I_B = \frac{\text{const}}{r_B{}^2}$, $I_C = \frac{\text{const}}{r_C{}^2}$.

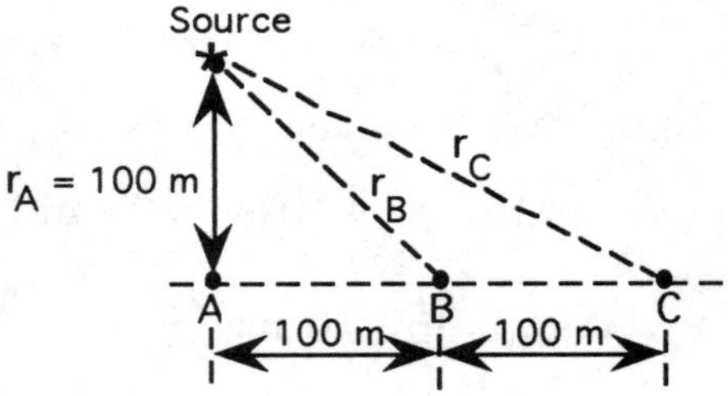

Thus, (a) $\frac{I_A}{I_B} = \frac{r_B{}^2}{r_A{}^2}$

$= \frac{(100\ \text{m})^2 + (100\ \text{m})^2}{(100\ \text{m})^2} = 2$

and (b) $\frac{I_A}{I_C} = \frac{r_C{}^2}{r_A{}^2}$

$= \frac{(100\ \text{m})^2 + (200\ \text{m})^2}{(100\ \text{m})^2} = 5$

14.16 Using, $f' = f\frac{v \pm v_o}{v \pm v_s}$, with $v_o = -30.0$ m/s (away) and $v_s = 0$, we obtain: $f' = (1000\text{ Hz})\frac{345\text{ m/s} - 30.0\text{ m/s}}{345\text{ m/s}} = 913\text{ Hz}$.

14.17 When the observer is at rest, the general doppler effect equation,

$f' = f\frac{v \pm v_o}{v \pm v_s}$, reduces to $f' = f\frac{v}{v \pm v_s}$.

(a) If the source is approaching at half the speed of sound ($v_s = -\frac{v}{2}$),

we have: $f' = f\frac{v}{v - v/2} = 2f = 10.0\text{ kHz}$

(b) If the source is receeding at half the speed of sound ($v_s = +\frac{v}{2}$),

we have: $f' = f\frac{v}{v + v/2} = \frac{2}{3}f = 3.33\text{ kHz}$

14.18 Since the observer hears a reduced frequency, the source must be moving away from the observer. The cyclist must be behind the car. Since both source and observer are in motion, we use

$f' = f\frac{v \pm v_o}{v \pm v_s}$. Since the observer moves toward the source, use upper sign in numerator. Since the source moves away from observer, use plus sign in denominator. Then with $v_o = \frac{1}{3}v_s$, we have:

$415\text{ Hz} = 440\text{ Hz}\left(\frac{345\text{ m/s} + \frac{1}{3}v_s}{345\text{ m/s} + v_s}\right)$, which can be solved to find

$v_s = 32.1$ m/s = 72 mph with the cyclist behind the car.

14.19 Both observer and source are moving, so we use $f' = f\frac{v \pm v_o}{v \pm v_s}$ with

v_s, = - 90.0 km/h = -25.0 m/s (source moves toward observer) and

v_o = +130 km/h = +36.1 m/s (observer moves toward source)

Thus, $f' = (500\text{ Hz})\frac{345\text{ m/s} + 36.1\text{ m/s}}{345\text{ m/s} - 25.0\text{ m/s}} = 595\text{ Hz}$

14.20 The wall will reflect a frequency of f_{wall} given by (source approaches a stationary observer): $f_{wall} = (40\text{ kHz})\frac{345\text{ m/s}}{345\text{ m/s} - 5.0\text{ m/s}} = 40.6\text{ kHz}$.

Treating the wall as a stationary source of sound having frequency 40.6 kHz, we have for the return signal (observer approaching stationary source):

$$f'_{bat} = (40.6\text{ kHz})\frac{345\text{ m/s} + 5.0\text{ m/s}}{345\text{ m/s}} = 41\text{ kHz}.$$

14.21 When the train is moving toward the observer at a speed v, we have

$$442\text{ Hz} = f\frac{345}{345 - v}. \quad (1)$$

When the train is moving away from the observer, at v, we have

$$441\text{ Hz} = f\frac{345}{345 + v}\,. \qquad (2)$$

Divide equation (1) by (2), f cancels, and the resulting equation can be solved for v. We find: $v = 0.391$ m/s.

14.22 (a) The wave travels a distance of 20,000 m at a speed of 345 m/s so it takes 58.0 s before one encounters the shock wave.

(b) In that time, the plane would have traveled a distance of $d = v_{plane}t = 3\,v_{sound}t = 3(345\text{ m/s})(58.0\text{ s}) = 60$ km (about 37 miles).

14.23 The half-angle of the cone of the shock wave is θ where: $\sin\theta = \frac{v}{vs} = \frac{1}{1.5} = 0.667$, or $\theta = 42°$. The angle between the direction of propagation of the shock wave and the direction of the plane's velocity is: $\phi = 90° - \theta$, or $\phi = 48°$ as shown in the diagram.

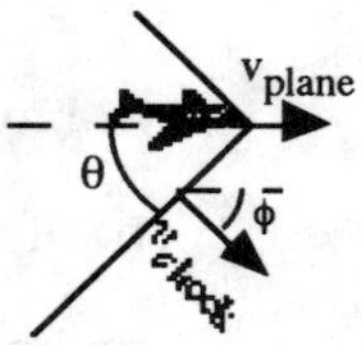

14.24 (a) The wavelength emitted by the speaker is:

$$\lambda = \frac{v}{f} = \frac{345\text{ m/s}}{400\text{ Hz}} = 0.863\text{ m}.$$

If destructive interference is presently taking place, one must increase the path length by $\lambda/2$ in order to change this to constructive interference. Thus, the increase is 0.431 m.

(b) To hear destructive interference once again, one needs a total increase (from the initial position) of one wavelength. Thus, the increase is 0.863 m.

14.25 The length of the diagonal of the triangle formed by the two sides 800 m and 600 m is found from the Pythagorean theorem to be $d_1 = 1000$ m. The extra distance of travel of the wave from A over that from B is 400 m. For destructive interference, we must have $d_1 - d_2 = \frac{\lambda}{2} = 400$ m,

or $\lambda = 800$ m.

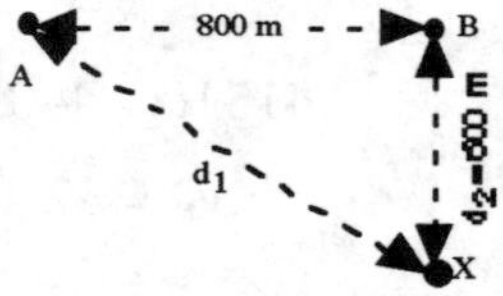

14.26 (a) The wavelength emitted by the speakers has a length of $\lambda = \frac{v}{f} = \frac{345\text{ m/s}}{500\text{ Hz}} = 0.69$ m. To produce destructive interference, the path difference should be $\lambda/2$. Therefore, the top speaker must be moved back 34.5 cm.

(b) If the path difference is λ, constructive interference will occur.

14.27 Since $f = 690$ Hz, we have $\lambda = \frac{345\text{ m/s}}{690\text{ Hz}} = 0.500$ m.

(a) At the first relative maximum (constructive interference), $\Delta = \lambda = 0.500$ m.

Thus, the Pythagorean theorem gives

$$(d + 0.500\text{ m})^2 = (0.700\text{ m})^2 + d^2,$$

or $d = 0.240$ m.

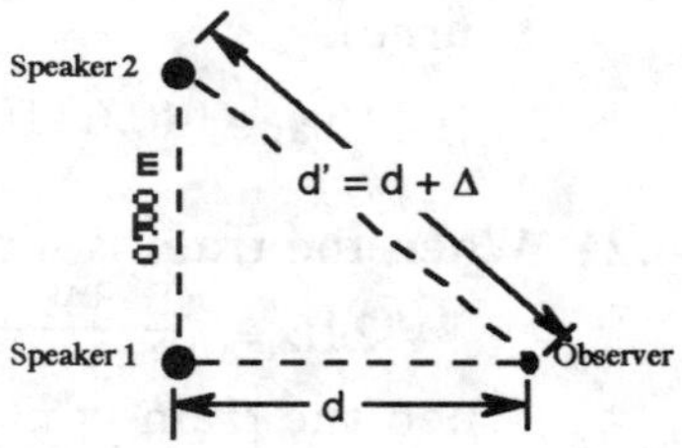

(b) At the first relative minimum (destructive interference), $\Delta = \lambda/2 = 0.250$ m. Therefore,
$(d + 0.250 \text{ m})^2 = (0.700 \text{ m})^2 + d^2$,
or $d = 0.855$ m.

14.28 $\mu = \frac{m}{L} = \frac{4.300 \times 10^{-3} \text{ kg}}{0.700 \text{ m}} = 6.14 \times 10^{-3}$ kg/m.
For the fundamental, $\lambda = 2L = 2(0.700 \text{ m}) = 1.40$ m, and if $f = 261.6$ Hz,
$v = \lambda f = 1.40 \text{ m}(261.6 \text{ Hz}) = 366.2$ m/s. The required tension is then
$F = \mu v^2 = (6.14 \times 10^{-3} \text{ kg/m})(366.2 \text{ m/s})^2 = 824$ N.

14.29 $\mu = \frac{m}{L} = \frac{0.04 \text{ kg}}{8.0 \text{ m}} = 5.00 \times 10^{-3}$ kg/m, and

$$v = \sqrt{\frac{F}{\mu}} = \sqrt{\frac{49.0 \text{ N}}{5.0 \times 10^{-3} \text{ kg/m}}} = 99 \text{ m/s}.$$

For the third harmonic, $L = \frac{3\lambda}{2} = 8.0$ m, giving $\lambda = 5.33$ m.

(a) Therefore nodes occur at 0, 2.67 m, 5.33 m, and 8.0 m from one end, and antinodes occur at 1.33 m, 4.0 m, and 6.67 m from the end.

(b) $f = v/\lambda = (99 \text{ m/s})/(5.33 \text{ m}) = 18.6$ Hz.

14.30 With successive antinodes at each end, the length of the rod is half of a wavelength: $L = \frac{\lambda}{2}$, or $\lambda = 2L = 2.00$ m. From Table 14.1, the speed of sound in aluminum is $v = 5100$ m/s. Therefore, the frequency of the wave associated with the resonance is $f = \frac{v}{\lambda} = \frac{5100 \text{ m/s}}{2.00 \text{ m}} = 2550$ Hz.

14.31 The mass per unit length of the string is:

$\mu = \frac{m}{L} = \frac{3.00 \times 10^{-4} \text{ kg}}{0.70 \text{ m}} = 4.29 \times 10^{-4}$ kg/m, and the wave speed is

$$v = \sqrt{\frac{F}{\mu}} = \sqrt{\frac{600 \text{ N}}{4.29 \times 10^{-4} \text{ kg/m}}} = 1183 \text{ m/s}.$$

The fundamental resonance mode, has a wavelength of $\lambda = 2L = 1.4$ m.

Thus, the first harmonic is: $f_1 = \frac{v}{\lambda} = \frac{1183 \text{ m/s}}{1.4 \text{ m}} = 845$ Hz.

The second harmonic is: $f_2 = 2f_1 = 1.69 \times 10^3$ Hz.

The third harmonic is: $f_3 = 3f_1 = 2.54 \times 10^3$ Hz.

14.32 In the diagram, observe that: $\sin\theta = \frac{1 \text{ m}}{1.5 \text{ m}} = \frac{2}{3}$ or $\theta = 41.8°$. Considering the mass, $\Sigma F_y = 0$ gives

$2T\cos\theta = mg$, or $T = \frac{(12 \text{ kg})(9.80 \text{ m/s}^2)}{2\cos 41.8°} = 78.9$ N.

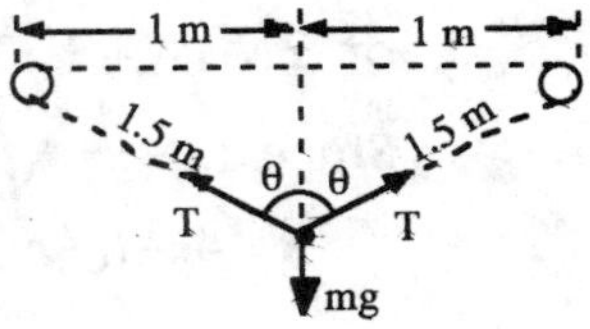

Therefore, the speed of the transverse waves in the string is $v = \sqrt{\frac{T}{\mu}} = \sqrt{\frac{78.9 \text{ N}}{0.001 \text{ kg/m}}} = 280.9$ m/s. For the shown standing wave pattern, $d = \frac{3}{2}\lambda$, or $\lambda = \frac{2(2 \text{ m})}{3} = 1.33$ m. Thus, the required frequency is

$$f = \frac{v}{\lambda} = \frac{280.9 \text{ m/s}}{1.33 \text{ m}} = 210 \text{ Hz}.$$

14.33 For standing waves in a string fixed at both ends, $L = n\frac{\lambda}{2}$ or $\lambda = \frac{2L}{n}$ where n is the number of loops.

a) From the figure, $n = 6$ and $f = 150$ Hz. Thus, $\lambda = \frac{2(2.00 \text{ m})}{6} = 0.667$ m, so $v = \lambda f = (0.667 \text{ m})(150 \text{ Hz}) = 100$ m/s. Then $v = \sqrt{\frac{T}{\mu}} = \sqrt{\frac{mg}{\mu}}$ gives

$$\mu = \frac{mg}{v^2} = \frac{(5.0 \text{ kg})(9.80 \text{ m/s}^2)}{(100 \text{ m/s})^2} = 4.9 \times 10^{-3} \text{ kg/m}.$$

(b) If $m = 45$ kg, $T = mg = 441$ N and $v = \sqrt{\frac{441 \text{ N}}{0.0049 \text{ kg/m}}} = 300$ m/s. Thus,

$\lambda = \frac{300 \text{ m/s}}{150 \text{ Hz}} = 2.0$ m,

so $n = \frac{2L}{\lambda} = \frac{2(2.0 \text{ m})}{2 \text{ m}} = 2$. (standing wave - 2 loops)

(c) If $m = 10$ kg, $T = mg = 98$ N and $v = \sqrt{\frac{98 \text{ N}}{0.0049 \text{ kg/m}}} = 141.4$ m/s.

Thus, $\lambda = \frac{141.4 \text{ m/s}}{150 \text{ Hz}} = 0.943$ m, so $n = \frac{2L}{\lambda} = \frac{2(2.00 \text{ m})}{0.943 \text{ m}} = 4.24$. (This is not an integer, so no standing wave exists.)

14.34 The wavelength of the fundamental mode of vibration is $\lambda = 2L$ where L is the length of the string. Also, μ is the same for both wires.

We have: $F_2 = 4F_1$. Since $v = \sqrt{\frac{F}{\mu}}$, $v_2 = 2v_1$.

Since $v = \lambda f$, this gives: $v_2 = 2(\lambda_1 f_1) = 2(2L_1)(60 \text{ Hz}) = (240 \text{ Hz})L_1$.

For a second haromic, $\lambda = L$. Thus, $f_2 = \frac{v_2}{\lambda_2} = \frac{v_2}{L_2} = \frac{(240 \text{ Hz})L_1}{2L_1}$, or

$f_2 = 120$ Hz. (frequency of 2nd harmonic in long wire).

14.35 Resonance of this system will occur when the push frequency, f, is given by $f = \frac{f_0}{n}$ where f_0 is the natural frequency of vibration and n is an integer

Let $2.4 \text{ Hz} = \frac{f_0}{N}$, then $1.2 \text{ Hz} = \frac{f_0}{N+1}$, giving $\frac{2.4 \text{ Hz}}{1.2 \text{ Hz}} = \frac{N+1}{N}$,

or $2N = N + 1$. Thus, $N = 1$ and we see that: $f_0 = 2.4$ Hz.

Since $f_0 = \frac{1}{2\pi}\sqrt{\frac{k}{m}}$, we have

$k = 4\pi^2 f_0^2 m$, or $k = 4\pi^2(2.4 \text{ Hz})^2(5.0 \text{ kg}) = 1.1 \times 10^3$ N/m.

14.36 The natural frequency of vibration of the swing is

$$f_0 = \frac{1}{2\pi}\sqrt{\frac{g}{L}} = \frac{1}{2\pi}\sqrt{\frac{(9.80 \text{ m/s}^2)}{2.00 \text{ m}}} = 0.352 \text{ Hz}.$$

Thus, for resonance, we can push the swing at frequencies of f_0, $f_0/2$, $f_0/3$, $f_0/4$, these correspond to frequencies of 0.352 Hz, 0.176 Hz, 0.117 Hz, and so forth.

14.37 (a) The space between successive resonance points is $\lambda/2$. Therefore, $\lambda/2 = (0.24\,\text{m} - 0.080\,\text{m}) = 0.16\,\text{m}$, or $\lambda = 0.32\,\text{m}$.
The third resonance point will be one-half wavelength further down the tube. This location is at $0.24\,\text{m} + 0.16\,\text{m} = 0.40\,\text{m}$.

(b) $f = \frac{v}{\lambda} = \frac{345\ \text{m/s}}{0.32\ \text{m}} = 1.1\times10^3\ \text{Hz}$.

14.38 For the open pipe (and the fundamental mode):

$$\lambda = \frac{v}{f} = \frac{345\ \text{m/s}}{261.6\ \text{Hz}} = 1.319\,\text{m}, \text{ and } L = \frac{\lambda}{2} = 0.659\,\text{m} = 65.9\,\text{cm}.$$

For the closed pipe (and the third harmonic), $\lambda = \frac{v}{f} = \frac{345\ \text{m/s}}{261.6\ \text{Hz}} = 1.319\,\text{m}$,

and $L = \frac{3}{4}(1.319\,\text{m}) = 0.989\,\text{m} = 98.9\,\text{cm}$.

14.39 Hearing would be best at the fundamental resonance, so we take

$$f_n = \frac{nv}{4L} = \frac{(1)(340)}{4(0.028)} = 3.0\times10^3\ \text{Hz}$$

14.40 (a) $\lambda = \frac{v}{f} = \frac{333\ \text{m/s}}{300\ \text{Hz}} = 1.11\ \text{m}$.

Thus, for the fundamental, $L = \frac{\lambda}{2} = 0.555\ \text{m}$.

(b) For the second harmonic, $\lambda = L$. So,: $f = \frac{v}{\lambda} = \frac{344\ \text{m/s}}{0.555\ \text{m}} = 620\,\text{Hz}$.

14.41 (a) At 0°C, the speed of sound is 331 m/s. The wavelength of the wave is:

$$\lambda = \frac{v}{f} = \frac{331\ \text{m/s}}{300\ \text{Hz}} = 1.10\,\text{m}.$$

For the fundamental mode of vibration, $\lambda = 2L$, or

$$L = \frac{\lambda}{2} = 0.55\,\text{m}.$$

(b) At T = 30 °C, the speed of sound is:

$$v = (331\ \text{m/s})\sqrt{1 + \frac{30}{273}} = 349\,\frac{\text{m}}{\text{s}}.$$

Thus, $f = \frac{v}{\lambda} = \frac{v}{2L} = \frac{349\ \text{m/s}}{2(0.55\ \text{m})} = 317\,\text{Hz}$.

14.42 For the open pipe, the frequency of the nth harmonic is, $f_n = n\frac{v}{2L}$.

Thus, $f_{n+1} - f_n = (n+1)\left(\frac{v}{2L}\right) - n\left(\frac{v}{2L}\right) = \frac{v}{2L}$. Thus, if $f_n = 410$ Hz, and

$f_{n+1} = 492$ Hz, when $L = 2.00$ m: $492\ \text{Hz} - 410\ \text{Hz} = \frac{v}{2(2.00\ \text{m})}$,

giving $v = 328\,\frac{\text{m}}{\text{s}}$

14.43 The speed of transverse waves in a string is $v = \sqrt{\frac{T}{\mu}}$.

Thus for $T = 200$ N, $v = \sqrt{\frac{200\ \text{N}}{\mu}}$, and for $T = 196$ N, $v' = \sqrt{\frac{196\ \text{N}}{\mu}}$.
Since $v = \lambda f$ and the length of the string (and hence λ) does not change:

$$\frac{f'}{f} = \frac{v'}{v}, \text{ or } f' = \sqrt{\frac{196\ \text{N}}{\mu}\ \frac{\mu}{200\ \text{N}}}\ f = 0.99(523\ \text{Hz}), \text{ giving } f' = 517.7\ \text{Hz}.$$

The beat frequency is $f_{beat} = f - f' = (523 - 517.7)\text{Hz} = 5.26\ \text{Hz}$

14.44 The wavelength of the sound emitted by the first violin is
$\lambda = 2L = 2(30.0\ \text{cm}) = 60.0\ \text{cm}$. As the second player shortens the length of her string, the frequency it emits will increase. Thus, the frequency her instrument emits is: $f' = f + 2\ \text{Hz} = 198\ \text{Hz}$.
The velocity of the waves are the same for both instruments.

Therefore, $\lambda f = \lambda' f'$, and $\lambda' = \frac{\lambda f}{f'} = \frac{(60.0\ \text{cm})(196\ \text{Hz})}{198\ \text{Hz}} = 59.4\ \text{cm}$.

The length of the shortened string is: $L' = \frac{0.594\ \text{m}}{2} = 0.297\ \text{m} = 29.7\ \text{cm}$.

14.45 The beat frequency is 2 Hz and $f = 180$ Hz. Thus, $f' = 182$ Hz if the moving train is coming toward the station, or $f' = 178$ Hz if the moving train is going away from the station.

Source moving toward stationary observer: $f' = f\frac{v}{v - v_s}$ becomes

$$182\ \text{Hz} = 180\ \text{Hz}\frac{345\ \text{m/s}}{345\ \text{m/s} - v_s}, \text{ from which, } \quad v_s = 3.8\ \text{m/s}.$$

Source moving away from stationary observer: $f' = f\ \frac{v}{v + v_s}$ becomes

$$178\ \text{Hz} = 180\ \text{Hz}\frac{345\text{m/s}}{345\ \text{m/s} + v_s}, \text{ from which, } \quad v_s = 3.9\ \text{m/s}.$$

Thus, the second train is either moving at 3.8 m/s toward the station or at 3.9 m/s away from the station.

14.46 The velocity of sound in the pipes is: $v_1 = 347$ m/s, and $v_2 = 350$ m/s.
Since the two pipes have the same length, $\lambda_1 = \lambda_2 = 4L$ (fundamental mode). Using $\lambda = v/f$, this gives: $f_2 = f_1\frac{v_2}{v_1} = (480\ \text{Hz})\frac{350}{347} = 484\ \text{Hz}$.
Therefore, the beat frequency is 4 Hz.

14.47 The speed of sound at $T = 37$ °C is 353 m/s, and the wavelength in the ear canal is, $\lambda = \frac{v}{f} = \frac{353\ \text{m/s}}{3000\ \text{Hz}} = 0.118\ \text{m}$.

In the fundamental resonance mode, we have $L = \frac{\lambda}{4} = 2.94\ \text{cm}$.

14.48 At normal body temperature of 37 °C, the speed of sound is 353 m/s, and the wavelength of a 20,000 Hz sound is

$$\lambda = \frac{v}{f} = \frac{353\ \text{m/s}}{20000\ \text{Hz}} = 1.76 \times 10^{-2}\ \text{m}.$$

Thus, the diameter of the eardrum is 1.76 cm.

14.49 Since there is no relative motion between the observer and the source in this case, there is no shift in frequency due to the Doppler effect. Thus, the answer is $f' = f = 300\ \text{Hz}$.

Mathematically, $f' = f\dfrac{v \pm v_O}{v \pm v_S}$.
But if $v_S = v_O$, this reduces to $f' = f(1) = f$.

14.50 (a) As the train approaches,

$$f' = f\left(\frac{v \pm v_O}{v \pm v_S}\right) = (320\text{ Hz})\left(\frac{345}{345 - 40.0}\right) = 362\text{ Hz}.$$

(b) As the train recedes, $f' = f\dfrac{v \pm v_O}{v \pm v_S} = (320\text{ Hz})\left(\dfrac{345}{345 + 40.0}\right) = 287\text{ Hz}.$

(c) The wavelength when the train is approaching is

$$\lambda = \frac{v}{f} = \frac{345\text{ m/s}}{362\text{ Hz}} = 0.953\text{ m}.$$

For the receding train, $\lambda = \dfrac{v}{f} = \dfrac{345\text{ m/s}}{287\text{ Hz}} = 1.20\text{ m}.$

14.51 On the weekend, there are one-fourth as many cars passing per minute as on a week day. Thus, the intensity, I_2, of the sound on the weekend is one-fourth that, I_1, on a week day. The difference in the decibel levels is therefore:

$$\beta_1 - \beta_2 = 10\log\left(\frac{I_1}{I_0}\right) - 10\log\left(\frac{I_2}{I_0}\right) = 10\log\left(\frac{I_1}{I_2}\right) = 10\log(4) = 6\text{dB}.$$

Therefore, $\beta_2 = \beta_1 - 6\text{ dB} = 70\text{ dB} - 6\text{ dB} = 64\text{ dB}.$

14.52 The first resonance in the air column will occur for $L_{air} = \dfrac{\lambda_{air}}{4} = 0.34\text{ m}.$

Therefore, $\lambda_{air} = 1.36\text{ m}$ and $f = \dfrac{v_{air}}{\lambda_{air}} = \dfrac{340\text{ m/s}}{1.36\text{ m}} = 250\text{ Hz}$ is the frequency of both the sound wave and the vibrating wire. Since the wire is vibrating in its third harmonic, $L_{wire} = \dfrac{3\lambda_{wire}}{2}$, or $\lambda_{wire} = \dfrac{2}{3}L_{wire} =$ 0.800 m. The wave velocity in the wire is then

$$v_{wire} = f\lambda_{wire} = (250\text{ Hz})(0.800\text{ m}) = 200\text{ m/s}.$$

14.53 (a) The speed of sound in air at 20 °C is:

$$v = \left(331\ \frac{\text{m}}{\text{s}}\right)\sqrt{1 + \frac{20}{273}} = 343\ \frac{\text{m}}{\text{s}}$$

and the wavelength of the sound is: $\lambda = \dfrac{v}{f} = \dfrac{343\text{ m/s}}{261.6\text{ Hz}} = 1.31\text{ m}.$

The length of the open tube is: $L = \dfrac{\lambda}{2} = 0.655\text{ m} = 65.5\text{ cm}.$

(b) In the colder room, the pipe has essentially the same length. Therefore, the wavelength of the fundamental, $\lambda = 2L$, is unchanged. $\lambda' = 1.31\text{ m}.$
Since the temperature is lower in the colder room, the speed of sound and hence the frequency of the fundamental will be lower. Thus, if the beat frequency is 3.00 Hz, the frequency in the colder room is $f' = 258.6\text{ Hz}.$

Therefore, $v' = \lambda' f' = (1.31\ \text{m})(258.6\ \text{Hz}) = 339\ \text{m/s}$, and the temperature is found from: $339\ \text{m/s} = (331\ \text{m/s})\sqrt{1 + \frac{T_C}{273}}$ which gives, $T_C = 13.4\ °\text{C}$.

14.54 We use $f' = f\,\frac{v \pm v_O}{v \pm v_S}$ with both sources moving toward a stationary observer. For train 1: $f_1' = (300\ \text{Hz})\left(\frac{345\ \text{m/s}}{345\ \text{m/s} - 30.0\ \text{m/s}}\right) = 328.6\ \text{Hz}$.
Since train 2 moves toward the observer faster than train 1, $f_2' > f_1'$. Then, if the beat frequency is 3 Hz, f_2' 331.6 Hz. Therefore,

$$331.6\ \text{Hz} = (300\ \text{Hz})\left(\frac{345\ \text{m/s}}{345\ \text{m/s} - v_{S2}}\right).$$ which yields: $v_{S2} = 32.9\ \text{m/s}$.

14.55 We use: $f' = f\frac{v \pm v_O}{v \pm v_S}$, with f_1' = frequency of the speaker in front of the student and f_2' = frequency of the speaker behind the student.

$$f_1' = (456\ \text{Hz})\frac{(345\ \text{m/s} + 1.50\ \text{m/s})}{(345\ \text{m/s} - 0)} = 458.0\ \text{Hz},\ \text{and}$$

$$f_2' = (456\ \text{Hz})\frac{(345\ \text{m/s} - 1.50\ \text{m/s})}{(345\ \text{m/s} - 0)} = 454.0\ \text{Hz}$$

Therefore, the beat frequency is 4.0 Hz.

14.56 The wavelength upstream, λ_2, is related to the wavelength downstream, λ_1, as $\lambda_2 = 1.5\lambda_1$. Thus, $\frac{v}{f_2} = 1.5\frac{v}{f_1}$, or $f_1 = 1.5\,f_2$.

But: $f_1 = f\frac{v}{v - v_S}$, and $f_2 = f\frac{v}{v + v_S}$, so $f\frac{v}{v - v_S} = 1.5\,f\frac{v}{v + v_S}$.

From which, $v_S = \frac{v}{5}$. Thus, if $v = 0.500\ \text{m/s}$, $v_S = 0.1\ \text{m/s}$.

14.57 Sound takes this time to reach the man:

$$\frac{(20.0\ \text{m} - 1.75\ \text{m})}{343\ \text{m/s}} = 5.32 \times 10^{-2}\ \text{s}$$

so the warning should be shouted no later than $0.300\ \text{s} + 5.32 \times 10^{-2}\ \text{s}$ before the pot strikes.
Since the whole time of fall is given by

$$y = \frac{1}{2}gt^2 \qquad 18.25\ \text{m} = \frac{1}{2}(9.80\ \text{m/s}^2)\,t^2$$

From which $t = 1.93\ \text{s}$
The warning needs to come
$1.93\ \text{s} - 0.353\ \text{s} = 1.58\ \text{s}$
into the fall, when the pot has fallen
$\frac{1}{2}(9.80\ \text{m/s}^2)(1.58\ \text{s})^2 = 12.2\ \text{m}$
to be above the ground by
$20.0\ \text{m} - 12.2\ \text{m} = 7.8\ \text{m}$

14.58 Call the speed of the plane v and its altitude h. Then
$\frac{h}{2} = v(2.00\ \text{s})$

The sound reaching the plane travels a distance

$$\sqrt{h^2 + \frac{h^2}{4}} = (343 \text{ m/s})(2.00 \text{ s})$$

It is easiest to solve part (b) of this problem first. We have

(b) $h = \frac{686 \text{ m}}{1.12} = 614 \text{ m}$

(a) $v = \frac{614 \text{ m}}{4.00 \text{ s}} = 153 \text{ m/s}$

14.59 $f_o = f\left(\frac{v}{v + v_s}\right)$ gives $485 = 512\left(\frac{340}{340 + 9.80 t_{fall}}\right)$

From which $t_{fall} = 1.93 \text{ s}$

$d_1 = 18.278 \text{ m}$

$t_{return} = \frac{18.3 \text{ m}}{340} = 0.05376 \text{ s}$

The fork continues to fall while the sound returns.

$t_{total\ fall} = 1.9851 \text{ s}$

$d_{total} = 19.3 \text{ m}$

14.60 The maximum speed of the speaker is described by

$$\frac{1}{2} m v^2_{max} = \frac{1}{2} k A^2$$

$$v = \sqrt{\frac{k}{m}}\, A$$

The frequencies heard by the stationary observer range from

$$f'_{min} = f\left(\frac{v}{v + \sqrt{\frac{k}{m}}\, A}\right) \quad \text{to} \quad f'_{max} = f\left(\frac{v}{v - \sqrt{\frac{k}{m}}\, A}\right)$$

We find $f'_{min} = 440 \text{ Hz}\left(\frac{343 \text{ m/s}}{343 \text{ m/s} + \sqrt{\frac{20.0}{5}}\, 0.500 \text{ m/s}}\right) = 439 \text{ Hz}$

$$f'_{max} = 440 \text{ Hz}\left(\frac{343 \text{ m/s}}{343 \text{ m/s} - \sqrt{\frac{20.0}{5}}\, 0.500 \text{ m/s}}\right) = 441 \text{ Hz}$$

14.61 (a) $f_g = f_e\left(\frac{v}{v - v_{diver}}\right)$ From which $v_{diver} = v\left(1 - \frac{f_e}{f_g}\right)$

With $v = 343$ m/s and $f_e = 1800$ Hz and $f_g = 2150$ Hz, we find

$v_{diver} = 55.8 \text{ m/s}$

(b) If the waves are reflected, and the skydiver is moving into them,

we have $f'_{rec} = f_g \frac{v + v_{diver}}{v}$

or $f'_{rec} = f_e\left(\frac{v}{v - v_{diver}}\right)\frac{v + v_{diver}}{v} = 1800\frac{343 + 55.8}{343 - 55.8} = 2500 \text{ Hz}$

14.62 (a) First we calculate the wavelength: $\lambda = \frac{v}{f} = \frac{344\text{ m/s}}{21.5\text{ Hz}} = 16$ m. Then we note that the path difference equals 9 m - 1m = $\frac{1}{2}\lambda$. Therefore, the receiver will record a minimum in sound intensity.

(b) If the receiver is located at point (x,y) then we must solve:

$$\sqrt{(x+5)^2+y^2} - \sqrt{(x-5)^2+y^2} = \frac{\lambda}{2}.$$

Then, $\sqrt{(x+5)^2+y^2} = \sqrt{(x-5)^2+y^2} + \frac{1}{2}\lambda$. Square both sides and simplify to get: $20x - \frac{\lambda^2}{4} = \lambda\sqrt{(x-5)^2+y^2}$. Upon squaring again, this reduces to: $400x^2 - 10\lambda^2 x + \frac{\lambda^4}{16} = \lambda^2(x-5)^2 + \lambda^2 y^2$.

Substituting $\lambda = 16$ m, and reducing, we have: $9x^2 - 16y^2 = 144$, or $\frac{x^2}{16} - \frac{y^2}{9} = 1$. (When plotted this yields a curve called a hyperbola.)

14.63 We have: $v_{long} = \sqrt{\frac{Y}{\rho}}$, and $v_{trans} = \sqrt{\frac{F}{\mu}}$.

If $\frac{v_l}{v_t} = 8$, then $\sqrt{\frac{Y/\rho}{F/\mu}} = 8$, or $\frac{Y\mu}{\rho F} = 64$. But, $\frac{\mu}{\rho} = \frac{V}{L} = A$. Thus, $\frac{(Y)(A)}{F} = 64$.

We solve the above for F, to find:

$$F = \frac{YA}{64} = \frac{(6.8 \times 10^{11}\text{ dynes/cm}^2)(4.00 \times 10^{-2}\,\pi\text{ cm}^2)}{64} = 1.34 \times 10^9$$

dynes

or $F = 1.34 \times 10^4$ N.

14.64 The moving student hears two frequencies: that due to receding from the source $f_1' = f\,\frac{(v - v_0)}{v}$, and that due to approaching the reflected wave

$f_2' = f\,\frac{(v + v_0)}{v}$. The number of beats per second = $f_2' - f_1' = f\frac{2v_0}{v}$

Therefore, $v_0 = \frac{v}{2f}$(#beats/s), but $f = \frac{v}{\lambda}$ where: $v = \sqrt{\frac{T}{m/L}}$, and $\lambda = \frac{2L}{3}$.

Thus, $f = \frac{3}{2}\sqrt{\frac{T}{mL}} = \frac{3}{2}\sqrt{\frac{400\text{ N}}{(2.25 \times 10^{-3}\text{ kg})(0.75\text{ m})}} = 7.3 \times 10^2$ Hz,

and $v_0 = \frac{v}{2f}(\#\text{beats/s}) = \frac{(340\text{ m/s})(8.3\text{ beats/s})}{(2)(7.3 \times 10^2\text{ Hz})} = 1.93$ m/s.

14.65 When observer is moving in front of and in the same direction as the source, $f_0 = f_s\,\frac{v - v_0}{v - v_s}$ where v_0 and are v_s measured relative to the medium in which the sound is propagated. In this case the ocean current is opposite the direction of travel of the ships and
v_0 = 45.0 km/h -(- 10.0 km/h) = 55.0 km/h = 15.29 m/s, and
v_s = 64.0 km/h -(- 10.0 km/h) = 74.0 km/h = 20.57 m/s

Therefore, $f_0 = (1200\text{ Hz})\,\frac{1520\text{ m/s} - 15.29\text{ m/s}}{1520\text{ m/s} - 20.57\text{ m/s}} = 1204.2$ Hz.

14.66 (a) If the source and the observer are moving away from each other, we have: $\theta_S = \theta_O = 180°$, and since $\cos 180° = -1$, we get Equation 14.15 with the lower signs.

(b) If $v_O = 0$ m/s, then $f' = \frac{v}{v - v_S \cos\theta_S} f$. Also, when the train is 40 m from the intersection, and the car is 30 m from the intersection, $\cos\theta_S = \frac{4}{5}$, so: $f' = \frac{343 \text{ m/s}}{343 \text{ m/s} - 0.8(25 \text{ m/s})}(500 \text{ Hz})$, or $f' = 531$ Hz.

Note that as the train approaches, passes, and departs from the intersection, θ_S varies from 0° to 180° and the frequency heard by the observer varies from:

$$f'_{max} = \frac{v}{v - v_S \cos 0°} f = \frac{343 \text{ m/s}}{343 \text{ m/s} - 25.0 \text{ m/s}}(500 \text{ Hz}) = 539 \text{ Hz}$$

to $$f'_{min} = \frac{v}{v - v_S \cos 180°} f = \frac{343 \text{ m/s}}{343 \text{ m/s} + 25.0 \text{ m/s}}(500 \text{ Hz}) = 466 \text{ Hz}.$$

ANSWERS TO CONCEPTUAL QUESTIONS

2. Air flowing fast by a rim of the pipe creates a "shshshsh" sound called edgetone noise, a mixture of all frequencies, as the air turbulently switches between flowing on one side of the edge and the other. The air column inside the pipe finds one or more of its resonance frequencies in the noise. The air column starts vibrating with large amplitude in a standing vibration mode and radiates this sound into the surrounding air.

4. The distance around the opening of the bell must be an integral multiple of the wavelength. Actually, the circumference being equal to the wavelength would describe the bell moving from side to side without bending, which it can do without producing any sound. A tuned bell is cast and shaped so that some of these vibrations will have their frequencies constitute higher harmonics of a musical note, the strike tone. This tuning is lost if a crack develops in the bell. The sides of the crack vibrate as antinodes. Energy of vibration may be rapidly lost into thermal energy at the end of the crack, so the bell may not ring for so long a time.

6. The sound waves created in the shower stall can vibrate in standing wave patterns to amplify certain frequencies in your voice. The hard walls of the bathroom reflect sound very well to make your voice louder at all frequencies, giving the room a longer reverberation time. The reverberant sound may help you to stay on key.

8. Refer to Table 14.2 to see that a rock concert has an intensity level of about 120 dB, the turning of a page in a textbook about 30 dB, a normal conversation is about 50 dB, background noise at a church is about 30 dB. This leaves a cheering crowd at a football game to be about 60 dB.

10. Imagine yourself at a concert hall listening to an orchestra. If the speed of sound depended on frequency, the sound from the high frequency instruments might reach you sooner than the sound from the lower frequency bass instruments. The notes are supposed to be played at precise instants of time, so if they arrived out of sequence, the music would turn to a jumble of noise.

12. A beam of radio waves of known frequency is sent toward a speeding car, which reflects the beam back to a detector in the police car. The amount the returning frequency has been shifted depends on the velocity of the oncoming car.

14. Consider the level of fluid in the bottle to be adjusted so that the air column above it resonates at the first harmonic. This is given by $f = \frac{v}{4L}$ This equation indicates that as the length L of the column decreases (fluid level increases), the resonant frequency increases.

16. Walking makes the person's hand vibrate a little. If the frequency of this motion equals the natural frequency of coffee sloshing from side to side in a cup, then a large-amplitude vibration of the coffee will build up in resonance. To get off resonance and back to the normal case of a small-amplitude disturbance producing a small-amplitude result, the person can walk faster, walk slower, vary his speed, or get a larger or smaller cup. Alternatively, even at resonance, he can reduce the amplitude by adding damping, as by stirring high-fiber quick cooking oat meal into the hot coffee.

18. The two engines are running at slightly different frequencies, thus producing a beat frequency between the two.

CHAPTER FIFTEEN SOLUTIONS

Chapter Fifteen Readings

Holt, C., "Working Knowledge: Photocopiers," *Scientific American*, v. 275 (Oct. '96) p 128.

Kaner, R.B, and MacDiarmid, A.G., "Plastics That Conduct Electricity," *Scientific American*, February 1988, p. 106.

Moore, A.D., "Electrostatics," *Scientific American*, March 1972, p. 46.

Roller, D, and Roller, D.H.D., "T*he Development of the Concept of Electric Charge*," Cambridge, Mass., Harvard University Press, 1954.

Williams, E.R., "The Electrification of Thunderstorms," *Scientific American*, November 1988, p. 88.

Review (a) $F = \frac{ke^2}{r^2} = (8.99 \times 10^9 \text{ Nm}^2/\text{C}^2)\frac{(1.60 \times 10^{-19} \text{ C})^2}{(0.53 \times 10^{-10} \text{ m})^2} = 8.2 \times 10^{-8} \text{ N}$

(b) We have: $F = \frac{mv^2}{r}$, or $v = \sqrt{\frac{Fr}{m}}$. Therefore,

$$v = \sqrt{\frac{(8.2 \times 10^{-8} \text{ N})(0.53 \times 10^{-10} \text{ m})}{(9.11 \times 10^{-31} \text{ kg})}} = 2.2 \times 10^6 \text{ m/s}.$$

15.1 $q = 1.60 \times 10^{-6} \text{ C} = ne = n(1.60 \times 10^{-19} \text{ C})$

(a) Therefore, $n = \frac{1.60 \times 10^{-6} \text{ C}}{1.60 \times 10^{-19} \text{ C}} = 10^{13}$ electrons.

(b) 27 g of aluminum is 1 mole and thus contains Avogadro's number of aluminum atoms, each having 13 electrons. Originally there were $13(6.02 \times 10^{23}) = 7.83 \times 10^{24}$ electrons in the aluminum. The fraction removed was $\frac{10^{13}}{7.83 \times 10^{24}} = 1.28 \times 10^{-12}$

15.2 The force is one of attraction. Its magnitude is:

$$F = \frac{kq_1q_2}{r^2} = (8.99 \times 10^9 \text{ Nm}^2/\text{C}^2)\ \frac{(4.5 \times 10^{-9} \text{ C})(2.8 \times 10^{-9} \text{ C})}{(3.2 \text{ m})^2}$$
$$= 1.1 \times 10^{-8} \text{ N}$$

15.3 (a) The force is one of attraction. The distance r in Coulomb's law is the distance between centers. The magnitude of the force is

$$F = \frac{kq_1q_2}{r^2} = \left(8.99 \times 10^9 \frac{\text{Nm}^2}{\text{C}^2}\right)\frac{(12 \times 10^{-9} \text{ C})(18 \times 10^{-9} \text{ C})}{(0.30 \text{ m})^2} = 2.2 \times 10^{-5} \text{ N}$$

(b) The net charge of -6.0×10^{-9} C will be equally split between the two spheres, or -3.0×10^{-9} C on each. The force is one of repulsion, and its magnitude is:

$$F = \frac{kq_1q_2}{r^2} = \left(8.99 \times 10^9 \frac{\text{Nm}^2}{\text{C}^2}\right)\frac{(3.0 \times 10^{-9} \text{ C})(3.0 \times 10^{-9} \text{ C})}{(0.30 \text{ m})^2} = 9.0 \times 10^{-7} \text{ N}$$

CHAPTER FIFTEEN SOLUTIONS

15.4 $F = k\frac{q_1 q_2}{r^2} = (8.99 \times 10^9 \text{ Nm}^2/\text{C}^2)\frac{(2e)(79e)}{(2.0 \times 10^{-14} \text{ m})^2} = 91 \text{ N}$

15.5 (a) $F = k\frac{q_1 q_2}{r^2} = (8.99 \times 10^9 \text{ Nm}^2/\text{C}^2)\frac{[(2)(1.60 \times 10^{-19} \text{ C})]^2}{(5.00 \times 10^{-15} \text{ m})^2} = 36.8 \text{ N}$

(b) $a = \frac{F}{m} = \frac{36.8 \text{ N}}{4(1.67 \times 10^{-27} \text{ kg})} = 5.51 \times 10^{27} \text{ m/s}^2$

15.6 1.00 g of hydrogen contains $N_A = 6.02 \times 10^{23}$ atoms, each containing one proton and one electron. Thus,

$$q = N_A e = (6.02 \times 10^{23})(1.60 \times 10^{-19} \text{C}) = 9.63 \times 10^4 \text{C}.$$

The distance of separation of these charges = $2R_e = 1.276 \times 10^7$ m.

Thus, $F = \frac{kq_1 q_2}{r^2} = (8.99 \times 10^9 \text{ Nm}^2/\text{C}^2)\frac{(9.63 \times 10^4 \text{ C})^2}{(1.276 \times 10^7 \text{ m})^2}$

$= 5.12 \times 10^5$ N.

15.7 We have $F_e = mg$, or $\frac{ke^2}{r^2} = mg$, from which

$$r = \sqrt{\frac{(8.99 \times 10^9 \text{ Nm}^2/\text{C}^2)(1.60 \times 10^{-19} \text{ C})^2}{(9.11 \times 10^{-31} \text{ kg})(9.80 \text{ m/s}^2)}} = 5.08 \text{ m}$$

15.8 The force exerted on the 3.5×10^{-9} C charge by the 2.2×10^{-9} C charge is in the positive x direction (a force of repulsion) and has a magnitude of

$F_1 = \frac{kq_1 q_3}{r^2} = \left(8.99 \times 10^9 \frac{\text{Nm}^2}{\text{C}^2}\right)\frac{(2.2 \times 10^{-9} \text{ C})(3.5 \times 10^{-9} \text{ C})}{(1.5 \text{ m})^2}$

$= 3.08 \times 10^{-8}$ N

and the force exerted on the 3.5×10^{-9} C charge by the 5.4×10^{-9} C charge is in the negative x direction (also a force of repulsion). Its magnitude is:

$F_2 = \frac{kq_2 q_3}{r^2} = (8.99 \times 10^9 \text{ Nm}^2/\text{C}^2)\frac{(5.4 \times 10^{-9} \text{ N})(3.5 \times 10^{-9} \text{ N})}{(2 \text{ m})^2}$

$= 4.25 \times 10^{-8}$ N

The net force is:

$F_{net} = -4.25 \times 10^{-8} \text{ N} + 3.08 \times 10^{-8} \text{ N} = -1.2 \times 10^{-8}$ N (negative x direction)

15.9 The distance of separation between the two charges at equilibrium, r, is

$r = 2(0.300 \text{ m})\sin 5.0° = 5.23 \times 10^{-2}$ m.

Therefore, $F = \frac{kQ^2}{r^2} = \frac{(8.99 \times 10^9 \text{ Nm}^2/\text{C}^2)Q^2}{(5.23 \times 10^{-2} \text{ m})^2}$

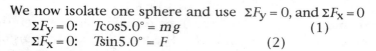

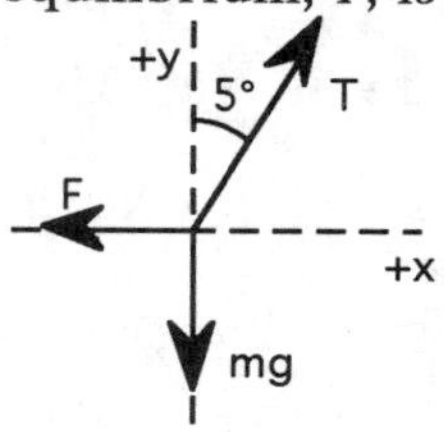

We now isolate one sphere and use $\Sigma F_y = 0$, and $\Sigma F_x = 0$

$\Sigma F_y = 0$: $T\cos 5.0° = mg$ (1)

$\Sigma F_x = 0$: $T\sin 5.0° = F$ (2)

Divide (2) by (1), yielding $\frac{F}{mg} = \tan 5.0°$, or

$$\frac{(8.99 \times 10^9\ \text{Nm}^2/\text{C}^2)Q^2}{(2.0 \times 10^{-4}\ \text{kg})(9.80\ \text{m/s}^2)(5.23 \times 10^{-2}\ \text{m})^2} = \tan 5.0°$$

Thus, $Q = 7.2 \times 10^{-9}$ C

15.10 The forces are as shown in the sketch below.

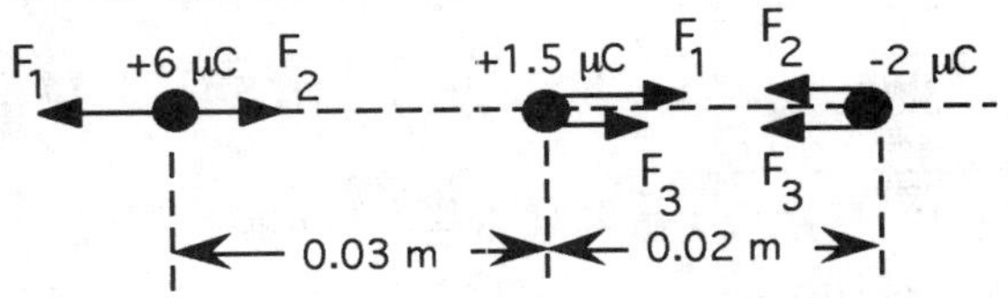

$$F_1 = \frac{kq_1q_2}{r_{12}^2} = (8.99 \times 10^9\ \text{Nm}^2/\text{C}^2)\ \frac{(6.00 \times 10^{-6}\ \text{C})(1.50 \times 10^{-6}\ \text{C})}{(3.00 \times 10^{-2}\ \text{m})^2}$$

$= 89.9$ N

$$F_2 = \frac{kq_1q_3}{r_{13}^2} = (8.99 \times 10^9\ \text{Nm}^2/\text{C}^2)\ \frac{(6.00 \times 10^{-6}\ \text{C})(2.00 \times 10^{-6}\ \text{C})}{(5.00 \times 10^{-2}\ \text{m})^2}$$

$= 43.2$ N

$$F_3 = \frac{kq_2q_3}{r_{23}^2} = (8.99 \times 10^9\ \text{Nm}^2/\text{C}^2)\ \frac{(1.50 \times 10^{-6}\ \text{C})(2.00 \times 10^{-6}\ \text{C})}{(2.00 \times 10^{-2}\ \text{m})^2}$$

$= 67.4$ N

The net force on the 6 μC charge = $F_1 - F_2 = 46.7$ N (toward left).
The net force on the 1.5 μC charge = $F_1 + F_3 = 157.3$ N (toward right).
The net force on the -2 μC charge = $F_2 + F_3 = 110.6$ N (toward left).

15.11 The force exerted on the charge at the origin by the charge on the x axis is in the negative x direction (repulsive). Its magnitude is:

$$F_2 = (8.99 \times 10^9\ \text{Nm}^2/\text{C}^2)\ \frac{(5.00 \times 10^{-9}\ \text{C})(6.00 \times 10^{-9}\ \text{C})}{(0.300\ \text{m})^2} = 3.00 \times 10^{-6}\ \text{N}.$$

The force exerted on the charge at the origin by the charge on the y axis is in the negative y direction (attractive), with magnitude:

$$F_3 = (8.99 \times 10^9\ \text{Nm}^2/\text{C}^2)\ \frac{(3.00 \times 10^{-9}\ \text{C})(5.00 \times 10^{-9}\ \text{C})}{(0.100\ \text{m})^2} = 1.35 \times 10^{-5}\ \text{N}.$$

The resultant is found from the Pythagorean theorem, as:

$$F = \sqrt{(F_2)^2 + (F_3)^2} = 1.38 \times 10^{-5}\ \text{N}.$$

The angle θ is: $\tan\theta = \dfrac{F_3}{F_2} = 4.5$, or $\theta = 77.5°$.

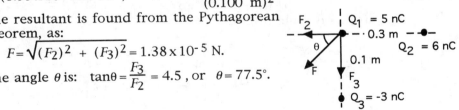

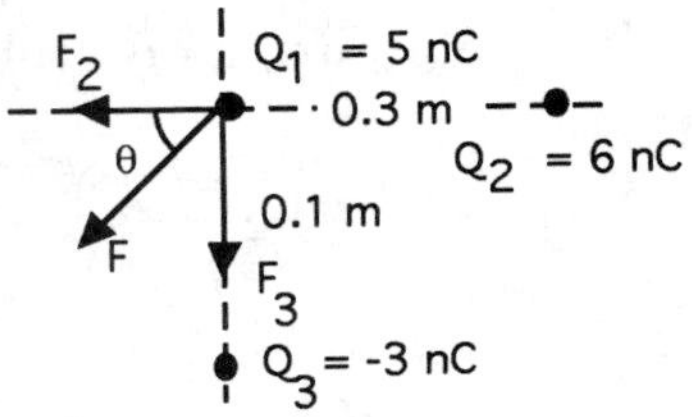

15.12 The force F_1 exerted on the 6.00×10^{-9} C charge by the 2.00×10^{-9} C is repulsive and in the direction indicated in the sketch. Its magnitude is

$$F_1 = (8.99 \times 10^9\ \text{Nm}^2/\text{C}^2)\ \frac{(2.00 \times 10^{-9}\ \text{C})(6.00 \times 10^{-9}\ \text{C})}{2(0.500\ \text{m})^2} = 2.16 \times 10^{-7}\ \text{N}.$$

The force F_2 on the 6.00×10^{-9} C charge by the 3.00×10^{-9} C is repulsive and in the direction shown. The magnitude is

$$F_2 = (8.99 \times 10^9\ \text{Nm}^2/\text{C}^2)\ \frac{(3.00 \times 10^{-9}\ \text{C})(6.00 \times 10^{-9}\ \text{C})}{2(0.500\ \text{m})^2} = 3.24 \times 10^{-7}\ \text{N}.$$

Now, resolve the forces into their x and y components as:

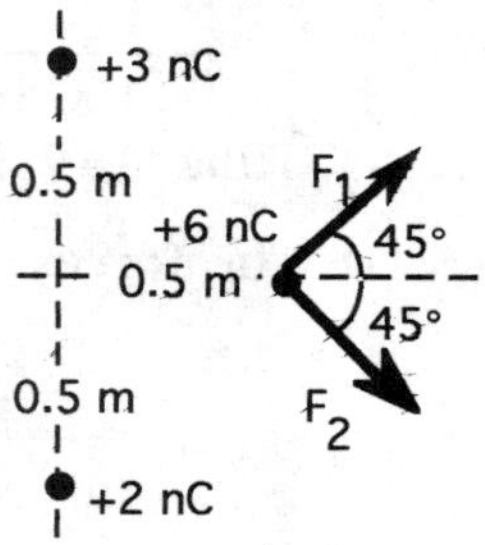

Force	x-component	y-component
F_1	$+1.53 \times 10^{-7}$ N	$+1.53 \times 10^{-7}$ N
F_2	$+2.29 \times 10^{-7}$ N	-2.29×10^{-7} N
F_R	3.82×10^{-7} N	-7.61×10^{-8} N

$F_R = \sqrt{(F_{Rx})^2 + (F_{Ry})^2} = 3.90 \times 10^{-7}$ N, and

$\tan\theta = \dfrac{F_{Ry}}{F_{Rx}} = 0.199$, or $\theta = 11.3\,°$

15.13 The required position is indicated in the sketch. We find

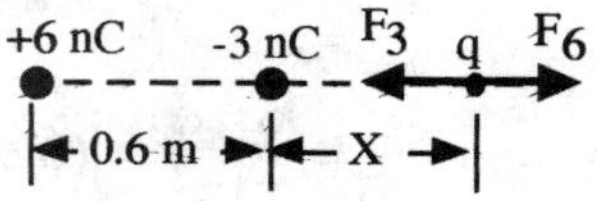

$$\frac{k(6.00 \times 10^{-9}\ \text{C})q}{(x + .600\ \text{m})^2} = \frac{k(3.00 \times 10^{-9}\ \text{C})q}{(x)^2},$$

which gives:

$2x^2 = (x + .600\ \text{m})^2$, or $\quad x\sqrt{2} = x + 0.600$ m.

We must choose the signs as shown in order to have $x > 0$ so that the forces on the charge q will be in opposite directions. We solve for x, obtaining:

$x = 1.45$ m (beyond the -3.00×10^{-9} C charge).

15.14 If the net force is zero, $F_1 = F_2$. (See the sketch.) We see that:

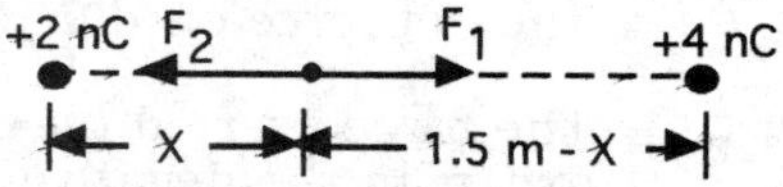

$$\frac{k(2.00 \times 10^{-9}\ \text{C})q}{x^2} = \frac{k(4.00 \times 10^{-9}\ \text{C})q}{(1.50\ \text{m} - x)^2}$$

which reduces to: $(1.50\ \text{m} - x)^2 = 2.00x^2$

Now take square root of both sides of the equation to yield

$(1.50\ \text{m} - x) = \sqrt{2.00}\,x$. Note that the square root of 2.00 can be either plus or minus. We select, the plus sign so that the position of equilibrium will be between the two charges. We find, $\quad x = 0.621$ m.

15.15 $E = \dfrac{kq}{r^2} = \dfrac{(8.99 \times 10^9\ \text{Nm}^2/\text{C}^2)(1.60 \times 10^{-19}\ \text{C})}{(0.510 \times 10^{-10}\ \text{m})^2} = 5.53 \times 10^{11}$ N/C (directed outward, away from proton)

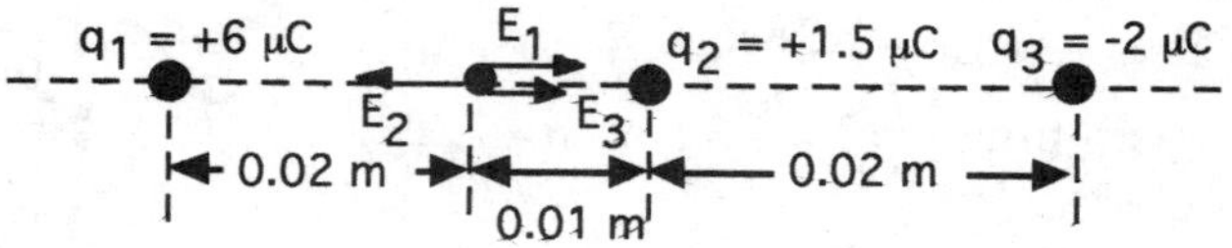

15.16

(a) (See the above sketch) $\quad E = E_1 - E_2 + E_3$, or

$$E = (8.99 \times 10^9\ \text{N m}^2/\text{C}^2)\left(\frac{6.00 \times 10^{-6}\ \text{C}}{(2.00 \times 10^{-2}\ \text{m})^2} - \frac{1.50 \times 10^{-6}\ \text{C}}{(1.00 \times 10^{-2}\ \text{m})^2} + \frac{2.00 \times 10^{-6}\ \text{C}}{(3.00 \times 10^{-2}\ \text{m})^2}\right)$$

Giving: $\quad E = 2.0 \times 10^7$ N/C (directed toward the right).

(b) $F = |q|E = (2.0 \times 10^{-6}\ \text{N})(2.0 \times 10^7\ \text{N/C}) = 40$ N (toward the left).

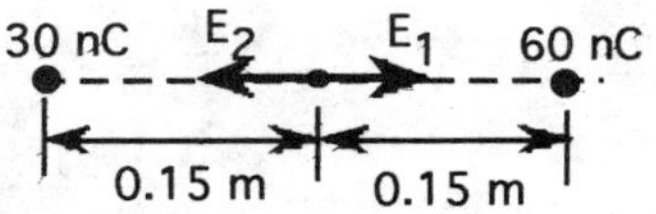

15.17 (a) E_1 = field due to 30.0×10^{-9} C charge.

$$E_1 = \frac{kq}{r^2}$$

$$= \frac{(8.99 \times 10^9 \text{ Nm}^2\text{ C}^2)(30.0 \times 10^{-9} \text{ C})}{(0.150 \text{ m})^2}$$

$$= 1.20 \times 10^4 \text{ N/C}.$$

E_2 (the field due to the 60.0×10^{-9} C charge is: $E_2 = 2.40 \times 10^4$ N/C . The directions of E_1 and E_2 are shown in the sketch. The resultant electric field is: $E_2 - E_1 = 1.20 \times 10^4$ N/C (directed toward the 30.0×10^{-9} C charge).

(b) If $q_2 = -60.0 \times 10^{-9}$ C, then E_2 is of the same magnitude, but opposite in direction. Thus, the net electric field is $E_2 + E_1 = 3.60 \times 10^4$ N/C (toward the -60.0×10^{-9} C charge).

15.18 (a) The magnitude of the force on the electron is:

$F = qE = (1.60 \times 10^{-19})(300 \text{ N/C}) = 4.80 \times 10^{-17}$ N.

Hence, from Newton's second law, the acceleration is:

$$a = \frac{F}{m} = \frac{4.80 \times 10^{-17} \text{ N}}{9.11 \times 10^{-31} \text{ kg}} = 5.27 \times 10^{13} \text{ m/s}^2.$$

(b) We use: $v = v_0 + at = 0 + (5.27 \times 10^{13} \text{ m/s}^2)(10^{-8} \text{ s}) = 5.27 \times 10^5$ m/s.

15.19 If there is zero tension in the string, $qE = mg$.
Thus, $(3.00 \times 10^{-6} \text{ C})E = 0.490$ N, and $E = 1.63 \times 10^5$ N/C.

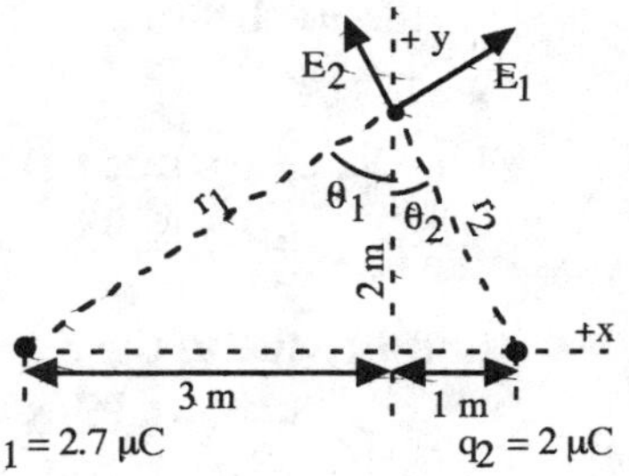

15.20 From the sketch: $\theta_1 = \tan^{-1}\left(\frac{3.0 \text{ m}}{2.0 \text{ m}}\right) =$ 56.31°,

$\theta_2 = \tan^{-1}\left(\frac{1.0 \text{ m}}{2.0 \text{ m}}\right) = 26.57°$,

$r_1^2 = (3.0 \text{ m})^2 + (2.0 \text{ m})^2 = 13 \text{ m}^2$,

$r_2^2 = 5.0 \text{ m}^2$.

Now compute the field due to each charge:

$$E_1 = (8.99 \times 10^9 \text{ N m}^2/\text{C}^2) \left(\frac{2.7 \times 10^{-6} \text{ C}}{(13 \text{ m})^2}\right.$$

or $E_1 = 1867$ N/C,

and $E_2 = (8.99 \times 10^9 \text{ N m}^2/\text{C}^2) \left(\frac{2.0 \times 10^{-6} \text{ C}}{(5 \text{ m})^2}\right) = 3596$ N/C

$E_x = E_1\sin\theta_1 - E_2\sin\theta_2 = -55.0$ N/C, and $E_y = E_1\cos\theta_1 - E_2\cos\theta_2 = 4252$ N/C.

Thus, $E = \sqrt{(E_x)^2 + (E_y)^2} = 4.3 \times 10^3$ N/C, at

$$\theta = \tan^{-1}\left(\frac{E_y}{E_x}\right) = 91° \text{ CCW from the } +x \text{ axis.}$$

15.21 The force on the proton is:

$F = qE = (1.60 \times 10^{-19} \text{ C})(640 \text{ N/C}) = 1.02 \times 10^{-16}$ N

(a) The acceleration is found from Newton's second law:

$$a = \frac{F}{m} = \frac{1.02 \times 10^{-16}\ \text{N}}{1.67 \times 10^{-27}\ \text{kg}} = 6.11 \times 10^{10}\ \text{m/s}^2.$$

(b) $t = \frac{v}{a} = \frac{1.20 \times 10^{6}\ \text{m/s}}{6.11 \times 10^{10}\ \text{m/s}^2} = 1.96 \times 10^{-5}\ \text{s} = 19.6\ \mu\text{s}.$

(c) $s = \frac{v^2}{2a} = \frac{(1.20 \times 10^{6}\ \text{m/s})^2}{2(6.11 \times 10^{10}\ \text{m/s}^2)} = 11.8\ \text{m}.$

(d) $KE = \frac{1}{2} m v^2 = \frac{1}{2}(1.67 \times 10^{-27}\ \text{s})(1.20 \times 10^{6}\ \text{m/s})^2 = 1.20 \times 10^{-15}\ \text{J}.$

15.22 The required electric field must be directed opposite to the motion.

We know: Work done = ΔKE, so $-Fs = -\frac{1}{2} m v_0^2$ (since $v_f = 0$).

With $F = eE$, this becomes: $eEs = \frac{1}{2} m v_0^2$, or $E = \frac{m v_0^2}{2es} = \frac{KE_0}{es}$. Thus,

$E = \frac{3.25 \times 10^{-15}\ \text{J}}{(1.60 \times 10^{-19}\ \text{J})(1.25\ \text{m})} = 1.63 \times 10^{4}$ N/C directed opposite to the motion.

15.23 The length of the diagonal can be shown, from the Pythagorean theorem, to be 0.63 m. Also, the angle ϕ (see figure) is found from the tangent function to be 18.4°

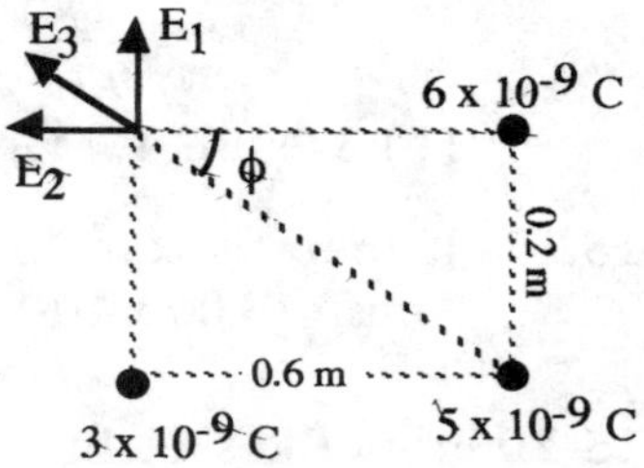

The field, E_1, due to the 3.00×10^{-9} C charge is (direction shown on sketch).

$E = (8.99 \times 10^{9}\ \text{N m}^2/\text{C}^2)\left(\frac{3 \times 10^{-9}\ \text{C}}{(0.200\ \ \text{m})^2}\right)$

= 674 N/C

Likewise, E_2, due to the 6.00×10^{-9} C charge is:

$$E_2 = \frac{kq}{r^2} = \frac{(8.99 \times 10^{9}\ \text{Nm}^2/\text{C}^2)(6.00 \times 10^{-9}\ \text{C})}{(0.600\ \text{m})^2} = 150\ \text{N/C},$$

and E_3, due to the 5×10^{-9} C charge is:

$$E_3 = \frac{kq}{r^2} = \frac{(8.99 \times 10^{9}\ \text{Nm}^2/\text{C}^2)(5.00 \times 10^{-9}\ \text{C})}{(0.630\ \text{m})^2} = 113.2\ \text{N/C}.$$

Now, resolve the fields into their x and y components as

Field	x-comp	y-comp
E_1	0	674 N/C
E_2	-150 N/C	0
E_3	-106 N/C	35.7 N/C
E_R	-256 N/C	710 N/C

$E_R = \sqrt{(E_{Rx})^2 + (E_{Ry})^2} = 756$ N/C, and

$\theta = \tan^{-1}\left(\frac{E_{Ry}}{E_{Rx}}\right) = 70.1$ ° (CW from - x axis).

15.24 Students should recognize that $E_{net} = 0$ at the center from the symmetry of the arrangement. If not; $E_1 = E_2 = E_3$, where E_1 is the field due to the - 5.0 μC charge in the upper right quadrant, E_2 is the field due to the - 5.0 μC in the upper left quadrant, and E_3 is the field due to the - 5.0 μC charge directly below the point.

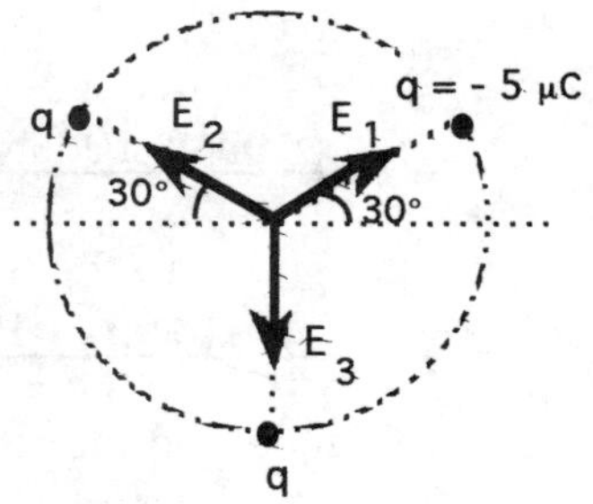

$E_x = E_{1x} - E_{2x} = E_1\cos 30° - E_2\cos 30° = 0$

and

$E_y = E_{1y} + E_{2y} - E_{3y} = 2E_1\sin 30° - E_3 = E_1 - E_3 = 0$. Thus, $E = 0$.

15.25 (a) The initial speed of these electrons is:

$$v_0 = \sqrt{\frac{2\ KE}{m}} = \sqrt{\frac{2(1.60 \times 10^{-17}\ \text{J})}{9.11 \times 10^{-31}\ \text{kg}}} = 5.93 \times 10^6 \text{ m/s}$$

The acceleration needed to stop these electrons in a distance of 10.0 cm is:

$$a = \frac{v_f^2 - v_0^2}{2s} = \frac{0 - (5.93 \times 10^6 \text{ m/s})^2}{2(0.100 \text{ m})} = -1.76 \times 10^{14} \text{ m/s}^2$$

Hence, the field needed is:

$$E = \frac{F}{q} = \frac{ma}{-e} = \frac{(9.11 \times 10^{-31}\text{ kg})(-1.76 \times 10^{14}\text{ m/s}^2)}{(-1.60 \times 10^{-19}\text{ C})} = 1000 \text{ N/C}$$

(b) Using $v = v_0 + at$: $t = \dfrac{v - v_0}{a} = \dfrac{0 - 5.93 \times 10^6 \text{ m/s}}{-1.76 \times 10^{14} \text{ m/s}^2} = 3.37 \times 10^{-8} \text{ s}$

(c) Turn around and start to accelerate at $a = 1.76 \times 10^{14}$ m/s² in the direction opposite that of the electric field.

15.26 The field, E_1, due to the 8×10^{-9} C charge is:

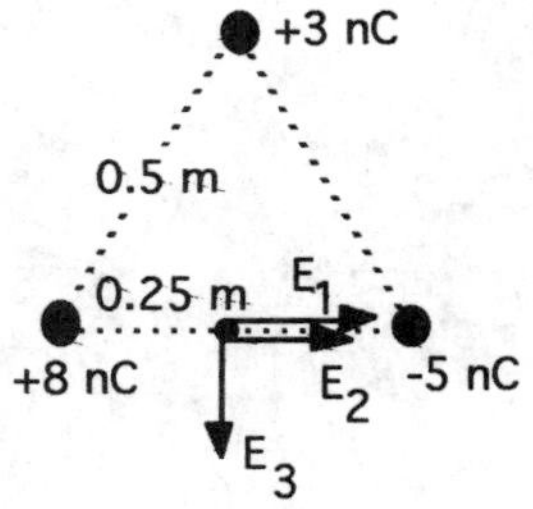

$$E_1 = \frac{kq}{r^2} = \frac{(8.99 \times 10^9 \text{ Nm}^2/\text{C}^2)(8.00 \times 10^{-9}\text{ C})}{(0.250 \text{ m})^2}$$

= 1151 N/C (direction shown on sketch).

Likewise, E_2, due to the -5.00×10^{-9} C charge is:

$$E_2 = \frac{kq}{r^2} = \frac{(8.99 \times 10^9 \text{ Nm}^2/\text{C}^2)(5.00 \times 10^{-9}\text{ C})}{(0.250 \text{ m})^2}$$

= 719 N/C,

and E_3, due to the 3.00×10^{-9} C charge is:

$$E_3 = \frac{kq}{r^2} = \frac{(8.99 \times 10^9 \text{ Nm}^2/\text{C}^2)(3.00 \times 10^{-9}\text{ C})}{(0.500 \text{ m})^2 - (0.250 \text{ m})^2} = 144 \text{ N/C},$$

$E_{Rx} = \Sigma E_x = E_1 + E_2 = 1870$ N/C and $E_{Ry} = \Sigma E_y = -E_3 = -144$ N/C

$E_R = \sqrt{(E_{Rx})^2 + (E_{Ry})^2} = 1875$ N/C, and $\theta = \tan^{-1}\dfrac{E_{Ry}}{E_{Rx}} = -4.4°$ (below x axis)

15.27 The point is designated in the sketch.
The electric field, E_1, due to the -2.5×10^{-6} C charge is:

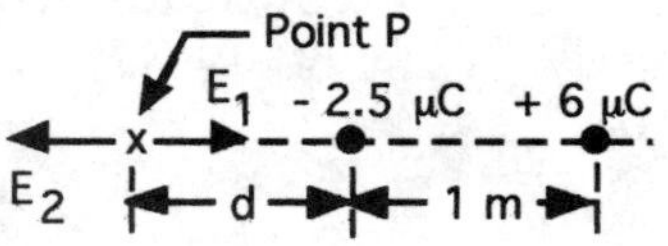

$$E_1 = \frac{kq}{r^2} = \frac{(8.99 \times 10^9 \text{ Nm}^2/\text{C}^2)(2.5 \times 10^{-6} \text{ C})}{d^2}$$

and E_2 due to the 6 x 10^{-6} C charge is:

$$E_2 = \frac{kq}{r^2} = \frac{(8.99 \times 10^9 \text{ Nm}^2/\text{C}^2)(6 \times 10^{-6} \text{ C})}{(d + 1 \text{ m})^2}$$ Since we wish these fields to cancel, equate the magnitudes of E_1 and E_2 to obtain:

$(d + 1 \text{ m})^2 = 2.4d^2$, or $d + 1 \text{ m} = \pm 1.55d$, which yields $d = 1.82$ m or $d = -0.392$ m. The negative value for d is unsatisfactory because that locates a point between the charges where both fields are in the same direction. Thus, $d = 1.82$ m to the left of the -2.5 x 10^{-6} C charge.

15.28 (a) The magnitude of q_2 is three times the magnitude of q_1 because 3 times as many lines emerge from q_2 as enter q_1. ($|q_2| = 3|q_1|$)

(b) $q_2 > 0$ because lines emerge from it, and $q_1 < 0$ because lines terminate on it.

15.29 Note in the sketches at the right that electric field lines originate on positive charges and terminate on negative charges. The density of lines is twice as great for the -2q charge in (b) as they are for the 1q charge in (a).

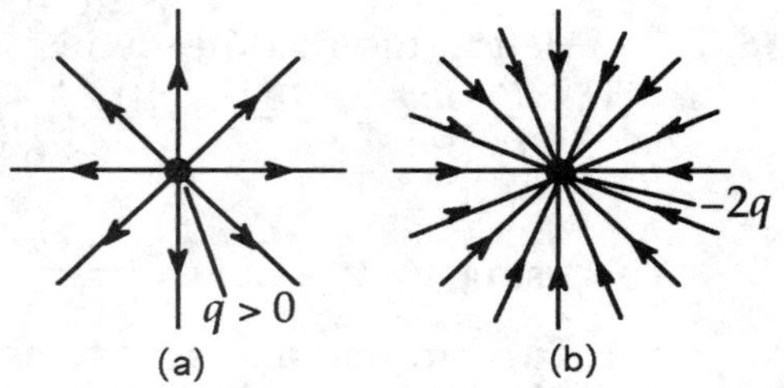

15.30 Rough sketches for these charge configurations are shown below.

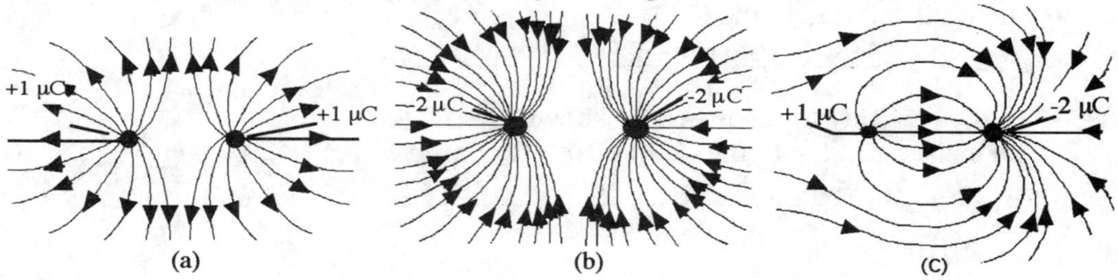

15.31 (a) The sketch for (a) is shown at the right. Note that approximately four times as many lines leave q_1 as emerge from q_2.

(b) The field pattern looks the same here as that shown for (a) if the arrowheads are reversed on the field lines.

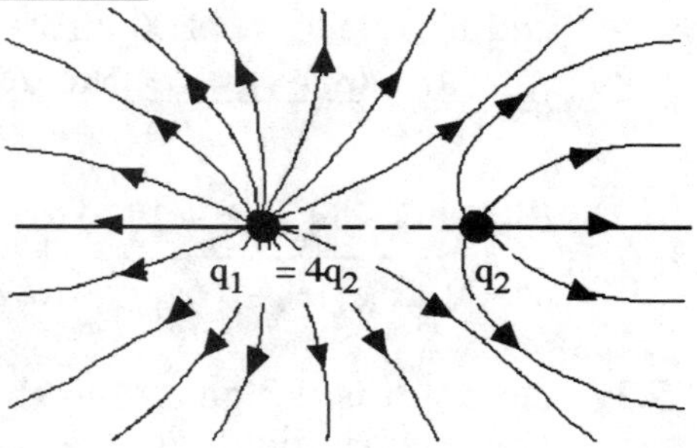

15.32 (a) In the sketch for (a) below, note that there are no lines inside the sphere. On the outside of the sphere, the field lines are uniformly spaced and radially outward.

(b) In the sketch for (b) below, not that the lines are perpendicular to the surface and symmetrical about the symmetry axes of the cube. The field is zero inside the cube.

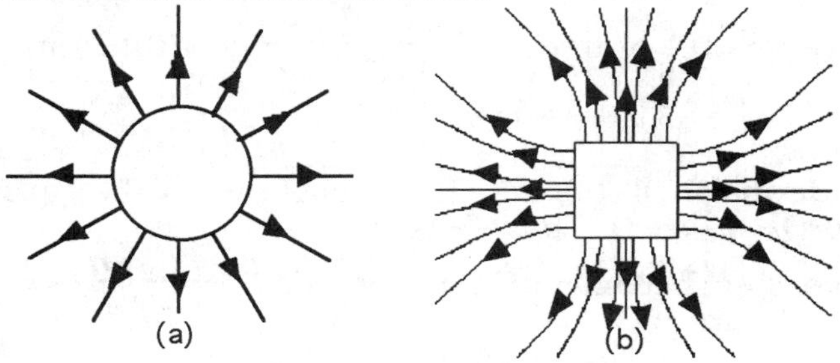

15.33 (a) Zero net charge on inside and outside surface of the sphere.

(b) The positive charge lowered into the sphere attracts -5 μC of negative charge to the inside surface of the sphere, and +5 μC is left behind on the outside surface of the sphere.

(c) The negative charge on the inside surface of the sphere neutralizes the positive charge lowered inside the sphere. However, +5 μC is left on the outside surface of the sphere.

(d) When the object is removed from the sphere, the +5 μC remains on the outside of the sphere.

15.34 (a) The dome is a closed conducting surface. Therefore, the electric field is zero inside.

(b) $E = \frac{kq}{R^2} = \frac{(8.99 \times 10^9 \text{ Nm}^2/\text{C}^2)(2.0 \times 10^{-4} \text{ C})}{(1.0 \text{ m})^2} = 1.8 \times 10^6 \text{ N/C}$

(c) $E = \frac{kq}{r^2} = \frac{(8.99 \times 10^9 \text{ Nm}^2/\text{C}^2)(2.0 \times 10^{-4} \text{ C})}{(4.0 \text{ m})^2} = 1.1 \times 10^5 \text{ N/C}$

15.35 The field is strongest just outside the surface of a sphere. Thus,

$$E_{max} = \frac{kq_{max}}{R^2}, \text{ and } q_{max} = \frac{E_{max}R^2}{k} = \frac{3.0 \times 10^6 \text{ N/C}(2.0 \text{ m})^2}{8.99 \times 10^9 \text{ Nm}^2/\text{C}^2} = 1.3 \times 10^{-3} \text{ C}.$$

15.36 (a) $a = \frac{F}{m} = \frac{qE}{m} = \frac{(1.60 \times 10^{-19} \text{ C})(3.0 \times 10^6 \text{ N/C})}{9.11 \times 10^{-31} \text{ kg}} = 5.3 \times 10^{17} \text{ m/s}^2.$

(b) Anticipating that this distance is very small, we assume the field is uniform over this short distance:

work done = $\Delta KE = KE_f - KE_i = KE_f - 0$, so $Fs = mv^2/2$, and

$$s = \frac{mv^2}{2qE} = \frac{(9.11 \times 10^{-31} \text{ kg})(3.0 \times 10^7)^2}{2(1.60 \times 10^{-19} \text{ C})(3.0 \times 10^6 \text{ N/C})} = 8.5 \times 10^{-4} \text{ m} = 0.85 \text{ mm}.$$

15.37 (a) $F = qE = (1.60 \times 10^{-19} \text{ C})(3.0 \times 10^4 \text{ N/C}) = 4.8 \times 10^{-15} \text{ N}$

(b) $a = \frac{F}{m} = \frac{4.8 \times 10^{-15} \text{ N}}{1.67 \times 10^{-27} \text{ kg}} = 2.9 \times 10^{12} \text{ m/s}^2$

15.38 (a) $\Phi = EA\cos\theta = EA = (6.2 \times 10^5 \text{ N/C})(3.2 \text{ m}^2)(1) = 2.0 \times 10^6 \text{ N m}^2/\text{C}$

(b) $\Phi = EA\cos\theta = EA\cos 90° = 0$

15.39 $E = \frac{\Phi}{A} = \frac{5.2 \times 10^5 \text{ N m}^2/\text{C}}{\pi(0.20 \text{ m})^2} = 4.1 \times 10^6 \text{ N/C}$

15.40 $\Phi = EA = (8.99 \times 10^9 \text{ N m}^2/\text{C}^2)\left(\frac{5.00 \times 10^{-6} \text{ C}}{(0.120 \text{ m})^2}\right) 4\pi(0.120 \text{ m})^2$
$= 5.65 \times 10^5 \text{ N m}^2/\text{C}$

15.41 (a) Outside the shell, the net charge enclosed in the gaussian surface is zero, $Q = q - q = 0$. Thus, $E = 0$.

(b) $\Sigma EA\cos\theta = \frac{Q}{\varepsilon_0}$ becomes $E(4\pi r^2) = \frac{q}{\varepsilon_0}$ or $E = \frac{1}{4\pi\varepsilon_0}\frac{q}{r^2} = k\frac{q}{r^2}$

15.42 Construct a gaussian surface just barely inside the surface of the conductor, where $E = 0$. Since $E = 0$ inside, Gauss' law says $\frac{Q}{\varepsilon_0} = 0$ inside. Thus, any excess charge the conductor possesses must be outside our gaussian surface, i.e., on the surface of the conductor.

15.43 E inside the conductor = 0, and $\cos\theta = \cos 90° = 0$ on the cylindrical surface. Thus, the only flux through the gaussian surface is on the outside end cap and Gauss' law reduces to:

$\Sigma EA\cos\theta = EA_{\text{outsidecap}} = \frac{Q}{\varepsilon_0}$ which becomes $EA = \frac{\sigma A}{\varepsilon_0}$ or $E = \frac{\sigma}{\varepsilon_0}$

15.44 We use a gaussian surface in the shape of a cylinder with A as the area of each end cap. $\cos\theta = \cos 90° = 0$ on the cylindrical surface. $E = 0$ inside the conductor, so Φ through the end cap inside the conductor is zero. For the endcap outside the conductor, $\Sigma EA\cos\theta = EA$ and $\frac{Q}{\varepsilon_0} = \frac{\sigma A}{\varepsilon_0}$

Thus, $E = \frac{\sigma}{\varepsilon_0}$.

15.45 The field, E_1, due to the 4.0×10^{-9} C charge is in the $-x$ direction and has the value: $E_1 = \frac{kq}{r^2} = \frac{(8.99 \times 10^9 \text{ Nm}^2/\text{C}^2)(4.0 \times 10^{-9} \text{ C})}{(2.5 \text{ m})^2} = 5.75 \text{ N/C}$.

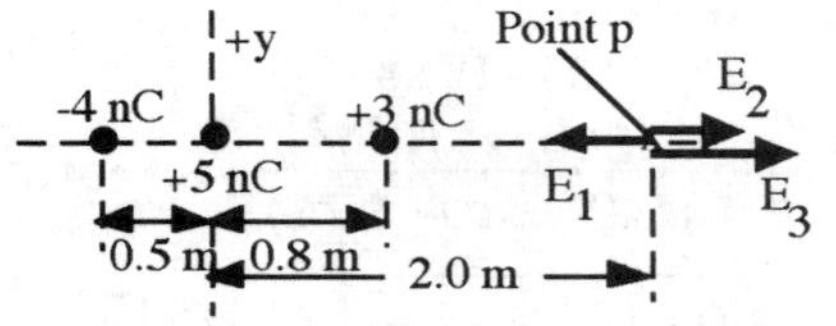

(a)

Likewise, E_2, due to the 5.0×10^{-9} C charge is in the $+x$ direction and has the value:

$E_2 = \frac{(8.99 \times 10^9 \text{ Nm}^2/\text{C}^2)(5.0 \times 10^{-9} \text{ C})}{(2.0 \text{ m})^2}$

giving $E_2 = 11.2\,\text{N/C}$.

E_3, due to the 3.0×10^{-9} C charge is also in the $+x$ direction and has a magnitude of:

$$E_3 = \frac{(8.99 \times 10^9\ \text{Nm}^2/\text{C}^2)(3.0 \times 10^{-9}\ \text{C})}{(1.2\ \text{m})^2} = 18.7\,\text{N/C}.$$

$E_R = -E_1 + E_2 + E_3 = 24\,\text{N/C}$ in $+x$ direction.

15.46 In order to have the net force on q_3 be zero, the forces due to the other two charges must be in opposite directions and of the same magnitude. Careful consideration shows these two condition can only be met at a point between the two charges. Thus, we have:

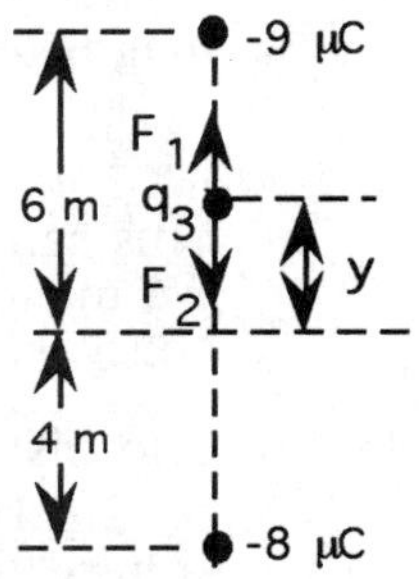

$$\frac{k(9.0\ \mu\text{c})q_3}{(6.0 - y)^2} = \frac{k(8.0\ \mu\text{c})q_3}{(4.0 + y)^2}.$$ This reduces to:

$9(4+y)^2 = 8(6-y)^2$. Solving this equation and choosing the solution related to a position between the first two charges gives: $y = +0.85\,\text{m}$.

15.47 From the free body diagram shown,

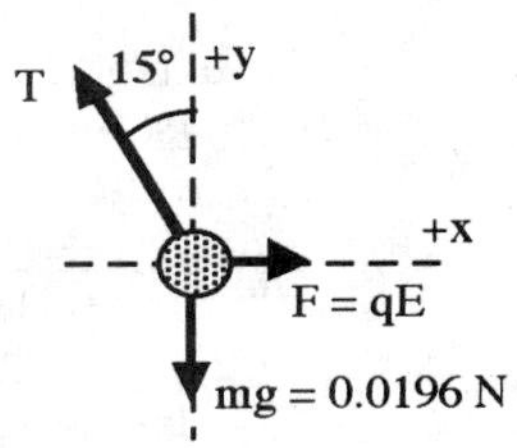

$\Sigma F_y = 0$ becomes $T\cos 15° = mg = 1.96 \times 10^{-2}$ N, or

$T = 2.03 \times 10^{-2}$ N.

From $\Sigma F_x = 0$, we have: $qE = T\sin 15°$, or

$$q = \frac{T\sin 15°}{\text{E}} = \frac{(2.03 \times 10^{-2}\ \text{N})\sin\ 15°}{10^3\ \text{N/C}}$$

$q = 5.25 \times 10^{-6}\,\text{C} = 5.25\,\mu\text{C}$

15.48 (a) The y components of E_1 and E_2 are equal in magnitude, but oppositely directed and therefore cancel.

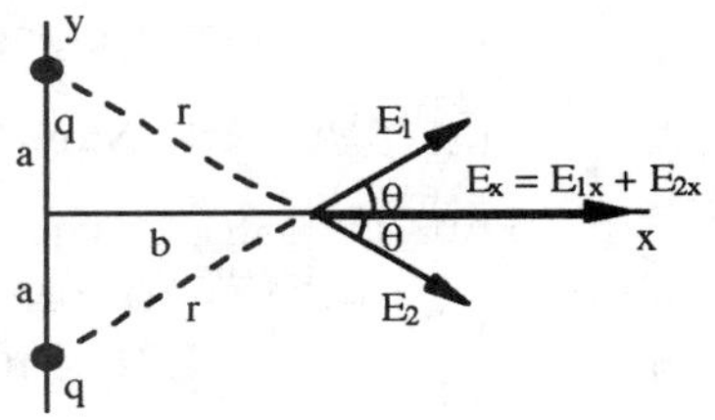

$$E_{x2} = E_{x1} = \frac{kq}{r^2}\cos\theta \quad \text{where } r = \sqrt{a^2 + b^2}$$

The resultant field is therefore:

$$E_x = E_{x1} + E_{x2} = 2\frac{kq}{r^2}\cos\theta$$

Since $\cos\theta = \dfrac{b}{r}$, we obtain

$$E_{x2} = 2\frac{kq}{r^2}\frac{b}{r} = \frac{k(2q)b}{r^3} = \frac{k(2q)b}{[a^2 + b^2]^{3/2}}$$

(b) Consider the ring of charge to consist of a large (essentially infinite) number of pairs of charges, each pair having total charge Δq, positioned across the ring as shown. All components perpendicular to the x-axis cancel. The contribution to the total field from each pair of charges is (see part (a) above):

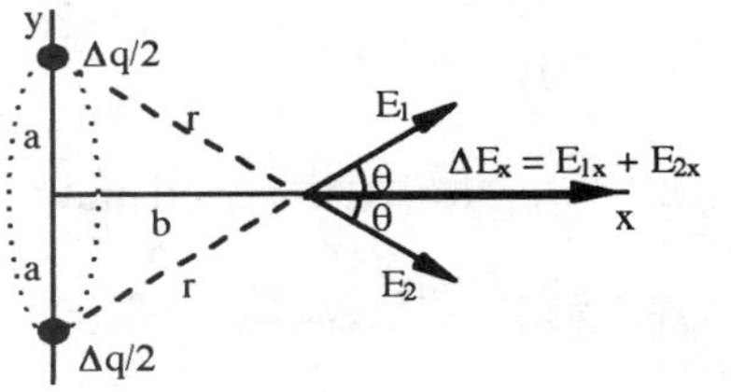

$$\Delta E_x = \frac{k(\Delta q)b}{[a^2 + b^2]^{3/2}}$$

The total field due to the entire ring is therefore:

$$E_x = \Sigma \Delta E_x = \Sigma \frac{k(\Delta q)\,b}{[a^2 + b^2]^{3/2}} = \frac{kb}{[a^2 + b^2]^{3/2}}\Sigma(\Delta q) = \frac{kQb}{[a^2 + b^2]^{3/2}}$$

15.49 The fields must be in opposite directions to cancel. Therefore, the point must be between the two charges. We equate the magnitudes of the fields as:

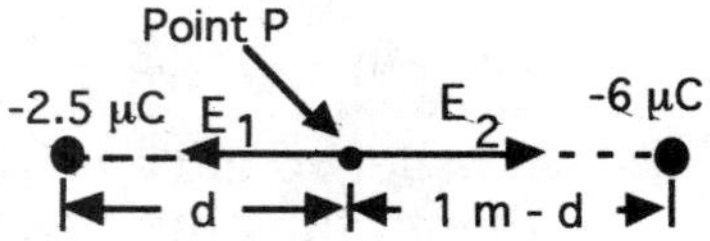

$$\frac{k(2.50 \times 10^{-6}\ C)}{d^2} = \frac{k(6.00 \times 10^{-6}\ C)}{(1.0m - d)^2}.$$

This can be reduced to: $1.00\ m - d = \pm 1.55d$.

We must choose the + sign to make d > 0 so the point is between the two charges. Thus, $d = 0.392$ m.

15.50 The distance between the two charges at equilibrium is: $r = 2(0.100\ m)\sin 10° = 3.47 \times 10^{-2}$ m. Now consider the forces on the sphere with charge $+q$ [see sketch (a)], and use $\Sigma F_y = 0$ to obtain:

$$T\cos 10° = mg, \text{ or} \qquad T = \frac{mg}{\cos 10°}. \qquad (1)$$

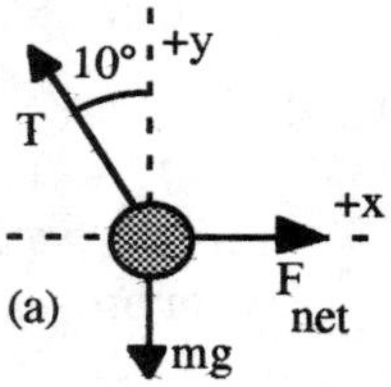

Now use $\Sigma F_x = 0$: $\quad F_{net} = T\sin 10°. \qquad (2)$

F_{net} is the net electrical force on the charged sphere. Eliminate T from (2) by use of (1).

$$F_{net} = \frac{mg\sin 10°}{\cos 10°} = mg\tan 10°, \text{ or}$$

$$F_{net} = (2.00 \times 10^{-3}\ kg)(9.80\ m/s^2)\tan 10° = 3.46 \times 10^{-3}\ N.$$

F_{net} is the resultant of two forces, F_1 and F_2 [see sketch (b)]. F_1 is the attractive force on $+q$ exerted by $-q$, and F_2 is the force exerted on $+q$ by the external electric field. $F_{net} = F_2 - F_1$ or, $F_2 = F_{net} + F_1$, and

$$F_1 = (8.99 \times 10^9\ Nm^2/C^2)\frac{(5.00 \times 10^{-8}\ C)(5.00 \times 10^{-8}\ C)}{(3.47 \times 10^{-2}\ m)^2} = 1.86 \times 10^{-2}\ N.$$

Thus, $F_2 = F_{net} + F_1$ yields:

$$F_2 = 3.46 \times 10^{-3}\ N + 1.86 \times 10^{-2}\ N = 2.21 \times 10^{-2}\ N,$$

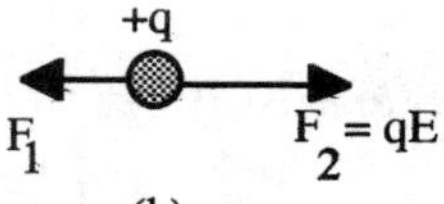

and $E = \dfrac{F_2}{q} = \dfrac{2.21 \times 10^{-2}\ N}{5.0 \times 10^{-8}\ C} = 4.4 \times 10^5\ \dfrac{N}{C}.$

15.51 (a) E = 0

(b) $E = \dfrac{kQ}{r^2} = \dfrac{(8.99 \times 10^9\ Nm^2/C^2)(8.00 \times 10^{-6})}{(0.0300)^2} = 8.00 \times 10^7\ \dfrac{N}{C}.$

(c) E = 0

(d) $E = \dfrac{kQ}{r^2} = \dfrac{(8.99 \times 10^9\ Nm^2/C^2)(4.00 \times 10^{-6})}{(0.0700)^2} = 7.35 \times 10^6\ \dfrac{N}{C}.$

15.52 We find the equal-magnitude charges on both spheres:

$$F = k\frac{q_1 q_1}{r^2} = k\frac{q^2}{r^2}$$

$$q = r\sqrt{\frac{F}{k}} = 1.00\ m\sqrt{\frac{10^4\ N\ C^2}{8.99 \times 10^9\ Nm^2/C^2}} = 1.05 \times 10^{-3}\ C$$

The number of electrons transferred is then

$$(1.05 \times 10^{-3}\ \mathrm{C})\left(\frac{1\ \mathrm{e}}{1.60 \times 10^{-19}\ \mathrm{C}}\right) = 6.59 \times 10^{15}\ \text{electrons}$$

The whole number of electrons on each sphere is

$$(100\ \mathrm{g})\left(\frac{1\ \mathrm{mol}}{107.87\ \mathrm{g}}\right)\left(\frac{6.02 \times 10^{23}\ \text{atoms}}{1\ \mathrm{mol}}\right)\left(\frac{47\ \mathrm{e}}{\text{atom}}\right) = 2.62 \times 10^{25}\ \mathrm{e}$$

The fraction transferred is then

$$\left(\frac{6.59 \times 10^{15}}{2.62 \times 10^{25}}\right) = 2.51 \times 10^{-10} = 2.51 \text{ charges in every 10 billion}$$

15.53 The required electric field will be in the direction of motion.

Work done = ΔK

so, $-Fd = -\frac{1}{2} m v_0^2$ (since ther final velocity = 0)

which becomes $eEd = K$ and $E = \frac{K}{ed}$

15.54 $F_{compression} = \frac{kq_1q_2}{r^2}$

$$= \left(8.99 \times 10^9\ \frac{\mathrm{Nm}^2}{\mathrm{C}^2}\right)\frac{(1.60 \times 10^{-19}\ \mathrm{C})^2}{(2.17 \times 10^{-6}\ \mathrm{m})^2} = 4.89 \times 10^{-17}\ \mathrm{N}$$

This force causes the molecule to compress by a distance of $0.01(2.17 \times 10^{-6}\ \mathrm{m}) = 2.17 \times 10^{-8}$ m. Thus, the effective force constant is: $k = \frac{F}{x} = \frac{4.89 \times 10^{-17}\ \mathrm{N}}{2.17 \times 10^{-8}\ \mathrm{m}} = 2.25 \times 10^{-9}$ N/m.

15.55 (a) First, we determine the proton's downward acceleration using $F = ma = qE$, so that $a = \frac{qE}{m}$ where we have ignored effects due to gravity. Since the motion is that of a projectile, we can use the expression for the range of a projectile,

$R = \frac{v^2_o}{g}\sin(2\theta)$ with g replaced by a to get: $R = \frac{v^2_o}{a}\sin(2\theta)$.

Therefore, $\sin(2\theta) = \frac{Ra}{v^2_o} = \frac{qER}{mv^2_o}$, or

$$\sin(2\theta) = \frac{(1.60 \times 10^{-19}\ \mathrm{C})(720\ \mathrm{N/C})(1.27 \times 10^{-3}\ \mathrm{m})}{(1.67 \times 10^{-27}\ \mathrm{kg})(9550\ \mathrm{m/s})^2} = 0.9606, \text{ so}$$

$2\theta = 73.86°$, or $106.14°$. This yields: $\theta = 36.9°$, or $53.1°$.

(b) Using $R = v_{ox}\, t = v_0 \cos(\theta)\, t$ yields: $t = \frac{R}{v_0 \cos(\theta)}$, so

$$t = \frac{1.27 \times 10^{-3}\ \mathrm{m}}{(9550\ \mathrm{m/s})\cos 36.9°} = 1.66 \times 10^{-7}\ \mathrm{s}, \text{ or}$$

$$t = \frac{1.27 \times 10^{-3}\ \mathrm{m}}{(9550\ \mathrm{m/s})\cos 53.1°} = 2.21 \times 10^{-7}\ \mathrm{s}$$

15.56 (a) The magnitude of the acceleration is given by $|a| = \frac{qE}{m}$ as

$|a| = \frac{(1.60 \times 10^{-19}\ C)(2.5 \times 10^{4}\ N/C)}{9.11 \times 10^{-31}\ kg} = 4.4 \times 10^{15}\ m/s^2$, or calling the direction of initial motion the positive direction, the acceleration is: $a = -4.4 \times 10^{15}\ m/s^2$.

(b) $v = v_o + at$ becomes: $0 = 4.0 \times 10^6\ m/s + (-4.4 \times 10^{15}\ m/s^2)t$, giving $t = 9.1 \times 10^{-10}\ s$.

(c) $x = v_o t + \frac{1}{2}at^2$, becomes:

$$x = \left(4.0 \times 10^6\ \frac{m}{s}\right)(9.1 \times 10^{-10} s) + \frac{1}{2}(-4.4 \times 10^{15}\ \frac{m}{s^2})(9.1 \times 10^{-10} s)^2,$$

or $x = 1.8 \times 10^{-3}$ m.

15.57 (a) The total non-contact force on the cork ball is:

$F = qE + mg = m\left(g + \frac{qE}{m}\right)$, which is constant and directed downward.

Therefore, it behaves like a simple pendulum in the presence of a modified uniform gravitational field with a period given by:

$$T = 2\pi\sqrt{\frac{L}{g + \frac{qE}{m}}} = 2\pi\sqrt{\frac{0.500\ m}{9.80\ m/s^2 + \frac{(2.00 \times 10^{-6}\ C)(10^5\ N/C)}{0.001\ kg}}},$$

or $T = 0.307$ s.

(b) Yes. Without gravity in part a, we get

$$T = 2\pi\sqrt{\frac{L}{\frac{qE}{m}}} = 2\pi\sqrt{\frac{0.500\ m}{\frac{(2.00 \times 10^{-6}\ C)(10^5\ N/C)}{0.001\ kg}}} = 0.314\,s$$ which

is a 2.28% difference.

15.58 The electric field at any point x is:

$E = \frac{kq}{(x - a)^2} - \frac{kq}{(x - (-a))^2} = \frac{kq(4ax)}{(x^2 - a^2)^2}$. When x is much, much greater than a, we find: $E = \frac{(4a)(kq)}{x^3}$.

15.59 Observe that $r_1 = r_2 = \sqrt{y^2 + a^2}$, and

$\cos\theta = \frac{y}{r_1} = \frac{y}{r_2} = \frac{y}{\sqrt{y^2 + a^2}}$.

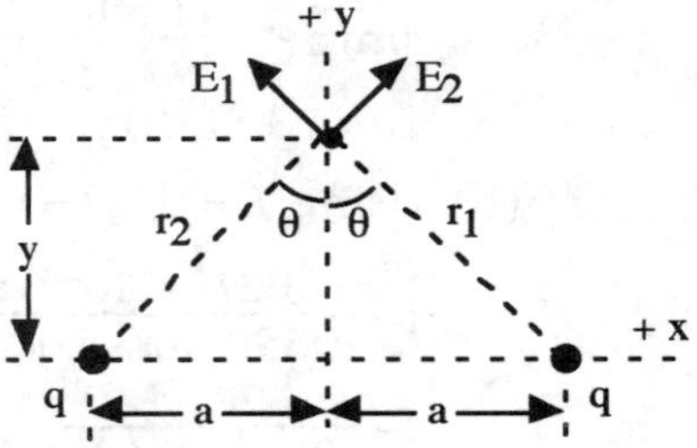

Also, note that $E_1 = E_2 = E = \frac{kq}{r^2}$,

where $r = r_1 = r_2$.

Then:

$E_x = E_{1x} + E_{2x} = 0$, and

$E_y = E_{1y} + E_{2y} = 2E\cos\theta = 2\ \frac{kq}{r^2}\ \frac{y}{r} = \frac{2kqy}{[a^2 + y^2]^{3/2}}$

Thus E is in the positive y direction with magnitude:

$E = E_y = 2kqy(y^2 + a^2)^{-3/2}$.

15.60 (a) Let us sum forces as follows

$$\Sigma F_x = qE_x - T\sin\theta = 0,$$

and $\Sigma F_y = qE_y + T\cos\theta - mg = 0.$

Combining these two equations, we get

$$q = \frac{mg}{(E_x\cot\theta + E_y)} = \frac{(0.001)(9.80)}{(3.00\cot 37^\circ + 5.00) \times 10^5} = 1.09 \times 10^{-8}\,\mathrm{C}$$

(b) Also from the force equations,

$$T = \frac{qE_x}{\sin 37^\circ} = 5.43 \times 10^{-3}\,\mathrm{N}$$

ANSWERS TO CONCEPTUAL QUESTIONS

2. Electrons are more mobile than protons and are more easily freed from atoms than are protons.

4. To avoid making a spark. Rubber-soled shoes acquire a charge by friction with the floor and could discharge with a spark, possibly causing an explosive burning situation, where the burning is enhanced by the oxygen.

6. So the electric field from the test charge does not distort the electric field you are trying to measure by moving the charges that create it.

8. She is not shocked. She becomes part of the dome of the Van de Graaff, and charges flow onto her body. They do not jump to her body via a spark, however, so she is not shocked.

10. An electric field once established by a positive or negative charge extends in all directions from the charge. Thus, it can exist in empty space if that is what surrounds the charge.

12. The magnitude of the electric force is given by $F = qE$ and is the same for both. The proton because of its positive charge will move in the direction of the electric field while the negatively charged electron will move in the opposite direction. Because of its much smaller mass, a given electric field will produce a much greater acceleration of an electron than a proton.

14. The antenna is similar to a lightning rod and can induce a bolt to strike it. A wire from the antenna to the ground provides a pathway for the charges to move away from the house in case a lightning strike does occur.

16. Lightning usually strikes the tallest object in the affected area. If you are under the tree, the charges passing though it and the earth can also cause damage to you.

18. No. Life would be no different if electrons were positively charged and protons were negatively charged. Opposite charges would still attract, and like charges would still repel. The designation of charges as positive and negative is merely a definition.

CHAPTER SIXTEEN SOLUTIONS

Chapter Sixteen Readings

Einstein A., and Infeld, L., "*The Evolution of Physics,*" New York, Simon and Shuster, 1938.

Sperling, D., "The Case for Electric Vehicles," *Scientific American*, v. 275 (Nov. '96) p. 54-9

Standford Jr., A.L, *Foundations of Biophysics*, New York, Academic Press, 1975.

16.1 (a) The force exerted on the proton by the field is:

$F = qE = (1.60 \times 10^{-19}\ C)(200\ N/C) = 3.2 \times 10^{-17}\ N.$

The work done is:

$W = Fs(\cos\theta) = (3.2 \times 10^{-17}\ N)(2.0 \times 10^{-2}\ m)(1) = 6.4 \times 10^{-19}\ J.$

(b) $\Delta PE = -W = -6.4 \times 10^{-19}\ J.$

(c) $\Delta V = \Delta PE/q = (-6.4 \times 10^{-19}\ J.)/(1.60 \times 10^{-19}\ C) = -4.0\ V.$

16.2 (a) We follow the path from (0,0) to (20 cm,0) to (20 cm,50 cm).
ΔPE = - (work done) = -(work from origin to (20 cm,0)) - (work from (20 cm,0) to (20 cm,50 cm)). The last term = 0 because the force is perpendicular to the displacement.

So, $\Delta PE = -(qE_x)(\Delta x) = -(12 \times 10^{-6}\ C)(250\ V/m)(0.20\ m)$

$= -6.0 \times 10^{-4}\ J.$

(b) $\Delta V = \dfrac{\Delta PE}{q} = -\dfrac{6.0 \times 10^{-4}\ J}{12 \times 10^{-6}\ C} = -50\ J/C = -50\ V.$

16.3 $W = q\Delta V = (+e)\Delta V = (1.60 \times 10^{-19}\ C)(90.0 \times 10^{-3}\ J/C) = 1.44 \times 10^{-20}\ J$

16.4 From the definition of potential difference,

$q = \dfrac{\Delta PE}{\Delta V} = \dfrac{1.92 \times 10^{-17}\ J}{60\ V} = 3.2 \times 10^{-19}\ C.$

16.5 $E = \dfrac{\Delta V}{d} = \dfrac{25 \times 10^{3}\ J/C}{1.5 \times 10^{-2}\ m} = 1.7 \times 10^{6}\ N/C$

16.6 Since potential difference is work per unit charge ($\Delta V = \dfrac{W}{q}$), we find:

$W = q\Delta V = (3.6 \times 10^{5}\ C)(12\ V) = 4.3 \times 10^{6}\ J.$

16.7 (a) $E = \dfrac{\Delta V}{d} = \dfrac{600\ V}{5.33 \times 10^{-3}\ m} = 1.13 \times 10^{5}\ V/m$

(b) $F = qE = (1.60 \times 10^{-19}\ C)(1.13 \times 10^{5}\ V/m) = 1.80 \times 10^{-14}\ N$

(c) Work = $Fs = qEs = (1.80 \times 10^{-14}\ N)(5.33 \times 10^{-3}\ m - 2.90 \times 10^{-3}\ m)$, or
Work = $4.38 \times 10^{-17}\ J.$

16.8 $W = \Delta KE = q\Delta V$ gives: $\dfrac{1}{2}mv^2 = e(120\ V) = 1.92 \times 10^{-17}\ J.$

Thus, $v = \sqrt{\dfrac{3.84 \times 10^{-17}\ \text{J}}{\text{m}}}$.

(a) For a proton, this becomes $v = \sqrt{\dfrac{3.84 \times 10^{-17}\ \text{J}}{1.607 \times 10^{-27}\ \text{kg}}} = 1.52 \times 10^5$ m/s.

(b) If an electron: $v = \sqrt{\dfrac{3.84 \times 10^{-17}\ \text{J}}{9.11 \times 10^{-31}\ \text{kg}}} = 6.49 \times 10^6$ m/s.

16.9 Conservation of energy yields $\frac{1}{2}mv^2 = q\Delta V$, or $v = \sqrt{\dfrac{2q\Delta V}{m}}$.

(a) For an electron:

$$v = \sqrt{\frac{2q\Delta V}{m}} = \sqrt{\frac{2(1.60 \times 10^{-19}\ \text{C})(2000\ \text{V})}{9.11 \times 10^{-31}\ \text{kg}}} = 2.65 \times 10^7\ \text{m/s}.$$

(b) For a proton:

$$v = \sqrt{\frac{2q\Delta V}{m}} = \sqrt{\frac{2(1.60 \times 10^{-19}\ \text{C})(2000\ \text{V})}{1.67 \times 10^{-27}\ \text{kg}}} = 6.19 \times 10^5\ \text{m/s}.$$

16.10 Sixty percent of the speed of light (3.00×10^8 m/s) is 1.80×10^8 m/s.

From conservation of energy, we have: $\frac{1}{2}mv^2 = q\Delta V$, or $\Delta V = \dfrac{mv^2}{2q}$.

(a) For an electron:

$$|\Delta V| = \frac{mv^2}{2q} = \frac{(9.11 \times 10^{-31})(1.80 \times 10^8\ \text{m/s})^2}{2(1.60 \times 10^{-19}\ \text{C})} = 9.22 \times 10^4\ \text{V}.$$

(b) For a proton:

$$|\Delta V| = \frac{mv^2}{2q} = \frac{(1.67 \times 10^{-27})(1.80 \times 10^8\ \text{m/s})^2}{2(1.60 \times 10^{-19}\ \text{C})} = 1.69 \times 10^8\ \text{V}.$$

16.11 (a) The potential at 1 cm is:

$$V_1 = k\frac{q}{r} = \frac{(8.99 \times 10^9\ \text{N m}^2/\text{C}^2)(1.60 \times 10^{-19}\ \text{C})}{1.00\ 10^{-2}\ \text{m}} = 1.44 \times 10^{-7}\ \text{V}.$$

(b) The potential at 2 cm is:

$$V_2 = k\frac{q}{r} = \frac{(8.99 \times 10^9\ \text{N m}^2/\text{C}^2)(1.60 \times 10^{-19}\ \text{C})}{2.00 \times 10^{-2}\ \text{m}} = 0.719 \times 10^{-7}\ \text{V}.$$

Thus, the difference in potential between the two points is:

$$\Delta V = V_2 - V_1 = -7.19 \times 10^{-8}\ \text{V}.$$

16.12 The net potential is the algebraic sum of the potentials set up by the individual charges. Thus, $V = k\left(\dfrac{q_1}{r_1} + \dfrac{q_2}{r_2}\right)$. At $y = 0.600$ m, $r_1 = 0.600$ m and $r_2 = 0.300$ m. We have:

$$V = (8.99 \times 10^9\ \text{N m}^2/\text{C}^2)\left(\frac{3.00 \times 10^{-9}\ \text{C}}{0.600\ \text{m}} + \frac{6.00 \times 10^{-9}\ \text{C}}{0.300\ \text{m}}\right) = 230\ \text{V}.$$

16.13 The total electric potential is the scalar sum of the potentials due to the individual charges, $V = \Sigma V_i = \Sigma\dfrac{kq_i}{r_i}$. Thus,

$$V = (8.99 \times 10^9\ \text{N m}^2/\text{C}^2)\left(\frac{8.0 \times 10^{-6}\ \text{C}}{6.0 \times 10^{-2}\ \text{m}} + \frac{4.0 \times 10^{-6}\ \text{C}}{3.0 \times 10^{-2}\ \text{m}} + \frac{2.0 \times 10^{-6}\ \text{C}}{\sqrt{45} \times 10^{-2}\ \text{m}}\right)$$

or $V = 2.7 \times 10^6$ J/C.

16.14 Work done on 8.0 μC charge = $\Delta PE = PE_f - PE_i = 0 - PE_i$. ($PE_f = 0$ because, at the end, the charge is at an infinite distance from all other charges.)
So, $W = -(PE_{\text{due to presence of 2 μC charge}} + PE_{\text{due to presence of 4 μC charge}})$

$$= -\left(\frac{(8.99 \times 10^9 \text{ N m}^2/\text{C}^2)(8.0 \times 10^{-6} \text{ C})(2.0 \times 10^{-6} \text{ C})}{3.0 \times 10^{-2} \text{ m}}\right) - \left(\frac{(8.99 \times 10^9 \text{ N m}^2/\text{C}^2)(8.0 \times 10^{-6} \text{ C})(4.0 \times 10^{-6} \text{ C})}{\sqrt{(0.03 \text{ m})^2 + (0.06 \text{ m})^2}}\right),$$

or $W = -9.1$ J.

16.15 (a) $V = (8.99 \times 10^9 \text{ N m}^2/\text{C}^2)\left(\frac{5.00 \times 10^{-9} \text{ C}}{0.175 \text{ m}} + \frac{-3.00 \times 10^{-9} \text{ C}}{0.175 \text{ m}}\right) = 103$ V.

(b) $PE = k\frac{q_1 q_2}{r_{12}} = \frac{(8.99 \times 10^9 \text{ N m}^2/\text{C}^2)(5.00 \times 10^{-9} \text{ C})(-3.00 \times 10^{-9} \text{ C})}{0.35 \text{ m}}$,
or PE = -3.85×10^{-7} J.
Positive work must be done on them to separate the charges.

16.16 (a) 1 eV = 1.60×10^{-19} J. Thus, this is the kinetic energy of the electron. $KE = \frac{1}{2}mv^2 = \frac{1}{2}(9.11 \times 10^{-31} \text{ kg})v^2 = 1.60 \times 10^{-19}$ J.
From which, $v = 5.93 \times 10^5$ m/s.

(b) If the particle is a proton, we have
$KE = \frac{1}{2}mv^2 = \frac{1}{2}(1.67 \times 10^{-27} \text{ kg})v^2 = 1.60 \times 10^{-19}$ J, and
$v = 1.38 \times 10^4$ m/s.

16.17 $W = q'\Delta V = q(V_f - V_i) = q'\left(k\frac{q}{r_f} - k\frac{q}{r_i}\right)$, but $k\frac{q}{r_i} = 0$ (r_i = infinity).
Thus,

$$W = k\frac{q'q}{r_f} = (8.99 \times 10^9 \text{ N m}^2/\text{C}^2)\ \frac{(3.00 \times 10^{-9} \text{ C})(9.00 \times 10^{-9} \text{ C})}{0.300 \text{ m}}$$
$$= 8.09 \times 10^{-7} \text{ J}.$$

16.18 Using conservation of energy, we have:

$\frac{keQ}{r_1} = \frac{keQ}{r_2} + \frac{1}{2}mv^2$, which gives: $v = \sqrt{\frac{2keQ}{m}\left(\frac{1}{r_1} - \frac{1}{r_2}\right)}$, or

$$v = \sqrt{\frac{(2)(8.99 \times 10^9 \text{ N m}^2/\text{C}^2)(-1.60 \times 10^{-19} \text{ C})(10^{-9} \text{ C})}{9.11 \times 10^{-31} \text{ kg}}\left(\frac{1}{0.0300 \text{ m}} - \frac{1}{0.0200 \text{ m}}\right)}$$

$v = 7.25 \times 10^6$ m/s.

16.19 Using conservation of energy, we have $KE_i + PE_i = KE_f + PE_f$.
But $PE_i = k\frac{q_\alpha q_{gold}}{r_i}$, and $r_i = \infty$. Thus, $PE_i = 0$.
Also $KE_f = 0$ ($v_f = 0$ at turning point), so $PE_f = KE_i$, or

$$k\frac{q_\alpha q_{gold}}{r_{min}} = \frac{1}{2} m_\alpha v_\alpha^2, \text{ and}$$

$$r_{min} = \frac{2kq_\alpha q_{gold}}{m_\alpha v_\alpha^2} = \frac{2(8.99 \times 10^9 \text{ N m}^2/\text{C}^2)(2e)(79e)}{(6.6 \times 10^{-27} \text{ kg})(2 \times 10^7 \text{ m/s})^2} = 2.8 \times 10^{-14} \text{ m}.$$

16.20 By definition, the work required to move a charge from one point to any other point on an equipotential surface is zero. From the definition of work, $W = (F\cos\theta)s$, the work is zero only if $s = 0$ or $(F\cos\theta) = 0$. The displacement s cannot be assumed to be zero in all cases. Thus, one must require that $(F\cos\theta) = 0$. The force F is given by $F = qE$ and neither the charge q nor the field strength E can be assumed to be zero in all cases. Therefore, the only way the work can be zero in all cases is if $\cos\theta = 0$. but if $\cos\theta = 0$, then $\theta = 90°$ or the force (and hence the electric field) must be perpendicular to the displacement s (which is tangent to the surface). That is, the field must be perpendicular to the equipotential surface at all points on that surface.

16.21 (a) $Q = C\Delta V = (4.00 \times 10^{-6} \text{ F})(12.0 \text{ V}) = 4.80 \times 10^{-5} \text{ C} = 48.0\,\mu\text{C}$

(b) $Q = C\Delta V = (4.00 \times 10^{-6} \text{ F})(1.50 \text{ V}) = 6.00 \times 10^{-6} \text{ C} = 6.00\,\mu\text{C}$

16.22 (a) $C = \frac{\varepsilon_0 A}{d} = \frac{(8.85 \times 10^{-12} \text{ F/m})(1.0 \times 10^6 \text{ m}^2)}{800 \text{ m}} = 1.1 \times 10^{-8} \text{ F}.$

(b) $\Delta V_{max} = E_{max} d = (3.0 \times 10^6 \text{ V/m})(800 \text{ m}) = 2.4 \times 10^9 \text{ V}$, and

$Q_{max} = C\Delta V_{max} = (1.1 \times 10^{-8} \text{ F})(2.4 \times 10^9 \text{ V}) = 26 \text{ C}.$

16.23 (a) If d is doubled while A and Q remain constant, then when d doubles, C is reduced by a factor of 2. Thus, if Q remains constant, then

$$\Delta V_2 = \frac{Q_2}{C_2} = \frac{Q_1}{\frac{1}{2}C_1} = 2\frac{Q_1}{C_1}, \text{ or } \quad \Delta V_2 = 2\Delta V_1 = 800 \text{ V}.$$

(b) If d is doubled the capacitance reduced by a factor of 2. Thus, if ΔV is held constant:

$Q_2 = C_2 \Delta V_2 = \left(\frac{1}{2} C_1\right)(\Delta V_1) = \frac{1}{2} C_1 \Delta V_1 = \frac{1}{2} Q_1$, or the charge must be halved.

16.24 $C = \frac{\varepsilon_0 A}{d} = \frac{(8.85 \times 10^{-12} \text{ F/m})(2.0 \times 10^{-4} \text{ m}^2)}{2.0 \times 10^{-3} \text{ m}} = 8.85 \times 10^{-13} \text{ F}$, and

$Q = C\Delta V = (8.85 \times 10^{-13} \text{ F})(6.0 \text{ V}) = 5.3 \times 10^{-12} \text{ C}.$

16.25 $C = \frac{\varepsilon_0 A}{d}$ gives: $A = \frac{Cd}{\varepsilon_0} = \frac{(2.00 \times 10^{-12} \text{ F})(1.00 \times 10^{-4} \text{ m})}{8.85 \times 10^{-12} \text{ F/m}} = 2.26 \times 10^{-5} \text{ m}^2.$

16.26 (a) $C = \frac{\varepsilon_0 A}{d} = \frac{(8.85 \times 10^{-12} \text{ F/m})(5.00 \times 10^{-4} \text{ m}^2)}{1.00 \times 10^{-3} \text{ m}} = 4.43 \times 10^{-12} \text{ F}$, and

$$\Delta V = \frac{Q}{C} = \frac{400 \times 10^{-12} \text{ C}}{4.43 \times 10^{-12} \text{ F}} = 90.3 \text{ V}.$$

(b) $E = \frac{\Delta V}{d} = \frac{90.3 \text{ V}}{10^{-3} \text{ m}} = 9.03 \times 10^4 \text{ V/m}$

16.27 (a) $\frac{1}{C_{eq}} = \frac{1}{0.050\ \mu F} + \frac{1}{0.100\ \mu F}$, and $C_{eq} = 0.0333\ \mu F$.

Thus, $Q = C_{eq}\Delta V = (0.0333\ \mu F)(400\ V) = 13.3\ \mu C$ on each capacitor.

(b) The voltage is the same across both capacitors and equal to 400 V.

Thus, $Q_1 = C_1\Delta V = (0.050\ \mu F)(400\ V) = 20.0\ \mu C$, and

$Q_2 = C_2\Delta V = (0.100\ \mu F)(400\ V) = 40.0\ \mu C$.

16.28 (a) $C_{eq} = C_1 + C_2 + C_3 = 5.00\ \mu F + 4.00\ \mu F + 9.00\ \mu F = 18.0\ \mu F$.

(b) $\frac{1}{C_{eq}} = \frac{1}{C_1} + \frac{1}{C_2} + \frac{1}{C_3} = \frac{1}{5.00\ \mu F} + \frac{1}{4.00\ \mu F} + \frac{1}{9.00\ \mu F}$,

giving $C_{eq} = 1.78\ \mu F$.

16.29 (a) Using the rules for combining capacitors in series and in parallel, the circuit is reduced in steps as shown below. The equivalent capacitor is shown to be a 2 μF capacitor.

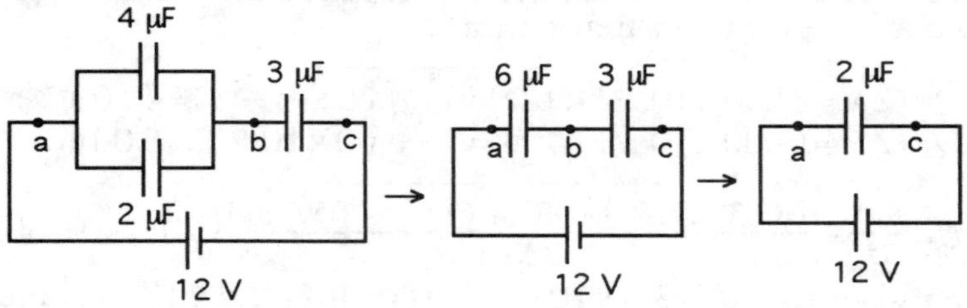

Figure 1 Figure 2 Figure 3

(b) From Fig. 3: $Q_{ac} = C_{ac}\Delta V_{ac} = (2.0\ \mu F)(12\ V) = 24\ \mu C$.

From Fig. 2: $Q_{ab} = Q_{bc} = Q_{ac} = 24\ \mu C$

Thus, the charge on the 3.0 μF capacitor is: $Q_3 = 24\ \mu C$.

We now find the potential differences between the points indicated in Fig. 2: $\Delta V_{ab} = \frac{Q_{ab}}{C_{ab}} = \frac{24\ \mu C}{6.0\ \mu F} = 4.0\ V$, and $\Delta V_{bc} = \frac{Q_{bc}}{C_{bc}} = \frac{24\ \mu C}{3.0\ \mu F} = 8.0\ V$

Finally, usingFig. 1: $Q_4 = C_4\Delta V_{ab} = (4.0\ \mu F)(4.0\ V) = 16\ \mu C$,

and $Q_2 = C_2\Delta V_{ab} = (2.0\ \mu F)(4.0\ V) = 8.0\ \mu C$.

16.30 (a) The largest occurs when they are all in parallel, yielding

$C_{max} = 2.0\ \mu F + 2.0\ \mu F + 2.0\ \mu F = 6.0\ \mu F$.

(b) The smallest occurs when they are all in series, yielding

$\frac{1}{C_{min}} = \frac{1}{2.0\ \mu F} + \frac{1}{2.0\ \mu F} + \frac{1}{2.0\ \mu F} = \frac{3}{2.0\ \mu F}$, or $C_{min} = \frac{2}{3}\ \mu F$.

(c) Putting two of them in series, and that combination in parallel with the third yields an equivalent capacitance of 3.0 μF.

16.31 (a) The combination reduces to an equivalent capacitance of 12 μF in stages shown below.

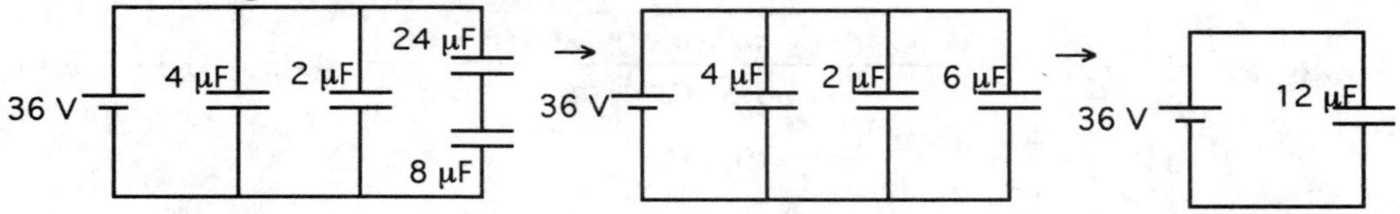

Figure 1 Figure 2 Figure 3

(b) From Fig. 2, $Q_4 = (4.0\ \mu F)(36\ V) = 144\ \mu C$, $Q_2 = (2.0\ \mu F)(36\ V) = 72\ \mu C$,

and $Q_6 = (6.0\ \mu F)(36\ V) = 216\ \mu C$
Then, from Fig. 1: $Q_{24} = Q_8 = Q_6 = 216\ \mu C$

16.32

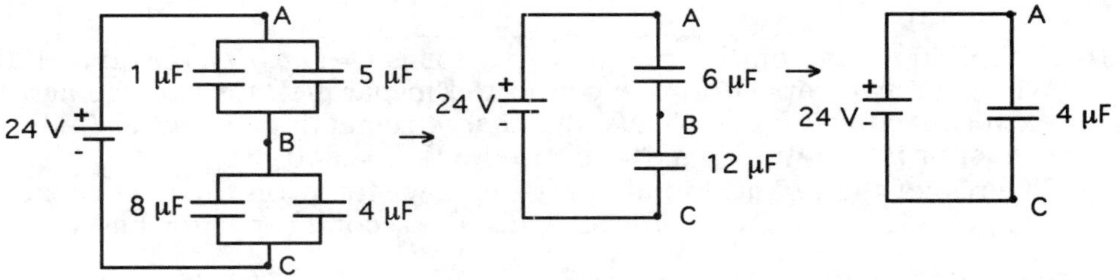

We reduce the circuit in steps as shown above. Using the equivalent circuit, we find: $Q_{total} = C\Delta V = (4.0\ \mu F)(24\ V) = 96\ \mu C$

Then in the second circuit:

$$\Delta V_{AB} = \frac{Q_{total}}{C_{AB}} = \frac{96\ \mu C}{6.0\ \mu F} = 16\ V, \text{ and } \Delta V_{BC} = \frac{Q_{total}}{C_{BC}} = \frac{96\ \mu C}{12\ \mu F} = 8\ V$$

Finally, using the original circuit:
$Q_1 = C_1 \Delta V_{AB} = (1.0\ \mu F)(16\ V) = 16\ \mu C$ $Q_5 = C_5 \Delta V_{AB} = (5.0\ \mu F)(16\ V) = 80\ \mu C$,
$Q_8 = C_8 \Delta V_{BC} = (8.0\ \mu F)(8\ V) = 64\ \mu C$, and $Q_4 = C_4 \Delta V_{BC} = (4.0\ \mu F)(8\ V) = 32\ \mu C$

16.33 (a) All four should be connected in parallel.
(b) Two in parallel followed by another group of two in parallel. Or, two in series which are in parallel with another group of two in series.
(c) One in series with a group of three in parallel.
(d) All four in series.

16.34 The technician combines two of the capacitors in parallel making a capacitor of capacitance 200 µF. Then she does it again with two more of the capacitors. Then the two resulting 200 µF capacitors are connected in series to yield an equivalent capacitance of 100 µF. Because of the symmetry of the solution, every capacitor in the combination has the same voltage across it, 50 V.

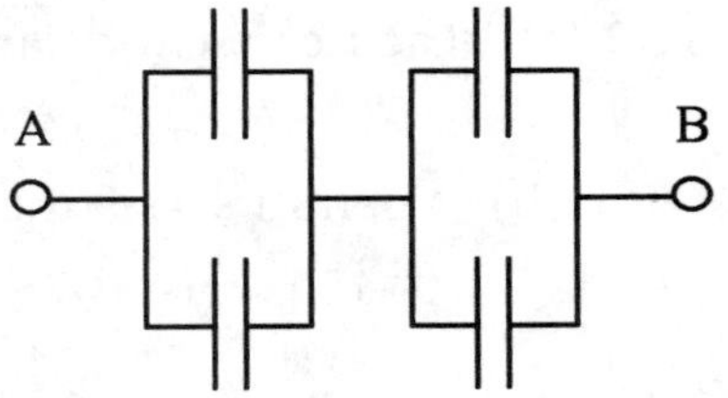

16.35 (a) Using $Q = C\Delta V$, we have: $Q_1 = (25.0 \times 10^{-6}\ F)(50.0\ V) = 1.25 \times 10^3\ \mu C$,
and $Q_2 = (40.0 \times 10^{-6}\ F)(50.0\ V) = 2.00 \times 10^3\ \mu C$
on the 25.0 µF and 40.0 µF capacitors, respectively.

(b) Let Q_1' and Q_2' be the final charges on each capacitor. Since charge is conserved, we have:

$$Q_1' + Q_2' = (-Q_1) + Q_2 = -1250\ \mu C + 2000\ \mu C = 750\ \mu C. \quad (1)$$

In addition, the capacitors are now in parallel and the potentials across them are equal, so

$$\frac{Q_1'}{C_1} = \frac{Q_2'}{C_2}, \text{ giving } Q_1' = \frac{25}{40} Q_2' = 0.625 Q_2'. \quad (2)$$

Substitute eq. (2) into (1) to obtain: $Q_2 = 462\ \mu C$.
Then equation (2) yields: $Q_1 = 288\ \mu C$.

The potential across the 40 μF capacitor is: $\Delta V = \frac{Q}{C} = \frac{462\ \mu C}{40\ \mu F} = 11.6\ V$.

16.36 The initial charge on the 10.0 μF capacitor is $Q = (12.0\ V)(10.0\ \mu F) = 120\ \mu C$.
When the two capacitors are connected in parallel, the voltage across each capacitor is 3.0 V. Thus, the charge remaining on the 10.0 μF capacitor is: $Q_{10} = C_{10}\Delta V' = (10.0\ \mu F)(3.0\ V) = 30.0\ \mu F$.
The rest of the 120 μC initial charge is now stored on the new capacitor (i.e., $Q_c = 120\ \mu C - 30\ \mu C = 90\ \mu C$). Thus, the second capacitor has a capacitance of: $C = \frac{Q_c}{\Delta V'} = \frac{90\ \mu F}{3.0\ V} = 30\ \mu F$.

16.37 When the 1.00 μF capacitor is connected across the battery, it receives a charge of: $Q = C\Delta V = (1.00\ \mu F)(10.0\ V) = 10.0\ \mu C$.
When connected in parallel with the 2.00 μF capacitor, the voltages are the same across each capacitor:

$$\Delta V' = \frac{Q_1}{1.00\ \mu F} = \frac{Q_2}{2.00\ \mu F},\ \text{so}\ Q_1 = \frac{1}{2}Q_2 \qquad (1)$$

Since charge is conserved, the sum of the charges on the two capacitors must equal the original charge, or: $Q_1 + Q_2 = 10.0\ \mu C$ (2)

Combining equations (1) and (2) gives: $Q_1 = \frac{10}{3}\ \mu C$, and $Q_2 = \frac{20}{3}\ \mu C$.

16.38 $C = \frac{\varepsilon_0 A}{d} = \frac{(8.85 \times 10^{-12}\ F/m)(2.00 \times 10^{-4}\ m^2)}{5.00 \times 10^{-3}\ m} = 3.54 \times 10^{-13}\ F$, and

$$W = \frac{1}{2}C\Delta V^2 = \frac{1}{2}(3.54 \times 10^{-13}\ F)(12.0\ V)^2 = 2.55 \times 10^{-11}\ J.$$

16.39 (a) Each capacitor has voltage V, so:

$$W = \frac{1}{2}(C_1 + C_2)\Delta V^2 = \frac{1}{2}(25 \times 10^{-6}\ F + 5.0 \times 10^{-6}\ F)(100\ V)^2 = 0.15\ J.$$

(b) When in series the equivalent capacitance is 4.167 μF, and

$$0.15\ J = \frac{1}{2}(4.167 \times 10^{-6}\ F)\Delta V'^2,\ \text{or}\ \Delta V' = 270\ V.$$

16.40 The capacitance of the Earth-cloud system is:

$$C = \frac{\varepsilon_0 A}{d} = \frac{(8.85 \times 10^{-12}\ F/m)(1.0 \times 10^6\ m^2)}{800\ m} = 1.1 \times 10^{-8}\ F,$$

Just before discharge, the potential difference between the Earth and cloud is:

$$\Delta V = E_{max}d = (3.0 \times 10^6\ V/m)(800\ m) = 2.4 \times 10^9\ V.$$

Thus, the energy stored in this capacitor (and released during the lightning strike, assuming total discharge) is:

$$W = \frac{1}{2}C\Delta V^2 = \frac{(1.1 \times 10^{-8}\ F)(2.4 \times 10^9\ V)^2}{2} = 3.2 \times 10^{10}\ J$$

16.41 Initially, the potential difference across the capacitor is: $\Delta V_0 = \frac{Q}{C_0}$.
After removal of the capacitor from the circuit and insertion of the glass, the charge is unchanged but the potential difference is:

$\Delta V' = \frac{Q}{C'}$. Thus, $\kappa = \frac{C}{C_0} = \frac{\Delta V_0}{\Delta V'} = \frac{100\ \text{V}}{25\ \text{V}} = 4.0$

16.42 (a) Using $Ed = \Delta V$, we get $E = \frac{6.00\ \text{V}}{0.002\ \text{m}} = 3000\ \text{V/m}$

(b) With water (κ = 80) between the plates:

$$C = \frac{\kappa \varepsilon_0 A}{d} = \frac{80(8.85\ \text{x}\ 10^{-12}\ \text{F/m})(2.00\ \text{x}\ 10^{-4}\ \text{m}^2)}{(2.00\ \text{x}\ 10^{-3}\ \text{m})} = 7.08 \text{x} 10^{-11}\ \text{F},$$

and the stored charge is:

$$Q = C\Delta V = (7.08 \text{x} 10^{-11}\ \text{F})(6.00\ \text{V}) = 4.25 \text{x} 10^{-10}\ \text{C} = 0.425\ \text{nC}.$$

(c) When the water is replaced by air, (κ = 1), the capacitance is reduced by a factor of 80, so the new capacitance is:

$C = \frac{C}{80} = 8.85 \text{x} 10^{-13}$ F, and the stored charge is now:

$$Q = C\Delta V = (8.85 \text{x} 10^{-13}\ \text{F})(6.00\ \text{V}) = 5.31 \text{x} 10^{-12}\ \text{C} = 5.31\ \text{pC}.$$

16.43 (a) $C = \frac{\kappa \varepsilon_0 A}{d} = \frac{2.1(8.85\ \text{x}\ 10^{-12}\ \text{F/m})(1.75\ \text{x}\ 10^{-2}\ \text{m}^2)}{4.00\ \text{x}\ 10^{-5}\ \text{m}}$, or

$C = 8.1 \text{x} 10^{-9}\ \text{F} = 8.1\ \text{nF}.$

(b) $\Delta V_{max} = E_{max}d = (60 \text{x} 10^6\ \text{V/m})(4.00 \text{x} 10^{-5}\ \text{m}) = 2.4 \text{x} 10^3\ \text{V} = 2.4\ \text{kV}.$

16.44 When the electric field, E, surpasses the dielectric strength of air)see Table 16.1), a spark will occur. The potential difference in this case is:

$$\Delta V = Ed = (3 \text{x} 10^6\ \text{V/m})(0.50\ \text{inch})(2.54\ \text{x}\ 10^{-2}\ \text{m/inch}) = 3.8\ \text{x}\ 10^4\ \text{V}$$

16.45 (a) Using Volume = $\frac{\text{mass}}{\text{density}}$, we get:

Volume = $\frac{10^{-12}\ \text{kg}}{1100\ \text{kg/m}^3} = 9.09 \text{x} 10^{-16}\ \text{m}^3$. But Volume = $\frac{4\pi r^3}{3}$, so that

$r = 6.00 \text{x} 10^{-6}$ m, and hence: $A = 4\pi r^2 = 4.54 \text{x} 10^{-10}\ \text{m}^2$.

(b) Treat the membrane as a parallel plate capacitor, so

$$C = \frac{\kappa \varepsilon_0 A}{d} = \frac{(5)(8.85\ \text{x}\ 10^{-12}\ \text{F/m})(4.54\ \text{x}\ 10^{-10}\ \text{m}^2)}{(100\ \text{x}\ 10^{-9}\ \text{m})} = 2.00 \text{x} 10^{-13}\ \text{F}.$$

(c) Using $Q = C\Delta V$, we get $(2.00 \text{x} 10^{-13})(100 \text{x} 10^{-3}) = 2.00 \text{x} 10^{-14}$ C. This represents: $n = \frac{Q}{e} = \frac{2.00\ \text{x}\ 10^{-14}\ \text{C}}{1.60\ \text{x}\ 10^{-19}\ \text{C}} = 1.25 \text{x} 10^5$ electronic charges.

16.46 Since the capacitors are in parallel, the equivalent capacitance is"

$$C_{eq} = C_1 + C_2 + C_3 .$$

$$C_{eq} = \frac{\varepsilon_0 A_{eq}}{d} = \frac{\varepsilon_0 A_1}{d} + \frac{\varepsilon_0 A_2}{d} + \frac{\varepsilon_0 A_3}{d} = + \frac{\varepsilon_0 (A_1 + A_2 + A_3)}{d}$$

16.47 Since the capacitors are in series, the equivalent capacitance is:

$$\frac{1}{C_{eq}} = \frac{1}{C_1} + \frac{1}{C_2} + \frac{1}{C_3}$$

$$\frac{1}{C_{eq}} = \frac{d_{eq}}{\varepsilon_0 A} = \frac{d_1}{\varepsilon_0 A} + \frac{d_2}{\varepsilon_0 A} + \frac{d_3}{\varepsilon_0 A} = \frac{d_1 + d_2 + d_3}{\varepsilon_0 A}$$

$$C_{eq} = \frac{\varepsilon_0 A}{d_1 + d_2 + d_3}$$

16.48 The length of the diagonal is (from the Pythagorean theorem):

$d = \sqrt{(0.35\ \text{m})^2 + (0.20\ \text{m})^2} = 0.403$ m. Thus,

$$V = \Sigma \frac{q_i}{r_i}$$

$$= (8.99 \times 10^9\ \text{N m}^2/\text{C}^2)\left(\frac{8.00 \times 10^{-6}\ \text{C}}{0.200\ \text{m}} + \frac{12.0 \times 10^{-6}\ \text{C}}{0.403\ \text{m}} - \frac{8.00 \times 10^{-6}\ \text{C}}{0.350\ \text{m}}\right)$$

or: $V = 4.22 \times 10^5$ V.

16.49 The distance from the charge at the apex of the triangle to the mid-point of the base is found from the Pythagorean theorem to be:

$d = \sqrt{(4.0\ \text{cm})^2 - (1.0\ \text{cm})^2} = 3.87$ cm. Thus, $V = \Sigma \frac{q_i}{r_i}$ becomes

$$V = (8.99 \times 10^9\ \text{N m}^2/\text{C}^2)\left(\frac{5.0 \times 10^{-9}\ \text{C}}{0.01\ \text{m}} + \frac{5.0 \times 10^{-9}\ \text{C}}{0.01\ \text{m}} - \frac{5 \times 10^{-9}\ \text{C}}{0.0387\ \text{m}}\right)$$

or: $V = +7.8 \times 10^3$ V.

16.50 The stages for the reduction of this circuit are shown below.

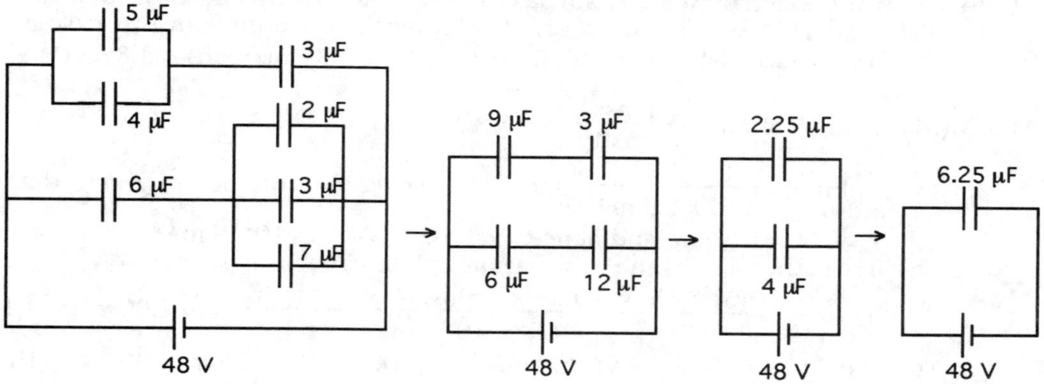

16.51 The capacitance with and without the dielectric is:

$C = \frac{Q}{\Delta V'}$, and $C_0 = \frac{Q_0}{\Delta V_0}$. Thus, the dielectric constant is given by

$\kappa = \frac{C}{C_0} = \frac{Q \Delta V_0}{Q_0 \Delta V'}$. But $\Delta V' = \Delta V_0$, so $\kappa = \frac{Q}{Q_0} = \frac{150\ \mu\text{C} + 200\ \mu\text{C}}{150\ \mu\text{C}} = 2.33$.

16.52 Let C_x represent the unknown capacitance. The original charge stored in this capacitor is $Q_0 = C_x \Delta V_0 = C_x(100\ \text{V})$. After connecting in parallel with a neutral 10 μF capacitor, the voltage is 30.0 V across each capacitor. Thus, the charge stored in each capacitor is:

$Q_{10} = C_{10} \Delta V = (10\ \mu\text{F})(30.0\ \text{V}) = 300\ \mu\text{C}$, and $Q_x = C_x \Delta V = C_x(30.0\ \text{V})$.

From conservation of charge, we must require that:

$Q_0 = Q_x + Q_{10}$, or $C_x(100\ \text{V}) = C_x(30.0\ \text{V}) + 300\ \mu\text{C}$.

Thus, $C_x(70.0\text{ V}) = 300\ \mu\text{C}$, or $C_x = \frac{300\ \mu\text{C}}{70.0\ \text{V}} = 4.29\ \mu\text{F}$.

16.53 If d is the distance separating the plates, the electric field between the plates is $E = \frac{\Delta V}{d} = \frac{500\ \text{V}}{5 \times 10^{-2}\ \text{m}} = 10^4\ \text{V/m}$. This field exerts a force of: $F = qE = (1.60 \times 10^{-19}\ \text{C})(10^4\ \text{V/m}) = 1.6 \times 10^{-15}\ \text{N}$ on a particle of charge e. The electron is given an acceleration of:

$$a_e = \frac{F}{m_e} = \frac{(1.6 \times 10^{-15}\ \text{N})}{9.11 \times 10^{-31}\ \text{kg}} = 1.76 \times 10^{15}\ \text{m/s}^2 \text{ toward the positive plate,}$$

while the proton has an acceleration of:

$$a_p = \frac{F}{m_p} = \frac{(1.6 \times 10^{-15}\ \text{N})}{1.67 \times 10^{-27}\ \text{kg}} = 9.58 \times 10^{11}\ \text{m/s}^2 \text{ toward the negative plate.}$$

In time t, the distance each particle has traveled (starting from rest) is

$$x_e = \frac{1}{2} a_e t^2 = (8.78 \times 10^{14}\ \text{m/s}^2)t^2, \text{ and}$$

$$x_p = \frac{1}{2} a_p t^2 = (4.79 \times 10^{11}\ \text{m/s}^2)t^2. \qquad (1)$$

(a) When the particles pass, $x_e + x_p = 5 \times 10^{-2}$ m. Substituting for x_e and x_p from (1) and solving for t gives: $t = 7.54 \times 10^{-9}$ s when they pass.

(b) At the time computed in (a), the speed of each particle is
$v_e = a_e t = (1.76 \times 10^{15}\ \text{m/s}^2)(7.54 \times 10^{-9}\ \text{s}) = 1.33 \times 10^7\ \text{m/s}$, and
$v_p = a_p t = (9.58 \times 10^{11}\ \text{m/s}^2)(7.54 \times 10^{-9}\ \text{s}) = 7230\ \text{m/s}$.

(c) Setting $x_e = d = 5 \times 10^{-2}$ m in equation (1) above and solving gives: $t_e = 7.55 \times 10^{-9}\ \text{s} = 7.55$ ns as the time the electron reaches the positive plate.

(d) Setting $x_p = d = 5 \times 10^{-2}$ m in equation (1) above and solving gives: $t_p = 3.23 \times 10^{-7}\ \text{s} = 0.323\ \mu\text{s}$ as the time the proton reaches the negative plate.

16.54 Initially (capacitors charged in parallel),

$Q_1 = C_1\Delta V = (6.0\ \mu\text{V})(250\ \text{V}) = 1.5 \times 10^3\ \mu\text{C}$, and

$Q_2 = C_2\Delta V = (2.0\ \mu\text{V})(250\ \text{V}) = 5.0 \times 10^2\ \mu\text{C}$

After reconnecting (positive plate to negative plate), the capacitors are in parallel and $Q_{total} = Q_1 - Q_2 = 1.0 \times 10^3\ \mu\text{C}$

Thus, $\Delta V' = \frac{Q_{total}}{C_{total}} = \frac{1.0 \times 10^3\ \mu\text{C}}{8.0\ \mu\text{F}} = 125\ \text{V}$.

Therefore:

$Q_1 = C_1\Delta V' = (6.0\ \mu\text{F})(125\ \text{V}) = 7.5 \times 10^2\ \mu\text{C}$, and

$Q_2 = C_2\Delta V' = (2.0\ \mu\text{F})(125\ \text{V}) = 2.5 \times 10^2\ \mu\text{C}$

16.55 Initially with the capacitors in series, $Q_1 = Q_2 = C_{eq}\Delta V$, and

$\frac{1}{C_{eq}} = \frac{1}{4.0\ \mu\text{F}} + \frac{1}{2.0\ \mu\text{F}}$, or $C_{eq} = 1.33\ \mu\text{F}$. Thus, the initial charge on each capacitor is: $Q_1 = Q_2 = C_{eq}\Delta V = (1.33\ \mu\text{F})(100\ \text{V}) = 133\ \mu\text{C}$

After reconnection in parallel, $Q_{total} = Q_1 + Q_2 = 266\ \mu\text{C}$, and

$C_{eq} = C_1 + C_2 = 6.0\ \mu\text{F}$, so $\Delta V' = \frac{Q_{total}}{C_{eq}} = \frac{266\ \mu\text{C}}{6.0\ \mu\text{F}} = 44.3\ \text{V}$.

Therefore, $Q_1 = C_1 \Delta V' = (4.0\ \mu F)(44.3\ V) = 1.8 \times 10^2\ \mu C,$
and $Q_2 = C_2 \Delta V' = (2.0\ \mu F)(44.3\ V) = 8.9 \times 10^1\ \mu C,$

16.56 For the whole motion

$$y = v_{yo}t + \frac{1}{2}a_y t^2$$

$$0 = vt + \frac{1}{2}a_y t^2 \quad \text{or} \quad a_y = -\frac{2v}{t}$$

Now from $\Sigma F_y = ma_y$

we have $-mg - qE = -\frac{2mv}{t}$

$$E = \frac{m}{q}\left(\frac{2v}{t} - g\right)$$ where E is in the y direction.

For the upward flight,

$$v^2 = v_{yo}^2 + 2a_y y$$

$$0 = v^2 + 2\left(\frac{-2v}{t}\right)y_{max}$$

$$y_{max} = \frac{1}{4}vt$$

and $\Delta V = Ey$ gives

$$\Delta V = \frac{m}{q}\left(\frac{2v}{t} - g\right)\frac{1}{4}vt$$

$$= \frac{2.00\ kg}{5.00 \times 10^{-6}\ C}\left(\frac{2(20.1\ m/s)}{4.10\ s} - 9.80\ m/s^2\right)\frac{1}{4}(20.1\ m/s)(4.10\ s) = 40.2\ kV$$

16.57 When the two capacitors are connected in series, the equivalent capacitance is $\frac{1}{C_{series}} = \frac{1}{C_1} + \frac{1}{C_2} = \frac{1}{2.00\ pF}$. [Equation 1]

When they are connected in parallel, the equivalent capacitance is $C_{parallel} = C_1 + C_2 = 9.00\ pF$, which may be written as $C_2 = 9.00\ pF - C_1$.

Substituting this result into Equation 1 yields

$$\frac{1}{C_1} + \frac{1}{9.00\ pF - C_1} = \frac{1}{2.00\ pF}.$$

Finding a common denominator gives

$$\frac{(9.00\ pF - C_1) + C_1}{C_1(9.00\ pF - C_1)} = \frac{1}{2.00\ pF},$$

or $(9.00\ pF)(2.00\ pF) = C_1(9.00\ pF - C_1)$.

Expanding and rearranging yields the equation

$$C_1^2 - (9.00\ pF)C_1 + 18.0(pF)^2 = 0$$

which may be solved with the quadratic formula:

$$C_1 = \frac{(9.00\ pF) \pm \sqrt{(9.00\ pF)^2 - 72.0(pF)^2}}{2} = \frac{(9.00\ pF) \pm (3.00\ pF)}{2}.$$

Thus, there are two possible values for C_1:

$$C_1 = 6.00\ pF \quad \text{or} \quad C_1 = 3.00\ pF.$$

Then, using $C_2 = 9.00\text{ pF} - C_1$ from above, two possible values for C_2 are found: $C_2 = 3.00\text{ pF}$ or $C_2 = 6.00\text{ pF}$. The conclusion is that one of the unknown capacitances is 3.00 pF and the other is 6.00 pF.

16.58 $C_p = C_1 + C_2 \quad \frac{1}{C_s} = \frac{1}{C_1} + \frac{1}{C_2}$

Substitute $C_2 = C_p - C_1 \quad \frac{1}{C_s} = \frac{1}{C_1} + \frac{1}{C_p - C_1} = \frac{C_p - C_1 + C_1}{C_1(C_p - C_1)}$

which reduces to $C_1^2 - C_1C_p + C_pC_s = 0$

Solving $\quad C_1 = \frac{C_p \pm \sqrt{C_p^2 - 4C_pC_s}}{2} = \frac{1}{2}C_p + \sqrt{\frac{1}{4}C_p^2 - C_pC_s}$

We choose arbitrarily the + sign. Then

$$C_2 = C_p - C_1 = \frac{1}{2}C_p - \sqrt{\frac{1}{4}C_p^2 - C_pC_s}$$

If we had chosen the - sign, we would get the same two answers with their names interchanged.

16.59 (a) The 15.0 μF and 3.00 μF in series reduces to $\frac{1}{C_s} = \frac{1}{15.0} + \frac{1}{3.00}$

from which $C_s = 2.50\ \mu\text{F}$

This 2.50 μF replacement is now in parallel with the 6.00 μF capacitor. This combination can be replaced with their sum, an 8.50 μF capacitor. Finally, this 8.5 μF capacitor is in series with the 20.0 μF. This combination becomes $\frac{1}{C_{eq}} = \frac{1}{8.50} + \frac{1}{20.0} = 5.96\ \mu\text{F}$

(b) $Q = \Delta VC = (15.0)(5.96\ \mu\text{F}) = 89.5\ \mu\text{C}$ on the 20.0 μF

$\Delta V = \frac{Q}{C} = \frac{89.5\ \mu\text{C}}{20.0\ \mu\text{F}} = 4.48\text{ V}$

$15.0 - 4.48 = 10.52\text{ V}$

$Q = \Delta VC = (10.52)(6.00\ \mu\text{F}) = 63.1\ \mu\text{C}$ on 6.00 μF

$89.5 - 63.1 = 26.4\ \mu\text{C}$ on 15.0 μC and 3.00 μF

16.60 (a) $V = kQ\left(\frac{1}{x+d} - \frac{2}{x} + \frac{1}{x-d}\right)$

$$= kQ\left(\frac{x(x-d) - 2(x+d)(x-d) + x(x+d)}{x(x+d)(x-d)}\right)$$

$$V = \frac{2kQd^2}{x^3 - xd^2}$$

(b) $V = \frac{2kQd^2}{x^3}$ for $\frac{d}{x} << 1$

16.61 $W = \frac{1}{2}C\Delta V^2$ and $Q = mc\Delta T + mL$

$\frac{1}{2}C\Delta V^2 = m(c\Delta T + L_f)$

$$\frac{1}{2}(52.0 \times 10^{-6}\text{ F})\Delta V^2 = (6.00 \times 10^{-6}\text{ kg})\left(\left(\frac{128}{\text{kg }^\circ\text{C}}\right)(327.3 - 20.0)^\circ\text{C} + 2.45 \times 10^4\text{ J/kg}\right)$$

gives $\quad \Delta V = 121\text{ V}$

16.62 The stored charge will be $Q = C\Delta V = (20\,\mu F)(100\,V) = 2.0 \times 10^{-3}\,C$. For a parallel plate capacitor, the capacitance is $C = \frac{\kappa \varepsilon_0 A}{d}$, so we observe that $\kappa \varepsilon_0 A = Cd = (20\,\mu F)(2.01 \times 10^{-3}\,m)$ in this case. Therefore,

$$F = \frac{Q^2}{2Cd} = \frac{(2.0 \times 10^{-3}\,C)^2}{2(20 \times 10^{-6}\,F)(2.01 \times 10^{-3}\,m)} = 50\,N.$$

16.63 The electric field between the plates is $E = \frac{\Delta V}{d} = \frac{100\,V}{2.0 \times 10^{-3}\,m} = 5.0 \times 10^4$ V/m and this will exert an upward force $F = qE = (1.60 \times 10^{-19}\,C)(5.0 \times 10^4\,V/m) = 8.0 \times 10^{-15}\,N$ on the electron. Thus, the upward acceleration of the electron is:

$$a_y = \frac{F}{m} = \frac{8.0 \times 10^{-15}\,N}{9.11 \times 10^{-31}\,kg} = 8.78 \times 10^{15}\,m/s^2.$$

Now the problem is one of projectile motion.

(a) We first use: $v_y = v_{oy} + at$, with

$$v_{oy} = \left(5.60 \times 10^6\,\frac{m}{s}\right)\sin(-45°) = -3.96 \times 10^6\,\frac{m}{s}$$ and $v_y = 0$ at the lowest point on the path.

The time when $v_y = 0$ is $t = -\frac{v_{oy}}{a_y} = 4.51 \times 10^{-10}\,s$.

At this time, the vertical displacement (from point O) is:

$$y = \frac{\bar{v}_y}{2}t = \frac{(-3.96 \times 10^6\,m/s + 0)}{2}(4.51 \times 10^{-10}\,s) = -8.9 \times 10^{-4}\,m,$$ or

$y = -0.89$ mm. Thus, at its closest approach, the electron is:
$d = 1.00\,mm - 0.89\,mm = 0.11$ mm above the lower plate.

(b) The vertical position of the electron at any time is $y = v_{oy}t + \frac{1}{2}a_y t^2$.
When the electron reaches the upper plate, $y = 1.00$ mm. Thus,

$$10^{-3}\,m = (-3.96 \times 10^6\,m/s)t + \frac{1}{2}(8.78 \times 10^{15}\,m/s^2)t^2.$$

Solving this for t gives $t = 1.11 \times 10^{-9}$ s. At this time, the horizontal displacement is:

$$x = v_{ox}t = (3.96 \times 10^6\,m/s)(1.11 \times 10^{-9}\,s) = 4.39 \times 10^{-3}\,m = 4.39\,mm.$$

ANSWERS TO CONCEPTUAL QUESTIONS

2. Electric potential V is a measure of the potential energy per unit charge. Electrical potential energy, $PE = QV$, gives the energy of the total charge Q.

4. A sharp point on a charged conductor would produce a large electric field in the region near the point. An electric discharge could most easily take place at the point.

6. Individual C_1, C_2, C_3.
Parallel $C_1 + C_2 + C_3$, $C_1 + C_2$, $C_1 + C_3$, $C_2 + C_3$.

Series-Parallel $\left(\frac{1}{C_1} + \frac{1}{C_2}\right)^{-1} + C_3$, $\left(\frac{1}{C_1} + \frac{1}{C_3}\right)^{-1} + C_2$, $\left(\frac{1}{C_2} + \frac{1}{C_3}\right)^{-1} + C_1$.

Series $\left(\frac{1}{C_1} + \frac{1}{C_2} + \frac{1}{C_3}\right)^{-1}$, $\left(\frac{1}{C_1} + \frac{1}{C_2}\right)^{-1}$, $\left(\frac{1}{C_2} + \frac{1}{C_3}\right)^{-1}$, $\left(\frac{1}{C_1} + \frac{1}{C_3}\right)^{-1}$.

8. Nothing happens to the charge if the wires are disconnected. If the wires are connected to each other, the charge recombines, rapidly.

10. The plates have the same charge.

12. All connections of capacitors are not simple combinations of series and parallel circuits. As an example of such a complex circuit, start with five capacitors C_1, C_2, C_3, C_4, and C_5. Now form a parallel circuit with C_1 and C_2 in series in the upper branch and C_3, and C_4 in series in the lower branch. Now, connect C_5 with one lead between the two in the upper branch and the other lead between the two in the lower branch. The combination cannot be reduced to a simple equivalent by the techniques of combining series and parallel capacitors.

14. The material of the dielectric may be able to support a larger electric field than air without breaking down to pass a spark between the capacitor plates.

16. If two points on a conducting object were at different potentials, then free charges in the object would move, and we would have a nonstatic situation, in contradiction to the initial assumption. (Free positive charges would migrate from higher to lower potential locations; free electrons would rapidly move from lower to higher potential locations.) The charges would continue to move until the potential became equal everywhere in the conductor.

18. The work done in pulling the capacitor plates further apart is transferred into additional electric energy stored in the capacitor. The charge is constant and the capacitance decreases, but the potential difference between the plates increases, which results in an increase in the stored electric energy.

CHAPTER SEVENTEEN SOLUTIONS

Chapter Seventeen Readings

Azbel, M. et al., "Conduction Electrons in Metals," *Scientific American*, January 1973, p. 88.

Cava, R.J., "Superconductors Beyond 1-2-3,:"*Scientific American*, August 1990, p. 60.

de Bruyn, O.R., "Heike Kamerlingh Onnes's Discovery of Superconductivity," *Scientific American*, v. 276 (Mar. '97) p98-103.

Ehrenreich, "The Electrical Properties of Materials," *Scientific American*, September 1967, p. 194.

Hazen, R.M., *The Breakthrough: The Race for the Superconductor*, New York, Summit Books, 1988.

Mende, S.B., Sentman, D.D., and Westcott, E.M., "Lightning between Earth and Space," *Scientific American*, August 1997, p. 56.

Williams, L.P., "Andre-Marie Ampere," *Scientific American*, January 1989, p.90.

Wolsky, A.M., Giese, R.F., and Daniels, E.J., "The New Superconductors: Prospects for Applications," *Scientific American*, February 1989, p. 60.

17.1 $\Delta Q = I(\Delta t) = (80.0 \times 10^{-3}\text{ C/s})(600\text{ s}) = 48.0\text{ C}$. The number of electrons is:

$$n = \frac{\Delta Q}{e} = \frac{48.0\text{ C}}{1.60 \times 10^{-19}\text{ C/electron}} = 3.00 \times 10^{20}\text{ electrons.}$$

The direction of the current is opposite to the direction of the electron's velocity.

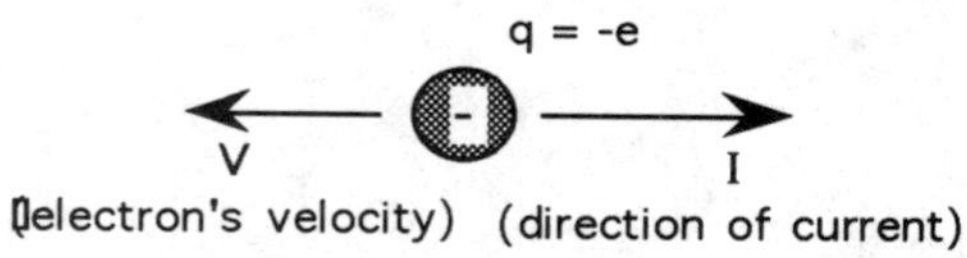

17.2 $\Delta Q = I\Delta T = (90\text{ A})(0.50\text{ s}) = 45\text{ C}$.

17.3 Using $I = \frac{\Delta Q}{\Delta t}$, we get: $I = \frac{6.0\text{ mC}}{2.0} = 3.0\text{ mA}$.

17.4 $I = ne = 60 \times 10^{-6}$ A. Thus, $n = \frac{I}{e} = \frac{60 \times 10^{-6}\text{ A}}{1.60 \times 10^{-19}\text{ C}} = 3.75 \times 10^{14}$ electrons/s.

17.5 The time for the electron to revolve around the proton once is:

$$t = \frac{2\pi r}{v} = \frac{2\pi(5.29 \times 10^{-11}\text{ m})}{(2.19 \times 10^{6}\text{ m/s})} = 1.52 \times 10^{-16}\text{ s.}$$

The total charge flow in this time is 1.60×10^{-19} C, so the current is $I = \frac{1.60 \times 10^{-19}\ \text{C}}{1.52 \times 10^{-16}\ \text{s}} = 1.05 \times 10^{-3}\ \text{A} = 1.05\ \text{mA}$.

17.6 The atomic weight of gold = 197, so the mass of one atom is:

$$\text{mass of atom} = \frac{197\ \text{g}}{6.02 \times 10^{23}\ \text{atoms}} = 3.27 \times 10^{-22}\ \text{g} = 3.27 \times 10^{-25}\ \text{kg}.$$

The number of gold atoms deposited is:

$N = \frac{3.25 \times 10^{-3}\ \text{kg}}{3.27 \times 10^{-25}\ \text{kg/atom}} = 9.93 \times 10^{21}$ ions, and the charge deposited $= (9.93 \times 10^{21}\ \text{ions})(1.60 \times 10^{-19}\ \text{C/ion}) = 1.59 \times 10^{3}\ \text{C}$.

The elapsed time = 2.78 h = 1.00×10^{4} s, so

$$I = \frac{\Delta Q}{\Delta t} = \frac{1.59 \times 10^{3}\ \text{C}}{1.00 \times 10^{4}\ \text{s}} = 1.59 \times 10^{-1}\ \text{C/s} = 0.159\ \text{A}.$$

17.7 The density of charge carriers is given as $8.5 \times 10^{28}\ \text{m}^{-3}$, and the drift velocity of each electron is:

$$v_d = \frac{I}{nqA} = \frac{1000\ \text{C/s}}{(8.5 \times 10^{28}\ \text{m}^{-3})(1.60 \times 10^{-19}\ \text{C})\pi(0.01\ \text{m})^2} = 2.34 \times 10^{-4}\ \frac{\text{m}}{\text{s}}.$$

In order to travel the length of the cable, 200×10^{3} m, it will take:

$$t = \frac{200 \times 10^{3}\ \text{m}}{2.34 \times 10^{-4}\ \text{m/s}} = 8.55 \times 10^{8}\ \text{s} = 27\ \text{y}.$$

17.8 The atomic weight of gold = 197, and its density = $19.3 \times 10^{3}\ \text{kg/m}^3$. The mass of 1 m^3 = 19.3×10^{3} kg, and the number of gold atoms in 1 m^3

is: $N = 19.3 \times 10^{3}\ \text{kg}\left(\frac{6.02 \times 10^{26}\ \text{atoms/kg-mol}}{197\ \text{kg/kg mol}}\right) = 5.90 \times 10^{28}\ \text{atoms/m}^3$

The number of free electrons per m^3 is:

n = (number atom/m^3)(number of free electrons/atom), or

$n = (5.90 \times 10^{28}\ \text{atoms/m}^3)$(number of free electrons/atom), or

$n = (5.90 \times 10^{28}\ \text{atoms/m}^3)(1\ \text{electron/atom})$

$= 5.90 \times 10^{28}\ \text{electrons/m}^3$

17.9 We use, $I = nqAv_d$, where n = (number of charge carriers per unit volume) = (number of atoms per unit volume). We assume a contribution of 1 free electron per atom in the relationship above. For aluminum, which has a molecular weight of 27, we know that Avogadro's number of atoms, N_a, has a mass of 27 g. Thus, the mass per

atom is: $m_{atom} = \frac{27\ \text{g}}{N_a} = \frac{27\ \text{g}}{6.02 \times 10^{23}} = 4.49 \times 10^{-23}\ \text{g/atom}.$

Thus, $n = \frac{\text{density of aluminum}}{\text{mass per atom}} = \frac{2.7\ \text{g/cm}^3}{4.49 \times 10^{-23}\ \text{g/atom}}$, or

$$n = 6.02 \times 10^{22}\ \frac{\text{atoms}}{\text{cm}^3} = 6.02 \times 10^{28}\ \frac{\text{atoms}}{\text{m}^3}.$$

Therefore, the drift velocity is:

$$v_d = \frac{I}{nqA} = \frac{5\ \text{A}}{(6.02 \times 10^{28}\ \text{m}^{-3})(1.60 \times 10^{-19}\ \text{C})(4 \times 10^{-6}\ \text{m}^2)},\ \text{or}$$

$v_d = 1.3 \times 10^{-4}\ \text{m/s} = 0.13\ \text{mm/s}.$

17.10 If $R = 4.0 \times 10^5\ \Omega$, then: $\Delta V_{max} = (4.0 \times 10^5\ \Omega)(8.0 \times 10^{-5}\ A) = 32\ V$.
If $R = 2000\ \Omega$, we have: $\Delta V_{max} = (2.0 \times 10^3\ \Omega)(8.0 \times 10^{-5}\ A) = 0.16\ V$.

17.11 (a) The resistance of the device is: $R = \frac{\Delta V}{I} = \frac{120\ V}{0.50\ A} = 240\ \Omega$.

If the voltage is lowered to 90 V, we have: $I = \frac{\Delta V}{R} = \frac{90\ V}{240\ \Omega} = 0.38\ A$.

(b) If the voltage is raised to 130 V, we have: $I = \frac{\Delta V}{R} = \frac{130\ V}{240\ \Omega} = 0.54\ A$.

17.12 $A = \frac{\rho L}{R} = \frac{(5.6 \times 10^{-8}\ \Omega\ m)(2.0 \times 10^{-2}\ m)}{5.0 \times 10^{-2}\ \Omega} = 2.24 \times 10^{-8}\ m^2$.
But, $A = \pi d^2/4$. From which, $d = 1.7 \times 10^{-4}\ m = 0.17\ mm$.

17.13 $R = \frac{\rho L}{A} = \frac{(1.7 \times 10^{-8}\ \Omega\ m)(15\ m)}{8.24 \times 10^{-7}\ m^2} = 0.31\ \Omega$.

17.14 (a) The resistance of the wire is: $R = \frac{\Delta V}{I} = \frac{12\ V}{0.40\ A} = 30\ \Omega$, and

(b) $\rho = \frac{RA}{L} = \frac{30\ \Omega\ \pi(4.0 \times 10^{-3}\ m)^2}{3.2\ m} = 4.7 \times 10^{-4}\ \Omega m$

17.15 The area A' of the new "wire" is 3 times the area A_0 of the original wire.

The length of the new "wire" is $L' = \frac{L_0}{3}$ as given in the problem.

The new resistance: $R' = \frac{\rho L'}{A'} = \frac{\rho(L_0/3)}{3A_0} = \frac{1}{9}\left(\frac{\rho L_0}{A_0}\right) = \frac{R_0}{9}$

17.16 Using $\Delta V = IR = I\left(\frac{\rho L}{A}\right)$, we get: $\rho = \frac{\Delta VA}{IL} = \frac{(9.11\ V)\pi(0.001\ m)^2}{(36\ A)(50.0\ m)}$, or
$\rho = 1.59 \times 10^{-8}\ \Omega\ m$, which is the resistivity for silver.

17.17 From $R = \frac{\rho L}{A}$ we see that the minimum resistance occurs for the minimum L and the maximum A. The maximum resistance will occur with maximum length and minimum area. The possible cross-sectional areas and the associated lengths are:

$A_1 = (20\ cm)(40\ cm) = 800\ cm^2$, $L = 10\ cm$;
$A_2 = (10\ cm)(40\ cm) = 400\ cm^2$, $L = 20\ cm$; and
$A_3 = (20\ cm)(10\ cm) = 200\ cm^2$, $L = 40\ cm$.

Thus, $R_{min} = (1.7 \times 10^{-8}\ \Omega\ m)\left(\frac{0.10\ m}{800 \times 10^{-4}\ m^2}\right) = 2.13 \times 10^{-8}\ \Omega$,

and $R_{max} = (1.7 \times 10^{-8}\ \Omega\ m)\left(\frac{0.40\ m}{200 \times 10^{-4}\ m^2}\right) = 3.40 \times 10^{-7}\ \Omega$.

Using the information above:

(a) $I_{max} = \frac{\Delta V}{R_{min}} = \frac{6\ V}{2.13 \times 10^{-8}\ \Omega} = 2.82 \times 10^8\ A$.

(b) $I_{min} = \frac{\Delta V}{R_{max}} = \frac{6\ V}{3.4 \times 10^{-7}\ \Omega} = 1.76 \times 10^7\ A$.

17.18 (a) First, we find the resistance as:

$$R = \frac{\rho L}{A} = \frac{(1.7 \times 10^{-8}\ \Omega\ \text{m})(34.5\ \text{m})}{\pi(0.25 \times 10^{-3}\ \text{m})^2} = 2.987\ \Omega.$$

The current then follows from $I = \frac{\Delta V}{R} = \frac{9\ \text{V}}{2.987\ \Omega} = 3.0\ \text{A}.$

(b) Heating the wire increases the resistance to:

$R = R_0[1 + \alpha(T - T_0)] = (2.987\ \Omega)[1 + (3.9 \times 10^{-3}\ °\text{C}^{-1})(30\ °\text{C} - 20\ °\text{C})],$

$R = 3.104\ \Omega$. Thus,the current is decreased to $I = \frac{9\ \text{V}}{3.104\ \Omega} = 2.9\ \text{A}.$

17.19 The resistance of the hot wire is given by: $R = \frac{\Delta V^2}{P} = \frac{(120\ \text{V})^2}{1050\ \text{W}} = 13.7\ \Omega$

The resistivity of nichrome at 320° C is given by:

$\rho = \rho_0[1 + \alpha(\Delta T)] = (150 \times 10^{-8}\ \Omega\ \text{m})[1 + (0.4 \times 10^{-3}\ °\text{C}^{-1})(300\ °\text{C})]$

$= 1.68 \times 10^{-6}\ \Omega\ \text{m}$

The area is then found from: $A = \frac{\rho L}{R} = \frac{(1.68 \times 10^{-6}\ \Omega\ \text{m})(4.0\ \text{m})}{13.7\ \Omega}$

$= 4.9 \times 10^{-7}\ \text{m}^2$

17.20 The volume of copper is:

$V_{ol} = AL = \frac{m}{\mu} = \frac{1 \times 10^{-3}\ \text{kg}}{8.92 \times 10^3\ \text{kg/m}^3}$, or $AL = 1.12 \times 10^{-7}\ \text{m}^3$ (1)

Also, $A = \frac{\rho L}{R} = \frac{1.7 \times 10^{-8}\ \Omega\ \text{m}}{0.50\ \Omega} L$, or $A = (3.4 \times 10^{-8}\ \text{m})L.$ (2)

(a) Solving equations (1) and (2) simultaneously gives: $L = 1.8\ \text{m}.$

(b) Then, equation (2) gives $A = \pi r^2 = 6.1 \times 10^{-8}\ \text{m}^2$, and $r = 0.14\ \text{mm}.$

17.21 $R = R_0[1 + \alpha(\Delta T)]$ gives: $140\ \Omega = 19\ \Omega[1 + (4.5 \times 10^{-3}\ °\text{C}^{-1})(\Delta T)].$

Thus, $\Delta T = 1.415 \times 10^3\ °\text{C}$, and the final temperature is: $T = 1435\ °\text{C}.$

17.22 $R = R_0(1 + \alpha(\Delta T)) = 10.0\ \Omega[1 + (3.8 \times 10^{-3}\ °\text{C}^{-1})(20.0\ °\text{C})] = 10.8\ \Omega.$

17.23 At 80 °C the resistance has decreased to:

$R = R_0[1 + \alpha(\Delta T)] = 200\ \Omega[1 + (-0.5 \times 10^{-3}\ °\text{C}^{-1})(60\ °\text{C})] = 194\ \Omega.$

Thus, $I = \frac{\Delta V}{R} = \frac{5.0\ \text{V}}{194\ \Omega} = 2.58 \times 10^{-2}\ \text{A} = 26\ \text{mA}.$

17.24 We use, $R = R_0[1 + \alpha(\Delta T)]$, and find the resistance at 20°C:

$100\ \Omega = R_0[1 + (3.4 \times 10^{-3}\ °\text{C}^{-1})(20\ °\text{C})] = R_0(1.068).$

From which: $R_0 = 93.63\ \Omega.$

At the unknown temperature; $R = 97\ \Omega$. Thus,

$97\ \Omega = (93.63\ \Omega)[1 + (3.4 \times 10^{-3}\ °\text{C}^{-1})(\Delta T)]$

From which, we find $\Delta T = 10.6\ °\text{C}$, and $T = 30.6\ °\text{C}.$

17.25 $A = 3\ \text{mm}^2 = 3 \times 10^{-6}\ \text{m}^2$. At 20 °C the resistance of the wire is:

$$R = \frac{\rho L}{A} = \frac{(1.7 \times 10^{-8}\ \Omega\ \text{m})(10\ \text{m})}{3 \times 10^{-6}\ \text{m}^2} = 5.67 \times 10^{-2}\ \Omega.$$

(a) At $T = 30\ °\text{C}$, we have:

$R = R_0(1 + \alpha(\Delta T)) = 5.67 \times 10^{-2}\ \Omega(1 + (3.9 \times 10^{-3}\ °\text{C}^{-1})(10\ °\text{C}))$, or

$R = 5.89 \times 10^{-2}\ \Omega$.

(b) At $T = 10\ ^\circ C$,

$R = R_0(1 + \alpha(\Delta T)) = 5.67 \times 10^{-2}\ \Omega(1 + (3.9 \times 10^{-3}\ ^\circ C^{-1})(-10.0\ ^\circ C))$, or

$R = 5.45 \times 10^{-2}\ \Omega$.

17.26 $R = R_0[1 + \alpha(\Delta T)]$ gives: $41.4\Omega = 41.0\Omega[1 + \alpha(9.0^\circ C)]$, and

$\alpha = 1.08 \times 10^{-3}\ ^\circ C^{-1}$.

17.27 (a) The resistance of the wire is:

$$R = \frac{\rho L}{A} = \frac{(1.7 \times 10^{-8}\ \Omega\ m)(1.0\ m)}{\pi(0.50 \times 10^{-2}\ m)^2} = 2.165 \times 10^{-4}\ \Omega.$$

Then, $\Delta V = IR = (3.0\ A)(2.165 \times 10^{-4}\ \Omega) = 6.49 \times 10^{-4}\ V = 0.65\ mV$.

(b) At $T = 200\ ^\circ C$, the resistance is:

$R = R_0[1 + \alpha(\Delta T)] = 2.165 \times 10^{-4}\ \Omega[1 + (3.9 \times 10^{-3}\ ^\circ C^{-1})(180\ ^\circ C)]$, or

$R = 3.69 \times 10^{-4}\ \Omega$.

Thus, $\Delta V = IR = (3.0\ A)(3.69 \times 10^{-4}\ \Omega) = 1.11 \times 10^{-3}\ V = 1.1\ mV$.

17.28 (a) Using $R = \frac{\rho L}{A}$, we get: $R = \frac{(9.4 \times 10^{-7}\ \Omega\ m)(1\ m)}{\pi(0.0005\ m)^2} = 1.1968\ \Omega$.

(b) If the length is increased to $L' = 1.0004\,m$:

Since the volume of mercury is constant, $LA = L'A'$, so

$$A' = \frac{LA}{L'} = \frac{(1\ m)\pi(0.0005\ m)^2}{1.0004\ m} = 7.8508 \times 10^{-7}\ m^2, \text{ so}$$

$R' = \frac{\rho L'}{A'}$ becomes: $R' = \frac{(94 \times 10^{-8}\ \Omega\ m)(1.0004\ m)}{(7.8508 \times 10^{-7}\ m^2)} = 1.19780\ \Omega$.

The fractional change in the resistance is:

$$\frac{R' - R}{R} = 8 \times 10^{-4} = 0.08\%.$$

17.29 Using $R = R_0[1 + \alpha(T - T_0)]$ with $T = 0$, $R = 200.0\ \Omega$, $T_0 = 20.0\ ^\circ C$, and $\alpha = 3.92 \times 10^{-3}\ ^\circ C^{-1}$ (at 20.0 °C), we find that:

$$R_0 = \frac{R}{[1 + \alpha(T - T_0)]} = \frac{200\ \Omega}{1 + (3.92 \times 10^{-3}\ C^{-1})(0 - 20.0\ ^\circ C)} = 217\Omega.$$

Then we use $R = R_0[1 + \alpha(T - T_0)]$ again with $R = 253.8\ \Omega$. We get:

$$T = T_0 + \left(\frac{R - R_0}{\alpha R_0}\right) = 20.0\ ^\circ C + \frac{253.8\ \Omega - 217\ \Omega}{(3.92 \times 10^{-3}\ C^{-1})(217\ \Omega)} = 63.2\ ^\circ C$$

17.30 $$\%\text{ change} = \left(\frac{P_f - P_i}{P_i}\right) 100\% = \left(\frac{\frac{\Delta V_f^2}{R} - \frac{\Delta V_i^2}{R}}{\frac{\Delta V_i^2}{R}}\right) 100\% = \left(\frac{\Delta V^2_f - \Delta V^2_i}{V^2_i}\right) 100\%,$$

or

$$\%\text{ change} = \left(\frac{(140\ \Delta V)^2 - (120\ V)^2}{(120\ V)^2}\right) 100\% = 36.1\%\ \text{(increase)}$$

17.31 The maximum power that can be dissipated in the circuit is:

$P = \Delta VI = (120\ V)(15\ A) = 1800\ W$.

Thus, one can operate at most 18 bulbs rated at 100 W per bulb.

17.32 (a) $P_{loss} = I^2R = (1000\text{ A})^2[(0.31\ \Omega/\text{km})(160\text{ km})] = 4.96 \times 10^7\text{ W} = 50\text{ MW}.$

(b) The total power transmitted is:

$P = I\Delta V = (1000\text{ A})(700 \times 10^3\text{ V}) = 7 \times 10^8\text{ W} = 700\text{ MW}.$

Of this, 50 MW, or 7.1% is lost due to the resistance.

17.33 (a) The energy W = power times the time used. Thus,

$$W = Pt = (90\text{ J/s})(3600\text{ s}) = 3.2 \times 10^5\text{ J}.$$

(b) The power consumed by the color set is,

$$P = \Delta VI = (120\text{ V})(2.5\text{ A}) = 300\text{ W}.$$

Thus, $t = \frac{W}{P} = \frac{3.24 \times 10^5\text{ J}}{300\text{ W}} = 1.1 \times 10^3\text{ s} = 18\text{ min}.$

17.34 $R = \frac{\Delta V^2}{P} = \frac{(120\text{ V})^2}{1500\text{ W}} = 9.6\ \Omega$, and

$$A = \frac{\rho L}{R} = \frac{(5.6 \times 10^{-8}\ \Omega\text{ m})(3.0\text{ m})}{9.6\ \Omega} = 1.75 \times 10^{-8}\text{ m}^2.$$

17.35 The heat that must be added to the water is:

$$Q = mc\Delta T = (1.50\text{ kg})(4186\text{ J/kg °C})(40\text{ °C}) = 2.51 \times 10^5\text{ J}.$$

Thus, the power supplied by the heater is:

$P = \frac{W}{t} = \frac{Q}{t} = \frac{2.51 \times 10^5\text{ J}}{600\text{ s}} = 419\text{ W}$, and the

resistance is: $R = \frac{\Delta V^2}{P} = \frac{(120\text{ V})^2}{419\text{ W}} = 34.4\ \Omega.$

17.36 Find the resistance of a 1 meter length from $P = I^2R$, or

$R = \frac{P}{I^2} = \frac{2\text{ W/m}}{(300\text{ A})^2} = 2.22 \times 10^{-5}\ \Omega/\text{m}$. Now use $R = \frac{\rho L}{A}$ to solve for the needed cross sectional area

$A = \frac{\rho L}{R} = \frac{(1.7 \times 10^{-8}\ \Omega\text{ m})(1.00\text{ m})}{2.22 \times 10^{-5}\ \Omega/\text{m}} = 7.65 \times 10^{-4}\text{ m}^2 = \pi r^2$, so

$r = 1.56 \times 10^{-2}\text{ m} = 1.56\text{ cm}.$

17.37 (a) The power input to the motor is:

$$P_{input} = \Delta VI = (120\text{ V})(1.75\text{ A}) = 210\text{ W} = 0.282\text{ hp}.$$

The energy used in four hours is:

$W = Pt = (0.21\text{ kW})(4\text{ h}) = 0.84\text{ kWh}$, and

the cost is: cost = (\$0.06/kWh)(0.84 kWh) = \$ 0.0504 = 5 ¢.

(b) $Eff = \frac{P_{output}}{P_{input}} = \frac{0.2\text{ hp}}{0.282\text{ hp}} = 0.71$, or 71 %.

17.38 $W = Pt = (90\text{ W})(21\text{ h}) = 1890\text{ Wh} = 1.89\text{ kWh}.$

Thus, the cost is: cost = (7 cents/kWh) (1.89 kWh) = 13.2 cents

---

17.39 The total energy used was:

$$\text{energy} = \frac{\text{cost}}{\text{rate}} = \frac{200\text{ dollars}}{0.080\text{ dollars/kWh}} = 2.50 \times 10^3\text{ kWh}.$$

The time required to use this much energy at a rate of 24.0 kW is:

$t = \frac{\text{total energy used}}{\text{power}} = \frac{2.50 \times 10^3\text{ kWh}}{24.0\text{ kW}} = 104.2\text{ h}$. Since there are 31 days in January, the average time per day was:

$$\text{average} = \frac{104.2\ \text{h}}{31\ \text{days}} = 3.36\ \text{h/day}.$$

17.40 (power output) = (efficiency)(power input)

$$(2.50\ \text{hp})\left(\frac{746\ \text{W}}{1\ \text{hp}}\right) = (0.900)\, P_{input}, \text{ so} \qquad P_{input} = 2070\ \text{W} = 2.070\ \text{kW}.$$

(a) $I = \frac{P}{\Delta V} = \frac{2070\ \text{W}}{110\ \text{V}} = 18.8\ \text{A}.$

(b) $W = Pt = (2.07\ \text{kW})(1\ \text{h}) = 2.07\ \text{kWh}$

$$= (2.07\ \text{kWh})\left(\frac{3.60 \times 10^6\ \text{J}}{1\ \text{kWh}}\right) = 7.45 \times 10^6\ \text{J}.$$

(c) cost = (energy used)(rate) = (2.07 kWh)(8.0 cents/kWh) = 17 cents.

17.41 The power savings is 40 W - 11 W = 29 W. Saving 29 W for 100 hours of use represents an energy savings of:
$E = (29\ \text{W})(100\ \text{h}) = 2900\ \text{W h} = 2.9\ \text{kWh}.$

The monetary saving is thus $2.9\ \text{kWh}\left(\frac{\$0.08}{\text{kWh}}\right) = \$0.23$ or 23 cents.

17.42 $P = 1500\ \text{kcal/h} = 1744\ \text{W}$, and

$I = \frac{P}{\Delta V} = \frac{1744\ \text{W}}{110\ \text{V}} = 15.9\ \text{A}.$ (A 20 Ampere fuse is required.)

17.43 The energy, Q needed to raise 200 kg from 15°C to 80 °C is:

$$Q = mc\Delta T = (200\ \text{kg})(4186\ \text{J/kg °C})(80\ \text{°C} - 15\ \text{°C}) = 5.44 \times 10^7\ \text{J},$$

$$Q = (5.44 \times 10^7\ \text{J})\left(\frac{1\ \text{kWh}}{3.6 \times 10^6\ \text{J}}\right) = 15.1\ \text{kWh}.$$

The total cost at \$0.080 per kWh is then (15.1kWh)(\$0.080/kWh) = \$1.21.

17.44 The current drawn by the wire is: $I = \frac{P}{\Delta V} = \frac{48\ \text{W}}{20\ \text{V}} = 2.4\ \text{A},$

and the resistance of the wire is: $R = \frac{\Delta V}{I} = \frac{20\ \text{V}}{2.4\ \text{A}} = 8.33\ \Omega.$

Thus, from $R = \frac{\rho L}{A}$ we have: $L = \frac{RA}{\rho} = \frac{(8.33\ \Omega)\ 4 \times 10^{-6}\ \text{m}^2}{3 \times 10^{-8}\ \Omega\ \text{m}} = 1.1 \times 10^3\ \text{m}.$

17.45 (a) Using $P = I\Delta V$, we get $P = (6.0\ \text{A})(120\ \text{V}) = 720\ \text{W} = 720\ \text{J/s}.$
In 20 min = 1200 s, a total of $(720\ \text{J/s})(1200\ \text{s}) = 8.6 \times 10^5$ J of thermal energy is produced.

(b) Since $8.64 \times 10^5\ \text{J} = 0.24\ \text{kWh}$, we see that it costs

$$\left(\frac{\$0.08}{\text{kWh}}\right)(0.24\ \text{kWh}) = \$0.0192 = 1.9\ \text{cents}.$$

17.46 $Q = IA = (90\ \text{A})(1\ \text{h}) = (90.0\ \text{C/s})(3600\ \text{s}) = 3.24 \times 10^5\ \text{C}.$

17.47 The resistance of the 4.0 cm length of wire between the feet is:

$$R = \frac{\rho L}{A} = \frac{\left(1.7 \times 10^{-8}\ \Omega\ \text{m}\right)(0.040\ \text{m})}{\pi(1.1 \times 10^{-2}\ \text{m})^2} = 1.8 \times 10^{-6}\ \Omega.$$

The voltage between the feet is:

$$\Delta V = IR = (50\ \text{A})(1.8 \times 10^{-6}\ \Omega) = 9.0 \times 10^{-5}\ \text{V} = 90\ \mu\text{V}$$

17.48 The time required for one revolution is: $T = \frac{2\pi}{\omega} = \frac{2\pi}{100\pi \text{ rad/s}} = 0.020\text{ s}$.
The charge that passes a fixed point in the circular path in this time is $\Delta Q = 8.00 \times 10^{-9}$ C. The average current is then:

$$I = \frac{\Delta Q}{\Delta t} = \frac{8.00 \times 10^{-9}\text{ C}}{0.020\text{ s}} = 4.00 \times 10^{-7}\text{ C/s} = 0.400\ \mu\text{A}$$

17.49 (a) From the definition of current, we see that: $\Delta Q = I(\Delta T)$.
From this, we see that the charge can be found by finding the total area under a curve of I versus t. Thus,
Q= (area of rectangle A_1) + 2(area of triangle A_2)
+ (rectangular area A_3).

$$Q = (2\text{ A})(5\text{ s}) + 2\left(\frac{(1\text{ s})(4\text{ A})}{2}\right) + (1\text{ s})(4\text{ A}) = 10\text{ C} + 4\text{ C} + 4\text{ C} = 18\text{ C}.$$

(b) The constant current would be: $I = \frac{\Delta Q}{\Delta t} = \frac{18\text{ C}}{5\text{ s}} = 3.6\text{ A}$.

17.50 The volume of aluminum present is:

$$V_{ol} = \frac{m}{\mu} = \frac{0.115\text{ kg}}{2.70 \times 10^3\text{ kg/m}^3} = 4.26 \times 10^{-5}\text{ m}^3$$

(a) For the cylindrical volume described,

$$V_{ol} = Ah = \left(\frac{\pi L^2}{4}\right)L = \frac{\pi L^3}{4}.$$

Thus, $\frac{\pi L^3}{4} = 4.26 \times 10^{-5}$ m, so $L = 3.79 \times 10^{-2}$ m.
The resistance between the ends is then:

$$R = \rho\frac{L}{A} = 4\rho\frac{L}{(\pi L^2)} = \frac{4\rho}{\pi L} = \frac{4(2.82 \times 10^{-8}\ \Omega\text{ m})}{\pi(3.78 \times 10^{-2}\text{ m})} = 9.48 \times 10^{-7}\ \Omega$$

(b) For a cube, $V_{ol} = L^3 = 4.26 \times 10^{-5}\text{ m}^3$. Thus, $L = 3.49 \times 10^{-2}$ m
and the resistance between opposite faces is:

$$R = \frac{\rho L}{A} = \frac{\rho L}{L^2} = \frac{\rho}{L} = \frac{2.82 \times 10^{-8}\ \Omega\text{ m}}{3.49 \times 10^{-2}\text{ m}} = 8.07 \times 10^{-7}\ \Omega$$

17.51 The area of the wire is: $A = 7.85 \times 10^{-5}\text{ m}^2$.
The current in the wire is: $I = \frac{\Delta V}{R} = \frac{15\text{ V}}{0.1\ \Omega} = 150\text{ A}$.
We now can find the density of free electrons from $I = nqAv_d$.

$$n = \frac{I}{qv_dA} = \frac{150\text{ A}}{(1.60 \times 10^{-19}\text{ C})(3.17 \times 10^{-4}\text{ m/s})(7.85 \times 10^{-5}\text{ m}^2)}, \text{ or}$$

$n = 3.77 \times 10^{28}\text{ electrons/m}^3$.

17.52 (a) The volume of the wire is: $\text{Vol} = \frac{50\text{ g}}{7.86\text{ g/cm}^3} = 6.36\text{ cm}^3$.
We also know that:

$$\text{Volume} = AL, \text{ or } A = \frac{\text{Vol}}{L} = \frac{6.36\text{ cm}^3}{L} = \frac{6.36 \times 10^{-6}\text{ m}^3}{L}. \quad (1)$$

From the definition of resistance, we find:

$$R = \frac{\rho L}{A} \text{ becomes, } 1.5\ \Omega = (11 \times 10^{-8}\ \Omega\text{ m})\frac{L}{A}, \text{ or}$$

$$A = \left(7.33 \times 10^{-8}\ \text{m}\right)L. \qquad (2)$$

Solving (1) and (2) simultaneously gives:

$L = 9.3$ m, and $A = 6.83 \times 10^{-7}$ m^2.

(b) From the area of the wire, we can find its diameter to be:

$d = 9.3 \times 10^{-4}$ m $= 0.93$ mm.

17.53 $R = R_c + R_n = R_c(1 + \alpha_c(T - T_0)) + R_n(1 + \alpha_n(T - T_o))$

$0 = R_c\alpha_c(T - T_0) + R_n\alpha_n(T - T_0)$

$$R_c = -R_n \frac{\alpha_n}{\alpha_c}$$

$$R = -R_n \frac{\alpha_n}{\alpha_c} + R_n$$

$$R_n = R(1 - \frac{\alpha_n}{\alpha_c})^{-1} \qquad R_c = R(1 - \frac{\alpha_c}{\alpha_n})^{-1}$$

$$R_n = 10.0\,\text{k}\Omega\,[1 - \frac{(0.4 \times 10^{-3}/\text{C}°)}{(-0.5 \times 10\text{-}3/\text{C}°)}]^{-1}$$

$R_n = 5.6\,\text{k}\Omega$ and $R_c = 4.4\,\text{k}\Omega$

17.54 Let α be the temperature coefficient at 20 °C, and α' be the temperature coefficient at 0°C. Then $R = R_0[1 + \alpha_0(T - 20\ °\text{C})]$, and $R = R'[1 + \alpha'(T - 0°\text{C})]$ must both give the correct resistance at any temperature T. That is, we must have:

$$R_0[1 + \alpha(T - 20\ °\text{C})] = R'[1 + \alpha'_1(T - 0°\text{C})]. \qquad (1)$$

Setting $T = 0$ in equation (1) yields: $R' = R_0[1 + \alpha'(20\ °\text{C})]$, and setting $T = 20°$C in equation (1) gives: $R_0 = R'[1 - \alpha(20\ °\text{C})]$. Put R' from the first of these results into the second to obtain:

$R_0 = R_0[1 - \alpha(20\ °\text{C})]\,[1 + \alpha'(20\ \text{C})]$, and therefore

$$1 + \alpha'(20°\text{C}) = \frac{1}{1 - \alpha(20°\text{C})}, \text{ which simplifies to}$$

$$\alpha' = \frac{\alpha}{[1 - \alpha(20°\text{C})]}.$$

From this, the temperature coefficient, based on a reference temperature of 0°C, may be computed for any material. For example, using this, the table of temperature coefficients becomes at 0°C (°C^{-1}):

Material	Temp Coefficients at 0°C
Silver	4.1×10^{-3}
Copper	4.2×10^{-3}
Gold	3.6×10^{-3}
Aluminum	4.2×10^{-3}
Tungsten	4.9×10^{-3}
Iron	5.6×10^{-3}
Platinum	4.25×10^{-3}
Lead	4.2×10^{-3}
Nichrome	0.4×10^{-3}
Carbon	-0.5×10^{-3}
Germanium	-24×10^{-3}
Silicon	-30×10^{-3}

17.55 (a) Using $P = \frac{\Delta V^2}{R}$ with $\Delta V = 120$ V, gives $R = 144\ \Omega$.

(b) $R = \frac{\rho L}{A}$ and $A = 10^{-2}\ \text{mm}^2 = 10^{-8}\ \text{m}^2$. Therefore,

$$L = \frac{RA}{\rho} = \frac{(144\ \Omega)(10^{-8}\ \text{m}^2)}{5.6 \times 10^{-8}\ \Omega\ \text{m}} = 26\ \text{m}.$$

(c) To fit the required length in a small space.

(d) From $L = L_0[1 + \alpha(T - T_0)]$ we find:

$$25.7\ \text{m} = L_0[1 + (4.5 \times 10^{-6})^\circ\text{C}^{-1})(2600\ ^\circ\text{C} - 20^\circ\text{C})] = 1.011 L_0, \text{ and}$$

$$L_0 = 25\ \text{m}.$$

17.56 Each speaker receives 60 W of power. Using $P = I^2R$, we then have $I = \sqrt{\frac{P}{R}} = \sqrt{\frac{60\ \text{W}}{4\ \Omega}} = 3.87$ A, so the system is not adequately protected since the fuse should be set to melt at 3.87 A, or less.

17.57 $R = \frac{\rho L}{A} = \frac{\rho L}{\pi(r_b^2 - r_a^2)} = \frac{(3.5 \times 10^5\ \Omega\ \text{m})(0.04\ \text{m})}{\pi((0.012\ \text{m})^2 - (0.005\ \text{m})^2)} = 37\ \text{M}\Omega.$

17.58 The volume of the wire remains a constant during the stretching process. Thus, $V = LA = \text{constant}$. If $r = \frac{r_0}{4}$, then $A = \pi r^2 = \pi\frac{r_0^2}{16} = \frac{A_0}{16}$.

Therefore, $LA = L(\frac{A_0}{16}) = L_0A_0$, or $L = 16L_0$, and

$$R = \frac{\rho L}{A} = \frac{\rho(16L_0)}{\frac{A_0}{16}} = 256\frac{\rho L_0}{A_0} = 256\ R_0.$$ If $R_0 = 1\ \Omega$, then $R = 256\ \Omega$.

17.59 The power in the beam is $(4.0 \times 10^6\ \text{V})(25 \times 10^{-3}\ \text{A}) = 10^5$ W.
The energy absorbed per kg of water as it warms by 50°C is:

$$\frac{Q}{m} = c\Delta T = (4186\ \text{J/kg}\ ^\circ\text{C})(50\ ^\circ\text{C}) = 2.1 \times 10^5\ \text{J/kg}.$$

Thus, $\frac{\Delta m}{\Delta t} = \frac{P}{Q/m} = \frac{(10^5\ \text{J/s})}{2.1 \times 10^5\ \text{J/kg}} = 0.48\ \frac{\text{kg}}{\text{s}}$

17.60 (a) $R = \frac{\rho L}{A} = \frac{(1.7 \times 10^{-8})(0.24)}{(0.08)(0.002)} = 2.6 \times 10^{-5}\ \Omega.$

(b) $m = (\text{volume})(\text{density})$ but $R = \frac{\rho L}{A}$ and $A = \frac{\text{volume}}{L}$. Therefore,

$$m = \frac{\rho L^2}{R}(\text{density}) = \frac{1.7 \times 10^{-8}(1.5 \times 10^3)^2}{(4.5)}(8.92 \times 10^3) = 76\ \text{kg}.$$

ANSWERS TO CONCEPTUAL QUESTIONS

2. The number of cars would correspond to charge Q. The rate of flow of cars past a point would correspond to current.

4. To analyze this situation, it is important to note that the voltage V across each lightbulb is the same. Since the power is $P = \Delta V^2/R$, the 25-W bulb would have the higher resistance. Furthermore, since $P = I\,\Delta V$, we see that the 100-W bulb carries the greater current.

6. Since the current is not proportional to the applied voltage, the conductor does not obey Ohm's law. This occurs, for example, in an electronic device known as a diode.

8. Let us assume that we use the dryer for about one-half hour per day, for a total of about 180 h per year. Thus, for the 1.5 kW dryer, the total amount of energy consumed in kWh is E = (1.5 kW)(180 h) = 270 kWh. At a cost of eight cents per kWh, the cost for this much energy is almost twenty-two dollars.

10. The knob is connected to a variable resistor. As you increase the magnitude of the resistance in the circuit, the current is reduced and the bulb dims.

12. Superconducting devices are expensive to operate primarily because they must be kept at very low temperatures. As the onset temperature for superconductivity is increased toward room temperature, it becomes easier to accomplish this reduction in temperature. In fact, if room temperature superconductors could be achieved, this requirement would disappear altogether.

14. The potential difference across each conductor is the same. Since the power dissipated in a conductor is $P = \Delta V^2/R$, the conductor with the lower resistance will dissipate more power.

16. Because an ampere is a coulomb per second, an ampere-hour is equal to 3600 C. This is the amount of charge that the battery can "push" through itself, increasing the energy of each bit of this charge by the advertised voltage.

CHAPTER EIGHTEEN SOLUTIONS

Chapter Eighteen Readings

Baker, P.F., "The Nerve Axon," *Scientific American*, March 1966, p. 74.

Debuvitz, W., "Christmas Tree Lights: A Continuing Series?" *The Physics Teacher*, 30, 530, 1992.

Katz, B., "The Nerve Impulse," *Scientific American*, November 1952, p. 55.

Kordesch, K and Tomantschger, K., "Primary Batteries," *The Physics Teacher*, January 1981, p. 12.

Robinson, T.F, Factor, S.M, and Sonnenblick, E.H., "The Heart as a Suction Pump," Scientific American, June 1986, p. 84.

Scher, A.M., "The Electrocardiagram," Scientific American, November 1961, p. 132.

Shepherd, G.M., "Microcircuits in the Nervous System," *Scientific American*, February 1978, p. 92

Solomon, A.K., "Pumps in the Living Cell," *Scientific American*, August 1962, p. 100.

18.1 Using $\Delta V = I(R + r)$. we get: $r = \frac{\Delta V}{I} - R = \frac{9.00\ \text{V}}{117 \times 10^{-3}\text{A}} - 72.0 = 4.92\ \Omega$.

18.2 (a) Resistors in series add. Thus, the equivalent resistance is:

$$R_{eq} = R_1 + R_2 + R_3 = 4.0\ \Omega + 8.0\ \Omega + 12\ \Omega = 24\ \Omega.$$

(b) The current is the same for resistors in series: $I = \frac{\Delta V}{R_{eq}} = \frac{24\ \text{V}}{24\ \Omega} = 1.0\ \text{A}$

18.3 (a) The equivalent resistor for the two in series is:

$$R_{eq} = R_1 + R_2 = 18\ \Omega + 6.0\ \Omega = 24\ \Omega.$$

From this, we can find the current through the circuit as,

$$I = \frac{\Delta V}{R_{eq}} = \frac{18\ \text{V}}{24\ \Omega} = 0.75\ \text{A}.$$

Since resistors in series carry the same current, this is the current through both the 18 Ω and the 6 Ω resistors. The voltage drop across each resistor can now be found as:

$$\Delta V_{18} = IR_{18} = (0.75\ \text{A})(18\ \Omega) = 13.5\ \text{V}, \text{ and}$$

$$\Delta V_6 = IR_6 = (0.75\ \text{A})(6.0\ \Omega) = 4.5\ \text{V}.$$

(b) For the parallel combination, the potential difference is the same across both resistors and equal to that of the battery. Thus,

$$\Delta V_{18} = \Delta V_6 = 18\ \text{V}.$$

The currents are given by:

$$I_{18} = \frac{\Delta V}{R_{18}} = \frac{18\ \text{V}}{18\ \Omega} = 1.0\ \text{A, and} \quad I_6 = \frac{\Delta V}{R_6} = \frac{18\ \text{V}}{6.0\ \Omega} = 3.0\ \text{A}.$$

18.4 (a) The equivalent resistance for a parallel combination of resistors is given by:

$$\frac{1}{R_{eq}}=\frac{1}{R_1}+\frac{1}{R_2}+\frac{1}{R_3}=\frac{1}{4.0\ \Omega}+\frac{1}{8.0\ \Omega}+\frac{1}{12\ \Omega}.$$

From which, $R_{eq}=\frac{24}{11}\ \Omega$.

(b) The potential difference across each parallel element is the same.

Thus, $I_4=\frac{24\ \text{V}}{4.0\ \Omega}=6.0\ \text{A}$, $I_8=\frac{24\ \text{V}}{8.0\ \Omega}=3.0\ \text{A}$, and $I_{12}=\frac{\Delta V}{R_{12}}=\frac{24\ \text{V}}{12\ \Omega}=$ 2.0 A.

18.5 (a) We are given that, $\Delta V_{bc}=12$ V (See the sketch.)

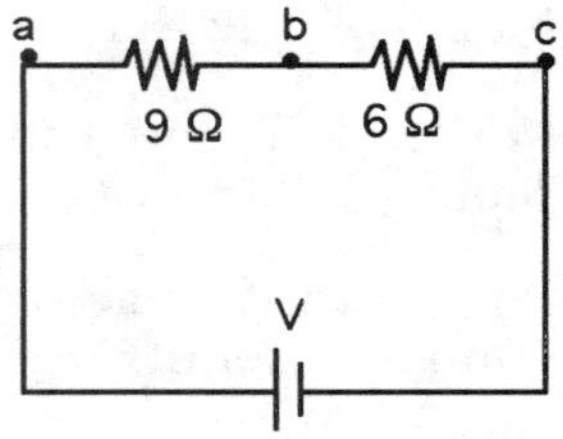

Therefore, $I=\frac{\Delta V_{bc}}{R_{bc}}=\frac{12\ \text{V}}{6.0\ \Omega}=2.0\ \text{A}$

From this, we can find the voltage drop across the 9 Ω resistor as:

$\Delta V_{ab}=IR_{ab}=(2.0\ \text{A})(9.0\ \Omega)=18\ \text{V}$.

Thus, the voltage of the battery is:

$\Delta V=\Delta V_{bc}+\Delta V_{ab}=18\ \text{V}+12\ \text{V}=30\ \text{V}$.

(b) The voltage setting of the power supply equals the voltage drop across the 9 Ω resistor: $\Delta V=IR=(0.25\ \text{A})(9.0\ \Omega)=2.3\ \text{V}$.

18.6 The three resistors in parallel are replaced by an equivalent resistance of:
$$\frac{1}{R_{eqp}}=\frac{1}{R_1}+\frac{1}{R_2}+\frac{1}{R_3}=\frac{1}{18\ \Omega}+\frac{1}{9.0\ \Omega}+\frac{1}{6.0\ \Omega}$$

From which, $R_{eqp}=3.0\ \Omega$.

This resistor is now in series with the 12 Ω resistor. The two add for an end result of: $R_{eq}=R_1+R_2=12\ \Omega+3.0\ \Omega=15\ \Omega$.

18.7 The resistor going upwards (with one free end) can be ignored. The two resistors in series have an equivalent resistance of 2 R and the two in parallel have a resistance of $R/2$. The two combinations are in series giving a total resistance of 2.5 R.

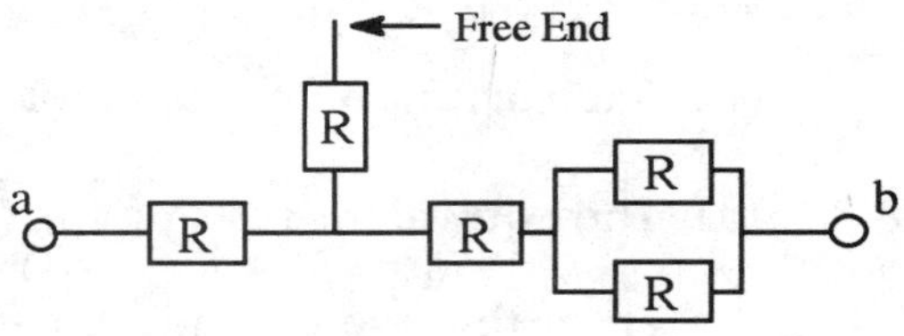

18.8 The rules for combining resistors in series and parallel are used to reduce the circuit to an equivalent resistor according to the stages indicated below. The resultant is 9.83 Ω.

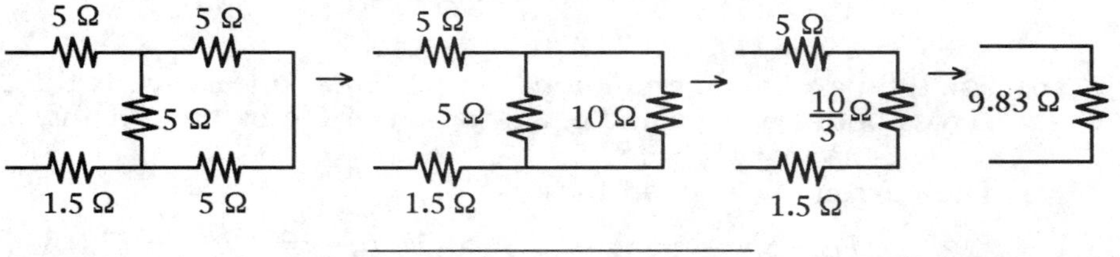

18.9 (a) The rules for combining resistors in series and parallel are used to reduce the circuit to an equivalent resistor according to the stages indicated below. The resultant is 5.13 Ω.

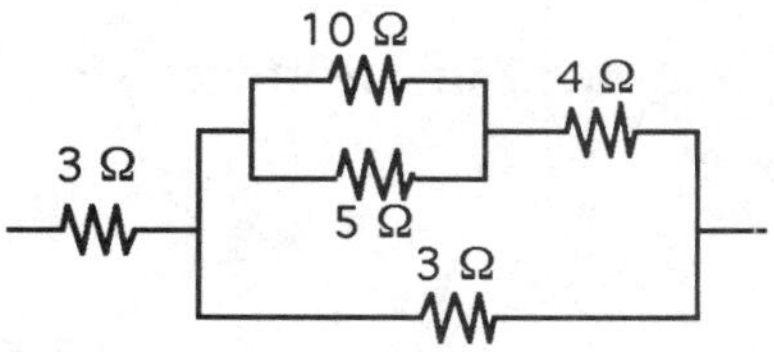

Figure 1

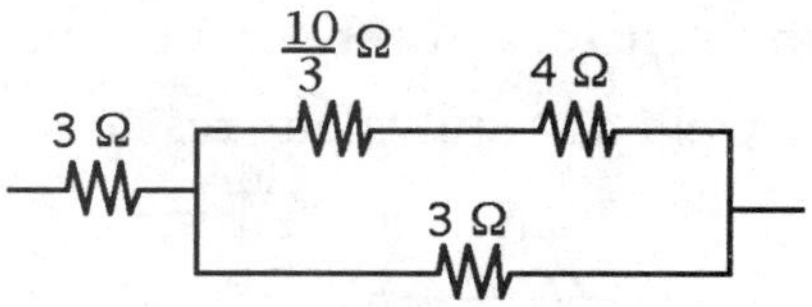

Figure 2

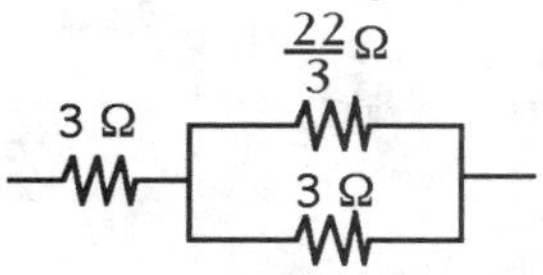

Figure 3

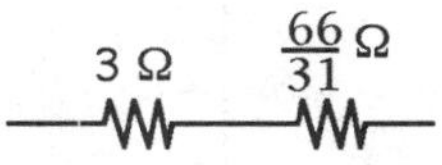

Figure 4

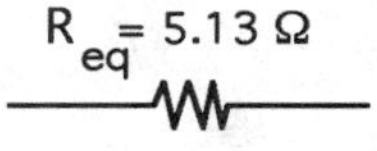

Figure 5

(b) $P = I^2 R_{eq} = \dfrac{\Delta V^2}{R_{eq}} = 4\text{ W}$, so $\Delta V^2 = (4.00\text{ W})(5.13\ \Omega) = 20.52\text{ V}^2$, or $\Delta V = 4.53\text{ V}$.

18.10 There are 7 distinct values possible:
(1) use one alone, value = R (2) use two in series, value = $2R$
(3) three in series, value = $3R$ (4) two in parallel, value = $R/2$
(5) three in parallel, value = $R/3$ (6) two in series with one in parallel, value = $(2/3)R$ (7) two in parallel with one in series, value = $(3/2)R$

18.11 First, consider the parallel case. We know the voltage drop across B is 6.0 V, and we are given that the current through it is 2.0 A. Thus, we can find the resistance of B as: $R_B = \dfrac{6.0\text{ V}}{2.0\text{ A}} = 3.0\ \Omega$.
Now, consider the series connection. We are given that the voltage across A is 4.0 V, but we also know that the voltage across B must be 2.0 V. Thus, let us apply Ohm's law to B to find the current in the circuit. We find: $I = \dfrac{\Delta V}{R_B} = \dfrac{2.0\text{ V}}{3.0\ \Omega} = \dfrac{2}{3}\text{ A}$. Thus, the resistance of A can now be found as:

$$R_A = \frac{\Delta V}{I} = \frac{4.0\text{ V}}{\frac{2}{3}\text{ A}} = 6.0\ \Omega.$$

18.12 (a) Put two 50 Ω resistors in parallel to get 25 Ω, and then put that combination in series with a 20 Ω resistor for an equivalent resistance of 45 Ω.
(b) Put two 50 Ω resistors in parallel to get 25 Ω, and put two 20 Ω resistors in parallel to get 10 Ω. We then put these two combinations in series to get 35 Ω.

18.13 The equivalent resistance is given by $R_{eq} = R + R_1$, where
$\dfrac{1}{R_1} = \dfrac{1}{120} + \dfrac{1}{40} + \dfrac{1}{R+5} = \dfrac{1}{30} + \dfrac{1}{R+5} = \dfrac{R+35}{30(R+5)}$, or $R_1 = \dfrac{30(R+5)}{R+35}$.
Therefore, $R_{eq} = R + \dfrac{30(R+5)}{R+35} = \dfrac{(R^2 + 65R + 150)}{R+35}$
Since $R_{eq} = 75\ \Omega$, we get $R^2 + 65R + 150 = 75R + 2625$, or
$R^2 - 10R - 2475 = 0$, yielding: $R = 55\ \Omega$.

18.14 The resistors in the circuit can be combined in the stages shown below to yield an equivalent resistance of $\frac{63}{11}\ \Omega$.

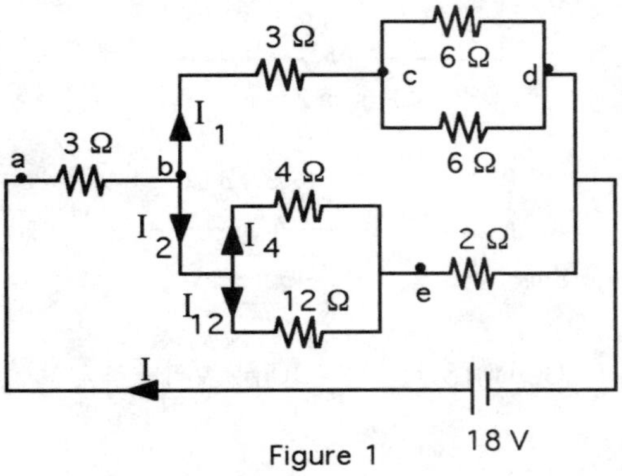

Figure 1

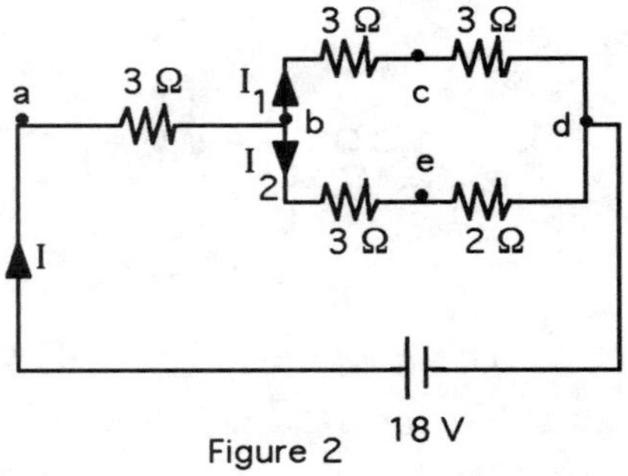

Figure 2

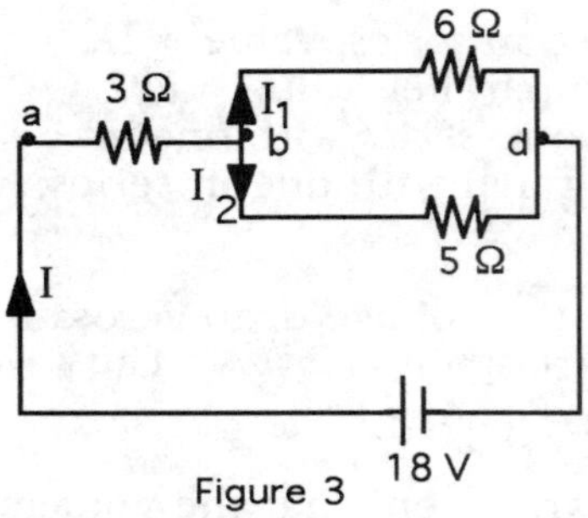

Figure 3

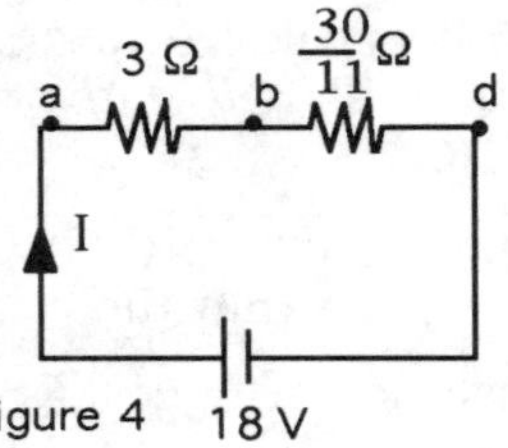

Figure 4

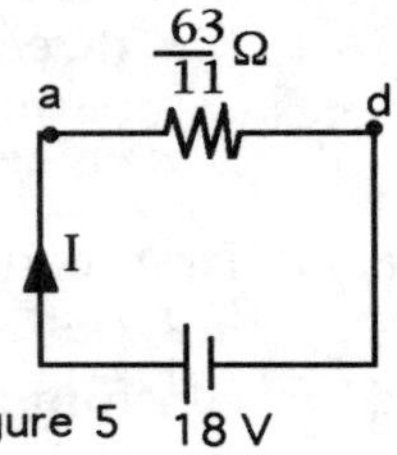

Figure 5

From Fig. 5, we have: $I = \frac{\Delta V}{R} = \frac{18\ \text{V}}{\frac{63}{11}\ \Omega} = 3.14\ \text{A}.$

Then, from Fig. 4, $\Delta V_{bd} = (3.14\ \text{A})\left(\frac{30}{11}\ \Omega\right) = 8.57\ \text{V}.$

From Fig. 3, $I_2 = \frac{\Delta V_{bd}}{5\ \Omega} = \frac{8.57\ \text{V}}{5\ \Omega} = 1.71\ \text{A}.$

From Fig. 2, $\Delta V_{be} = (1.71\ \text{A})(3\ \Omega) = 5.14\ \text{V}.$

Finally, from Fig. 1, $I_{12} = \frac{5.14\ \text{V}}{12\ \Omega} = 0.429\ \text{A}.$

18.15 Since the center branch is not a continuous conducting path, no current flows in that branch. We apply the loop rule to the outer loop of the circuit.

$$12\ \text{V} - 10I - 5.0I - 8.0\text{V} - 2.0I - 3.0I = 0,$$

so $I = \frac{4.0\ \Delta\text{V}}{20\ \Omega} = 0.20\ \text{A}.$

Now, start at b and go around the upper loop:

$$V_{ab} + 10(0.20) - 12\ \text{V} + (3.0)(0.20) + 0 + 4.0\ \text{V} = 0$$

from which, $V_{ab} = 5.4$ V (with point a at a higher potential than b).

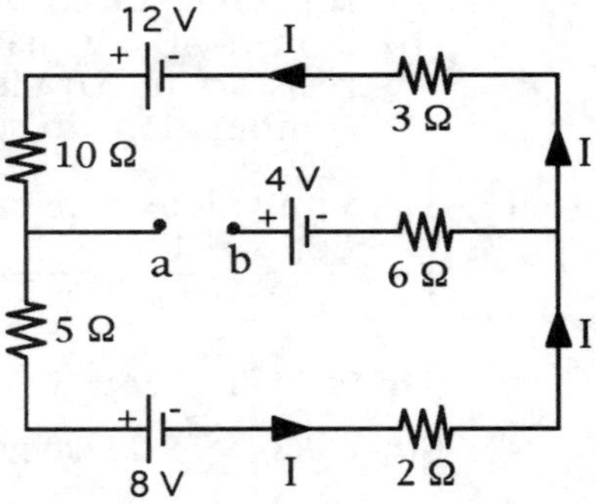

18.16 (a) Moving clockwise around the loop, we find:

$$20.0 - 2000\,I - 30.0 - 2500\,I + 25.0 - 500\,I = 0, \text{ from which}$$
$$I = 0.003 \text{ A} = 3 \text{ mA.}$$

(b) Start at the grounded point and move up the left side.

$V_A = 20.0 \text{ V} - 2000\,\Omega(0.003 \text{ A}) - 30.0 \text{ V} - 1000\,\Omega(0.003 \text{ A})$, which gives

$$V_A = -19.0 \text{ V.}$$

(c) $V_{1500} = (1500\,\Omega)(0.003 \text{ A}) = 4.5 \text{ V.}$

(The upper end is at the higher potential.)

18.17 The change in potential between a and b, following the path taken by the current I_1 is:

$$\Delta V_{ba} = 24 \text{ V} - 6.0(3.0) = +6.0 \text{ V}$$

Then calculating ΔV_{ba} along the path followed by I_2 yields:

$$\Delta V_{ba} = -3.0 I_2 = +6.0, \text{ so } I_2 = -2.0 \text{ A.}$$

Thus, I_2 must flow from b toward a through the 3 Ω resistor. Applying the junction rule at point b gives:

$$I_3 = I_1 + I_2 = 3.0 - 2.0 = +1.0 \text{ A.}$$

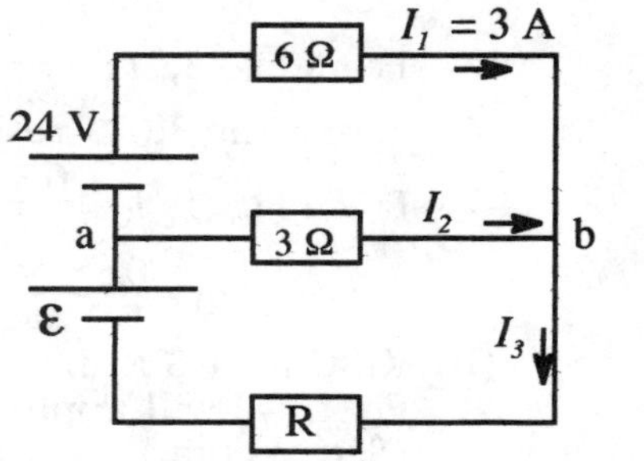

18.18 Apply the junction rule at point a:

$$I_1 + I_2 = 2.00, \text{ or}$$
$$I_2 = 2.00 - I_1.$$

Apply the loop rule to the right hand loop moving CW from a:

$-8.00 \text{ V} + 6.00 I_1 - 12.0(2.00 - I_1) = 0.$ From which,

$I_1 = 1.78$ A.

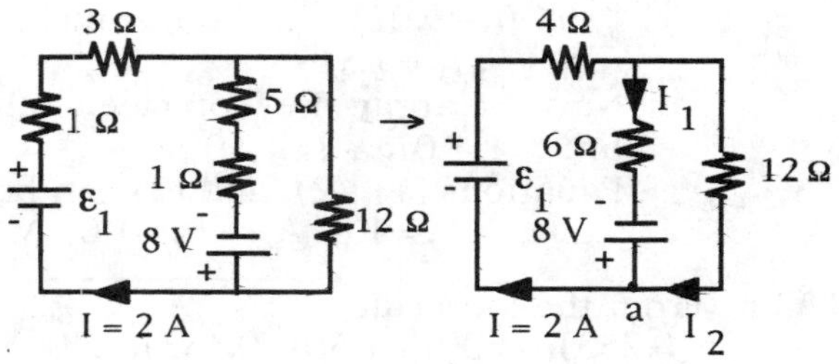

Finally, use the loop rule on the left hand loop moving CW from a:

$$+\varepsilon_1 - (4.00\,\Omega)(2.00 \text{ A}) - (6.00\,\Omega)(1.78 \text{ A}) + 8.00 \text{ V} = 0$$

gives $\varepsilon_1 = 10.67$ V with the polarity indicated.

18.19 Applying the loop rule to loop aefba gives:

$$+24 - 3(6) - 3(I_2) = 0,$$

or $I_2 = -2$ A.

Then the junction rule at point b yields

$$I_3 = 3 \text{ A} - 2 \text{ A} = +1 \text{ A.}$$

Finally, the loop rule applied to loop aefbhga gives:

$$+24 - 3(6) - 12(1) + \varepsilon = 0,$$

or $\varepsilon = 6$ V.

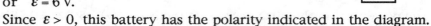

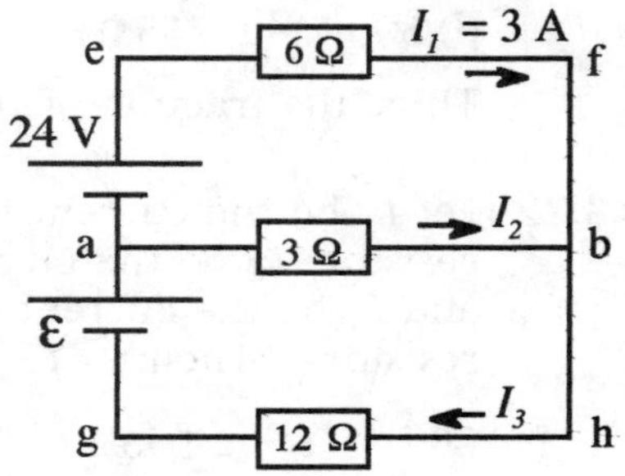

Since $\varepsilon > 0$, this battery has the polarity indicated in the diagram.

18.20 (a) The resistors can be combined as shown below to yield an equivalent of 6.6 Ω.

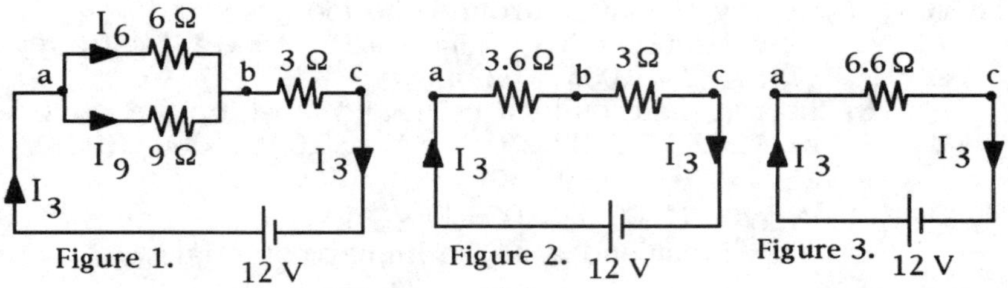

(a)

From Fig. 3, $I_3 = \dfrac{12\text{ V}}{6.6\ \Omega} = 1.82\text{ A}$. Then from Fig. 2, the voltage drop across the 3.6 Ω resistor is $\Delta V_{3.6} = (1.82\text{ A})(3.6\ \Omega) = 6.55\text{ V}$.

From Fig. 1, $I_6 = \dfrac{6.55\text{ V}}{6.0\ \Omega} = 1.09\text{ A}$, and

$$I_9 = \frac{6.55\text{ V}}{9.0\ \Omega} = 0.727\text{ A},$$

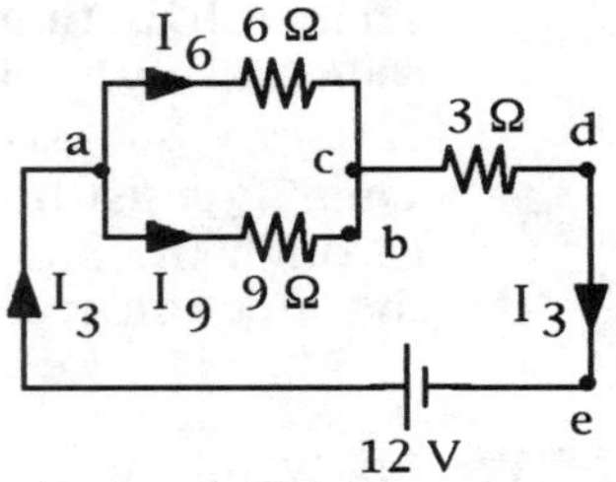

(b)

(b) KIRCHOFF'S RULES

First, we will apply the junction rule at a. (See sketch.) $I_3 = I_6 + I_9$ (1)

Now, we apply the loop rule to acba:

$-6.0I_6 + 9.0I_9 = 0$, from which, we find

$I_6 = 1.5I_9$ (2)

Next, we apply the loop rule to abcdea to find: $-9.0I_9 - 3.0I_3 + 12 = 0$,

or $3.0I_9 + I_3 = 4.0$ (3)

Equations (1), (2), and (3) can be solved simultaneously to find :

$I_3 = 1.82\text{ A}$, $I_6 = 1.09\text{ A}$, and $I_9 = 0.727\text{ A}$.

18.21 From the loop rule:

$-(0.255)(0.600) + 1.50 - (0.153)(0.600) + 1.50 - (0.600)R = 0$

From which, $R = 4.59\ \Omega$.

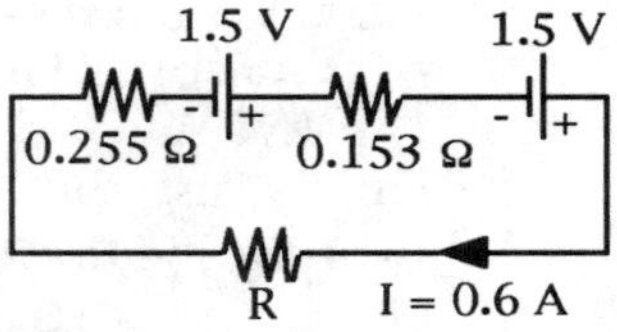

The total power dissipated = I^2R_{total}, or

$P = (0.600\text{ A})^2(0.255\ \Omega + 0.153\ \Omega + 4.59\ \Omega) = 1.8\text{ W}$,

and the total power dissipated within the batteries is:

$(0.600\text{ A})^2(0.255\ \Omega) + (0.600\text{ A})^2(0.153\ \Omega) = 0.147\text{ W}$.

Thus, the fraction of the power dissipated internally $= \dfrac{0.147}{1.8\text{ W}} = 0.082$.

18.22 Let I_1 be the current flowing toward the right through the 20 Ω resistor, I_2 be the current flowing leftward through the 90 Ω resistor, and I_3 be the current flowing leftward through the 30 Ω and 50 Ω resistors. Then: $12 - 90I_2 - 20I_1 = 0$, $12 - 50I_3 - 30I_3 - 20I_1 = 0$,

and $I_1 = I_2 + I_3$. Solving these simultaneously gives $I_3 = \dfrac{27}{250}\text{ A}$.

The power lost in the 50 Ω resistor is then: $P = (I_3)^2(50\ \Omega) = 0.58\text{ W}$.

18.23 Junction rule at point a:

$I_1 = I_2 + I_3$ (1)

Loop rule on upper loop:

$-3.0(I_3) + 24 - 2.0(I_2 + I_3) - 4.0(I_2 + I_3) = 0$

which reduces to: $2.0I_2 + 3.0I_3 = 8.0$, (2)

and the loop rule for the lower loop

$-(I_2) - 5.0(I_2) + 12 + 3.0(I_3) = 0$,

or $2.0I_2 - I_3 = 4.0$.

(3)

Solve (1), (2), and (3) together, to find:

$I_1 = 3.5$ A, $I_2 = 2.5$ A, and $I_3 = 1.0$ A.

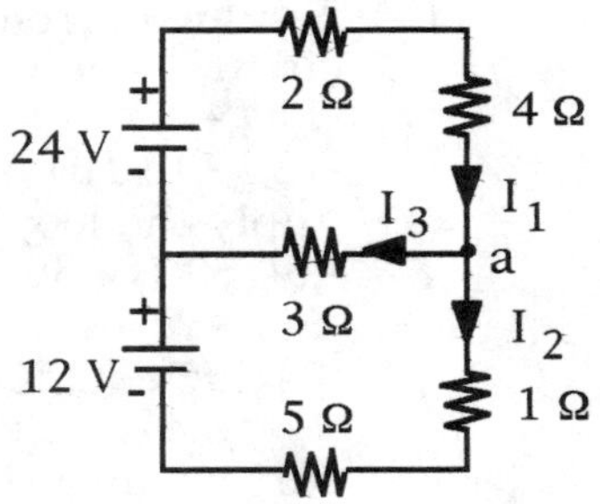

18.24 For the situation shown first:

$-\varepsilon_x - 0.01\ r + 5.60 = 0$.

For the second situation:

$5.60 - 0.025\ r + \varepsilon_x = 0$.

These two equations can be solved together to find: $r = 320\ \Omega$, and $\varepsilon_x = 2.4$ V.

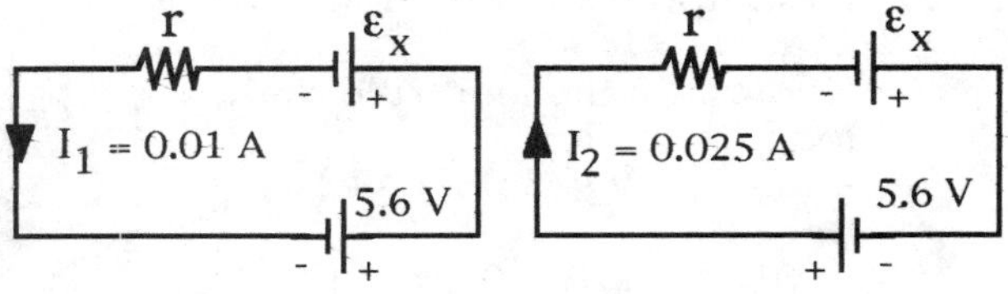

18.25 See sketch for the designation of currents and their directions. We apply the junction rule at point a:

$I_3 = I_1 + I_2$. (1)

Use the loop rule on the upper loop:

$+20.0 - 30.0I_1 + 5.00I_2 - 10.0 = 0$, or

$6.00I_1 - I_2 = 2.00$. (2)

Finally, apply the loop rule to the lower loop: $10.0 - 5.00I_2 - 20.0I_3 = 0$, or $I_2 + 4.00I_3 = 2.00$ (3)

Equations (1), (2), and (3) can be solved together to find,

$I_1 = 0.353$ A, $I_2 = 0.118$ A, and $I_3 = 0.471$ A.

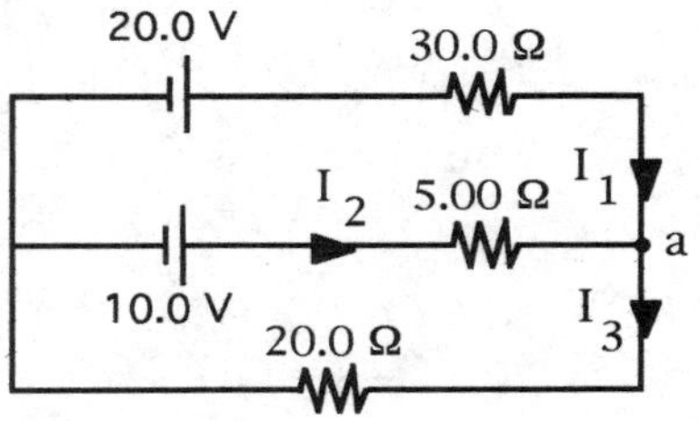

18.26 (a) Since there is not a continuous path in the center branch, no current flows in that part of the circuit. Then, applying the loop rule to the outer perimeter gives:

$-I - 4.0I + 36 - 3.0I - 8.0I - 2.0I + 18 = 0$, or

$18I = 54$. Hence, $I = 3.0$A.

Now, go CCW around the lower loop as:

$V_{ab} = V_a - V_b$

$= -36 + 4.0(3.0) + 1.0(3.0) + 6.0(0) + 5.0(0) + 12$.

Thus, $V_{ab} = V_a - V_b = -9.0$ V, or point a is 9.0 V lower in potential than point b.

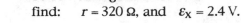

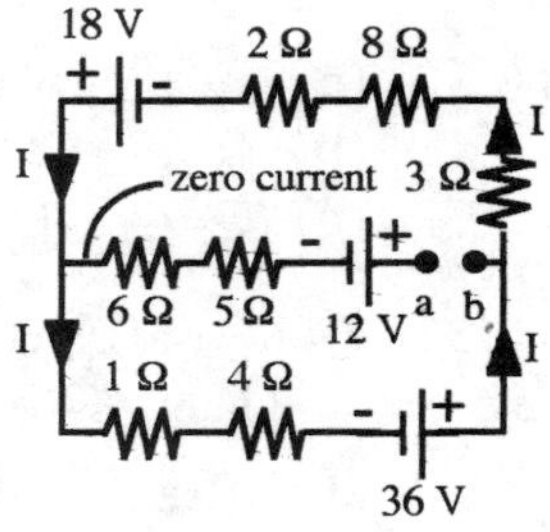

(b) Assume currents as shown in the modified circuit. Apply the loop rule to the upper loop: $-11\,I + 12 - 7\,I - 3\,I_1 - 10\,I_1 + 18 = 0$, giving $-18\,I - 13\,I_1 + 30 = 0$, or $18\,I + 13\,I_1 = 30$. (1)
Apply the loop rule to the lower loop: $-5(I_1 - I) + 36 + 7\,I - 12 + 11\,I = 0$, giving $-5I_1 + 23\,I + 24 = 0$, or $23I - 5I_1 = -24$. (2)
Solving equations (1) and (2) together yields: $I = -0.416$ A, and $I_1 = 2.884$ A. Thus, the current through the 7 Ω resistor is 0.416 A directed from b to a.

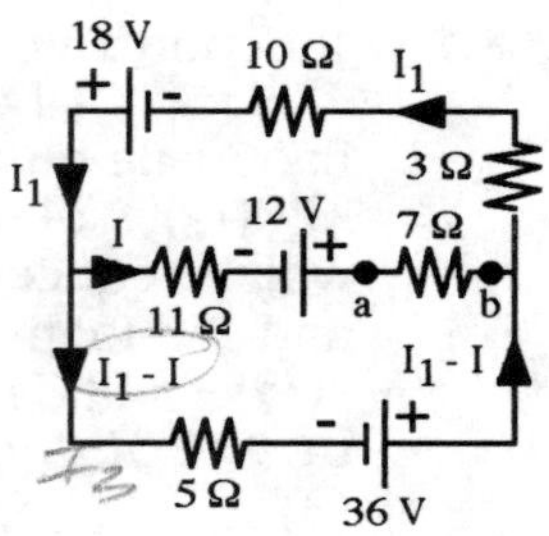

18.27 First, apply the junction rule at a: $I_3 = I_1 + I_2$ (1)
Now apply the loop rule to the loop on the left:
$-3.00 - 4.00I_3 - 5.00I_1 + 12.0 = 0$,
or
$4.00I_3 + 5.00I_1 = 9.00$ (2)
Apply loop rule to right loop:
$-18.0 + 2.00I_2 + 3.00I_2 + 4.00I_3 + 3.00 = 0$,
or $5.00I_2 + 4.00I_3 = 15.0$ (3)
Solving (1), (2), and (3) simultaneously yields:
$I_1 = 0.323$ A, $I_2 = 1.523$ A, and $I_3 = 1.846$ A.
Thus: $\Delta V_2 = 2I_2 = 3.05$ V, $\Delta V_3 = 3I_2 = 4.57$ V,
$\Delta V_4 = 4I_3 = 7.38$ V, and $\Delta V_5 = 5I_1 = 1.62$ V.

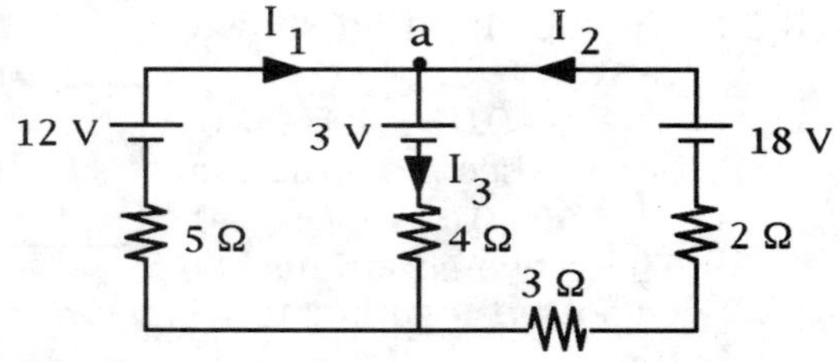

18.28 (a) $\tau = RC = (2.0 \times 10^{6}\ \Omega)(6.0 \times 10^{-6}\ \text{F}) = 12$ s.
(b) $Q_{max} = C\Delta V = (6.0 \times 10^{-6}\ \text{F})(20\ \text{V}) = 120\ \mu\text{C}$

18.29 Proceed as follows: $\tau = RC = \Omega\,\text{F} = \frac{\text{V}}{\text{A}}\frac{\text{C}}{\text{V}} = \frac{\text{C}}{\text{A}} = \frac{\text{C}}{\frac{\text{C}}{\text{s}}} = \text{s}$.

Thus, RC has units of time.

18.30 (a) $\tau = RC = (100\ \Omega)(20.0 \times 10^{-6}\ \text{F}) = 2.00 \times 10^{-3}$ s.
(b) $Q_{max} = C\Delta V = (20.0 \times 10^{-6}\ \text{F})(9.00\ \text{V}) = 180\ \mu\text{C}$
(c) $Q = Q_{max}(1 - e^{-1}) = 0.63Q_{max} = 113\ \mu\text{C}$

18.31 $\tau = RC = (10^{6}\ \Omega)(5.0 \times 10^{-6}\ \text{F}) = 5.0$ s. Thus, at $t = 10$ s, $t = 2\tau$.
$Q_{max} = C\mathcal{E} = (5.0 \times 10^{-6}\ \text{F})(30\ \text{V}) = 150\ \mu\text{C}$
at $t = 2\tau$, $q = Q_{max}(1 - e^{-t/\tau}) = (150\ \mu\text{C})(1 - \frac{1}{e^{2}}) = 130\ \mu\text{C}$

18.32 The voltage across the capacitor is given by $\Delta V_c = \mathcal{E}(1 - e^{-t/RC})$ and solving for C gives: $\frac{-t}{RC} = \ln\left(1 - \frac{V_c}{\varepsilon}\right)$, or

$$C = \frac{-t}{R\ \ln\left(1 - \frac{V_c}{\varepsilon}\right)} = \frac{-1\ \text{s}}{(12000\ \Omega)\ln\left(1 - \frac{10.0\ \text{V}}{12.0\ \text{V}}\right)} = 46.5\ \mu\text{F}.$$

18.33 (a) The time constant is given by: $\tau = RC = 0.960$ s. (1)
and the resistance can be found from the maximum current as: $R = \frac{\Delta V}{I_{max}} = \frac{48.0 \text{ V}}{0.50 \text{ A}} = 96.0\,\Omega$.
Thus, from (1), $C = 10^{-2}$ F.

(b) After two time constants, (two time constants equal 1.92 s), the charge is:

$$q = Q_{max}(1 - e^{-t/\tau}) = C\varepsilon\,(1 - e^{-2\tau/\tau}) = (10^{-2}\text{ F})(48.0\text{ V})(1 - \frac{1}{e^2}) = 0.415\text{ C}.$$

18.34 (a) The current drawn by the heater is: $I = \frac{P}{V} = \frac{1300\text{ W}}{120\text{ V}} = 10.8$ A.

Toaster: $I = \frac{P}{V} = \frac{1000\text{ W}}{120\text{ V}} = 8.33$ A.

Grill: $I = \frac{P}{V} = \frac{1500\text{ W}}{120\text{ V}} = 12.5$ A.

(b) The total current in the wire leading directly to the power source is the sum of the currents drawn by each element. This is 31.6 A. Thus, a 30 A circuit is insufficient.

18.35 (a) The current drawn by each individual element is found below.

lamp: $I = \frac{\Delta V}{R} = \frac{120\text{ V}}{150\ \Omega} = 0.80$ A heater: $I = \frac{\Delta V}{R} = \frac{120\text{ V}}{25\ \Omega} = 4.8$ A

fan: $I = \frac{\Delta V}{R} = \frac{120\text{ V}}{50\ \Omega} = 2.4$ A

The total current drawn by the combination is 8.0 A.

(b) The elements are connected in parallel to the source. Thus, the voltage across each is also 120 V.

(c) The current in the lamp has been found above to be 0.8 A.

(d) The heater power is: $P = I\Delta V = (120\text{ V})(4.8\text{ A}) = 580$ W

18.36 Let us first find the current that would be drawn by the heating element when connected to 240 V. This is: $I = \frac{P}{\Delta V} = \frac{3000\text{ W}}{240\text{ V}} = 12.5$ A
Ohm's law gives us the resistance of the element:

$$R = \frac{\Delta V}{I} = \frac{240\text{ V}}{12.5\text{ A}} = 19.2\,\Omega.$$

If the element is connected to a 120 V source, the current drawn is:

(a) $I = \frac{\Delta V}{R} = \frac{120\text{ V}}{19.2\ \Omega} = 6.25$ A, and the power dissipated is

(b) $P = \Delta V I = (120\text{ V})(6.25\text{ A}) = 750$ W.

18.37 Each use a current of $I = \frac{P}{\Delta V} = \frac{1200\text{ W}}{120\text{ V}} = 10$ A. In total, 20 A are needed, but the circuit breaker is rated at 15 A. Therefore, you may not use both of them at the same time.

18.38 If the capacitor is uncharged at time $t = 0$ when the switch is first closed in a RC circuit, the charge on the capacitor at time t later is given by:
$q = Q(1 - e^{-t/\tau})$ Thus, at a time $t = 2\tau$, we have: $q = Q(1 - \frac{1}{e^2}) = 0.865Q$

18.39 The 5.1 Ω and 3.5 Ω resistors are in series and reduce to an equivalent of 8.6 Ω. This 8.6 Ω resistor is in parallel with the 1.8 Ω resistor, and these two reduce to an equivalent of 1.50 Ω. Finally, the 1.5 Ω resistor is in series with the 2.4 Ω and 3.6 Ω resistors. These three add to give a resultant resistance of 7.5 Ω.

18.40 (a) The circuit reduces as shown below to an total resistance of 14 Ω.

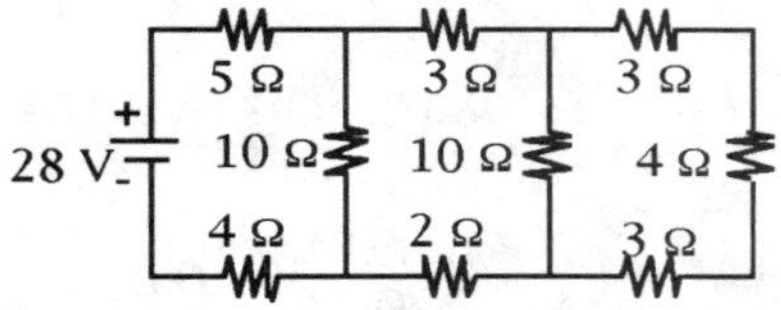

Figure 1

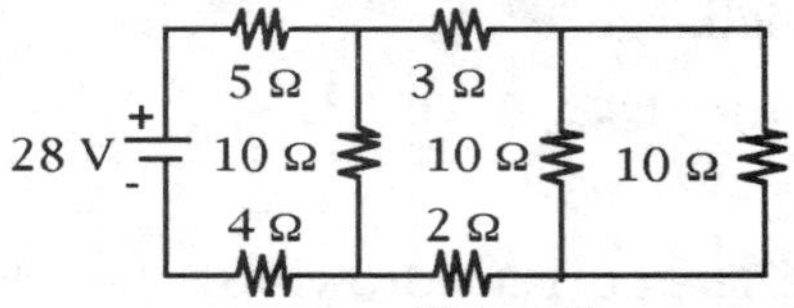

Figure 2

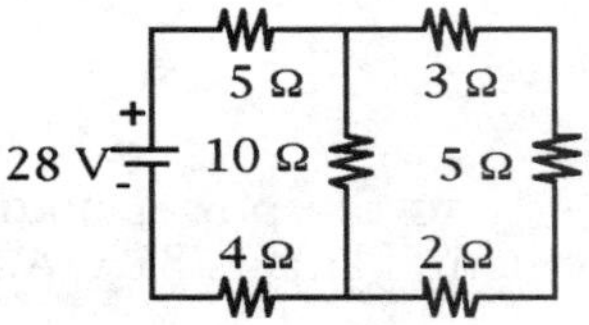

Figure 3

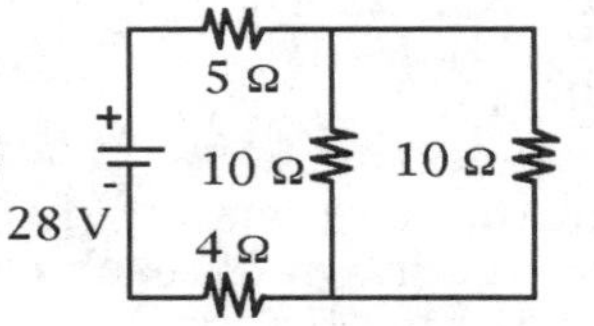

Figure 4

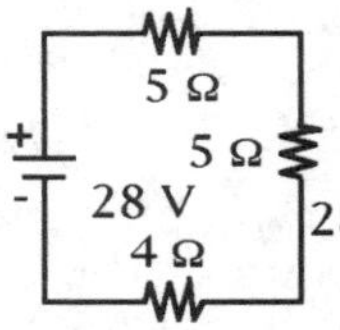

Figure 5

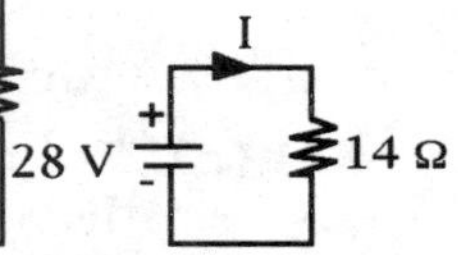

Figure 6

(b) The power dissipated in the circuit is: $P = I^2 R_{eq} = (2.0\text{ A})^2(14\,\Omega) = 56$ W

(c) From Fig. 6, we have: $I = \dfrac{28\text{ V}}{14\ \Omega} = 2.0\text{ A}.$

18.41 The resistors combine to an equivalent resistance of 15 Ω as shown.

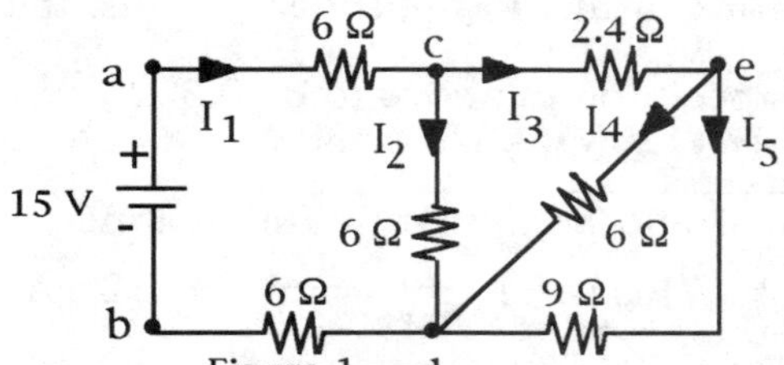

Figure 1 d

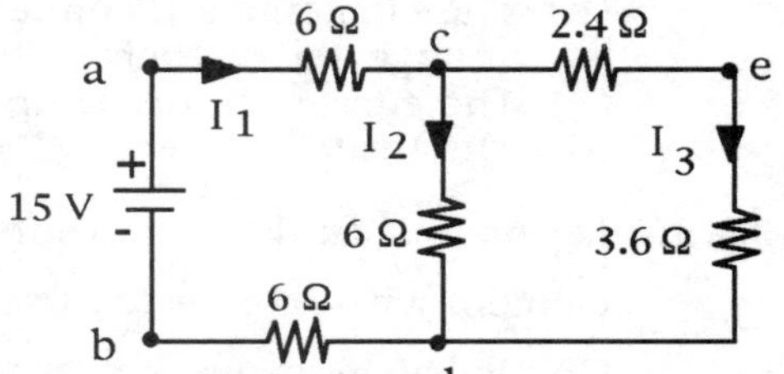

Figure 2 d

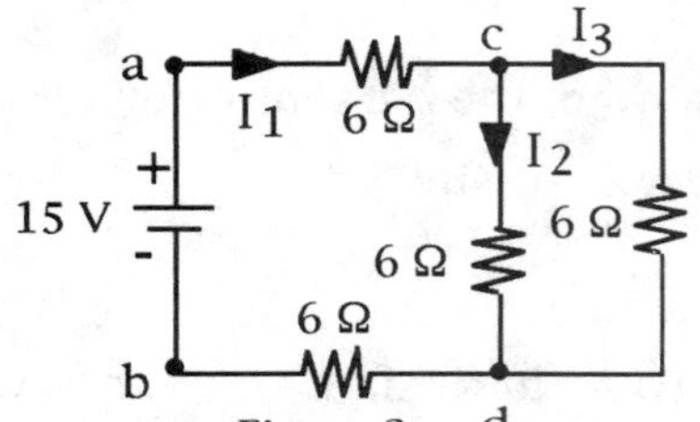

Figure 3 d

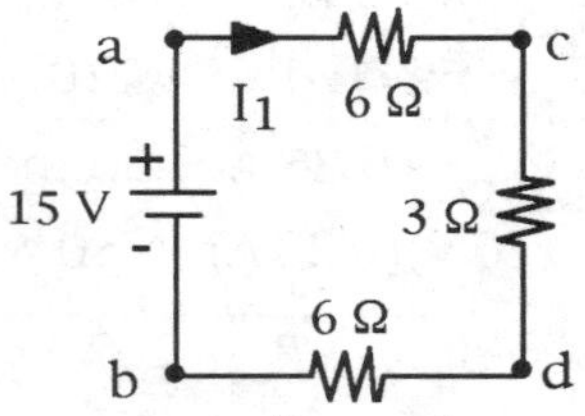

Figure 4

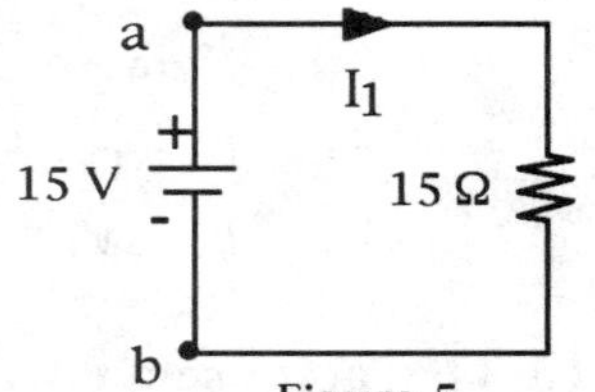

Figure 5

18.42 (a) From Fig. 4 of the solution to problem 41, we find:

$$I_1 = \frac{\Delta V_{ab}}{R_{ab}} = \frac{15\text{ V}}{15\ \Omega} = 1.0\text{ A}.\ \text{ Then } \Delta V_{cd} = I_1 R_{cd} = (1.0\text{ A})(3.0\,\Omega) = 3.0\text{ V}.$$

From Fig. 3: $I_2 = \dfrac{\Delta V_{cd}}{6.0\ \Omega} = \dfrac{3.0\text{ V}}{6.0\ \Omega} = 0.50\text{ A}$, and

$$I_3 = \frac{\Delta V_{cd}}{6\ \Omega} = \frac{3.0\ \text{V}}{6.0\ \Omega} = 0.50\ \text{A}.$$

From Fig. 2: $\Delta V_{ed} = I_3 R_{ed} = (0.50\ \text{A})(3.6\ \Omega) = 1.8\ \text{V}.$

Finally, from Fig. 1: $I_4 = \frac{\Delta V_{ed}}{6\ \Omega} = \frac{1.8\ \text{V}}{6\ \Omega} = 0.3\ \text{A}$, and

$$I_5 = \frac{\Delta V_{ed}}{9\ \Omega} = \frac{1.8\ \text{V}}{9\ \Omega} = 0.2\ \text{A}.$$

(b) $\Delta V_{ac} = I_1(6\ \Omega) = 6\ \text{V}$; $\Delta V_{ce} = I_3(2.4\ \Omega) = 1.2\ \text{V}$; $\Delta V_{ed} = I_4(6\ \Omega) = 1.8\ \text{V}$;
$\Delta V_{fd} = I_5(9\ \Omega) = 1.8\ \text{V}$; $\Delta V_{cd} = I_2(6\ \Omega) = 3\ \text{V}$; and $\Delta V_{db} = I_1(6\ \Omega) = 6\ \text{V}$.

(c) $P_{ac} = I_1^2(6\ \Omega) = 6\ \text{W}$; $P_{ce} = I_3^2(2.4\ \Omega) = 0.6\ \text{W}$;
$P_{ed} = I_4^2(6\ \Omega) = 0.54\ \text{W}$; $P_{fd} = I_5^2(9\ \Omega) = 0.36\ \text{W}$;
$P_{cd} = I_2^2(6\ \Omega) = 1.5\ \text{W}$; and $P_{db} = I_1^2(6\ \Omega) = 6\ \text{W}$;

18.43 (a) Here $\varepsilon = I(R + r)$, so $I = \frac{\varepsilon}{R + r} = \frac{12.60\ \text{V}}{(5.00\ \Omega + 0.080\ \Omega)} = 2.48\ \text{A}.$
Then, $\Delta V = IR = 5.00\ \Omega(2.48\ \text{A}) = 12.4\ \text{V}.$

(b) Let I_1 and I_2 be the currents flowing through the battery, connected in parallel, and the headlights, respectively. Then,
$I_1 = I_2 + 35.0\ \text{A}$, and $\varepsilon - rI_1 - RI_2 = 0$, so
$\varepsilon = 0.08\ \Omega(I_2 + 35.0\ \text{A}) + (5\ \Omega)I_2 = 12.6\ \text{V}$, giving $I_2 = 1.93\ \text{A}.$
Thus: $\Delta V_2 = 1.93\ \text{A}(5.00\ \Omega) = 9.65\ \text{V}.$

18.44 Connect the 5 resistors as shown in the diagram at the right to obtain the desired equivalent of 14 Ω.

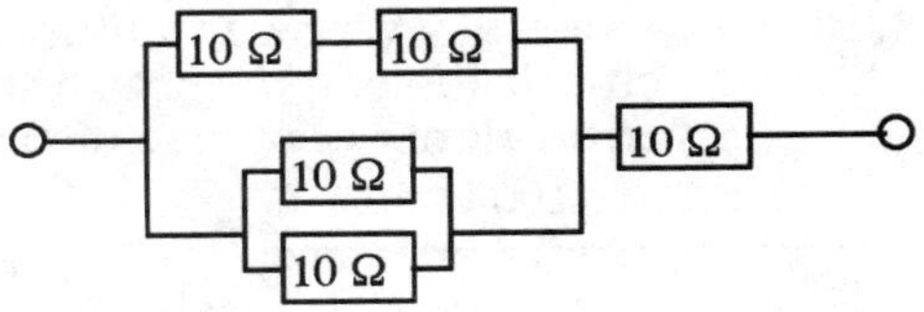

18.45 When the resistors are in series: $R_1 + R_2 = 690\ \Omega.$ (1)

When in parallel: $\frac{1}{R_1} + \frac{1}{R_2} = \frac{1}{150\ \Omega}$, or $\frac{R_1 R_2}{R_1 + R_2} = 150\ \Omega$ (2)

From (1): $R_2 = 690\ \Omega - R_1$. Substitute this into (2) to find:

$$\frac{R_1(690\ \Omega - R_1)}{690\ \Omega} = 150\ \Omega, \text{ or } R^2{}_1 - (690\ \Omega)R_1 + 103{,}500\ \Omega^2 = 0.$$

Solving this quadratic equation for R_1 gives:
$R_1 = 220.4\ \Omega$ or $R_1 = 469.6\ \Omega$
Then equation (1) yields: $R_2 = 469.6\ \Omega$ or $R_2 = 220.4\ \Omega$
Thus, the values of the two resistors are: 220.4 Ω, and 469.6 Ω.

18.46 Apply the junction rule at a. (See sketch.)

$I_2 = I_1 + I_3.$ (1)

Now use the loop rule on the left loop.

$-4.0 - 10I_2 + 9.0 - 5.0I_1 = 0,$

or $I_1 + 2.0I_2 = 1.0.$ (2)

Now apply the loop rule to the right loop.

$-4.0 - 10I_2 + 14 - 10I_3 = 0$, or

$I_2 + I_3 = 1.0.$ (3)

Solving (1), (2), and (3) simultaneously yields: $I_1 = 0$; $I_2 = I_3 = 0.5$ A.

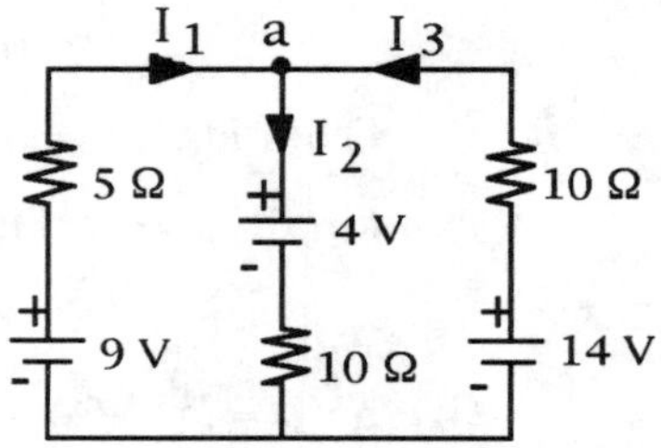

18.47 With the switch open, the circuit may be reduced as follows:

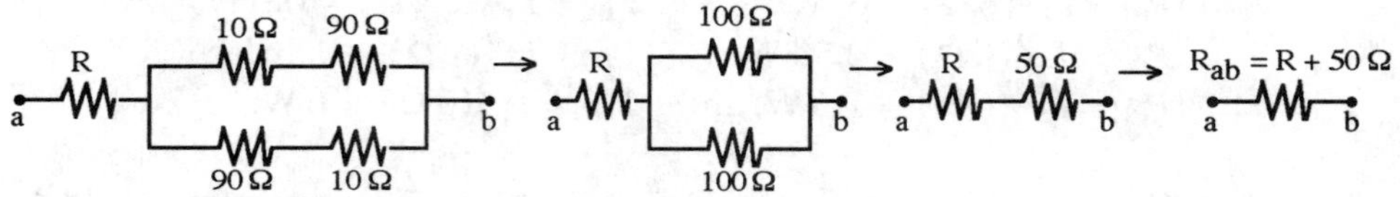

With the switch closed, the circuit reduces as follows:

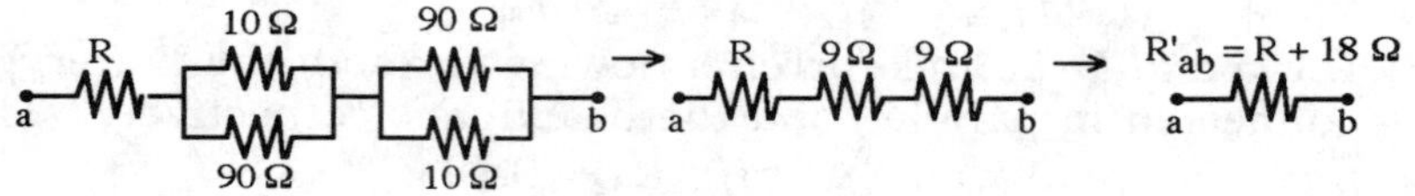

We are told that $R'_{ab} = \frac{1}{2}R_{ab} =$. Thus, $R + 18\ \Omega = \frac{1}{2}(R + 50\ \Omega)$, or $\frac{1}{2}R = 7\ \Omega$.

Therefore, $R = 14\ \Omega$.

18.48 (a) When a 5 V power supply is connected between points a and b, the circuit looks like that shown below, and reduces as shown to an equivalent resistance of 0.0999 Ω.

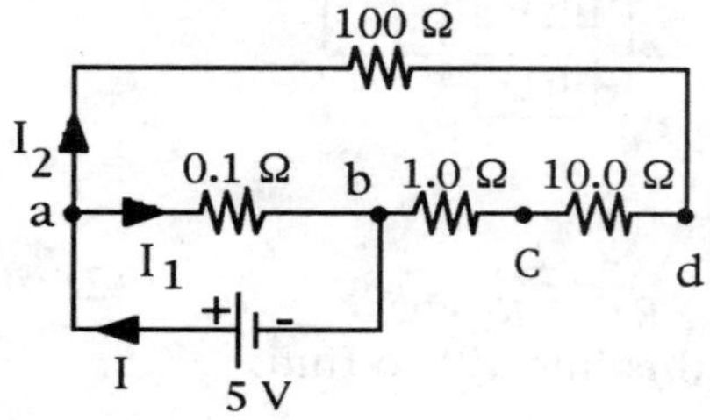

Figure 1

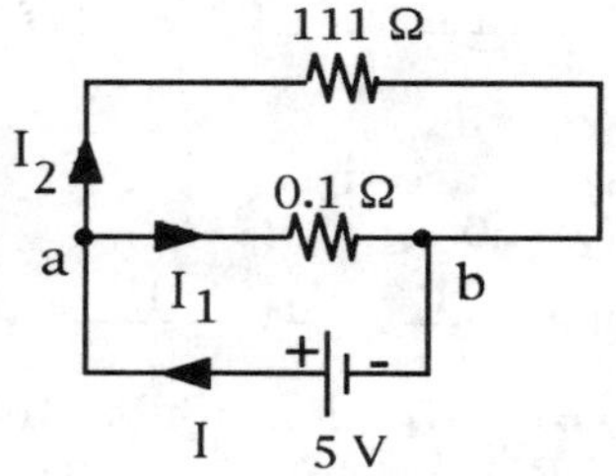

Figure 2

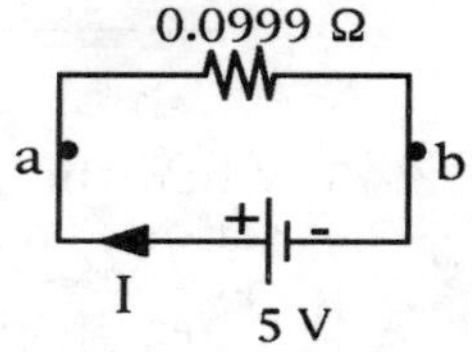

Figure 3

In Fig. 2, we find: $I_1 = \frac{5\ \text{V}}{0.1\ \Omega} = 50$ A, and $I_2 = \frac{5\ \text{V}}{111\ \Omega} = 0.045$ A.

(b) When the 5 V source is connected between points a and c, the circuit reduces to an equivalent resistance as shown.

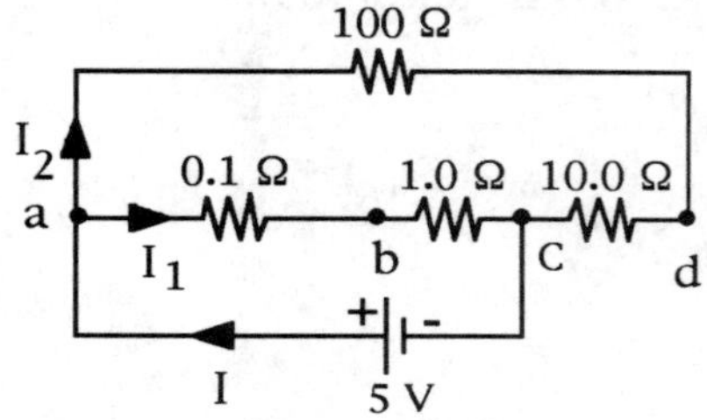

Figure 1

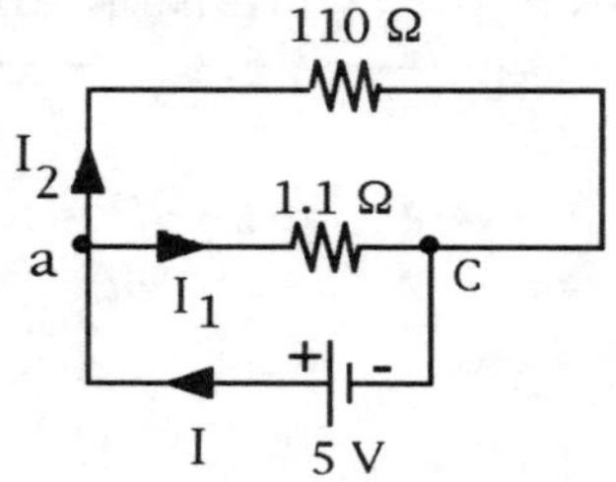

Figure 2

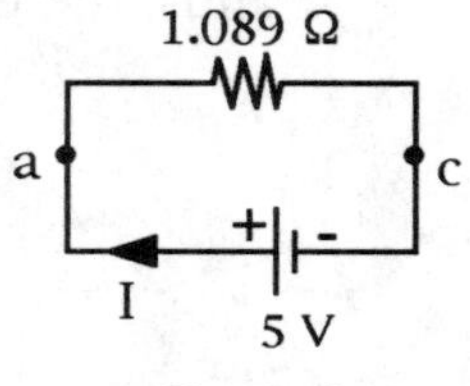

Figure 3

From Fig. 2, we find: $I_1 = \frac{5\ \text{V}}{1.1\ \Omega} = 4.55$ A, and $I_2 = \frac{5\ \text{V}}{110\ \Omega} = 0.045$ A.

(c) Finally, when the 5 V source is connected between points a and d, we have an equivalent resistance of 9.99 Ω.

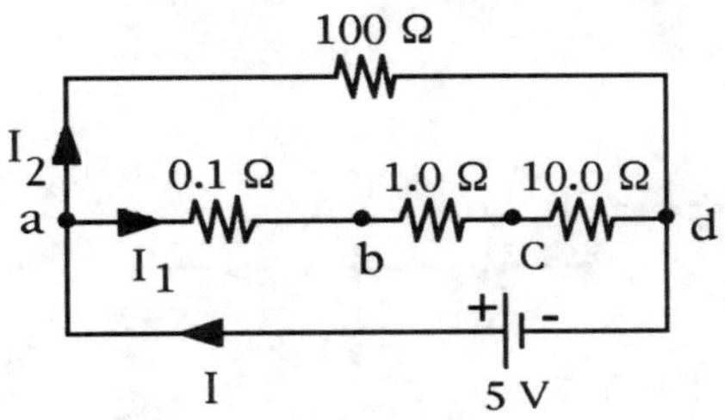

Figure 1

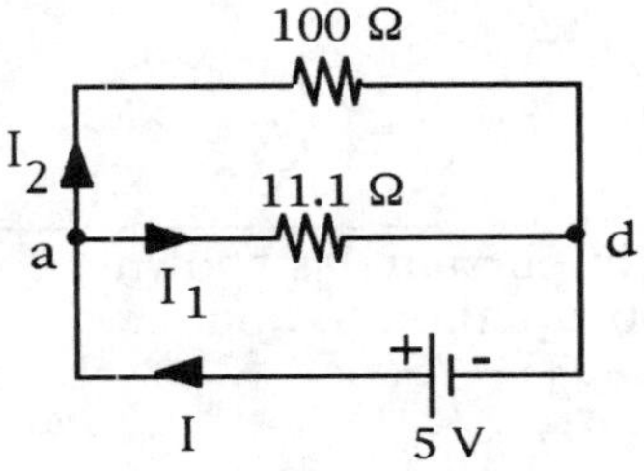

Figure 2

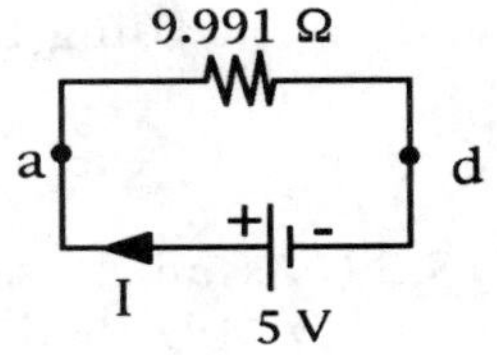

Figure 3

and from Fig. 2: $I_1 = \frac{5\ \text{V}}{11.1\ \Omega} = 0.45$ A, and $I_2 = \frac{5\ \text{V}}{100\ \Omega} = 0.05$ A,

---

18.49 Labeling currents and directions as shown in the sketch, we have:

$I_1 + I_4 = I_2 + I_3$

$6.00I_1 - 6.00I_4 = 0$

$6.00I_1 + 5.00I_3 - 4.50 = 0$

$6.00I_1 + 10.0I_2 - 6.00 = 0$

Solution of these equations yield an ammeter reading of

$I_4 = 0.39$ A.

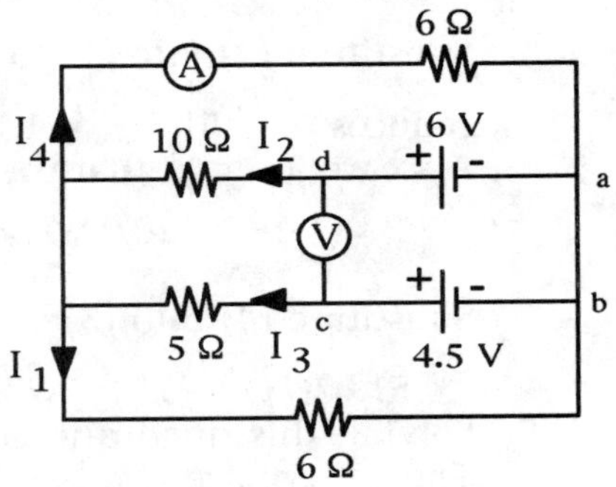

Going around the closed path abcda, we have: $+4.50\ \text{V} + V_m - 6.00\ \text{V} = 0$.

Thus, $V_m = 1.5$ V.

18.50 The terminal voltage is: $\Delta V = \varepsilon - Ir$.

For the generator, $\Delta V = 110$ V when $I = 10.0$ A, so

$110\ \text{V} = \varepsilon - (10.0\ \text{A})r,$ (1)

and $\Delta V = 106$ V when $I = 30.0$ A, giving

$106\ \text{V} = \varepsilon - (30.0\ \text{A})r.$ (2)

Subtract (2) from (1) to obtain:

$4\ \text{V} = (20.0\ \text{A})r$ which yields $r = 0.20\ \Omega$.

Then equation (1) gives: $\varepsilon = 110\ \text{V} + (10.0\ \text{A})(0.20\ \Omega)$, or $\varepsilon = 112$ V.

18.51 The time constant is: $\tau = RC = (2.0 \times 10^6\ \Omega)(3 \times 10^{-6}\ \text{F}) = 6.0$ s.

$Q = Q_{max}(1 - e^{-t/\tau})$, from which: $e^{-t/\tau} = 1 - \frac{Q}{Q_{max}}$.

If $Q = 0.9\ Q_{max}$, then $e^{-t/\tau} = 1 - 0.9 = 0.1$.

Now take antilog of the above: $\ln(e^{-t/\tau}) = \ln(0.1)$, or

$-\frac{t}{\tau} = \ln(0.1)$, and $t = -(6\ \text{s})\ln(0.1) = 14$ s.

18.52 (a) By the loop rule, we have: $\varepsilon - \Delta V_C - \Delta V_R = 0$, so that $\varepsilon - \frac{q}{C} - IR = 0$.

Using this, we get: $I(t) = \frac{\varepsilon}{R} - \frac{q(t)}{RC}$, or

$$I(t) = \frac{\varepsilon}{R} - \frac{C\varepsilon}{RC}\left(1 - e^{-t/RC}\right) = \frac{\varepsilon}{R}\left(1 - [1 - e^{-t/RC}]\right) = \left(\frac{\varepsilon}{R}\right) e^{-t/RC}.$$

(b) By the loop rule, we have $\Delta V_C - \Delta V_R = 0$, so that $\frac{q}{C} - IR = 0$.

Using this, we get:

$$I(t) = \frac{q(t)}{RC} = \left(\frac{Q}{RC}\right) e^{-t/RC}.$$

18.53 Assume a set of currents as shown.

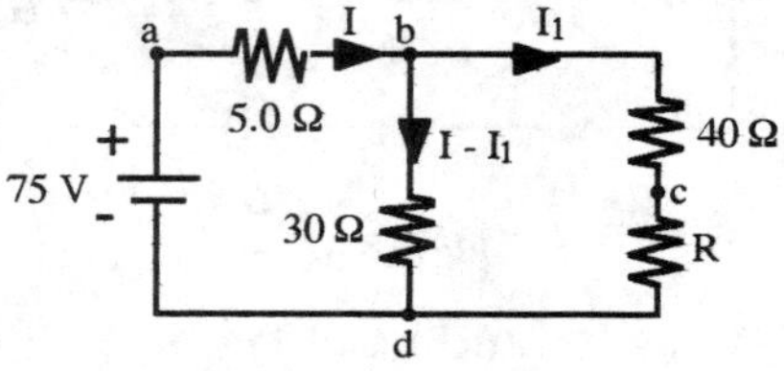

Apply the loop equation to abda:

$5.0I + 30(I - I_1) = 75$, or

$35I - 30I_1 = 75.$ (1)

Apply the loop equation to bdcb:

$-30(I - I_1) + RI_1 + 40I_1 = 0$, or

$30\,I = (70 + R)I_1$, giving

$I = (\frac{7}{3} + \frac{R}{30})\,I_1.$ (2)

Substitute (2) into (1) to obtain: $35\left(\frac{7}{3} + \frac{R}{30}\right)I_1 - 30I_1 = 75$, which reduces to $51.67I_1 + 1.167(I_1R) = 75.$ (3)

Also, we are told that the power dissipated by R is 20.0 W. Thus,

$P = (I_1)^2R = 20.0$ W, or $(I_1R) = \frac{20.0\text{ W}}{I_1}.$ (4)

Substitute (4) into (3) to find: $51.67I_1 + \frac{23.33}{I_1} = 75$, or

$51.67(I_1)^2 - 75I_1 + 23.33 = 0$

Solving this quadratic equation gives: $I_1 = 1.0$ A or $I_1 = 0.4515$ A.

Thus, there are two possible values for R given by the equation:

$(I_1)^2\,R = 20.0$ W, or $R = \frac{20.0\text{ W}}{(I_1)^2}$. This gives: $R = 20.0\ \Omega$, or $R = 98.1\ \Omega$.

18.54 Notice first that the 20.0 Ω and 5.00 Ω are in series and combine to an equivalent of 25.0 Ω.

This resultant 25.0 Ω resistor, the 5.00 Ω and the 10.0 Ω resistor are now seen to be in parallel. We can solve for their equivalent resistance as:

$$R_{eq} = \frac{1}{\left(\frac{1}{10.0\ \Omega} + \frac{1}{5.00\ \Omega} + \frac{1}{25.0\ \Omega}\right)} = 2.94\ \Omega$$

This 2.94 Ω resistor is in series with the 10.0 Ω resistor adjacent to the battery. Thus, the equivalent resistor for the entire circuit is 12.94 Ω. The current drawn from the 25.0 V battery is found as

$$I = \frac{\Delta V}{R} = \frac{25.0\text{ V}}{12.94\ \Omega} = 1.93\text{ A}$$

This 1.93 A goes through the 2.94 Ω equivalent resistor producing a voltage drop of

$$\Delta V = IR = (1.93\text{ A})(2.94\ \Omega) = 5.68\text{ V}$$

This, however, is the voltage drop across the 10Ω resistor, the 5.00 Ω resistor, and the 25.0 Ω equivalent.

(b) Therefore, $\Delta V_{ab} = 5.68$ V.

(a) $I = \frac{\Delta V_{ab}}{R_{ab}} = \frac{5.68\text{ V}}{25\Omega} = 0.227$ A

18.55 Call the current in the left-most branch I_1 and select its direction to be down. The center branch has a current I_2 and a downward direction. Finally, the current is chosen to be I_3 in the right branch with direction upward.
The junction rule gives $I_3 = I_1 + I_2$
From the loop rule applied to the loop containing I_2 and I_3.
$12\text{ V} - 4I_3 - 6I_2 - 4\text{ V} = 0$ or $8 = 4I_3 + 6I_2$
From the loop rule applied to the loop containing I_1 and I_2.
$-6I_2 - 4\text{ V} + 8I_1 = 0$ or $8I_1 = 4 + 6I_2$
Solving, we find $I_1 = \frac{11}{13}\text{ A}$, $I_2 = \frac{6}{13}\text{ A}$, $I_3 = \frac{17}{13}\text{ A}$

18.56 The current through R_1 is I_1 chosen to be left to right. I_2 is the current through R_2 and is upward. I_3 is the current through R_3 and is left to right.
We have $70 - 60 + I_2(3.00\text{ k}\Omega) + I_1(2.00\text{ k}\Omega) = 0$ (1)
$80 - I_3(4.00\text{ k}\Omega) - 60.0 + I_2(3.00\text{ k}\Omega) = 0$ (2)
$I_2 = I_1 + I_3$ (3)
(a) Solving, we find $I_1 = -0.385\text{ mA}$, $I_3 = -2.692\text{ mA}$, $I_2 = -3.08\text{ mA}$
(b) $\Delta V_{cf} = -60.0\text{ V} - (3.08\text{ mA})(3.00\text{ k}\Omega) = -69.2\text{ V}$

18.57 (a) For the first measurement, the equivalent circuit is as shown in Figure 1. Thus,

$$R_{ab} = R_1 = R_y + R_y = 2R_y, \text{ so } R_y = \frac{1}{2}R_1. \quad (1)$$

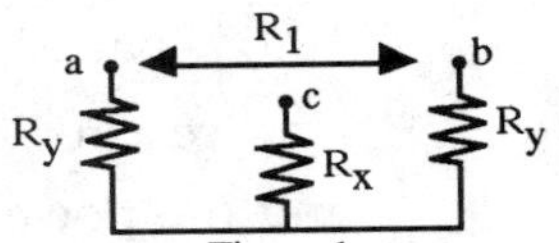

Figure 1

For the second measurement, the equivalent circuit is shown in Figure 2. Thus,

$$R_{ac} = R_2 = \frac{1}{2}R_y + R_x. \quad (2)$$

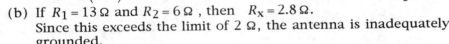

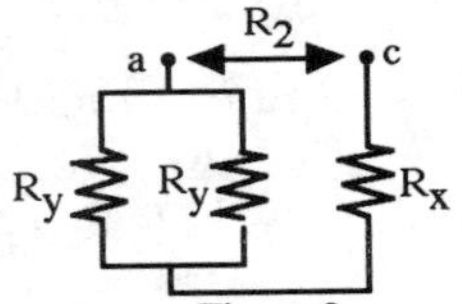

Figure 2

Substitute (1) into (2) to obtain:

$$R_2 = \frac{1}{2}\left(\frac{1}{2}R\right) + R_x, \text{ or } R_x = R_2 - \frac{1}{4}R_1.$$

(b) If $R_1 = 13\,\Omega$ and $R_2 = 6\,\Omega$, then $R_x = 2.8\,\Omega$.
Since this exceeds the limit of $2\,\Omega$, the antenna is inadequately grounded.

18.58 In series, $R_{eq} = R_1 + R_2 + R_3 + \ldots + R_n$, and if each resistor equals R then $R_{eq} = nR$. Thus, the current and power dissipations will be:

$$I_s = \frac{\Delta V}{R_{eq}} = \frac{\Delta V}{nR}, \text{ and } P_s = I_s^2 R_{eq} = \frac{\Delta V^2}{n^2R^2}\,nR = \frac{\Delta V^2}{nR}.$$

In parallel, $\frac{1}{R_{eq}} = \frac{1}{R_1} + \frac{1}{R_2} + \frac{1}{R_3} + \ldots$, and if each resistor equals R

then: $\frac{1}{R_{eq}} = \frac{n}{R}$, or $R_{eq} = \frac{R}{n}$. In this case, the current and power are:

$$I_p = \frac{\Delta V}{R_{eq}} = \frac{n\Delta V}{R}, \text{ and } P_p = I_p^2 R_{eq} = \frac{n^2\Delta V^2}{R^2}\frac{R}{n} = \frac{n\Delta V^2}{R}.$$

Therefore, $\frac{P_s}{P_p} = \frac{1}{n^2}$, or $P_s = \frac{P_p}{n^2}$.

18.59 Consider a battery of emf ε connected to the circuit as shown. Apply the loop rule to acbea to obtain:

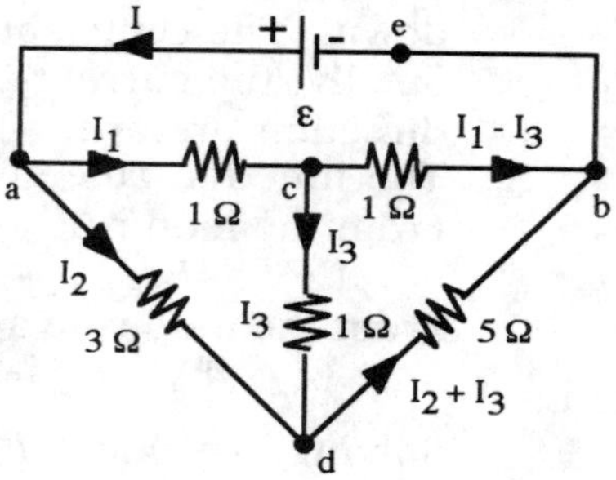

$- I_1 - (I_1 - I_3) + \varepsilon = 0,$

or $2.0I_1 - I_3 = \varepsilon.$ (1)

Apply the loop rule to adbea to obtain:

$-3.0I_2 - 5.0(I_2 + I_3) + \varepsilon = 0$

or $8.0I_2 + 5.0I_3 = \varepsilon.$ (2)

Apply the loop rule to adca to obtain:

$-3.0I_2 + I_3 + I_1 = 0$

or $I_1 = 3I_2 - I_3.$ (3)

Solving (1), (2), and (3) simultaneously gives:

$$I_1 = \frac{13}{27}\varepsilon, \quad I_2 = \frac{4}{27}\varepsilon, \text{ and } I_3 = \frac{-\varepsilon}{27}.$$

Apply the point rule at point a to obtain:

$$I = I_1 + I_2 = \frac{13}{27}\varepsilon + \frac{4}{27}\varepsilon = \frac{17}{27}\varepsilon. \quad \text{Thus, } R_{ab} = \frac{\varepsilon}{I} = \frac{\varepsilon}{\frac{17}{27}\varepsilon} = \frac{27}{17}\,\Omega.$$

18.60 With R the value of the load resistor, the current in a series circuit composed of a 12.0 V battery, a resistor of 10.0 Ω, and a load resistor is: $I = \dfrac{12.0 \text{ V}}{R + 10.0\ \Omega}$

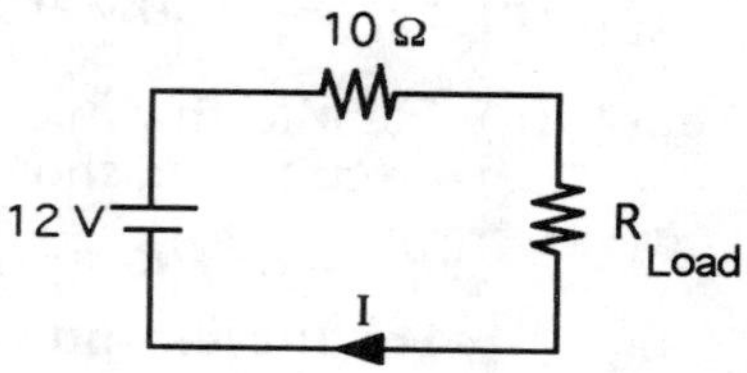

and the power delivered to the load resistor is: $P = I^2R = \dfrac{(144\ V^2)R}{(R + 10.0\ \Omega)^2}$

Some typical values are

R	P_{load}
1 Ω	1.19 W
5 Ω	3.20 W
10 Ω	3.60 W
15 Ω	3.46 W
20 Ω	3.20 W
25 Ω	2.94 W
30 Ω	2.70 W

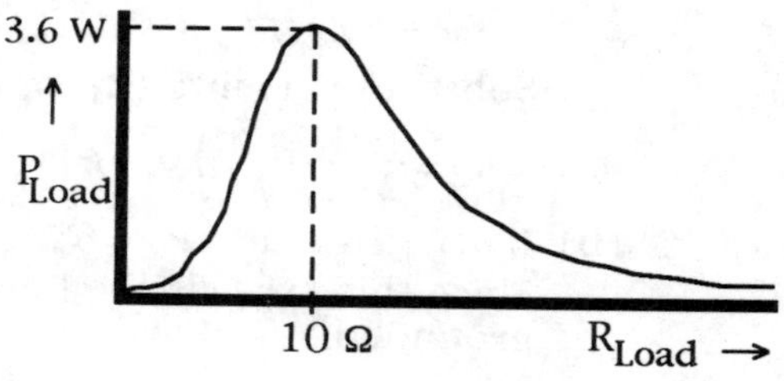

The curve peaks at $P_{load} = 3.6$ W at a load resistance of $R = 10.0\ \Omega$.

18.61 The total resistance between points b and c is:

$$\frac{1}{R} = \frac{1}{2.0\text{ k}\Omega} + \frac{1}{3.0\text{ k}\Omega}, \text{ or } R = \frac{6}{5}\text{ k}\Omega = 1.2\text{ k}\Omega = 1200\ \Omega.$$ The total capacitance betwen points d and e is $C = 2.0\ \mu\text{F} + 3.0\ \mu\text{F} = 5.0\ \mu\text{F}$. The total charge stored between points d and e in this series RC circuit at any time is:

$$Q = C\varepsilon[1 - e^{-t/RC}], \text{ or } Q = (600\ \mu\text{C})(1 - e^{-1000t/6}).$$

Since the two capacitors are in parallel, the voltage is the same for each capacitor. That is:

$$\Delta V_1 = \frac{Q_1}{C_1} = \frac{Q_2}{C_2} = \Delta V_2, \text{ or } \quad Q_2 = \frac{C_2}{C_1}Q_1 = \frac{3.0\ \mu\text{F}}{2.0\ \mu\text{F}}Q_1 = 1.5\,Q_1. \quad (1)$$

Also: $Q = Q_1 + Q_2.$ (2)

Solving (1) and (2) together gives:

$Q_1 = 0.4\ Q = 240\ \mu C((1 - e^{-1000t/6})$ for 2.0 μF capacitor

$Q_2 = 0.6\ Q = 360\ \mu C((1 - e^{-1000t/6})$ for 3.0 μF capacitor

ANSWERS TO CONCEPTUAL QUESTIONS

2. The resistors should be connected in series. For example, connecting three resistors of 5 Ω, 7 Ω, and 2 Ω in series gives a resultant resistance of 14 Ω.

4. The equivalent resistance is always smaller than the smallest in the combination when resistors are connected in parallel. For example, connecting a 6 Ω in parallel with a 12 Ω resistor gives an equivalent resistance of $\frac{1}{6\Omega} + \frac{1}{12\ \Omega} = \frac{1}{R_{eq}}$. The result is $R_{eq} = 4\ \Omega$.

6. A short circuit can develop when the last bit of insulation frays away between the two conductors in a lamp cord. Then the two conductors touch each other, opening a low resistance branch in parallel with the lamp. The lamp will immediately go out, carrying no current and presenting no danger. A very large current will be produced in the power source, the house wiring, and the wire in the lamp cord up to and through the short. The circuit breaker will interrupt the circuit quickly but not before considerable heat and sparking is produced in the short-circuit path.

8. A wire or cable in a transmission line is thick and made of material with very low resistivity. Only when its length is very large does its resistance become significant. To transmit power over a long distance it is most efficient to use low current at high voltage, minimizing the I^2R power loss in the transmission line.

10. The bulbs of set A are wired in parallel. The bulbs of set B are wired in series, so removing one bulb produces an open circuit with infinite resistance and zero current.

12. Car headlights are wired in parallel. If they were in series, both would go out when the filament of one burned out. An important safety factor would be lost.

14. Compare two runs in series to two resistors connected in series.
Compare three runs in parallel to three resistors connected in parallel.
Compare one run followed by two runs in parallel to a battery followed immediately by two resistors in parallel.

The junction rule for ski resorts says that the number of skiers coming into a junction must be equal to the number of skiers leaving. The loop rule would be stated as the total change in altitude must be zero for any skier completing a closed path.

16. Because water is a good conductor, if you should become part of a short circuit while fumbling with any electrical circuit while in a bathtub, the current would follow a pathway through you, the water, and to ground. Electrocution would be the obvious result.

18. Even if the fuse were to burn out, there would still be a current path through the devices, and they would not be protected.

CHAPTER NINETEEN SOLUTIONS

Chapter Nineteen Readings

Akasofu, S., "The Dynamic Aurora," *Scientific American*, May 1989, p. 90.

Banerjee, S., "Polar Flip-Flops," *The Sciences*, November/December 1984, p. 24.

Bitter, F., *Magnets: The Education of a Physicist*, Science Study Series, Garden City, N.Y., Doubleday, 1959.

Bloxham, J, and Gubbins, D., "The Evolution of the Earth's Magnetic Field," *Scientific American*, December 1989, p. 68.

Carrigan Jr, R.A. and Trower, W.P., "Superheavy Magnetic Monopoles," *Scientific American*, April 1982, p. 106.

Felch, S., "Searches for Magnetic Monopoles and Fractional Electric Charge," *The Physics Teacher*, March 1984, p. 142.

Hoffman, K.A., "Ancient Magnetic Reversals: Clues to the Geodynamo," *Scientific American*, May 1988, p. 76.

Kolm, H.H, and Freeman, A.J., "Intense Magnetic Fields," *Scientific American*, April 1965, p. 66.

Rillings, J.H., "Automated Highways," *Scientific American*, October 1997, p. 80.

Yam, P., "Medical Technology: Magnet on the Brain," *Scientific American*, October 1997, p. 80.

Review The resistance of the wire used to make the solenoid is $R = \frac{\rho L}{A}$.
Hence, the length of the wire to be used is:

$$L = \frac{RA}{\rho} = \frac{(5.00\ \Omega)[\pi(2.50 \times 10^{-4}\ \text{m})^2]}{1.70 \times 10^{-8}\ \Omega\ \text{m}} = 57.8\ \text{m}.$$

The number of times this length will wrap around a 1.00 cm radius cylinder (i.e., the total number of turns of wire that will be on the solenoid) is: $N = \frac{L}{2\pi r} = \frac{57.8\ \text{m}}{2\pi(10^{-2}\ \text{m})} = 920$. Since the magnetic field inside a solenoid is given by $B = \mu_0 n I$, the number of turns of wire needed per unit length of solenoid is given by:

$$n = \frac{B}{\mu_0 I} = \frac{4.00 \times 10^{-2}\ \text{T}}{(4\pi \times 10^{-7}\ \text{N/A}^2)(4.00\ \text{A})} = 7.96 \times 10^3\ \text{m}^{-1}.$$

Thus, the needed length of the solenoid is;

$$l = \frac{N}{n} = \frac{920}{7.96 \times 10^3\ \text{m}^{-1}} = 1.16 \times 10^{-1}\ \text{m} = 11.6\ \text{cm}.$$

19.1 (a), (b), and (c) The direction is given by the right hand rule and recognizing that electrons are negatively charged.
(d) $F = qvB\sin\theta = qvB\sin(180°) = 0$.

19.2 (a) These are all applications of the right hand rule:
(a) to left, (b) into page (c) out of page
(d) toward top of page (e) into page (f) out of page
(b) If the charge is negative, the right hand rule is still used, but the direction for the force is changed by 180°. Thus, the answers here are reversed in direction from those given above.

19.3 Use the right hand rule. The answers are:
(a) into page, (b) toward the right (c) toward bottom of page

19.4 $F = qvB\sin\theta = (4.0 \times 10^{-8}\ \text{C})(5.0 \times 10^{-5}\ \text{T})(15\ \text{m/s})\sin 60°$, or
$F = 2.6 \times 10^{-11}$ N, directed due west.

19.5 (a) $F = qvB\sin\theta = (1.60 \times 10^{-19}\ \text{C})(3.0 \times 10^{6}\ \text{m/s})(3.0 \times 10^{-1}\ \text{T})\sin 37°$, or
$F = 8.7 \times 10^{-14}$ N.
(b) $a = \dfrac{F}{m} = \dfrac{8.67 \times 10^{-14}\ \text{N}}{1.67 \times 10^{-27}\ \text{kg}} = 5.2 \times 10^{13}\ \text{m/s}^2$.

19.6 The gravitational force is small enough to be ignored, so the magnetic force must supply the needed centripetal acceleration, or:
$qvB = \dfrac{mv^2}{R}$, or $v = \dfrac{qBR}{m}$ where $R = R_{earth} + 1000$ km. Therefore,
$$v = \frac{(1.60 \times 10^{-19}\ \text{C})(4.00 \times 10^{-8}\ \text{T})(7.38 \times 10^{6}\ \text{m})}{1.67 \times 10^{-27}\ \text{kg}} = 2.83 \times 10^{7}\ \text{m/s}$$

19.7 First find the speed of the electron: $\Delta KE = \frac{1}{2}mv^2 = e\Delta V = \Delta PE$ gives
$$v = \sqrt{\frac{2e\Delta V}{m}} = \sqrt{\frac{2(1.60 \times 10^{-19}\ \text{C})(2400\ \text{J/C})}{(9.11 \times 10^{-31}\ \text{kg})}} = 2.9 \times 10^{7}\ \text{m/s}.$$
(a) $F_{max} = qvB = (1.60 \times 10^{-19}\ \text{C})(2.9 \times 10^{7}\ \text{C})(1.70\ \text{T}) = 7.90 \times 10^{-12}$ N.
(b) $F_{min} = 0$ occurs when v is either parallel to or anti-parallel to B.

19.8 $F = ma = (1.67 \times 10^{-27}\ \text{kg})(2.0 \times 10^{13}\ \text{m/s}^2) = 3.34 \times 10^{-14}$ N.
$$B = \frac{F}{qv} = \frac{3.34 \times 10^{-14}\ \text{N}}{(1.60 \times 10^{-19}\ \text{C})(1.0 \times 10^{7}\ \text{m/s})} = 2.1 \times 10^{-2}\ \text{T}$$
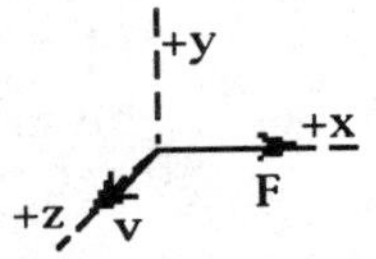

The right hand rule shows that B must be in the $-y$ direction to yield a force in the $+x$ direction when v is in the z direction.

19.9 n = number of Na^+ ions present = $(3.00 \times 10^{20}/\text{cm}^3)(100\ \text{cm}^3) = 3 \times 10^{22}$.
The force on a single ion is:
$F = qvB\sin\theta = (1.60 \times 10^{-19}\ \text{C})(0.851\ \text{m/s})(0.254\ \text{T})\sin 51.0° = 2.69 \times 10^{-20}$ N
Thus, assuming all ions move in the same direction through the field, the total force is:
$F_{total} = nF = (3 \times 10^{22}\ \text{ions})(2.69 \times 10^{-20}\ \text{N}) = 806$ N

19.10 The work done by a force is $W = Fs\cos\theta$ where θ is the angle between the direction of the force and the direction of the displacement s. But, if F is a magnetic force acting on a charged particle, then F is always perpendicular to the direction of the velocity and hence the displacement. Therefore, $\theta = 90°$, and $\cos\theta = 0$. Thus, $W = 0$.

19.11 $\frac{F}{L} = BI$. Thus, $(0.12\ \text{N/m}) = B(15\ \text{A})$, and $B = 8.0 \times 10^{-3}\ \text{T}$.
The direction of B must be out of the page (in $+z$ direction) to have F directed as specified.

19.12 (a) into page (b) toward right (c) toward bottom of page

19.13 (a) to the left, (b) into page (c) out of page
(d) toward top of page (e) into page (f) out of page

19.14 $F = BIL\sin\theta = (0.300\ \text{T})(10.0\ \text{A})(5.00\ \text{m})\sin 30.0° = 7.5\ \text{N}$.

19.15 (a) $F = BIL\sin\theta = (0.60 \times 10^{-4}\ \text{T})(15\ \text{A})(10.0\ \text{m})\sin 90° = 9.0 \times 10^{-3}\ \text{N}$.
F is perpendicular to B and, by the right hand rule, is directed at 15° above the horizontal in the northward direction.
(b) $F = BIL\sin\theta = (0.60 \times 10^{-4}\ \text{T})(15\ \text{A})(10.0\ \text{m})\sin 165° = 2.3 \times 10^{-3}\ \text{N}$.
The right hand rule shows F is horizontal and directed due west.

19.16 To find the minimum B field, B must be perpendicular to I, and from the right hand rule, it must be directed downward to produce a northward horizontal force. The friction force per unit length = $\mu N = \mu$(mass per unit length)(g),

or $\frac{f}{L} = 0.200\left(\frac{10^{-3}\ \text{kg}}{10^{-2}\ \text{m}}\right)(9.80\ \text{m/s}^2) = 0.196\ \text{N/m}$.

Thus, the magnetic force per unit length must be 0.196 N/m to overcome the friction force.

$$\frac{F}{L} = BI = 0.196\ \text{N/m}, \text{ or } \quad B = \frac{0.196\ \text{N/m}}{1.50\ \text{A}} = 0.131\ \text{T}.$$

19.17 For the wire to move upward at constant speed, the net force acting on it must be zero. Therefore, $F_{magnetic} = mg$, or $BIL\sin\theta = mg$.

At $\theta = 90°$, we have $B = \frac{mg}{IL} = \frac{(0.015\ \text{kg})(9.80\ \text{m/s}^2)}{(5.0\ \text{A})(0.15\ \text{m})} = 0.20\ \text{T}$.

The magnetic force must be directed upward. Therefore, B must be directed out of page.

19.18 In order for the rod to float, the magnetic force must have the same magnitude as the weight of the rod. Thus: $F = BIL\sin\theta = mg$, or

$I = \frac{mg}{BL\sin\theta}$ The minimum value of I occurs when $\sin\theta = 1$.

Thus, $$I_{min} = \frac{(5.00 \times 10^{-2}\ \text{kg})(9.80\ \text{m/s}^2)}{(2.00\ \text{T})(1.00\ \text{m})} = 0.245\ \text{A}.$$

19.19 The area of the circular loop is $0.785\ \text{m}^2$, and $\tau = NBIA\sin\theta$.
(a) For τ_{max}, $\theta = 90°$, and we have:

$$\tau_{max} = BIA = (0.400\ \text{T})(2.00\ \text{A})(0.785\ \text{m}^2) = 0.628\ \text{N m}.$$

(b) If $\tau = \frac{1}{2}\tau_{max}$, then $\sin\theta = \frac{1}{2}$, and $\theta = 30°$. This is the angle between the field and the line perpendicular to the plane of the loop. The angle between the plane of the loop and the field will therefore be:

$\phi = 90° - 30° = 60°$.

19.20 The area of the ellipse is $A = \pi(0.200\,\text{m}(0.150\,\text{m}) = 9.42 \times 10^{-2}\,\text{m}^2$. The torque on the coil is given by:

$$\tau = NBIA\,\sin\theta = 8(2.00 \times 10^{-4}\,\text{T})(6.00\,\text{A})(9.42 \times 10^{-2}\,\text{m}^2)\,\sin 90°$$
$$= 9.04 \times 10^{-4}\,\text{Nm.}$$ (independent of the shape of the area, A)

19.21 Note that the angle between the line perpendicular to the plane of the coil and the field is: $\theta = 90° - 30° = 60°$. Therefore, the torque is:

$$\tau = NBIA\sin\theta = 100(0.80\,\text{T})(1.2\,\text{A})(0.12\,\text{m}^2)\sin 60.0° = 10\,\text{N m.}$$

The right hand rule shows the torque will tend to rotate the coil clockwise as viewed from above.

19.22 Each side of the loop will have a length of $b = \frac{L}{3} = \frac{2}{3}\,\text{m}$. Since the loop is an equilateral triangle, all angles are 60°. The altitude of the triangle is therefore $A = b\sin 60° = 0.577$ m and the enclosed area is:

$$A = \frac{1}{2}bh = \frac{1}{2}(\tfrac{2}{3}\text{m})(0.577\,\text{m}) = 0.192\,\text{m}^2.$$

The maximum torque occurs when the plane of the loop is parallel to the magnetic field ($\theta = 90°$) and is given by:

$$\tau_{max} = BIA = (0.500\,\text{T})(2.00\,\text{A})(0.192\,\text{m}^2) = 0.192\,\text{N m.}$$

19.23 First find the current that flows in the wire:

$$R = \frac{\rho L}{A} = \frac{(1.70 \times 10^{-8}\ \Omega\ \text{m})(8.00\ \text{m})}{(1.00 \times 10^{-4}\ \text{m}^2)} = 1.36 \times 10^{-3}\,\Omega, \text{ so}$$

$$I = \frac{\Delta V}{R} = \frac{0.100\ \text{V}}{1.36 \times 10^{-3}\ \Omega} = 73.5\,\text{A.}$$

Each side of the square loop formed by the wire is 2.00 m long so the enclosed area is $A = (2.00\,\text{m})^2 = 4.00\,\text{m}^2$. Then the maximum torque on the loop is: $\tau_{max} = IAB = (73.5\,\text{A})(4.00\,\text{m}^2)(0.400\,\text{T}) = 118\,\text{N m}$.

19.24 (See sketch) The current through the parallel resistor is: $I = 3.00\,\text{A} - 10\,\text{mA} = 2.99\,\text{A}$.
Use the loop rule on the closed loop, and find

$$-(0.01\,\text{A})(50.0\,\Omega) + R_p(2.99\,\text{A}) = 0.$$

This yields, $R_p = 0.167\,\Omega$.

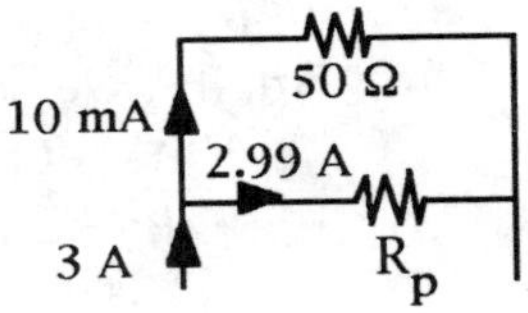

19.25 The current through the coil at full scale deflection is:

$$i_c = \frac{50.0 \times 10^{-3}\ \text{V}}{50.0\ \Omega} = 10^{-3}\,\text{A.}$$

Hence, the current that must exist in the parallel branch is: $I_p = 10\,\text{A} - i_c = 10\,\text{A} - 10^{-3}\,\text{A} = 9.999\,\text{A}$.
Therefore, the parallel resistor has a value of:

$$R_p = \frac{50.0 \times 10^{-3}\ \text{V}}{9.999\ \text{A}} = 5.00 \times 10^{-3}\,\Omega.$$

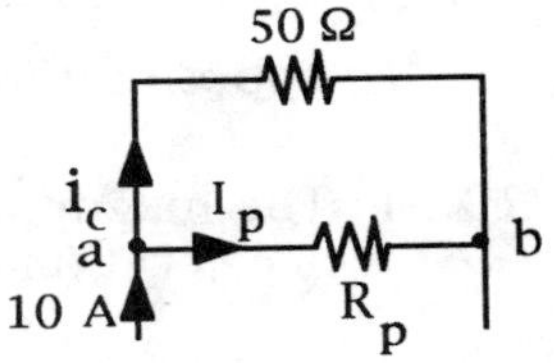

19.26 The voltage drop across the terminals is given by $\Delta V_{AB} = iR + ir = i(R + r)$ where $r = 60.0\,\Omega$, and R is the unknown resistance connected in series with the meter movement.

$1\ V = (5 \times 10^{-4}\ A)(R + 60.0\ \Omega)$ gives $R = 1940\ \Omega$.

19.27 The series resistor that must be used has a value found as:

$\Delta V = 150\ V = (R_s + 40\ \Omega)(2.0 \times 10^{-3}\ A)$,

Which yields, $R_s = 7.5 \times 10^4\ \Omega$.

19.28 See sketch. If $I = 0.300$ A, and a and d are the terminals, $I_p(R_1 + R_2 + R_3) = i_c(100\ \Omega)$.

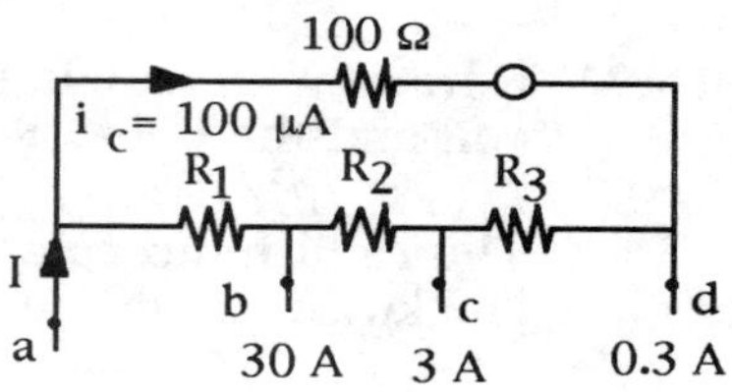

In this case, $I_p = 0.2999$ A and $i_c = 100 \times 10^{-6}$ A.

Thus, $R_1 + R_2 + R_3 = 3.33 \times 10^{-2}\ \Omega$ (1)

If $I = 3.00$ A, and a and c are the terminals:

$I_p(R_1 + R_2) = i_c(100\ \Omega + R_3)$.

Here, $I_p = 2.9999$ A and $i_c = 100 \times 10^{-6}$ A.

Thus, we have $R_1 + R_2 - 3.33 \times 10^{-5} R_3 = 3.33 \times 10^{-3}\ \Omega$ (2)

Finally, if $I = 30.0$ A and a and b are the terminals:

$I_p R_1 = i_c(100\ \Omega + R_2 + R_3)$.

With $I_p = 29.9999$ A and $i_c = 100 \times 10^{-6}$ A, this reduces to:

$R_1 - 3.33 \times 10^{-6} R_2 - 3.33 \times 10^{-6} R_3 = 3.33 \times 10^{-4}\ \Omega$. (3)

Solving (1), (2), and (3) simultaneously, we find:

$R_1 = 3.33 \times 10^{-4}\ \Omega$, $R_2 = 2.998 \times 10^{-3}\ \Omega$, and $R_3 = 2.997 \times 10^{-2}\ \Omega$.

19.29 (See sketch.) We have

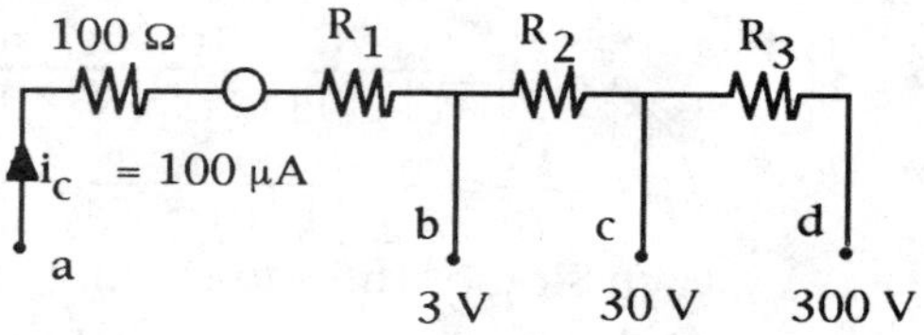

$\Delta V_{ab} = i_c(R_1 + 100\ \Omega)$, or

$3.00\ V = (100 \times 10^{-6}\ A)(R_1 + 100\ \Omega)$.

From which, $R_1 = 2.99 \times 10^4\ \Omega$.

Likewise,:

$\Delta V_{ac} = i_c(R_1 + R_2 + 100\ \Omega)$,

and,

$30.0\ V = (100 \times 10^{-6}\ A)(R_2 + 2.99 \times 10^4\ \Omega + 100\ \Omega)$,

Which yields, $R_2 = 2.70 \times 10^5\ \Omega$.

Finally, we see that: $\Delta V_{ad} = i_c(R_1 + R_2 + R_3 + 100\ \Omega)$. or

$300\ V = (100 \times 10^{-6}\ A)(R_3 + 2.99 \times 10^4\ \Omega + 2.7 \times 10^5\ \Omega + 100\ \Omega)$, and

$R_3 = 2.70 \times 10^6\ \Omega$.

19.30 To pass through undeflected, the magnitude of the magnetic force must equal the magnitude of the electric force, and the two forces must be opposite in direction so they will cancel. Thus, $qvB = qE$, and $v = \frac{E}{B}$

19.31 The magnetic force is the force that causes the centripetal acceleration. Thus,

$qvB = \frac{mv^2}{R}$, which reduces to $qBR = mv$. Therefore,

$(qBR)^2 = m^2v^2 = 2m(\frac{1}{2}mv^2) = 2mKE$, which gives $m = \frac{(qBR)^2}{2(KE)}$

Hence, $m = \frac{((2.0 \times 10^{-6}\ C)(0.1\ T)(3.0\ m))^2}{2(0.09\ J)} = 2.0 \times 10^{-12}$ kg

19.32 First, find the speed of the particle: $v = \frac{E}{B} = \frac{950\ \text{V/m}}{0.930\ \text{T}} = 1.02 \times 10^{3}\ \text{m/s}$

Now, note that the magnetic force causes the centripetal acceleration:

$$qvB = \frac{mv^2}{R}.$$

Thus, $$R = \frac{mv}{qB} = \frac{(2.18 \times 10^{-26}\ \text{kg})(1.02 \times 10^{3}\ \text{m/s})}{(1.60 \times 10^{-19}\ \text{C})(0.930\ \text{T})} = 1.49 \times 10^{-4}\ \text{m}$$

19.33 We use conservation of energy to find the velocity of the ion upon entering the field: $\frac{1}{2}mv^2 = q\Delta V$,

or $$v = \sqrt{\frac{2(1.60 \times 10^{-19}\ \text{C})(250\ \text{V})}{2.50 \times 10^{-26}\ \text{kg}}} = 5.66 \times 10^{4}\ \text{m/s}$$

The magnetic force causes the centripetal acceleration.

Then: $qvB = \frac{mv^2}{R}$,

and $$R = \frac{mv}{qB} = \frac{(2.50 \times 10^{-26}\ \text{kg})(5.66 \times 10^{4}\ \text{m/s})}{(1.60 \times 10^{-19}\ \text{C})(0.500\ \text{T})}$$
$$= 1.77 \times 10^{-2}\ \text{m} = 1.77\ \text{cm}.$$

19.34 $$r = \frac{mv}{qB} = \text{m}\left(\frac{v}{qB}\right) = m\left(\frac{3.00 \times 10^{5}\ \text{m/s}}{(1.60 \times 10^{-19}\ \text{C})(0.600\ \text{T})}\right) = \text{m}\left(3.125 \times 10^{24}\ \frac{\text{m}}{\text{kg}}\right).$$

For U^{235}: $m = 235(1.67 \times 10^{-27}\ \text{kg}) = 3.925 \times 10^{-25}\ \text{kg}$.

Thus, $r = (3.125 \times 10^{24}\ \text{m/kg})(3.925 \times 10^{-25}\ \text{kg}) = 1.227\ \text{m}$.

For U^{238}: $m = 238(1.67 \times 10^{-27}\ \text{kg}) = 3.975 \times 10^{-25}\ \text{kg}$,

and $r = (3.125 \times 10^{24}\ \text{m/kg})(3.975 \times 10^{-25}\ \text{kg}) = 1.242\ \text{m}$.

Therefore: $\Delta d = 2(\Delta r) = 2(1.242 - 1.227) = 3.0 \times 10^{-2}\ \text{m} = 3.0\ \text{cm}$.

19.35 The magnetic force produces the centripetal acceleration:

$qvB = \frac{mv^2}{R}$, or $R = \frac{mv}{qB}$. The time to complete one orbit is then:

$$T = \frac{\text{circumference}}{\text{speed}} = \frac{2\pi R}{v} = \frac{2\pi\frac{mv}{qB}}{v} = \frac{2\pi m}{qB}$$
$$= \frac{2\pi(1.67 \times 10^{-27}\ \text{kg})}{(1.60 \times 10^{-19}\ \text{C})(0.758\ \text{T})} = 8.65 \times 10^{-8}\ \text{m}$$

19.36 (a) right to left, (b) out of page, (c) lower left to upper right.

19.37 We use $B = \frac{\mu_0 I}{2\pi r}$ to find: $r = \frac{\mu_0 I}{2\pi B} = \frac{(4\pi \times 10^{-7}\ \text{T m/A})(5.0\ \text{A})}{2\pi(5.0 \times 10^{-5}\ \text{T})}$, or

$r = 2 \times 10^{-2}\ \text{m} = 2.0\ \text{cm}$.

19.38 The magnitude of the field due to a single wire is given by:

$$B = \frac{\mu_0 I}{2\pi r} = \frac{(4\pi \times 10^{-7}\ \text{T m/A})(5.00\ \text{A})}{2\pi r} = \frac{1.00 \times 10^{-6}\ \text{T m}}{r}.$$

Call the wire on the left wire 1 and the wire on the right wire 2.

(a) At a point midway between the wires, $r_1 = r_2 = 5.00$ cm. Thus,:

$B_1 = B_2 = \dfrac{1.00 \text{ x } 10^{-6} \text{ T m}}{0.0500 \text{ m}} = 2.00 \times 10^{-5}$ T. Using the right hand rule, we see that both fields are in the same direction (into the page), which gives us a resultant field of:

$B_{net} = B_1 + B_2 = 4.00 \times 10^{-5}$ T (directed into page).

(b) At the point P_1: $B_1 = \dfrac{1.00 \text{ x } 10^{-6} \text{ T m}}{0.200 \text{ m}} = 5.00 \times 10^{-6}$ T (into the page), and $B_2 = \dfrac{1.00 \text{ x } 10^{-6} \text{ T m}}{0.100 \text{ m}} = 10.0 \times 10^{-6}$ T (out of the page).

Thus, $B_{net} = 5.00 \times 10^{-6}$ T (out of page).

(c) At P_2,: $B_1 = \dfrac{1.00 \text{ x } 10^{-6} \text{ T m}}{0.200 \text{ m}} = 5.00 \times 10^{-6}$ T (out of the page), and

$B_2 = \dfrac{1.00 \text{ x } 10^{-6} \text{ T m}}{0.300 \text{ m}} = 3.33 \times 10^{-6}$ T (into the page),

for $B_{net} = 1.67 \times 10^{-6}$ T (out of page).

19.39 Call the wire on the left 1 and the wire on the right 2.

(a) $B_1 = \dfrac{\mu_0 I}{2\pi r} = \dfrac{(4\pi \text{ x } 10^{-7} \text{ T m/A})(3.00 \text{ A})}{2\pi(1.00 \text{ x } 10^{-1} \text{ m})} = 6.00 \times 10^{-6}$ T (upward).

$B_2 = \dfrac{\mu_0 I}{2\pi r} = \dfrac{(4\pi \text{ x } 10^{-7} \text{ T m/A})(5.00 \text{ A})}{2\pi(1.00 \text{ x } 10^{-1} \text{ m})} = 10.0 \times 10^{-6}$ T (downward),

so $B_{net} = 4.00 \times 10^{-6}$ T (downward).

(b) (See the sketch) The distance R is

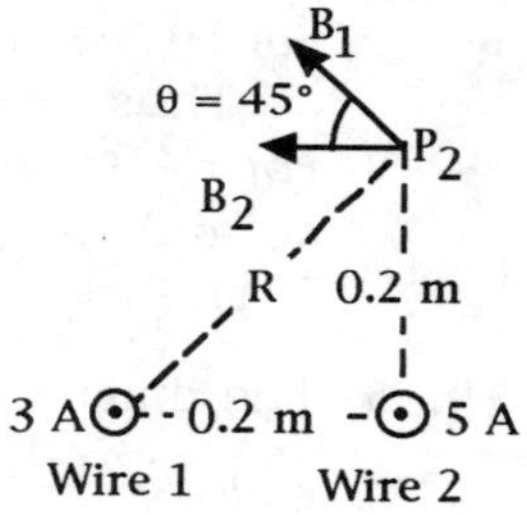

$R = \sqrt{(0.2 \text{ m})^2 + (0.2 \text{ m})^2} = 0.283$ m.

The field produced by wire 2 at P_2 is:

$B_2 = \dfrac{\mu_0 I}{2\pi r} = \dfrac{(4\pi \text{ x } 10^{-7} \text{ T m/A})(5 \text{ A})}{2\pi(0.2 \text{ m})}$

$= 5.00 \times 10^{-6}$ T

and the field from wire 1 at point P_2 is

$B_1 = \dfrac{\mu_0 I}{2\pi R} = \dfrac{(4\pi \text{ x } 10^{-7} \text{ T m/A})(3 \text{ A})}{2\pi(0.283 \text{ m})}$, or

$B_1 = 2.12 \times 10^{-6}$ T. The angle θ shown in the sketch is 45 °. Thus, the fields can be broken into their x and y components. These resultant components are: $B_x = -6.5 \times 10^{-6}$ T, $B_y = 1.5 \times 10^{-6}$ T. The Pythagorean theorem gives a resultant field of: $B = 6.67 \times 10^{-6}$ T at 77 ° to the left of the vertical.

19.40 The magnitude of the field produced by either wire is given by $B = \dfrac{\mu_0 I}{2\pi r}$.

At point P, the field due to the wire along the x-axis ($I = 7.00$ A) is directed out of the page while the field due to the wire along the y-axis ($I = 6.00$ A) is directed into the page. Taking out of the page as positive,

we then have $B_{net} = B_7 - B_6 = \dfrac{\mu_0(7.00 \text{ A})}{2\pi(3.00 \text{ m})} - \dfrac{\mu_0(6.00 \text{ A})}{2\pi(4.00 \text{ m})} = 1.67 \times 10^{-7}$ T.

Thus, the resultant field at point P is 1.67×10^{-7} T directed out of the page.

19.41 From Ampere's law, the magnetic field at point A is given by:

$$B_A = \frac{\mu_0 I_A}{2\pi r_A},$$ where I_A is the net current flowing through the area of the circle of radius r_A. In this case, I_A = 1.00 A out of the page (the current in the inner conductor), so

$$B_A = \frac{(4\pi \times 10^{-7}\ \text{T m/A})(1.00\ \text{A})}{2\pi(1.00 \times 10^{-3}\ \text{m})} = 2.00 \times 10^{-4}\ \text{T counterclockwise.}$$

Similarly at point B: $B_B = \frac{\mu_0 I_B}{2\pi r_B}$, where I_B is the net current flowing through the area of the circle having radius r_B. Taking out of the page as positive, I_B = 1.00A - 3.00 A = -2.00 A, or I_B = 2.00 A into the page. Therefore,

$$B_B = \frac{(4\pi \times 10^{-7}\ \text{T m/A})(2.00\ \text{A})}{2\pi(3.00 \times 10^{-3}\ \text{m})} = 1.33 \times 10^{-4}\ \text{T clockwise.}$$

19.42 (a) $\frac{F}{L} = \frac{\mu_0 I_1 I_2}{2\pi d} = \left(2 \times 10^{-7}\ \frac{\text{N}}{\text{A}^2}\right)\left(\frac{(10.0\ \text{A})^2}{0.100\ \text{m}}\right) = 2.00 \times 10^{-4}$ N/m (attracted).

(b) The magnitude remains the same as calculated in (a), but the wires are repelled.

19.43 In order for the system to be in equilibrium, the magnetic force per unit length on the top wire must be equal to its weight per unit length. Thus, $\frac{F}{L}$ = weight per unit length, where: $\frac{F}{L} = \frac{\mu_0 I_1 I_2}{2\pi d}$.

We have, $(2 \times 10^{-7}\ \text{T m/A})\left(\frac{(30.0\ \text{A})(60.0\ \text{A})}{d}\right) = 0.080$ N/m, and find

$d = 4.50 \times 10^{-3}$ m = 4.50 mm.

19.44 The magnetic force exerted on B by A is directed upward and has a magnitude given by: $F_m = \frac{\mu_0 I_A I_B L}{2\pi r}$, where r is the distance between the two wires. At equilibrium: $F_m = mg = \frac{\mu_0 I_A I_B L}{2\pi r}$,

or $I_B = \frac{2\pi r}{\mu_0 I_A}\frac{m}{L}g$.

This gives:

$$I_B = \frac{2\pi(0.025\ \text{m})}{(4\pi \times 10^{-7}\ \text{T m/A})(150\ \text{A})}(0.010\ \text{kg/m})(9.80\ \text{m/s}^2) = 82\ \text{A}.$$

19.45 The magnetic field at the center of the solenoid is:

$B = \mu_0 n I = (4\pi \times 10^{-7}$ T m/A)(3000 turns/m)(15.0 A) = 5.65×10^{-2} T.

The force on one of the sides of the loop is:

$F = BIL = (5.65 \times 10^{-2}$ T)(0.200 A)(0.0200 m) = 2.26×10^{-4} N.

With the loop aligned as in the problem, all the forces are directed such that they tend to stretch the loop. There is no tendency for the forces to cause rotation. Thus, $\tau = 0$.

19.46 The resistance of the wire is $R = \frac{\rho L}{\pi r^2}$, so it carries current $I = \frac{\varepsilon}{R} = \frac{\varepsilon \pi r^2}{\rho L}$

If there is a single layer of windings, the number of turns per unit length is the reciprocal of the wire diameter: $n = \frac{1}{2}r$.

So $B = n\mu_0 I = \frac{\mu_0 \varepsilon \pi r^2}{\rho L 2r} = \frac{\mu_0 \varepsilon \pi r}{\rho L 2}$

$$= \frac{(4\pi \times 10^{-7} \text{ T m/A})(20 \text{ V})\pi(2 \times 10^{-3} \text{ m})}{2(1.7 \times 10^{-8} \ \Omega \text{ m})10 \text{ m}} = 0.464 \text{ T}$$

19.47 (a) The magnetic force provides the centripetal acceleration

$qvB = \frac{mv^2}{R}$, or $B = \frac{mv}{qr} = \frac{(9.11 \times 10^{-31} \text{ kg})(10^4 \text{ m/s})}{(1.60 \times 10^{-19} \text{ C})(2.0 \times 10^{-2} \text{ m})} = 2.8 \times 10^{-6}$ T

(b) From $B = \mu_0 n I$: $I = \frac{B}{\mu_0 n} = \frac{2.8 \times 10^{-6} \text{ T}}{(4\pi \times 10^{-7} \text{ Tm/S})(2500 \text{ turns/m})} =$ 8.9×10^{-4} A = 0.89 mA.

19.48 Note that the angle between the field and the line perpendicular to the plane of the coil is $90° - 35° = 55°$. Therefore, the torque is:

$$\tau = NBIA\sin\theta = (1)(0.30 \text{ T})(25 \text{ A})[\pi(0.30 \text{ m})^2]\sin 55° = 1.7 \text{ N·m}$$

19.49 Call the wire along the y-axis #1 and the wire along the x-axis #2.

(a) The field at P produced by wire 1 is

$B_1 = \frac{\mu_0 I_1}{2\pi r_1} = \frac{(4\pi \times 10^{-7} \text{ T m/A})(3.00 \text{ A})}{2\pi(0.300 \text{ m})} = 2.00 \times 10^{-6}$ T (into page),

and the field due to wire 2 is

$B_2 = \frac{\mu_0 I_2}{2\pi r_2} = \frac{(4\pi \times 10^{-7} \text{ T m/A})(5.00 \text{ A})}{2\pi(0.400 \text{ m})} = 2.50 \times 10^{-6}$ T (out of page), Thus, the net field is $B_{net} = 5.0 \times 10^{-7}$ T (out of page).

(b) We use the same designation for discussing the wires as above. The field due to wire 1 is:

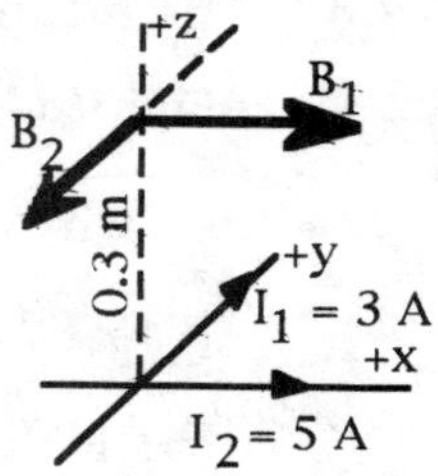

$$B_1 = \frac{\mu_0 I_1}{2\pi r_1} = \frac{(4\pi \times 10^{-7} \text{ T m/A})(3.00 \text{ A})}{2\pi(0.300 \text{ m})} = 2.00 \times 10^{-6} \text{ T}$$

The sketch indicates the direction of the field. The field due to wire 2 is:

$$B_2 = \frac{\mu_0 I_2}{2\pi r_2} = \frac{(4\pi \times 10^{-7} \text{ T m/A})(5.00 \text{ A})}{2\pi(0.300 \text{ m})} = 3.33 \times 10^{-6} \text{ T}$$

(For direction, see sketch.

The net field is found from the Pythagorean theorem to be

$B_{net} = 3.89 \times 10^{-6}$ T.

The angle, as seen from above the wires (second sketch) is:

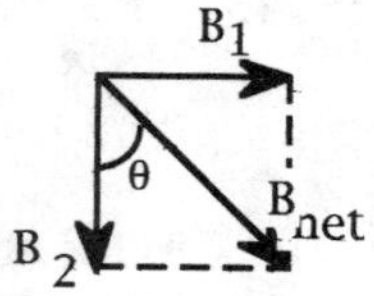

$\tan\theta = \frac{B_1}{B_2} = 0.6$ and $\theta = 31°$ (CCW from $-y$ direction).

19.50 A kinetic energy of 400 eV is equivalent to 6.4×10^{-17} J. We find the velocity v as: $v = \sqrt{\frac{2 \ KE}{m}} = \sqrt{\frac{2(6.4 \times 10^{-17} \text{ J})}{9.11 \times 10^{-31} \text{ kg}}} = 1.19 \times 10^7$ m/s

Thus, $B = \frac{mv}{qr} = \frac{(9.11 \times 10^{-31}\ \text{kg})(1.19 \times 10^{7}\ \text{m/s})}{(1.60 \times 10^{-19}\ \text{C})(0.80\ \text{m})} = 8.5 \times 10^{-5}\,\text{T}$

19.51 The centripetal acceleration is produced by the magnetic force as

$M\left(\frac{v^2}{r}\right) = qvB,$

or $r = \frac{Mv}{qB} = \frac{M(1.00 \times 10^{5}\ \text{m/s})}{(1.60 \times 10^{-19}\ \text{C})(0.200\ \text{T})} = M(3.13 \times 10^{24}\ \text{m/kg})$

For the first particle, $M = 20.0 \times 10^{-27}$ kg, thus

$r_1 = (20.0 \times 10^{-27}\ \text{kg})(3.13 \times 10^{24}\ \text{m/kg}) = 6.26 \times 10^{-2}\ \text{m}$

For the second particle, $M = 23.4 \times 10^{-27}$ kg, and

$r_2 = (23.4 \times 10^{-27}\ \text{kg})(3.13 \times 10^{24}\ \text{m/kg}) = 7.32 \times 10^{-2}\ \text{m}$

Thus, after half a revolution, $\Delta = 2(r_2 - r_1) = 2.12\ \text{cm}$

19.52 (a) At point C, the two currents give rise to oppositely directed magnetic fields. Therefore, to have $B = 0$ at C, we require $B_1 = B_2$, where B_1 is due to 1 and B_2 is due to the 10 A current. From $B = \frac{\mu_0 I}{2\pi r}$, we have: $\frac{I_1}{r_1} = \frac{I_2}{r_2}$, or $I = I_2\left(\frac{r_1}{r_2}\right) = (10.0\ \text{A})\left(\frac{15.0\ \text{cm}}{5.00\ \text{cm}}\right) = 30.0\ \text{A}.$

(b) At point A, between the wires:

$B_1 = \frac{\mu_0 I_1}{2\pi r_1} = \frac{(4\pi \times 10^{-7}\ \text{T m/A})(30.0\ \text{A})}{2\pi(5.00 \times 10^{-2}\ \text{m})} = 1.20 \times 10^{-4}\ \text{T (out of page)},$

$B_2 = \frac{\mu_0 I_2}{2\pi r_2} = \frac{(4\pi \times 10^{-7}\ \text{T m/A})(10.0\ \text{A})}{2\pi(5.00 \times 10^{-2}\ \text{m})} = 4.00 \times 10^{-5}\ \text{T (out of page)}.$

Thus, $B_{total} = B_1 + B_2 = 1.60 \times 10^{-4}\ \text{T}$ (out of page).

19.53 The distance to the center of the square is found from the Pythagorean theorem to be: $r = 0.141$ m.

The magnitude of the magnetic field of each wire is equal to:

$B_1 = B_2 = B_3 = B_4 = \frac{\mu_0 I}{2\pi r} = \frac{(4\pi \times 10^{-7}\ \text{T m/A})(4.00\ \text{A})}{2\pi(0.141\ \text{m})} = 5.66 \times 10^{-6}\,\text{T}.$

The directions of these fields are indicated in the sketch. The net field pointing toward wire 4, B_{IV} is: $B_{IV} = B_1 + B_3 = 1.13 \times 10^{-5}\,\text{T}.$

The net field toward wire 1, B_I is:

$B_I = B_2 + B_4 = 1.13 \times 10^{-5}$ T. These two fields are perpendicular. Thus, from the Pythagorean theorem, we find: $B_{net} = 1.6 \times 10^{-5}$ T.

The direction is toward top of page.

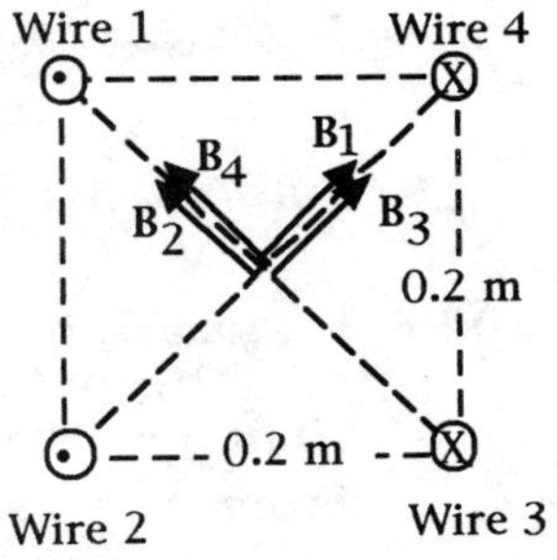

19.54 The magnetic force produces the centripetal acceleration, or: $qvB = \frac{mv^2}{R}$, giving $v = \frac{qRB}{m}$.

But the time for one complete revolution is: $T = \frac{2\pi R}{v}$,

The frequency of revolution is $f = \frac{1}{T} = \frac{v}{2\pi R} = \frac{qB}{2\pi m}$. Therefore, $m = \frac{qB}{2\pi f}$

We are told that $f = \frac{5 \text{ rev}}{1.50 \times 10^{-3} \text{ s}} = 3.33 \times 10^3$ Hz. Thus,

$$m = \frac{(1.60 \times 10^{-19} \text{ C})(0.050 \text{ T})}{2\pi(3.33 \times 10^3 \text{ Hz})}, \text{ or } m = 3.82 \times 10^{-25} \text{ kg}$$

19.55 The magnetic force produces the centripetal acceleration,

or: $qvB = \frac{mv^2}{R}$, giving $B = \frac{mv}{qR}$. But the time for one complete revolution is $T = \frac{2\pi R}{v}$, so $v = \frac{2\pi R}{T}$ and the field becomes:

$$B = \frac{m}{qR}\left(\frac{2\pi R}{T}\right) = \frac{2\pi m}{qT} = \frac{2\pi(1.67 \times 10^{-27} \text{ kg})}{(1.60 \times 10^{-19} \text{ C})(1.00 \times 10^{-6} \text{ s})} = 6.56 \times 10^{-2} \text{ T}$$

19.56 The magnetic forces on the top and bottom segments of the rectangle are equal in magnitude and opposite in direction. Hence, they cancel. The force on the left vertical segment is:

$$F_L = \frac{\mu_0 I_1 I_2}{2\pi c} L = (2 \times 10^{-7} \text{ N/A}^2)\frac{(5.0 \text{ A})(10.0 \text{ A})(0.45 \text{ m})}{0.10 \text{ m}}$$

$$= 4.5 \times 10^{-5} \text{ N (to left)}$$

The force on the right vertical segment is:

$$F_R = \frac{\mu_0 I_1 I_2}{2\pi(c + a)} L = (2 \times 10^{-7} \text{ N/A}^2)\frac{(5.0 \text{ A})(10.0 \text{ A})(0.45 \text{ m})}{0.25 \text{ m}}$$

$$= 1.8 \times 10^{-5} \text{ N (to right)}$$

Finding the resultant of the two ($F_R - F_L$) gives:

$$F_{net} = 2.7 \times 10^{-5} \text{ N (to left)}$$

19.57 First find the force constant of the spring system from the elongation produced by the weight of the wire, $mg = 9.80 \times 10^{-2}$ N, alone:

$$k = \frac{F}{\Delta x} = \frac{mg}{\Delta x} = \frac{9.80 \times 10^{-2} \text{ N}}{5.0 \times 10^{-3} \text{ m}} = 19.6 \text{ N/m}.$$

When the magnetic field is on, the total force pulling down on the wire is given by: $F_{down} = F_m + mg = k(\Delta x)_{total}$.

Thus, the magnetic force, F_m is:

$$F_m = k(\Delta x)_{total} - mg = (19.6 \text{ N/m})(8.0 \times 10^{-3} \text{ m}) - 9.80 \times 10^{-2} \text{ N}$$

$$= 5.88 \times 10^{-2} \text{ N}$$

But, $F_m = BIL$. Thus, $B = \frac{F_m}{IL} = \frac{F_m R}{VL} = \frac{(5.88 \times 10^{-2} \text{ N})(12 \ \Omega)}{(24 \text{ V})(5.0 \times 10^{-2} \text{ m})} = 0.59 \text{ T}.$

19.58 Let us assume the magnetic force is small compared to gravity. Then, its horizontal velocity component stays nearly constant. We call its value v in the x direction.

From $v_y^2 = v_{oy}^2 + 2a_y y$, the vertical component at impact is $\sqrt{2gh}$ in the downward direction.

Thus, from $F = qvB\sin\theta$, we find there is a magnetic force on the ball in the horizontal direction given by

$$F_h = Q\sqrt{2gh}B$$

and a force in the vertical direction given by $F_v = QvB$

$$F_h = 5.0 \times 10^{-6} \text{ C}\sqrt{2(9.80)(20.0)}\ (0.0100 \text{ T}) = 0.990 \times 10^{-6} \text{ N}$$

$$F_v = 5.0 \times 10^{-6} \text{ C}(20.0 \text{ m/s})(0.0100 \text{ T}) = 1.00 \times 10^{-6} \text{ N}$$

19.59 $F = qvB = \frac{mv^2}{r}$

$$B = \frac{mv}{qr} = \frac{4.80 \times 10^{-16}\ \text{kg m/s}}{(1.60 \times 10^{-19}\ \text{C})(1000\ \text{m})} = 3.00\,\text{T}$$

19.60 Model the two wires as straight parallel wires.

(a) $F = \frac{\mu_0 I^2 L}{2\pi a} = \frac{(4\pi 10^{-7})(140)^2 2\pi(0.1)}{2\pi 10^{-3}} = 2.46\,\text{N}$

(b) $a_{loop} = \frac{2.46\ \text{N} - m_{loop}g}{m_{loop}} = 107.3\ \text{m/s}^2.$

19.61 (a) At any point on the ring, the magnetic field has a horizontal component, $B_H = B\sin\theta$, and a vertical component $B_V = B\cos\theta$. Treat these as two separate fields and consider the forces they exert on the ring. At any point on the ring, the vertical field exerts a horizontal force directed inward toward the center of the ring. The horizontal forces exerted on diametrically opposite points in the ring cancel each other, so the resultant horizontal force on the ring is zero. At any point on the ring, the outward horizontal field, B_H, exerts an upward force on the ring. The total upward force on the ring is: $F = B_H I L = (B\sin\theta)I(2\pi r)$, or

$$F = (0.01\ \text{T})\sin 30°(2.0\ \text{A})(2\pi)(2 \times 10^{-2}\ \text{m}) = 1.3 \times 10^{-3}\ \text{N}.$$

(b) To levitate the ring, the upward magnetic force must equal the weight of the ring: $B_H I L = mg$, or

$$I = \frac{m}{L}\frac{g}{B_H} = \frac{(0.01\ \text{kg})(9.80\ \text{m/s}^2)}{(0.01\ \text{T})\sin 30°} = 19.6\ \text{A}.$$

19.62 (a) The net upward force on the wire is: $F_y = ma_y = ILB - mg$, so the upward acceleration is: $a_y = \frac{IBL}{m} - g = \frac{BI}{\lambda} - g$, where λ is the mass per unit length of the wire. Thus,

$$a_y = \frac{(2\ \text{A})(40 \times 10^{-4}\ \text{T})}{5 \times 10^{-4}\ \text{kg/m}} - 9.80\ \text{m/s}^2 = 6.2\ \text{m/s}^2.$$

(b) Using $y = \frac{at^2}{2}$, we get:

$$t = \sqrt{\frac{2y}{a}} = \sqrt{2\left(\frac{0.5\ \text{m}}{6.2\ \text{m/s}^2}\right)} = 0.40\ \text{s when } y = 0.5\ \text{m}.$$

19.63 (a) The radius of the path as a function of charge is given by

$$r = \frac{mv}{qB} = \frac{(6.64 \times 10^{-27}\ \text{kg})(10^6\ \text{m/s})}{q(0.20\ \text{T})} = \frac{3.32 \times 10^{-20}\ \text{C m}}{q}. \quad (1)$$

If the ion is singly ionized ($q = 1.60 \times 10^{-19}$ C) then (1) gives the radius of the orbit as $r_1 = 2.1 \times 10^{-1}$ m = 21 cm, and for the doubly charged ion ($q = 3.2 \times 10^{-19}$ C), we have $r_2 = 1.0 \times 10^{-1}$ m = 10 cm.

(b) Their distance of separation after one-half their circular path is:

$$\Delta = 2(21\ \text{cm} - 10\ \text{cm}) = 22\ \text{cm}.$$

19.64 Label the wires 1, 2, and 3 as shown and let the magnetic field created by the currents in the wires be B_1, B_2, and B_3, respectively. (Note that $\theta = 45°$.)

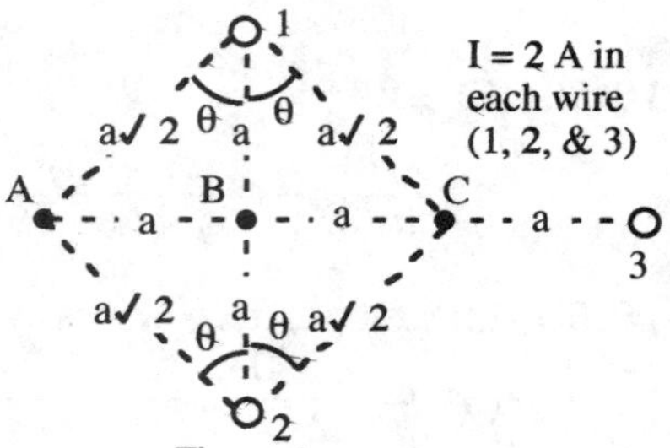

Figure 1

(a) At point A: $B_1 = B_2 = \frac{\mu_0 I}{2\pi a\sqrt{2}}$

$$B_1 = B_2 = \frac{(2 \times 10^{-7} \text{ T m/A})(2.0 \text{ A})}{(0.01 \text{ m})\sqrt{2}}$$

$B_1 = B_2 = 2.83 \times 10^{-5}$ T, and

$$B_3 = \frac{\mu_0 I}{2\pi 3a} = \frac{(2 \times 10^{-7} \text{ T m/A})(2.0 \text{ A})}{3(0.01 \text{ m})} = 1.33 \times 10^{-5} \text{ T.}$$

The direction of these three fields are as shown in Figure 2. Observe that the horizontal components of B_1 and B_2 cancel while the vertical components add to B_3. Thus, the net field at A is:

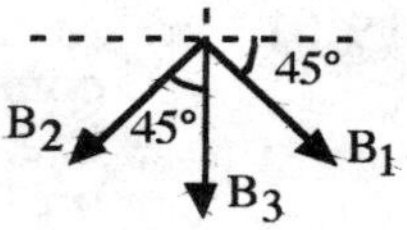

Figure 2

$$B_A = B_1\cos 45 + B_2\cos 45 + B_3$$
$$= 2(2.83 \times 10^{-5} \text{ T})\cos 45° + 1.33 \times 10^{-5} \text{ T} = 5.3 \times 10^{-5} \text{ T.}$$

(b) At point B, $B_1 = B_2 = \frac{\mu_0 I}{2\pi a} = 4 \times 10^{-5}$ T and $B_3 = \frac{\mu_0 I}{2\pi 2a} = 2 \times 10^{-5}$ T.

The directions of these fields at B are as shown in Figure 3. Thus, B_1 and B_2 cancel leaving

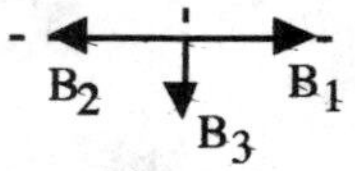

Figure 3

$B_B = B_3 = 2.0 \times 10^{-5}$ T downward.

(c) At point C, $B_1 = B_2 = \frac{\mu_0 I}{2\pi a\sqrt{2}} = 2.83 \times 10^{-5}$ T, and

$B_3 = \frac{\mu_0 I}{2\pi a} = 4 \times 10^{-5}$ T. The directions of these 3 fields at C are as shown in Figure 4: Again, the horizontal components of B_1 and B_2 cancel. The vertical components of B_1 and B_2 both oppose B_3 giving:

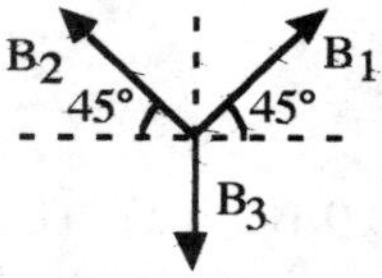

Figure 4

$$B_C = B_1\cos 45 + B_2\cos 45 - B_3 = 2(2.83 \times 10^{-5} \text{ T})\cos 45° - 4 \times 10^{-5} \text{ T} = 0.$$

19.65 (a) Since the magnetic field is pointing from N to S, a magnetic force will exist pushing positive charges toward point A and negative charges toward point B. This separation of charges will then set up an electric field directed from A toward B. At equilibrium, the electric force caused by this field must balance the magnetic force,

so $qvB = qE = q\left(\frac{V}{d}\right)$,

or $v = \frac{\Delta V}{Bd} = \frac{160 \times 10^{-6} \text{ V}}{(0.040 \text{ T})(3.0 \times 10^{-3} \text{ m})} = 1.33$ m/s.

(b) The magnetic field is directed from N to S. If the charge carriers are negative moving in the direction of v, the magnetic force is directed toward point B. Negative charges build up at point B, placing A at a higher potential than B. If the charge carriers are positive moving in the direction of v, the magnetic force is directed toward A, so positive charges build up at A. This also places A at a higher potential than B. Therefore the sign of the potential difference does not depend on whether the ions in the blood are positively or negatively charged.

19.66 (a) Since one wire repels the other, the currents in the two wires are in opposite directions.

(b) Consider a free body diagram of one of the wires as shown at the right.

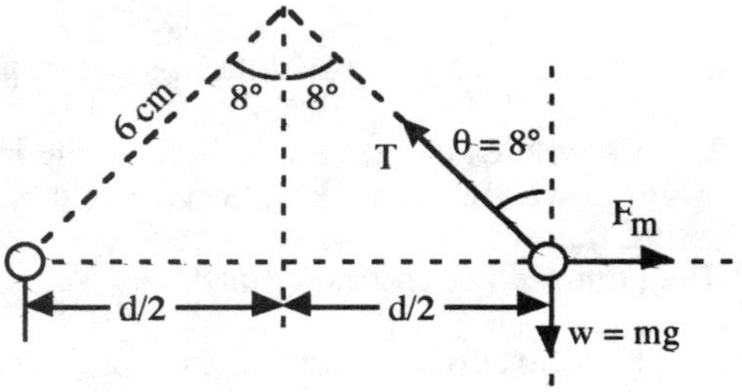

$\Sigma F_x = 0 \Rightarrow F_m = T\sin 8°$, and $\Sigma F_y = 0 \Rightarrow mg = T\cos 8°$, so dividing the first equation by the second gives: $\frac{F_m}{mg} = \tan 8°$, or $F_m = mg\tan 8°$.

Also observe that $\frac{d}{2} = (6\text{ cm})\sin 8°$, or $d = (0.12\text{ m})\sin 8°$ is the distance between the two wires. Thus: $F_m = \frac{\mu_0 I_1 I_2 L}{2\pi d} = mg\tan 8°$,

and since $I_1 = I_2 = I$, this becomes: $I^2 = \left(\frac{2\pi g}{\mu_0}\right)\left(\frac{m}{L}\right) d\tan 8°$, or

$$I^2 = \left(\frac{2\pi(9.80\text{ m/s}^2)}{4\pi \times 10^{-7}\text{ T m/A}}\right)\left(0.04\ \frac{\text{kg}}{\text{m}}\right)(0.12\text{ m}\sin 8°)(\tan 8°) = 4600\text{ A}^2,$$

and $I = 67.8$ A.

19.67 The velocity is given by

$$v = \sqrt{\frac{2K}{m}} = \sqrt{\frac{2(5.00 \times 10^{6}\text{ eV})(1.60 \times 10^{-19}\text{ J/eV})}{1.67 \times 10^{-27}\text{ kg}}} = 3.10 \times 10^{7}\text{ m/s}$$

and $r = \frac{mv}{qB} = \frac{1.67 \times 10^{-27}\text{ kg}(3.10 \times 10^{7}\text{ m})}{(1.60 \times 10^{-19}\text{ m})(0.05\text{ T})} = 6.46\text{ m}$

(b) The angle α is the angle with which the particle leaves the field measured with respect to the horizontal. It is found as

$$\sin\alpha = \frac{1\text{ m}}{6.46\text{ m}} = 8.90°$$

(a) The magnitude of the proton momentum remains constant, and its final y component is

$$-(1.67 \times 10^{-27}\text{ kg})(3.10 \times 10^{7}\text{ m/s})\sin 8.90° = -8.00 \times 10^{-21}\text{ kg m/s}$$

ANSWERS TO CONCEPTUAL QUESTIONS

2. If the current is in a direction parallel or antiparallel to the magnetic field, then there is no force.

4. Straight down toward the surface of the Earth.

6. The magnet causes domain alignment in the iron such that the iron becomes magnetic and is attracted to the original magnet. Now that the iron is magnetic, it can produce an identical effect in another piece of iron.

8. The magnet produces domain alignment in the nail such that the nail is attracted to the magnet. Regardless of which pole is used, the alignment in the nail is such that it is attracted to the magnet.

10. The shock shakes the domains out of alignment.

12. At the poles the magnetic field of the Earth points almost straight downward (or straight upward), in the direction (or opposite to the direction) the charges are moving. As a result, there is little or no magnetic force exerted on the charged particles at the pole to deflect them away from the Earth.

14. The loop can be mounted on an axle that can rotate. The current loop will rotate when placed in an external magnetic field for some arbitrary orientation of the field relative to the loop. As the current in the loop is increased, the torque on it will increase.

16. Yes, if the magnetic field is directed perpendicular to the plane of the loop, the forces on opposite sides of the loop will be equal and opposite, but will produce no net torque on the loop.

18. A charge at rest is completely unaffected by a magnetic field.

20. Such levitation would never occur. At the north pole of the Earth where the field of the Earth is downward, toward the equivalent of a buried south pole, a coffin would be repelled if its south pole were directed downward. However, equilibrium would be only transitory as any slight disturbance would overcome the balance.

CHAPTER TWENTY SOLUTIONS

Chapter Twenty Readings

Kondo, H., "Michael Faraday," *Scientic American*, October 1953, p. 90.

McDonald, D.K.C., *Faraday, Maxwell and Kelvin*, New York Doubleday Anchor, 1964.

Sharlin, H.L., "From Faraday to the Dynamo," *Scientific American*, May 1961, p. 107.

Shiers, G., "The Induction Coil," *Scientific American*, May 1971, p. 80.

Stix, G., "Maglev: Racing to Oblivion?" *Scientific American*, October 1997, p 109.

20.1 The magnetic flux through the area enclosed by the loop is given by:
$\Phi = BA\cos\theta = B(\pi r^2) = (0.30\ \text{T})\pi(0.25\ \text{m})^2 = 5.9 \times 10^{-2}\ \text{T m}^2$.

20.2 $\Phi = BA\cos\theta = (0.300\ \text{T})(4.00\ \text{m}^2)\cos 50° = 7.71 \times 10^{-1}\ \text{T m}^2$.

20.3 $\Phi = BA\cos\theta$ Thus,
(a) $\Phi = (5.00 \times 10^{-5}\ \text{T})(20.0 \times 10^{-4}\ \text{m}^2)\cos(0°) = 1.00 \times 10^{-7}\ \text{T m}^2$.
(b) $\Phi = (5.00 \times 10^{-5}\ \text{T})(20.0 \times 10^{-4}\ \text{m}^2)\cos(30°) = 8.66 \times 10^{-8}\ \text{T m}^2$.
(c) $\Phi = (5.00 \times 10^{-5}\ \text{T})(20.0 \times 10^{-4}\ \text{m}^2)\cos(90°) = 0$.

20.4 The magnetic field lines are tangent to the surface of the cylinder, so that no magnetic field lines penetrate the cylinder. The total flux through the cylinder is zero.

20.5 (a) Every field line that comes up through the area *A* on one side of the wire goes back down through area *A* on the other side of the wire. Thus, $\Phi_{net} = 0$.
(b) The magnetic field lines are all parallel to the plane of the coil and do not thread through it. $\Phi = 0$.

20.6 We have $B = \mu_0 n I$, where $n = \dfrac{250\ \text{turns}}{0.20\ \text{m}} = 1250\ \text{turns/m}$.
Thus, $\Phi = BA\cos\theta = \mu_0 n I A$, or

$$\Phi = \left(4\pi \times 10^{-7}\ \text{T}\ \frac{\text{m}}{\text{A}}\right)\left(1250\ \frac{\text{turns}}{\text{m}}\right)(15.0\ \text{A})\pi(2 \times 10^{-2}\ \text{m})^2 = 2.96 \times 10^{-5}\ \text{T m}^2.$$

20.7 $\Phi = BA\cos\theta =$ (component of B perpendicular to surface)A

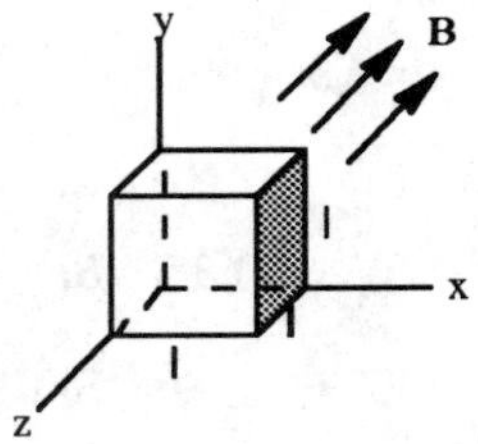

(a) $\Phi_{\text{shaded side}} = B_x A = (5.0\ \text{T})(2.5 \times 10^{-2}\ \text{m})^2 = 3.1 \times 10^{-3}\ \text{T m}^2$.
(b) Magnetic field lines have no beginning and no end. Thus, with a uniform magnetic field, any field line that emerges from the cube through one face entered the cube through the opposite

face. Therefore, the net flux (number of field lines) emerging from the cube is zero. $\Phi_{total} = 0$.

20.8 The initial flux through the coil is

$$\Phi_i = B_i A = (0.20\,\mathrm{T})\pi(0.20\,\mathrm{m})^2 = 2.51 \times 10^{-2}\,\mathrm{T\,m^2},$$

and the final flux linkage is $\Phi_f = 0$.

Thus, $\Delta\Phi = \Phi_f - \Phi_i = -2.51 \times 10^{-2}\,\mathrm{T\,m^2}$, and the magnitude of the induced emf is: $\langle\mathcal{E}\rangle = N\frac{\Delta\Phi}{\Delta t} = \frac{2.51 \times 10^{-2}\,\mathrm{T\,m^2}}{0.30\,\mathrm{s}} = 8.38 \times 10^{-2}\,\mathrm{V} = 84\,\mathrm{mV}$.

20.9 $\mathcal{E} = N\left(\frac{\Delta\Phi}{\Delta t}\right)$ but, $\frac{\Delta\Phi}{\Delta t} = \frac{\Delta(BA)}{\Delta t} = B\left(\frac{\Delta A}{\Delta t}\right)$ so $\langle\mathcal{E}\rangle = NB\left(\frac{\Delta A}{\Delta t}\right)$.

This gives: $18 \times 10^{-3}\,\mathrm{V} = (1)\,B(0.10\,\mathrm{m^2/s})$, and $B = 0.18\,\mathrm{T}$.

20.10 $\Delta\Phi = (A_f - A_i)B = (0 - A_i)B = -(0.15\,\mathrm{T})\,\pi(0.12\,\mathrm{m})^2 = -6.79 \times 10^{-3}\,\mathrm{T\,m^2}$.

The magnitude of the average value of the induced emf is:

$$\langle\mathcal{E}\rangle = \frac{\Delta\Phi}{\Delta t} = \frac{6.79 \times 10^{-3}\,\mathrm{T\,m^2}}{0.20\,\mathrm{s}} = 3.39 \times 10^{-2}\,\mathrm{V} = 34\,\mathrm{mV}.$$

20.11 To produce 0.10 A in an 8.0 Ω coil, the induced emf must be

$\mathcal{E} = IR = (0.10\,\mathrm{A})(8.0\,\Omega) = 0.80\,\mathrm{V}$.

Also, $\mathcal{E} = N\frac{\Delta\Phi}{\Delta t}$ where, $\frac{\Delta\Phi}{\Delta t} = \frac{\Delta(BA)}{\Delta t} = A\frac{\Delta B}{\Delta t}$.

Thus, $0.80\,\mathrm{V} = (75)\frac{\Delta B}{\Delta t}(0.050\,\mathrm{m})(0.080\,\mathrm{m})$, and $\frac{\Delta B}{\Delta t} = 2.7\,\mathrm{T/s}$.

20.12 $\Delta\Phi = \Phi_i - \Phi_f = B\left(\frac{\pi d^2}{4}\right) - 0 = B\left(\frac{\pi d^2}{4}\right)$, and $\langle\mathcal{E}\rangle = N\left(\frac{\Delta\Phi}{\Delta t}\right) = N\frac{B}{\Delta t}\frac{\pi d^2}{4}$.

Thus, $B = \frac{4\,\Delta t\langle\mathcal{E}\rangle}{N\pi d^2} = \frac{4(2.77 \times 10^{-3}\,\mathrm{s})(0.166\,\mathrm{V})}{(500)\pi(15.0 \times 10^{-2}\,\mathrm{m})^2} = 5.2 \times 10^{-5}\,\mathrm{T}$.

20.13 $\Delta\Phi = (B_f - B_i)A = (-0.20\,\mathrm{T} - 0.30\,\mathrm{T})\,\pi(0.30\,\mathrm{m})^2 = -1.41 \times 10^{-1}\,\mathrm{T\,m^2}$.

Thus, the magnitude of the average value of the induced emf is

$$\langle\mathcal{E}\rangle = \frac{\Delta\Phi}{\Delta t} = \frac{1.41 \times 10^{-1}\,\mathrm{T\,m^2}}{1.5\,\mathrm{s}} = 9.42 \times 10^{-2}\,\mathrm{V} = 94\,\mathrm{mV}.$$

20.14 (a) The magnetic field set up inside the solenoid is:

$$B = \mu_0 n I = (4\pi \times 10^{-7}\,\mathrm{Tm/A})\frac{100\,\mathrm{turns}}{0.200\,\mathrm{m}}(3.00\,\mathrm{A}) = 1.88 \times 10^{-3}\,\mathrm{T}, \text{ and}$$

$$\Phi_i = BA = (1.88 \times 10^{-3}\,\mathrm{T})(10^{-2}\,\mathrm{m})^2 = 1.88 \times 10^{-7}\,\mathrm{T\,m^2}.$$

(b) When the current is reduced to zero, $\Phi_f = 0$.

Therefore, $\Delta\Phi = 1.88 \times 10^{-7}\,\mathrm{T\,m^2}$, and

$$\langle\mathcal{E}\rangle = N\frac{\Delta\Phi}{\Delta t} = \frac{1.88 \times 10^{-7}\,\mathrm{T\,m^2}}{3.00\,\mathrm{s}} = 6.28 \times 10^{-8}\,\mathrm{V}.$$

20.15 $B_i = \mu_0 n I_i = (4\pi \times 10^{-7}\,\mathrm{Tm/A})\frac{300\,\mathrm{turns}}{0.20\,\mathrm{m}}(2.0\,\mathrm{A}) = 3.77 \times 10^{-3}\,\mathrm{T}$, and

$B_f = \mu_0 n I_f = (4\pi \times 10^{-7}\,\mathrm{Tm/A})\frac{300\,\mathrm{turns}}{0.20\,\mathrm{m}}(5.0\,\mathrm{A}) = 9.42 \times 10^{-3}\,\mathrm{T}$.

(a) $\Delta\Phi = (B_f - B_i)A = (9.42 \times 10^{-3}\,\mathrm{T} - 3.77 \times 10^{-3}\,\mathrm{T})\pi(0.015\,\mathrm{m})^2$, or

$\Delta\Phi = 4.0 \times 10^{-6}$ T m^2.

(b) $<\varepsilon> = N\dfrac{\Delta\Phi}{\Delta t} = 4\left(\dfrac{4.0 \times 10^{-6} \text{ T m}^2}{0.90 \text{ s}}\right) = 1.8 \times 10^{-5}$ V.

20.16 Take upward through the plane of the coil as the positive direction for the magnetic flux. Then, the initial flux through the coil is:

$\Phi_i = N\phi = NBA\cos\theta. = 200(1.1 \text{ T})(100 \times 10^{-4} \text{ m}^2)\cos 0° = +2.2$ T m^2.

After the field reversed direction, the flux through the coil is:

$\Phi_f = N\phi = NBA\cos\theta. = 200(1.1 \text{ T})(100 \times 10^{-4} \text{ m}^2)\cos 180° = -2.2$ T m^2.

Therefore, the magnitude of the change in flux is $\Delta\Phi = \Phi_i - \Phi_f = 4.4$ T m^2.

The average induced emf in the coil is: $<\varepsilon> = \dfrac{\Delta\Phi}{\Delta t} = \dfrac{4.4 \text{ T m}^2}{0.10 \text{ s}} = 44$ V,

and the average current is $<I> = \dfrac{<\varepsilon>}{R} = \dfrac{44 \text{ V}}{5.0\ \Omega} = 8.8$ A.

20.17 To produce a 0.50 A current through 6.0 Ω of resistance, the induced emf in the bar must be: $\varepsilon = IR = (0.50 \text{ A})(6.0\ \Omega) = 3.0$ V.

But, $v = \dfrac{\varepsilon}{Bl}$, so $v = \dfrac{3.0 \text{ V}}{(2.5 \text{ T})(1.2 \text{ m})} = 1.00$ m/s.

20.18 $\varepsilon = Blv = (40.0 \times 10^{-6} \text{ T})(5.00 \text{ m})(10.0 \text{ m/s}) = 2.00 \times 10^{-3} \text{ V} = 2.00$ mV. Using the right hand rule shows that the direction of the magnetic force on a positive charge in the wire is directed toward the west. Thus, a charge will drift to the western end of the wire, so the western end is positive relative to the eastern end.

20.19 The time for the blade to complete one revolution is $\Delta t = 0.50$ s. During this time, the blade sweeps out an area of $A = \pi l^2 = \pi(3.0 \text{ m})^2 = 9.0\pi$ m^2. The number of field lines (flux) cut by the blade in this time is therefore

$\Delta\Phi = B_{perpendicular}A = (5.0 \times 10^{-5} \text{ T})(9.0\pi \text{ m}^2) = 1.4 \times 10^{-3}$ T m^2, and

the magnitude of the induced emf is:

$\varepsilon = \dfrac{\Delta\Phi}{\Delta t} = \dfrac{1.4 \times 10^{-3} \text{ T m}^2}{0.50 \text{ s}} = 2.8 \times 10^{-3} \text{ V} = 2.8$ mV

20.20 We must first find the speed of the beam just before impact. We use conservation of mechanical energy: $\frac{1}{2}mv^2 = mgh$, or

$v = \sqrt{2gh} = \sqrt{2(9.80 \text{ m/s}^2)(9.0 \text{ m})} = 13.3$ m/s.

The magnitude of the induced field is:

$\varepsilon = BLv = (18 \times 10^{-6} \text{ T})(12.0 \text{ m})(13.3 \text{ m/s}) = 2.87 \times 10^{-3} \text{ V} = 2.87$ mV.

20.21 (a) The top of the loop must behave as a south pole in order to oppose the approaching south pole of the bar magnet. Thus, the current must be clockwise as viewed from above.

(b) After the magnet falls through the loop, the lower side of the loop must act as a south pole to oppose the movement of the north pole of the falling magnet. Thus, the current is counterclockwise as viewed from above.

20.22 The current is left to right.

20.23 The current is left to right.

20.24 (a) The current is left to right. (b) The current is right to left.

20.25 (a) The current is left to right.
(b) No current is present since B is constant.
(c) The current is right to left.

20.26 (a) The current is right to left. (b) The current is right to left.
(c) The current is left to right. (d) The current is left to right.

20.27 (a) The maximum induced emf in a rotating coil may be written as: $\mathcal{E}_{max} = NAB_{perpendicular}\omega$, where $B_{perpendicular}$ is the magnetic field perpendicular to the axis of rotation. In this case, $\omega = 100$ rpm = 10.5 rad/s and the area enclosed by the rotating coil is:

$$A = \pi ab = \pi(5.00 \times 10^{-2}\text{ m})(2.00 \times 10^{-2}\text{ m}) = \pi \times 10^{-3}\text{ m}^2.$$

Therefore,

$$\mathcal{E}_{max} = (10.0)(\pi \times 10^{-3}\text{ m}^2)(5.5 \times 10^{-5}\text{ T})(10.5\text{ rad/s}) = 1.81 \times 10^{-5}\text{ V} = 18.1\ \mu\text{V}$$

(b) In this case, the field lines are always parallel to the plane of the coil. Therefore, the flux through the coil has a constant value (of zero) and there is no induced emf. $\mathcal{E}_{max} = (\frac{\Delta\Phi}{\Delta t})_{max} = 0$

20.28 $\mathcal{E}_{max} = NBA\omega = (100)(2.0 \times 10^{-5}\text{ T})(4.0 \times 10^{-2}\text{ m}^2)(157\text{ rad/s}) = 1.3 \times 10^{-2}\text{ V}.$

20.29 (a) $I_o = \frac{\mathcal{E}}{R} = \frac{240\text{ V}}{30\ \Omega} = 8.0\text{ A}.$

(b) $I = \frac{\mathcal{E} - \mathcal{E}_{back}}{R} = \frac{240\text{ V} - 145\text{ V}}{30\ \Omega} = 3.2\text{ A}.$

(c) $\mathcal{E}_{back} = \mathcal{E} - IR = 240\text{ V} - (6.0\text{ A})(30\ \Omega) = 60\text{ V}.$

20.30 When $\omega = 0$, $\mathcal{E}_{back} = 0$ and $I = 11$ A.

(a) The resistance of the windings is found as

$$R = \frac{\mathcal{E}}{I} = \frac{120\text{ V}}{11\text{ A}} = 10.9\ \Omega.$$

(b) When the motor has reached operating speed, the current is 4.0 A, and $\mathcal{E} - \mathcal{E}_{back} = IR$. Thus,

$$\mathcal{E}_{back} = \mathcal{E} - IR = 120\text{ V} - (4.0\text{ A})(10.9\ \Omega) = 76\text{ V}.$$

20.31 (a) Using $\mathcal{E}_{max} = NBA\omega$, we get:

$$\mathcal{E}_{max} = (1000)(0.20\text{ T})(0.10\text{ m}^2)(120\pi\text{ rad/s}) = 7.5 \times 10^3\text{ V}.$$

(b) $\mathcal{E}_{max}$ occurs when the flux through the loop is changing the most rapidly. This is when the plane of the loop is parallel to the magnetic field.

20.32 (a) $\omega = 120$ rev/min = 12.6 rad/s, and

$$\mathcal{E}_{max} = NAB\omega = (500)(0.60\text{ T})(0.080\text{ m})(0.2\text{ m})(12.6\text{ rad/s}) = 60\text{ V}.$$

(b) $\mathcal{E} = \mathcal{E}_{max}\sin\omega t = (60\text{ V})\sin(12.6\text{ s}^{-1}(\pi/32)) = 57\text{ V}.$

(c) The emf will be a maximum at:

$$t = T/4 = \frac{2\pi/\omega}{4} = \frac{\pi}{2\omega} = \frac{\pi}{2(12.6\ \text{rad/s})} = 0.12\ \text{s}.$$

20.33 The inductance of a solenoid is $L = \frac{\mu_0 N^2 A}{l}$, where N is the number of turns, A is the cross-sectional area, and l is the length. In this case, $L = \frac{(4\pi \times 10^{-7}\ \text{N/A}^2)(510)^2[\pi(8.00 \times 10^{-2}\ \text{m})^2]}{1.40\ \text{m}} = 4.69 \times 10^{-3}\ \text{H} = 4.69\ \text{mH}.$

20.34 The units of $\frac{N\Phi}{I} = \frac{\text{T m}^2}{\text{A}}$ and the units of $\frac{\varepsilon}{\Delta I/\Delta t}$ are $\frac{\text{V s}}{\text{A}}$. Comparing the two, we see that the proof is equivalent to showing that T m^2 = V s. The basic units of the Tesla, from $F = qvB$, are: $\text{T} = \frac{\text{N s}}{\text{C m}}$.

Substituting these, we have: $\frac{\text{N s}}{\text{C m}}\ \text{m}^2 = \frac{(\text{N m})\ \text{s}}{\text{C}} = \frac{\text{J}}{\text{C}}\text{s} = \text{V s}$. Thus, the units are the same in the two expressions.

20.35 $\varepsilon = L\left(\frac{\Delta I}{\Delta t}\right) = (3.0 \times 10^{-3}\ \text{H})\left(\frac{1.5\ \text{A} - 0.20\ \text{A}}{0.20\ \text{s}}\right) = 1.95 \times 10^{-2}\ \text{V} = 20\ \text{mV}.$

20.36 (a) $L = \frac{\mu_0 N^2 A}{l} = \frac{(4\pi \times 10^{-7}\ \text{N/A}^2)(400)^2\pi(2.5 \times 10^{-2}\ \text{m})^2}{(0.20\ \text{m})}$, or $L = 1.97 \times 10^{-3}\ \text{H} = 1.97\ \text{mH}.$

(b) From $\varepsilon = L\frac{\Delta I}{\Delta t}$, $\frac{\Delta I}{\Delta t} = \frac{\varepsilon}{L} = \frac{75 \times 10^{-3}\ \text{V}}{1.97 \times 10^{-3}\ \text{H}} = 38\ \text{A/s}.$

20.37 From $\varepsilon = L\frac{\Delta I}{\Delta t}$, we have: $L = \frac{\varepsilon}{\frac{\Delta I}{\Delta t}} = \frac{24.0 \times 10^{-3}\ \text{V}}{10.0\ \text{A/s}} = 2.40 \times 10^{-3}\ \text{H},$

and from $L = \frac{N\Phi}{I}$, we have: $\Phi = \frac{LI}{N} = \frac{(2.40 \times 10^{-3}\ \text{H})(4\ \text{A})}{500}$, or $\Phi = 1.92 \times 10^{-5}\ \text{T m}^2.$

20.38 Let us use $\varepsilon = L\frac{\Delta I}{\Delta t}$ to find the fundamental units of L.

$$L = \frac{\varepsilon}{\left(\frac{\Delta I}{\Delta t}\right)} = \frac{\text{V s}}{\text{A}} = \Omega\ \text{s}. \quad \text{Thus,} \qquad \tau = \frac{L}{R} = \frac{\Omega\ \text{s}}{\Omega} = \text{s}.$$

20.39 (a) Using $\tau_C = \tau_L$, or $RC = \frac{L}{R}$, we get $R = \sqrt{\frac{L}{C}} = \sqrt{\frac{3\ \text{H}}{3 \times 10^{-6}\ \text{F}}} = 1000\ \Omega.$

(b) $\tau = RC = (1000\ \Omega)(3 \times 10^{-6}\ \text{F}) = 3 \times 10^{-3}\ \text{s} = 3\ \text{ms}.$

20.40 $\tau = \frac{L}{R} = 600 \times 10^{-6}\ \text{s} = 6.00 \times 10^{-4}\ \text{s}$. $I_{max} = \frac{\Delta V}{R} = \frac{6.0\ \text{V}}{\text{R}} = 0.300\ \text{A}$, which yields

$R = 20\ \Omega$. Therefore, $L = \tau R = (6.00 \times 10^{-4}\ \text{s})(20\ \Omega) = 1.2 \times 10^{-2}\ \Omega\text{s} = 12\ \text{mH}.$

20.41 (a) $\Delta V_R = iR$ At $t = 0, i = 0$. thus, $\Delta V_R = 0$.

(b) At $t=\tau$, $i = 63.2\%$ of I_{max}.

Thus, $i=(0.632)\left(\frac{\Delta V}{R}\right)=(0.632)\left(\frac{6.0\ \text{V}}{8.0\ \Omega}\right)=0.474\,\text{A}$,

and $\Delta V_R = iR = (0.474\,\text{A})(8.0\,\Omega) = 3.8\,\text{V}$.

(c) At $t = 0$, the voltage drop across the resistor is zero. Thus, the total voltage of the battery is dropped across the inductor. $\Delta V_L = 6.0\,\text{V}$.

(d) At $t=\tau$, the Voltage drop across the resistor is 3.8 V. Thus, the voltage drop across the inductor is 6.0 V - 3.8 V = 2.2 V.

20.42 (a) $I_{max}=\frac{\varepsilon}{R}=\frac{24.00\ \text{V}}{6.00\ \Omega}=4.00\,\text{A}$.

(b) The time constant of the circuit is $\tau=\frac{L}{R}=\frac{3.00\ \text{H}}{6.00\ \Omega}=0.500\,\text{s}$. Thus, at $t = 0.500$ s the current is: $i=(0.632)I_{max}=(0.632)(4.00\,\text{A})=2.53\,\text{A}$.

20.43 $W=\frac{1}{2}LI^2=\frac{1}{2}(70.0\times10^{-3}\,\text{H})(2.00\,\text{A})^2=0.140\,\text{J}$.

20.44 The inductance is;

$$L=\frac{\mu_0 N^2 A}{l}=\frac{(4\pi\ \text{x}\ 10^{-7}\ \text{N/A}^2)(300)^2\pi(0.0500\ \text{m})^2}{0.200\ \text{m}}=4.44\times10^{-3}\,\text{H},$$

and $W=\frac{1}{2}LI^2=\frac{1}{2}(4.44\times10^{-3}\,\text{H})(0.500\,\text{A})^2=5.55\times10^{-4}\,\text{J}$.

20.45 (a) $I_{max}=\frac{\varepsilon}{R}=\frac{24\ \text{V}}{8\ \Omega}=3\,\text{A}$, and $W=\frac{1}{2}LI^2=\frac{1}{2}(4.0\,\text{H})(3.0\,\text{A})^2=18\,\text{J}$.

(b) At $t=\tau$, $i=0.632I_{max}=(0.632)(3.0\,\text{A})=1.90\,\text{A}$, and

$W=\frac{1}{2}LI^2=\frac{1}{2}(4.0\,\text{H})(1.90\,\text{A})^2=7.2\,\text{J}$.

20.46 We use $\varepsilon=N\frac{\Delta\Phi}{\Delta t}$, with $\Delta\Phi=\Delta BA=(0.30\,\text{T}-0)\pi(0.20\,\text{m})^2=3.77\times10^{-2}\,\text{T m}^2$.

Thus, $\varepsilon=\frac{50(3.77\ \text{x}\ 10^{-2}\ \text{T m}^2)}{0.40\ \text{s}}=4.7\,\text{V}$.

20.47 Treating the telephone cord as a solenoid, we have:

$$L=\frac{\mu_0 N^2 A}{l}=\frac{(4\pi\ \text{x}\ 10^{-7}\ \text{T m/A})(70)^2(\pi)(0.0065\ \text{m})^2}{0.60\ \text{m}}=1.4\times10^{-6}\,\text{H}.$$

20.48 From $\varepsilon_{max}=NAB\omega$, we find:

$$B=\frac{\varepsilon_{max}}{NA\omega}=\frac{0.5\ \text{V}}{(50)(0.20\ \text{m})(0.30\ \text{m})(90\ \text{rad/s})}=1.9\times10^{-3}\,\text{T}.$$

20.49 According to Lenz's law, a current will be induced in the coil to oppose the change in magnetic flux due to the magnet. Therefore, current must flow from b to a through the resistor. Hence $V_a - V_b$ will be negative.

20.50 The flux passing through the coil when $B=0.15$ T is;

$\Phi_i = NB_iA = (5)(0.15\,\text{T})\pi(0.15\,\text{m})^2 = 5.30\times10^{-2}\,\text{T m}^2$.

When $B = 0.20$ T, the flux is:

$\Phi_f = NB_fA = (5)(0.20\text{ T})\pi(0.15\text{ m})^2 = 7.07\times10^{-2}\text{ T m}^2$. Thus,

$\Delta\Phi = 1.77\times10^{-2}\text{ T m}^2$, and $\langle\varepsilon\rangle = \frac{\Delta\Phi}{\Delta t} = \frac{1.77\times10^{-2}\text{ T m}^2}{3.0\text{ s}} = 5.89\times10^{-3}\text{ V}$.

With the average induced emf found above during the 3.0 seconds, the average induced current is: $I = \frac{\varepsilon}{R} = \frac{5.89\times10^{-3}\text{ V}}{8.0\ \Omega} = 7.4\times10^{-4}\text{ A}$.

20.51 (a) The primary circuit (containing the battery and solenoid) is an RL circuit with $R = 14.0\ \Omega$ and $L = \frac{\mu_o N^2 A}{l}$, or

$L = \frac{(4\pi\times10^{-7}\text{ T m/A})(12500)^2(10^{-4}\text{ m}^2)}{0.0700\text{ m}} = 0.28\text{ H}$. The time for the current to reach 0.63 times its maximum is one time constant which is: $\tau = \frac{L}{R} = \frac{0.28\text{ H}}{14.0\ \Omega} = 0.020\text{ s}$.

(b) The average emf is $\langle\mathcal{E}\rangle = L\frac{\Delta I}{\Delta t} = L\frac{(I - 0)}{\tau}$, where

$I = 0.63 I_{max} = 0.63\left(\frac{60.0\text{ V}}{14.0\ \Omega}\right) = 2.7\text{ A}$.

Thus, $\langle\mathcal{E}\rangle = (0.28\text{ H})\left(\frac{2.7\text{ A}}{0.020\text{ s}}\right) = 37.8\text{ V}$.

(c) The rate of change of flux in the 820 turn coil is the same as that in the solenoid. This rate can be found by realizing that the back emf in the solenoid at any time is $\varepsilon = N(\frac{\Delta\phi}{\Delta t})$ when N is the number of turns on the solenoid and $\frac{\Delta\phi}{\Delta t}$ is the rate of change of flux in each turn. Thus, $\langle\varepsilon\rangle = N(\frac{\Delta\phi}{\Delta t})$ or $\frac{\Delta\phi}{\Delta t} = \frac{\langle\varepsilon\rangle}{N} = \frac{37.8\text{ V}}{12\ 500} = 3.02\times10^{-3}\text{ V}$.

(d) The average induced emf in the coil is:

$\langle\mathcal{E}\rangle_{coil} = N_{coil}(\frac{\Delta\phi}{\Delta t}) = 820(3.02\times10^{-3}\text{ V}) = 2.48\text{ V}$, and the average induced current is: $\langle I\rangle_{coil} = \frac{\langle\varepsilon\rangle_{coil}}{R_{coil}} = \frac{2.48\text{ V}}{24.0\ \Omega} = 0.103\text{ A}$.

20.52

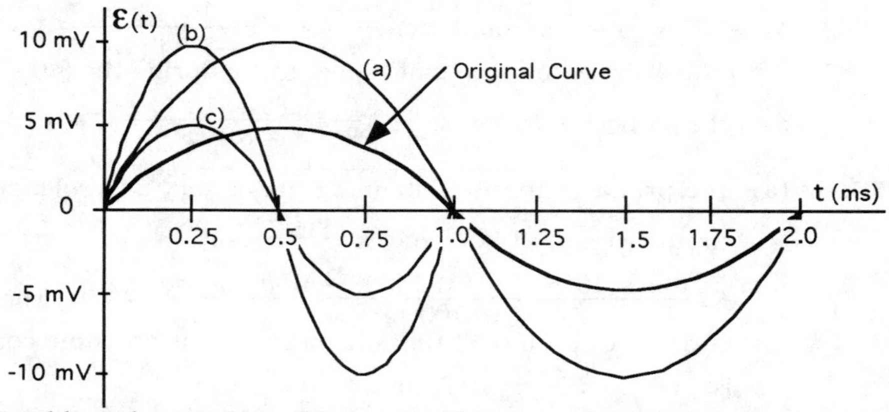

(a) Doubling the number of turns doubles the amplitude but does not alter the period.
(b) Doubling the angular velocity doubles the amplitude and also cuts the period in half.
(c) Doubling the angular velocity while reducing the number of turns to one half the original value leaves the amplitude unchanged but does cut the period in half.

20.53 When not rotating, $\varepsilon = IR$, and from this, $R = \frac{\varepsilon}{I} = \frac{12\text{ V}}{18\text{A}} = 0.67\ \Omega$.

When rotating, $\varepsilon - \varepsilon_{back} = IR$, or

$\varepsilon_{back} = \varepsilon - IR = 12\text{ V} - (3.5\text{ A})(0.67\ \Omega) = 9.7\text{ V}$.

20.54 The flux through the coil at any instant is the same as the flux through the solenoid. The magnetic field along the axis of the solenoid is given by $B_s = \mu_0 n I$.

The rate of change of this field is:

$$\frac{\Delta B_s}{\Delta t} = \mu_0 n\left(\frac{\Delta I}{\Delta t}\right)$$

$$= (4\pi \times 10^{-7}\text{ N/A}^2)\left(\frac{1600}{0.80\text{ m}}\right)\left(\frac{1.5\text{ A} - 6.0\text{ A}}{0.20\text{ s}}\right) = -5.6 \times 10^{-2}\text{ T/s}$$

Thus, the rate of change of flux through the solenoid (and therefore the coil) is:

$$\left(\frac{\Delta \phi}{\Delta t}\right) = \left(\frac{\Delta B_s}{\Delta t}\right)A_{solenoid} = (-5.6 \times 10^{-2}\text{ T/s})[\pi(0.05\text{ m})^2] = -4.4 \times 10^{-4}\text{ V}$$

The induced emf in the coil is then:

$$\langle\varepsilon\rangle_{coil} = -N_{coil}\frac{\Delta \phi}{\Delta t} = -(1)(-4.4 \times 10^{-4}\text{ V}) = 4.4 \times 10^{-4}\text{ V} = 440\ \mu\text{V}.$$

20.55 When the wire is moving downward at speed v, an emf, $\varepsilon = Blv$, is induced in the wire. The left end of the wire is at a higher potential than the right end. Thus, an induced current, $I = \frac{\varepsilon}{R} = \frac{Blv}{R}$, flows counterclockwise around the circuit and right to left through the wire. The magnetic field exerts an upward force of

$F_m = BIl = \frac{B^2 l^2 v}{R}$ on the wire. The wire will reach terminal speed when this force equals the downward gravitation force on the wire. When this occurs, $F_m = mg$,

or $\frac{B^2 l^2 v_t}{R} = mg$. Thus, $v_t = \frac{mgR}{B^2 l^2}$

20.56 $F = ILB$ and $\varepsilon = BLv$

$I = \frac{\varepsilon}{R} = \frac{BLv}{R}$, so $B = \frac{IR}{Lv}$

(a) Therefore, $F = \frac{I^2 LR}{Lv}$ and $I = \sqrt{\frac{Fv}{R}} = 0.500\text{ A}$

(b) $I^2 R = 2.00\text{ W}$

(c) For constant force, $P = FV = (1.00\text{ N})(2.00\text{ m/s}) = 2.00\text{ W}$.

20.57 At a distance r from the long straight current,

$B_i = \frac{\mu_o i}{2\pi r} = \frac{2 \times 10^{-7}\text{ Tm/A}(6.02 \times 10^6\text{ A})}{200\text{ m}} = 6.02 \times 10^{-3}\text{ T}$, and

$B_f = 0$, since $I_f = 0$. Therefore,

$\Phi_i = B_i A = (6.02 \times 10^{-3}\text{ T})\pi(0.8\text{ m})^2 = 1.21 \times 10^{-2}\text{ T m}^2$, giving

$\langle \mathcal{E} \rangle = N\frac{\Delta\Phi}{\Delta t} = (100)\frac{1.21 \times 10^{-2}\text{ T m}^2 - 0}{10.5 \times 10^{-6}\text{ s}} = 1.15 \times 10^5\text{ V}$.

20.58 The average induced emf is given by:

$$\langle \mathcal{E} \rangle = -\frac{\Delta(N\Phi)}{\Delta t} = -\frac{N'\Phi' - N\Phi}{\Delta t} = -\frac{B(N'A' - NA)}{\Delta t}.$$

In this case, $N = 2$ turns, $N' = 1$ turn, and $A = \pi r^2 = \pi(0.500\text{ m})^2 = 0.7854\text{m}^2$. Since the total length of the wire is constant, the circumference of the 1 turn coil must be twice the circumference of the 2 turn coil, C' = 2C. Thus, $2\pi r' = 2(2\pi r)$, or $r' = 2r = 1.00\text{ m}$ and $A' = \pi r^{2\prime} = \pi(1.00\text{ m})^2 = \pi\text{ m}^2$.

Therefore, $\langle \varepsilon \rangle = -\frac{(0.40\text{ T})((1)\pi\text{ m}^2 - (2)(0.7854\text{ m}^2))}{0.10\text{ s}} = -6.28\text{ V}$.

20.59 The area of the tent that is effective in intercepting magnetic field lines is the area perpendicular to the direction of the magnetic field. This is the same as the base of the tent. In the initial configuration, this is $A_1 = L(2L\cos\theta) = 2(1.5\text{ m})^2\cos 60 = 2.25\text{ m}^2$. After the tent is flattened, the area of the base is $A_2 = L(2L) = 2L^2 = 2(1.5\text{ m})^2 = 4.5\text{ m}^2$. Thus, the initial flux is:

$$\Phi_1 = BA_1 = (0.30\text{ T})(2.25\text{ m}^2) = 0.675\text{ T m}^2,$$

and the final flux is: $\Phi_2 = BA_2 = (0.30\text{ T})(4.5\text{ m}^2) = 1.35\text{ T m}^2$.

The average induced emf is:

$$\langle \mathcal{E} \rangle = -\frac{\Delta\phi}{\Delta t} = -\frac{(\Phi_2 - \Phi_1)}{\Delta t} = -\frac{(1.35\text{ T m}^2 - 0.675\text{ T m}^2)}{0.10\text{ s}} = -6.8\text{ V}.$$

20.60 (a) $\varepsilon = BLv = (40.0 \times 10^{-6}\text{ T})(0.500\text{ m})(5.00\text{ m/s}) = 1.00 \times 10^{-4}\text{ V} = 100\ \mu\text{V}$.

(b) $i = \dfrac{\mathcal{E}}{R} = \dfrac{1.00 \times 10^{-4}\text{ V}}{5.00\ \Omega} = 2.00 \times 10^{-5}\text{ A} = 20\ \mu\text{A}.$

(c) $P_{supplied} = \mathcal{E}i = (1.00 \times 10^{-4}\text{ V})(2.00 \times 10^{-5}\text{ A}) = 2.00 \times 10^{-9}\text{ W}$
= 2 nanowatts.

(d) $P_{dissipated} = i^2R = (2 \times 10^{-5}\text{ A})^2(5.00\ \Omega) = 2.00 \times 10^{-9}\text{ W}$ = 2 nanowatts.

(e) $F_{applied} = F_{\text{retarding force exerted by magnetic field}} = BIL.$ Thus,
$F = (40 \times 10^{-6}\text{ T})(2.00 \times 10^{-5}\text{ A})(0.500\text{ m}) = 4.00 \times 10^{-10}\text{ N}.$

(f) $P = Fv = (4.00 \times 10^{-10}\text{ N})(5.00\text{ m/s}) = 2.00 \times 10^{-9}\text{ W}$ = 2 nanowatts.

20.61 (a) $A_i = \pi r_i = \pi(10^{-2}\text{ m})^2 = \pi 10^{-4}\text{ m}^2$ and $A_f = 0$. Therefore,
$\Delta\Phi = BA_i - BA_f = BA_i = (25.0 \times 10^{-3}\text{ T})(\pi 10^{-4}\text{ m}^2) = 7.85\text{ X }10^{-6}\text{ T m}^2.$

Thus, $<\mathcal{E}> = N\dfrac{\Delta\Phi}{\Delta t} = \dfrac{7.85 \times 10^{-6}\text{ T m}^2}{50.0 \times 10^{-3}\text{ s}} = 1.57 \times 10^{-4}\text{ V} = 0.157\text{ mV},$
and Lenz' law shows that the induced current will flow from A to B. (End B will be positive.)

(b) $\Delta\Phi = B_fA - B_iA = (100\text{ mT})A - (25.0\text{ mT})A = (75.0\text{ X }10^{-3}\text{ T})(\pi 10^{-4}\text{ m}^2),$
or $\Delta\Phi = 2.36\text{ X }10^{-5}\text{ T m}^2$, and $<\mathcal{E}> = N\dfrac{\Delta\Phi}{\Delta t}$ gives

$<\mathcal{E}> = \dfrac{2.36 \times 10^{-5}\text{ T m}^2}{4.00 \times 10^{-3}\text{ s}} = 5.89 \times 10^{-3}\text{ V} = 5.89\text{ mV}.$ In this case, the magnetic force on a positive charge in the wire causes it to drift toward end A, so end A is positive. (Current flow is from B to A.)

20.62 I is proportional to $<\mathcal{E}> = N\dfrac{\Delta\Phi}{\Delta t}$, so I is proportional to the rate of change of the flux, or slope of the Φ versus time graph. (The maximum flux occurs when the magnet is perpendicular to the plane of the coil.) The curve will be somewhat like the sketch at the right.

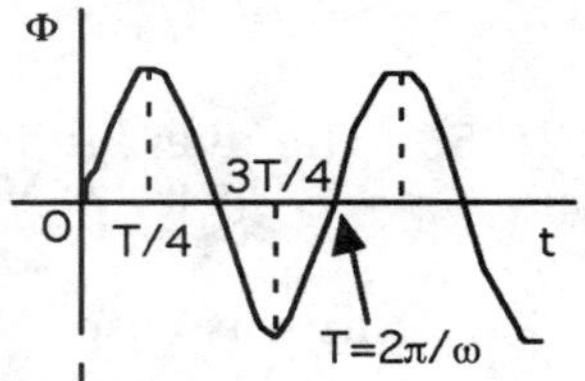

The induced current versus time curve is somewhat like the sketch at the right. Notice the phase difference between this curve and the Φ versus time curve sketched above.

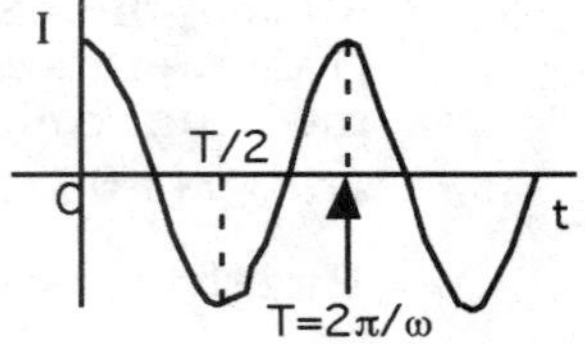

20.63 Using $\mathcal{E} = I_{ring}R = \dfrac{\Delta\Phi}{\Delta t}$ we get: $I = \left(\dfrac{1}{R}\right)\left(\dfrac{\Delta\Phi}{\Delta t}\right).$

When current I flows in the solenoid, the magnetic field is $B = \dfrac{1}{2}\mu_0 n I$, so the rate of change of the field is:

$$\frac{\Delta B}{\Delta t} = \frac{1}{2}\mu_0 n\left(\frac{\Delta I}{\Delta t}\right) = \frac{1}{2}(4\pi \times 10^{-7}\text{ T m/A})(1000/\text{m})(270\text{ A/s}) = 0.170\text{ T/s},$$

and the rate of change of flux is:

$$\frac{\Delta\Phi}{\Delta t} = \left(\frac{\Delta B}{\Delta t}\right)A = (0.170\text{ T/s})(\pi(0.030\text{ m})^2) = 4.80 \times 10^{-4}\text{ V}.$$

so $I = 1.6$ A

20.64 (a) We begin with: $\varepsilon = -N\dfrac{\Delta\Phi}{\Delta t} = -N\dfrac{\Delta(BA)}{\Delta t} = -N\dfrac{\Delta\left(\dfrac{B\theta a^2}{2}\right)}{\Delta t} = -\dfrac{NBa^2}{2}\left(\dfrac{\Delta\theta}{\Delta t}\right)$,

   or: $\varepsilon = -\dfrac{1}{2}NBa^2\omega = -\dfrac{(1)(0.500\ \text{T})(0.500\ \text{m})^2(2.00\ \text{rad/s})}{2} = -0.125\ \text{V}.$

   (b) At $t = 0.250$ s, $\theta = \omega t = (2.00\ \text{rad/s})(0.250\ \text{s}) = 0.500$ radians, and the arc length from P to Q is: $s = a\theta = (0.500\ \text{m})(0.500\ \text{rad}) = 0.250\ \text{m}$. The total length of material in the loop is $a + a + a\theta = 0.500\ \text{m} + 0.500\ \text{m} + 0.250\ \text{m} = 1.25\ \text{m}$, and the resistance is: $R = (5.00\ \Omega/\text{m})(1.25\ \text{m}) = 6.25\ \Omega$.

   Therefore, the induced current is: $I = \dfrac{\varepsilon}{R} = \dfrac{0.125\ \text{V}}{6.25\ \Omega} = 0.02\ \text{A}.$

20.65 (a) Motional emf $\varepsilon = Bwv$ appears in the conducting water. Its resistance, if the plates are submerged is

   $\dfrac{\rho L}{A} = \dfrac{\rho w}{ab}$

   Kirchoff's loop rule says

   $Bwv - IR - \dfrac{I\rho w}{ab} = 0$

   Therefore, $I = \dfrac{Bwv}{R + \dfrac{\rho w}{ab}} = \dfrac{abvB}{\rho + \dfrac{abR}{w}}$

   (b) $I_{sc} = \dfrac{(100\ \text{m})(5.00\ \text{m})(3.00\ \text{m/s})(50.0 \times 10^{-6}\ \text{T})}{100\ \Omega\ \text{m}} = 0.75\ \text{mA}$

23.66 (a) $\varepsilon = BLv = 0.36\ \text{V}$ $\qquad I = \dfrac{\varepsilon}{R} = 0.900\ \text{A}$

   (b) $F = ILB = 0.108\ \text{N}$

   (c) Since the magnetic flux through the area of the coil is decreasing, the induced current flow through R is from b to a. b is at the higher potential.

   (d) No.

ANSWERS TO CONCEPTUAL QUESTIONS

2. Consider the copper tube to be a large set of rings stacked one on top of the other. As the magnet falls toward or falls away from each ring, a current is induced in the ring. Thus, there is a current in the copper tube around its circumference.

4. The tape has small pieces of iron oxide embedded in it. A nearby magnet will attract these pieces of iron, drawing the tape toward it. This experiment will cause the alignment of the oxide to be altered to what it was before. Thus, the information encoded on the tape will be lost. Try this with an old tape.

6. Let us assume the north pole of the magnet faces the ring. As the bar magnet falls toward the conducting ring, a magnet field is induced in the ring pointing upward. This upward directed field will oppose the motion of the magnet preventing it from moving as a freely-falling body. Try it for yourself to show that an upward force also acts on the falling magnet if the south end faces the ring.

8. As the aluminum plate moves into the field, eddy currents are induced in the metal by the changing magnetic field at the plate. The magnetic field of the electromagnet interacts with this current producing a retarding force on the plate, slowing it down. In a similar fashion, as the plate leaves the magnetic field, a current is induced, and once again there is an upward force to slow the plate.

10. If an external battery is acting to increase the current in the inductor, an emf is induced in a direction to oppose the increase of current. Likewise, if one attempts to reduce the current in the inductor, the emf set up tries to support the current. Thus, the induced emf always acts to oppose the change occurring in the circuit, or it acts in the "back" direction to the change.

12. As water falls, it gains velocity and kinetic energy. It then pushes against the blades of a turbine transferring this energy to the rotor or coil of a large alternating current generator. This rotor moves in a strong external magnetic field and a voltage is induced in the coil. This induced emf is the voltage source for the current in our electric power lines.

14. If the bar were moving to the left, the magnetic force on the negative charges in the bar would be upward, causing an accumulation of negative charge on the top, and positive charges at the bottom. Hence, the electric field in the bar would be upward.

CHAPTER TWENTY-ONE SOLUTIONS

Chapter Twenty-One Readings

Barthold, L and Pfeiffer, H.G., "High-Voltage Transmission," *Scientific American*, May 1964, p. 38.

Bohren, C.F., *What Light Through Yonder Window Breaks?*, John Wiley & Sons, New York, 1991

Carlson, S., "Detecting Natural Electromagnetic Waves," *Scientific American*, May 1996, p. 98.

Coltman, J.W., "The Transformer," Scientific American, January 1988, p. 86.

Kedem, O and Ganiel, U., "Solar Energy, How Much Do We Receive?" *The Physics Teacher*, December 1983, p. 573.

Leffell, D.J., "Sunlight and Skin Cancer," *Scientific American*, July 1996, p. 52.

Stolarski, R.S., "The Antarctic Ozone Hole," Scientific American, January 1988, p. 30.

Review (a) The number of turns a 100 m wire can make on a 2.0 cm radius cylindrical form is:

$$N = \frac{l_{\text{wire}}}{\text{circumference}} = \frac{100\text{ m}}{2\pi(0.020\text{ m})} = 8.0 \times 10^2 \text{ turns}$$

The length of the solenoid will then be:

$l_{\text{sol}} = (\#\text{turns})(\text{diameter of wire}) = 800(6.0 \times 10^{-4}\text{ m}) = 0.48\text{ m}.$

(b) The self inductance will be:

$$L = \frac{\mu_o N^2 A_{\text{sol}}}{l_{\text{sol}}} = \frac{(4\pi \times 10^{-7}\text{ N/A}^2)(800)^2[\pi(0.020\text{ m})^2]}{0.48\text{ m}}$$

$$= 2.1 \times 10^{-3}\text{ H} = 2.1\text{ mH}.$$

(c) The completed solenoid will have a resistance of:

$$R = \frac{\rho l_{\text{wire}}}{A_{\text{wire}}} = \frac{(1.7 \times 10^{-8}\ \Omega\text{ m})(100\text{ m})}{[\pi(0.3 \times 10^{-3}\text{ m})]} = 6.0\,\Omega.$$

(d) At 400 Hz, the inductive reactance of the solenoid is:

$X_L = 2\pi f L = 2\pi(400\text{ s}^{-1})(2.1 \times 10^{-3}\ \Omega\text{ s}) = 5.3\ \Omega$, and the impedance of the solenoid is

$$Z = \sqrt{R^2 + X_L^2} = \sqrt{(6.0\ \Omega)^2 + (5.3\ \Omega)^2} = 8.0\,\Omega.$$

The current that will flow in the coil is then $I = \frac{\Delta V}{Z} = \frac{5.0\text{ V}}{8.0\ \Omega} = 0.63\text{ A}$,

and the power dissipation will be: $P = I^2 R = (0.63\text{ A})^2(6.0\,\Omega) = 2.4\text{ W}$

21.1 (a) $V = \frac{V_m}{\sqrt{2}}$, so $V_m = \sqrt{2}\,V = \sqrt{2}\,(100\text{ V}) = 141\text{ V}.$

(b) $\Delta V = IR$ and $I = \frac{\Delta V}{R} = \frac{100\text{ V}}{5.00\ \Omega} = 20.0\text{ A}.$

(c) Use either $I_m = \sqrt{2}\, I$, or $I_m = \dfrac{\Delta V_m}{R} = \dfrac{100\ \sqrt{2}\ \text{V}}{5.00\ \Omega} = 20.0\sqrt{2}\,\text{A} = 28.3\ \text{A}$.

(d) $P = I^2 R = (20.0\ \text{A})^2(5.00\ \Omega) = 2.00 \times 10^3\ \text{W} = 2.00\ \text{kW}$.

21.2 We must compare the expression given for the voltage, $\Delta v = 150 \sin 377t$, with the general expression for an ac voltage, $\Delta v = \Delta V_m \sin 2\pi f t$. By comparison, we see:

(a) $\Delta V_m = 150$ V, and from this, $\Delta V = \dfrac{\Delta V_m}{\sqrt{2}} = \dfrac{150\ \text{V}}{\sqrt{2}} = 106\ \text{V}$

(b) We also see that: $\omega = 2\pi f = 377$ rad/s. Thus, $f = \dfrac{377\ \text{rad/s}}{2\pi} = 60\ \text{Hz}$.

(c) At $t = \dfrac{1}{120\ \text{s}}$, $v = 150 \sin\left(\dfrac{377}{120}\right) = 150 \sin\pi = 0$.

(d) $I_m = \dfrac{\Delta V_m}{R} = \dfrac{150\ \text{V}}{50.0\ \Omega} = 3.0\ \text{A}$.

21.3 $\Delta V = \dfrac{\Delta V_m}{\sqrt{2}} = \dfrac{170\ \text{V}}{\sqrt{2}} = 120\ \text{V}$. $\qquad R = \dfrac{\Delta V^2}{P} = \dfrac{(120\ \text{V})^2}{P}$.

(1)

(a) If $P = 75$ W, equation (1) gives: $R = 190\ \Omega$.
(b) If $P = 100$ W, equation (1) gives: $R = 140\ \Omega$.

21.4 $R_{total} = 8.20\ \Omega + 10.4\ \Omega = 18.6\ \Omega$, and $I = \dfrac{\Delta V}{R} = \dfrac{15.0\ \text{V}}{18.6\ \Omega} = 0.806\ \text{A}$.

$P_{speaker} = I^2_{speaker} R_{speaker} = (0.806\ \text{A})^2(10.4\ \Omega) = 6.76\ \text{W}$.

21.5 The ammeter and voltmeter measure rms current and potential difference, respectively. Therefore,

$$\Delta V_{rms} = \frac{100\ \text{V}}{\sqrt{2}} = 70.71\ \text{V, and} \quad I_{rms} = \frac{\Delta V_{rms}}{R} = \frac{70.71\ \text{V}}{24\ \Omega} = 3.0\ \text{A}.$$

21.6 Capacitive reactance is $X_C = \dfrac{1}{2\pi f C}$ and the units of capacitance are Farads where 1 Farad = 1 $\dfrac{\text{Coulomb}}{\text{Volt}}$, and the units of frequency are $\dfrac{1}{\text{second}}$.

Thus, $X_C = \dfrac{1}{(\text{s}^{-1})(\text{C/V})} = \dfrac{\text{V}}{\text{C/s}} = \dfrac{\text{V}}{\text{A}} = \Omega$.

21.7 $X_C = \dfrac{1}{2\pi f C} = \dfrac{\Delta V_C}{I} = \dfrac{30\ \text{V}}{0.30\ \text{A}} = 1.0 \times 10^2\ \Omega$

Thus, $f = \dfrac{1}{2\pi C X_C} = \dfrac{1}{2\pi(4.0 \times 10^{-6}\ \text{F})(1.0 \times 10^2\ \Omega)} = 4.0 \times 10^2\ \text{Hz}$.

21.8 The ratio of the capacitive reactance at the higher frequency to that at the lower is: $\dfrac{X_{C(high)}}{X_{C(low)}} = \dfrac{2\pi f_{low} C}{2\pi f_{high} C} = \dfrac{f_{low}}{f_{high}} = \dfrac{120}{10000}$.

Thus, $X_{C(high)} = (30.0\ \Omega)\left(\dfrac{120}{10000}\right) = 0.36\ \Omega$.

21.9 The rms voltage is $\Delta V = \frac{\Delta V_m}{\sqrt{2}} = \frac{170\ \text{V}}{\sqrt{2}} = 120\ \text{V}$, and $X_C = \frac{\Delta V}{I} = \frac{120\ \text{V}}{0.75\ \text{A}} = 160\ \Omega$.

So, $C = \frac{1}{2\pi f X_C} = \frac{1}{2\pi(60\ \text{Hz})(160\ \Omega)} = 1.66 \times 10^{-5}\ \text{F} = 17\ \mu\text{F}$.

21.10 $X_C = \frac{1}{\omega C}$, where $\omega = 2\pi f$ = the angular frequency.

Thus, $X_C = \frac{1}{(120\pi\ \text{rad/s})(6.00 \times 10^{-6}\ \text{F})} = 442\ \Omega$.

Also, $\Delta V = \frac{\Delta V_m}{\sqrt{2}} = \frac{140\ \text{V}}{\sqrt{2}} = 99.0\ \text{V}$. Thus, $I = \frac{\Delta V}{X_C} = \frac{99.0\ \text{V}}{442\ \Omega} = 0.224\ \text{A}$.

21.11 The basic unit for self inductance is $1\ \text{H} = \frac{1\ \text{V}}{1\ \text{A/s}} = 1\ (\frac{\text{V}}{\text{A}})\ \text{s} = 1\ \Omega\ \text{s}$, and the unit of frequency is 1/s. Therefore, $X_L = 2\pi f L = \frac{1}{\text{s}}(\Omega\ \text{s}) = \Omega$.

21.12 First, we note that $\Delta V_{rms} = \frac{140\ \text{V}}{\sqrt{2}} = 99.0\ \text{V}$. The inductive reactance is:

$X_L = 2\pi f L = \omega L = (120\pi\ \text{rad/s})(0.100\ \text{H}) = 37.7\ \Omega$, and

$I_{rms} = \frac{\Delta V_{rms}}{X_L} = \frac{99.0\ \text{V}}{37.7\ \Omega} = 2.63\ \text{A}$.

21.13 $X_L = 2\pi f L = 120\pi\ \text{rad/s}\,L = 54.0\ \Omega$, so $L = \frac{54.0\ \Omega}{120\pi\ \text{rad/s}} = 0.143\ \text{H}$.

Thus, when $f = 50.0\ \text{Hz}$ and $\Delta V = 100\ \text{V}$,

$I = \frac{\Delta V}{X_L} = \frac{100\ \text{V}}{(100\pi\ \text{rad/s})(0.143\ \text{H})} = 2.22\ \text{A}$, and

$I_{max} = \sqrt{2}\,I = \sqrt{2}\,(2.22\ \text{A}) = 3.14\ \text{A}$.

21.14 $X_L = 2\pi f L = \frac{\Delta V}{I}$ and $I = \frac{I_m}{\sqrt{2}}$. Thus, $L = \frac{\Delta V \sqrt{2}}{2\pi f I_m}$

Therefore, if $I_m < 80.0\ \text{mA}$,

then $L > \frac{(50.0\ \text{V})\sqrt{2}}{2\pi(20.0\ \text{Hz})(80.0 \times 10^{-3}\ \text{A})}$, or $L > 7.03\ \text{H}$

21.15 (a) $X_C = \frac{\Delta V}{I} = \frac{9.00\ \text{V}}{25.0 \times 10^{-3}\ \text{A}} = 360\ \Omega$, or $\frac{1}{2\pi f C} = 360\ \Omega$.

Thus, $f = \frac{1}{2\pi(360\ \Omega.)\left(2.40 \times 10^{-6}\ \text{F}\right)} = 184\ \text{Hz}$.

(b) $X_L = 2\pi f L = 2\pi(184\ \text{Hz})(0.160\ \text{H}) = 185\ \Omega$,

$I = \frac{\Delta V}{X_L} = \frac{9.00\ \text{V}}{185\ \Omega} = 4.86 \times 10^{-2}\ \text{A} = 48.6\ \text{mA}$.

21.16 We have:

$X_L = 2\pi f L = 2\pi(60.0\text{ Hz})(2.0 \times 10^{-2}\text{ H}) = 7.54\ \Omega$, thus

$Z = \sqrt{R^2 + (X_L - X_C)^2} = \sqrt{R^2 + (X_L)^2} = 21.4\ \Omega$.

(a) $I = \frac{\Delta V}{Z} = \frac{100\text{ V}}{21.4\ \Omega} = 4.67\text{ A}$.

(b) $\Delta V_L = IX_L = (4.67\text{ A})(7.54\ \Omega) = 35.2\text{ V}$.

(c) $\Delta V_R = IR = (4.67\text{ A})(20.0\ \Omega) = 93.4\text{ V}$.

(d) $\tan\phi = \frac{X_L - X_C}{R} = \frac{X_L}{R} = \frac{7.54\ \Omega}{20.0\ \Omega} = 0.377$, and $\phi = 20.7°$.

(e)

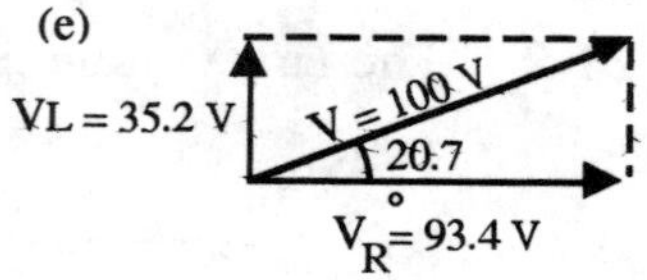

21.17 We have:

$X_C = \frac{1}{2\pi fC} = \frac{1}{2\pi(60.0\text{ Hz})(10^{-5}\text{ F})} = 265\ \Omega$, and

$X_L = 2\pi f L = 2\pi(60.0\text{ Hz})(2.00\text{ H}) = 754\ \Omega$, so

$Z = \sqrt{R^2 + (X_L - X_C)^2} = \sqrt{(X_L - X_C)^2} = 489\ \Omega$.

(a) $I = \frac{\Delta V}{Z} = \frac{100\text{ V}}{489\ \Omega} = 0.204\text{ A}$.

(b) $\Delta V_L = IX_L = (0.204\text{ A})(754\ \Omega) = 154\text{ V}$.

(c) $\Delta V_C = IX_C = (0.204\text{ A})(265\ \Omega) = 54.1\text{ V}$.

(d) $\tan\phi = \frac{X_L - X_C}{R} = \frac{489\ \Omega}{0\ \Omega}$ = infinity, and $\phi = 90°$.

(e)

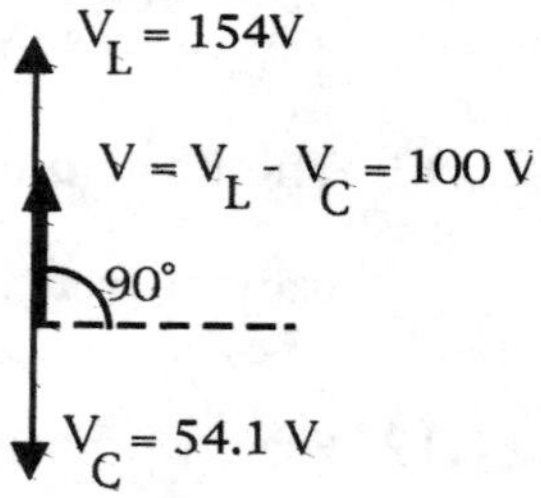

21.18 We have, $X_C = \frac{1}{2\pi fC} = \frac{1}{2\pi(60.0\text{ Hz})(40.0 \times 10^{-6}\text{ F})} = 66.3\ \Omega$.

Thus, $Z = \sqrt{R^2 + (X_L - X_C)^2}$ becomes:

$Z = \sqrt{R^2 + (X_C)^2} = \sqrt{(150\ \Omega)^2 + (66.3\ \Omega)^2} = 83.0\ \Omega$

(a) $I = \frac{\Delta V}{Z} = \frac{30.0\text{ V}}{83.0\ \Omega} = 0.361\text{ A}$.

(b) $\Delta V_R = IR = (0.361\text{ A})(50.0\ \Omega) = 18.1\text{ V}$.

(c) $\Delta V_C = IX_C = (0.361\text{ A})(66.3\ \Omega) = 23.9\text{ V}$.

(d) $\tan\phi = \frac{X_L - X_C}{R} = \frac{-X_C}{R} = \frac{-66.3\ \Omega}{50.0\ \Omega} = -1.33$,

and $\phi = -53.0°$.

(e)

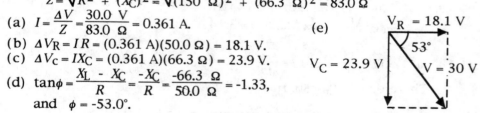

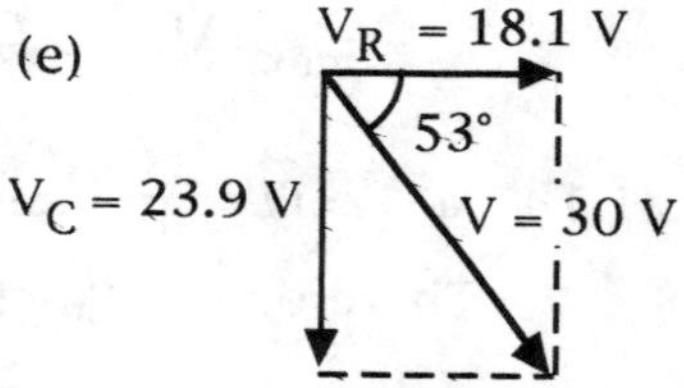

21.19 $X_L = 2\pi f L = (1.51 \times 10^3\text{ rad/s})(2.5\text{ H}) = 3.8 \times 10^3\ \Omega$.

$X_C = \frac{1}{2\pi fC} = \frac{1}{(1.51 \times 10^3\text{ rad/s})(0.25 \times 10^{-6}\text{ F})} = 2.7 \times 10^3\ \Omega$.

(a) $Z = \sqrt{(900\ \Omega)^2 + (3.8 \times 10^3\ \Omega - 2.7 \times 10^3\ \Omega)^2} = 1.4 \times 10^3\ \Omega$.

(b) $I_{max} = \frac{\Delta V_{max}}{Z} = \frac{140\text{ V}}{1.4 \times 10^3\ \Omega} = 1.0 \times 10^{-1}\text{ A} = 0.10\text{ A}$.

(c) $\tan\phi = \frac{X_L - X_C}{R} = \frac{3.8 \times 10^3\ \Omega - 2.7 \times 10^3\ \Omega}{900\ \Omega} = 1.22$, and $\phi = 51°$.

(d) $X_L > X_C$ ϕ is greater than zero, so the voltage leads the current.

21.20 $X_C = \frac{1}{2\pi fC} = \frac{1}{2\pi(60.0\ \text{Hz})(10.0 \times 10^{-6}\ \text{F})} = 265\ \Omega$, and
$X_L = 2\pi fL = 2\pi(60.0\ \text{Hz})(0.100\ \text{H}) = 37.7\ \Omega$.
(a) $\Delta V_R = IR = (2.75\ \text{A})(50.0\ \Omega) = 138\ \text{V}$
(b) $\Delta V_L = IX_L = (2.75\ \text{A})(37.7\ \Omega) = 104\ \text{V}$
(c) $\Delta V_C = IX_C = (2.75\ \text{A})(265\ \Omega) = 729\ \text{V}$
(d) $\Delta V = \sqrt{\Delta V_R^2 + (\Delta V_L - \Delta V_C)^2}$, or
$\Delta V = \sqrt{(138\ \text{V})^2 + (104\ \text{V} - 729\ \text{V})^2} = 640\ \text{V}$.
(e) The phasor diagram is sketched at the right.

(e) 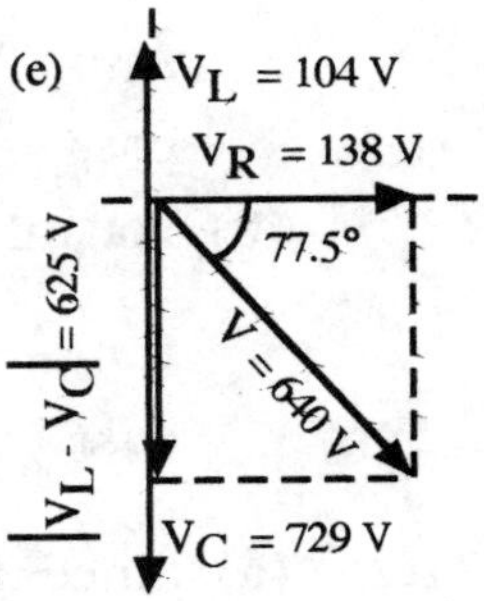

21.21 $X_C = \frac{1}{2\pi fC} = \frac{1}{2\pi(60\ \text{Hz})(3 \times 10^{-6}\ \text{F})} = 884\ \Omega$, and
$X_L = 2\pi fL = 2\pi(60.0\ \text{Hz})(0.400\ \text{H}) = 151\ \Omega$. Thus,
$Z = \sqrt{(60.0\ \Omega)^2 + (151\ \Omega - 884\ \Omega)^2} = 735\ \Omega$, and
$I = \frac{\Delta V}{Z} = \frac{90.0\ \text{V}}{735\ \Omega} = 0.122\ \text{A}$.
(a) The voltage drop across the capacitor-inductor combination is:
$\Delta V_{LC} = IZ_{LC} = I\sqrt{(X_L - X_C)^2} = (0.122\ \text{A})(|151\ \Omega - 884\ \Omega|) = 89.4\ \text{V}$
(b) The voltage drop across the *RC* combination is:
$\Delta V_{RC} = IZ_{RC} = I\sqrt{R^2 + (X_C)^2} = (0.122\ \text{A})\sqrt{(60.0\ \Omega)^2 + (884\ \Omega)^2} = 108\ \text{V}$

21.22 (a) $X_C = \frac{1}{2\pi fC} = \frac{1}{2\pi(60.0\ \text{Hz})(15.0 \times 10^{-6}\ \text{F})} = 177\ \Omega$, and
$Z = \sqrt{R^2 + (X_L - X_C)^2} = \sqrt{R^2 + (X_C)^2} = 184\ \Omega$.
$I = \frac{\Delta V}{Z} = \frac{120\ \text{V}}{184\ \Omega} = 0.652\ \text{A} = 652\ \text{mA}$.
(b) If $I_2 = \frac{1}{2} I_1$, then $Z_2 = 2Z_1$ therefore, $Z_2^2 = 4Z_1^2$, or
$R^2 + (X_L - X_C)^2 = 4[R^2 + (X_C)^2]$. This reduces to:
$X_L = X_C \pm 364\ \Omega = 177\ \Omega \pm 364\ \Omega$. We must use the + sign so that the inductive reactance will be greater than zero. Thus,
$X_L = 541\ \Omega = 2\pi fL$, and $L = \frac{541\ \Omega}{2\pi(60\ \text{Hz})} = 1.44\ \text{H}$.

21.23 We find: $\Delta V = \frac{\Delta V_m}{\sqrt{2}} = 106\ \text{V}$, $X_C = \frac{1}{2\pi fC} = 49.0\ \Omega$, and $X_L = 2\pi fL = 58.1\ \Omega$.
Thus, $Z = \sqrt{R^2 + (X_L - X_C)^2} = 41.0\ \Omega$, and $I = \frac{\Delta V}{Z} = \frac{106\ \text{V}}{41.0\ \Omega} = 2.59\ \text{A}$.
Therefore:
(a) $\Delta V_{ab} = IR = (2.59\ \text{A})(40.0\ \Omega) = 104\ \text{V}$.
(b) $\Delta V_{bc} = IX_L = (2.59\ \text{A})(58.1\ \Omega) = 150\ \text{V}$.
(c) $\Delta V_{cd} = IX_C = (2.59\ \text{A})(49.0\ \Omega) = 127\ \text{V}$.
(d) $\Delta V_{bd} = I\sqrt{(X_L - X_C)^2} = (2.59\ \text{A})\sqrt{(58.1\ \Omega - 49.0\ \Omega)^2} = 23.6\ \text{V}$.

21.24 (a) We find: $X_C = 88.4\ \Omega$, $Z = 102\ \Omega$, and $I = \frac{\Delta V}{Z} = \frac{100\ \text{V}}{102\ \Omega} = 0.980\ \text{A}$.

Also, $\tan\phi = \frac{X_L - X_C}{R} = \frac{-X_C}{R} = \frac{-88.4}{50.0} = -1.77$, and $\phi = -60.5°$. Thus, $\cos\phi = 0.492$, and $P = I\Delta V\cos\phi = (0.980\text{ A})(100\text{ V})(0.492) = 48.2\text{ W}$.

(b) For this case: $X_L = 113\ \Omega$, $Z = 124\ \Omega$, and $I = \frac{\Delta V}{Z} = \frac{100\text{ V}}{124\ \Omega} = 0.806\text{ A}$.

$\tan\phi = \frac{X_L - X_C}{R} = \frac{X_L}{R} = \frac{113}{50.0} = 2.26$, and $\phi = 66.1°$. Thus, $\cos\phi = 0.405$, and $P = I\Delta V\cos\phi = (0.806\text{ A})(100\text{ V})(0.405) = 32.6\text{ W}$.

21.25 (a) Since $\Delta V = IZ$, we have $Z = \frac{\Delta V}{I} = \frac{104\text{ V}}{0.500\text{ A}} = 208\ \Omega$.

(b) The power dissipated is: $P = I^2R$, so that $R = \frac{P}{I^2} = \frac{10.0\text{ W}}{(0.500\text{ A})^2} = 40.0\ \Omega$.

(c) In an RL circuit, $Z = \sqrt{R^2 + X_L^2}$, or
$X_L^2 = Z^2 - R^2 = (208\ \Omega)^2 - (40.0\ \Omega)^2$, giving $X_L = 204\ \Omega$.
But, $X_L = 2\pi f L = 204\ \Omega$, so $L = 0.541\text{ H}$.

21.26 (a) $Z = \frac{\Delta V}{I} = \frac{240\text{ V}}{6.0\text{ A}} = 40\ \Omega$, and $R = Z\cos\phi = (40\ \Omega)\cos(-53°) = 24\ \Omega$.

(b) From $\tan\phi = \frac{X_L - X_C}{R}$, we find: $X_L - X_C = R\tan\phi = -32\ \Omega$.

(c) $P = I\Delta V\cos\phi = (6.0\text{ A})(240\text{ V})\cos(-53°) = 8.7 \times 10^2\text{ W}$.

21.27 (a) We know, $\frac{\Delta V_R}{\Delta V} = \cos\phi = \frac{50\text{ V}}{90\text{ V}} = 0.56$. Thus,

$I = \frac{P}{V_R} = \frac{14\text{ W}}{50\text{ V}} = 0.28\text{ A}$, and $R = \frac{\Delta V_R}{I} = \frac{50\text{ V}}{0.28\text{ A}} = 1.8 \times 10^2\ \Omega$.

(b) From $\cos\phi = 0.56$, we find: $\phi = 56°$.

For the circuit: $\tan\phi = \frac{X_L - X_C}{R} = \frac{X_L}{R}$, so $X_L = R\tan\phi$. Thus,

$X_L = (1.8 \times 10^2\ \Omega)\tan(56°) = 267\ \Omega$, and $L = \frac{X_L}{\omega} = \frac{267\ \Omega}{2\pi(60\text{ Hz})} = 0.71\text{ H}$.

21.28 (a) The needed relations are: $\Delta V = \frac{\Delta V_{max}}{\sqrt{2}} = \frac{100\text{ V}}{\sqrt{2}} = 70.7\text{ V}$,

$X_L = 2\pi f L = 37.7\ \Omega$, and $X_C = \frac{1}{2\pi f C} = 13.3\ \Omega$. Then,

$Z = \sqrt{R^2 + (X_L - X_C)^2} = \sqrt{(20.0\ \Omega)^2 + (37.7\ \Omega - 13.3\ \Omega)^2} = 31.5\ \Omega$.

Therefore, $I = \frac{\Delta V}{Z} = \frac{70.7\text{ V}}{31.5\text{ A}} = 2.24\text{ A}$, and the dissipated power is

$P = I^2R = (2.24\text{ A})^2(20.0\ \Omega) = 100\text{ W}$, and

the power factor is $\cos\phi = \frac{P}{VI} = \frac{100\text{ W}}{(70.7\text{ V})(2.24\text{ A})} = 0.631$.

(b) If $f = 50$ Hz, these relations have the following values:

$X_C = \frac{1}{2\pi f C} = 15.9\ \Omega$, $X_L = 31.4\ \Omega$, $Z = 25.3\ \Omega$, $P = 156\text{ W}$, and $\cos\phi = 0.791$.

21.29 The resonance frequency of the circuit should match the broadcast frequency of the station. Thus, $f = \frac{1}{2\pi\sqrt{LC}} = f_{station}$, or

$$L = \frac{1}{4\pi^2 f^2 C} = \frac{1}{4\pi^2(88.9 \times 10^6 \text{ s}^{-1})^2(1.40 \times 10^{-12} \text{ F})} = 2.29 \times 10^{-6}\text{ H} = 2.29\ \mu\text{H}.$$

21.30 The frequency of the station is equal to the resonant frequency of the tuning circuit: $f_0 = \frac{1}{2\pi\sqrt{LC}} = \frac{1}{2\pi\sqrt{(2.00 \times 10^{-4} \text{ H})(30.0 \times 10^{-12} \text{ F})}}$, or

$f_0 = 2.05 \times 10^6$ Hz $= 2.05$ MHz, and $\lambda = \frac{c}{f} = \frac{3.00 \times 10^8 \text{ m/s}}{2.05 \times 10^6 \text{ Hz}} = 146$ m.

21.31 For f_{min}: $C_{max} = \frac{1}{[2\pi(5.0 \times 10^5 \text{ Hz})]^2(2.0 \times 10^{-6} \text{ H})} = 5.1 \times 10^{-8}$ F.

For f_{max}: $C_{min} = \frac{1}{[2\pi(1.6 \times 10^6 \text{ Hz})]^2(2.0 \times 10^{-6} \text{ H})} = 4.9 \times 10^{-9}$ F.

21.32 (a) At the resonant frequency, $Z = R = 30.0\ \Omega$. The current in the circuit is: $I = \frac{\Delta V}{Z} = \frac{120 \text{ V}}{30.0\ \Omega} = 4.00$ A, and the power is

$P = I^2R = (4.00 \text{ A})^2(30.0\ \Omega) = 480$ W.

(b) At one-half the resonant frequency, the following is easily calculated: $X_C = 2000\ \Omega$, $X_L = 500\ \Omega$, and $Z = 1500\ \Omega$.

Thus, $I = \frac{\Delta V}{Z} = \frac{120 \text{ V}}{1500\ \Omega} = 0.080$ A, and $P = I^2R = 0.192$ W.

(c) At one-fourth the resonant frequency, we find: $X_C = 4000\ \Omega$, $X_L = 250\ \Omega$, and $Z = 3750\ \Omega$, $I = 0.03$ A, and $P = 0.03$ W.

(d) At twice the resonant frequency: $X_C = 500\ \Omega$, $X_L = 2000\ \Omega$, $Z = 1500\ \Omega$, $I = 0.080$ A, and $P = 0.192$ W.

(e) At four times the resonant frequency: $X_C = 250\ \Omega$, $X_L = 4000\ \Omega$, $Z = 3750\ \Omega$, $I = 0.030$ A, and $P = 0.030$ W.

The power delivered to the circuit is maximum when the frequency of the source is equal to the resonant frequency of the circuit.

21.33 (a) $Q = \frac{\Delta V_L}{\Delta V_R}$ (at the resonant frequency).

Thus, $Q = \frac{\Delta V_L}{\Delta V_R} = \frac{2\pi f_0 L\, I_{max}}{R\, I_{max}} = \frac{2\pi f_0 L}{R}$.

(b) In Problem 32, $f_0 = 53.1$ Hz. Thus, $Q = \frac{2\pi(53.1 \text{ Hz})(3.00 \text{ H})}{30.0\ \Omega} = 33.3$.

21.34 (a) For the circuit of Problems 32 and 33: $f_0 = 53.1$ Hz and $Q = 33.3$.

Thus, $\Delta f = (53.1 \text{ Hz}/33.3) = 1.59$ Hz.

(b) If $R = 300\ \Omega$, $Q = (2\pi f_0 L/R) = (333.3 \text{ rad/s})(3.00 \text{ H}/300\ \Omega) = 3.33$, and $\Delta f = (53.1 \text{ Hz}/3.33) = 15.9$ Hz.

21.35 (a) For an ideal transformer, $\frac{\Delta V_2}{\Delta V_1} = \frac{N_2}{N_1}$,

so $N_2 = N_1\frac{\Delta V_2}{\Delta V_1} = 80\frac{2200 \text{ V}}{110 \text{ V}} = 1600$

(b) Also, for an ideal transformer, $\Delta V_2 I_2 = \Delta V_1 I_1$.

Thus, $I_1 = I_2 \frac{\Delta V_2}{\Delta V_1} = 1.5\text{ A}\left(\frac{2200\text{ V}}{110\text{ V}}\right) = 30\text{ A}.$

21.36 (a) The total power required by the city is:
$P = (2.00 \times 10^4)(100\text{ W}) = 2.00 \times 10^6\text{ W}.$
So, $I = \frac{P}{\Delta V} = \frac{2.00 \times 10^6\text{ W}}{120\text{ V}} = 1.67 \times 10^4\text{ A}.$

(b) $I = \frac{P}{\Delta V} = \frac{2.00 \times 10^6\text{ W}}{200\,000\text{ V}} = 10.0\text{ A}.$

(c) If $I = 1.67 \times 10^4$ A, then:
$P_{loss} = I^2R = (1.67 \times 10^4\text{ A})^2(5.00 \times 10^{-4}\ \Omega/\text{m}) = 1.39 \times 10^5\text{ W/m}.$
If $I = 10.0$ A,
then: $P_{loss} = I^2R = (10.0\text{ A})^2(5.00 \times 10^{-4}\ \Omega/\text{m}) = 5.00 \times 10^{-2}\text{ W/m}.$

(d) Case a:

number of lines needed $= \frac{I}{100\text{ A/line}} = \frac{1.67 \times 10^4\text{ A}}{100\text{ A/line}} = 167$ lines.

Case b: number lines needed $= \frac{I}{100\text{ A/line}} = \frac{10\text{ A}}{100\text{ A/line}} = 0.1$ line,
or 1 line is more than sufficient.

21.37 (a) We are given that $P_{out} = 0.90 P_{in}$. Thus, $P_{in} = \frac{1000\text{ kW}}{0.90} = 1.1 \times 10^3$ kW.

(b) We have: $I_p = \frac{P_{in}}{V_p} = \frac{1.1 \times 10^6\text{ W}}{3600\text{ V}} = 3.1 \times 10^2\text{ A}.$

(c) $I_s = \frac{P_{out}}{V_s} = \frac{1000 \times 10^3\text{ W}}{120\text{ V}} = 8.3 \times 10^3\text{ A}.$

21.38 The current in the secondary is: $I_2 \Delta V_2 = I_1 \Delta V_1$, or
$I_2 = \frac{(50\text{ A})(3600\text{ V})}{100000\text{ V}} = 1.8\text{ A}.$ Then, $P_{lost} = I^2{}_2 R = (1.8)^2(100) = 324\text{ W}.$
The original power is $P = I\Delta V = (50\text{ A})(3600\text{ V}) = 180{,}000\text{W}$, so
only $\left(\frac{324\text{ W}}{180\,000\text{ W}}\right)100\,\% = 0.18\%$ is lost.

21.39 Using $\lambda = \frac{c}{f}$ gives: $\lambda = \frac{3.00 \times 10^8\text{ m/s}}{75\text{ Hz}} = 4.0 \times 10^6\text{ m} = 4000\text{ km}.$ One-quarter of this is 1000 km (about 621 miles). Not very practical.

21.40 $c = \frac{1}{\sqrt{\mu_0 \varepsilon_0}}$. If $\mu_0 = 4\pi \times 10^{-7}\text{ Ns}^2/\text{C}^2$ and $\varepsilon_0 = 8.854 \times 10^{-12}\text{ C}^2/\text{Nm}^2$, then
$c = \frac{1}{\sqrt{1.1126 \times 10^{-17}\text{ s}^2/\text{m}^2}} = 2.99796 \times 10^8$ m/s, or rounding to four significant figures, $c = 2.998 \times 10^8$ m/s.

21.41 (a) The magnitudes of the fields associated with an electromagnetic wave are related by $\frac{E}{B} = c$.
Therefore, $E = cB = (3.00 \times 10^8\text{ m/s})(1.5 \times 10^{-7}\text{ T}) = 45\text{ N/C}$
(b) The average power per unit area may be computed as

Average power per unit area $= \dfrac{E_m B_m}{2\mu_0} = \dfrac{45\ \text{N/C}(1.5 \times 10^{-7}\ \text{T})}{2(4\pi \times 10^{-7}\ \text{N/A}^2)} = 2.7\ \text{W/m}^2$

21.42 $I = \dfrac{P}{A} = \dfrac{P}{4\pi r^2}$, so $P = (4\pi r^2)I = 4\pi(1.49 \times 10^{11}\ \text{m})^2\left(1340\ \dfrac{\text{W}}{\text{m}^2}\right) = 3.74 \times 10^{26}$ W.

21.43 From Average Power per unit area $= \dfrac{E_{max}^2}{2\mu_0 c} = 1340\ \text{W/m}^2$, we have:

$E_{max} = \sqrt{(2\mu_0 c)(1340\ \text{W/m}^2)}$, giving

$E_{max} = \sqrt{2(4\pi \times 10^{-7}\ \text{N s}^2/\text{C}^2)(3.00 \times 10^8\ \text{m/s})(1340\ \text{W/m}^2)} = 1.01 \times 10^3\ \dfrac{\text{N}}{\text{C}}$

and $B_{max} = \dfrac{E_{max}}{c} = \dfrac{1.01 \times 10^3\ \text{N/C}}{3.00 \times 10^8\ \text{m/s}} = 3.35 \times 10^{-6}\ \text{T}$.

21.44 The wavelength and frequency of any wave are related by $\lambda f = v$. The speed of electromagnetic waves (in a vacuum) is $v = c = 3.00 \times 10^8$ m/s.

Thus, $f = \dfrac{c}{\lambda} = \dfrac{3.00 \times 10^8\ \text{m/s}}{\lambda}$, and the desired frequencies are:

$f_{min} = \dfrac{c}{\lambda_{max}} = \dfrac{3.00 \times 10^8\ \text{m/s}}{700 \times 10^{-9}\ \text{m}} = 4.29 \times 10^{14}$ Hz, and

$f_{max} = \dfrac{c}{\lambda_{min}} = \dfrac{3.00 \times 10^8\ \text{m/s}}{400 \times 10^{-9}\ \text{m}} = 7.50 \times 10^{14}$ Hz,

---

21.45 (a) $\lambda_{max} = \dfrac{c}{f_{min}} = \dfrac{3.00 \times 10^8\ \text{m/s}}{540 \times 10^3\ \text{Hz}} = 556$ m,

$\lambda_{min} = \dfrac{c}{f_{max}} = \dfrac{3.00 \times 10^8\ \text{m/s}}{1600 \times 10^3\ \text{Hz}} = 188$ m.

(b) For the FM band: $\lambda_{max} = \dfrac{c}{f_{min}} = \dfrac{3.00 \times 10^8\ \text{m/s}}{88 \times 10^6\ \text{Hz}} = 3.4$ m,

$\lambda_{min} = \dfrac{c}{f_{max}} = \dfrac{3.00 \times 10^8\ \text{m/s}}{108 \times 10^6\ \text{Hz}} = 2.78$ m.

21.46 Using $\lambda = \dfrac{c}{f}$, we have $\lambda = \dfrac{3.00 \times 10^8\ \text{m/s}}{27.33 \times 10^6\ \text{Hz}} = 11.0$ m.

21.47 The time for the radio signal to travel 100 km is:

$t_r = \dfrac{100 \times 10^3\ \text{m}}{3.00 \times 10^8\ \text{m/s}} = 3.33 \times 10^{-4}$ s.

The time for the sound wave to travel 3 m across the room is:

$t_s = \dfrac{3.0\ \text{m}}{343\ \text{m/s}} = 8.7 \times 10^{-3}$ s. Therefore, listeners 100 km away will receive the news $\Delta t = 8.7 \times 10^{-3}\ \text{s} - 3.33 \times 10^{-4}\ \text{s} = 8.4 \times 10^{-3}$ s before the people in the newsroom.

21.48 For an ideal transformer: $\dfrac{\Delta V_{out}}{\Delta V_{in}} = \dfrac{N_{secondary}}{N_{primary}}$,

and [Power input] = [Power output]

(a) $N_{secondary} = N_{primary} \frac{\Delta V_{out}}{\Delta V_{in}}, = 240 \frac{9.0\ V}{120\ V} = 18$ turns.

(b) $P_{in} = P_{out} = \Delta V_{out} I_{out} = (9.0\ V)(0.400\ A) = 3.6\ V$

21.49 (a) $X_L = 942\ \Omega$, and $Z = 945\ \Omega$, so $I = \frac{\Delta V}{Z} = \frac{110\ V}{945\ \Omega} = 0.116\ A$.

(b) $I = \frac{\Delta V}{R} = \frac{110\ V}{80.0\ \Omega} = 1.38\ A$.

(c) $P = I^2 R = (0.116\ A)^2 (80.0\ \Omega) = 1.08\ W$ for case (a),
$P = I^2 R = (1.38\ A)^2 (80.0\ \Omega) = 152\ W$ for case (b).

21.50 For $\lambda = 5.25$ m, $f_o = \frac{c}{\lambda} = \frac{3.00 \times 10^8\ m/s}{5.25\ m} = 5.71 \times 10^7$ Hz.

From $f_o = \frac{1}{2\pi\sqrt{LC}}$, we have: $L = \frac{1}{4\pi^2 C f_o^2}$, or

$$L = \frac{1}{4\pi^2 (1.50 \times 10^{-12}\ F)(5.71 \times 10^7\ Hz)^2} = 5.17 \times 10^{-6}\ H = 5.17\ \mu H$$

21.51 (a) $N_s = \frac{\Delta V_s}{\Delta V_p} N_p = \frac{6.0\ V}{110\ V}(220) = 12$ turns.

(b) The impedance of the primary, $Z = X_L = 2\pi(60\ Hz)(0.150\ H) = 56.5\ \Omega$.

Thus, $I = \frac{\Delta V}{Z} = \frac{110\ V}{56.5\ \Omega} = 1.9\ A$.

(c) $P = I \Delta V \cos\phi$, but $\cos\phi = \frac{R}{Z} = 0$. Therefore, $P = 0$.

21.52 $X_C = 531\ \Omega$, and $Z = 567\ \Omega$. Thus, $I = \frac{\Delta V}{Z} = \frac{120\ V}{567\ \Omega} = 0.212$ A, and the power dissipated is: $P = I^2 R = (0.212\ A)^2 (200\ \Omega) = 8.99\ W = 8.99 \times 10^{-3}$ kW.
The energy used in 24 h is: $E = Pt = (8.99 \times 10^{-3}\ kW)(24\ h) = 0.22$ kWh,
and the cost is: cost = (0.22 kWh)(8.0 cents/kWh) = 1.8 cents.

21.53 Combining $X_L = \omega L = 12\ \Omega$, and $X_C = \frac{1}{\omega C} = 8.0\ \Omega$, we find: $L = (96\ \Omega^2)\ C$

Substitute this into the expression $f_o = \frac{1}{2\pi\sqrt{LC}} = \frac{2000\ s^{-1}}{\pi}$ to find:

$C = 26\ \mu F$, and $L = 2.5$ mH.

21.54 $X_L = 2\pi f L = 2\pi(60.0\ Hz)(0.700\ H) = 264\ \Omega$.
Now use $\Delta V^2 = \Delta V_R^2 + \Delta V_L^2$: $(120\ V)^2 = (40.0\ V)^2 + \Delta V_L^2$, from which,

$\Delta V_L = 113$ V. But, $\Delta V_L = I X_L$, so $I = \frac{\Delta V_L}{X_L} = \frac{113\ V}{264\ \Omega} = 0.428\ A = 428$ mA.

21.55 (a) and (b) When a dc source is connected, there is a current in the circuit. Thus, neither of the two elements in the box can be a capacitor since a steady dc current can not flow in branch containing a capacitor. Also, because the direct current is finite, one of the elements must be a resistor. The value of this resistance is: $R = \frac{\Delta V}{I} = \frac{3.0\ V}{0.300\ A} = 10\ \Omega$.

When an ac source is used, we find that the alternating current is less than the direct current. Thus, one of the elements must be an inductor. The impedance is: $Z = \frac{\Delta V}{I} = \frac{3.0\ \text{V}}{0.200\ \text{A}} = 15\ \Omega$. Therefore, we use: $Z^2 = (15\ \Omega)^2 = (10\ \Omega)^2 + X_L{}^2$ to find: $X_L = 11\ \Omega = 2\pi f L$, and

$$L = \frac{11\ \Omega}{2\pi(60\ \text{Hz})} = 3.0 \times 10^{-2}\ \text{H} = 30\ \text{mH}.$$

21.56 (a) We begin with $f = \frac{c}{\lambda} = \frac{3.0 \times 10^8\ \text{m/s}}{0.030\ \text{m}} = 1.0 \times 10^{10}$ Hz. This must be the same as the resonant frequency, $f_0 = \frac{1}{2\pi\sqrt{LC}}$, so

$$C = \frac{1}{4\pi^2 f^2 L} = \frac{1}{4\pi^2(10^{10})^2(400 \times 10^{-12})} = 6.3 \times 10^{-13} = 0.63\ \text{pF}.$$

(b) Using $C = \frac{\varepsilon_0 A}{d}$, we get: $A = \frac{Cd}{\varepsilon_0} = \frac{(0.63 \times 10^{-12}\ \text{F})(10^{-3}\ \text{m})}{(8.85 \times 10^{-12}\ \text{F/m})}$, or

$A = 7.12 \times 10^{-5}\ \text{m}^2$, so that each side has length 8.4 mm.

(c) At resonance $X_C = X_L = 2\pi f L = 2\pi(10^{10}\ \text{Hz})(400 \times 10^{-12}\ \text{H}) = 25\ \Omega$

21.57 (a) $B_{max} = \frac{E_{max}}{c} = \frac{2.0 \times 10^{-7}\ \text{V/m}}{3.0 \times 10^8\ \text{m/s}} = 6.7 \times 10^{-16}\ \text{T}.$

(b) $I = \frac{E^2_{max}}{2\mu_0 c} = \frac{(2.0 \times 10^{-7}\ \text{V/m})^2}{2(4\pi \times 10^{-7}\ \text{Ns}^2/\text{C}^2)(3.0 \times 10^8\ \text{m/s})} = 5.3 \times 10^{-17}\ \text{W/m}^2.$

(c) $P = IA = (5.3 \times 10^{-17}\ \text{W/m}^2)(100\pi\ \text{m}^2) = 1.7 \times 10^{-14}\ \text{W}.$

21.58 (a) $B = \frac{E}{c} = \frac{6.0\ \text{V/m}}{3.0 \times 10^8\ \text{m/s}} = 2.0 \times 10^{-8}\ \text{T}.$

(b) $I = \frac{E_{max}B_{max}}{2\mu_0} = \frac{(6.0\ \text{V/m})(2.0 \times 10^{-8}\ \text{T})}{2(4\pi \times 10^{-7}\ \text{Ns}^2/\text{C}^2)} = 4.8 \times 10^{-2}\ \text{W/m}^2$, and

$P = IA = 4\pi r^2 I = 4\pi(10^3\ \text{m})^2(4.8 \times 10^{-2}\ \text{W/m}^2) = 6.0 \times 10^5\ \text{W} = 600\ \text{kW}.$

21.59 The intensity is:

$$I = \frac{cB_{max}{}^2}{2\mu_0} = \frac{(3.0 \times 10^8\ \text{m/s})(7.0 \times 10^{-8}\ \text{T})^2}{2(4\pi \times 10^{-7}\ \text{Ns}^2/\text{C}^2)} = 0.585\ \text{W/m}^2.$$

At $r = 2.0$ m, $P = IA = (0.585\ \text{W/m}^2)[4\pi(2.0\ \text{m})^2] = 30\ \text{W}.$

21.60 (a) Since $F = ma = qE$, we have:

$$a = \frac{qE}{m} = \frac{(1.60 \times 10^{-19}\ \text{C})(100\ \text{N/C})}{9.11 \times 10^{-31}\ \text{kg}} = 1.76 \times 10^{13}\ \text{m/s}^2.$$

(b) Using the given equation, $P = \frac{2kq^2a^2}{3\ c^3}$, we find:

$$P = \frac{2(8.99\ 10^9\ \text{N m}^2/\text{C}^2)(1.60 \times 10^{-19}\ \text{C})^2(1.76 \times 10^{13}\ \text{m/s}^2)}{3(3.00 \times 10^8\ \text{m/s})^3}$$, or

$P = 1.75 \times 10^{-27}$ W.

(c) We have: $$\frac{\left(\frac{\text{Nm}^2}{\text{C}^2}\right)(\text{C}^2)(\text{m/s}^2)^2}{(\text{m/s}^2)^3} = \frac{\text{Nm}^4}{\text{s}^4\text{m}^3/\text{s}^3} = \frac{\text{N m}}{\text{s}} = \frac{\text{J}}{\text{s}} = \text{W}.$$

21.61 (a) When connected to the battery, the only impedance to the current is the resistance of the coil. Thus, the coil resistance is:

$R = \frac{\Delta V}{I} = \frac{12\ \text{V}}{3.0\ \text{A}} = 4.0\ \Omega$. The impedance when connected to the ac source is: $Z = \frac{\Delta V}{I} = \frac{12\ \text{V}}{2.0\ \text{A}} = 6.0\ \Omega$.

(b) We now find X_L as: $Z^2 = R^2 + X_L{}^2$, or $(6.0\ \Omega)^2 = (4.0\ \Omega)^2 + X_L{}^2$. This yields, $X_L = 4.47\ \Omega$, and

$$L = \frac{X_L}{2\pi f} = \frac{4.47\ \Omega}{2\pi(60\ \text{Hz})} = 1.2 \times 10^{-2}\ \text{H} = 12\ \text{mH}.$$

21.62 (a) $R = (4.50 \times 10^{-4}\ \Omega/\text{m})(6.44 \times 10^5\ \text{m}) = 290\ \Omega$, and

$I = \frac{P}{V} = \frac{5.0 \times 10^6\ \text{W}}{5.0 \times 10^5\ \Delta\text{V}} = 10\ \text{A}$. $P_{loss} = I^2 R = (10\ \text{A})^2(290\ \Omega) = 2.9 \times 10^4\ \text{W}$.

(b) $\frac{P_{loss}}{P} = \frac{2.9 \times 10^4\ \text{W}}{5.0 \times 10^6\ \text{W}} = 0.0058\ (0.58\,\%)$.

(c) It is impossible to deliver 5000 kW of power to the customer through this transmission line with an input voltage of only 4500 V. With an input voltage of 4500 V, the power input from the generator is $P_{input} = \Delta VI = (4500\ \text{V})I$. The maximum current that can exist in this line with a 4500 V input occurs when the transmission line is shorted out at the customer's end, and the minimum resistance of the circuit is $R_{min} = R_{line} = 290\ \Omega$. Hence, $I_{max} = \frac{\Delta V}{R_{min}} = \frac{4500\ \text{V}}{290\ \Omega} = 15.5\ \text{A}$, and the maximum power input to the transmission line with an input voltage of 4500 V is $(P_{input})_{max} = (4500\ \text{V})(15.5\ \text{A}) = 6.98 \times 10^4\ \text{W} = 69.8\ \text{kW}$. This is far less than the power the customer wants delivered 5000 kW, and it is all dissipated in the transmission line.

21.63 (a) The radiation pressure is $\frac{(2)(1340\ \text{W/m}^2)}{3.00 \times 10^8\ \text{m/s}^2} = 8.93 \times 10^{-6}\ \text{N/m}^2$.

Multiplying by the total area, $A = 6.00 \times 10^4\ \text{m}^2$ gives: $F = 0.536\ \text{N}$.

(b) The acceleration is: $a = \frac{F}{m} = \frac{0.536\ \text{N}}{6000\ \text{kg}} = 8.93 \times 10^{-5}\ \text{m/s}^2$.

(c) It will take a time t where:

$d = \frac{1}{2}at^2$, or $t = \sqrt{\frac{2d}{a}} = \sqrt{\frac{2(3.84 \times 10^8\ \text{m})}{(8.93 \times 10^{-5}\ \text{m/s}^2)}} = 2.93 \times 10^6\ \text{s} = 33.9$ days.

21.64 We know $\frac{N_1}{N_2} = \frac{\Delta V_1}{\Delta V_2}$. Let the output impedance be $Z_1 = \frac{\Delta V_1}{I_1}$ and the input impedance $Z_2 = \frac{\Delta V_2}{I_2}$, so $\frac{N_1}{N_2} = \frac{Z_1 I_1}{Z_2 I_2}$. But we also know: $\frac{I_1}{I_2} = \frac{\Delta V_2}{\Delta V_1} = \frac{N_2}{N_1}$. Combining with the previous result, we have:

$$\frac{N_1}{N_2} = \left(\frac{Z_1}{Z_2}\right)^{1/2} = \left(\frac{8000}{8}\right)^{1/2} = 32.$$

21.65 First determine the energy density in this sunlight (at the top of the atmosphere) by considering a shaft of sunlight one square meter in cross-sectional area and 1.00 m long (i.e one cubic meter of sunlight). All the energy in this volume strikes one square meter of the atmosphere in a time of: $t = \frac{d}{v} = \frac{1.00\text{ m}}{3.00 \times 10^{8}\text{ m/s}} = 3.33 \times 10^{-9}$ s.

The energy striking a unit area in time t is given by:

$$E = It = (\frac{\text{power}}{\text{area}})\ t = \frac{\text{energy}}{\text{area}}$$

Thus, if $I = 1340\text{ W/m}^2$, the energy striking one square meter in 3.33×10^{-9} s is: $U = (1340\text{ J/s/m}^2)(3.33 \times 10^{-9}\text{ s/m}) = 4.47 \times 10^{-6}\text{ J/m}^3$.

Thus, the energy in 1.00 liter of sunlight is:

E = (energy density)(volume) = $(4.47 \times 10^{-6}\text{ J/m}^3)(10^{-3}\text{ m}^3)$, or

$E = 4.47 \times 10^{-9}$ J.

ANSWERS TO CONCEPTUAL QUESTIONS

2. At resonance $X_L = X_C$. This means that the impedance $Z = \sqrt{R^2 + (X_L - X_C)^2}$ reduces to $Z = R$.

4. The purpose of the iron coil is to increase the flux and to provide a pathway in which nearly all the flux through one coil is led through the other.

6. The fundamental source of an electromagnetic wave is a moving charge. For example, in a transmitting antenna of a radio station, charges are caused to move up and down at the frequency of the radio station. These moving charges set up electric and magnetic fields, the electromagnetic wave, in the space around the antenna.

8. As an electromagnetic wave moves through space, the only things associated with the wave that move are alternating electric and magnetic fields at right angles to one another.

10. The average value of an alternating current is zero because its direction is positive as often as it is negative, and its time average is zero. The average value of the square of the current is not zero, however, since the square of positive and negative values are always positive and cannot cancel.

12. The brightest portion of your face shows where you radiate the most. Your nostrils and the openings of your ear canals are particularly bright. Brighter still are the pupils of your eyes.

14. No, the only element that dissipates energy in an ac circuit is a resistor. Inductors and capacitors store energy during one half of a cycle and release that energy during the other half of the cycle, so they dissipate no net energy.

CHAPTER TWENTY-TWO SOLUTIONS

Chapter Twenty-Two Readings

Bell, A.E., "Next Generation Compact Discs," *Scientific American*, July 1996, p. 42.

Boyle, W.S., "Light-Wave Communications, " *Scientific American*, August 1977, p. 40.

Fraser, A.B. and Mach, W.H., "Mirages," *Scientific American*, January 1976, p. 102.

Kapany, N.S., "Fiber Optics," *Scientific American*, November 1960, p. 72.

MacChesney, J., "Working Knowledge: Optical Fibers," *Scientific American*, August 1997, p 96.

Mandoli, D.F and Briggs, W.R., "Fiber Optics in Plants," *Scientific American*, August 1984, p. 90.

Morrison, P. and Morrison, P., "Bandwith Galore," *Scientific American*, July 1997, p. 102.

Stark, E.W., "Diffuse Reflection:Uses That Affect Our Lives," *The Physics Teacher*, March 1986, p. 144.

Williamson, S, and Cummins, H., *Light and Color in Nature and Art*, John Wiley and Son, 1983.

22.1 The Moon's radius is 1.74×10^6 m and the Earth's radius is 6.38×10^6 m. The total distance traveled by the light is:

$$d = 2(3.84 \times 10^8 \text{ m} - 1.74 \times 10^6 - 6.38 \times 10^6) = 7.518 \times 10^8 \text{ m}.$$

This takes 2.51 s, so $v = \dfrac{7.518 \times 10^8 \text{ m}}{2.51 \text{ s}} = 2.995 \times 10^8$ m/s.

22.2 (a) The time for the light to travel 40 m is:

$t = \dfrac{40.0 \text{ m}}{3.00 \times 10^8 \text{ m/s}} = 1.33 \times 10^{-7}$ s. At the lowest speed, the wheel will have turned through 1/360 rev in the time *t*. Thus,

$$\omega = \frac{\Delta\theta}{\Delta t} = \frac{1/360 \text{ rev}}{1.33 \times 10^{-7} \text{ s}} = 2.1 \times 10^4 \text{ rev/s}.$$

The next lowest speed occurs when the wheel turns through 2/360 rev in the time t: $\omega = \dfrac{\Delta\theta}{\Delta t} = \dfrac{2/360 \text{ rev}}{1.33 \times 10^{-7} \text{ s}} = 4.2 \times 10^4$ rev/s.

(b) The steps are identical to those used in part a. The flight time of the light is 1.33×10^{-5} s, and the lowest speed is 2.1×10^2 rev/s. The next lowest speed is 4.2×10^2 rev/s.

22.3 (a) The time for the light to travel to the mirror and back is:

$t = \frac{2(35.0 \times 10^3 \text{ m})}{3.00 \times 10^8 \text{ m/s}} = 2.33 \times 10^{-4}$ s. At the lowest speed, the mirror will turn 1/8 rev in time t. Thus, $\omega = \frac{\Delta\theta}{\Delta t} = \frac{1/8 \text{ rev}}{2.33 \times 10^{-4} \text{ s}} = 536$ rev/s.

(b) The next higher speed will occur when the wheel makes 2/8 rev in time t. The angular velocity for this case is: $\omega = \frac{\Delta\theta}{\Delta t} = 1.07 \times 10^3$ rev/s.

22.4 (a) For the light beam to make it through both slots, the time for the light to travel the distance s must equal the time for the disks to rotate through the angle θ. Therefore, if c is the speed of light,

$$t = \frac{s}{c} = \frac{\theta}{\omega}, \text{ so } \quad c = \frac{s\omega}{\theta}$$

(b) Given: $s = 2.500 \text{ m}$, $\theta = \frac{1}{60}\left(\frac{\pi \text{ rad}}{180^\circ}\right) = 2.909 \times 10^{-4}$ rad, and

$\omega = (5555 \text{ rev/s})(2\pi \text{ rad/rev}) = 3.490 \times 10^4$ rad/s, so

$$c = \frac{2.500 \text{ m}(3.490 \times 10^4 \text{ rad/s})}{(2.909 \times 10^{-4} \text{ rad})} = 2.999 \times 10^8 \text{ m/s.}$$

22.5 (a) From geometry, $1.25 \text{ m} = d \sin 40^\circ$
so $d = 1.94$ m.
(b) At 50° above horizontal, or parallel to the incident ray.

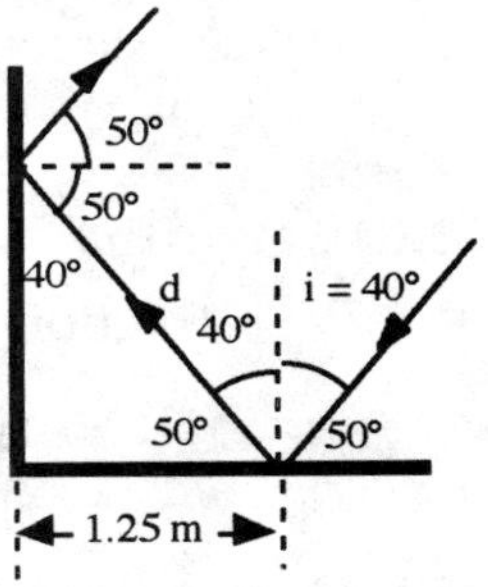

22.6 The speed of light in water is $v_w = \frac{c}{n_w} = \frac{3.00 \times 10^8 \text{ m/s}}{1.333} = 2.25 \times 10^8$ m/s,

and its speed in lucite is $v_{luc} = \frac{c}{n_{luc}} = \frac{3.00 \times 10^8 \text{ m/s}}{1.59} = 1.89 \times 10^8$ m/s,

The time to travel through each layer is then:

$$t_{water} = \frac{1.00 \times 10^{-2} \text{ m}}{2.25 \times 10^8 \text{ m/s}} = 4.44 \times 10^{-11} \text{ s and}$$

$$t_{lucite} = \frac{0.500 \times 10^{-2} \text{ m}}{1.89 \times 10^8 \text{ m/s}} = 2.65 \times 10^{-11} \text{ s}$$

The time to travel an equal distance in air is:

$$t_{lucite} = \frac{1.50 \times 10^{-2} \text{ m}}{3.00 \times 10^8 \text{ m/s}} = 5.00 \times 10^{-11} \text{ s}$$

Therefore, with the two layers present, the excess travel time is

$$\Delta t = (t_{water} + t_{lucite}) - t_{air} = 2.09 \times 10^{-11} \text{ s}$$

22.7 (a) $v = \frac{c}{n} = \frac{3.00 \times 10^8 \text{ m/s}}{1.66} = 1.81 \times 10^8$ m/s

(b) $v = \frac{c}{n} = \frac{3.00 \times 10^8 \text{ m/s}}{1.333} = 2.25 \times 10^8$ m/s

(c) $v = \frac{c}{n} = \frac{3.00 \times 10^8 \text{ m/s}}{1.923} = 1.56 \times 10^8$ m/s

---

22.8 (a) $\lambda_o = n_w \lambda_w = (1.333)(438 \text{ nm}) = 584$ nm

(b) $\lambda_o = n_b \lambda_b =$, or $\frac{n_b}{n_w} = \frac{\lambda_w}{\lambda_b} = \frac{438 \text{ nm}}{390 \text{ nm}} = 1.12$

22.9 (a) $\lambda_{water} = \frac{\lambda_{vac}}{n_{water}} = \frac{436 \text{ nm}}{1.333} = 327$ nm

(b) $\lambda_{glass} = \frac{\lambda_{vac}}{n_{glass}} = \frac{436 \text{ nm}}{1.52} = 287$ nm

---

22.10 From Snell's Law, $n_1 \sin\theta_1 = n_2 \sin\theta_2$, or
(1) $\sin 36° = (1.33)\sin\theta_2$, so $\theta_2 = 26°$.

22.11 The air is medium 1, and the ice is medium 2.
Snell's law gives the angle of refraction as:
$n_2 \sin\theta_2 = n_1 \sin\theta_1$, or $1.309 \sin\theta_2 = \sin 40.0°$.
Thus, $\sin\theta_2 = 0.491$, and $\theta_2 = 29.4°$.
Also, from the law of reflection, $\Phi = 40.0°$.
The angle between the reflected and refracted ray (see sketch) is found as: $\theta_2 + \alpha + \Phi = 180°$.
Thus, $\alpha = 110.6°$.

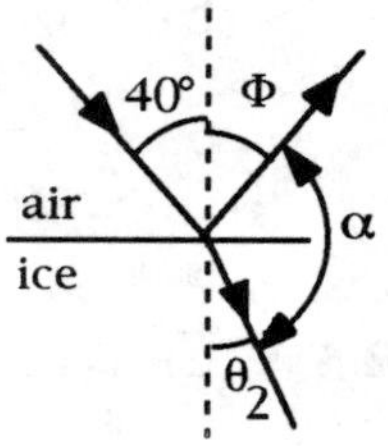

22.12 $n_2 \sin\theta_2 = n_1 \sin\theta_1$, or $\frac{4}{3} \sin\theta_2 = (1.0)\sin 35°$, so the angle of refraction is: $\theta_2 = 25.5°$. The wavelength in water is:

$\lambda_2 = \lambda_1 (\frac{n_1}{n_2}) = (589 \text{ nm})\frac{1.00}{1.333} = 442$ nm.

22.13 $n_{oil} = \frac{c}{v_{oil}} = \frac{3.00 \times 10^8 \text{ m/s}}{2.17 \times 10^8 \text{ m/s}} = 1.382$. Thus, from Snell's law gives:
$n_{oil} \sin\theta_2 = n_{air} \sin\theta_1$, or $1.382 \sin\theta_2 = (1.0)\sin 23.1°$, and $\theta_2 = 16.5°$.

22.14 The angle of incidence is given by θ where $\tan\theta = \frac{2.00 \text{ m}}{4.00 \text{ m}}$, or $\theta = 26.6°$.
Then, Snell's law gives $1.333 \sin 26.6° = 1.00 \sin\phi$, or $\phi = 36.6°$.

22.15 Snell's law may be written as $\frac{\sin\theta_2}{\sin\theta_1} = \frac{n_1}{n_2} = \frac{v_2}{v_1}$. Thus, $\sin\theta_2 = \frac{v_2}{v_1} \sin\theta_1$

or $\sin\theta_2 = \frac{1510 \text{ m/s}}{340 \text{ m/s}} \sin 12.0° = 0.923$, and $\theta_2 = 67.4°$

22.16 At the first surface, call the air medium 1 and the glass medium 2. We find the angle of refraction from Snell's law: $n_2 \sin\theta_2 = n_1 \sin\theta_1$, or
$1.50 \sin\theta_2 = \sin 30.0°$, and $\sin\theta_2 = 0.333$, giving $\theta_2 = 19.5°$.
At the second surface, we call medium 2 the glass and medium 3 the air into which the light exits. We find: $n_3 \sin\theta_3 = n_2 \sin\theta_2$, or
$1.00 \sin\theta_3 = 1.50 \sin 19.5°$, and $\sin\theta_3 = 0.50$, giving $\theta_3 = 30.0°$.
Thus, the light emerges traveling parallel to the incident beam.

22.17 The angle of refraction, θ_2, equals 19.5° (see problem 16). Let h represent the distance from point a to c (i.e., the hypotenuse of triangle abc). Then, h is found by use of triangle abc as:

$$\frac{2.00\ \text{cm}}{h} = \cos 19.5°, \text{ from which, } \quad h = 2.12\ \text{cm}.$$

We also see that: $\theta_2 + \alpha = \theta_1$, or,

$$\alpha = \theta_1 - \theta_2 = 30.0° - 19.5° = 10.5°$$

Finally, $d = h \sin\alpha = (2.12\ \text{cm})\sin 10.5° = 0.386\ \text{cm}.$

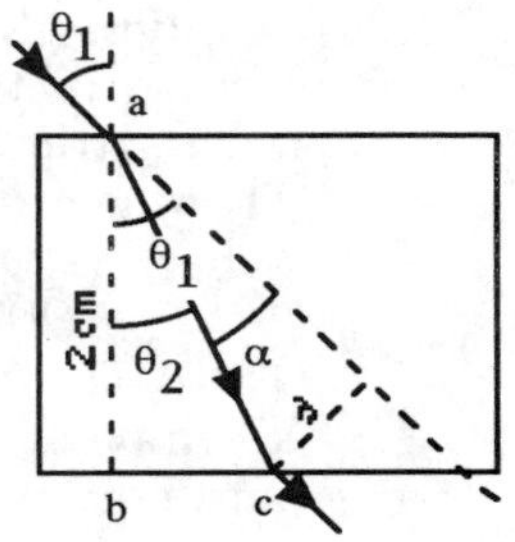

22.18 Applying Snell's law at the air-oil interface,
$n_{air} \sin\theta = n_{oil} \sin 20.0°$ yields $\theta = 30.4°$.
Applying Snell's law at the oil-water interface
$n_w \sin\theta' = n_{oil} \sin 20°$ yields $\theta' = 22.3°$.

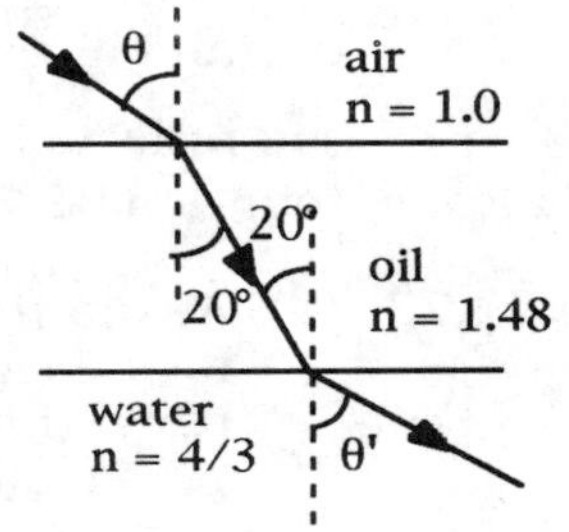

22.19 (See sketch.)

$$\tan\theta_1 = \frac{90}{100} = 0.90, \text{ and}$$

$$\theta_1 = 42.0°.$$

From Snell's law, we find:

$$n_2 \sin\theta_2 = n_1 \sin\theta_1$$

$$1 \sin\theta_2 = 1.333 \sin 42.0°,$$

or $\theta_2 = 63.1°$.

Finally,

$$h = \frac{210\ \text{m}}{\tan 63.1°} = 107\ \text{m}.$$

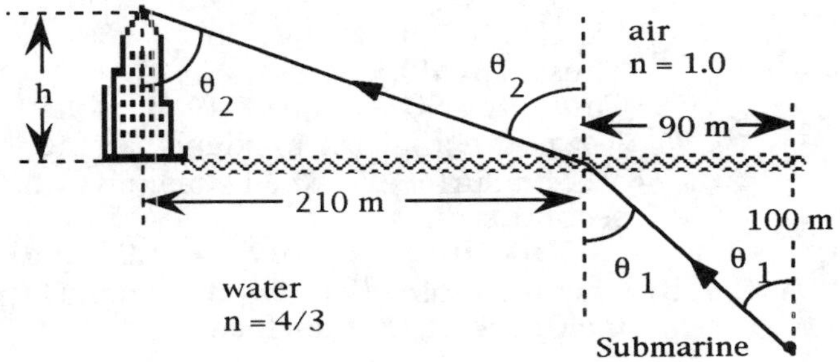

22.20 Using the law of reflection, we find that $d = 6.00$ cm. Then, from Snell's law:

$$n_m \sin 50.0° = n_L \sin\theta,$$

$$\sin\theta = \frac{n_m}{n_L} \sin 50.0° = \frac{v_L}{v_w} \sin 50.0°$$

$$= (0.900) \sin 50.0°$$

Thus, $\theta = 43.6°$, and $h = \dfrac{d}{\tan 43.6°} = 6.30\ \text{cm}.$

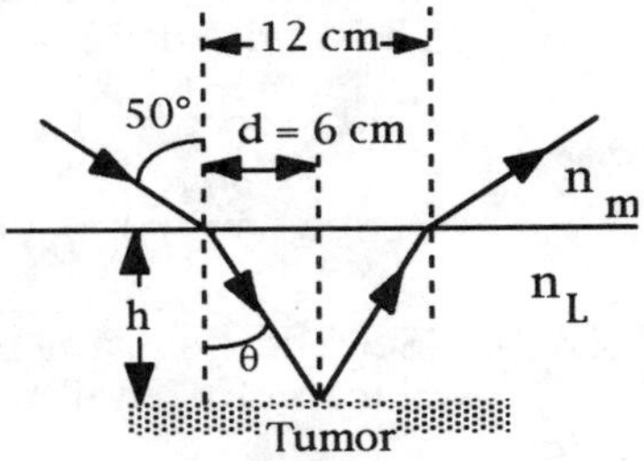

22.21 Applying Snell's law to the refraction shown in the figure at the right gives:

$n_g \sin\theta_2 = (1)\sin\theta_1$, (1)

From geometry, $\alpha + \beta + \theta_2 = 180°$

When $\beta = 90°$ as desired, this reduces to:

$\theta_2 = 90° - \alpha$

But $\alpha = \theta_1$ from the law of reflection. Thus, we have $\theta_2 = 90° - \theta_1$

and equation (1) yields:

$\sin\theta_1 = n_g \sin(90° - \alpha) = n_g \cos(\theta_1)$

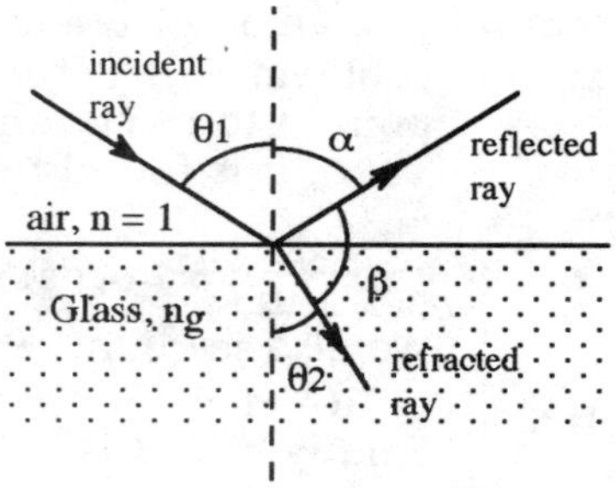

or $\tan\theta_1 = \dfrac{\sin\theta_1}{\cos\theta_1} = n_g$. Therefore, the angle of incidence for which the reflected and refracted rays will be perpendicular to each other is found to be $\theta_1 = \tan^{-1}(n_g) = \text{Arctan}(n_g)$.

22.22 (a) At the first surface, the angle of incidence is 30° and the angle of refraction is found from Snell's law:

$n_2 \sin\theta_2 = n_1 \sin\theta_1$

$1.50 \sin\theta_2 = 1.00 \sin 30.0°$, or $\theta_2 = 19.5°$.

At the first surface, we see:

$\alpha + \theta_2 = 90°$, or $\alpha = 90° - 19.5° = 70.5°$.

We also see that: $\alpha + \beta + 60° = 180°$.

Thus, $\beta = 49.5°$.

Thus, $\theta_3 = 90° - \beta = 90° - 49.5° = 40.5°$.

θ_3 is the angle of incidence at the second surface.

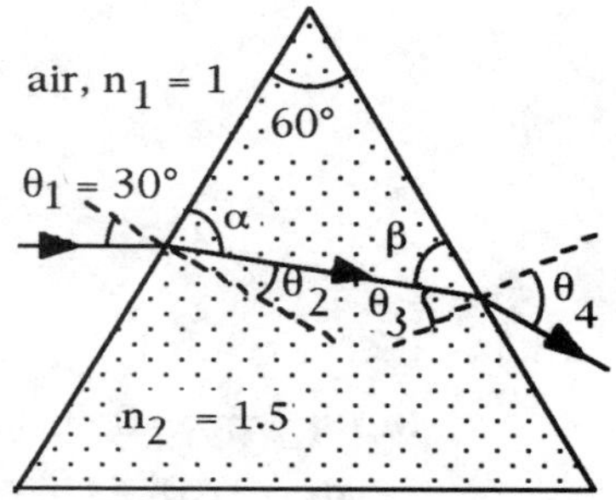

Snell's law gives us the angle of refraction at the second surface:

$n_4 \sin\theta_4 = n_3 \sin\theta_3 \Rightarrow 1.00 \sin\theta_4 = 1.50 \sin 40.5°$, or $\theta_4 = 77.1°$.

(b) The angle of reflection at each surface is the same as the angle of incidence at that surface.

22.23 When the Sun is 28.0° from horizon, incident rays are 62.0° from normal at the air-water interface. (See the sketch at the right.)

Thus, $n_w \sin\theta_w = 1.00 \sin 62.0°$, or

$\sin\theta_w = \dfrac{\sin 62.0°}{4/3} = 0.662$, and $\theta_w = 41.5°$.

Hence, $\dfrac{3.00 \text{ m}}{h} = \tan\theta_w$, so $h = \dfrac{3.00 \text{ m}}{\tan 41.5°} = 3.39 \text{ m}$.

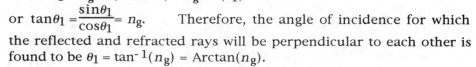

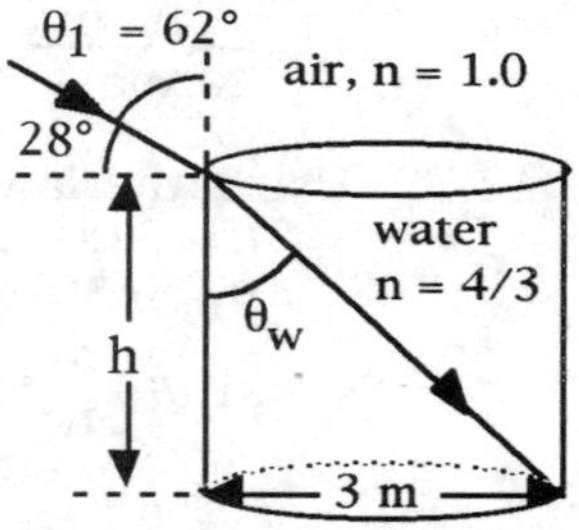

22.24 (See the diagram below.) For the first placement, Snell's law becomes, with 1 referring to the upper sheet and 2 to the lower, $n_2 = n_1 \dfrac{\sin 26.5°}{\sin 31.7°}$. (1)

Given Conditions and Observed Results

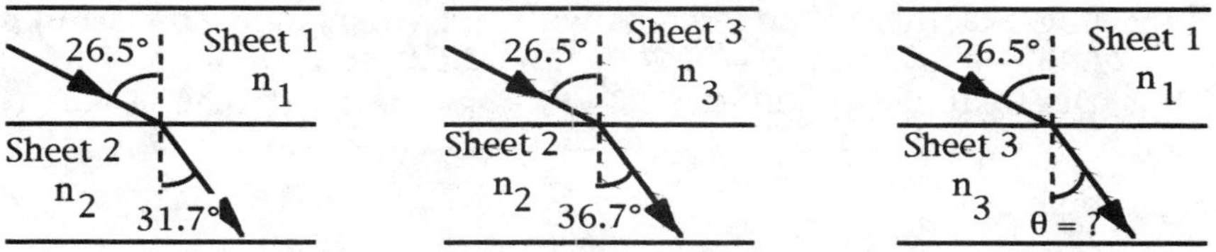

Case (a) Case (b) Case (c)

For the second placement, with 3 referring to the remaining sheet,

$$n_3 = n_2 \frac{\sin 36.7°}{\sin 26.5°} \ . \qquad (2)$$

Combining (1) and (2), we have: $n_3 = n_1 \frac{\sin 36.7°}{\sin 31.7°}$. (3)

Applying Snell's law to the final situation, we have:

$$\sin\theta = n_1\left(\frac{\sin 26.5°}{n_3}\right) = \left(\frac{\sin 31.7°}{\sin 36.7°}\right)\sin 26.5°, \text{ or } \quad \theta = 23.1°.$$

22.25 From the sketch, observe that:

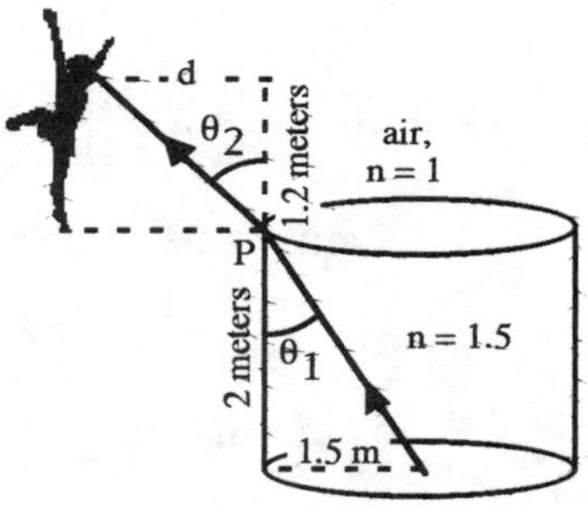

$$\tan\theta_1 = \frac{R}{h} = \frac{1.5 \text{ m}}{2.0 \text{ m}} = 0.75,$$

so $\theta_1 = 36.9°$.

Application of Snell's law at point P yields:

$1.0 \sin\theta_2 = 1.5 \sin 36.9°$, or $\theta_2 = 64.2°$.

Then observe that:

$\tan\theta_2 = \frac{d}{1.2 \text{ m}}$, or $d = 1.2 \text{ m} \tan 64.2°$, giving

$d = 2.5$ m.

22.26 For acrylic with $\lambda = 400$ nm, we find $n = 1.507$. (See dispersion graph in text.) To be refracted at the same angle in the fused quartz, the wavelength used must have the same index of refraction as the 400 nm light had in the acrylic. From Fig. 22.15, it is seen that the wavelength for which $n = 1.507$ in fused quartz is: $\lambda = 245$ nm.

22.27 Using Snell's law gives: $1.00 \sin 83.0° = 1.331 \sin\theta_r$, and

$1.00 \sin 83.0° = 1.340 \sin\theta_b$, so $\theta_r = 48.2°$, and $\theta_b = 47.8°$

22.28 The angle of refraction for the blue light is found from Snell's law as:

$$\sin\theta_B = \frac{1}{2(1.650)} = 0.3030, \text{ and } \theta_B = 17.64°.$$

Likewise, for red, we have: $\sin\theta_R = \frac{1}{2(1.615)} = 0.3096$, and $\theta_R = 18.03°$.

Thus, the angle between the two rays is: $\Delta\theta = 0.39°$.

22.29 First we do some geometry (see sketch):

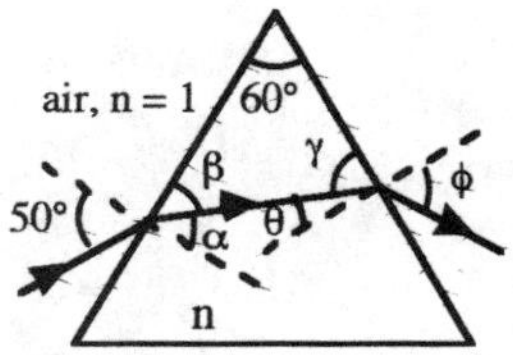

$\beta = 90° - \alpha$, $\gamma + \beta + 60 = 180°$ gives: $\gamma = 120° - \beta$.

The angle of incidence at the second surface is:

$\theta = 90° - \gamma$. Now consider the red light ($n = 1.62$).

Snell's law at the first surface gives:

$1.62 \sin\alpha = 1.0 \sin 50°$, and $\alpha = 28.22°$. Then the above relations give: $\beta = 61.78°$, $\gamma = 58.22°$, and $\theta = 31.78°$. Thus, Snell's law at the second surface gives:

$1.00 \sin\phi_R = 1.62 \sin(31.78°)$, or $\phi_R = 58.56°$.
Following exactly the same steps with the violet light ($n = 1.66$) gives:
$\alpha = 27.48°$, $\beta = 62.52°$, $\gamma = 57.48°$, $\theta = 32.52°$, and $\phi_V = 63.17°$.
Thus, the total dispersion is: $D = \phi_V - \phi_R = 63.17° - 58.56° = 4.61°$.

22.30 We use $\sin\theta_c = \frac{n_2}{n_1}$:

(a) For zircon: $\sin\theta_c = \frac{1}{1.923} = 0.5200$, and $\theta_c = 31.3°$.

(b) For Fluorite: $\sin\theta_c = \frac{1}{1.434} = 0.6973$, and $\theta_c = 44.2°$.

(c) For Ice: $\sin\theta_c = \frac{1}{1.309} = 0.7639$, and $\theta_c = 49.8°$.

22.31 From Snell's law, we find the index of refraction of the fluid:
$n_2 \sin\theta_2 = n_1 \sin\theta_1 \Rightarrow n_2 \sin 22° = 1.0 \sin 30.0°$, or $n_2 = 1.335$.
Then, from $\sin\theta_c = \frac{n_2}{n_1}$: $\sin\theta_c = \frac{1}{1.335} = 0.749$, and $\theta_c = 48.5°$.

22.32 $\sin\theta_c = \frac{n_2}{n_1} = \frac{1}{2.419} = 0.4134$, and $\theta_c = 24.4°$.

22.33 Given: $\sin\theta_c = n_2/n_1$.

(a) If surrounded by air: $\sin\theta_c = \frac{n_2}{n_1} = \frac{1.00}{1.53} = 0.6535$, or $\theta_c = 40.8°$

(b) If surrounded by water: $\sin\theta_c = \frac{n_2}{n_1} = \frac{1.333}{1.53} = 0.8714$, or $\theta_c = 60.6°$

22.34 Given: $\sin\theta_c = \frac{n_c}{n_p}$, so $n_c = n_p \sin\theta_c = 1.60 \sin 59.5° = 1.38$.

22.35 Given: $\sin\theta_c = \frac{n_{air}}{n_{pipe}}$, or $\sin\theta_c = \frac{1.00}{1.36} = 0.7353$, and $\theta_c = 47.3°$.
Geometry shows that the angle of refraction at the end is:
$\theta_r = 90° - \theta_c = 90° - 47.3° = 42.7°$.
Then, applying Snell's law at the end gives:
$1.00 \sin\theta = 1.36 \sin 42.7°$, or $\theta = 67.2°$.

22.36 Looking at the sketch at the right, it is seen that if θ is the angle of incidence at one of the clear faces, $\sin\theta = \frac{d}{L}$, where

$d = \frac{1}{2}$ diagonal of the base of the cube.

$(\text{diagonal})^2 = (2d)^2 = t^2 + t^2 = 2t^2$, so

$2d = \sqrt{2}\, t$, or $d = \frac{t}{\sqrt{2}}$.

Also, $L^2 = d^2 + t^2 = \frac{t^2}{2} + t^2 = \frac{3}{2} t^2$, or

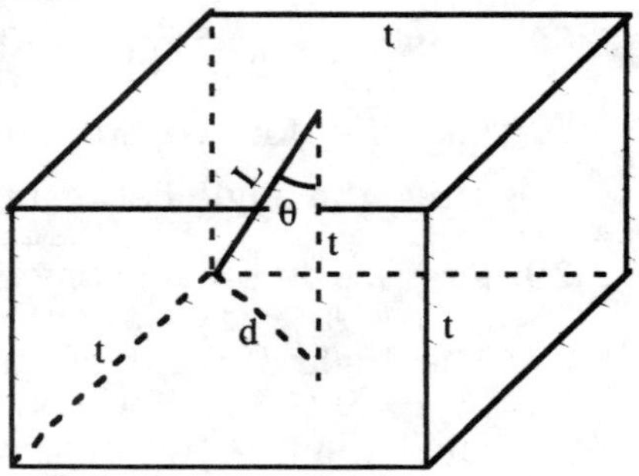

$L = \sqrt{\frac{3}{2}}\,t$. Thus, $\sin\theta = \left(\frac{t}{\sqrt{2}}\right)\left(\frac{\sqrt{2}}{\sqrt{3}\,t}\right) = \frac{1}{\sqrt{3}}$.

For total internal reflection for this ray, it is necessary to have $\theta > \theta_C$, or $\sin\theta > \sin\theta_C$. But, $n \sin\theta_C = n_{air} \sin 90°$, or $\sin\theta_C = \frac{1}{n}$. Thus, the requirement is: $\sin\theta > \frac{1}{n}$, or $n > \frac{1}{\sin\theta} = \sqrt{3}$.

22.37 The critical angle for a water-air boundary is:

$$\sin\theta_c = \frac{n_2}{n_1} = \frac{1}{4/3} = \frac{3}{4}, \text{ and } \theta_c = 48.6°.$$

The circular raft must cover the area of the surface through which light from the diamond could emerge. Thus, it must form the base of a cone (with apex at the diamond) whose half angle is θ, where θ is greater than or equal to the critical angle. We have:

$$\frac{r_{min}}{h} = \tan\theta_c, \text{ or } r_{min} = (2.00\text{ m})\tan 48.6° = 2.27\text{ m, and the diameter}$$

is $d_{min} = 2\,r_{min} = 4.54$ m.

22.38 If the beam follows the path shown in figure in the text, the angle of incidence when it strikes the short face of the prism is 45°. The index of refraction of the prism must be such that θ_c is less than or equal to 45°.

We find: $\sin\theta_c = \frac{n_2}{n_1} = \frac{1}{n}$ where n is the index of refraction of the prism material. Thus, $n = \frac{1}{\sin\theta_c}$. However, if the critical angle is less than or equal to 45°, then $\sin\theta_c$ is less than or equal to $\sin 45°$, and

$$n \text{ is greater than or equal to } \frac{1}{\sin 45°} = \frac{2}{\sqrt{2}} = \sqrt{2}$$

22.39 At Surface 2:

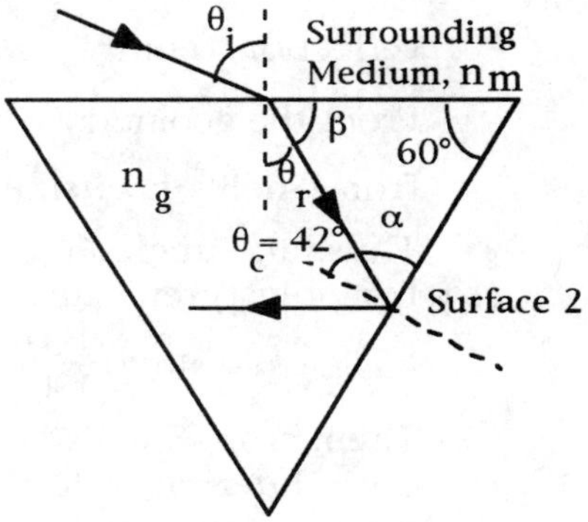

$$\sin\theta_c = \frac{n_m}{n_g} = \sin 42° = 0.669,$$

and $n_m = 0.669 n_g$.

$\alpha = 90° - \theta_c = 48°$, therefore

$\beta = 180° - 60° - \alpha = 72°$.

Thus, $\theta_r = 90° - \beta = 90° - 72° = 18°$.

Then, Snell's law applied at the first surface gives:

$n_m \sin\theta_i = n_g \sin\theta_r$

$$\sin\theta_i = \left(\frac{n_g}{0.669\, n_g}\right)\sin 18° = 0.462, \text{ or}$$

$$\theta_i = 27.5°.$$

22.40 (See sketch.)

$\alpha + (90° - \theta) + 90° = 180°$, gives

$\alpha - \theta = 0$, or, $\alpha = \theta$.

The angle of incidence at the second mirror is: $90° - \theta$, where θ is an arbitrary angle of incidence at the first mirror. Thus, we see that the emerging ray makes an angle θ with the second mirror (a vertical surface which is parallel to the normal line for the first mirror. Therefore, the emerging ray is parallel to the incident ray.

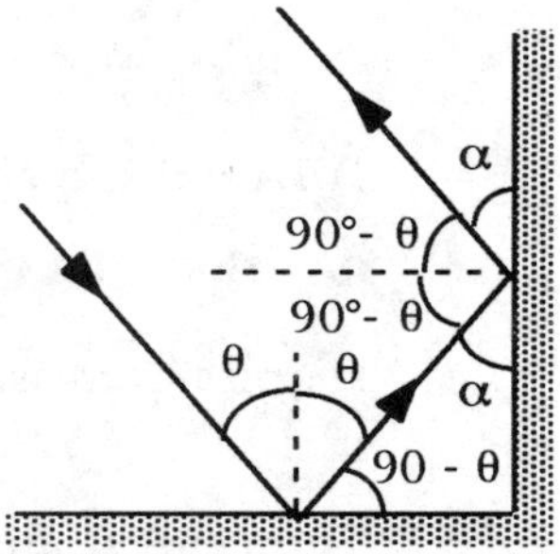

22.41 To have total internal reflection at the diagonal surface, it is necessary that the critical angle be less than the angle of incidence, 45°. From Snell's law, we have: $n_1 \sin\theta_1 = n_2 \sin\theta_2$.

At the critical angle: $\sin\theta_2 = 1$ and, $n_1 \sin\theta_c = n_2$.

Therefore, if the critical angle is less than or equal to 45°, we have

$n_1 \sin 45° \geq n_2$, or $n_2 \leq 0.707 n_1 = 0.707(1.80) = 1.27$,

where n_1 is the index of refraction of the prism material, and n_2 is the index of refraction of the surrounding fluid.

22.42 First, use Snell's law to find the angle of refraction in the ice:

$n_2 \sin\theta_2 = n_1 \sin\theta_1 = (1.00)\sin 30.0°$. Thus, $n_2 \sin\theta_2 = 0.500$.

Since the ice layer has parallel sides, the angle of incidence at the lower surface is the same as the angle of refraction at the upper surface. Then, applying Snell's law to the refraction at the ice-water boundary gives: $n_3 \sin\theta_3 = n_2 \sin\theta_2$,

or $\sin\theta_3 = \dfrac{n_2 \sin\theta_2}{n_3} = \dfrac{0.500}{1.333} = 0.375$.

Therefore, the angle of refraction in the water is

$\theta_3 = \sin^{-1}(0.375) = 22.0°$.

22.43 (a) For polystyrene surrounded by air, internal reflection requires: $\theta_3 \geq \sin^{-1}\left(\dfrac{1.00}{1.49}\right) \geq 42.2°$.

From the geometry: $\theta_2 = 90° - \theta_3 \leq 47.8°$, and

from Snell's law: $\sin\theta_1 \leq \dfrac{(1.49)\sin 47.8°}{1.00} = 1.10$

Thus, any angle $\theta_1 \leq 90.0°$ meets the criteria.

(b) For polystyrene surrounded by water, we have: $\theta_3 = \sin^{-1}\left(\dfrac{1.33}{1.49}\right) = 63.2°$, and $\theta_2 = 26.8°$.

Then, from Snell's law, $\theta_1 = 30.3°$.

(c) Total internal reflection is not possible since the beam is initially traveling in a medium of lower index of refraction.

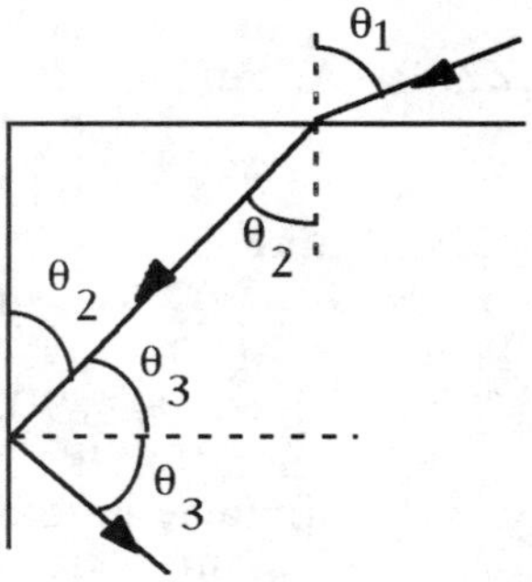

22.44 The angles of incidence and refraction at each boundary are shown in the sketch. Applying Snell's law at points A, B, and C gives:

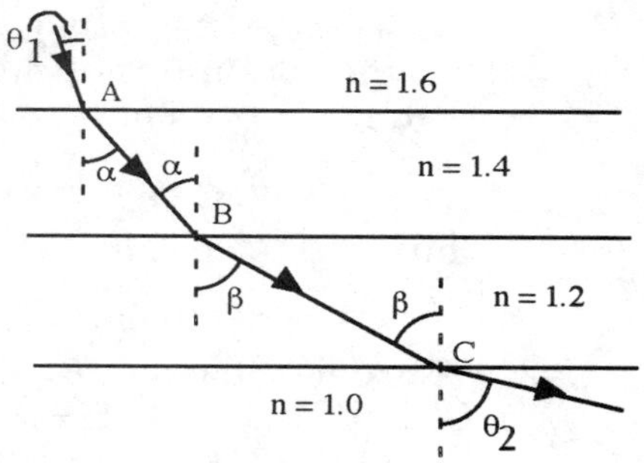

$1.60 \sin\theta_1 = 1.40 \sin\alpha$,
$1.40 \sin\alpha = 1.20 \sin\beta$,
and $1.20 \sin\beta = 1.00 \sin\theta_2$.
Combining these equations gives:

$$\sin\theta_2 = 1.60 \sin\theta_1. \qquad (1)$$

(a) If $\theta_1 = 30.0°$, then equation (1) gives:

$\sin\theta_2 = 1.60 \sin 30° = 0.800$, or

$\theta_2 = 53.1°$.

(b) At the critical angle of incidence, $\theta_2 = 90.0°$, so equation (1) gives:

$\sin\theta_1 = \dfrac{\sin 90.0°}{1.60} = 0.625$, and $\theta_1 = 38.7$. Therefore, one must have:

$\theta_1 \geq 38.7°$ to obtain total internal reflection at the last boundary.

22.45 (a) Water $= n_2 = 1.333$
From geometry $\theta_1 = 60.0°$, and the law of reflection gives $\theta_2 = 60.0°$.
Thus, $\alpha = 90° - \theta_2 = 30.0°$, and
$(\theta_3 + 90°) + 30.0° + 30.0° = 180°$
(sum of angles in triangle)
so $\theta_3 = 30.0°$.

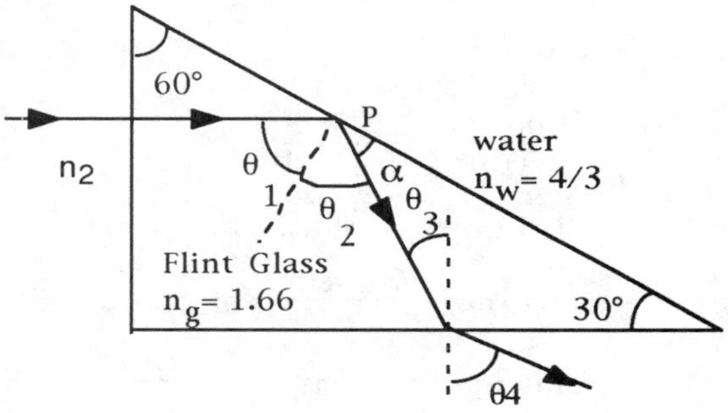

From Snell's law:

$\sin\theta_4 = (1.66)\left(\dfrac{\sin 30.0°}{1.333}\right)$, and $\theta_4 = 38.5°$.

(b) To have refraction occur at point P, it is necessary that the critical angle be greater than $\theta_1 = 60.0°$.

Thus, $\sin\theta_c = \dfrac{n_2}{n_g} > \sin 60.0°$, or $n_2 > n_g \sin 60.0°$,

or it is necessary that: $n_2 > (1.66)(0.866) = 1.44$

22.46 The sketch of the light path is shown. Starting at the lower boundary, we have: $n_3 \sin\theta_3 = n_1 \sin\theta_4$,
$1.50 \sin\theta_3 = 1.00 \sin 40.0°$, or $\theta_3 = 25.4°$.
Then at the middle boundary,
$n_2 \sin\theta_2 = n_3 \sin\theta_3$ gives:
$1.66 \sin\theta_2 = 1.50 \sin 25.4°$, and $\theta_2 = 22.8°$.
Finally, at the upper surface,
$n_1 \sin\theta_1 = n_2 \sin\theta_2$, or
$1.00 \sin\theta_1 = 1.66 \sin 22.8°$, and $\theta_1 = 40.0°$.

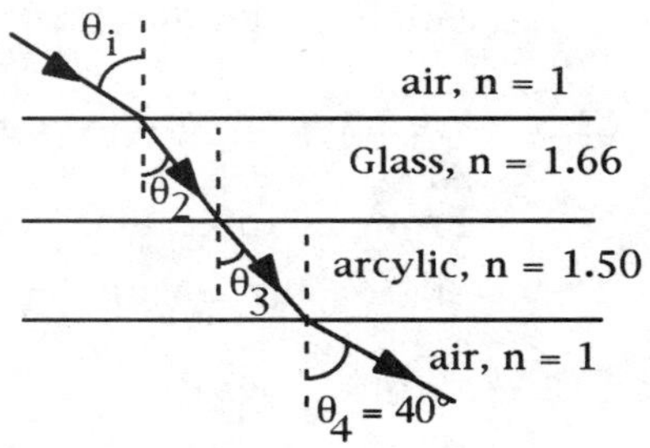

22.47 Applying Snell's law to this refraction gives:

$n_g \sin\theta_2 = n_{air} \sin\theta_1$, or $1.56 \sin\theta_2 = \sin\theta_1$.

But, the conditions of the problem are such that $\theta_1 = 2\theta_2$. Thus, we have $1.56 \sin\theta_2 = \sin(2\theta_2)$. Now use the suggested double angle formula:

$$1.56 \sin\theta_2 = 2(\sin\theta_2)(\cos\theta_2), \text{ or } \cos\theta_2 = \frac{1.56}{2} = 0.780, \text{ and } \theta_2 = 38.7°.$$

Thus, $\theta_1 = 2\theta_2 = 77.5°$.

22.48 We are to show that $B = 2A$. (See sketch.)

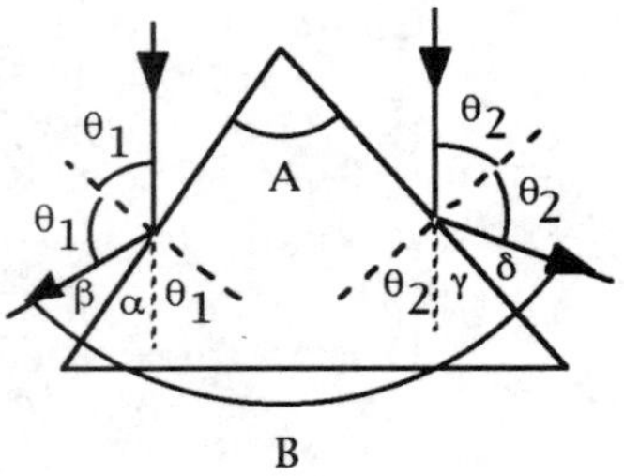

Observe that: $B = A + \beta + \delta$, and $\alpha + \gamma = A$.

But, observing the reflection on the left side:

$\beta + \theta_1 = 90°$, and $\alpha + \theta_1 = 90°$. Thus, $\beta = \alpha$.

So far, we have: $B = A + (\alpha + \delta)$, and $\alpha + \gamma = A$.

Now, consider the reflection on the right side:

$\gamma + \theta_2 = 90°$, and $\delta + \theta_2 = 90°$.

Therefore, $\gamma = \delta$ and we now see that

$B = A + (\alpha + \delta)$, and $\alpha + \delta = A$, or

$B = A + (A) = 2A$

22.49 From Snell's law we see: (see sketch)

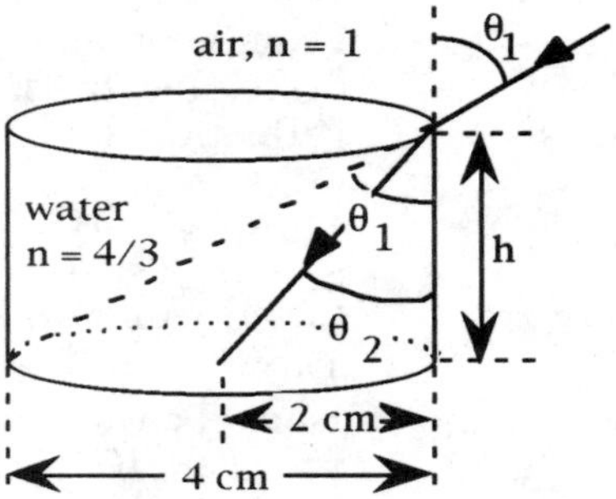

$n_2 \sin\theta_2 = n_1 \sin\theta_1$

$$\frac{\sin\theta_2}{\sin\theta_1} = \frac{1}{4/3} = \frac{3}{4}. \qquad (1)$$

Also observe that, $\tan\theta_1 = \dfrac{4.0 \text{ cm}}{h}$, and

$\tan\theta_2 = \dfrac{2.0 \text{ cm}}{h}$, or $\tan\theta_1 = 2\tan\theta_2$.

This may be written as $\dfrac{\sin\theta_1}{\cos\theta_1} = 2\left(\dfrac{\sin\theta_2}{\cos\theta_2}\right)$,

which, using Eq. (1), gives:

$$\cos\theta_2 = 2\left(\frac{\sin\theta_2}{\sin\theta_1}\right)\cos\theta_1 = 2\left(\frac{3}{4}\right)\cos\theta_1, \text{ or } \cos\theta_2 = \frac{3}{2}\cos\theta_1. \qquad (2)$$

Then, $\sin^2\theta_2 + \cos^2\theta_2 = 1$, or making use of equations (1) and (2):

$\dfrac{9}{16}\sin^2\theta_1 + \dfrac{9}{4}\cos^2\theta_1 = 1$, which reduces to: $\sin^2\theta_1 + 4\cos^2\theta_1 = \dfrac{16}{9}$, or

$(1 - \cos^2\theta_1) + 4\cos^2\theta_1 = \dfrac{16}{9}$. This can be solved for θ_1 to find: $\theta_1 = 59.4°$.

Finally, $\tan\theta_1 = \dfrac{4 \text{ cm}}{h}$ becomes $\tan 59.4° = \dfrac{4 \text{ cm}}{h}$, so $h = 2.4 \text{ cm}$.

22.50 We have: $\delta_{min} = \alpha + \varepsilon$.

Also, $\beta + \theta_2 = 90°$. (1)

From triangle abc:

$\beta + \dfrac{A}{2} + 90° = 180°$, or

$\beta + \dfrac{A}{2} = 90°$. (2)

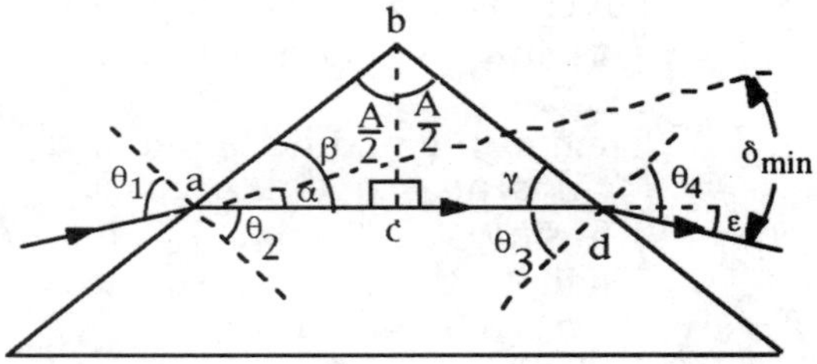

Comparing (1) and (2), we see that: $\theta_2 = \dfrac{A}{2}$. Using triangle

bcd, we have: $\frac{A}{2} + 90° + \gamma = 180°$, or $\gamma = 90° - \frac{A}{2} = 90° - \theta_2$.
Therefore, $\gamma + \theta_3 = 90°$, or $(90° - \theta_2) + \theta_3 = 90°$, which gives: $\theta_3 = \theta_2$.
We also have, $1.0 \sin\theta_1 = n \sin\theta_2$, and $n \sin\theta_3 = 1.0 \sin\theta_4$.
Since $\theta_3 = \theta_2$, these equations show that: $\theta_4 = \theta_1$.
Therefore, $\alpha = \theta_1 - \theta_2 = \theta_1 - \frac{A}{2}$, and $\varepsilon = \theta_4 - \theta_3 = \theta_1 - \theta_2 = \theta_1 - \frac{A}{2}$.

Then, $\delta_{min} = \alpha + \varepsilon = \theta_1 - \frac{A}{2} + \theta_1 - \frac{A}{2} = 2\theta_1 - A$ or, $2\theta_1 = A + \delta_{min}$.

From which, $\theta_1 = \frac{A + \delta_{min}}{2}$. Finally, from equation (1):

$\sin\theta_1 = n \sin\theta_2$, we have: $n = \frac{\sin\theta_1}{\sin\theta_2} = \sin\left(\frac{A + \delta_{min}}{2}\right) / \sin\frac{A}{2}$.

22.51 time difference = (time for light to travel 6.20 m in ice) - (time to travel 6.20 m in air) = $\Delta t = \frac{6.20\text{ m}}{v_{ice}} - \frac{6.20\text{ m}}{c}$

but $v = \frac{c}{n}$ so $\Delta t = (6.20\text{ m})\left(\frac{1.309}{c} - \frac{1}{c}\right) = \frac{(6.20\text{ m})}{c}(0.309) = 6.39 \times 10^{-9}\text{ s}$

$\Delta t = 6.39\text{ ns}$

22.52 Consider light from the bottom end of the wire that happens to be headed up along the surface of the wire before and after refraction with angle of incidence ϕ_1 and angle of refraction $\phi_2 = 60°$. Then

$1.50 \sin\phi_1 = 1 \sin 60.0°$

so $\phi_1 = 35.3°$

and $\theta = 60.0° - 35.3° = 24.7°$

22.53 Consider glass of index 1.5, 3 mm thick. The speed of light in the glass is $\frac{3.00 \times 10^8\text{ m/s}}{1.5} = 2.00 \times 10^8\text{ m/s}$

The extra travel time is $\frac{3.00 \times 10^{-3}\text{ m}}{2.00 \times 10^8\text{ m/s}} - \frac{3.00 \times 10^{-3}\text{ m}}{3.00 \times 10^8\text{ m/s}} \cong 10^{-11}\text{ s}$

For light of wavelength 600 nm in vacuum and wavelength $\frac{600\text{ nm}}{1.5} = 400\text{ nm}$ in glass, the extra path length as a number of wavelengths is $\frac{3.00 \times 10^{-3}\text{ m}}{4 \times 10^{-7}\text{ m}} - \frac{3.00 \times 10^{-3}\text{ m}}{6 \times 10^{-7}\text{ m}} \cong 10^3$ wavelengths

---

22.54 Horizontal light rays from the setting Sun pass above the hiker. The light rays are twice refracted and once reflected. Those special rays deviated by 40° and 42° reach the hiker as a rainbow. Let us consider the red outer edge. The radius R of the circle of droplets is

$R = (8.00\text{ km})(\sin 42.0°) = 5.35\text{ km}$

Then the angle ϕ, between the vertical and the radius where the bow touches the ground , is given by

$\cos\phi = \frac{2.00\text{ km}}{R} = \frac{2.00\text{ km}}{5.35\text{ km}} = 0.374$ or $\phi = 68.1°$

The angle filled by the visible bow is 360° - (2 x 68.1°) = 223.8°, so the visible bow is $\frac{223.8°}{360°} = 62.2\%$ of a circle.

22.55 The angle of refraction as the light enters the slab is: $1.48\sin\alpha = (1)\sin 50.0°$, or $\alpha = 31.17°$. The horizontal distance traveled for each internal reflection that occurs (see sketch) is $2d$, where:

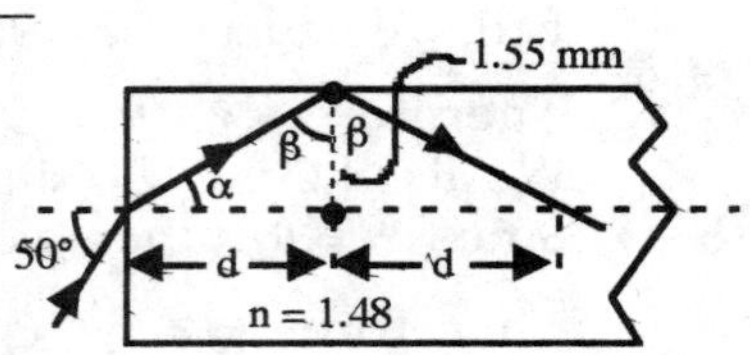

$$\tan\alpha = \frac{1.55\ \text{m}}{d}. \text{ Thus, } \quad 2d = \frac{2(1.55\ \text{mm})}{\tan 31.17°},$$

which gives: $2d = 5.125$ mm. Therefore, the number of internal reflections made before reaching the other end of the slab is

$$N = \frac{L}{2d}, \text{ or } \quad N = \frac{420\ \text{mm}}{5.125\ \text{mm}} = 82.$$

22.56 As shown in the sketch, the angle of incidence at point A is:

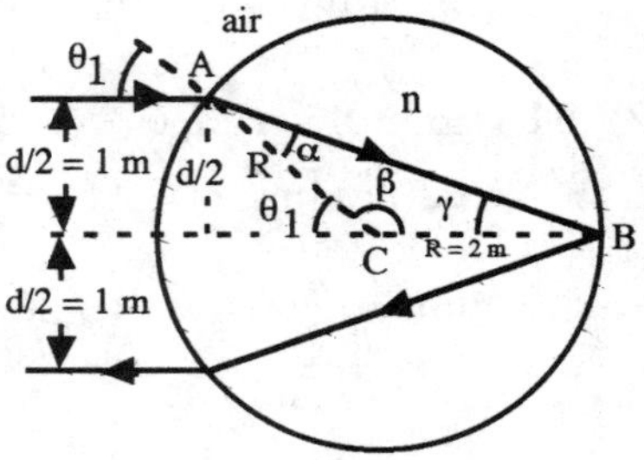

$$\sin\theta_1 = \frac{(d/2)}{R} = \frac{1.00\ \text{m}}{2.00\ \text{m}} = 0.50,$$

or $\theta_1 = 30.0°$.

If the emerging ray is to be parallel to the incident ray, the light path must be symmetric about the center line CB of the cylinder. In the isosceles triangle ABC, $\gamma = \alpha$ and, $\beta = 180° - \theta_1$.

Since $\alpha + \beta + \gamma = 180°$, this gives:

$$\alpha + \alpha + 180° - \theta_1 = 180°, \text{ so } \quad 2\alpha - \theta_1 = 0, \text{ or } \quad \alpha = \frac{\theta_1}{2}.$$

Since $\theta_1 = 30.0°$, $\alpha = 15.0°$. Applying Snell's law at point A, we find:

$$n\sin\alpha = 1.00\sin\theta_1, \text{ or } \quad n = \frac{\sin\theta_1}{\sin\alpha} = \frac{\sin 30.0°}{\sin 15.0°} = 1.93.$$

22.57 (a) At the boundary of the air and glass, the critical angle is defined by:

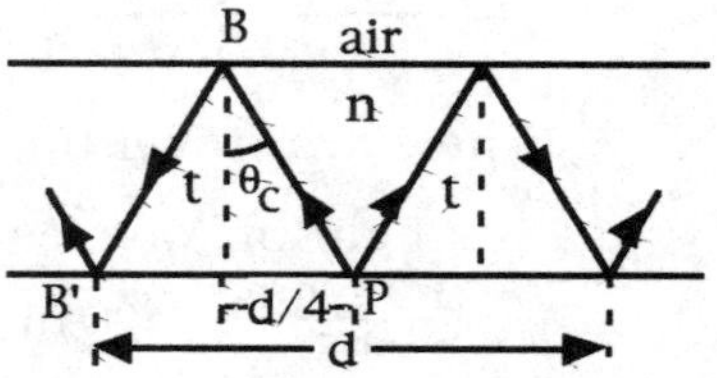

$$n\sin\theta_c = 1\sin 90°, \text{ or } \quad \sin\theta_c = \frac{1}{n}, \quad (1)$$

where n is the index of refraction of the glass. Now consider the critical ray PBB' shown in the diagram and observe

that: $\tan\theta_c = \frac{(d/4)}{t}$, or $\frac{\sin\theta_c}{\cos\theta_c} = \frac{d}{4t}$. Squaring both sides of this

equation gives: $\frac{\sin^2\theta_c}{\cos^2\theta_c} = \frac{\sin^2\theta_c}{1 - \sin^2\theta_c} = \left(\frac{d}{4t}\right)^2$, and solving for n

gives: $n = \sqrt{1 + (4t/d)^2}$.

(b) Solving for d, we have: $d = \frac{4t}{\sqrt{n^2 - 1}}$. (2)

Thus, if $n = 1.52$ and $t = 0.600$ cm, we obtain:

$$d = \frac{4(0.600\ \text{cm})}{\sqrt{(1.52)^2 - 1}} = 2.10\ \text{cm}.$$

(c) Since violet light has a larger index of refraction, it will lead to a smaller critical angle so that the inner edge of the white halo will be tinged with violet light.

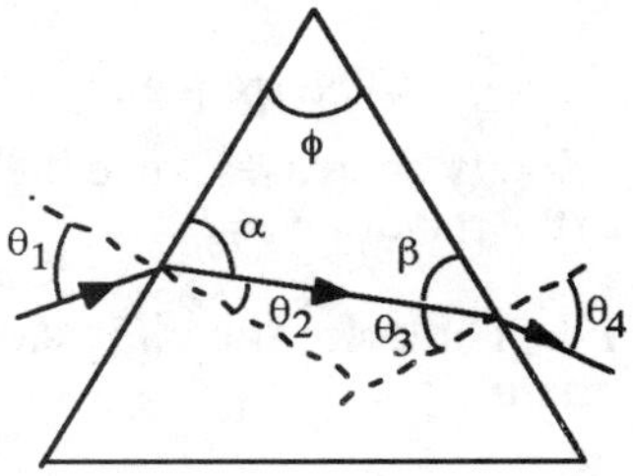

22.58 Refer to the sketch.
We see that: $\theta_2 + \alpha = 90°$,
and $\theta_3 + \beta = 90°$, so $\theta_2 + \theta_3 + \alpha + \beta = 180°$.
Also, from the figure we see: $\alpha + \beta + \phi = 180°$.
Therefore, $\phi = \theta_2 + \theta_3$.
By applying Snell's law at the first and second surfaces, we find: $\theta_2 = \sin^{-1}\left(\frac{\sin\theta_1}{n}\right)$,
and $\theta_3 = \sin^{-1}\left(\frac{\sin\theta_4}{n}\right)$. Substituting these values into the expression for ϕ yields: $\phi = \sin^{-1}\left(\frac{\sin\theta_1}{n}\right) + \sin^{-1}\left(\frac{\sin\theta_4}{n}\right)$. The limiting condition for internal reflection at the second surface is θ_4 approaches 90°. Under these conditions we have $\phi = \sin^{-1}\left(\sin\theta_1/n\right) + \sin^{-1}(1/n)$, or

$\sin\theta_1 = n\sin\left(\phi - \sin^{-1}\frac{1}{n}\right)$. Using the trigonometry identity for the sine of the difference of two angles, this may be written as:

$\sin\theta_1 = n\left\{\sin\phi \cos[\sin^{-1}\left(\frac{1}{n}\right)] - \cos\phi \sin[\sin^{-1}\left(\frac{1}{n}\right)]\right\}$. But,

$\sin[\sin^{-1}\left(\frac{1}{n}\right)] = \frac{1}{n}$ and $\cos[\sin^{-1}\left(\frac{1}{n}\right)] = \frac{(n^2 - 1)^{1/2}}{n}$. Therefore,

$\sin\theta_1 = (n^2 - 1)^{1/2}\sin\phi - \cos\phi$ or $\theta_1 = \sin^{-1}\left[(n^2 - 1)^{1/2}\sin\phi - \cos\phi\right]$

ANSWERS TO CONCEPTUAL QUESTIONS

2. At the altitude of the plane the surface of the Earth does not block off the lower half of the rainbow. Thus, you can see the full circle. You can show such a rainbow to your children by letting them climb a stepladder above a garden sprinkler in the middle of a sunny day.

4. The spectrum of the light sent back to you from a drop at the top of the rainbow arrives such that the red light (deviated by an angle of 42°) strikes the eye while the violet light (deviated by 40°) passes over your head. Thus, the top of the rainbow looks red. At the bottom of the bow, violet light arrives at your eye and red light is deviated toward the ground. Thus, the bottom part of the bow appears violet.

6. A mirage occurs when light changes direction as it moves between batches of air having different indices of refraction. The different indices of refraction occur because the air has different densities at different temperatures. Two images are seen. One from a direct path from the object to you, and the second arriving by refracted rays heading toward the earth but refracted to your eye. The latter produces an inverted image of the original object. On a hot day, the Sun makes the surface of blacktop hot, so the air is hot directly above it, becoming cooler as one moves higher into the sky. The water we see far in front of us is an image of the blue sky. Adding to the effect is the effect that the image shimmers as the air changes in temperature, adding to the appearance of moving water.

8. The wavelength decreases since it depends on the index of refraction of the medium as $\lambda n = \frac{\lambda_0}{n}$. The frequency does not change; it depends on the nature of the light source. The velocity decreases since it also depends on the index of refraction of the medium according to the relation $v = c/n$. .

10. The color traveling slowest is bent the most. Thus, X travels more slowly in the glass prism.

12. Total internal reflection occurs only when light attempts to move from a medium of high index of refraction to a medium of lower index of refraction. Thus, light moving from air ($n = 1$) to water ($n = 1.33$) cannot undergo total internal reflection.

14. Objects beneath the surface of water appear to be raised toward the surface by refraction. Thus, the bottom of the oar appears to be closer to the surface than it really is, and the oar looks to be bent.

CHAPTER TWENTY-THREE SOLUTIONS

Chapter Twenty-Three Readings

Ansbacher, T.H., "Left-Right Semantics?" *The Physics Teacher*, 30, 70, 1992.

Fraser, A.B, and Hirsch, M.W., *Mirages*, Springer-Verlag, 1975.

Galili, I., Goldberg, F. and Bendall, S., "Some Reflections on Plane Mirrors and Images," *The Physics Teacher*, 29, 471, 1991.

Galili, I., Bendall, S. and Goldberg, F., "Author's Response to 'Left-Right Semantics?'", *The Physics Teacher*, 30, 70, 1992.

Galili, I. and Goldberg, F., "Left-Right Conversions in a Plane Mirror," *The Physics Teacher*, 31, 463, 1993.

Greenslade, T.B., "Multiple Image in Plane Mirrors," *The Physics Teacher*, January 1982, p. 29.

Jones, R.C., "How Images are Detected," *Scientific American*, September 1968, p. 111.

Smith, F.D., "How Images are Formed," *Scientific American*, September 1968, p. 97.

Thomas, D.E., "Mirror Images," *Scientific American*, December 1980, p. 206.

Veldkamp, W.B, and McHugh, T.J., "Binary Optics," *Scientific American*, May 1992, p. 92.

Winston, R., "Nonimaging Optics," *Scientific American*, March 1991, p. 76.

23.1 (1) The first image in the left mirror is 5.00 ft behind the mirror, or 10.0 ft from the position of the person.

(2) The first image in the right mirror is located 10.0 ft behind the right mirror, but this location is 25.0 ft from the left mirror. Thus, the second image in the left mirror is 25.0 ft behind the mirror, or 30.0 ft from the person.

(3) The first image in the left mirror serves as an object for the right mirror. It is located 20 ft in front of the right mirror and forms an image 20 ft behind that mirror. This image then serves as an object for, and forms an image in, the left mirror. The distance from this image to the left mirror is 35.0 ft. The third image in the left mirror is, thus, 35.0 ft behind the mirror, or 40.0 ft from the person.

23.2 (See sketch.)

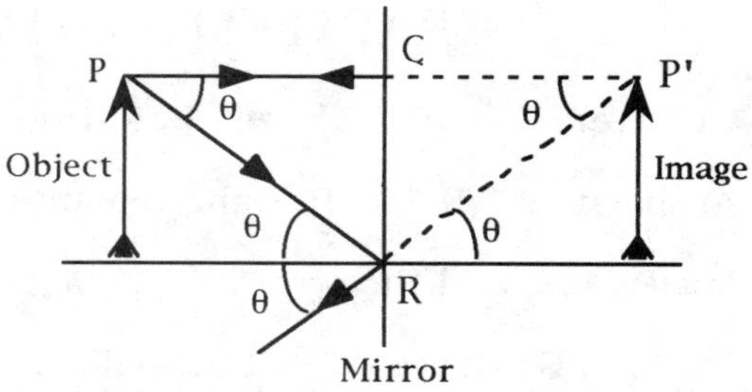

(1) angle PRQ = angle P'RQ
($90° - \theta = 90° - \theta$)

(2) angle PQR = angle P'QR
(both 90°)

(3) side QR = side QR

Therefore, triangle PQR is congruent to triangle P'QR
(angle-side-angle)

Hence, the distance PQ = QP'
or, the image is as far behind the mirror as the object is in front of the mirror.

23.3 (a) For a plane mirror, R is infinite.

(b) $\frac{1}{p} + \frac{1}{q} = \frac{2}{R} = 0$, or $q = -p$. Additionally, $M = -\left(\frac{q}{p}\right) = -\left(\frac{-p}{p}\right) = +1$.

(c) Since, $q = -p$, the image is virtual and as far behind the mirror as the object is in front of the mirror. Also, since $M = +1$, the image is erect and the same size as the object. These agree with the earlier discussion of plane mirrors.

23.4 From the sign conventions for convex mirrors, we see that $R = -3.00$ cm and $f = -1.50$ cm. Also, $p = 10.0$ cm. Thus,

$$\frac{1}{q} = \frac{1}{f} - \frac{1}{p} = \frac{1}{-1.50\ \text{cm}} - \frac{1}{10.0\ \text{cm}} = -\frac{23.0}{30.0\ \text{cm}},\ \text{and}\quad q = -1.30\ \text{cm}.$$

$$M = -\frac{q}{p} = -\left(\frac{-1.30\ \text{cm}}{10.0\ \text{cm}}\right) = +0.130.$$

23.5 For a concave mirror, both R and f are positive. Also, $f = \frac{R}{2} = 10.0$ cm.

The mirror equation gives: $\frac{1}{q} = \frac{1}{f} - \frac{1}{p}$,

or $q = \frac{pf}{p - f} = \frac{p(10.0\ \text{cm})}{p - (10.0\ \text{cm})}$

(a) If $p = 40.0$ cm, $q = \frac{(40.0\ \text{cm})(10.0\ \text{cm})}{(40.0\ \text{cm}) - (10\ \text{cm})} = 13.3$ cm,

$M = -\frac{q}{p} = -\frac{13.3\ \text{cm}}{40.0\ \text{cm}} = -0.333$.

The image is 13.3 cm in front of the mirror, is real, and inverted.

(b) If $p = 20.0$ cm, $q = \frac{(20.0\ \text{cm})(10.0\ \text{cm})}{(20.0\ \text{cm}) - (10\ \text{cm})} = 20.0$ cm,

$M = -\frac{q}{p} = -\frac{20.0\ \text{cm}}{20.0\ \text{cm}} = -1.00$.

The image is 20 cm in front of the mirror, is real, and inverted.

(c) If $p = 10.0$ cm, $q = \frac{(10.0\ \text{cm})(10.0\ \text{cm})}{(10.0\ \text{cm}) - (10.0\ \text{cm})} = \infty$,

No image is formed. The rays are reflected parallel to each other.

23.6 (a) $\frac{1}{f} = \frac{1}{p} + \frac{1}{q} = \frac{1}{1.00\ \text{cm}} - \frac{1}{10.0\ \text{cm}}$, or $f = 1.11$ cm and $R = 2f = 2.22$ cm.

(b) $M = -\left(\frac{q}{p}\right) = -\left(\frac{-10.0\ \text{cm}}{1.00\ \text{cm}}\right) = +10.0.$

23.7 $f = R/2 = -0.275$ cm. $\frac{1}{q} = \frac{1}{f} - \frac{1}{p} = -\frac{1}{0.275\ \text{m}} - \frac{1}{10.0\ \text{m}}$ gives $q = -0.268$ m.

Thus, the image is virtual. $M = -\frac{q}{p} = -\left(\frac{-0.268}{10.0\ \text{m}}\right) = 0.0268$

Thus, the image is erect ($M > 0$).

23.8 Since the image is projected on a screen, it is a real image. Therefore, q is positive. We have: $\frac{1}{f} = \frac{1}{p} + \frac{1}{q} = \frac{1}{10.0\ \text{cm}} + \frac{1}{200\ \text{cm}} = \frac{+21}{200\ \text{cm}}$, and $f = +9.52$ cm. Thus, because f is positive, we need a concave mirror.

$M = -\frac{q}{p} = -\frac{200\ \text{cm}}{10.0\ \text{cm}} = -20.0.$

23.9 We know that for a convex mirror R and f are negative, and we also are given that $M = 1/2$. M is positive because convex mirrors only form erect virtual images of real objects. Therefore, $M = -\frac{q}{p} = \frac{1}{2}$, or $q = -\frac{p}{2}$.

Thus, $\frac{1}{p} = \frac{1}{f} - \frac{1}{q} = \frac{1}{-20.0\ \text{cm}} - \left(\frac{-2}{p}\right)$, which gives: $p = 20.0$ cm.

The object should be 20.0 cm in front of the mirror.

23.10 Since we have a real object and want a magnified image, the mirror must be concave. (A convex mirror forms diminished images of all real objects.) Since image is erect, it must be virtual. (All real images formed by concave mirrors of real objects are inverted.)

Thus, $q < 0$, $f > 0$, and $p = 10$ cm.

$M = \frac{h'}{h} = \frac{4.00\ \text{cm}}{2.00\ \text{cm}} = +2.00 = -\frac{q}{p'}$

$Q = -20.0$ cm.

Thus, $\frac{1}{f} = \frac{1}{p} + \frac{1}{q} = \frac{1}{10.0\ \text{cm}} + \left(\frac{1}{-20.0\ \text{cm}}\right)$, or $f = 20.0$ cm, and $R = 2f =$ 40.0 cm.

23.11 For a concave mirror, R and f are positive. Also, $M = \frac{h'}{h} = -\frac{q}{p}$. We are given that $h' = 5.0$ cm (erect...thus h' is positive), $h = 2.0$ cm, and $p = 3.0$ cm. Therefore, $q = -p\left(\frac{h'}{h}\right) = -(3.0\ \text{cm})\left(\frac{5.0\ \text{cm}}{2.0\ \text{cm}}\right) =$ -7.5 cm.

And, $\frac{1}{f} = \frac{1}{p} + \frac{1}{q} = \frac{1}{3.0\ \text{cm}} - \frac{1}{7.5\ \text{cm}} = \frac{3.0}{15\ \text{cm}}$, and $f = 5.0$ cm.

23.12 Realize that the nearer image ($q = -10.0$ cm) occurs when using the convex side of the hubcap. Applying the mirror equation to both cases gives:

(concave side: $f = \frac{|R|}{2}$, $q = -30.0$ cm):

$$\frac{1}{p}+\frac{1}{q}=\frac{2}{|R|},\ \text{or}\ \frac{2}{|R|}=\frac{1}{p}+\left(\frac{1}{-30.0}\right) \qquad (1)$$

(convex side: $f=-\frac{|R|}{2}$, $q=-10.0\text{ cm}$):

$$\frac{1}{p}+\frac{1}{q}=-\frac{2}{|R|},\ \text{or}\ \frac{2}{|R|}=-\left(\frac{1}{p}\right)-\left(\frac{1}{-10.0}\right) \qquad (2)$$

(a) Equating equations (1) and (2) gives: $\frac{2}{p}=\frac{1}{10.0}+\frac{1}{30.0}$,
or $p=+15.0\text{ cm}$.
Thus, his face is 15.0 cm in front of the hubcap.

(b) Using the above result (p = 15 cm) in equation (1) gives:
$\frac{2}{|R|}=\frac{1}{15.0}+\left(\frac{1}{-30.0}\right)$, or $\frac{2}{|R|}=\frac{1}{30.0\text{ cm}}$, and $|R|=60.0\text{ cm}$.
The radius of the hubcap is 60.0 cm

23.13 We know that R and f are positive for a concave mirror. Also, since a concave mirror only forms magnified, erect images when the image is virtual, we know that q is negative.

Thus, $M=2$, and $M=-\frac{q}{p}=2.0$, or $q=-2.0(25\text{ cm})=-50\text{ cm}$.

Thus, $\frac{1}{f}=\frac{1}{p}+\frac{1}{q}=\frac{1}{25\text{ cm}}+\left(\frac{1}{-50\text{ cm}}\right)=\frac{1}{50\text{ cm}}$, and $f=50\text{ cm}$.

But, $R=2f=100\text{ cm}=1.0\text{ m}$.

23.14 A convex mirror has R and f negative. Thus, $f=\frac{R}{2}=-5.00\text{ cm}$. For a virtual image, q is negative. Therefore, $M=-\frac{q}{p}=\frac{1}{3}$, and $q=-\frac{p}{3}$.

Therefore, $\frac{1}{f}=\frac{1}{p}+\frac{1}{q}$ becomes $\frac{1}{-5.00\text{ cm}}=\frac{1}{p}-\frac{3}{p}$, or $p=10.0\text{ cm}$.

The object must be 10.0 cm in front of the mirror.

23.15 $\frac{1}{f}=\frac{1}{p}+\frac{1}{q}=\frac{1}{1.52\text{ m}}+\frac{1}{0.180\text{ m}}$, or $f=0.161\ m=16.1\text{ cm}$.

Now, to get an erect image which is twice the size of the object, we need: $M=-\frac{q}{p}=+2.00$, so $q=-2.00p$.

Thus, $\frac{1}{p}+\frac{1}{q}=\frac{1}{f}$ becomes $\frac{1}{p}-\frac{1}{2p}=\frac{1}{f}$, or $p=\frac{f}{2}$.

Thus, $p=\frac{16.1\text{ cm}}{2}=8.05\text{ cm}$ is the required object distance.

23.16 For a concave mirror, R and f are positive. Also, for an erect image M is positive. Therefore, $M=-\frac{q}{p}=4$, or $q=-4p$.

$\frac{1}{f}=\frac{1}{p}+\frac{1}{q}$ becomes: $\frac{1}{40.0\text{ cm}}=\frac{1}{p}-\frac{1}{4p}=\frac{3}{4p}$, giving $p=30.0\text{ cm}$.

23.17 For a convex mirror, R and f are negative. Since we have a real object, the image will be virtual and erect. Thus, q is negative and the magnification is positive. $M = -\left(\frac{q}{p}\right) = \frac{1}{2}$, and $q = -\left(\frac{p}{2}\right) = -5.00\text{ cm}$.

Thus, $\frac{1}{f} = \frac{1}{p} + \frac{1}{q} = \frac{1}{10.0\text{ cm}} + \frac{1}{-5.00\text{ cm}} = -\frac{1}{10.0\text{ cm}}$, and $f = -10.0\text{ cm}$.

But, $R = 2f$. Therefore, the radius of curvature is $R = -20.0\text{ cm}$.

23.18 We know that R and f are positive for a concave mirror, and we are given that $p = 30.0\text{ cm}$, and $M = -4.00$. ($M < 0$ since the only magnified real images formed by a concave mirror of real objects are inverted images.) Hence, $M = -\frac{q}{p} = -4.00$, or $q = 4p$.

Since $p = 30.0\text{ cm}$, $q = 120\text{ cm}$.

Thus, $\frac{1}{f} = \frac{1}{p} + \frac{1}{q} = \frac{1}{30.0\text{ cm}} + \frac{1}{120\text{ cm}} = \frac{5}{120\text{ cm}}$, giving $f = 24.0\text{ cm}$, and $R = 2f = 48.0\text{ cm}$.

23.19 (a) In this case, both the object and the image are real. To form a real image of a real object, a concave mirror must be used.

(b) We are given $q = +5.0\text{ m}$, and $M = -\frac{q}{p} = -5.0$ (a concave mirror forms inverted real images, hence the negative sign on the value of the magnification.) Therefore, $q = 5p$, and since we know that $q = 5.0\text{ m}$, we find that $p = 1.0\text{ m}$ as the distance the object must be from the mirror.

23.20 We are given that $q = -35.0\text{ cm}$. The negative sign arises because we have a virtual image on the same side of the boundary as is the object. $p = -\frac{n_1}{n_2} q = -\frac{1.50}{1.00}(-35.0\text{ cm}) = 52.5\text{ cm}$. The benzene is 52.5 cm deep.

23.21 $q = -\frac{n_2}{n_1} p = -\frac{1}{1.309}(50.0\text{ cm}) = -38.2\text{ cm}$. Thus, the virtual image of the dust speck is 38.2 cm below the top surface of the ice.

23.22 (a) For a plane refracting surface, we have: $q = -\frac{n_2}{n_1} p = -\frac{3}{4} p$.

Thus, for $p = 2.00\text{ m}$, $q = -1.50\text{ m}$. The pool appears to be 1.50 m deep.

(b) If the pool is half filled, $p = 1.00\text{ m}$, and $q = -\frac{3}{4}(1.00\text{ m}) = -0.75\text{ m}$.

The bottom surface appears to be 0.75 m below the water surface, or 1.75 m below ground level (or the top of the pool).

23.23 We have $R = -4.0\text{ cm}$ (center of curvature is on side light is coming from), and $p = 4.0\text{ cm}$. Thus, $\frac{n_1}{p} + \frac{n_2}{q} = \frac{n_2 - n_1}{R}$ becomes:

$\frac{1.5}{4.0\text{ cm}} + \frac{1}{q} = \frac{1.0 - 1.5}{-4.0\text{ cm}}$. This gives $q = -4.0\text{ cm}$. Note that the location of the virtual image is at the same position as the object.

$M = \frac{h'}{h} = -\left(\frac{n_1}{n_2}\right)\left(\frac{q}{p}\right)$ gives: $\frac{h'}{2.5\ \text{mm}} = -\frac{(1.5)(-4\ \text{cm})}{(1.0)(4\ \text{cm})} = 1.5$, or $h' = 3.8\ \text{mm}$.

23.24 We use: $\frac{n_1}{p} + \frac{n_2}{q} = \frac{n_2 - n_1}{R}$.

(a) $\frac{1}{20.0\ \text{cm}} + \frac{1.50}{q} = \frac{0.50}{8.0\ \text{cm}}$ gives $q = 120\ \text{cm}$.

(b) $\frac{1}{8.00\ \text{cm}} + \frac{1.50}{q} = \frac{0.50}{8.00\ \text{cm}}$ gives $q = -24.0\ \text{cm}$.

(c) $\frac{1}{4.00\ \text{cm}} + \frac{1.50}{q} = \frac{0.50}{8.00\ \text{cm}}$ gives $q = -8.00\ \text{cm}$.

(d) $\frac{1}{2.00\ \text{cm}} + \frac{1.50}{q} = \frac{0.50}{8.00\ \text{cm}}$ gives $q = -3.43\ \text{cm}$.

23.25 $\frac{n_1}{p} + \frac{n_2}{q} = \frac{n_2 - n_1}{R}$. But the object is at infinity, and $q = 2R$, so

$\frac{n_2}{2R} = \frac{n_2 - 1.00}{R}$, which gives: $n_2 = 2.00$

23.26 Use $\frac{n_1}{p} + \frac{n_2}{q} = \frac{n_2 - n_1}{R}$ to find the apparent depth of the top and the bottom of the glass plate first, then subtract to find the apparent thickness. Note that for a plane surface, $R = \infty$, so we have: $q = -\frac{n_2}{n_1}p$.

First consider the bottom of the plate as the object and locate the image formed by refraction at the glass-water boundary. Here, $p = 8.00\ \text{cm}$, $n_1 = 1.66$, and $n_2 = 1.333$, so $q_{1b} = -\left(\frac{1.333}{1.66}\right)(8.00\ \text{cm}) = -6.42\ \text{cm}$.

Now use this image as the object for refraction at the water-air boundary. In this case, $p = 12.0\ \text{cm} + 6.42\ \text{cm} = 18.42\ \text{cm}$, $n_1 = 1.333$, and $n_2 = 1.0$. Thus, $q_{2b} = -\left(\frac{1.00}{1.333}\right)(18.42\ \text{cm}) = -13.8\ \text{cm}$. The bottom of the plate appears to be 13.8 cm below the water surface.

Now, locate the image formed of the top of the plate by refraction at the water-air boundary. Here $p = 12.0\ \text{cm}$, $n_1 = 1.333$, and $n_2 = 1.00$, so $q_{2t} = -\left(\frac{1.00}{1.333}\right)(12.0\ \text{cm}) = -9.00\ \text{cm}$ below the water surface and the apparent thickness of the plate is:

$t = q_{2b} - q_{2t} = 13.8\ \text{cm} - 9.00\ \text{cm} = 4.80\ \text{cm}$.

23.27 $\frac{1}{f} = (n - 1)\left(\frac{1}{R_1} - \frac{1}{R_2}\right)$ becomes: $\frac{1}{60.0\ \text{cm}} = (n - 1)\left(\frac{1}{52.5\ \text{cm}} - \frac{1}{-61.9\ \text{cm}}\right)$, which gives $n = 1.47$.

23.28 $\frac{1}{f} = (n - 1)\left(\frac{1}{R_1} - \frac{1}{R_2}\right)$ becomes: $\frac{1}{25.0\ \text{cm}} = 0.58\left(\frac{1}{R_1} - \frac{1}{1.80\ \text{cm}}\right)$, which gives $R_1 = 1.60\ \text{cm}$.

23.29 (a) We find the focal length from:

$\frac{1}{f} = (n - 1)\left(\frac{1}{R_1} - \frac{1}{R_2}\right) = 0.50\left(\frac{1}{15.0\ \text{cm}} - \frac{1}{-10.0\ \text{cm}}\right)$, or $f = 12.0$ cm.

(b) When $p = \infty$, $\frac{1}{q} = \frac{1}{f}$, or $q = f = 12.0$ cm.

(c) $\frac{1}{q} = \frac{1}{f} - \frac{1}{p} = \frac{1}{12.0\ \text{cm}} - \frac{1}{36.0\ \text{cm}} = \frac{2}{36.0\ \text{cm}}$, or $q = 18.0$ cm.

(d) $\frac{1}{q} = \frac{1}{f} - \frac{1}{p} = \frac{1}{12.0\ \text{cm}} - \frac{1}{12.0\ \text{cm}} = 0$, or q = infinity (no image formed)

(e) $\frac{1}{q} = \frac{1}{f} - \frac{1}{p} = \frac{1}{12.0\ \text{cm}} - \frac{1}{6.00\ \text{cm}} = -\frac{1}{12.0\ \text{cm}}$, gives $q = -12.0$ cm.

23.30 For a converging lens, f is positive. We use: $\frac{1}{p} + \frac{1}{q} = \frac{1}{f}$.

(a) $\frac{1}{q} = \frac{1}{f} - \frac{1}{p} = \frac{1}{20.0\ \text{cm}} - \frac{1}{40.0\ \text{cm}} = \frac{1}{40.0\ \text{cm}}$, or $q = 40.0$ cm.

$M = -\frac{q}{p} = -\frac{40.0}{40.0} = -1.00$. (real, inverted, and 40.0 cm past the lens)

(b) $\frac{1}{q} = \frac{1}{f} - \frac{1}{p} = \frac{1}{20.0\ \text{cm}} - \frac{1}{20.0\ \text{cm}} = 0$, giving q = infinity.

No image is formed. (parallel rays emerge from the lens)

(c) $\frac{1}{q} = \frac{1}{f} - \frac{1}{p} = \frac{1}{20.0\ \text{cm}} - \frac{1}{10.0\ \text{cm}} = -\frac{1}{20.0\ \text{cm}}$, or $q = -20.0$ cm.

$M = -\frac{q}{p} = -\left(\frac{-20.0}{10.0}\right) = 2.00$. (erect, virtual, and 20.0 cm in front of lens)

23.31 (a) $\frac{1}{f} = (n - 1)\left(\frac{1}{R_1} - \frac{1}{R_2}\right) = 0.50\left(-\frac{1}{15.0\ \text{cm}} - \frac{1}{10.0\ \text{cm}}\right)$, or $f = -12.0$ cm.

(b) When p = infinity, $q = f = -12.0$ cm.

(c) $p = 36.0$ cm, $\frac{1}{q} = \frac{1}{f} - \frac{1}{p} = -\frac{1}{12.0\ \text{cm}} - \frac{1}{36.0\ \text{cm}} = -\frac{1}{9.00\ \text{cm}}$, or $q = -9.00$ cm.

(d) $p = 12.0$ cm, $\frac{1}{q} = \frac{1}{f} - \frac{1}{p} = -\frac{1}{12.0\ \text{cm}} - \frac{1}{12.0\ \text{cm}} = -\frac{1}{6.00\ \text{cm}}$, or $q = -6.00$ cm.

(e) $p = 6.00$ cm, $\frac{1}{q} = \frac{1}{f} - \frac{1}{p} = -\frac{1}{12.0\ \text{cm}} - \frac{1}{6.00\ \text{cm}} = -\frac{1}{4.00\ \text{cm}}$, or $q = -4.00$ cm.

23.32 For a diverging lens, f is negative.

(a) $\frac{1}{q} = \frac{1}{f} - \frac{1}{p} = -\frac{1}{20.0\ \text{cm}} - \frac{1}{40.0\ \text{cm}} = -\frac{3}{40.0\ \text{cm}}$, or $q = -13.3$ cm.

$M = -\frac{q}{p} = -\frac{-13.3\ \text{cm}}{40\ \text{cm}} = \frac{1}{3}$.

The image is virtual, erect, and 13.3 cm in front of the lens.

(b) $\frac{1}{q} = \frac{1}{f} - \frac{1}{p} = -\frac{1}{20.0\ \text{cm}} - \frac{1}{20.0\ \text{cm}} = -\frac{1}{10.0\ \text{cm}}$, or $q = -10.0$ cm.

$M = -\frac{q}{p} = -\frac{-10.0\ \text{cm}}{20.0\ \text{cm}} = \frac{1}{2}$

The image is virtual, erect, and 10 cm in front of the lens.

(c) $\frac{1}{q}=\frac{1}{f}-\frac{1}{p}=-\frac{1}{20.0\text{ cm}}-\frac{1}{10.0\text{ cm}}=-\frac{3}{20.0\text{ cm}}$, or $q=-6.67$ cm.

$M=-\frac{q}{p}=-\frac{-6.67\text{ cm}}{10.0\text{ cm}}=0.667.$

The image is virtual, erect, and 6.67 cm in front of the lens.

23.33 We want $|M|=1$. Using $M=-\left(\frac{q}{p}\right)$, and $\frac{1}{p}+\frac{1}{q}=\frac{1}{f}$, we have:

$\frac{1}{p}-\frac{1}{Mp}=\frac{1}{f}$, or $p=f\left(1-\frac{1}{M}\right)$.

(a) converging lens: $p=(12.00\text{ cm})\left(1-\frac{1}{M}\right)$.

If $M=+1$, $p=0$ (object against lens).
If $M=-1$, $p=24.0$ cm

(b) diverging lens: $p=(-12.00\text{ cm})\left(1-\frac{1}{M}\right)$.

If $M=+1$, $p=0$ (object against lens).
If $M=-1$, $p=-24.0$ cm.

Note that in both cases, M approaches +1.00 only in the limit as p approaches zero. Note also that in part (b), the object must be virtual to obtain $M=-1.00$.

23.34 We want $M=+2.00$, so $M=-\left(\frac{q}{p}\right)=2.00$, or $q=-2.00p$.

$\frac{1}{p}+\frac{1}{q}=\frac{1}{f}$ becomes: $\frac{1}{p}+\frac{1}{-2.00p}=\frac{1}{+15.0\text{ cm}}$, giving $p=+7.50$ cm.

23.35 We must first realize that we are looking at an erect, magnified, virtual image. Thus, we have a real object located inside the focal point of a converging lens. Thus, $p>0$, $q<0$, and $f>0$.

$M=2.00=-\left(\frac{q}{p}\right)$, or $q=-2.00p=-2(2.84\text{ cm})=-5.68$ cm.

Thus, $\frac{1}{p}+\frac{1}{q}=\frac{1}{f}$, or $\frac{1}{f}=\frac{1}{2.84\text{ cm}}-\frac{1}{5.68\text{ cm}}$, giving $f=5.68$ cm.

23.36 Start with the thin lens equation $\frac{1}{p}+\frac{1}{q}=\frac{1}{f}$ and solve for the image distance to get $q=\frac{pf}{p-f}$. In this case, $f=10.0$ cm and the object distance can vary from a minimum of $p=10.2$ cm to a maximum of $p=11.0$ cm. When $p=11.0$ cm, $q=\frac{(11.0\text{ cm})(10.0\text{ cm})}{11.0\text{ cm}-10.0\text{ cm}}=110$ cm. When $p=10.2$ cm, $q=\frac{(10.2\text{ cm})(10.0\text{ cm})}{10.2\text{ cm}-10.0\text{ cm}}=510$ cm. Thus, the screen should be between 1.10 m and 5.10 m from the lens.

23.37 Given $f=-40.0$ cm, and $|q|=30.0$ cm. But for a real object, a diverging lens can only form virtual images ($q<0$). Therefore, $q=-30.0$ cm.

$$\frac{1}{p}=\frac{1}{f}-\frac{1}{q}=\left(\frac{1}{-40.0\ \text{cm}}\right)-\left(\frac{1}{-30.0\ \text{cm}}\right), \text{ and } \quad p=120\ \text{cm}.$$

The object should be 120 cm in front of lens.

$$M=-\frac{q}{p}=-\left(\frac{-30.0\ \text{cm}}{120\ \text{cm}}\right)=+\frac{1}{4}.$$

23.38 Given: $f>0$, and $p=10f$.

Thus, $\frac{1}{q}=\frac{1}{f}-\frac{1}{p}=\frac{1}{f}-\frac{1}{10f}$, and $q=\frac{10}{9}f$, or, the image is distance of $\frac{1}{9}f$ outside the focal point.

23.39 For a virtual image, the image distance is negative and the magnification is positive (assuming a real object).

Thus, $M=-\frac{q}{p}=\frac{1}{3}$, and $q=-\frac{p}{3}$.

So, $\frac{1}{p}+\frac{1}{q}=\frac{1}{f}$ becomes $\frac{1}{p}-\frac{3}{p}=\frac{1}{f}$, or $p=-2f$.

23.40 We are given that $p=80.0$ cm and $q=-40.0$ cm. Thus,

$$\frac{1}{f}=\frac{1}{p}+\frac{1}{q}=\frac{1}{80.0\ \text{cm}}-\frac{1}{40.0\ \text{cm}}=-\frac{1}{80.0\ \text{cm}}, \text{ and } \quad f=-80.0\ \text{cm}.$$

23.41 $\frac{1}{p}=\frac{1}{f}-\frac{1}{q}=\frac{1}{12.5\ \text{cm}}-\left(\frac{1}{-30.0\ \text{cm}}\right)$, and $p=8.82$ cm.

$$M=-\frac{q}{p'}=-\left(\frac{-30.0\ \text{cm}}{8.82\ \text{cm}}\right)=+3.40 \quad \text{(image is erect since } M>0\text{)}.$$

23.42 Let us consider the first lens. We find the image position and magnification as:

$$\frac{1}{q_1}=\frac{1}{f_1}-\frac{1}{p_1}=\frac{1}{15.0\ \text{cm}}-\frac{1}{30.0\ \text{cm}}=\frac{1}{30.0\ \text{cm}}, \text{ or } \quad q_1=30.0\ \text{cm}.$$

$$M_1=-\frac{q_1}{p_1}=-\frac{30.0\ \text{cm}}{30.0\ \text{cm}}=-1.00.$$

Now consider the second lens. The image produced by the first lens becomes the object for this second lens. Thus,

$p_2=40.0\ \text{cm}-q_1=40.0\ \text{cm}-30.0\ \text{cm}=10.0$ cm. The thin lens equation then gives: $\frac{1}{q_2}=\frac{1}{f_2}-\frac{1}{p_2}=\frac{1}{15.0\ \text{cm}}-\frac{1}{10.0\ \text{cm}}=-\frac{1}{30.0\ \text{cm}}$, or $q_2=-30.0$ cm.

$$M_2=-\frac{q_2}{p_2}=-\left(\frac{-30.0\ \text{cm}}{10.0\ \text{cm}}\right)=3.00.$$

The overall magnification M is: $\quad M=(M_1)(M_2)=(-1.00)(3.00)=-3.00.$

23.43 For the diverging lens, (parallel incident rays $\Rightarrow p_1=\infty$):

Using the thin lens equation, $\frac{1}{\infty}+\frac{1}{q_1}=\frac{1}{-10\ \text{cm}}$, or $q_1=-10.0$ cm.

The image formed by the diverging lens is the object for the converging lens. Thus, $p_2=30.0\ \text{cm}-q_1=30.0\ \text{cm}-(-10.0\ \text{cm})=40.0$ cm. Also, since the emerging rays are parallel, $q_2=\infty$.

For the converging lens: $\frac{1}{40.0\ \text{cm}} + \frac{1}{\infty} = \frac{1}{f_C}$, gives $f_C = +40.0$ cm.

23.44 Consider the first lens.: $\frac{1}{q_1} = \frac{1}{f_1} - \frac{1}{p_1} = \frac{1}{25\ \text{cm}} - \frac{1}{20\ \text{cm}} = -\frac{1}{100\ \text{cm}}$, so

$q_1 = -100$ cm, and $M_1 = -\frac{q_1}{p_1} = -\left(\frac{-100\ \text{cm}}{20\ \text{cm}}\right) = +5.$

The object position for the second lens is: $p_2 = 125$ cm. Thus,

$\frac{1}{q_2} = \frac{1}{f_2} - \frac{1}{p_2} = \left(\frac{1}{-10\ \text{cm}}\right) - \frac{1}{125\ \text{cm}}$, and $q_2 = -9.3$ cm.

$M_2 = -\frac{q_2}{p_2} = -\left(\frac{-9.3\ \text{cm}}{125\ \text{cm}}\right) = 0.074,$ the overall magnification M is:

$M = (M_1)(M_2) = (5.0)(0.074) = 0.37.$

23.45 (a) Note that: $q = 12.9\ \text{cm} - p$, so $\frac{1}{p} + \frac{1}{12.9 - p} = \frac{1}{2.44}$

which yields:

$-p^2 + 12.9p = 31.48.$

This has solutions:

$p = 9.63$ cm, or $p = 3.27$ cm, and both solutions are valid.

(b) For a virtual image:

$|q| = -q = p + 12.9$ cm, so

$\frac{1}{p} - \frac{1}{12.9 + p} = \frac{1}{2.44}$, or

$p^2 + 12.9p = 31.48$, from which

$p = 2.10$ cm, or $p = -15$ cm.

We must have a real object, so the -15 cm solution must be rejected.

(b)

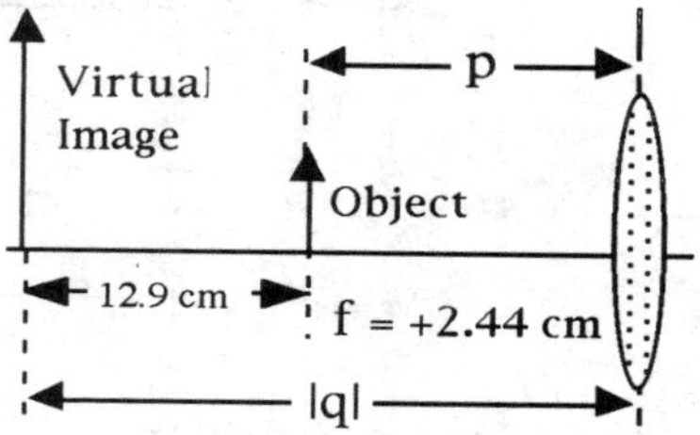

23.46 (a) The distance from the object to the lens is p, so the image distance is $q = 5.00\ \text{m} - p$. Thus, $\frac{1}{p} + \frac{1}{q} = \frac{1}{f}$ becomes:

$\frac{1}{p} + \frac{1}{5.00\ \text{m} - p} = \frac{1}{0.800\ \text{m}}$. This reduces to a quadratic equation:

$p^2 - 5.00p + 4.00 = 0$, which yields $p = 4.00$ m, or $p = 1.00$ m.

Thus, there are two possible object distances, both corresponding to real objects.

(b) For $p = 4.00$ m: $q = 5.00\ \text{m} - 4.00\ \text{m} = 1.00$ m, and $M = -\frac{1.00}{4.00} = -\frac{1}{4}$.

For $p = 1.00$ m: $q = 5.00\ \text{m} - 1.00\ \text{m} = 4.00$ m, and $M = -\frac{4.00}{1.00} = -4.00.$

Both images are real and inverted, but the magnifications are different, with one being 4 times the size of the object and the other one-fourth the size of the object.

23.47 Treating the first lens: $\frac{1}{q_1} = \frac{1}{f_1} - \frac{1}{p_1} = \frac{1}{8.00\ \text{cm}} - \frac{1}{4.00\ \text{cm}}$,

or $q_1 = -8.0$ cm.

Thus, $p_2 = 14.0$ cm, and $\frac{1}{q_2} = \frac{1}{f_2} - \frac{1}{p_2} = \frac{1}{-16.0 \text{ cm}} - \frac{1}{14.0 \text{ cm}}$, or $q_2 =$ -7.47 cm

$M_1 = -\frac{q_1}{p_1} = 2.00$, and $M_2 = -\frac{q_2}{p_2} = 0.533$, and $M = M_1 M_2 = 1.07$.

Thus, if the object is 1.00 cm in height, the erect ($M > 0$), virtual image ($q_2 < 0$) is 1.07 cm tall.

23.48 (a) Start with the second lens and work backward.

$f_2 = 20.0$ cm, $\quad q_2 = -(50.0 \text{ cm} - 31.0 \text{ cm}) = -19.0$ cm

$\frac{1}{p_2} + \frac{1}{q_2} = \frac{1}{f}$ becomes, $\frac{1}{p_2} - \frac{1}{19.0} = \frac{1}{20.0}$, from which $p_2 = 9.74$ cm.

Now, treat the first lens, recognizing that the object of the second lens is the image of the first lens: $q_1 = (50.0 \text{ cm} - 9.74 \text{ cm}) = 40.26$ cm, and $f_1 = 10.0$ cm, so $\frac{1}{p_1} = \frac{1}{f_1} - \frac{1}{q_1} = \frac{1}{10.0 \text{ cm}} - \frac{1}{40.26 \text{ cm}}$,

or $\quad p_1 = 13.3$ cm.

(b) $M_1 = -\frac{q_1}{p_1} = -\frac{40.26 \text{ cm}}{13.3 \text{ cm}} = -3.03$, and $M_2 = -\frac{q_2}{p_2} = -\frac{-19.0 \text{ cm}}{9.74 \text{ cm}} = 1.95$.

Thus, $M_{overall} = M_1 M_2 = -5.91$.

(c) The overall magnification is less than 0, so the final image is inverted. Also, the final image is virtual (before final lens).

23.49 The final image will be on the film, so let us start with the second lens. If $d = 5.00$ cm, then the lenses are 7.00 cm apart and $q_2 = 5.00$ cm.

$\frac{1}{p_2} = \frac{1}{f_2} - \frac{1}{q_2} = \frac{1}{13.3 \text{ cm}} - \frac{1}{5.00 \text{ cm}}$, so $\quad p_2 = -8.01$ cm.

Thus, $q_1 = 7.00 \text{ cm} + 8.01 \text{ cm} = 15.01$ cm.

Then, $\frac{1}{p_1} = \frac{1}{f_1} - \frac{1}{q_1} = \frac{1}{15.0 \text{ cm}} - \frac{1}{15.01 \text{ cm}}$, and $p_1 = 225$ m (max dist).

Similarly, if $d = 10.0$ cm, the lenses are 2.00 cm apart and $q_2 = 10$ cm.

$\frac{1}{p_2} = \frac{1}{f_2} - \frac{1}{q_2} = \frac{1}{13.3 \text{ cm}} - \frac{1}{10.0 \text{ cm}}$, giving $\quad p_2 = -40.3$ cm.

Thus, $q_1 = 2.00 \text{ cm} + 40.3 \text{ cm} = 42.3$ cm, so

$\frac{1}{p_1} = \frac{1}{f_1} - \frac{1}{q_1} = \frac{1}{15.0 \text{ cm}} - \frac{1}{42.3 \text{ cm}}$, and $p_1 = 0.232$ m (min dist).

23.50 The image, I_1, formed by the first lens serves as the object for the second lens. With the two lenses in contact with each other, this is a virtual object. If the thicknesses of the two lenses are ignored, the image distance of the first lens and the object distance for the second lens have the same magnitude but opposite signs (i.e., $p_2 = -q_1$). Thus, the thin lens equation applied to the second lens gives:

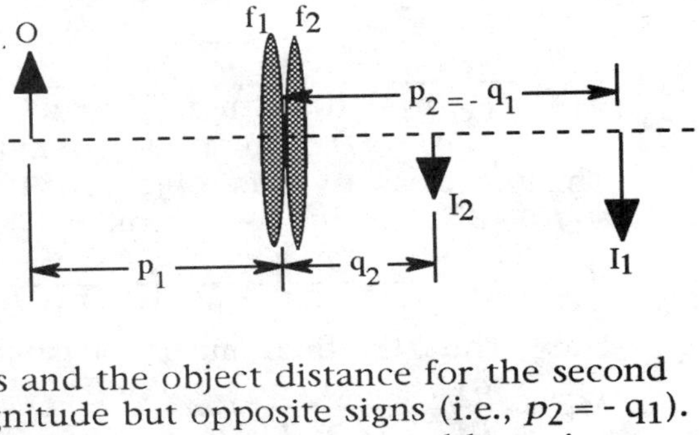

$$\frac{1}{-q_1} + \frac{1}{q_2} = \frac{1}{f_2}$$

Applying the thin lens equation to the first lens, we have

$\frac{1}{p_1} + \frac{1}{q_1} = \frac{1}{f_1}$ Adding these two equations yields:

$\frac{1}{p_1} + \frac{1}{q_2} = \frac{1}{f_1} + \frac{1}{f_2}$. This equation gives the relation between the position of the object, O, and the position of the final image, I_2. Note that this is in the form of a thin lens equation. Thus, we see that a pair of thin lenses in contact behaves like a thin lens having a focal length, f, given by $\frac{1}{f} = \frac{1}{f_1} + \frac{1}{f_2}$.

23.51 We first find the focal length of the mirror.

$$\frac{1}{f} = \frac{1}{p} + \frac{1}{q} = \frac{1}{10.0\text{ cm}} + \frac{1}{8.00\text{ cm}} = \frac{9.00}{40.0\text{ cm}}, \text{ and } f = 4.44\text{ cm}.$$

Hence, if $p = 20.0$ cm:

$$\frac{1}{q} = \frac{1}{f} - \frac{1}{p} = \frac{1}{4.44\text{ cm}} - \frac{1}{20.0\text{ cm}} = \frac{15.56}{88.8\text{ cm}}, \text{ and } q = 5.71\text{ cm (real image)}$$

23.52 For the first lens, $\frac{1}{f} = \frac{1}{p} + \frac{1}{q}$ becomes: $\frac{1}{-6.0\text{ cm}} = \frac{1}{12\text{ cm}} + \frac{1}{q_1}$, giving $q_1 = -4.0$ cm. When we require that q_2 approach infinity, we see that p_2 must be the focal length of the second lens. In this case: $p_2 = d - (-4.0\text{ cm})$. Therefore, $d + 4.0\text{ cm} = f_2 = 12$ cm, and $d = 8.0$ cm.

23.53 Since the object is very far from the lens, we approximate $p \approx \infty$, and the thin lens equation becomes

$$\frac{1}{\infty} + \frac{1}{q} = \frac{1}{50.0\text{ mm}}$$

which gives $q = 50.0$ mm.

Then, if the angular field of view is α as shown at the right, we have

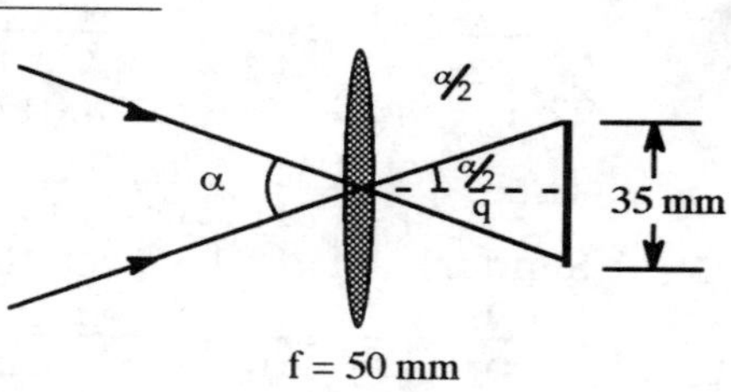

$$\tan\left(\frac{\alpha}{2}\right) = \frac{\frac{1}{2}(35.0\text{ mm})}{50.0\text{ mm}} = 0.350.$$

Therefore, $\frac{\alpha}{2} = 19.3°$, or the angular field of view is: $\alpha = 38.6°$.

23.54 $\frac{1}{q_1} = \frac{1}{f_1} - \frac{1}{p_1} = \frac{1}{10.0\text{ cm}} - \frac{1}{12.5\text{ cm}}$,

giving $q_1 = 50.0$ cm. (to left of mirror)

This serves as a virtual object for the lens, so $p_2 = 25.0\text{ cm} - q_1 = -25.0$ cm.

$\frac{1}{q_2} = \frac{1}{f_2} - \frac{1}{p_2} = \frac{1}{-16.7\text{ cm}} - \left(\frac{1}{-25.0\text{ cm}}\right)$, or $q_2 = -50.3$ cm. (to right of lens) Thus, the final image is located 25.3 cm to right of mirror.

$$M_1 = -\frac{q_1}{p_1} = -\frac{50.0\text{ cm}}{12.5\text{ cm}} = -4.00, \quad M_2 = -\frac{q_2}{p_2} = -\left(\frac{-50.3\text{ cm}}{-25.0\text{ cm}}\right) = -2.01,$$

and $M = M_1 M_2 = 8.05$.
Thus, the final image is virtual, erect, 8.05 times the size of object, and 25.3 cm to right of the mirror.

23.55 Start with the first pass through the lens:

$$\frac{1}{q_1} = \frac{1}{f_1} - \frac{1}{p_1} = \frac{1}{80.0 \text{ cm}} - \frac{1}{100 \text{ cm}}, \text{ so } q_1 = 400 \text{ cm}.$$ (to right of lens)

For the mirror, $p_2 = -300$ cm, so $\frac{1}{q_2} = \frac{1}{f_2} - \frac{1}{p_2} = \frac{1}{-50.0 \text{ cm}} - \frac{1}{(-300 \text{ cm})}$.

This yields: $q_2 = -60.0$ cm.

For the second pass through the lens: $p_3 = +160$ cm

$$\frac{1}{q_3} = \frac{1}{f_1} - \frac{1}{p_3} = \frac{1}{80.0 \text{ cm}} - \frac{1}{160 \text{ cm}}, \text{ giving } q_3 = 160 \text{ cm}.$$ (to left of lens)

$$M_1 = -\frac{q_1}{p_1} = -\frac{400 \text{ cm}}{100 \text{ cm}} = -4.00, \quad M_2 = -\frac{q_2}{p_2} = -\left(\frac{-60.0 \text{ cm}}{-300 \text{ cm}}\right) = -\frac{1}{5.00}$$

$$M_3 = -\frac{q_3}{p_3} = -\frac{160 \text{ cm}}{160 \text{ cm}} = -1.00, \text{ and } \quad M = M_1 M_2 M_3 = -0.800.$$

Since $M < 0$, the final image is inverted relative to the original object.

23.56 (a) We find the image position produced by the first lens.

$$\frac{1}{q_1} = \frac{1}{f_1} - \frac{1}{p_1} = \frac{1}{20.0 \text{ cm}} - \frac{1}{40.0 \text{ cm}} = \frac{1}{40 \text{ cm}}, \text{ so } q_1 = 40.0 \text{ cm, and}$$

$$M_1 = -\frac{q_1}{p_1} = -\frac{40.0 \text{ cm}}{40.0 \text{ cm}} = -1.00.$$

For the second lens, $p_2 = 10.0$ cm. Thus,

$$\frac{1}{q_2} = \frac{1}{f_2} - \frac{1}{p_2} = \frac{1}{5.00 \text{ cm}} - \frac{1}{10.0 \text{ cm}}, \text{ and } q_2 = 10.0 \text{ cm}$$ (to right of 2nd lens)

$$M_2 = -\frac{q_2}{p_2} = -\frac{10.0 \text{ cm}}{10.0 \text{ cm}} = -1.00.$$

(b) The overall magnification M is:
$M = (M_1)(M_2) = (-1.00)(-1.00) = +1.00$.
Thus, the final image is real ($q_2 > 0$), erect, and the same size (2.00 cm) as the object.

(c) With the two lenses in contact, the effective focal length is calculated using

$$\frac{1}{f_{eff}} = \frac{1}{f_1} + \frac{1}{f_2} = \frac{1}{20.0 \text{ cm}} + \frac{1}{5.00 \text{ cm}} \quad \text{yielding } f_{eff} = 4.00 \text{ cm}$$

The final image is then located by: $\frac{1}{q} = \frac{1}{f_{eff}} - \frac{1}{p} = \frac{1}{4.00 \text{ cm}} - \frac{1}{5.00 \text{ cm}}$

which gives $q = 20.0$ cm.

23.57 We use $\frac{n_1}{p} + \frac{n_2}{q} = \frac{n_2 - n_1}{R}$ applied to each surface in turn.

At the first surface, we have: $\frac{1}{1.00 \text{ cm}} + \frac{1.50}{q_1} = \frac{1.50 - 1}{2.00 \text{ cm}}$, or $q_1 = -2.00$ cm.

Thus, the image is formed 2.00 cm to the left of the surface, a distance of 16 cm from the second surface. This image becomes the object for the second surface (hence, $p_2 = +16.0$ cm).

We again use, $\frac{n_1}{p} + \frac{n_2}{q} = \frac{n_2 - n_1}{R}$:

$$\frac{1.50}{16.0\ \text{cm}} + \frac{1}{q_2} = \frac{1.00 - 1.50}{-4.00\ \text{cm}}, \text{ or } \quad q_2 = 32.0\ \text{cm}.$$

The final image is a real image 32.0 cm to the right of the second surface.

23.58 First locate the image of the coins formed by the upper mirror:

$\frac{1}{p_1} + \frac{1}{q_1} = \frac{1}{f}$ gives: $\frac{1}{7.5\ \text{cm}} + \frac{1}{q_1} = \frac{1}{7.5\ \text{cm}}$, so $q_1 = \infty$., or the reflected rays are parallel as they leave this mirror.

Now, locate the final image, realizing that parallel rays are reflected toward the lower mirror by the upper mirror (thus. $p_2 = \infty$).

$\frac{1}{p_2} + \frac{1}{q_2} = \frac{1}{f}$, gives $\frac{1}{\infty} + \frac{1}{q_2} = \frac{1}{7.5\ \text{cm}}$, and $q_2 = 7.5$ cm.

Thus, the final image is located at the center of the upper mirror, is real, and is erect (having undergone two inversions—one due to each mirror). It is also the same size as the object.

23.59 (a) Using $\frac{1}{p} + \frac{1}{q} = \frac{1}{f}$ we make the following table, with $f = \frac{R}{2} = \frac{1.00\ \text{m}}{2} =$ 0.500 m

Between $p = 3.00$ m and $p = 0.50$ m above the mirror, the ball's image is real and moves from + 0.60 m to + infinity. Between 0.50 m and contact with the mirror, the ball's image is virtual and moves from - infinity to 0. (Note the "jump" of image location as the ball passes through the focal point of the mirror.)

p = 3 m	q = 0.6 m
p = 0.5 m	q = +∞/-∞
p = 0	q = 0

(b) For the ball and its image to coincide, the image must be real with

$q = p$, so $\frac{1}{p} + \frac{1}{q} = \frac{1}{f}$ becomes: $\frac{1}{p} + \frac{1}{p} = \frac{1}{f}$; $\frac{2}{p} = \frac{1}{f}$; $p = 2f = 1.00$ m.

The time it takes for the ball to fall 2.00 m to this point is found using

$x = v_0 t + \frac{1}{2}at^2$: $-2.00\ \text{m} = 0 + \frac{1}{2}(-9.80\ \text{m/s}^2)t^2$, or $\quad t = 0.639$ s.

23.60 (a) The lensmakers equation, $\frac{1}{f} = (n - 1)\left(\frac{1}{R_1} - \frac{1}{R_2}\right)$, becomes:

$$\frac{1}{5.00\ \text{cm}} = (n - 1)\left(\frac{1}{9.00\ \text{cm}} - \frac{1}{-11.0\ \text{cm}}\right), \text{ giving } \quad n = 1.99.$$

(b) As the light passes through the lens for the first time, the thin lens equation, $\frac{1}{p_1} + \frac{1}{q_1} = \frac{1}{f}$ becomes: $\frac{1}{8.00\ \text{cm}} + \frac{1}{q_1} = \frac{1}{5.00\ \text{cm}}$, or

$q_1 = 13.33$ cm, and $M_1 = \frac{-q_1}{p_1} = -\frac{13.33\ \text{cm}}{8.00\ \text{cm}} = -1.67$. This image becomes the object for the concave mirror with:

$p_m = 20.0\ \text{cm} - q_1 = 20.0\ \text{cm} - 13.33\ \text{cm} = 6.67$ cm,

and $f = \frac{R}{2} = +4.00$ cm.

The mirror equation becomes: $\frac{1}{6.67\text{ cm}} + \frac{1}{q_m} = \frac{1}{4.00\text{ cm}}$,
giving
$q_m = 10.0$ cm, and $M_2 = \frac{-q_m}{p_m} = -\frac{10.0\text{ cm}}{6.67\text{ cm}} = -1.50$.
The image formed by the mirror serves as a real object for the lens on the second pass of the light through the lens with:
$p_3 = 20\text{ cm} - q_m = +10.0$ cm. The thin lens equation yields:
$\frac{1}{10.0\text{ cm}} + \frac{1}{q_3} = \frac{1}{5.00\text{ cm}}$, or $q_3 = 10.0$ cm,
and $M_3 = \frac{-q_3}{p_3} = -\frac{10.0\text{ cm}}{10.0\text{ cm}} = -1.00$. The final image is a real image located 10.0 cm to the left of the lens. Since the total magnification $(M_{total} = M_1 M_1 M_1 = -2.50)$ is negative, this final image is inverted.

23.61 (a) $\frac{1}{q_1} = \frac{1}{f_1} - \frac{1}{p_1} = \frac{1}{10.0\text{ cm}} - \frac{1}{15.0\text{ cm}}$, giving $q_1 = 30.0$ cm.
Therefore: $p_2 = -20.0$ cm, and $q_2 = -25.0$ cm.
Thus, $\frac{1}{f_2} = \frac{1}{-20.0\text{ cm}} + \frac{1}{-25.0\text{ cm}}$, and $f_2 = -11.1$ cm.
(b) $M_1 = -\frac{q_1}{p_1} = -\frac{30.0\text{ cm}}{15.0\text{ cm}} = -2.00$, $M_2 = -\frac{q_2}{p_2} = -\frac{-25.0\text{ cm}}{-20.0\text{ cm}} = -1.25$, and
$M_{overall} = (M_1)(M_2) = (-2.00)(-1.25) = 2.50$.
(c) The final image is virtual, erect, and enlarged.

23.62 With the given radii of curvature, the lens maker's equation becomes:
$$\frac{1}{f} = \left(\frac{n_1}{n_2} - 1\right)\left(\frac{1}{-3.0\text{ m}} - \frac{1}{-6.0\text{ m}}\right) = \left(\frac{n_1}{n_2} - 1\right)\left(\frac{-2+1}{6.0\text{ m}}\right) = \left(\frac{n_1}{n_2} - 1\right)\left(\frac{-1}{6.0\text{ m}}\right),$$
or $$\frac{1}{f} = \frac{1}{6.0\text{ m}}\left(1 - \frac{n_1}{n_2}\right). \quad (1)$$
(a) When $n_1 = 1.5$ and $n_2 = 1$, the focal length of the lens is:
$\frac{1}{f} = \frac{1}{6.0\text{ m}}(-0.5\text{ m})$, or $f = -12.0$ m, so the thin lens equation gives
$\frac{1}{10.0\text{ m}} + \frac{1}{q} = \frac{1}{-12\text{ m}}$, which yields: $q = -5.50$ m, or the image is 5.50 m to left of the lens.
(b) When $n_1 = 1.5$, and $n_2 = 1.333$, the above yields:
$f = -48.0$ m, and $q = -8.30$ m, or 8.30 m to left of lens.
(c) When $n_1 = 1.5$, and $n_2 = 2.0$, the above yields:
$f = 24$ m, and $q = -17$ m, or 17 m to left of lens.
(d) As shown in equation (1), the focal length will be positive if
$\left(1 - \frac{n_1}{n_2}\right) > 0$, or $\frac{n_1}{n_2} < 1$, meaning $n_1 < n_2$. That is; the surrounding material should have a higher index of refraction than the lens material.

23.63 We solve $\frac{1}{f} = \frac{1}{p} + \frac{1}{q}$ for p to find: $p = \frac{fq}{(q - f)}$ and we use $M = -\frac{q}{p}$.
(a) For $q = 4f$: $p = \frac{f(4f)}{(4f - f)} = \frac{4f}{3}$.

(b) For $q = -3f$: $p = \frac{f(-3f)}{(-3f - f)} = \frac{3f}{4}$.

(c) For case (a), $M = -\frac{4f}{\frac{4f}{3}} = -3.00$, and for case (b), $M = -\frac{-3f}{\frac{3f}{4}} = 4.00$

ANSWERS TO CONCEPTUAL QUESTIONS

2. Because of refraction, the fish appears to be at a depth that is less than its actual depth. Therefore, the person should aim below the image of the fish to hit it.

4. Chromatic aberration is produced when light passes *through* a material, as it does when passing through the glass of a lens. A mirror, silvered on its front surface never has light passing through it, so this aberration cannot occur. This is only one of many reasons why large telescopes use mirrors rather than lenses for their optical elements.

6. Make the mirror an efficient reflector (shiny); use a parabolic shaped mirror so that it reflects all rays to the image point, even those far from the axis; most important, use a large-diameter mirror in order to collect more solar power.

8. A convex mirror is being used. Since a demagnified image is produced, the driver may think the small truck bearing down on him is far away; thus, the warning. This kind of mirror is used so that a large area behind the car can be seen.

10. All objects beneath the stream appear to be closer to the surface than they really are because of refraction. Thus, the pebbles on the bottom of the stream appear to be close to the surface of a shallow stream.

12. An effect similar to a mirage is produced except the "mirage" is seen hovering in the air. Ghost lighthouses in the sky have been seen over bodies of water by this effect.

14. Actually no physics is involved here. The design is chosen so your eyelashes will not brush against the glass as you blink. A reason involving a little physics is that with this design, when you direct your gaze near the outer circumference of the lens you receive a ray that has passed through glass with more nearly parallel surfaces of entry and exit. Then the lens minimally distorts the direction to the object you are looking at.

16. Both words are inverted. However OXIDE looks the same right side up and upside down. LEAD does not.

CHAPTER TWENTY-FOUR SOLUTIONS

Chapter Twenty-Four Readings

Baumeister, P. and Pincus, G., "Optical Interference Coatings," *Scientific American*, December 1970, p. 59.

Bohrens, C. and Fraser, A., "Colors of the Sky," *The Physics Teacher*, May 1985, p. 267.

Kettler, J.E., "The Compact Disk as a Diffraction Grating," *American Journal of Physics*, 59, 367, 1991.

Kruglak, H., "The Compact Disc as a Diffraction Grating," *Physics Education*, 25, 255, 1990.

Nemecek, S., "Coat of Many Colors," *Scientific American*, August 1996, p. 34.

Nussenvieg, H.M., "The Theory of the Rainbow," *Scientific American*, April 1977, p. 116.

Scientific American, September 1968. The entire issue is devoted to light.

Shurcliffe, W.A. and Ballard, S.S., *Polarized Light*, Van Nostrand, 1964.

Slusher, R.E. and Yurke, B., "Squeezed Light," *Scientific American*, May 1988, p. 50.

Von Baeyer, H.D., "Rainbows, Whirlpools, and Clouds," *The Scientist*, July/August 1984, p. 24.

Wehner, R., "Polarized Light Navigation by Insects," *Scientific American*, July 1976, p. 106.

Wood, A. and Oldham, *F., Thomas Young, Natural Philosopher, 1773-1829*, Cambridge, England, Cambridge University Press, 1954.

Review No phase shift upon reflection from the upper surface (glass to air) of the film, but there will be a shift of $\lambda/2$ due to the reflection at the lower surface of the film (air to metal). The total phase difference in the two reflected beams is then $\delta = 2n_f t + \lambda/2$. For constructive interference,
$\delta = m\lambda$, or $2(1.00)t + \lambda/2 = m\lambda$ Thus, the film thickness for the mth order bright fringe is: $t_m = \left(m - \frac{1}{2}\right)\frac{\lambda}{2} = m\left(\frac{\lambda}{2}\right) - \frac{\lambda}{4}$, and the thickness for the m - 1 bright fringe is: $t_{m-1} = (m-1)\left(\frac{\lambda}{2}\right) - \frac{\lambda}{4}$.

Therefore, $\Delta t = t_m - t_{m-1} = \frac{\lambda}{2}$. This is the change in thickness required to go from one bright fringe to the next bright fringe. To go through 200 bright fringes, the change in thickness of the air film must be: $200\left(\frac{\lambda}{2}\right) = 100\,\lambda$. Thus, the increase in the length of the rod is:

$$\Delta L = 100\lambda = (100)(5.00 \times 10^{-7}\ \text{m}) = 5.00 \times 10^{-5}\ \text{m}, \text{ and from } \Delta L = L_0 \alpha \Delta T,$$

we have: $\alpha = \frac{\Delta L}{L_0 \Delta T}$, or $\alpha = \frac{5.00 \times 10^{-5}\ \text{m}}{(1 \times 10^{-1}\ \text{m})(25\ °\text{C})} = 20.0 \times 10^{-6}\ °\text{C}^{-1}$.

24.1 (a) For a bright fringe (constructive interference), the difference in the path lengths to the two slits must be given by $\delta = m\lambda$ where $m = 0, 1, 2, 3, \ldots$ For a third order bright fringe, $m = 3$. Therefore, the path difference is: $\delta = 3\lambda = 3(589\ \text{nm}) = 1767\ \text{nm} = 1.77\ \mu\text{m}$.

(b) For a dark fringe (destructive interference), the required path difference is $\delta = (m + \frac{1}{2})\lambda$ where $m = 0, 1, 2, 3, \ldots$ For a third order dark fringe, $m = 2$, and $\delta = 2.5\lambda = 2.5(589\ \text{nm}) = 1473\ \text{nm} = 1.47\ \mu\text{m}$.

24.2 (a) The position of the mth fringe is given by: $\left(y_{bright}\right)_m = \frac{m\lambda L}{d}$.

For m = 1, $\left(y_{bright}\right)_1 = \frac{(1)(546 \times 10^{-9}\ \text{m})(1.2\ \text{m})}{0.250 \times 10^{-3}\ \text{m}} = 2.62\ \text{mm}$

(b) The mth dark fringe occurs at: $\left(y_{dark}\right)_m = \left(m + \frac{1}{2}\right)\frac{\lambda L}{d}$, from

which $\Delta y = \left(y_{dark}\right)_2 - \left(y_{dark}\right)_1 = \frac{\lambda L}{d} = 2.62\ \text{mm}$.

24.3 The position of the mth bright fringe is given by $y_m = m\frac{\lambda L}{d}$.

Thus, $\Delta y = y_{m+1} - y_m = \frac{\lambda L}{d}$ is the spacing between consecutive bright fringes. With the given data this becomes:

$$\Delta y = \frac{(6.00 \times 10^{-7}\ \text{m})(2.50\ \text{m})}{5.00 \times 10^{-5}\ \text{m}} = 3.00 \times 10^{-2}\ \text{m} = 3.00\ \text{cm}.$$

24.4 Location of A = central maximum, and location of B = first minimum.

Thus, $\Delta y = \left(y_{first\ min}\right) - \left(y_{central\ max}\right) = \frac{\lambda L}{d}\left(0 + \frac{1}{2}\right) - 0 = \frac{1}{2}\left(\frac{\lambda L}{d}\right) = 20.0\ \text{m}$,

or $d = \frac{\lambda L}{2(\Delta y)} = \frac{(3.00\ \text{m})(150\ \text{m})}{2(20.0\ \text{m})} = 11.3\ \text{m}$.

24.5 For bright fringes, the condition is: $\delta = d\sin\theta = m\lambda$.

Thus, $d = \frac{m\lambda}{\sin\theta} = \frac{(1)(575 \times 10^{-9}\ \text{m})}{\sin 16.5°} = 2.02\ \mu\text{m}$.

24.6 The spacing of successive dark fringes is:

$\Delta y = \left(y_{dark}\right)_{m+1} - \left(y_{dark}\right)_m = \frac{\lambda L}{d}$. Therefore,

$$L = \frac{(\Delta y)d}{\lambda} = \frac{(4.00 \times 10^{-3}\ \text{m})(3.00 \times 10^{-4}\ \text{m})}{460 \times 10^{-9}\ \text{m}} = 2.61\ \text{m}.$$

24.7 For the first order ($m = 1$) bright fringe, $y = (1)\left(\frac{\lambda L}{d}\right)$. Thus, for violet light: $y_V = \frac{\lambda_V L}{d} = \frac{(4.0 \times 10^{-7}\text{ m})(1.5\text{ m})}{3.0 \times 10^{-4}\text{ m}} = 2.0 \times 10^{-3}\text{ m} = 2.0\text{ mm}$, and for red light: $y_r = \frac{\lambda_r L}{d} = \frac{(7.0 \times 10^{-7}\text{ m})(1.5\text{ m})}{3.0 \times 10^{-4}\text{ m}} = 3.5 \times 10^{-3}\text{ m} = 3.5\text{ mm}$.

Therefore, $\Delta y = y_r - y_V = 3.5\text{ mm} - 2.0\text{ mm} = 1.5\text{ mm}$.

24.8 Note, with the conditions given, the small angle approximation does not work well. The approach to be used is outlined below.

(a) At the m = 2 maximum: $\tan\theta = \frac{400\text{ m}}{1000\text{ m}} = 0.400$, and $\theta = 21.8°$.

So, $\lambda = \frac{d\sin\theta}{m} = \frac{(300\text{ m})\sin 21.8°}{2} = 55.7\text{ m}$.

(b) The next minimum encountered is the $m = 2$ minimum, and at that point: $d\sin\theta = (m + \frac{1}{2})\lambda$, which becomes $d\sin\theta = \frac{5}{2}\lambda$, or

$\sin\theta = \frac{5\lambda}{2d} = \frac{5(55.7\text{ m})}{2(300\text{ m})} = 0.464$, and $\theta = 27.7°$, so

$y = (1000\text{ m})\tan 27.7° = 524\text{m}$. Therefore, the car must travel an additional 124 m.

24.9 From $y_{bright} = m\left(\frac{\lambda L}{d}\right)$, $\lambda = \frac{(y_m)d}{mL} = \frac{(3.40 \times 10^{-3}\text{ m})(5.00 \times 10^{-4}\text{ m})}{(1)(3.30\text{ m})} = 515\text{ nm}$.

24.10 Note that we are neglecting any phase changes which may occur upon reflection from the mountain. If d is the distance to the mountain, we have a path difference of $\delta = 2d$.

For destructive interference: $\delta = (m + \frac{1}{2})\lambda$.

Therefore, $2d = (m + \frac{1}{2})\lambda$. For the minimum value of d, we use the smallest value of m, namely $m = 0$. Thus,

$2d = \frac{\lambda}{2}$, or $d = \frac{\lambda}{4} = \frac{300\text{ m}}{4} = 75.0\text{ m}$.

24.11 (See sketch.) For the minimum height h and hence the minimum path difference to give destructive interference, we have:

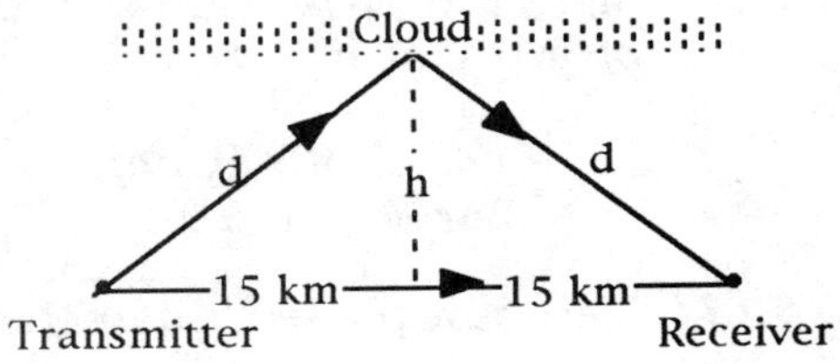

$\delta = 2d - 3.00 \times 10^4\text{ m} = \frac{\lambda}{2} = 200\text{ m}$.

Therefore, $d = 1.51 \times 10^4\text{ m}$. Then from the Pythagorean theorem: $d^2 = h^2 + (1.5 \times 10^4\text{ m})^2 = (1.51 \times 10^4\text{ m})^2$, and $h = 1.73\text{ km}$.

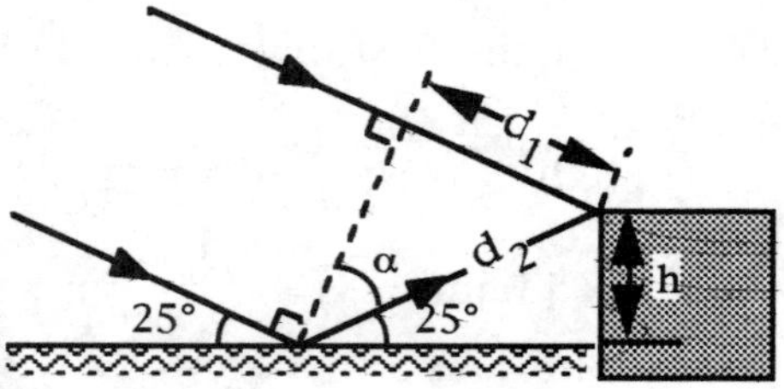

24.12 (See sketch.) We have:

$25.0° + 90.0° + \alpha + 25.0° = 180°.$

Thus, $\alpha = 40.0°.$

$\delta = d_2 - d_1 = d_2 - d_2 \sin\alpha$, or

$\delta = d_2(1 - \sin 40.0°) = (0.357)d_2.$

For first order destructive interference: $\delta = \frac{\lambda}{2} = 125$ m.

Therefore, $(0.357)d_2 = 125$ m, and $d_2 = 350$ m.

Then, $h = d_2 \sin 25° = (350 \text{ m})\sin 25.0° = 148$ m.

24.13 The phase difference because of the difference in path lengths is $2n_f t$, where n_f is the index of refraction of the film. The phase difference due to reflection at the upper surface is $\frac{\lambda}{2}$.

For constructive interference, $\delta = m\lambda$.

Thus, $2n_f t + \frac{\lambda}{2} = m\lambda$. For the minimum thickness, $m = 1$, and we have:

$$t = \frac{\lambda}{4n_f} = \frac{500 \text{ nm}}{4(1.36)} = 91.9 \text{ nm}.$$

24.14 There is a phase difference of $\frac{\lambda}{2}$ because of reflections and one of $2n_f t$ because of the path difference. We have, $\delta_{total} = 2n_f t + \frac{\lambda}{2} = (m + \frac{1}{2})\lambda$, or

$t = \frac{m\lambda}{2n_f} = m\left(\frac{580 \text{ nm}}{2(1)}\right)$, which reduces to: $t_m = m(290 \text{ nm})$. The first three non-zero distances are: $t_1 = 290$ nm, $t_2 = 580$ nm, and $t_3 = 870$ nm.

24.15 There is a phase shift due to reflection at the upper surface and none at the lower. We have: $\delta = 2n_f t + \frac{\lambda}{2} = m\lambda$ as the condition for constructive interference. Thus, $t = \left(m - \frac{1}{2}\right)\left(\frac{\lambda}{2n_f}\right) = (2m-1)\left(\frac{600 \text{ nm}}{4(1.756)}\right)$, or

$t = (2m-1)(85.4 \text{ nm})$ for $m = 1, 2, 3, \ldots$ That is, any odd multiple of 85.4 nm.

24.16 There is a phase shift at both the upper and lower film surfaces. Thus, for a bright fringe: $\delta_{total} = 2n_f t + 0 = m\lambda$, and

$$t = \frac{m\lambda}{2n_f} = \frac{(1)(600 \text{ nm})}{2(1.29)} = 233 \text{ nm}.$$

24.17 There is a phase shift at the upper surface, but none at the lower so the total phase difference in the two reflected waves is $\delta = 2n_f t + \frac{\lambda}{2}$.

For destructive interference, $2n_f t + \frac{\lambda}{2} = (2m + 1)\frac{\lambda}{2}$, or $\lambda = \frac{2n_f t}{m}$.

When $m = 1$, $\lambda = \frac{2(1.55)(177.4 \text{ nm})}{1} = 550$ nm (located at the center of the visible spectrum).

24.18 There is a phase shift due to reflection at the upper surface, but none at the lower. For constructive interference, $2n_f t + \frac{\lambda}{2} = m\lambda$, or

$$t = \left(m - \frac{1}{2}\right)\left(\frac{\lambda}{2n_f}\right), \quad \text{and} \quad m = 1 \quad \text{for minimum thickness.}$$

(a) $t = \frac{(656.3 \text{ nm})}{4(1.33)} = 123 \text{ nm}.$ (b) $t = \frac{(434.0 \text{ nm})}{4(1.33)} = 81.6 \text{ nm}.$

24.19 There is a phase shift due to reflection at the upper surface but not at the lower surface. For destructive interference, we have:

$$\delta_{\text{total}} = 2n_f t + \frac{\lambda}{2} = (m + \frac{1}{2})\lambda, \text{ or } t = \frac{m\lambda}{2n_f} = m\left(\frac{580 \text{ nm}}{2(1.50)}\right) = m(193 \text{ nm}).$$

For the smallest thickness other than zero, $m = 1$, and $t = 193$ nm.

24.20 Both reflections are of the same type. so there is no net phase difference due to reflections. Thus, for constructive interference: $\delta = 2n_f d = m\lambda$. For the minimum value of d, $m = 1$.

Thus, $d = \frac{\lambda}{2n_f} = \frac{580 \text{ nm}}{2(1.00)} = 290 \text{ nm}.$

24.21 There is a phase shift due to reflection at the bottom of the air film but not at the top of the film. For dark fringes: $\delta_{\text{total}} = 2n_f t + \frac{\lambda}{2} = (m + \frac{1}{2})\lambda$,

or $t = \frac{m\lambda}{2n_f} = m\left(\frac{500 \text{ nm}}{2(1.00)}\right) = m(250 \text{ nm})$. For the 19th order destructive interference, $t = 19(250 \text{ nm}) = 4.75 \times 10^3 \text{ nm} = 4.75\ \mu\text{m}$.

24.22 There is a half wavelength phase shift due to the reflection at the lower surface of the air film, giving a total phase difference of:

$\delta = 2n_f t + \frac{\lambda}{2}$. For destructive interference, $\delta = 2n_f t + \frac{\lambda}{2} = \left(m + \frac{1}{2}\right)\lambda$, or

$2n_f t = m\lambda$. Thus, $m = \frac{2(1.00)(2.00 \times 10^{-6} \text{ m})}{546.1 \times 10^{-9} \text{ m}} = 7.32$. The last dark fringe seen is the 7th order, and the total number of dark fringes seen (counting the zeroth order) is 7 + 1 = 8.

24.23 A phase shift due to reflection occurs at the top of the oil layer but not at the bottom surface. Thus, for constructive interference,

$$\delta_{\text{total}} = 2n_f t + \frac{\lambda}{2} = m\lambda, \text{ or } \lambda_m = \frac{4n_f t}{(2m - 1)} = \frac{4(1.38)(300 \text{ nm})}{(2m - 1)} = \frac{1660 \text{ nm}}{(2m - 1)}.$$

Thus, $\lambda_1 = 1660$ nm, $\lambda_2 = 553$ nm, $\lambda_3 = 332$, $\lambda_4 = 237$ nm, etc. Of these, only $\lambda_2 = 553$ nm is in the visible range. The surface will appear Green.

24.24

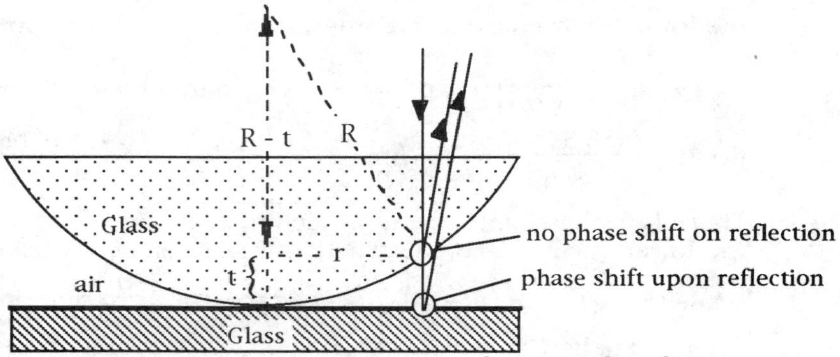

(See sketch.) From geometry, we have: $R^2 = (R - t)^2 + r^2$, or

$$t = R - \sqrt{R^2 - r^2} = 3.0\text{ m} - \sqrt{(3.0)^2 - (9.8 \times 10^{-3})^2} = 1.6 \times 10^{-5}\text{ m}.$$

At the mth bright fringe, $\delta_{total} = 2n_f t + \frac{\lambda}{2} = m\lambda$.

For $n_f = 1$ and $m = 50$, $(49.5)\lambda = 2t$, or $\lambda = \frac{2(1.6 \times 10^{-5}\text{ m})}{49.5} = 6.5 \times 10^2$ nm.

24.25 There is a phase shift of $\lambda/2$ due to reflections at both surfaces of the magnesium fluoride layer. Thus, there is no net phase difference in the two reflected waves due to reflection. All the phase difference is a result of difference in path lengths, $\delta_{total} = 2n_f t + 0$. For destructive interference, δ_{total} must be an odd multiple of half wavelengths, or $\delta_{total} = 2n_f t = (2m + 1)\left(\frac{\lambda}{2}\right)$ with $m = 0, 1, 2,...$ Thus, for minimum thickness, $m = 0$, and the required thickness is:

$$t = \frac{\lambda}{4n_f} = \frac{550\text{ nm}}{4(1.38)} = 99.6\text{ nm}.$$

24.26 There is a phase shift due to reflection at each surface of the film. Thus, there is no phase difference in the two relected waves due to reflection and $\delta_{total} = 2n_f t + 0$. For a bright fringe $\delta_{total} = m\lambda$, we must have: $\lambda = \frac{2n_f t}{m} = \frac{2(1.38)(100\text{ nm})}{m} = \frac{276\text{ nm}}{m}$ which gives $\lambda = 276$ nm, 138 nm, 92 nm, etc. (for $m = 1, 2, 3, \cdots$). Thus, no visible wavelengths produce constructive interference.

24.27 (a) The dark bands occur where $\sin\theta = m\frac{\lambda}{a}$. For the first dark band ($m = 1$), $\sin\theta = \frac{\lambda}{a}$. But $\sin\theta \cong \frac{y}{1.5\text{ m}}$. Thus, $\frac{y}{1.5\text{ m}} = \frac{\lambda}{a}$,

and $y = \frac{(1.5\text{ m})(600 \times 10^{-9}\text{ m})}{4.0 \times 10^{-4}\text{ m}} = 2.25$ mm.

(b) The width of the central maximum is the distance between the dark lines on each side of the central bright line. This is: 2(2.25 mm) = 4.50 mm.

24.28 (a) At the first dark band: $\sin\theta = \frac{\lambda}{a} = \frac{5.875 \times 10^{-7}\text{ m}}{7.5 \times 10^{-4}\text{ m}} = 7.83 \times 10^{-4}$.

But also, $\sin\theta = \frac{y}{L}$, so $L = \frac{y}{\sin\theta}$. Thus, $L = \frac{8.5 \times 10^{-4}\ \text{m}}{7.83 \times 10^{-4}} = 1.09$ m.

(b) The width of the central maximum $= 2y = 2(0.85\ \text{mm}) = 1.70$ mm.

24.29 For destructive interference,

$\sin\theta = m\left(\frac{\lambda}{a}\right) = \frac{\lambda}{a} = \frac{5.00\ \text{cm}}{36.0\ \text{cm}}$, or

$\sin\theta = 0.13889$, and $\theta = 7.98°$.

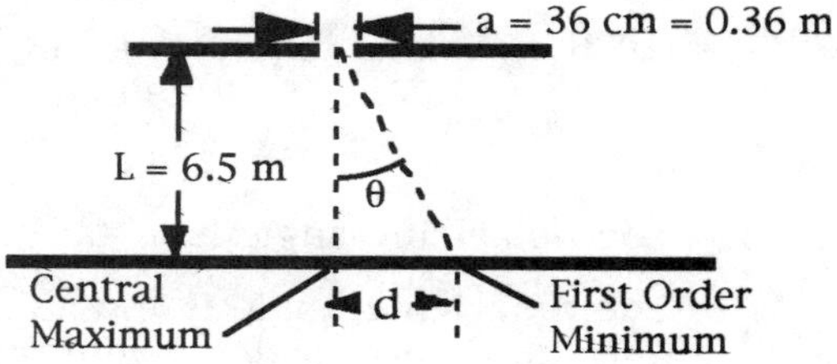

Then, $\frac{d}{L} = \tan\theta$ gives:

$d = L\tan\theta = (6.50\ \text{m})\tan 7.98°$, or

$d = 0.912\ \text{m} = 91.2$ cm.

24.30 The angles (measured from the line perpendicular to the plane of the single slit) at which dark fringes can occur are given by $\sin\theta = \frac{m\lambda}{a}$ with $m = 1, 2, 3, \ldots$. If $\lambda = a$, the first order ($m = 1$) dark fringe is at $\sin\theta = 1$, or at $\theta = 90°$. That is, the central maximum is infinitely wide. If $\lambda > a$, the condition for a dark fringe gives $\sin\theta > m$ which is mathematically impossible since $m \geq 1$. Thus, one must conclude that no dark fringe can be seen if $\lambda \geq a$, where a is the width of the slit.

24.31 The angles at which a dark fringe can occur are given by $\sin\theta = \frac{m\lambda}{a}$, and the screen positions of these dark fringes are: $y_m = L\tan\theta$. If we make the small angle approximation [$\sin\theta \approx \tan\theta$], we have:

$y_m = mL\left(\frac{\lambda}{a}\right)$ as the location of the mth order dark fringe. With $L =$ 120 cm, $a = 0.50$ mm, and $\lambda = 500$ nm, this gives: $y_1 = 1.20$ mm, $y_2 = 2.40$ mm, and $y_3 = 3.60$ mm. The width of the first order maximum is:

$y_2 - y_1 = (2.40 - 1.20)\ \text{mm} = 1.20$ mm, and the width of the second order maximum is: $y_3 - y_2 = (3.60 - 2.40)\ \text{mm} = 1.20$ mm.

24.32 The angles at which a dark fringe can occur are given by $\sin\theta = \frac{m\lambda}{a}$, and the screen positions of these dark fringes are: $y_m = L\tan\theta$. Making the small angle approximation [$\sin\theta \approx \tan\theta$] gives, $y_m = mL\left(\frac{\lambda}{a}\right)$ as the location of the mth order dark fringe. The distance from the first to the third dark fringes is then $\Delta y = y_3 - y_1 = 2L\left(\frac{\lambda}{a}\right)$. With $L = 50.0$ cm, $\lambda = 680$ nm, and $\Delta y = 3.00$ mm, this gives:

$$3.00 \times 10^{-3}\ \text{m} = 2(5.00 \times 10^{-1}\ \text{m})\left(\frac{6.80 \times 10^{-7}\ \text{m}}{a}\right), \text{ or } a = 0.227\ \text{mm}.$$

24.33 (a) $\tan\theta_p = \frac{n_2}{n_1} = n_2$ since $n_1 = 1.00$. Thus, $n_2 = \tan 48.0° = 1.11$.

(b) We know that the refracted angle is related to the polarizing angle as: $\theta_2 = 90.0° - \theta_p = 42.0°$.

24.34 The Brewster angle is given by: $\tan\theta_p = \frac{n_2}{n_1}$ (See problem 38).

(a) If $n_2 = 1.52$, and $n_1 = 1.0$ (air), then $\tan\theta_p = \frac{1.52}{1.00} = 1.52$, and $\theta_p = 56.7°$.

(b) If $n_2 = 1.52$, and $n_1 = 1.333$ (water), then $\tan\theta_p = \frac{1.52}{1.333} = 1.14$, and $\theta_p = 48.8°$.

24.35 The polarizing angle is: $\tan\theta_p = \frac{n_2}{n_1} = \frac{1.333}{1.00} = 1.333$, and $\theta_p = 53.1°$.
The polarizing angle is the angle between the ray of light and the normal to the surface, while the altitude is the angle between the ray of light and the horizontal. This angle is: $\alpha = 90.0° - \theta_p = 36.9°$.

24.36 $n_g = \tan\theta_p = 1.65$, so Brewster's angle is: $\theta_p = 58.8°$.
From Snell's law: $n_g \sin\theta_r = n_{air} \sin\theta_p$, which gives:

$$\sin\theta_r = \frac{(1)(\sin 58.8°)}{1.65} = 0.5183, \text{ and } \quad \theta_r = 31.2°.$$

24.37 The critical angle for total internal reflection is given by $\sin\theta_c = \frac{n_2}{n_1}$, where n_1 is the index of refraction of the material in which the light travels, and n_2 is the index of the surrounding material. Thus,

$n_1 = \frac{n_2}{\sin\theta_c} = \frac{1}{\sin 34.4°} = 1.77$. This is the index of refraction of sapphire.

The polarizing angle is given (see problem 38) by $\tan\theta_p = \frac{n_2}{n_1}$ where n_1 is the index of the material from which the light is incident and n_2 is the index of the material from which the light reflects. Thus,

$$\tan\theta_p = \frac{1.77}{1.00} = 1.77, \text{ and } \theta_p = 60.5°.$$

24.38 Starting with Snell's law, we have: $n_1 \sin\theta_1 = n_2 \sin\theta_2$.
At Brewster's angle: $\theta_1 + \theta_2 + 90° = 180°$, or $\theta_1 + \theta_2 = 90°$. (1)
If the material is incident from medium 1 and θ_1 is the polarizing angle, θ_p, equation (1) gives: $\theta_2 = 90° - \theta_p$.
Thus, $\sin\theta_2 = \sin(90° - \theta_p) = \cos\theta_p$, and Snell's law becomes:

$$n_1 \sin\theta_p = n_2 \cos\theta_p, \text{ or } \frac{\sin\theta_p}{\cos\theta_p} = \frac{n_2}{n_1}, \text{ so } \tan\theta_p = \frac{n_2}{n_1}.$$

24.39 We use Malus's law: $I = I_0 \cos^2\theta$.

(a) If $\theta = 45°$, then $\cos\theta = \frac{1}{\sqrt{2}}$, and $\frac{I}{I_0} = \frac{1}{2}$.

(b) If $\frac{I}{I_0} = \frac{1}{3}$, then $\cos^2\theta = \frac{1}{3}$, or $\cos\theta = \frac{1}{\sqrt{3}} = 0.577$, and $\theta = 54.7°$.

24.40 For $\theta_1 = 20°$, we have: $I_2 = I_i \cos^2\theta = 10\cos^2(20.0°) = 8.83$ units.
The light emerging from this plate is polarized at 20° with respect to the vertical. At the next plate:

$$I_3 = I_2 \cos^2(\theta_2 - \theta_1) = 8.83\cos^2(20.0°) = 7.80 \text{ units}.$$

The light emerging from the second polarizer has its plane of polarization at 40° from the vertical. At the final plate,
$I_f = I_3\cos^2(\theta_3 - \theta_2) = 7.80\cos^2(20°) = 6.89$ units.

24.41 (a) The wavelength in a medium of refractive index n is given by $\lambda = \frac{\lambda_{vac}}{n}$. Thus, the wavelengths of the component beams are:

$$\lambda_1 = \frac{546.1\ \text{nm}}{1.320} = 413.7\ \text{nm, and} \qquad \lambda_2 = \frac{546.1\ \text{nm}}{1.333} = 409.7\ \text{nm}.$$

(b) The thickness of the specimen is equivalent to a different number of wavelengths for these two waves. These numbers are

$$N_1 = \frac{t}{\lambda_1} = \frac{1.000 \times 10^{-6}\ \text{m}}{4.137 \times 10^{-7}\ \text{m}} = 2.417 \text{ (first component), and}$$

$$N_2 = \frac{t}{\lambda_2} = \frac{1 \times 10^{-6}\ \text{m}}{4.097 \times 10^{-7}\ \text{m}} = 2.441 \text{ (second component).}$$

Thus, when they emerge, the two waves are out of phase by $N_2 - N_1 = (2.441 - 2.417) = 0.024$ wavelengths. A full wavelength represents a phase angle of 360°. Therefore, when they emerge, the waves are out of phase by:

$$\Delta\phi = (0.024 \text{ wavelengths})\left(\frac{360°}{1 \text{ wavelength}}\right) = 8.64°.$$

24.42 Bright lines occur when $m\lambda = d\sin\theta$. For the light of wavelength λ_2, we have: $5\lambda_2 = d\sin\theta$. (1)
For the fourth order bright line of wavelength λ_1:
$4\lambda_1 = d\sin\theta$. (2)
Combining (1) and (2) gives: $5\lambda_2 = 4\lambda_1$.
Thus, $\lambda_2 = \frac{4}{5}\lambda_1 = 0.8(540\ \text{nm}) = 432\ \text{nm}$.

24.43 For destructive interference: $\left(m + \frac{1}{2}\right)\lambda = d\sin\theta \quad m = 0, 1, 2, 3.....$

The angle θ is 18 min of arc, or 0.300°. At the second minimum, $m = 1$.

Thus, $d = \frac{3\ \lambda}{2\ \sin\theta} = \frac{3\ (546 \times 10^{-9}\ \text{m})}{2\ \sin(0.300°)} = 1.56 \times 10^{-4}\ \text{m} = 0.156\ \text{mm}$.

24.44 There is a phase shift due to reflection at both surfaces. Thus, $\delta_{total} = 2n_f t + 0$. For constructive interference, $\delta_{total} = m\lambda$,

or $t = \frac{m\lambda}{2n_f} = m\left(\frac{525\ \text{nm}}{2(1.25)}\right) = m(210\ \text{nm})$. Thus, the possible thicknesses are any positive integral multiples of 210 nm.

24.45 The wavelength of the wave is:

$$\lambda = \frac{c}{f} = \frac{3.00 \times 10^8\ \text{m/s}}{7.5 \times 10^9\ \text{Hz}} = 4.0 \times 10^{-2}\ \text{m} = 4.0\ \text{cm}.$$

The mth destructive interference occurs at: $\sin\theta = m\frac{\lambda}{a}$, so (for $m = 1$)

$$\sin\theta = 1\left(\frac{4\ \text{cm}}{6\ \text{cm}}\right) = 0.667, \quad \theta = 42°.$$

24.46 We first find the index of refraction of the glass by use of Snell's law: $n_1 \sin\theta_1 = n_g \sin\theta_2$ becomes: $1.00 \sin 37° = n_g \sin 22.0°$, giving

$$n_g = 1.61. \quad \text{Then,} \quad \tan\theta_p = \frac{n_2}{n_1} = \frac{1.61}{1.00} = 1.61, \text{ and } \quad \theta_p = 58.2°.$$

24.47 According to Malus's law, the intensity transmitted through the first polarizer is: $I_1 = I_i \cos^2\theta_1$. Then, applying Malus's law again gives the intensity transmitted through the second polarizer as

$$I_2 = I_1 \cos^2(\theta_2 - \theta_1).$$

Applying Malus's law for the third time, we see that the final transmitted intensity is:

$$I_f = I_2 \cos^2(\theta_3 - \theta_2) = I_i \cos^2\theta_1 \cos^2(\theta_2 - \theta_1)\cos^2(\theta_3 - \theta_2).$$

(a) If $\theta_1 = 45°$, $\theta_2 = 90°$, and $\theta_3 = 0°$; then

$$I_f = I_i \cos^2 45° \cos^2(90° - 45°)\cos^2(0 - 90°) = 0.$$

(b) If $\theta_1 = 0°$, $\theta_2 = 45°$, and $\theta_3 = 90°$; then

$$I_f = I_i \cos^2 0° \cos^2(45° - 0°)\cos^2(90° - 45°) = 0.25 I_i$$

24.48 From the sketch, observe that:

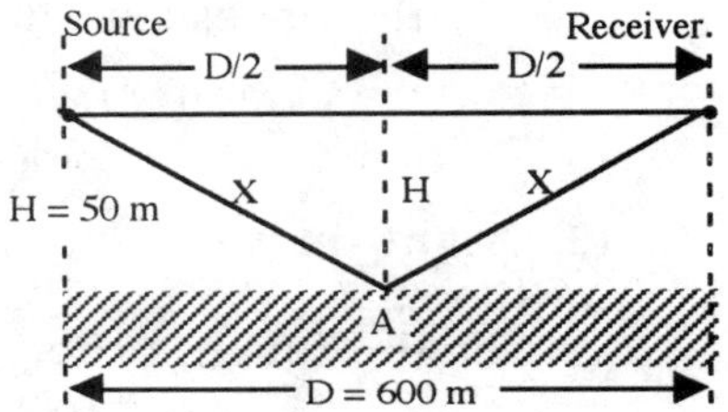

$$x = \sqrt{H^2 + \left(\frac{D}{2}\right)^2}$$

$$= \sqrt{(50.0 \text{ m})^2 + (300 \text{ m})^2} = 304 \text{ m}$$

Thus, the difference in the path lengths of the reflected and the direct waves is:

$$\delta_{path} = 2x - D = 2(304 \text{ m}) - 600 \text{ m} = 8.0 \text{ m}.$$

Also, there will be a half-wavelength phase shift due to the reflection at point A, and the total difference between the two waves is:

$$\delta_{total} = \delta_{path} + \delta_{reflection} = 8.0 \text{ m} + \frac{\lambda}{2}.$$

(a) For constructive interference, we must have:

$$\delta_{total} = 8.0 \text{ m} + \frac{\lambda}{2} = m\lambda, \text{ with } m = 1, 2, 3, \ldots \quad \text{Therefore,}$$

$$\lambda = \frac{8.0 \text{ m}}{m - 1/2}.$$ The longest wavelength corresponds to $m = 1$, so

$$\lambda = \frac{8.0 \text{ m}}{1/2}, \text{ or } \quad \lambda = 16 \text{ m (longest } \lambda \text{ for constructive interference).}$$

(b) For destructive interference interference, δ_{total} should equal an odd multiple of half-wavelengths:

$$\delta_{total} = 8.0 \text{ m} + \frac{\lambda}{2} = (2m + 1)\frac{\lambda}{2}, \quad \text{with } m = 1, 2, 3 \ldots \quad \text{This gives } \lambda = \frac{8 \text{ m}}{m}.$$

The longest wavelength for which this is true occurs when $m = 1$,

so $\lambda = \frac{8.0 \text{ m}}{(1)} = 8.0 \text{ m}$ is the longest wavelength for destructive interference.

24.49 (a) The path difference $\delta = d \sin\theta$, and when L is much much greater than y, we have $\sin\theta \approx \tan\theta = y/L$. Therefore,

$$\delta \approx \frac{yd}{L} = \frac{(1.80 \times 10^{-2} \text{ m})(1.50 \times 10^{-4} \text{ m})}{(1.40 \text{ m})} = 1.93 \times 10^{-6} \text{ m} = 1.93 \ \mu\text{m}.$$

(b) $\frac{\delta}{\lambda} = \frac{1.93 \text{ x } 10^{-6} \text{ m}}{6.43 \text{ x } 10^{-7} \text{ m}} = 3$, or $\delta = 3\lambda$.

(c) The interference will be a maximum since the path difference is an integer multiple of the wavelength.

24.50 (a) Since the light experiences a phase shift upon reflection at the top surface but not at the bottom surface, the total phase difference in the two reflected waves is:

$\delta_{total} = 2n_f x + \frac{\lambda}{2}$ where x is the

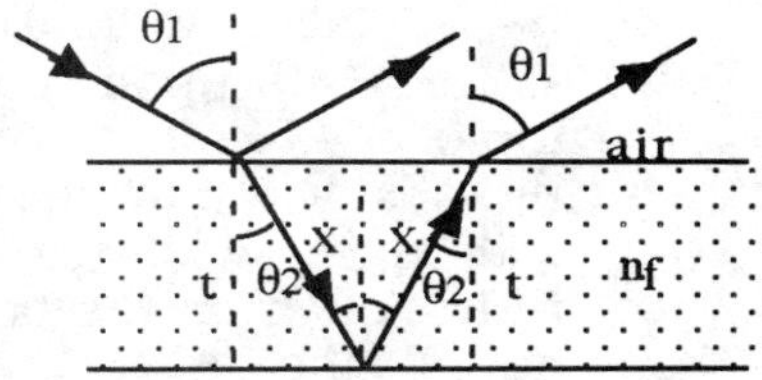

distance shown in the sketch. Since $\cos\theta_2 = \frac{t}{x}$, the extra path length of one of the waves is: $2x = \frac{2t}{\cos\theta_2}$. Thus, the total phase difference becomes: $\delta_{total} = \frac{2n_f t}{\cos\theta_2} + \frac{\lambda}{2}$. For constructive interference, this must be an integral multiple of wavelengths. Hence, we must require: $\delta_{total} = \frac{2n_f t}{\cos\theta_2} + \frac{\lambda}{2} = m\lambda$, where m is any positive integer.

This condition may be written as: $\frac{2n_f t}{\cos\theta_2} = (m - \frac{1}{2})\lambda$ where $m = 1, 2, 3,$

(b) Snell's law gives: $\sin\theta_2 = \frac{\sin\theta_1}{n_f} = \frac{\sin 30°}{1.38} = 0.362$, or $\theta_2 = 21.2°$.

The condition for constructive interference derived above (with m = 1 for <u>minimum</u> thickness)becomes: $\frac{2(1.38)t}{\cos 21.2°} = \frac{590 \text{ nm}}{2}$

Solving for t gives $t = \frac{(590 \text{ nm})\cos 21.2°}{4(1.38)} = 99.7$ nm

---

24.51 Consider a middle finger of width $d = 2$ cm.

(a) Two adjacent directions of constructive interference for 600 nm light are described by

$d\sin\theta = m\lambda$

$(2 \text{ x } 10^{-2} \text{ m})\sin\theta_1 = (1)(6 \text{ x } 10^{-7} \text{ m})$

$\theta_1 = 2 \text{ x } 10^{-3}$ degrees

So, if $\theta_0 = 0$, we have $\theta_1 - \theta_0 = 10^{-3}$ degrees

(b) Choose $\theta_1 = 20°$

$(2 \text{ x } 10^{-2} \text{ m})\sin 20° = (1)\lambda$

λ = 7 mm and millimeter waves are microwaves.

$f = \frac{c}{\lambda} = \frac{3 \text{ x } 10^{8} \text{ m/s}}{7 \text{ x } 10^{-3} \text{ m}}$ about 10^{11} Hz

---

24.52 For destructive interference, the path length must differ by $m\lambda$. We may treat this problem as a double slit experiment if we remember that the light undergoes a $\pi/2$ phase shift at the mirror. We have

$$y_{\text{dark}} = \frac{m\lambda L}{d} = \frac{1(5.0 \times 10^{-7}\ \text{m})(100\ \text{m})}{(2.0 \times 10^{-2}\ \text{m})} = 2.5\ \text{mm}$$

.0

24.53 If the index of refraction of the film, n_{film}, is greater than that of the glass, n_{glass}, then the light will be phase-shifted 180° upon reflection from the top of the film but not the bottom. If n_{film} is less than n_{glass}, then the light will be phase-shifted 180° upon reflection from the bottom of the film but not the top. So, in either case, for the dark rings (destructive interference), the extra path distance traveled by the light through the film should be an integral number of wavelengths of the light in the film. This requires that: $2t = \frac{m\lambda}{n_{\text{film}}}$. To find t in terms of r and R, note that: $R^2 = r^2 + (R - t)^2$, and solving for r^2 gives $r^2 = 2Rt + t^2$. Since t is much smaller than r or R, $t^2 \ll 2Rt$ so $r^2 \approx 2Rt$ and $t \approx \frac{r^2}{2R}$.

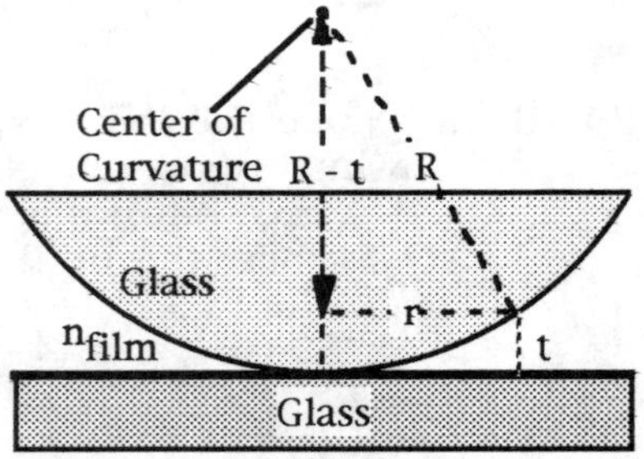

Thus, $2\left(\frac{r^2}{2R}\right) \approx \frac{m\lambda}{n_{\text{film}}}$, and $r \approx \sqrt{\frac{m\lambda R}{n_{\text{film}}}}$.

24.54 From problem 37, $r = \sqrt{\frac{m\lambda R}{n}}$ with m, λ and R the same in both instances. Thus $r^2 n = m\lambda R$ = constant, and $n_{\text{air}}r^2_{\text{air}} = n_{\text{liquid}}r^2_{\text{liquid}}$. Solving for n_{liquid} gives: $n_{\text{liquid}} = \frac{n_{\text{air}}r^2_{\text{air}}}{r^2_{\text{liquid}}} = \frac{(1.00)(1.50\ \text{cm})^2}{(1.31\ \text{cm})^2} = 1.31$.

24.55 (a) Applying Snell's law gives $n_2\sin\phi = n_1\sin\theta$. From the sketch, we also see that:

$\theta + \phi + \beta = \pi$, or $\phi = \pi - (\theta + \beta)$.

Thus, using the given identity:

$\sin\phi = \sin\pi\cos(\theta + \beta) - \cos\pi\sin(\theta + \beta)$, which reduces to: $\sin\phi = \sin(\theta + \beta)$.

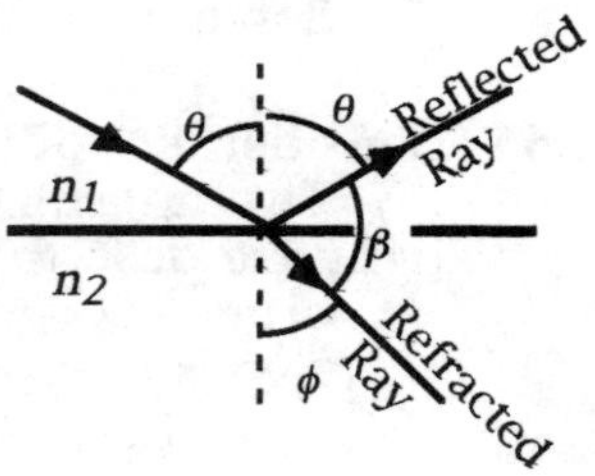

Applying the identity again gives:

$\sin\phi = \sin\theta\cos\beta + \cos\theta\sin\beta$, so

Snell's law becomes:

$n_2(\sin\theta\cos\beta + \cos\theta\sin\beta) = n_1\sin\theta$, or

(dividing by $\cos\theta$) $n_2(\tan\theta\cos\beta + \sin\beta) = n_1\tan\theta$.

Solving for $\tan\theta$ gives: $\tan\theta = \frac{n_2\sin\beta}{n_1 - n_2\cos\beta}$.

(b) If $\beta = 90°$, $n_1 = 1.0$, and $n_2 = n$, the above result becomes:

$\tan\theta = \frac{n(1)}{1.0 - 0}$, or $n = \tan\theta$, which is Brewster's law.

24.56 The wave must strike the water at the polarizing angle. Thus,

$$\tan\theta_p = \frac{n_2}{n_1} = \frac{1.33}{1.00} = 1.33.$$

But from triangle RST (see sketch), we have:

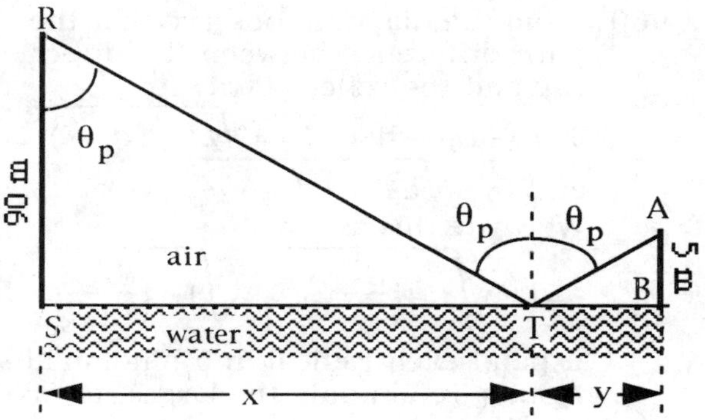

$$\tan\theta_p = \frac{x}{90.0\text{ m}}, \text{ or}$$

$$x = (90.0\text{ m})\tan\theta_p,$$

$$x = (90.0\text{ m})(1.33) = 120\text{ m}.$$

Also, using triangle ABT, we have:

$$\tan\theta_p = \frac{y}{5.00\text{ m}}, \text{ and } y = (5.00\text{ m})\tan\theta_p = (5.00\text{ m})(1.33) = 6.65\text{ m}.$$

The total distance from shore $= x + y = 126.7$ m.

24.57 We are assuming here (not really true) that the first order maximum occurs halfway between the first and second order minima. Then,

$$[y_{max}]_1 = \frac{[y_{dark}]_1 + [y_{dark}]_2}{2} = \frac{(1)\frac{\lambda}{a}L + (2)\frac{\lambda}{a}L}{2} = \frac{3}{2}\frac{\lambda}{a}L.$$

Thus,

$$a = \frac{3\lambda L}{2[y_{max}]_1} = \frac{3(5.00 \times 10^{-7}\text{ m})(1.40\text{ m})}{2(3.00 \times 10^{-3}\text{ m})} = 3.50 \times 10^{-4}\text{ m} = 0.350\text{ mm}.$$

24.58 There is zero net phase difference due to reflection from the surfaces of the film. Thus, $\delta_{total} = 2nft$. For destructive interference:

$$\delta_{total} = \left(m + \frac{1}{2}\right)\lambda, \text{ and for constructive interference: } \delta_{total} = m\lambda.$$

. Eliminating m and solving for t, we find

$$t = \frac{\lambda_d}{4n\left(1 - \frac{\lambda_d}{\lambda_b}\right)} = \frac{500\text{ nm}}{4(1.2)\left(1 - \frac{500}{750}\right)} = 313\text{ nm}.$$

24.59 Bright fringes occur when $2t = \frac{\lambda}{n}\left(m + \frac{1}{2}\right)$, and dark fringes occur when $2t = \frac{m\lambda}{n}$. The thickness of the film at x is: $t = \frac{hx}{l}$.

Therefore, $x_{bright} = \frac{\lambda l(m + 1/2)}{2hn}$, and $x_{dark} = \frac{\lambda l m}{2hn}$.

24.60 From the diagram, observe that the path difference between the direct ray and the reflected ray is:

$\delta = D_2 - D_1$, where $D_2 = \sqrt{L^2 + (d+y)^2}$,

and $D_1 = \sqrt{L^2 + (d-y)^2}$.

We write this as:

$$\delta = L\left(\sqrt{1 + \left(\frac{d+y}{L}\right)^2} - \sqrt{1 + \left(\frac{d-y}{L}\right)^2}\right)$$

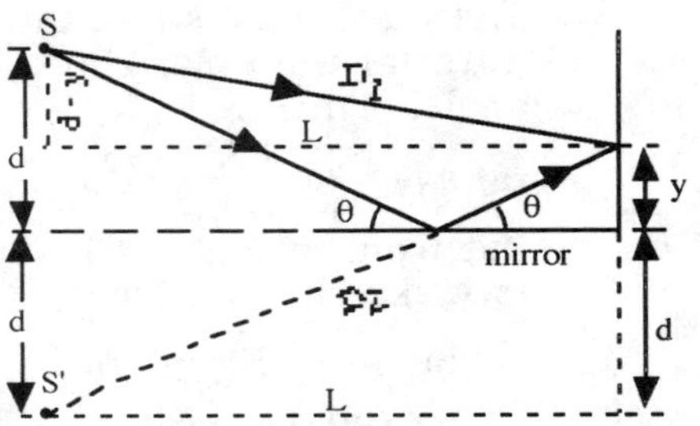

Expand each radical in a binominal series, and after subtracting the results, retain only the largest terms to find: $\delta \approx (2yd/L)$. Therefore,

$y \approx \frac{\delta L}{2d}$, and requiring that $\delta = \lambda$ (for first bright fringe) gives:

$$y \approx \frac{\lambda L}{2d} = \frac{(620 \times 10^{-9} \text{ m})(1.20 \text{ m})}{2(2.50 \times 10^{-3} \text{ m})} = 1.49 \times 10^{-4} \text{ m} = 0.149 \text{ mm}.$$

ANSWERS TO CONCEPTUAL QUESTIONS

2. The wavelength of light traveling in water would decrease, since the wavelength of light in a medium is given by $\lambda = \lambda_o/n$, where λ_o is the wavelength in vacuum and n is the index of refraction of the medium. Since the positions of the bright and dark fringes are proportional to the wavelength, the fringe separations would decrease.

4. Every color produces its own interference pattern and we see them superposed. The central maximum is white. The first maximum is a full spectrum with violet on the inside and red on the outside. The second maximum is also a full spectrum, with red in it overlapping with violet in the third maximum. At larger angles, the light soon starts mixing to white again.

6. (a) Two waves interfere constructively if their path difference is either zero or some integral multiple of the wavelength; that is, if the path difference is $m\lambda$, where m is an integer. (b) Two waves interfere destructively if their path difference is an odd multiple of one-half of a wavelength; that is, if the path difference equals $(m + \frac{1}{2})\lambda$.

8. The width of the central maximum increases as the width of the slit is made smaller. This can be seen by inspecting the condition for destructive interference, $\sin\theta = \lambda/a$. Since the width of the central maximum is proportional to $\sin\theta$, as the slit width a is reduced, the width of the central maximum increases.

10. Suppose the index of refraction of the coating is intermediate between vacuum and the glass. When the coating is very thin, light reflected from its top and bottom surfaces will interfere constructively, so you see the surface white and brighter. Once the thickness reaches one-quarter of the wavelength of violet light in the coating, destructive interference for violet light will make the surface look red. Then other colors in spectral order (blue, green, yellow, orange, and red) will interfere destructively, making the surface look red, violet, and then blue. As the coating gets thicker, constructive interference is observed for violet light and then for other colors in spectral order. Even thicker coatings give constructive and destructive interference for several visible wavelengths, so the reflected ligth starts looking white again.

12. The reflected light is partially polarized, with the component parallel to the reflecting surface being the most intense. Therefore, the polarizing material should have its transmission axis oriented in the vertical direction in order to minimize the intensity of the reflected light.

14. One way to produce interference patterns is to allow light to pass through very small openings. The opening between threads in a tautly stretched cloth like that in an umbrella is small enough for the effects to be observed.

16. Sound waves are longitudinal waves and cannot be polarized.

CHAPTER TWENTY-FIVE SOLUTIONS

Chapter Twenty-Five Readings

Bandana, E., "The Mystery of Myopia," *The Sciences*, Nov./Dec. 1985, p. 46.

Marr, D., *Vision*, New York, W.H. Freeman, 1982.

Michael, C.R., "Retinal Processing of Visual Images," *Scientific American*, May 1969, p. 105.

Neisser, U., "The Processes of Vision," *Scientific American*, September 1968, p. 204.

Price, W.H., "Photographic Lens," *Scientific American*, August 1976, p. 72.

Ruiz, M., "Camera Optics," *The Physics Teacher*, September 1982, p. 372.

Shankland, R.S., "Michelson and His Interferometer," *Physics Today*, April 1976, p. 72.

Stix, G., "Pictures Worth a Thousand Cameras," *Scientific American*, November 1996, p. 46.

Wald, G., "Eye and Camera," *Scientific American*, August 1950, p. 32.

Walker, T.D., *Light and its Uses*, New York, W.H. Freeman, 1980.

25.1 From $\frac{1}{p}+\frac{1}{q}=\frac{1}{f}$, we have: $\frac{1}{q}=\frac{1}{f}-\frac{1}{p}=\frac{1}{0.250\text{ m}}-\frac{1}{1.50\text{ m}}$, and from this, $q = 0.300$ m= 30.0 cm. Thus the image is formed 30.0 cm beyond the lens.

$$M = -\frac{q}{p} = -\frac{30\text{ cm}}{150\text{ cm}} = -\frac{1}{5}.$$

25.2 The magnitude of the magnification is: $|M| = \frac{h'}{h} = \frac{q}{p}$.

Therefore $h = h'\left(\frac{p}{q}\right)$

From the thin lens equation,

$$q = \frac{pf}{p-f} = \frac{(100\text{ m})(52.0\text{ mm})}{100\text{ m} - 52.0\times 10^{-3}\text{ m}} = 52.0\text{ mm}.$$

The object height is then: $h = h'\left(\frac{p}{q}\right) = (92.0\text{ mm})\left(\frac{100\text{ m}}{52.0\text{ mm}}\right) = 177\text{ m}$

25.3 Consider rays coming from opposite edges of the object and passing undeviated through the center of the lens as shown at the right. The angle between these rays is the angular width of the object. If the object is very distant, the image distance is equal to the focal length of the lens. Then, if $f = 55.0$ mm and $\theta = 20.0°$, the image size may be found as follows:

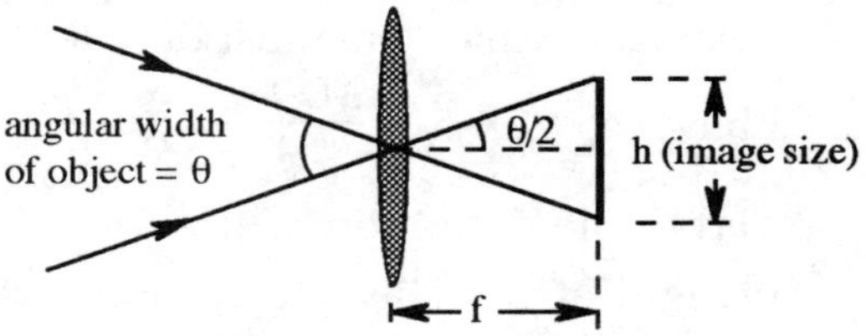

$$\frac{\frac{h}{2}}{f} = \tan\frac{\theta}{2}, \text{ or } h = (2f)\tan\frac{\theta}{2} = [2(55.0\text{ mm})]\tan\frac{20°}{2} = 19.4\text{ mm}.$$

Therefore, the image easily fits within a 23.5 mm by 35.0 mm space.

25.4 The magnitude of the magnification is $|M| = \frac{h'}{h} = \frac{q}{p}$.

Therefore $h' = h\left(\frac{q}{p}\right)$

The object distance is: $p = 3.84 \times 10^8$ m and with the object so far away, $q = f = 120$ mm. The object size is the *diameter* of the moon. Thus, $h = 2(1.74 \times 10^6\text{ m}) = 3.48 \times 10^6$ m and the image size is:

$$h' = \frac{(3.48 \times 10^6\text{ m})(120 \times 10^{-3}\text{ m})}{(3.84 \times 10^8\text{ m})} = 1.09 \times 10^{-3}\text{ m} = 1.09\text{ mm}.$$

25.5 The exposure time is being reduced by a factor of: $\dfrac{\frac{1}{256\text{ s}}}{\frac{1}{32\text{ s}}} = \frac{1}{8}$

Thus, to maintain correct exposure, you need to get 8 times more light on the film. To do this the aperture opening will have to be 8 times the original area, or: (new diameter) = $\sqrt{8}$ (original diameter), or $D_2 = \sqrt{8}\,D_1$.

From the definition of the f-number, $f\# = \frac{\text{focal length}}{\text{Diameter}}$ so

$$f\#_{new} = \frac{f\#_{lens}}{D_2} = \frac{f\#_{lens}}{\sqrt{8}D_1} = \frac{\frac{f\#_{lens}}{D_1}}{\sqrt{8}} = \frac{f\#_{old}}{\sqrt{8}} = \frac{4}{2.83} = 1.41.$$

We must use an $f/1.4$ setting.

25.6 To properly focus the image of a distant object, the lens must be a distance equal to the focal length away from the film ($q_1 = 65.0$ mm). For the closer object:

$\frac{1}{p_2} + \frac{1}{q_2} = \frac{1}{f}$ becomes $\frac{1}{2000\text{ mm}} + \frac{1}{q_2} = \frac{1}{65.0\text{ mm}}$, and $q_2 = 67.2$ mm.

The lens must be moved away a distance $D = q_2 - q_1 = 2.20$ mm.

25.7 To double the energy delivered to the film while using the same exposure time, you must double the area of the aperature. Then, we have $A_2 = 2A_1$ or $\frac{\pi D^2_{new}}{4} = 2\left(\frac{\pi D^2_{old}}{4}\right)$, or $D_{new} = \sqrt{2}\, D_{old}$.

From the definition of the f-number, $f\# = \frac{f_{lens}}{D}$. In this case, the focal length of the lens is constant.

Thus, $f\#_{new} = \frac{f_{lens}}{D_{new}} = \frac{f_{lens}}{\sqrt{2}D_{old}} = \frac{f\#_{old}}{\sqrt{2}} = \frac{11}{\sqrt{2}} = 7.78$.

There is no $f/7.78$ setting on a camera, so one should use the $f/8$ setting.

25.8 She needs a lens that forms a virtual image at the near point (q = - 60.0 cm) when the paper is held at 24.0 cm. $\frac{1}{p}+\frac{1}{q}=\frac{1}{f}$: becomes:

$$\frac{1}{24.0\ \text{cm}} + \left(\frac{1}{-60\ \text{cm}}\right) = \frac{1}{f},\quad \text{so}\quad f = +40.0\ \text{cm}.$$

25.9 For the right eye, a virtual image of the most distant object should be 8.44 cm in front of the lens (i.e., q = -8.44 cm when $p = \infty$). Thus,

$\frac{1}{p}+\frac{1}{q}=\frac{1}{f}$ gives: $0 + \frac{1}{-8.44\ \text{cm}} = \frac{1}{f}$, or $f = -8.44\ \text{cm} = -0.0844\ \text{m}$, and

$$P = \frac{1}{-0.0844\ \text{m}} = -11.8\ \text{diopters}.$$

For the left eye, as in the above, the needed lens has a focal length of: f = -(far point), so $f = -0.122$ m, and $P = \frac{1}{-0.122\ \text{m}} = -8.20$ diopters.

25.10 (a) When an object is at 25.0 cm in front of the lens (p = 25.0 cm), the image must be virtual and 100 cm in front of the lens so that the eye can focus on it. (q = -100 cm).

Thus, $\frac{1}{p}+\frac{1}{q}=\frac{1}{f}$ becomes: $\frac{1}{25.0\ \text{cm}} + \left(\frac{1}{-100\ \text{cm}}\right) = \frac{1}{f}$,

from which, $f = 33.3$ cm.

(b) $P = \frac{1}{f} = \frac{1}{0.333\ \text{m}} = +3.00$ diopters.

25.11 (a) If the far point is at 50.0 cm, we need an image distance of q = -50.0 cm when p = infinity. Thus, $\frac{1}{p}+\frac{1}{q}=\frac{1}{f}$ becomes:

$0 + \left(\frac{1}{-50.0\ \text{cm}}\right) = \frac{1}{f}$, and $f = -50.0\ \text{cm} = -0.500$ m, so the power is:

$$P = \frac{1}{f} = \frac{1}{-0.500\ \text{m}} = -2.00\ \text{diopters}.$$

(b) To be seen by the eye, the virtual image cannot be any closer than 13.0 cm to the lens. Thus, let us find the smallest value the object distance can have: $\frac{1}{p}+\frac{1}{q}=\frac{1}{f}$ becomes: $\frac{1}{p} + \left(\frac{1}{-0.130\ \text{m}}\right) = \frac{1}{-0.500\ \text{m}}$,

which gives $p = 0.176\ \text{m} = 17.6$ cm. Thus, the near point when glasses are worn is 17.6 cm.

25.12 Considering the image formed by the eye as a virtual object for the implanted lens, we have:

$$p = -(2.53\text{ cm} + 2.80\text{ cm}) = -5.33\text{ cm, and } q = 2.80\text{ cm}$$

Thus, $\frac{1}{p} + \frac{1}{q} = \frac{1}{f}$ becomes: $\left(\frac{1}{-5.33\text{ cm}}\right) + \frac{1}{2.80\text{ cm}} = \frac{1}{f}$, which gives

$f = +5.90$ cm and $P = \frac{1}{0.059\text{ m}} = +17.0$ diopters.

25.13 (a) To correct nearsightedness, the image of distant objects ($p = \infty$) should be virtual and located at the far point ($q = -1.5$ m). Thus,

$\frac{1}{p} + \frac{1}{q} = \frac{1}{f}$ becomes: $0 + \left(\frac{1}{-1.5\text{ m}}\right) = \frac{1}{f}$, or $f = -1.5$ m. The power is

then $P = \frac{1}{f} = \left(\frac{1}{-1.5\text{ m}}\right) = -0.67$ diopters.

(b) To correct farsightedness, objects at $p = 25$ cm should form a virtual image at the near point (q = -0.30 m). $\frac{1}{p} + \frac{1}{q} = \frac{1}{f}$ becomes:

$\frac{1}{0.25\text{ m}} + \left(\frac{1}{-0.30\text{ m}}\right) = \frac{1}{f}$, from which $f = +1.5$ m, and

$P = \frac{1}{f} = \frac{1}{1.5\text{ m}} = +0.67$ diopters.

25.14 (a) Objects at the far point ($p = 125$ cm) are focused on the retina ($q = 2.00$ cm). The focal length of the lens-cornea combination in this case is: $\frac{1}{125\text{ cm}} + \frac{1}{2.00\text{ cm}} = \frac{1}{f_{far}}$, or $f_{far} = 1.97$ cm,

and $P_{far} = \frac{1}{f_{far}} = \frac{1}{0.0197\text{ m}} = +50.8$ diopters.

Objects at the near point ($p = 10.0$ cm) are also focused on the retina ($q = 2.00$ cm). Thus, $\frac{1}{10.0\text{ cm}} + \frac{1}{2.00\text{ cm}} = \frac{1}{f_{near}}$, or

$f_{near} = 1.67$ cm, and $P_{near} = +60.0$ diopters.

(b) A diverging corrective lens must be used to form virtual images (located at the eye's far point) of very distant objects, ie., ($q = -125$ cm when $p = \infty$). Thus, $\frac{1}{p} + \frac{1}{q} = \frac{1}{f}$ gives:

$\frac{1}{\infty} - \frac{1}{125\text{ cm}} = \frac{1}{f}$, or $f = -125$ cm, and the power of the needed

corrective lens is: $P = \frac{1}{f} = \left(\frac{1}{-1.25\text{ m}}\right) = -0.800$ diopters.

25.15 (a) $\frac{1}{p} + \frac{1}{q} = \frac{1}{f}$ becomes: $\frac{1}{p} + \left(\frac{1}{-25\text{ cm}}\right) = \frac{1}{7.5\text{ cm}}$, giving $p = 5.8$ cm.

(b) With the virtual image at the normal near point, the angular magnification of a simple magnifier is $M = 1 + \frac{25\text{ cm}}{f}$. In this case,

we have: $M = 1 + \frac{25.0\text{ cm}}{5.8\text{ cm}} = 5.3$.

25.16 (a) With the image at the normal near point, the angular magnification is: $M = 1 + \frac{25 \text{ cm}}{f} = 1 + \frac{25 \text{ cm}}{25 \text{ cm}} = 2.0.$

(b) When the eye is relaxed: $M = \frac{25 \text{ cm}}{f} = \frac{25 \text{ cm}}{25 \text{ cm}} = 1.0.$

25.17 (a) We are given that: p = 3.50 cm, and q = -25.0 cm.

Thus, $\frac{1}{p} + \frac{1}{q} = \frac{1}{f}$ becomes: $\frac{1}{3.50 \text{ cm}} + \left(\frac{1}{-25.0 \text{ cm}}\right) = \frac{1}{f}$, so f = 4.07 cm.

(b) With the image at the normal near point, the angular magnification is: $M = 1 + \frac{25.0 \text{ cm}}{f} = 1 + \frac{25.0 \text{ cm}}{4.07 \text{ cm}} = 7.14$

25.18 (a) First, locate the image being formed by the lens.

$\frac{1}{p} + \frac{1}{q} = \frac{1}{f}$ becomes: $\frac{1}{71.0 \text{ cm}} + \frac{1}{q} = \frac{1}{39.0 \text{ cm}}$, so $q = 86.5$ cm

The magnitude of the lateral magnification is then:

$|M| = \frac{h'}{h} = |\frac{q}{p}| = \frac{86.5 \text{ cm}}{71.0 \text{ cm}} = 1.22$. Thus, $h' = 1.22\ h$.

(b) The angular size of the leaf if viewed directly from a distance of $d = 71.0 \text{ cm} + 126 \text{ cm} = 197$ would be $\theta_0 = \frac{h}{d} = \frac{h}{197 \text{ cm}}$. When the image is viewed from a distance of $d' = 126 \text{ cm} - 86.5 \text{ cm} = 39.5$ cm, its angular size is: $\theta = \frac{h'}{d'} = \frac{h'}{39.5 \text{ cm}}$. The angular magnification achieved by use of the lens is: $\frac{\theta}{\theta_0} = \frac{h'/39.5 \text{ cm}}{h/197 \text{ cm}} = \frac{h'}{h}\left(\frac{197 \text{ cm}}{39.5 \text{ cm}}\right) =$ 1.22(4.99) = 6.08.

25.19 (a) $M_1 = -\frac{L}{f_o} = -50.0$. Thus, $f_o = \frac{L}{50.0} = \frac{20.0 \text{ cm}}{50.0} = 0.400$ cm.

(b) $M_e = \frac{25.0 \text{ cm}}{f_e} = 20.0$, and $f_e = \frac{25.0 \text{ cm}}{20.0} = 1.25$ cm.

(c) $M = M_1 M_e = -(50.0)(20.0) = -1000.$

25.20 First, find the size of the final image: angular size $= \frac{h_e}{|q_e|} = \frac{h_e}{29.0 \text{ cm}} =$ 1.43×10^{-3} rad, so $h_e = 4.15 \times 10^{-2}$ cm.

Now apply thin lens equation to each lens to find the lateral magnification produced by each lens and hence the overall magnification:

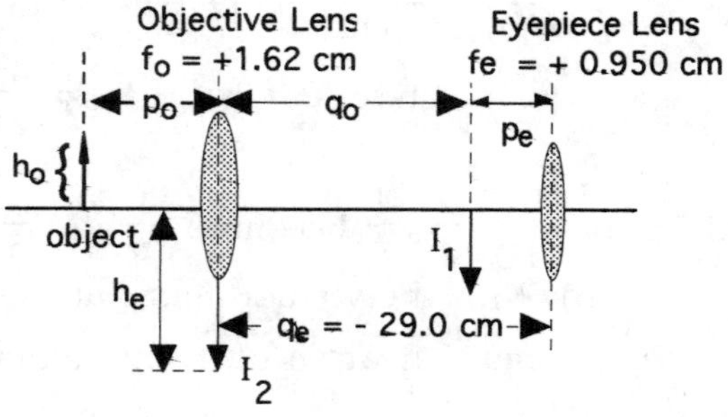

$\frac{1}{p} + \frac{1}{q} = \frac{1}{f}$ becomes:

$\frac{1}{p_e} + \frac{1}{-29.0 \text{ cm}} = \frac{1}{0.950 \text{ cm}}$, so

$p_e = 0.920$ cm, and

$M_e = -\frac{q_e}{p_e} = -\frac{29.0 \text{ cm}}{0.920 \text{ cm}} = 31.5$

For the objective lens, we have: $\frac{1}{p_o}+\frac{1}{q_o}=\frac{1}{f_o}$, or

$\frac{1}{p_o}+\frac{1}{28.1\ \text{cm}}=\frac{1}{1.622\ \text{cm}}$, so $p_o=1.72$ cm,

The magnitude of the lateral magnification produced by the objective is: $M_o=\frac{q_o}{p_o}=\frac{28.1\ \text{cm}}{1.72\ \text{cm}}=16.3$, and the overall magnification is:

$M=M_eM_o=(31.5)(16.3)=513.$

Therefore, $h_o=\frac{h_e}{M}=\frac{4.15\times10^{-2}\ \text{cm}}{513}=0.810\ \mu\text{m}.$

25.21 If the eye is relaxed, the final image is at infinity. Thus the object position for the eyepiece is: $p_e=f_e=2.50$ cm, and the angular magnification of the eyepiece is: $m_e=\frac{25.0\ \text{cm}}{f_e}=10.0$

The image position for the objective lens is:

$q_o=L-f_e=15.0\ \text{cm}-2.50\ \text{cm}=12.5\ \text{cm}.$

[*Note:* The approximation that the the image distance for the objective is nearly equal to the length of the microscope is a poor one in this case. Hence, we should not use $M_1=\frac{L}{f_o}$.]

We now find the object position for the objective:

$\frac{1}{p_o}+\frac{1}{q_o}=\frac{1}{f_o}$, becomes $\frac{1}{p_o}+\frac{1}{12.5\ \text{cm}}=\frac{1}{1.00\ \text{cm}}$, so $p_o=1.09$ cm.

Thus, the lateral magnification produced by the objective lens is:

$M_1=-\frac{q_o}{p_o}=-\frac{12.5\ \text{cm}}{1.09\ \text{cm}}=-11.5$, and the overall magnification of the microscope is: $M_{overall}=M_1m_e=(-11.5)(10)=-115$

25.22 $M=-\frac{f_o}{f_e}=-\frac{75\ \text{cm}}{4.0\ \text{cm}}=-19$

25.23 (a) The diameter of the lens is 5.00 in = 127 mm, so

$f_{number}=\frac{f_o}{D}=\frac{1250\ \text{mm}}{127\ \text{mm}}=9.84.$

(b) The angular magnification is: $M=-\frac{f_o}{f_e}=-\frac{1250\ \text{mm}}{25\ \text{mm}}=-50$

25.24 (See sketch.) The length, x, of an object on the moon, is found as

$\frac{x}{3.80\times10^{8}\ \text{m}}=\frac{1.00\times10^{-2}\ \text{m}}{15.0\ \text{m}}$

,and $x=2.53\times10^{5}$ m = 157 miles.

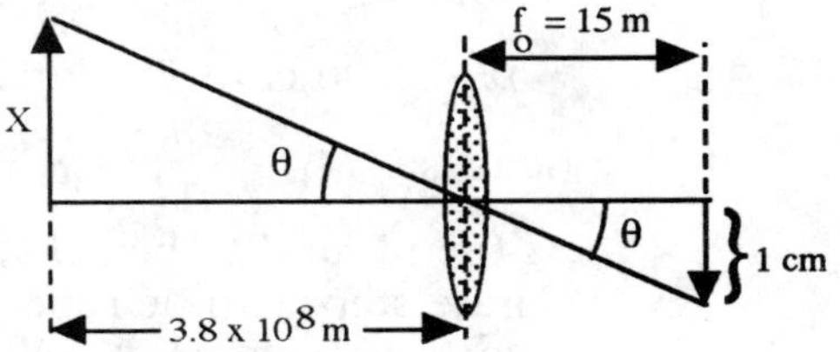

25.25 The length of the telescope is: $L=f_o+f_e=92$ cm. (1)

The angular magnification is: $M=\frac{f_o}{f_e}=45$, so $f_o=45f_e$ (2)

Substitute (2) into (1) to obtain: $45f_e+f_e=92$ cm, or $f_e=2.0$ cm

Then (2) gives: $f_o = 45(2.0\text{ cm})$ or $f_o = 90\text{ cm}$.

25.26 Use the larger focal length (lowest power) lens as the objective element and the shorter focal length (largest power) lens for the eye piece. The focal lengths are: $f_o = \frac{1}{1.20\text{ diopter}} = 0.833\text{ m} = 83.3\text{ cm}$, and

$f_e = \frac{1}{9.00\text{ diopters}} = 0.111\text{ m} = 11.1\text{ cm}$.

(a) The angular magnification (or magnifying power) of the telescope is then: $M = \frac{f_o}{f_e} = \frac{83.3\text{ cm}}{11.1\text{ cm}} = 7.50$.

(b) The length of the telescope is:
$L = f_o + f_e = 83.3\text{ cm} + 11.1\text{ cm} = 94.4\text{ cm}$.

25.27 Consider first the lens used for the left eye. The near point is at 50.0 cm ($q = -50.0\text{ cm}$ when $p = 25.0\text{ cm}$). Thus,

$\frac{1}{p} + \frac{1}{q} = \frac{1}{f}$ becomes: $\frac{1}{25.0\text{ cm}} + \left(\frac{1}{-50.0\text{ cm}}\right) = \frac{1}{f}$, and $f = 50.0\text{ cm}$.

For the right eye lens, we have a near point of 100 cm ($q = -100\text{ cm}$ when $p = 25\text{ cm}$).

$\frac{1}{p} + \frac{1}{q} = \frac{1}{f}$ becomes: $\frac{1}{25.0\text{ cm}} + \left(\frac{1}{-100\text{ cm}}\right) = \frac{1}{f}$, and $f = 33.3\text{ cm}$.

(a) The angular magnification of the telescope (using the longest focal length lens for the objective) is: $M = \frac{f_o}{f_e} = \frac{50.0\text{ cm}}{33.3\text{ cm}} = 1.50$.

(b) We shall use the 50.0 cm lens as the objective, and we shall require that a virtual final image be formed at $q_e = -25.0\text{ cm}$ for ***maximum*** magnification. The object distance for the eyepiece is:

$\frac{1}{p_e} + \frac{1}{q_e} = \frac{1}{f_e}$, or $\frac{1}{p_e} + \left(\frac{1}{-25.0\text{ cm}}\right) = \frac{1}{33.3\text{ cm}}$, yielding $p_e = 14.3$ cm.

When the image of the eyepiece (acting as a simple magnifier) is at the normal near point ($q_e = -25.0\text{ cm}$), the angular magnification produced by the eyepiece is: $m_e = 1 + \frac{25.0\text{ cm}}{f_e} = 1 + \frac{25.0\text{ cm}}{33.3\text{ cm}} = 1.75$.

The image position for the objective is:
$q_o = L - p_e = 10.0\text{ cm} - 14.3\text{ cm} = -4.30\text{ cm}$, and the object position is found as: $\frac{1}{p_o} + \frac{1}{q_o} = \frac{1}{f_o}$, or $\frac{1}{p_o} + \left(\frac{1}{-4.30\text{ cm}}\right) = \frac{1}{50.0\text{ cm}}$, yielding

$p_o = 3.96\text{ cm}$. The lateral magnification produced by the objective lens is: $M_1 = -\frac{q_o}{p_o} = -\left(\frac{-4.30\text{ cm}}{3.96\text{ cm}}\right) = 1.09$. The overall magnification is then found to be: $M_{overall} = M_1 m_e = (1.09)(1.75) = 1.91$.

These steps can be repeated with the 33.3 cm lens as the objective and the 50 cm as the eyepiece of the microscope. For that case, the overall magnification will be 1.80. Thus, the arrangement used above gives the greater magnification.

25.28 The angular resolution needed is:

$$\theta_m = \frac{s}{r} = \left(\frac{300 \text{ m}}{3.8 \times 10^8 \text{ m}}\right) = 7.9 \times 10^{-7} \text{ rad.}$$

For a circular aperture:

$$\theta_m = 1.22\frac{\lambda}{D}, \text{ so } D = 1.22\frac{\lambda}{\theta_m} = 1.22\left(\frac{500 \times 10^{-9} \text{ m}}{7.9 \times 10^{-7} \text{ rad}}\right)$$
$$= 0.77 \text{ m (about 30 inches.)}$$

25.29 If just resolved: $\theta = \theta_m = 1.22\frac{\lambda}{D} = 1.22\left(\frac{500 \times 10^{-9} \text{ m}}{0.300 \text{ m}}\right) = 2.03 \times 10^{-6}$ rad.

Thus the altitude is: $h = \frac{d}{\theta} = \frac{1.00 \text{ m}}{2.03 \times 10^{-6} \text{ rad}} = 4.93 \times 10^5 \text{ m} = 493 \text{ km}.$

25.30 The limit of resolution in air is: $\theta_{air} = 1.22\frac{\lambda}{D} = 0.60\,\mu\text{rad}$. In oil, the wavelength becomes $\lambda_{oil} = \frac{\lambda_{air}}{n_{oil}}$, so the limiting angle in oil is:

$$\theta_{oil} = 1.22\frac{\lambda_{oil}}{D} = \frac{1.22\left(\frac{\lambda_{air}}{n_{oil}}\right)}{D} = \frac{\theta_{air}}{n_{oil}} = \frac{0.60\ \mu\text{rad}}{1.5} = 0.40\,\mu\text{rad}.$$

25.31 $\theta = \frac{s}{r} = \left(\frac{2.0 \text{ m}}{10.0 \times 10^3 \text{ m}}\right) = 2.0 \times 10^{-4}$ rad.

If the two lights are to be just barely resolved,

$$\theta = \theta_m = 1.22\frac{\lambda}{D}, \text{ so } D = \frac{1.22\lambda}{\theta}, \text{ or}$$

$$D = 1.22\left(\frac{8.85 \times 10^{-7} \text{ m}}{2.0 \times 10^{-4} \text{ rad}}\right) = 5.4 \times 10^{-3} \text{ m} = 5.4 \text{ mm}.$$

25.32 (a) $\lambda_{medium} = \frac{\lambda_{vac}}{n_{medium}} = \frac{500 \text{ nm}}{1.33} = 376$ nm. The limiting angle is then:

$$\theta_m = 1.22\frac{\lambda}{D} = 1.22\left(\frac{3.76 \times 10^{-7} \text{ m}}{2.00 \times 10^{-3} \text{ m}}\right) = 2.29 \times 10^{-4} \text{ rad.}$$

(b) $r = \frac{s}{\theta_m} = \frac{1.00 \times 10^{-2} \text{ m}}{2.29 \times 10^{-4} \text{rad}} = 43.7 \text{ m}$

25.33 The diameter of the aperature is: $D = 20 \text{ in} = 51 \text{ cm} = 0.51 \text{ m}$. Since the two stars are barely resolved,

$$\theta = \theta_m = 1.22\frac{\lambda}{D} = 1.22\left(\frac{500 \times 10^{-9} \text{ m}}{0.51 \text{ m}}\right) = 1.2 \times 10^{-6} \text{ rad.}$$

Thus, $s = r\theta = (8.0 \text{ ly})\left(\frac{9.461 \times 10^{12} \text{ km}}{1 \text{ ly}}\right)(1.2 \times 10^{-6} \text{ rad.}) = 9.1 \times 10^7 \text{ km}$

25.34 If just resolved: $\theta = \theta_m = 1.22\frac{\lambda}{D} = 1.22\left(\frac{550 \times 10^{-9} \text{ m}}{0.35 \text{ m}}\right) = 1.9 \times 10^{-6}$ rad.

and $s = r\theta = (1.9 \times 10^{-6} \text{ rad.})(2.00 \times 10^5 \text{ m}) = 0.38 \text{ m} = 38 \text{ cm}.$

25.35 Under the conditions of this problem, the limit of resolution is:

$$\theta_m = 1.22\frac{\lambda}{D} = 1.22\left(\frac{500 \times 10^{-9}\ \text{m}}{5.00\ \text{m}}\right) = 1.22 \times 10^{-7}\ \text{rad}.$$ Thus, the minimum observable separation is:

$$s = r\theta_m = (1.22 \times 10^{-7}\ \text{rad})(8.0 \times 10^{7}\ \text{km}) = 9.8\ \text{km}$$

27.36 A fringe shift occurs when the mirror is moved a distance of $\frac{\lambda}{4}$. Thus, if the mirror is moved a distance $\Delta L = 0.180\ \text{mm} = 1.80 \times 10^{-4}$ m and the wavelength is λ = 550 nm, the number of fringe shifts observed is:

$$\text{fringe shifts} = \frac{\Delta L}{(\lambda/4)} = \frac{4(\Delta L)}{\lambda} = \frac{4(1.80 \times 10^{-4}\ \text{m})}{550 \times 10^{-9}\ \text{m}} = 1.31 \times 10^{3}\ \text{m}$$

25.37 A fringe shift occurs when the mirror is moved a distance of $\frac{\lambda}{4}$. Thus if 310 fringe shifts are counted, the interferometer mirror has moved a distance of $\Delta L = d = 310\left(\frac{650 \times 10^{-9}\ \text{m}}{4}\right) = 50.4\ \mu\text{m}$ (length of the amoeba).

25.38 If the number of wavelengths that will fit in the length of the tube changes by ΔN, there will be $4(\Delta N)$ fringe shifts observed. When the tube is evacuated, the number of wavelengths in its length is $N = \frac{L}{\lambda_{vac}}$

When the tube is filled with gas, the number of wavelengths is:

$$N' = \frac{L}{\lambda_{gas}} = \frac{L}{(\lambda_{vac}/n_{gas})} = \frac{n_{gas}L}{\lambda_{vac}}$$ Thus, the number of fringe shifts observed as the tube fills will be:

$$\text{fringe shifts} = 4(\Delta N) = 4\left(\frac{n_{gas}L}{\lambda_{vac}} - \frac{L}{\lambda_{vac}}\right) = \frac{4L}{\lambda_{vac}}(n_{gas} - 1).$$

Solving for the index of refraction gives:

$$n_{gas} = 1 + \frac{\lambda_{vac}}{4L}\ (\#\text{shifts})$$

If 600 nm light is used, L = 5.00 cm and 160 fringe shifts are observed, we have:

$$n_{gas} = 1 + \frac{600 \times 10^{-9}\ \text{m}}{4(5.00 \times 10^{-2}\ \text{m})}(160) = 1.0005$$

25.39 Note that changing the number of wavelengths that will fit within the length of the cell by ΔN will produce $4(\Delta N)$ fringe shifts since this is equivalent to increasing the length of the interferometer arm by $(\Delta N)\lambda$. As the air is evacuated from the cell, the wavelength of the light within the cell changes from $\lambda_{air} = \frac{\lambda_{vac}}{n_{air}}$ to λ_{vac}.

Thus, the number of wavelengths that will fit within the length of the cell changes from $N = \frac{L}{\lambda_{air}} = L\frac{n_{air}}{\lambda_{vac}}$ to $N' = \frac{L}{\lambda_{vac}}$ and the number of fringe shifts observed will be:

$$\#\text{fringe shifts} = 4(N - N')$$

$$= 4\left(L\frac{n_{air}}{\lambda_{vac}} - \frac{L}{\lambda_{vac}}\right) = \frac{4L}{\lambda_{vac}}(n_{air} - 1),\ \text{or}$$

$$\# \text{ fringe shifts} = \frac{4(5.00 \times 10^{-2}\text{ m})}{590 \times 10^{-9}\text{ m}}(1.00029 - 1) = 98.3, \text{ or } 98 \text{ complete}$$
shifts.

25.40 In a vacuum, the number of wavelengths in a distance t is $N = \frac{t}{\lambda_{vac}}$ When this space is filled by a medium of refractive index n_m, the number of wavelengths in the same distance t is $N' = \frac{t}{\lambda_{medium}} = \frac{n_m t}{\lambda_{vac}}$ Thus, the number of fringe shifts that will occur is:

$$\# \text{ fringe shifts} = 4(\Delta N) = 4\left(\frac{n_m t}{\lambda_{vac}} - \frac{t}{\lambda_{vac}}\right) = \frac{4t}{\lambda_{vac}}(n_m - 1).$$

If $t = 15 \times 10^{-6}$ m, $\lambda = 600$ nm, and $n_m = 1.4$, we have:

$$\# \text{ fringe shifts} = \frac{4(15 \times 10^{-6}\text{ m})}{600 \times 10^{-9}\text{ m}}(1.40 - 1) = 40$$

25.41 We first find the grating spacing as: $d = \frac{n\lambda}{\sin\theta} = \frac{(2)(502.\text{nm})}{\sin 30.0°} = 2008$ nm. Then for the 668 nm line, we have:

$$\sin\theta = \frac{n\lambda}{d} = \frac{(1)(668\text{ nm})}{2008\text{ nm}} = 0.333, \text{ from which: } \theta = 19.4°.$$

25.42 (a) $d = \frac{1}{3660\text{ lines/cm}} = 2.732 \times 10^{-4}\text{ cm} = 2.732 \times 10^{-6}\text{ m} = 2732$ nm.

The wavelength found at angle θ is: $\lambda = \frac{d \sin\theta}{n}$.

At $\theta = 10.1°$, $\lambda = 479$ nm; at $\theta = 13.7°$, $\lambda = 647$ nm; and at $\theta = 14.8°$, $\lambda = 698$ nm.

(b) The grating spacing is: $d = \frac{\lambda}{\sin\theta_1}$, and

for the second order: $(2)\lambda = d\sin\theta_2$. Combining these equations

gives: $\sin\theta_2 = \frac{2\lambda}{d} = 2\lambda\left(\frac{\sin\theta_1}{\lambda}\right) = 2\sin\theta_1$.

Therefore, if $\theta_1 = 10.1°$ then $\sin\theta_2 = 2\sin(10.1°)$ gives $\theta_2 = 20.5°$. Similarly, for $\theta_1 = 13.7°$, $\theta_2 = 28.3°$; and for $\theta_1 = 14.8°$, $\theta_2 = 30.7°$.

25.43 (a) The longest wavelength in the visible spectrum is 700 nm. The number of complete spectra that can be seen is therefore the same as the number of visible orders of the 700 nm light. From the grating equation, we have:

$n_{max}\lambda = d\sin\theta_{max}$, or $n_{max} = \frac{d\sin\theta_{max}}{\lambda}$. The slit spacing is:

$$d = \frac{1}{600\text{ line/mm}} = 1.67 \times 10^{-3}\text{ mm}.$$

Thus, $n_{max} = \frac{(1.67 \times 10^{-6}\text{ m})\sin 90°}{700 \times 10^{-9}\text{ m}} = 2.39$,

and we see that only two complete orders of the visible spectrum can be seen.

(b) For the violet edge of the first order:

$$\sin\theta_{V1} = \frac{n\lambda}{d} = \frac{(1)(400 \times 10^{-9}\ \text{m})}{1.67 \times 10^{-6}\ \text{m}} = 0.240, \text{ and } \theta_{V1} = 13.9°.$$

For the red edge of the first order:

$$\sin\theta_{R1} = \frac{n\lambda}{d} = \frac{(1)(700 \times 10^{-9}\ \text{m})}{1.67 \times 10^{-6}\ \text{m}} = 0.419, \text{ and } \theta_{V1} = 24.8°.$$

Therefore, the angular width of the first order visible spectrum is:

$$\Delta = \theta_{R1} - \theta_{V1} = 24.8° - 13.9° = 10.9°$$

25.44 (a) $d = \frac{1}{1500\ \text{lines/cm}} = 6.667 \times 10^{-4}\ \text{cm} = 6.667 \times 10^{-6}\ \text{m} = 6667\ \text{nm}$, and

$$n = \frac{d\sin\theta}{\lambda} = \frac{(6667\ \text{nm})\sin 90°}{500\ \text{nm}} = 13.3.$$

Thus, 13 complete orders will be observed.

(b) For 15,000 lines/cm: $d = 666.7$ nm, and

$$n = \frac{d\sin\theta}{\lambda} = \frac{(666.7\ \text{nm})\sin 90°}{500\ \text{nm}} = 1.33.$$

Only one complete order can be seen.

25.45 The wavelengths for the sodium doublet are: $\lambda_A = 588.995$ nm, and $\lambda_B = 589.592$ nm. For the given grating,

$d = \frac{1\ \text{cm}}{2500} = 4.0 \times 10^{-4}$ cm = 4000 nm. Using the grating equation,

$$d\sin\theta = m\lambda, \text{ or } \quad \sin\theta = \frac{m\lambda}{d}, \text{ and } \quad \theta = \arcsin\left(\frac{m\lambda}{d}\right).$$

Thus, for $m = 1$:

$$\theta_A = \arcsin\left(\frac{(1)(588.995\ \text{nm})}{4000\ \text{nm}}\right) = \arcsin(0.14725) = 8.4675°, \text{ and}$$

$$\theta_B = \arcsin\left(\frac{(1)(589.592\ \text{nm})}{4000\ \text{nm}}\right) = \arcsin(0.14740) = 8.4762°.$$

Thus, $\Delta\theta = \theta_B - \theta_A = 0.0087°$.

For $m = 2$: $\theta_A = 17.1274°$, $\theta_B = 17.1453°$; and $\Delta\theta = 0.0179°$.

For $m = 3$: $\theta_A = 26.2154°$, $\theta_B = 26.2440°$, and $\Delta\theta = 0.0286°$.

25.46 $d = \frac{n\lambda}{\sin\theta} = \frac{(1)(546.1\ \text{nm})}{\sin(21.0)°} = 1.524 \times 10^{3}\ \text{nm} = 1.524 \times 10^{-3}\ \text{mm}$, and the

number of lines per millimeter is: $\frac{1}{d} = \frac{1}{1.524 \times 10^{-3}\ \text{mm}} = 656$ line/mm.

25.47 We use $d\sin\theta = m\lambda$, with $m = 1$, and $d = \frac{1\ \text{cm}}{4000} = 2.5 \times 10^{-6}\ \text{m} = 2500\ \text{nm}$.

(a) For the blue light, $\sin\theta = \frac{m\lambda}{d} = \frac{(1)400\ \text{nm}}{2500\ \text{nm}} = 0.160$ and $\theta_{blue} = 9.21°$.

(b) For the red light $\sin\theta = \frac{m\lambda}{d} = \frac{(1)650\ \text{nm}}{2500\ \text{nm}} = 0.260$ and $\theta_{red} = 15.1°$.

25.48 $d = \frac{1}{5000\ \text{slits/cm}} = 2.00 \times 10^{-4}\ \text{cm} = 2000\ \text{nm}$.

In the second order, $2\lambda = d\sin\theta$ so $\sin\theta_1 = \frac{2\lambda_1}{d} = \frac{2(480\ \text{nm})}{2000\ \text{nm}} = 0.480$, and

$\theta_1 = 28.7°$. Also, $\sin\theta_2 = \frac{2(610\ \text{nm})}{2000\ \text{nm}} = 0.610$, giving $\theta_2 = 37.6°$.

$y_1 = L\tan\theta_1 = (2.00\ \text{m})\tan 28.7° = 1.095\ \text{m}$,

$y_2 = L\tan\theta_2 = (2.00\ \text{m})\tan 37.6° = 1.540\ \text{m}$, and

$\Delta y = y_2 - y_1 = 0.445\ \text{m} = 44.5\ \text{cm}$

25.49 (a) The resolving power is given by: $R = \frac{\lambda}{\Delta\lambda} = mN$. Thus, $N = \frac{\lambda}{m\Delta\lambda}$.

For the first order: $N = \frac{656.20\ \text{nm}}{(1)\ (0.18\ \text{nm})} = 3646$ slits.

(b) For the second order, $N = \frac{656.20\ \text{nm}}{(2)\ (0.18\ \text{nm})} = 1823$ slits.

25.50 $R = Nm = \frac{\lambda}{\Delta\lambda}$. The resolving power of the grating increases with the order. Thus, to have maximum resolving power, use the maximum order of the desired wavelength which can be observed. The grating spacing is: $d = \frac{1.00 \times 10^{-2}\ \text{m}}{6000} = 1.67 \times 10^{-6}\ \text{m} = 1670\ \text{nm}$.

The highest order of 600 nm light visible is:

$$m_{max} = \frac{d\sin\theta_{max}}{\lambda} = \frac{(1670\ \text{nm})\sin 90°}{600\ \text{nm}} = 2.78 \text{ or } 2 \text{ orders.}$$

The resolving power of this grating in the second order is

$$R = [(6000\ \text{slits/cm})(15.0\ \text{cm})]\ (2) = 1.80 \times 10^5,$$

and the resolving power needed to separate these two wavelengths is:

$$R = \frac{\lambda}{\Delta\lambda} = \frac{600.000\ \text{nm}}{0.003\ \text{nm}} = 2.00 \times 10^5.$$

These two spectral lines cannot be resolved using this grating.

25.51 (a) Corrective lenses must form a virtual image at $q = -75.0$ cm for objects which are 25.0 cm in front of the lens ($p = 25.0$ cm).

$\frac{1}{p} + \frac{1}{q} = \frac{1}{f}$ becomes: $\frac{1}{25.0\ \text{cm}} + \left(\frac{1}{-75.0\ \text{cm}}\right) = \frac{1}{f}$,

and $f = 37.5\ \text{cm} = 0.375\ \text{m}$.

Thus, $P = \frac{1}{f} = \frac{1}{0.375\ \text{m}} = 2.67$ diopters.

(b) If $q = -75.0$ cm when $p = 26.0$ cm rather than 25.0 cm as assumed in part(a), we have: $\frac{1}{26.0\ \text{cm}} + \left(\frac{1}{-75.0\ \text{cm}}\right) = \frac{1}{f'}$,

and $f' = 39.8\ \text{cm} = 0.398\ \text{m}$.

Thus, $P = \frac{1}{f'} = \frac{1}{0.398\ \text{m}} = 2.51$ diopters, (0.16 diopters too low).

25.52 (a) $\frac{1}{p} + \frac{1}{q} = \frac{1}{f}$ gives: $\frac{1}{100\ \text{cm}} + \left(\frac{1}{2.00\ \text{cm}}\right) = \frac{1}{f}$, and $f = 1.96$ cm

(b) and (c) $f_{max} = \frac{f}{D_{min}} = \frac{1.96\ \text{cm}}{0.200\ \text{cm}} = 9.80$,

and $f_{min} = \frac{f}{D_{max}} = \frac{1.96\ \text{cm}}{0.600\ \text{cm}} = 3.27$

25.53 (a) $L = f_o + f_e = 101.5$ cm. (b) $M = \frac{f_o}{f_e} = \frac{100 \text{ cm}}{1.50 \text{ cm}} = 67.$

25.54 $d = \frac{n\lambda}{\sin\theta} = \frac{(3)(546.1 \text{ nm})}{\sin 81.0^\circ} = 1.66 \times 10^3 \text{ nm} = 1.66 \times 10^{-3}$ mm.

Thus, $\text{lines/mm} = \frac{1}{d} = \frac{1}{1.66 \times 10^{-3} \text{ mm}} = 602.$

25.55 (a) The resolving power is given by: $R = \frac{\lambda}{\Delta\lambda} = mN.$

Thus, $N = \frac{\lambda}{m\Delta\lambda} = \frac{589.00 \text{ nm}}{(1)(0.60 \text{ nm})} = 980.$

(b) $N = \frac{\lambda}{m\Delta\lambda} = \frac{589.00 \text{ nm}}{(3)(0.60 \text{ nm})} = 330.$

25.56 In a distance t in a vacuum, the number of wavelengths that can be fitted in is $N = \frac{t}{\lambda_{vac}}$. If this space is then filled with material having a refractive index n, the number of wavelengths which can now be fitted in is $N' = \frac{t}{\lambda} = \frac{nt}{\lambda_{vac}}$. Since four fringe shifts occur when the path length increases by one wavelength, the number of fringe shifts observed as the material is introduced will be:

$$\# \text{ fringe shifts} = 4(\Delta N) = 4\left(\frac{nt}{\lambda_{vac}} - \frac{t}{\lambda_{vac}}\right). \text{ Therefore, } n = \left(1 + \frac{\lambda_{vac}}{4t}\right).$$

Therefore, $n = 1 + \frac{\lambda_{vac}}{4t}(\#\text{fringe shifts}).$

Thus, if $t = 2.5$ μm, $\lambda = 580 \times 10^{-9}$ m, and 12 fringe shifts are observed

$$n = 1 + \frac{(580 \times 10^{-9} \text{ m})12}{4(2.5 \times 10^{-6} \text{ m})} = 1.70 \text{ is the index of refraction.}$$

25.57 The grating spacing is: $d = \frac{1 \text{ cm}}{2750 \text{ lines}} = 3.64 \times 10^{-4} \text{ cm} = 3640 \text{ nm}.$

The violet end of the second order spectrum occurs at:

$\sin\theta = \frac{m\lambda}{d} = \frac{2(400 \text{ nm})}{3640 \text{ nm}} = 0.220$, or $\theta = 12.7^\circ = 0.222$ radians.

The red end of the second order spectrum is located at:

$\sin\theta = \frac{m\lambda}{d} = \frac{2(700 \text{ nm})}{3640 \text{ nm}} = 0.385$, or $\theta = 22.6^\circ = 0.395$ radians.

The angular width of the second order spectrum is thus:

$\Delta\theta = (0.395 - 0.222)$ radians $= 0.173$ radians.

At distance, L, the arc length included is: $\Delta s = L(\Delta\theta)$, so

$L = \frac{\Delta s}{\Delta\theta}$ If $\Delta s = 1.75$ cm, then: $L = \frac{1.75 \text{ cm}}{0.173 \text{ radians}} = 10.1$ cm.

25.58 (a) First find the location and size of the image formed by the objective lens: $\frac{1}{p_o} + \frac{1}{q_o} = \frac{1}{f_o}$ becomes:

$\frac{1}{40.0 \text{ m}} + \left(\frac{1}{q_o}\right) = \frac{1}{8.00 \times 10^{-2} \text{ m}}$, and $q_o = 8.02 \times 10^{-2}$ m is the image distance. The image size is:

$$h' = -\frac{h q_0}{p_0} = -\frac{(30.0\ \text{cm})(0.0802\ \text{m})}{(40.0\ \text{m})} = -6.02 \times 10^{-2}\ \text{cm}.$$

(b) Now, treat the eyepiece lens. With the image at $q = -\infty$, we have:

$$\frac{1}{p_e} + \frac{1}{\infty} = \frac{1}{-2.00\ \text{cm}},$$ so $p_e = -2.00$ cm. ($p < 0$ means a virtual object)

(c) Distance between lenses is $q_0 + p_e$,
or $L = 8.02\ \text{cm} - 2.00\ \text{cm} = 6.02$ cm.

(d) $$|M| = \left|\frac{f_0}{f_e}\right| = \left|\frac{8.00\ \text{cm}}{-2.00\ \text{cm}}\right| = 4.00.$$

25.59 The image of a very distant object is formed at $q = 5.0$ cm. Thus, the focal point is: $0 + \frac{1}{5.0\ \text{cm}} = \frac{1}{f}$, or $f = 5.0$ cm.

(a) The maximum magnification occurs when the image is at the near point of the eye. Thus, we see that $q = -15$ cm. We find:

$$\frac{1}{p} + \frac{1}{-15\ \text{cm}} = \frac{1}{5.0\ \text{cm}},$$ yields $p = \frac{15}{4}$ cm. The magnification is:

$$M = -\frac{q}{p} = -\frac{-15\ \text{cm}}{\frac{15}{4}\ \text{cm}} = 4.0.$$

(b) We have: $\theta_0 = \frac{h}{15\ \text{cm}}$, and $\theta = \frac{h}{f}$. Therefore,

$$M = \frac{\theta}{\theta_0} = \frac{15\ \text{cm}}{f} = \frac{15\ \text{cm}}{5.0\ \text{cm}} = 3.0.$$

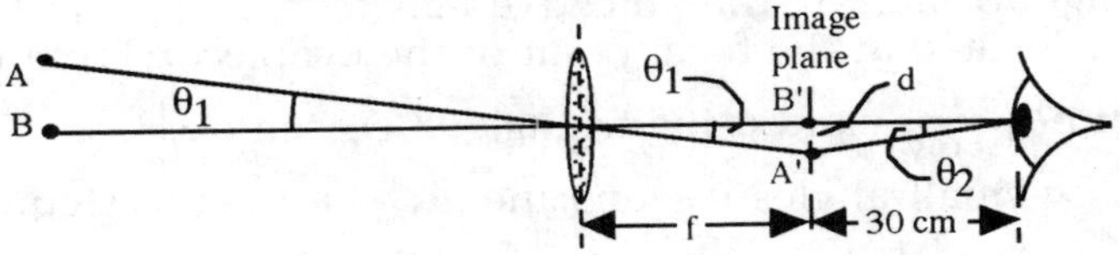

25.60 $$\theta_1 = \theta_m = 1.22\frac{\lambda}{D} = 1.22\left(\frac{500 \times 10^{-9}\ \text{m}}{0.100\ \text{m}}\right) = 6.10 \times 10^{-6}\ \text{rad}$$

$d = \theta_1 f$, and $\theta_2 = \frac{d}{30.0\ \text{cm}}$, so

$$\theta_2 = \frac{\theta_1 f}{30.0\ \text{cm}} = (6.10 \times 10^{-6}\ \text{rad})\left(\frac{140}{30.0}\right) = 2.85 \times 10^{-5}\ \text{rad} = 28.5\ \mu\text{rad}$$

25.61 First, find the longer wavelength: $y = \left(\frac{n\lambda}{d}\right)L$, and $y_2 - y_1 = \left(\frac{\lambda}{d}\right)L$,

or $0.844\ \text{cm} = \lambda\left(\frac{15\ \text{cm}}{8.333 \times 10^{-4}\ \text{cm}}\right)$, where

$$d = \frac{1}{1200\ \text{slits/cm}} = 8.333 \times 10^{-4}\ \text{cm} = 8333\ \text{nm}.$$ Thus,

$$\lambda_{long} = 4.689 \times 10^{-5}\ \text{cm} = 469\ \text{nm}.$$

The minima in intensity occur at angles of deviation for which the path difference for light passing through adjacent slits on the grating is $\delta = d\sin\theta = \left(m + \frac{1}{2}\right)\lambda$ with $m = 0, 1, 2, 3, \ldots$ Hence, at the first-order **minimum** for the longer wavelength,

$\sin\theta = \left(0+\frac{1}{2}\right)\frac{\lambda_{long}}{d} = \frac{\lambda_{long}}{2d}$. The angle at which the third-order **maximum** for the shorter wavelength λ_{short} occurs is

$\sin\theta = \frac{m\lambda}{d} = \frac{3\lambda_{short}}{d}$. If this maximum coincides with the first-order minimum for λ_{long}, then $\frac{3\lambda_{short}}{d} = \frac{\lambda_{long}}{2d}$, or

$$\lambda_{short} = \frac{\lambda_{long}}{6} = \frac{469 \text{ nm}}{6} = 78.2 \text{ nm}.$$

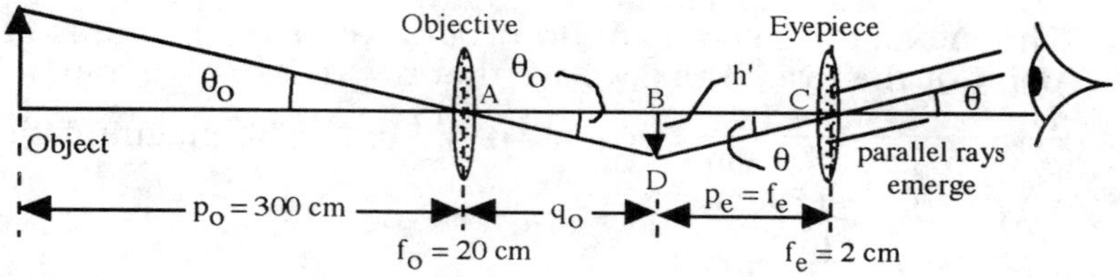

25.62 The angular magnification is $m=\frac{\theta}{\theta_0}$, where θ is the angle subtended by the final image, and θ_0 is the angle subtended by the object. These angles are labeled in the sketch. Note that since the telescope is adjusted for minimum eyestrain, the final image is at infinity. Thus, the image formed by the objective lens (serves as object for eyepiece) must be located at the focal point of the eyepiece. From triangle ABD,

$\tan\theta_0=\frac{h'}{q_0}$, and using triangle BCD, $\tan\theta=\frac{h'}{f_e}$.

Assuming small angles $\theta \approx \tan\theta$ and $\theta_0 \approx \tan\theta_0$, these equations become

$\theta_0 \approx \frac{h'}{q_0}$, and $\theta \approx \frac{h'}{f_e}$, so $M=\frac{\theta}{\theta_0} \approx \frac{q_0}{f_e}$.

To find q_0, apply the thin lens equation to the objective lens:

$\frac{1}{p_0}+\frac{1}{q_0}=\frac{1}{f_0}$ becomes: $\frac{1}{300 \text{ cm}}+\frac{1}{q_0}=\frac{1}{20.0 \text{ cm}}$, giving

q_0 =21.4 cm. Therefore, $M=\frac{21.4 \text{ cm}}{2.00 \text{ cm}}=10.7$.

25.63 We use: $\frac{n_1}{p}+\frac{n_2}{q}=\frac{n_2 - n_1}{R}$, with p = infinity.

Thus, $R=q\left(\frac{n_2 - n_1}{n_2}\right) = 2 \text{ cm}\left(\frac{1.34 - 1.00}{1.34}\right) = 0.507 \text{ cm} = 5.07 \text{ mm}.$

25.64 From the grating equation with d= 2500 nm, we find:

$\sin\theta=\frac{m\lambda}{d}=\frac{m\lambda}{2500 \text{ nm}}$.

Using the given wavelengths, with the restriction $\sin\theta \le 1$, we obtain the following table:

		sin θ					
Wavelength, (color)		m = 1	m = 2	m = 3	m = 4	m = 5	m = 6
400 nm	V	0.160	0.320	0.480	0.640	0.800	0.960
550 nm	G	0.220	0.440	0.660	0.880		
700 nm	R	0.280	0.560	0.840			

The order in which these lines are observed is:

V_1 G_1 R_1 V_2 G_2 V_3 R_2 V_4 G_3 V_5 G_4 R_3 V_6

ANSWERS TO CONCEPTUAL QUESTIONS

2. The light from the flashlight consists of many different wavelengths with random time differences between the individual waves. Thus, there is no coherence between the two sources and no possibility of interference.

4. The shutter of a camera is a close approximation to the iris of the eye. The retina of the eye corresponds to the film of the camera, and a close approximation to the cornea of the eye is the lens of the camera.

6. You want a real image formed at the location of the paper. To form such an image, the light source should be farther away from the paper than the focal point of the lens.

8. The telescope forms an inverted image. Thus, the astronauts could find themselves exploring the northern hemisphere when they were planning to explore the southern hemisphere. It is highly unlikely that a civilization advanced enough to travel to the Moon would ever face such a problem.

10. A magnified image of an object is produced by a converging lens when the object is placed somewhere between the focal point and the lens. Hence, the distance of the object from the lens should be less than 15 cm.

12. The image formed on the retina by the lens and cornea is already inverted.

CHAPTER TWENTY-SIX SOLUTIONS

Chapter Twenty-Six Readings

Bronowsky, J., "The Clock Paradox," *Scientific American*, February 1963, p. 134.

Clark, R.W., *Einstein: The Life and Times*, New York, World Publishing, 1971.

Crelinsten, J., "Relativity, Einstein, Physicists, and the Public," *The Physics Teacher*, February 1980, p. 115.

Crelinsten, J., "Physicists Receive Relativity: Revolution and Reaction," *The Physics Teacher*, February 1980, p. 187.

Einstein, A., *Out of My Later Years*, Secaucus, N.J., Citadel Press, 1973.

Gamow, G., *Mr. Tompkins in Wonderland*, New York, Cambridge University Press, 1939.

Hawkins, S.W. and Penrose, R., "The Nature of Space and Time," *Scientific American*, July 1996, p. 60.

Henry, R.D., "Special Relativity Made Transparent," *The Physics Teacher*, December 1985, p. 536.

Schwinger, J., *Einstein's Legacy*, Scientific American Library, New York, W.H. Freeman and Co., 1985.

Shankland, R.S., "The Michelson-Morley Experiment," *Scientific American*, November 1964, p. 107.

Review The internal energy of an ideal gas is the sum of the kinetic energies of its molecules. From chapter 10, the average kinetic energy per molecule in a monoatomic ideal gas is given by $\langle KE\rangle_{molecule} = \frac{3}{2}kT$, where the Boltzmann constant is given by $k = \frac{R}{N_A}$. Therefore, the internal energy of an ideal gas containing N molecules is

$$U = N\langle KE\rangle_{molecule} = \frac{3}{2}N\left(\frac{R}{N_A}\right)T = \frac{3}{2}nRT,$$

where n is the number of moles present. The energy added to 3.00 moles of an ideal gas when the temperature rises by $\Delta T = 900°F = 500°C = 500\ K$ is then: $\Delta U = \frac{3}{2}nR(\Delta T) = \frac{3}{2}(3.00\ mol)(8.31\ J/mol\ K)(500\ K) = 1.87 \times 10^4\ J$.

From $E = mc^2$, this increase in energy is equivalent to a mass increase of: $\Delta m = \frac{\Delta E}{c^2} = \frac{1.87 \times 10^4\ J}{(3.00 \times 10^8\ m/s)^2} = 2.08 \times 10^{-13}\ kg$.

26.1 (a) Along path I, the velocity along the ground is: $v_{ground} = 120\ m/s$.

Thus, $t_I = \frac{200 \times 10^3\ m}{120\ m/s} = 1.67 \times 10^3\ s$.

Along path II (see sketch), we have: $v^2_{air} = v^2_{ground} + v^2_{wind}$, =

$$(100\text{ m/s})^2 = v^2_{ground} + (20\text{ m/s})^2$$

gives $v_{ground} = 98.0$ m/s. Therefore, $t_{II} = \dfrac{200 \times 10^3 \text{ m}}{98.0 \text{ m/s}} = 2.04 \times 10^3$ s.

(b) Along path I: $v_{ground} = -100.0\text{ m/s} + 20.0\text{ m/s} = -80.0\text{ m/s}$,

and $t'_I = \dfrac{-200 \times 10^3 \text{ m}}{-80.0 \text{ m/s}} = 2.50 \times 10^3$ s.

Along path II:

$v^2_{air} = v^2_{ground} + v^2_{wind}$, $= 98.0$ m/s

as before. Thus,

$$t'_{II} = \frac{200 \times 10^3 \text{ m}}{98.0 \text{ m/s}} = 2.04 \times 10^3 \text{ s.}$$

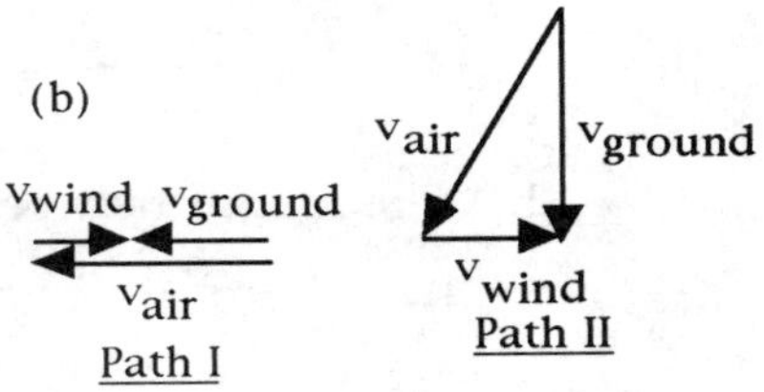

(c) $(t_I)_{total} = 1.67 \times 10^3\text{ s} + 2.50 \times 10^3\text{ s} = 4.17 \times 10^3$ s, and

$(t_{II})_{total} = 2.04 \times 10^3\text{ s} + 2.04 \times 10^3\text{ s} = 4.08 \times 10^3$ s, and

Thus, $\Delta t = 4.17 \times 10^3\text{ s} - 4.08 \times 10^3\text{ s} = 90$ s

---

26.2 (a) $\Delta t_{net} = \dfrac{2Lv^2}{c^3} = \dfrac{2(28 \text{ m})(3 \times 10^4 \text{ m/s})^2}{(3 \times 10^8 \text{ m/s})^3} = 1.9 \times 10^{-15}$ s.

(b) The path difference is:

$\Delta d_{net} = c(\Delta t)_{net} = (3 \times 10^8\text{ m/s})(1.9 \times 10^{-15}\text{ s}) = 5.6 \times 10^{-7}$ m.

Since a fringe shift occurs for every half wavelength change made in the optical path length, the number of shifts expected is:

$$N = \frac{\Delta d_{net}}{\lambda/2} = \frac{5.6 \times 10^{-7} \text{ m}}{275 \times 10^{-9} \text{ m}} = 2.0 \text{ fringe shifts.}$$

26.3 $\gamma = \dfrac{1}{\sqrt{1 - (v/c)^2}} = \dfrac{1}{\sqrt{1 - (0.80)^2}} = \dfrac{1}{0.6}$, so $\Delta T = \gamma(\Delta T_p) = \dfrac{1}{0.6}(3.0\text{ s}) = 5.0$ s.

26.4 (a) The time for 70 beats, as measured by the astronaut and any observer at rest with respect to the astronaut, is $\Delta t_p = 1.0$ min.

(b) When an observer moves at speed v = 0.90c relative to the astronaut, $\gamma = \dfrac{1}{\sqrt{1 - \dfrac{v^2}{c^2}}} = \dfrac{1}{\sqrt{1 - (0.90)^2}} = 2.3$.

Thus, the time for 70 beats as measured by an observer on earth is:

$\Delta t = \gamma(\Delta t_p) = 2.3$ min Therefore, the rate is $\dfrac{70 \text{ beats}}{2.3 \text{ min}} = 30 \dfrac{\text{beats}}{\text{min}}$.

26.5 (a) $T_p = 2.6 \times 10^{-8}$ s, $v = 0.98$ c, and $\gamma = \dfrac{1}{\sqrt{1 - \dfrac{v^2}{c^2}}} = \dfrac{1}{\sqrt{1 - (0.98)^2}} = 5.0$

Thus, $T = \gamma T_p = 5.0(2.6 \times 10^{-8}\text{ s}) = 1.3 \times 10^{-7}$ s.

(b) $d = vt = (0.98\,c)(1.3 \times 10^{-7}\text{ s}) = 38$ m.

(c) $d = vt = (0.98\,c)(2.6 \times 10^{-8}\text{ s}) = 7.6$ m.

26.6 (a) The time required in the Earth's frame of reference is:

$T_1 = \frac{4.20 \text{ light-yr}}{0.950} = 4.42$ yrs. Thus, the time measured in the ships reference frame (where $\gamma = \frac{1}{\sqrt{1 - (0.950)^2}} = 3.20$) is:

$$T_2 = \frac{T_1}{\gamma} = \frac{4.42 \text{ yr}}{3.20} = 1.38 \text{ years.}$$

(b) The length between Earth and the star as measured by astronauts is: $L = \frac{L_p}{\gamma} = \frac{4.20 \text{ ly}}{3.20} = 1.31$ ly.

26.7 As seen by an outside observer, the time for the muon to travel 4.6 km is: $\Delta t = \frac{d}{v} = \frac{4.6 \times 10^3 \text{ m}}{0.99c} = 1.6 \times 10^{-5}$ s. From the point of view of the muon, this time (its proper life time) is:

(a) $\Delta t_p = \Delta t\sqrt{1 - \frac{v^2}{c^2}} = (1.6 \times 10^{-5} \text{ s})\sqrt{1 - (0.99)^2} = 2.2 \times 10^{-6} \text{ s} = 2.2\ \mu\text{s}.$

(b) In this time, the muon travels a distance (measured in its own rest frame) of: $d_p = v(\Delta t_p) = (0.99c)(2.2 \times 10^{-6} \text{ s}) = 6.5 \times 10^2 \text{ m} = 0.65 \text{ km}.$

26.8 (a) Since your ship is identical to his, and you are at rest with respect to your own ship, its length is 20 m.

(b) His ship is in motion relative to you, so you see its length contracted to 19 m.

(c) We have, $L = L_p\sqrt{1 - \frac{v^2}{c^2}}$,

so $\sqrt{1 - \frac{v^2}{c^2}} = \frac{L}{D} = \frac{19\text{m}}{20 \text{ m}} = 0.95$, and $v = 0.31c$.

26.9 Length contraction occurs only in the dimension parallel to the motion. Thus, the sides labeled L_2 and L_3 are not affected. (See sketch.) However, the side labeled L_1 will exhibit length contraction. The dimensions of the block, as measured by the observer moving at $0.80c$ relative to it, will be:

$L_2 = L_{2p} = 2.0$ m, $L_3 = L_{3p} = 2.0$ m, and

$L_2 = L_{2p}/\gamma = (2.0 \text{ m})\sqrt{1 - (0.80)^2} = 1.2$ m.

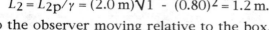

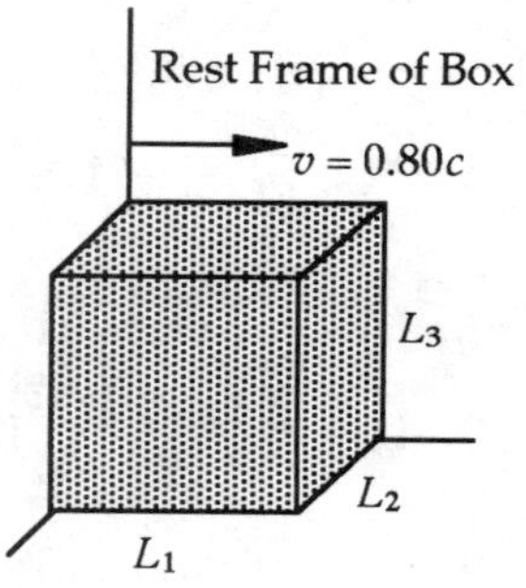

To the observer moving relative to the box,

(a) the box looks rectangular, with

(b) the sides perpendicular to the motion being 2.0 m long while the sides parallel to the motion are 1.2 m long.

26.10 If the frequency of a clock is one half its rest frequency, then the period = two times the rest period. Thus, $\Delta t = 2\Delta t_p$, and from $\Delta t = \gamma\Delta t_p$, we see that $\gamma = 2$. Therefore, $v = c\sqrt{1 - \frac{1}{\gamma^2}} = c\sqrt{1 - \frac{1}{4}} = 0.87\,c.$

26.11 The observed length of an object moving at speed v is $L = L_p\sqrt{1 - \frac{v^2}{c^2}}$, with L_p as the proper length. For the two ships, $L_2 = L_1$. Thus,

$L_{2p}\sqrt{1 - \frac{v_2^2}{c^2}} = L_{1p}\sqrt{1 - \frac{v_1^2}{c^2}}$. But, $L_{2p} = 3L_{1p}$ so this becomes

$3\sqrt{1 - \frac{v_2^2}{c^2}} = \sqrt{1 - \frac{v_1^2}{c^2}}$, or $9[1 - \frac{v_2^2}{c^2}] = 1 - \frac{v_1^2}{c^2}$. Since $v_1 = 0.35c$, this gives $9[1 - \frac{v_2^2}{c^2}] = 0.88$, or $\frac{v_2^2}{c^2} = 0.90$ and $v_2 = 0.95c$.

26.12 The trackside observer sees the supertrain length-contracted as:

$$L = L_p\sqrt{1 - \frac{v^2}{c^2}} = (100\text{ m})\sqrt{1 - \frac{(0.95c)^2}{c^2}} = 31\text{ m}.$$

The supertrain appears to fit in the tunnel with 50 m - 31 m = 19 m to spare.

26.13 $\gamma = 10.0$. Given: $L = 2.00$ m, and $\theta = 30.0°$ (both measured in the observer's rest frame). The components of the rod's length as measured in the observer's rest frame are therefore:

$L_x = L\cos\theta = (2.00\text{ m})\cos 30.0° = 1.73$ m, and

$L_y = L\sin\theta = (2.00\text{ m})\sin 30.0° = 1.00$ m.

The component of length parallel to the motion, L_x, has been contracted but the component perpendicular to the motion is unaltered. Thus, $L_{py} = L_y = 1.00$ m and

$L_{px} = \gamma L_x = 10.0(1.73\text{ m}) = 17.3$ m.

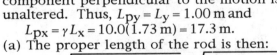

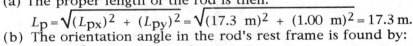

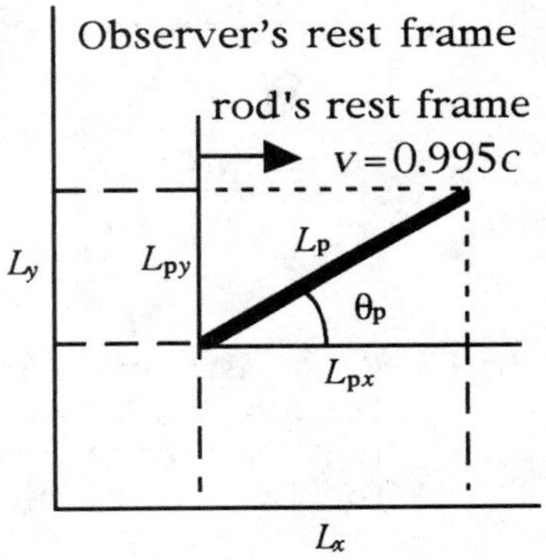

(a) The proper length of the rod is then:

$$L_p = \sqrt{(L_{px})^2 + (L_{py})^2} = \sqrt{(17.3\text{ m})^2 + (1.00\text{ m})^2} = 17.3\text{ m}.$$

(b) The orientation angle in the rod's rest frame is found by:

$$\tan\theta_p = \frac{L_{py}}{L_{px}} = \frac{1.00\text{ m}}{17.3\text{ m}} = 5.78 \times 10^{-2}, \text{ so } \theta_p = 3.31°.$$

26.14 $\gamma = 3.37$. Let L_0 = the common length the observer measures for the two rods. Then since rod A is at rest relative to this observer, the proper length of rod A is: $L_{pA} = L_0$. The proper length of B is given by: $L_{pB} = \gamma L_0 = 3.37L_0$. The length the observer in the rest frame of B will measure for rod A is: $L_{AB} = \frac{L_{pA}}{\gamma} = \frac{L_0}{3.37} = 0.297L_0$.

The ratio of lengths measured by the observer in B is:

$$\frac{L_{AB}}{L_{BB}} = \frac{\text{measured length of A}}{\text{measured length of B}} = \frac{0.297\ L_0}{3.37\ L_0} = 0.088.$$

26.15 The momentum of the electron is:

$$p_e = \gamma m_e v = \frac{(9.11 \times 10^{-31}\text{ kg})(0.90c)}{\sqrt{1 - (0.90)^2}} = (1.9 \times 10^{-30}\text{ kg})c.$$

For a proton to have the same momentum as the electron, we have:

$$p_p = \gamma m_p v = p_e = \frac{(1.67 \times 10^{-27}\ \text{kg})(v)}{\sqrt{1 - (v/c)^2}} = (1.9 \times 10^{-30}\ \text{kg})c.$$

This reduces to $880(v/c) = \sqrt{1 - (v/c)^2}$
and yields $v = (1.1 \times 10^{-3})c = 3.3 \times 10^5$ m/s

26.16 $p = \gamma m v$

(a) $v = 0.010c$, thus $\gamma = \dfrac{1}{\sqrt{1 - \dfrac{v^2}{c^2}}}, = \dfrac{1}{\sqrt{1 - (0.010)^2}} = 1.00005$(about 1.)

Therefore, $p = (1)(9.11 \times 10^{-31}\ \text{kg})(0.010)(3.00 \times 10^8\ \text{m/s})$
$= 2.7 \times 10^{-24}$ kg m/s.

(b) Following the same steps as used in part (a), we find
$\gamma = 1.15$, and $p = 1.6 \times 10^{-22}$ kg m/s.

(c) $\gamma = 2.29$, and $p = 5.6 \times 10^{-22}$ kg m/s.

26.17 $p = \dfrac{mv}{\sqrt{1 - \dfrac{v^2}{c^2}}}$, becomes $1 - \dfrac{v^2}{c^2} = \dfrac{m^2v^2}{p^2}$, which gives:

$$1 = v^2\left(\frac{m^2}{p^2} + \frac{1}{c^2}\right), \quad \text{or} \quad c^2 = v^2\left(\frac{m^2c^2}{p^2} + 1\right) \text{ and } \quad v = \frac{c}{\sqrt{\dfrac{m^2c^2}{p^2} + 1}}.$$

26.18 Relativistic momentum must be conserved:
For total momentum to be zero after as it was before, we must have (with subscript 2 referring to the heavier fragment, and subscript 1 to the lighter fragment): $p_2 = p_1$, or

$$\gamma_2 m_2 v_2 = \gamma_1 m_1 v_1 = \frac{(2.50 \times 10^{-28}\ \text{kg})(0.893c)}{\sqrt{1 - (0.893)^2}} = (4.96 \times 10^{-28}\ \text{kg})c.$$

This becomes $\dfrac{(1.67 \times 10^{-27}\ \text{kg})(v_2)}{\sqrt{1 - (v_2/c)^2}} = (4.96 \times 10^{-28}\ \text{kg})c,$

or $3.37(v_2/c) = \sqrt{1 - (v_2/c)^2}$

This yields $v_2 = 0.284c$.

26.19 Using the relativistic form,

$$p = = \frac{mv}{\sqrt{1 - \dfrac{v_2^2}{c^2}}}, = \gamma m v$$

we find the difference Δp from the classical momentum, mv:

$\Delta p = \gamma m v - mv = (\gamma - 1)mv.$

(a) The difference is 1% when $\gamma = 1.01$ or $v = 0.140c$.

(b) The difference is 10% when $\gamma = 1.10$ or $v = 0.417c$.

26.20 The relativistic velocity addition formula gives:
$v_{eo} = 0.90c$ = velocity of electron with respect to observer

v_{pe} = -0.70c =.velocity of proton with respect to electron
v_{po} = velocity of proton with respect to observer.

$$v_{po} = \frac{(v_{pe}) + (v_{eo})}{1 + \frac{(v_{pe})(v_{eo})}{c^2}} = \frac{(-0.70c) + (0.90c)}{1 + \frac{(-0.70c)(0.90c)}{c^2}} = 0.54c$$

26.21 We have, with to the right considered as positive,
v_{Re} = 0.70c = velocity of R with respect to Earth = - v_{eR}
v_{Le} = - 0.70c = velocity of L with respect to Earth.
v_{LR}= velocity of L with respect to R.

$$v_{LR} = \frac{(v_{Le}) + (v_{eR})}{1 + \frac{(v_{Le})(v_{eR})}{c^2}} = \frac{(-0.70c) - (0.70c)}{1 + \frac{(-0.70c)(-0.70c)}{c^2}} = -0.94c$$

26.22 Using the velocity addition formula,
v_{vo} = 0.75c = velocity of vehicle with respect to observer.
v_{pv} = 0.90c = velocity of particle with respect to vehicle.
v_{po} = velocity of particle with respect to observer.

$$v_{po} = \frac{(v_{pv}) + (v_{vo})}{1 + \frac{(v_{pv})(v_{vo})}{c^2}} = \frac{(0.90c) + (0.75c)}{1 + \frac{(0.90c)(0.75c)}{c^2}} = 0.99c$$

26.23 We have, with to the right considered as postive
v_{RA} = 0.92c = velocity of rocket with respect to A.
v_{RB} = - 0.95c = velocity of rocket with respect to B = - v_{BR}
v_{BA} = velocity of B relative to A.

$$v_{BA} = \frac{(v_{BR}) + (v_{RA})}{1 + \frac{(v_{BR})(v_{RA})}{c^2}} = \frac{(0.95c) + (0.92c)}{1 + \frac{(0.95c)(0.92c)}{c^2}} = 0.998c$$

26.24 We have, with the direction of the rocket considered as postive,
v_{pE} = -0.950c = velocity of pulsar with respect to Earth. = - v_{Ep}
v_{rE} = .995c = velocity of rocket with respect to Earth
v_{rp} = velocity of rocket relative to pulsar.

$$v_{rp} = \frac{(v_{rE}) + (v_{Ep})}{1 + \frac{(v_{rE})(v_{Ep})}{c^2}} = \frac{(0.995c) + (0.950c)}{1 + \frac{(0.995c)(0.950c)}{c^2}} = 0.99987c$$

Proper time = period of pulsar in its own rest frame $\Delta t_p = \frac{1}{10\text{ Hz}} = 0.100\text{ s.}$

The period of the pulsar in the rocket's rest frame is:

$$\Delta t = \gamma(\Delta t_p) = \left(\frac{1}{\sqrt{1 - u^2}}\right)(0.100\text{ s}) = 6.20\text{ s.}$$

The frequency is $f = \frac{1}{6.20\text{ s}} = 0.161\text{ Hz.}$

26.25 Using the velocity addition equation, the velocity of the students relative to the instructors (and hence the clock) is found as follows

v_{sE} = 0.60c = velocity of students with respect to Earth.

$v_{IE} = -0.28c$ = velocity of instructors with respect to Earth $= -v_{EI}$
v_{sI} = velocity of students relative to instructor.

$$v_{sI} = \frac{(v_{sE}) + (v_{EI})}{1 + \frac{(v_{sE})(v_{EI})}{c^2}} = \frac{(0.60c) + (0.28c)}{1 + \frac{(0.60c)(.28c)}{c^2}} = 0.75c$$

(students relative to instructors)

(a) With a proper time interval of Δt_p = 50 minutes (measured in the instructor's rest frame), the time interval measured by the students is: $\Delta t = \gamma \Delta t_p$ with $\gamma = \left(\frac{1}{\sqrt{1 - (0.75c/c)^2}}\right) = 1.51$. Thus, the students measure the exam to last $\Delta t = 1.51(50 \text{ min}) = 76$ min.

(b) The duration of the exam as measured by observers on Earth is:

$\Delta t = \gamma \Delta t_p$ with $\Delta t = \gamma \Delta t_p$ with $\gamma = \left(\frac{1}{\sqrt{1 - (0.28c/c)^2}}\right) = 1.04$,

so $\Delta t = 1.04(50 \text{ min}) = 52$ min.

26.26 At $v = 0.950\,c$, we find $\gamma = 3.20$.

(a) $E_0 = mc^2 = (1.67 \times 10^{-27} \text{ kg})(3.00 \times 10^8 \text{ m/s})^2$
$= 1.50 \times 10^{-10}$ J = 939 MeV

(b) $E = \gamma mc^2 = \gamma E_0 = (3.20)(939 \text{ MeV}) = 3.00 \times 10^9 \text{ eV} = 3.00$ GeV

(c) $KE = E - E_0 = 3.00 \times 10^9 \text{ eV} - 939 \text{ MeV} = 2.06$ GeV

26.27 (a) $E = mc^2 = (0.50 \text{ kg})(3.00 \times 10^8 \text{ m/s})^2 = 4.5 \times 10^{16}$ J.

(b) Power $= \frac{E}{t}$. Thus, $t = \frac{E}{\text{Power}} = \frac{4.5 \times 10^{16} \text{ J}}{100 \text{ J/s}} = 4.5 \times 10^{14} \text{ s} = 1.4 \times 10^7$ y.

26.28 (a) From $E = mc^2$, we have $m = \frac{E}{c^2} = \frac{4.0 \times 10^{26} \text{ J}}{(3.00 \times 10^8 \text{ m/s})^2} = 4.4 \times 10^9$ kg.

(b) $t = \frac{\text{total mass}}{\text{rate of use}} = \frac{2.0 \times 10^{30} \text{ kg}}{4.4 \times 10^9 \text{ kg/s}} = 4.5 \times 10^{20} \text{ s} = 1.4 \times 10^{13}$ years

---

26.29 We are given that: $KE = E_0$. But, the total energy is $E = E_0 + KE$, so we find: $E = 2E_0$, or $\gamma mc^2 = 2mc^2$. Thus, $\gamma = \left(\frac{1}{\sqrt{1 - (-v/c)^2}}\right) = 2$

from which $v = 0.866c$

26.30 The kinetic energy is given as: $KE = E - E_0 = 50.0 \text{ GeV} = 5.00 \times 10^4$ MeV. The total energy is:

$$E = E_0 + KE = 939 \text{ MeV} + 5.00 \times 10^4 \text{ MeV} = 5.09 \times 10^4 \text{ MeV}$$

(a) $E^2 = (pc)^2 + E_0^2$,
or $(pc)^2 = E^2 - E_0^2 = (5.09 \times 10^4 \text{ MeV})^2 - (939 \text{ MeV})^2$
Thus, $pc = 5.09 \times 10^4$ MeV, and $p = 5.09 \times 10^4$ MeV/c.

(b) From $E = \gamma E_0$ we have

$$\gamma = \left(\frac{1}{\sqrt{1 - (v/c)^2}}\right) = \frac{E}{E_0} = \frac{5.09 \times 10^4 \text{ MeV}}{939 \text{ MeV}} = 54.2,$$

from which $v = 0.9998c$.

26.31 The kinetic energy of the electron will equal its loss of potential energy, or: $KE = q\Delta V = (1.6 \times 10^{-19}\ \text{C})(2.0 \times 10^{4}\ \text{V}) = 3.2 \times 10^{-15}\ \text{J}$
The total energy of the electron is $E = E_0 + KE = \gamma E_0$. Then,

$$\gamma = \left(\frac{1}{\sqrt{1 - (v/c)^2}}\right) = 1 + \frac{KE}{E_0}$$

where $E_0 = mc^2 = (9.11 \times 10^{-31}\ \text{kg})c^2 = 8.2 \times 10^{-14}\ \text{J}$.

Thus, $\left(\dfrac{1}{\sqrt{1 - (v/c)^2}}\right) = 1 + \dfrac{3.2 \times 10^{-15}\ \text{J}}{8.2 \times 10^{-14}\ \text{J}} = 1.04,$

or $(v/c)^2 = 1 - \dfrac{1}{(1.04)^2} = 0.075$, and $v = 0.27c$

26.32 The relativistic kinetic energy of a particle is $KE = E - E_0 = (\gamma - 1)E_0$. When this is double the value from the classical expression, then

$(\gamma - 1)mc^2 = 2(\frac{1}{2}mv^2)$, or $(\gamma - 1) = (v/c)^2$. Since $\gamma = \left(\dfrac{1}{\sqrt{1 - (-v/c)^2}}\right)$,

this may be written as $1 = [1 + (v/c)^2]\sqrt{1 - (-v/c)^2}$. Squaring this result and combining terms gives: $(v/c)^2[(v/c)^4 + (v/c)^2 - 1] = 0$. Ignoring the trivial solution, $v = 0$, we see that it is necessary to have:

$(v/c)^4 + (v/c)^2 - 1 = 0$. This is a quadratic equation with $(v/c)^2$ as the variable. Using the quadratic formula, and rejecting the negative solution, gives: $(v/c)^2 = 0.618$, or $v = 0.786c$.

26.33 We must conserve both (i) mass-energy and (ii) relativistic momentum. With subscript 1 referring to the $0.868c$ particle and subscript 2 to the $0.987c$ particle, the total energy is:

$$E_{total} = E_1 + E_2 = \gamma_1 m_1 c^2 + \gamma_2 m_2 c^2 = m_{total}c^2,$$

with $\gamma_1 = \left(\dfrac{1}{\sqrt{1 - (-0.868)^2}}\right) = 2.01$, and $\gamma_2 = \left(\dfrac{1}{\sqrt{1 - (0.987)^2}}\right) = 6.22$

Then, mass-energy conservation reduces to:

$2.01m_1 + 6.22m_2 = 3.34 \times 10^{-27}\ \text{kg}$ (1).

Since the total momentum after the decay must equal zero,

$p_1 = p_2$, which gives: $\gamma_1 m_1 v_1 = \gamma_2 m_2 v_2$,

or $(2.01)(m_1)(0.868c) = (6.22)(m_2)(0.987c)$.

This reduces to: $m_1 = 3.52m_2$ (2)

Solving equations (1) and (2) simultaneously, gives:

$m_1 = 8.84 \times 10^{-28}\ \text{kg}$ and $m_2 = 2.51 \times 10^{-28}\ \text{kg}$

26.34 Since the proton starts from rest, its kinetic energy equals the work done on it: Thus, $KE = 3750$ MeV. The rest energy of a proton is

$$E_0 = mc^2 = (1.67 \times 10^{-27}\ \text{kg})c^2$$
$$= (1.503 \times 10^{-10}\ \text{J})\frac{1\ \text{MeV}}{1.60 \times 10^{-13}\ \text{J}} = 939\ \text{MeV}.$$

The relativistic energy for this proton is $E = E_0 + KE = 4689$ MeV.

Also, $E = mc^2 = \gamma E_0$, so $\gamma = \dfrac{E}{E_0} = \dfrac{4689\ \text{MeV}}{939\ \text{MeV}} = 4.99$ and $(v/c)^2 = 1 - \dfrac{1}{\gamma^2} = 0.960$

Therefore, $v = 0.980c$.

26.35 The energy required will be $\Delta E = E_f - E_i = (\gamma_f - \gamma_i)E_0$.
For an electron: $E_0 = mc^2 = 0.511$ MeV.

$$\Delta E = \left(\frac{1}{\sqrt{1 - (0.750)^2}} - \frac{1}{\sqrt{1 - (0.500)^2}}\right)(0.511 \text{ MeV}) = 0.183 \text{ MeV}.$$

(b) $$\Delta E = \left(\frac{1}{\sqrt{1 - (0.990)^2}} - \frac{1}{\sqrt{1 - (0.900)^2}}\right)(0.511 \text{ MeV}) = 2.45 \text{ MeV}.$$

26.36 The length contraction formula is $L = L_p\sqrt{1 - (v/c)^2}$. where L_p is the proper length and L is the observed length when the object is moving relative to the observer. In this case, $\frac{L}{L_p} = \frac{(0.500)}{(1.00)} = 0.500$.
Thus, $1 - (v/c)^2 = 0.500^2$ and from this $v = 0.866c$.

26.37 (a) $E = E_0 + KE = E_0 + qV = 939$ MeV + 500 eV. Thus, the total energy is still approximately equal to 939 MeV. As a result, $E = E_0$, $\gamma = 1$ and

Classically, $KE = \frac{1}{2}m_0 v^2 = qV$, from which

$$v = \sqrt{\frac{2(KE)}{m_0}} = \sqrt{\frac{2(500 \text{ eV})(1.60 \times 10^{-27} \text{ J/eV})}{1.67 \times 10^{-27} \text{ kg}}} = 3.10 \times 10^5 \text{ m/s} = 0.001c$$

(b) $E = E_0 + KE = E_0 + qV = 939$ MeV + 500 MeV = 1439 MeV,
and $\gamma = \frac{E}{E_0} = \frac{1439}{939} = 1.53$.

and $(v/c)^2 = 1 - \frac{1}{\gamma^2} = 1 - \frac{1}{(1.53)^2} = 0.574$, yielding $v = 0.757c$.

26.38 Given: $E = 5E_0$. Thus, $E^2 = (pc)^2 + E_0^2$ becomes:
$(pc)^2 = 24E_0^2$ or $p = \frac{4.9E_0}{c}$.

(a) For electron: $E_o = 0.511$ MeV, and $p = \frac{4.9(0.511 \text{ MeV})}{c} = 2.50$ MeV/c

(b) For a proton:
$E_0 = 939$ MeV, and $p = \frac{4.9(939 \text{ MeV})}{c} = 4.60 \times 10^3$ MeV/c

---

26.39 The relativistic momentum is related to the total energy by $E^2 = (pc)^2 + E_0^2$. For a 1.00 MeV electron, $E_o = 0.511$ MeV, and $E = KE + E_0 = 1.00$ MeV + 0.511 MeV = 1.51 MeV. Thus,
$(pc)^2 = (1.51 \text{ MeV})^2 - (0.511 \text{ MeV})^2 = 2.02 \text{ MeV}^2$ and $p = 1.42\frac{\text{MeV}}{c}$.

26.40 $$\gamma = \left(\frac{1}{\sqrt{1 - (v/c)^2}}\right) = \left(\frac{1}{\sqrt{1 - (0.75)^2}}\right) = 1.51.$$

Thus, $\Delta t = \gamma \Delta t_p = 1.51(10 \text{ h}) = 15.1$ h.
Therefore,
$d = v(\Delta t) = (0.75)(3.00 \times 10^8 \text{ m/s})(15.1 \text{ h})(3600 \text{ s/h}) = 1.2 \times 10^{13}$ m.

26.41 When the electron's mass equals the rest mass of a proton, we have $m = \frac{m_0}{\sqrt{1-(v/c)^2}}$ with $m = m_p$, and $m_o = m_e$. This becomes: $1-(v/c)^2 = (m_e/m_p)^2$,

or $$v = c\sqrt{1-(m_e/m_p)^2} = c\sqrt{1-\left(\frac{9.11 \times 10^{-31}\text{ kg}}{1.673 \times 10^{-27}\text{ kg}}\right)^2} = 0.99999985c.$$

26.42 We have

$v_{no} = v =$ velocity of nucleus with respect to observer

$v_{en} = 0.70c$ = velocity of electron with respect to the nucleus. $= -\ v_{ne}$

$v_{eo} = 0.85c$ = velocity of electron relative to observer.

$$v = v_{no} = \frac{(v_{ne}) + (v_{eo})}{1 + \frac{(v_{ne})(v_{eo})}{c^2}} = \frac{(-0.70c) + (0.850c)}{1 + \frac{(-0.70c)(0.850c)}{c^2}} = 0.37c$$

26.43 We have

$v_{qe} = 0.870c$ = velocity of quasar with respect to earth

$v_{mq} = -0.550c$ = velocity of material with respect to the quasar.

v_{me} = velocity of material relative to earth.

$$v_{me} = \frac{(v_{mq}) + (v_{qe})}{1 + \frac{(v_{mq})(v_{qe})}{c^2}} = \frac{(-0.550c) + (0.870c)}{1 + \frac{(-0.550c)(0.870c)}{c^2}} = 0.61c$$

or $0.61c$ away from earth.

26.44 The spaceship appears length-contracted to the Earth observer as given by $L = L_p\sqrt{1 - \frac{v^2}{c^2}}$, or $L^2 = L_p^2\,(1 - \frac{v^2}{c^2})$

Also, the contracted length is related to the time required to pass overhead by: $L = vt$, or $L^2 = v^2t^2 = \frac{v^2}{c^2}(ct)^2$. Equating these two expressions for L^2 gives: $L_p^2 - L_p^2\,(\frac{v^2}{c^2}) = (ct)^2(v/c)^2$,

or $$L_p^2 = (v/c)^2\,[L_p^2 + (ct)^2\,] = L^2$$

Using the given values: $L_p = 300$ m, and $t = 7.5 \times 10^{-7}$ s, this becomes

$$(1.4 \times 10^5\text{ m}^2\,)(\frac{v^2}{c^2}) = 9.00 \times 10^4\text{ m}^2,$$ giving $v = 0.80c$.

26.45 (a) Using the classical equation, we have

$$KE = \frac{1}{2}mv^2 = \frac{1}{2}(78.0\text{ kg})(1.06 \times 10^5\text{ m/s})^2 = 4.38 \times 10^{11}\text{ J}$$

(b) Using relativistic equations, we have

$$KE = \gamma mc^2 - mc^2 = (\gamma - 1)mc^2 = (\gamma - 1)(78.0\text{ kg})(3.00 \times 10^8\text{ m/s})^2$$
$$= (\gamma - 1) = (\gamma - 1)7.02 \times 10^{18}\text{ J}$$

but $\gamma = (1 - v^2/c^2)^{-1/2} = 1 + \frac{1}{2}\frac{v^2}{c^2}$ for v/c much smaller than 1.

Thus $(\gamma - 1) = \frac{1}{2}\frac{v^2}{c^2} = \frac{1}{2}\frac{(1.06 \times 10^5 \text{ m/s})^2}{(3.00 \times 108 \text{ m/s})^2} = 6.24 \times 10^{-8}$

so, $KE = (6.24 \times 10^{-8})7.02 \times 10^{18}\text{ J} = 4.38 \times 10^{11}\text{ J}$

Thus, in the limit of small speeds, the classical and relativistic equations yield the same results.

26.46 In this case, the proper time is T_0 (the time measured by the students on a clock at rest relative to them). The dilated time measured by the professor is: $\Delta t = \gamma T_0$, where $\Delta t = T + t$. Here T is the time she waits before sending a signal and t is the time required for the signal to reach the students. Thus, we have:

$$T + t = \gamma T_0. \qquad (1)$$

To determine the travel time t, realize that the distance the students will have moved beyond the professor before the signal reaches them is:

$$d = v(T + t)$$

The time required for the signal to travel this distance is:

$$t = \frac{d}{c} = \frac{v(T + t)}{c}.$$

Solving for t gives: $t = \frac{(v/c)T}{1 - (v/c)}$. Substituting this result into equation (1) yields: $T + \frac{(v/c)T}{1 - (v/c)} = \gamma T_0$, or $\frac{T}{1 - (v/c)} = \gamma T_0$.

Using the expression for γ, this becomes:

$$T = \frac{1 - (v/c)}{\sqrt{1 - (v/c)^2}} T_0.$$

or

$$T = T_0\sqrt{\frac{(1-(v/c))^2}{(1 - v/c)(1 + v/c)}} = T_0\sqrt{\frac{1 - v/c}{1 + v/c}}$$

26.47 If the energy required to remove a mass m from the surface is equal to its mass energy mc^2, then

$$G\frac{M_s m}{R_g} = mc^2$$

$$R_g = \frac{GM_s}{c^2} = \frac{(6.67 \times 10^{-11}\text{ N/m}^2/\text{kg}^2)(1.99 \times 10^{30}\text{ kg})}{(3 \times 10^8\text{ m/s})^2} = 1.47\text{ km}$$

26.48 (a) $L_0 = \sqrt{(L_{xp})^2 + (L_{yp})^2} = \sqrt{(L_0^2)\cos^2\theta + (L_0^2)\sin^2\theta}$, so that

$$L = \sqrt{\frac{(L_0^2)\cos^2\theta}{\gamma^2} + (L_0^2)\sin^2\theta} = L_0\sqrt{1 - \left(\frac{v}{c}\right)^2\cos^2\theta}.$$

(b) $\tan\theta_0 = \frac{L_{yp}}{L_{xp}} = \frac{L_y}{\gamma L_x} = \frac{1}{\gamma}\left(\frac{L_y}{L_x}\right) = \frac{1}{\gamma}\tan\theta.$

26.49 (a) Since Mary is in the same reference frame, S', as Ted, she observes it to have the same speed as Ted observes, namely $0.80c$.

(b) $t = \frac{x}{v} = \frac{(1.8 \times 10^{12}\text{ m})}{(0.80)(3.00 \times 10^8\text{ m/s})} = 7.5 \times 10^3\text{ s}.$

(c) $L = L_p\sqrt{1 - \frac{v^2}{c^2}} = (1.8 \times 10^{12}\text{ m})\sqrt{1 - \frac{(0.60c)^2}{c^2}} = 1.4 \times 10^{12}$ m.

v_{TJ} = 0.60c = velocity of Ted with respect to Jim
v_{BT} = -0.80c = velocity of ball with respect to Ted.
v_{BJ}= velocity of ball with respect to Jim.

$$v_{BJ} = \frac{(v_{BT}) + (v_{TJ})}{1 + \frac{(v_{BT})(v_{TJ})}{c^2}} = \frac{(-0.800c) + (0.60c)}{1 + \frac{(-0.80c)(0.60c)}{c^2}} = -0.39c$$

26.50 (a) If Newtonian mechanics remained valid, $KE = \frac{1}{2}mv^2$. When the electron starts from rest and moves through a potential difference V, the kinetic energy is qV. Thus, we would have $\frac{1}{2}mv^2 = qV$, or the required potential difference is:

$V = \frac{mv^2}{2q}$. Then, if $v = 2c = 6.00 \times 10^8$ m/s, we would find:

$$V = \frac{(9.11 \times 10^{-31}\text{ kg})(36.0 \times 10^{16}\text{ m}^2/\text{s}^2)}{2(1.60 \times 10^{-19}\text{ C})} = 1.02 \times 10^6\text{ V}.$$

(b) Considering relativistic effects, $KE = E - E_0 = \gamma E_0 - E_0$, or $KE = (\gamma - 1)E_0$. Thus, when accerated from rest through a potential difference V, we have: $(\gamma - 1)E_0 = qV$, or $\gamma = 1 + \frac{qV}{E_0} = 1 + \frac{qV}{m_0c^2}$.

For an electron with V = 1.02 x 10^6 V, this gives:

$$\gamma = 1 + \frac{(1.60 \times 10^{-19}\text{ V})(1.02 \times 10^6\text{ V})}{(9.11 \times 10^{-31}\text{ kg})(9.00 \times 10^{16}\text{ m}^2/\text{s}^2)} = 2.99,$$ from which

$$\gamma^2 = \frac{1}{1 - \frac{v^2}{c^2}} = 8.943,$$ giving $v = 0.942c$.

26.51 (a) Using the velocity addition equation, the velocity of the ball as measured by Jennifer is found as

v_{BM} = 0.80c = velocity of ball with respect to Matt
v_{MJ} = 0.60c = velocity of Matt with respect to Jennifer.
v_{BJ} = velocity of ball with respect to Jennifer.

$$v_{BJ} = \frac{(v_{BM}) + (v_{MJ})}{1 + \frac{(v_{BM})(v_{MJ})}{c^2}} = \frac{(0.80c) + (0.60c)}{1 + \frac{(0.80c)(0.60c)}{c^2}} = 0.95c$$

(b) According to Jennifer, the time required for the ball to arrive is:

$$t_J = \frac{L_p}{u} = \frac{(1.8 \times 10^{11}\text{ m})}{(0.946)(3 \times 10^8\text{ m/s})} = 630\text{ s}.$$

(c) The γ factor for the relative motion between the ball and Jennifer is: $\gamma_b = \frac{1}{\sqrt{1 - \frac{u^2}{c^2}}} = \frac{1}{\sqrt{1 - (0.946)^2}} = 3.08$. The ball sees the distance in S length contracted as: $L = \frac{L_p}{\gamma_b} = \frac{1.8 \times 10^{11}\text{ m}}{3.08} = 5.83 \times 10^{10}$ m and sees Jennifer moving toward it at speed $u_b = 0.946c$. Thus, the measured time for Jennifer to arrive is:

$$t_b = \frac{L}{u_b} = \frac{(5.83 \times 10^{10}\ \text{m})}{(0.946)(3 \times 10^8\ \text{m/s})} = 210\ \text{s}.$$

(d) The γ factor for the relative motion between Matt and Jennifer is:

$\gamma_m = \dfrac{1}{\sqrt{1 - (0.6)^2}} = 1.25$. Thus, the length-contracted distance Matt thinks the ball must travel to reach Jennifer is:

$L_m = \dfrac{L_p}{\gamma_m} = \dfrac{1.8 \times 10^{11}\ \text{m}}{1.25} = 1.44 \times 10^{11}$ m. Matt sees the ball moving toward Jennifer at a speed of $u' = 0.8c$, so the time he thinks it takes to reach her is: $t_m = \dfrac{L_m}{u'} = \dfrac{(1.44 \times 10^{11}\ \text{m})}{(0.8)(3 \times 10^8\ \text{m/s})} = 600$ s.

26.52 (a) $\tau = \gamma \tau_p = \dfrac{1}{\sqrt{1 - (0.95)^2}} (2.2\ \mu\text{s}) = 7.05\ \mu\text{s}$.

(b) $\Delta t_p = \dfrac{d'}{0.95c} = \dfrac{d}{\gamma(0.95c)} = \dfrac{3 \times 10^3\ \text{m}}{3.2(0.95c)} = 3.3\ \mu\text{s}$

Therefore, $N = (5 \times 10^4\ \text{muons})\, e^{(-3.3\ \mu\text{s})/(2.2\ \mu\text{s})} = 1.12 \times 10^4$ muons.

ANSWERS TO CONCEPTUAL QUESTIONS

2. All observers will agree on the speed of light.

4. Under certain circumstances energy can be converted into mass and, in a reciprocal fashion, mass can be converted into energy. The relationship that must be obeyed in these conversions is that $E = mc^2$. This is often summarized by saying that mass-energy is conserved.

6. You would see the same thing that you see when looking at a mirror when at rest. The theory of relativity tells us that all experiments will give the same results in all inertial frames of reference.

8. The clock in orbit will run more slowly. The experiment for clocks carried in airplanes is described in the Time Dilation section of the text as the Hafele and Keating experiment. The extra centripetal acceleration of the orbiting clock makes its history fundamentally different from that of the clock on Earth.

10. The 8 light-years represents the proper length of a rod from here to Sirius, measured by an observer seeing both the rod and Sirius nearly at rest. The astronaut sees Sirius coming toward her at 0.8c, but also sees the distance contracted to

$$\frac{8\ \text{light-years}}{\gamma} = (8\ \text{light-years})\sqrt{1 - \frac{v^2}{c^2}} = (8\ \text{light-years})\sqrt{1 - 0.8^2} = 5\ \text{light-years}$$

So, the travel time measured on her clock is $t = \dfrac{d}{v} = \dfrac{5\ \text{light-years}}{0.8c} = 6$ years

12. The equation $E = mc^2$, better written $\Delta E = \Delta mc^2$, relates any energy transferred into or removed from a system to the change in mass of the system. when work is done on an object to increase its speed, we can say that the increase in kinetic energy corresponds to an increase in its effective mass from m to γm. KE = $(\gamma m - m)c^2$, is one version of $\Delta E = \Delta mc^2$.

14. The light from the quasar moves at 3×10^8 m/s. The speed of light is independent of the motion of the source or observer.

CHAPTER TWENTY-SEVEN SOLUTIONS

Chapter Twenty-Seven Readings

Cassidy, D.C., "Heisenberg, Uncertainty and the Quantum Revolution," *Scientific American*, May 1992, p. 44.

Goldman, T. Hughes, R.J. and Nieto, M.M., "Gravity and Antimatter," *Scientific American*, March 1988, p. 48.

Heisenberg, W., *Physics and Beyond*, New York, Harper and Row, 1971 (A "biography of quantum mechanics)

Hoffman, B., *Strange Story of the Quantum*, New York, Dover 1959.

Howells, M.R. Kirz, J. and Sayre, D., "X-ray Microscopes," *Scientific American*, February 1991, p. 88.

Kinderman, J.V., "Investigating the Compton Effect with a Spreadsheet," *The Physics Teacher*, 30, 426, 1992

Reed, M.A., "Quantum Dots," *Scientific American*, January 1993, p. 118.

Shimony, A., "The Reality of the Quantum World," *Scientific American*, January 1988, p. 46.

Wagner, W.S., "Temperature and Color of Incandescent Lamps," *The Physics Teacher*, 29, 176, 1991

Wheaton, B., "Louis de Broglie and the Origin of Wave Mechanics," *The Physics Teacher*, May 1984, p. 297.

Wickramasinghe, H.K., "Scanned-Probe Microscopes," *Scientific American*, October 1989, p. 98.

Yam, P., "Exploiting Zero-Point Energy," *Scientific American*, December 1997, p. 82.

27.1 Wien's displacement law may be written as:

$$T = \frac{0.2898 \times 10^{-2} \text{ m K}}{\lambda_{max}} = \frac{2.898 \times 10^{6} \text{ nm K}}{\lambda_{max}}$$

(a) If $\lambda_{max} = 970$ nm, then $T = \frac{2.898 \times 10^{6} \text{ nm K}}{970 \text{ nm}} = 2.99 \times 10^{3}$ K, or T is about 3000 K.

(b) If $\lambda_{max} = 145$ nm, then $T = \frac{2.898 \times 10^{6} \text{ nm K}}{145 \text{ nm}} = 2.00 \times 10^{4}$ K (20,000 K)

27.2 $\lambda = \frac{c}{f} = \frac{3.00 \times 10^{8} \text{ m/s}}{1.00 \times 10^{15} \text{ Hz}} = 3.00 \times 10^{-7}$ m.

Thus, $T = \dfrac{0.2898 \times 10^{-2}\ \text{m K}}{\lambda_{max}} = \dfrac{0.2898 \times 10^{-2}\ \text{m K}}{3.00 \times 10^{-7}\ \text{m}} = 9.66 \times 10^{3}\ \text{K}.$

27.3 $\lambda_{max} T = 0.2898 \times 10^{-2}$ m K (Wien's displacement Law).

Thus, $\lambda_{max} = \dfrac{0.2898 \times 10^{-2}\ \text{m K}}{5800\ \text{K}} = 5.00 \times 10^{-7}\ \text{m} = 500\ \text{nm}.$

27.4 (a) Using $\lambda_{max} T = 0.2898 \times 10^{-2}$ m K, we get:

$$\lambda_{max} = \frac{0.2898 \times 10^{-2}\ \text{m}}{2900\ \text{K}} = 9.993 \times 10^{-7}\ \text{m} \approx 1{,}000\ \text{nm}.$$

(b) The peak wavelength is in the infrared, far from the visible region of the electromagnetic spectrum.

27.5 $E_\gamma = \dfrac{hc}{\lambda} = \dfrac{(6.63 \times 10^{-34}\ \text{J s})(3 \times 10^{8}\ \text{m/s})}{\lambda}$. The result of this calculation may be written in several forms:

$$E_\gamma = \frac{1.99 \times 10^{-25}\ \text{J m}}{\lambda} = \frac{1.243 \times 10^{-6}\ \text{eV m}}{\lambda} = \frac{1243\ \text{nm}}{\lambda}$$

(a) For $\lambda = 5.00\ \text{cm} = 5.00 \times 10^{-2}$ m, $E = 2.49 \times 10^{-5}$ eV.
(b) For $\lambda = 500$ nm, $E = 2.49$ eV.
(c) For $\lambda = 5.00$ nm, $E = 249$ eV.

27.6 $\lambda = \dfrac{hc}{E} = \dfrac{(6.63 \times 10^{-34}\ \text{J s})(3.00 \times 10^{8}\ \text{m/s})}{(2000\ \text{eV})(1.60 \times 10^{-19}\ \text{J/eV})} = 6.2 \times 10^{-10}\ \text{m} = 0.62\ \text{nm}.$

27.7 The total energy radiated each second is:

$$E = Pt = (150 \times 10^{3}\ \text{J/s})(1\ \text{s}) = 150 \times 10^{3}\ \text{J}.$$

The energy of each 99.7 MHz photon is:

$E_\gamma = hf = (6.63 \times 10^{-34}\ \text{J s})(99.7 \times 10^{6}\ \text{s}^{-1}) = 6.61 \times 10^{-26}$ J. The number of photons emitted per second is therefore:

$$n = \frac{E}{E_\gamma} = \frac{150 \times 10^{3}\ \text{J}}{6.61 \times 10^{-26}\ \text{photons/s}} = 2.27 \times 10^{30}\ \text{photons}.$$

27.8 Energy of a single 500 nm photon:

$$E_\gamma = hf = \frac{hc}{\lambda} = \frac{(6.63 \times 10^{-34}\ \text{J s})(3.00 \times 10^{8}\ \text{m/s})}{500 \times 10^{-9}\ \text{m}} = 3.98 \times 10^{-19}\ \text{J}.$$

The energy entering the eye each second is:

$$E = Pt = (IA)t = (4 \times 10^{-11}\ \text{W/m}^2)\frac{\pi}{4}(8.5 \times 10^{-3}\ \text{m})^2\ (1\ \text{s}) = 2.27 \times 10^{-15}\ \text{J}.$$

The number of photons required to yield this energy is:

$$n = \frac{E}{E_\gamma} = \frac{2.27 \times 10^{-15}\ \text{J}}{3.98 \times 10^{-19}\ \text{J/photon}} = 5.7 \times 10^{3}\ \text{photons}.$$

27.9 (a) $E = \dfrac{1}{2}kA^2 = \dfrac{1}{2}(20\ \text{N/m})(0.030\ \text{m})^2 = 9.0 \times 10^{-3}$ J, and

$f = \dfrac{1}{2\pi}\sqrt{\dfrac{k}{m}} = \dfrac{1}{2\pi}\sqrt{\dfrac{20\ \text{N/m}}{1.5\ \text{kg}}} = 0.58$ Hz. Therefore, if $E = nhf$, we have:

$$n = \frac{E}{hf} = \frac{9.0 \times 10^{-3}\ \text{J}}{(6.63 \times 10^{-34}\ \text{J s})(0.58\ \text{Hz})} = 2.3 \times 10^{31}.$$

(b) If $\Delta n = 1$, then $\Delta E = hf = 3.8 \times 10^{-34}$ J.

Thus, $\frac{\Delta E}{E} = \frac{3.8 \times 10^{-34}\ \text{J}}{9.0 \times 10^{-3}\ \text{J}} = 4.2 \times 10^{-32}$.

27.10 The energy which would be released is:
$mgh = (0.50\ \text{kg})(9.80\ \text{m/s}^2)(3.0\ \text{m}) = 14.7\ \text{J}$. The energy of a 500 nm photon is: $E = h\frac{c}{\lambda} = \frac{(6.63 \times 10^{-34}\ \text{J s})(3.00 \times 10^{8}\ \text{m/s})}{500 \times 10^{-9}\ \text{m}} = 3.98 \times 10^{-19}\ \text{J}$.

Thus, # photons released = $\frac{14.7\ \text{J}}{3.98 \times 10^{-19}\ \text{J/photon}} = 3.7 \times 10^{19}$ photons.

27.11 Energy needed = 1 eV = 1.6×10^{-19} J.
The energy absorbed in time t is $E = Pt = (IA)t$, so the required time is
$$t = \frac{E}{IA} = \frac{1.60 \times 10^{-19}\ \text{J}}{(500\ \text{J/s}\cdot\text{m}^2)(\pi(2.82 \times 10^{-15}\ \text{m})^2)} = 1.28 \times 10^{7}\ \text{s} = 148\ \text{days}.$$
This prediction from classical theory is incompatible with observation.

27.12 The maximum kinetic energy of the ejected electrons is:
$$\frac{1}{2}mv^2 = \frac{1}{2}(9.1 \times 10^{-31}\ \text{kg})(4.6 \times 10^{5}\ \text{m/s})^2 = 9.6 \times 10^{-20}\ \text{J}.$$
The work function is then found as: $\phi = h\frac{c}{\lambda} - KE_{max}$, so
$$\phi = \frac{(6.63 \times 10^{-34}\ \text{J s})(3.00 \times 10^{8}\ \text{m/s})}{(625 \times 10^{-9}\ \text{m})} - 9.6 \times 10^{-20}\ \text{J} = 2.2 \times 10^{-19}\ \text{J, and}$$
$\phi = 1.4$ eV. At the cutoff frequency, we have: $hf_c = \phi$, so
$$f_c = \frac{\phi}{h} = \frac{2.2 \times 10^{-19}\ \text{J}}{6.63 \times 10^{-34}\ \text{J s}} = 3.4 \times 10^{14}\ \text{Hz}.$$

27.13 (a) The photon energy is:
$$E = hf = \frac{hc}{\lambda} = \frac{(6.63 \times 10^{-34}\ \text{J s})(3.00 \times 10^{8}\ \text{m/s})}{350 \times 10^{-9}\ \text{m}} = 5.68 \times 10^{-19}\ \text{J, or}$$
$E = 3.55$ eV
and $\phi = E - KE_{max} = 3.55\ \text{eV} - 1.31\ \text{eV} = 2.24\ \text{eV}$.

(b) $\lambda_c = \frac{hc}{\phi} = \frac{(6.63 \times 10^{-34}\ \text{J s})(3.00 \times 10^{8}\ \text{m/s})}{(2.24\ \text{eV})(1.60 \times 10^{-19}\ \text{J/eV})}$
$= 5.55 \times 10^{-7}\ \text{m} = 555\ \text{nm}$

(c) $f_c = \frac{c}{\lambda_c} = \frac{3.00 \times 10^{8}\ \text{m/s}}{5.55 \times 10^{-7}\ \text{m}} = 5.41 \times 10^{14}\ \text{Hz}$.

27.14 The energy of a 300 nm wavelength photon is: $E = \frac{hc}{\lambda} = 4.14\ \text{eV}$.

(a) In order for the photoelectric effect to occur, the energy of the photon must be greater than the work function. Thus, the effect will occur in lithium and iron.

(b) For lithium: $KE_{max} = hf - \phi = 4.14\ \text{eV} - 2.3\ \text{eV} = 1.8\ \text{eV}$.
For iron; $KE_{max} = hf - \phi = 4.14\ \text{eV} - 4.1\ \text{eV} = 0.04\ \text{eV}$.

27.15 $\lambda = \frac{c}{f} = \frac{3.00 \times 10^{8}\ \text{m/s}}{3.0 \times 10^{15}\ \text{Hz}} = 1.0 \times 10^{-7}\ \text{m} = 100\ \text{nm}$. Thus, the photon energy is: $E_\gamma = h\frac{c}{\lambda} = 12.4\ \text{eV}$. Also, $KE_{max} = V_s e = (7.0\ \text{V})e = 7.0\ \text{eV}$.

Therefore, $\phi = E_\gamma - KE_{max} = 12.4\text{ eV} - 7.0\text{ eV} = 5.4\text{ eV}$.

27.16 The kinetic energy of the emitted electrons is:

$$KE = \frac{1}{2}mv^2 = 0.5(9.11\times10^{-31}\text{ kg})(1.0\times10^{6}\text{ m/s})^2 = 4.6\times10^{-19}\text{ J} = 2.9\text{ eV}$$

Then, from the photoelectric effect equation, the energy of the required photons is: $E_\gamma = KE + \phi = 2.9\text{ eV} + 2.46\text{ eV} = 5.36\text{ eV} = 8.57\times10^{-19}\text{ J}$.

The wavelength of such photons is:

$$\lambda = \frac{hc}{E_\gamma} = \frac{(6.63\times10^{-34}\text{ J s})(3.00\times10^{8}\text{ m/s})}{8.57\times10^{-19}\text{ J}} = 2.32\times10^{-7}\text{ m} = 232\text{ nm}.$$

27.17 The frequency of the 254 nm wavelength light is:

$$f = \frac{c}{\lambda} = \frac{3.00\times10^{8}\text{ m/s}}{254\times10^{-9}\text{ m}} = 1.18\times10^{15}\text{ Hz}.$$

Similarly, the frequency of the 436 nm light is 6.88×10^{14} Hz.
The graph you draw should look somewhat like the sketch below. The desired quantities are read from the graph as indicated. You should find that: $f_c = 4.77\times10^{14}$ Hz and $\phi = 2.03$ eV.

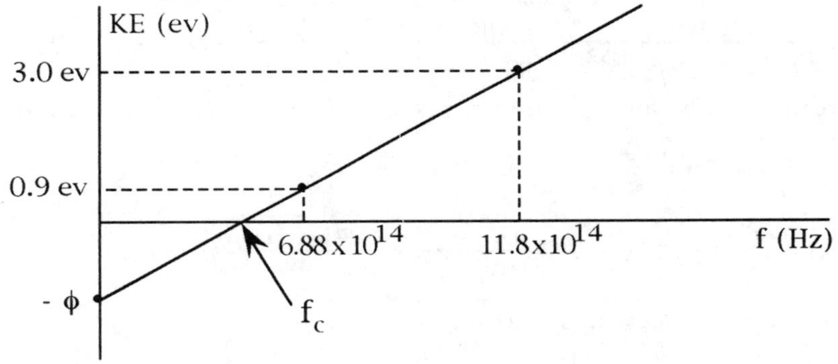

27.18 $\phi = 3.44\text{ eV} = 5.50\times10^{-19}\text{ J}$

$$KE = \frac{1}{2}mv^2 = \frac{1}{2}(9.11\times10^{-31}\text{ kg})(4.2\times10^{5}\text{ m/s})^2 = 8.0\times10^{-20}\text{ J}.$$

Energy absorbed = $E_\gamma = KE + \phi = 6.3\times10^{-19}$ J (per electron emitted)

Energy incident on one square centimeter of surface each second is:

$$E = Pt = (IA)t = (5.5\times10^{-2}\text{ J/sm}^2)((1.0\times10^{-2}\text{ m})^2)(1.0\text{ s}) = 5.5\times10^{-6}\text{ J}.$$

Therefore, the number of electrons liberated each second, n is:

$$n = \frac{5.5\times10^{-6}\text{ J}}{6.3\times10^{-19}\text{ J/electron}} = 8.7\times10^{12}\text{ electrons/s.} \quad (\text{per cm}^2)$$

27.19 From $V = \frac{KE_{max}}{e} = \frac{E_\gamma}{e} = \frac{hc}{e\lambda_{min}} = \frac{1.243\times10^{-6}\text{ eV m}}{e\lambda_{min}} = \frac{1.243\times10^{-6}\text{ V m}}{\lambda_{min}}$

If $\lambda = 1.0\times10^{-8}$ m, $V = \frac{1.243\times10^{-6}\text{ V m}}{1.0\times10^{-8}\text{ m}} = 1.2\times10^{2}$ V

If $\lambda = 1.0\times10^{-13}$ m, $V = \frac{1.243\times10^{-6}\text{ V m}}{1.0\times10^{-13}\text{ m}} = 1.2\times10^{7}\text{ V} = 12\text{ MV}$

27.20 A photon of maximum energy and minimum wavelength is produced when the electron gives up all its kinetic energy in one collision.

We have, $\lambda_{min} = \frac{hc}{E_\gamma} = \frac{1243 \text{ nm eV}}{E_\gamma}$.

(a) $E_\gamma = KE = 15.0$ keV, so $\lambda_{min} = \frac{1243 \text{ nm eV}}{1.50 \times 10^4 \text{ eV}} = 0.0828$ nm.

(b) $E_\gamma = KE = 100$ keV, and $\lambda_{min} = \frac{1243 \text{ nm eV}}{1.00 \times 10^5 \text{ eV}} = 0.0124$ nm.

27.21 $V = \frac{KE}{e} = \frac{E_\gamma}{e} = \frac{hc}{e\lambda} = \frac{(6.63 \times 10^{-34} \text{ J s})(3.00 \times 10^8 \text{ V})}{(1.60 \times 10^{-19} \text{ C})(0.0300 \times 10^{-9} \text{ m})} = 4.14 \times 10^4$ V

27.22 From Bragg's law: $\lambda = \frac{2d\sin\theta}{n} = \frac{2(0.353 \text{ nm}) \sin 20.5°}{(2)} = 0.124$ nm.

27.23 From Bragg's law, we have:

$\lambda = \frac{2d\sin\theta}{n} = \frac{2(0.296 \text{ nm}) \sin 7.6°}{(1)} = 0.078$ nm.

27.24 $\lambda = \frac{hc}{E_\gamma} = \frac{(6.63 \times 10^{-34} \text{ J s})(3.00 \times 10^8 \text{ m/s})}{(11.3 \times 10^3 \text{ eV})(1.60 \times 10^{-19} \text{ J/eV})} = 1.10 \times 10^{-10}$ m $= 0.110$ nm.

From Bragg's law: $\sin\theta = \frac{m\lambda}{2d}$, so if $m = 2$ and $d = 0.352$ nm,

$\sin\theta = \frac{2(0.110 \text{ nm})}{2(0.352 \text{ nm})} = 0.312$ and $\theta = 18.2°$.

27.25 From Bragg's law: $d = \frac{n\lambda}{2\sin\theta} = \frac{(1)(0.140 \text{ nm})}{2\sin 14.4°} = 0.281$ nm.

27.26 We have: $\Delta\lambda = \lambda_c(1 - \cos\theta)$, or,

$\cos\theta = 1 - \frac{\Delta\lambda}{\lambda_c} = 1 - \frac{1.50 \times 10^{-3} \text{ nm}}{2.43 \times 10^{-3} \text{ nm}} = 1 - 0.617 = 0.383$, and $\theta = 67.5°$.

27.27 For the recoiling electron to have a kinetic energy equal to the energy of the scattered photon, the energy of the incident photon must be split equally between the electron and the scattered photon.

Therefore, $E'_\gamma = \frac{1}{2} E_\gamma$, or $\frac{hc}{\lambda'} = \frac{1}{2}\frac{hc}{\lambda}$, so $\lambda' = 2\lambda$ and $\Delta\lambda = \lambda = 0.0016$ nm.

From the Compton equation:

$\cos\theta = 1 - \frac{\Delta\lambda}{\lambda_c} = 1 - \frac{0.0016 \text{ nm}}{0.00243 \text{ nm}} = 0.3416$, and $\theta = 70.0°$.

27.28 Using the Compton equation, the shift in wavelength for scattering at 45° is: $\Delta\lambda = (0.00243 \text{ nm})(1 - \cos 45°) = 7.1 \times 10^{-4}$ nm.

Thus, $\lambda = \lambda_0 + \Delta\lambda = 0.68 \text{ nm} + 7.1 \times 10^{-4} \text{ nm} = 0.6807$ nm.

The energy of these photons is:

$E_\gamma = \frac{hc}{\lambda} = \frac{(6.63 \times 10^{-34} \text{ J s})(3.00 \times 10^8 \text{ m/s})}{(0.6807 \times 10^{-9} \text{ m})} = 2.92 \times 10^{-16} \text{ J} = 1.8$ keV,

and the momentum is: $p = \frac{E_\gamma}{c} = 1.8$ keV/c $\quad (9.74 \times 10^{-25}$ kg m/s).

27.29 (a) From the Compton shift formula:

$$\Delta\lambda = \lambda_c(1 - \cos\theta) = (0.00243 \text{ nm})(1 - \cos 37°) = 4.89 \times 10^{-4} \text{ nm}.$$

(b) The wavelength of the original photon was:

$$\lambda_0 = \frac{hc}{E_{\gamma 0}} = \frac{(6.63 \times 10^{-34} \text{ Js})(3.00 \times 10^{8} \text{ m/s})}{(300 \text{ keV})(1.6 \times 10^{-16} \text{ J/keV})}$$

$$= 4.14 \times 10^{-12} \text{ m} = 4.14 \times 10^{-3} \text{ nm}$$

Thus, the scattered wavelength is:

$\lambda = \lambda_0 + \Delta\lambda = 4.14 \times 10^{-3}$ nm $+ 4.89 \times 10^{-4}$ m $= 4.63 \times 10^{-3}$ nm, and its energy is

$$E_\gamma = \frac{hc}{\lambda} = \frac{(6.63 \times 10^{-34} \text{ J s})(3.00 \times 10^{8} \text{ m/s})}{(4.63 \times 10^{-12} \text{ m})} = 4.29 \times 10^{-14} \text{ J} = 268 \text{ keV},$$

(c) The energy transferred to the recoiling electron is:

$$KE = E_{\gamma 0} - E_\gamma = 32 \text{ keV}$$

27.30 $KE = \frac{1}{2}mv^2 = \frac{1}{2}(9.11 \times 10^{-31} \text{ kg})(1.40 \times 10^{6} \text{ m/s})^2 = 8.93 \times 10^{-19}$ J, but

$$KE = E_\gamma - E'_\gamma = \frac{hc}{\lambda} - \frac{hc}{\lambda'} = hc\left(\frac{\lambda' - \lambda}{\lambda'\lambda}\right) \approx hc\left(\frac{\Delta\lambda}{\lambda^2}\right).$$

(a) Thus, $\Delta\lambda = \frac{\lambda^2(KE)}{hc} = \frac{(8.00 \times 10^{-10} \text{ m})^2(8.93 \times 10^{-19} \text{ J})}{(6.63 \times 10^{-34} \text{ J s})(3.00 \times 10^{8} \text{ m/s})}$, or

$$\Delta\lambda = 2.87 \times 10^{-12} \text{ m} = 2.87 \times 10^{-3} \text{ nm}.$$

(b) From the Compton equation: $1 - \cos\theta = \frac{\Delta\lambda}{\lambda_c} = \frac{2.87 \times 10^{-3} \text{ nm}}{2.43 \times 10^{-3} \text{ nm}} = 1.18,$

from which $\cos\theta = -0.18$, and $\theta = 100°$.

27.31 $E_{\gamma 0} = \frac{hc}{\lambda_0} = \frac{(6.63 \times 10^{-34} \text{ J s})(3.00 \times 10^{8} \text{ m/s})}{(0.450 \times 10^{-9} \text{ m})} = 4.42 \times 10^{-16}$ J.

With a scattering angle of $\theta = 23°$, the Compton equation gives:

$$\lambda' = \lambda_0 + \lambda_c(1 - \cos\theta) = 0.45 \text{ nm} + (2.43 \times 10^{-3} \text{ nm})(1 - \cos 23°) = 0.4502 \text{ nm}$$

$$E_\gamma = \frac{hc}{\lambda'} = \frac{(6.63 \times 10^{-34} \text{ J s})(3.00 \times 10^{8} \text{ m/s})}{(0.4502 \times 10^{-9} \text{ m})} = 4.418 \times 10^{-16} \text{ J}.$$

(a) Energy given to the electron $= KE = E_{\gamma 0} - E_\gamma = 2.0 \times 10^{-19}$ J.

(b) From $KE = \frac{1}{2}mv^2$:

$$v = \sqrt{\frac{2(KE)}{m}} = \sqrt{\frac{2(2.0 \times 10^{-19} \text{ J})}{(9.11 \times 10^{-31} \text{ kg})}} = 6.6 \times 10^{5} \text{ m/s}.$$

27.32 The kinetic energy of the pair will equal the energy of the photon that produced them minus the combined rest energy of the two. Thus,

$$KE = E_\gamma - 2E_0 = 3.00 \text{ MeV} - 2(0.511 \text{ MeV}) = 1.98 \text{ MeV}$$

27.33 (a) We have: $E = KE + 2E_0 = 2.50 \text{ MeV} + 2(0.511 \text{ MeV}) = 3.52$ MeV.

(b) $f = \frac{E}{h} = \frac{3.52 \text{ MeV}(1.60 \times 10^{-13} \text{ J/MeV})}{6.63 \times 10^{-34} \text{ J s}} = 8.50 \times 10^{20}$ Hz.

27.34 Assuming we are in the rest frame of the particles before annihilation, we have: $p_{before} = 0$, and as a result, $p_{after} = 0$. Thus,

$\frac{E_\gamma}{c} = \frac{E'_\gamma}{c}$, or $E_\gamma = E'_\gamma$. The two photons have equal energy.

From the energy-mass relationship:

$2E_0 = 2E_\gamma$, or $E_\gamma = E_0$. Therefore, $hf = m_p c^2$, which gives:

$$f = \frac{m_p c^2}{h} = \frac{(1.67 \times 10^{-27}\ \text{kg})(3.00 \times 10^8\ \text{m/s})^2}{6.63 \times 10^{-34}\ \text{J s}} = 2.27 \times 10^{23}\ \text{Hz}.$$

Then, $\lambda = \frac{c}{f} = \frac{3.00 \times 10^8\ \text{m/s}}{2.27 \times 10^{23}\ \text{Hz}} = 1.32 \times 10^{-15}$ m.

27.35 Total momentum is zero before and after the process, so the two emerging photons must have the same wavelength and hence energy. Next, look at conservation of energy:

$$E_\gamma + E_\gamma = 2(E_0 + KE) = 2[m_0 c^2 + m_0 c^2(\gamma - 1)] = 2\gamma m_0 c^2.$$

Thus, $E_\gamma = \gamma m_0 c^2 = \frac{0.511\ \text{MeV}}{\sqrt{1-(0.60)^2}} = 0.64$ MeV, and

$$p_\gamma = \frac{E_\gamma}{c} = 0.64\ \text{MeV/c} = 3.41 \times 10^{-22}\ \text{kg m/s}.$$

27.36 From conservation of energy: $\frac{1}{2}mv^2 = mgh$, or

$$v = \sqrt{2gh} = \sqrt{2(9.80\ \text{m/s}^2)(50.0\ \text{m})} = 31.3\ \text{m/s}.$$

Thus, $p = mv = (0.200\ \text{kg})(31.3\ \text{m/s}) = 6.26$ kg m/s, and

$$\lambda = \frac{h}{p} = \frac{6.63 \times 10^{-34}\ \text{J s}}{6.26\ \text{kg m/s}} = 1.06 \times 10^{-34}\ \text{m}.$$

27.37 (a) $\lambda = \frac{h}{p} = \frac{h}{mv}$,

so $v = \frac{h}{m\lambda} = \frac{6.63 \times 10^{-34}\ \text{J s}}{(9.11 \times 10^{-31}\ \text{kg})(500 \times 10^{-9}\ \text{m})} = 1.46 \times 10^3$ m/s

(b) $p = mv = (9.11 \times 10^{-31}\ \text{kg})(1.00 \times 10^7\ \text{m/s}) = 9.11 \times 10^{-24}$ kg m/s

Thus, $\lambda = \frac{h}{p} = \frac{6.63 \times 10^{-34}\ \text{J s}}{9.11 \times 10^{-24}\ \text{kg m/s}} = 7.28 \times 10^{-11}$ m

---

27.38 $p = \frac{h}{\lambda} = \frac{6.63 \times 10^{-34}\ \text{J s}}{1.0 \times 10^{-10}\ \text{m}} = 6.6 \times 10^{-24}$ kg m/s, and

$$pc = (6.6 \times 10^{-24}\ \text{kg m/s})(3.00 \times 10^8\ \text{m/s})\left(\frac{1\ \text{MeV}}{1.60 \times 10^{-13}\ \text{J}}\right) = 1.2 \times 10^{-2}\ \text{MeV}.$$

Thus, checking to see if this electron is relativistic,

$$E = \sqrt{p^2c^2 + E_0^2} = \sqrt{(1.24 \times 10^{-2}\ \text{MeV})^2 + (0.511\ \text{MeV})^2} = 0.511\ \text{MeV},$$

Thus E is approximately equal to E_0. (Thus, classical calculations suffice.)

From conservation of energy, $Ve = KE = \frac{p^2}{2m_0}$ or $V = \frac{p^2}{2m_0 e}$.

Thus, $$V = \frac{(6.63 \times 10^{-24}\ \text{kg m/s})^2}{2(9.11 \times 10^{-31}\ \text{kg})(1.60 \times 10^{-19}\ \text{C})} = 1.5 \times 10^2\ \text{V}.$$

27.39 (a) At 2.00×10^4 m/s, the proton is non-relativistic. Thus,
$p = m_0 v = (1.67 \times 10^{-27}\text{ kg})(2.00 \times 10^4\text{ m/s}) = 3.34 \times 10^{-23}$ kg m/s, and
$$\lambda = \frac{h}{p} = \frac{6.63 \times 10^{-34}\text{ J s}}{3.34 \times 10^{-23}\text{ kg m/s}} = 1.99 \times 10^{-11}\text{ m.}$$
(b) At 2.00×10^7 m/s, $\gamma = 1.005$. Thus, $p = \gamma m_0 v$ gives:
$p = (1.005)(1.67 \times 10^{-27}\text{ kg})(2.00 \times 10^7\text{ m/s}) = 5.04 \times 10^{-20}$ kg m/s,
and $$\lambda = \frac{h}{p} = \frac{6.63 \times 10^{-34}\text{ J s}}{5.04 \times 10^{-20}\text{ kg m/s}} = 1.32 \times 10^{-14}\text{ m.}$$

27.40 From the discussion of single slit diffraction in Chapter 24, the screen positions of the dark fringes are given by: $y_m = mL\left(\frac{\lambda}{a}\right)$. Thus, the spacing between successive minima is: $\Delta y = y_{m+1} - y_m = \frac{L\lambda}{a}$. The de Broglie wavelength of this electron is then:
$$\lambda = \frac{(\Delta y)a}{L} = \frac{(2.10\text{ cm})(0.500\text{ nm})}{20.0\text{ cm}} = 0.0525\text{ nm. Thus,}$$
$$p = \frac{h}{\lambda} = \frac{6.63 \times 10^{-34}\text{ J s}}{(5.25 \times 10^{-11}\text{ m})} = 1.26 \times 10^{-23}\text{ kg m/s.}$$
Classically, $KE = \frac{p^2}{2m_0} = \frac{(1.26 \times 10^{-23}\text{ kg m/s})^2}{2(9.11 \times 10^{-31}\text{ kg})} = 8.71 \times 10^{-17}\text{ J} = 545\text{ eV}$.
Relativistically, $KE = \sqrt{p^2c^2 + E_0^2} - E_0 = 8.71 \times 10^{-17}\text{ J} = 545\text{ eV}$.

27.41 This is a relativistic electron, so: $E = E_0 + KE$,
where $E_0 = m_0 c^2 = (9.11 \times 10^{-31}\text{ kg})(3.00 \times 10^8\text{ m/s})^2 = 8.20 \times 10^{-14}$ J
Since, $KE = 3.00$ MeV $= 4.80 \times 10^{-13}$ J, we have $E = E_0 + KE = 5.62 \times 10^{-13}$ J
Also, $p = \frac{1}{c}\sqrt{E^2 - E_0^2}$
$$= \frac{\sqrt{(5.62 \times 10^{-13}\text{ J})^2 - (8.20 \times 10^{-14}\text{ J})^2}}{3.00 \times 10^8\text{ m/s}} = 1.85 \times 10^{-21}\text{ kg m/s}$$
Then, $$\lambda = \frac{h}{p} = \frac{6.63 \times 10^{-34}\text{ J s}}{1.85 \times 10^{-21}\text{ kg m/s}} = 3.58 \times 10^{-13}\text{ m.}$$

27.42 The de Broglie wavelength is: $\lambda = \frac{h}{p} = \frac{h}{mv}$, where $m = \gamma m_0$.
Thus, $\lambda = \frac{h}{\gamma m_0 v} = \frac{h}{m_0(\gamma v)}$. The Compton wavelength is: $\lambda_0 = \frac{h}{m_0 c}$.
Therefore, we see that to have $\lambda = \lambda_0$, it is necessary that: $\gamma v = c$.
This gives: $\frac{v}{\sqrt{1 - (v/c)^2}} = c$, or $(v/c)^2 = 1 - (v/c)^2$, yielding $v = \frac{c}{\sqrt{2}}$.

27.43 (a) $p = \frac{h}{\lambda} = \frac{6.63 \times 10^{-34}\text{ J s}}{1.0 \times 10^{-11}\text{ m}} = 6.63 \times 10^{-23}$ kg m/s.
Relativistically: $E^2 = (pc)^2 + E_0^2$, which gives $E = 8.44 \times 10^{-14}$ J.
Then, $KE = E - E_0 = 8.44 \times 10^{-14}\text{ J} - (9.11 \times 10^{-31}\text{ J})(3.00 \times 10^8\text{ m/s})^2$,
or $KE = 2.38 \times 10^{-15}\text{ J} = 14.9$ keV.

If done classically: $KE = \frac{p^2}{2m_0} = 2.41 \times 10^{-15}$ J = 15.1 keV.

Therefore, to 2 significant figures, KE = 15 kev (for both cases)

(b) $E_\gamma = \frac{hc}{\lambda} = \frac{(6.63 \times 10^{-34}\text{ J s})(3.0 \times 10^{8}\text{ m/s})}{1.0 \times 10^{-11}\text{ m}} = 2.0 \times 10^{-14}$ J,

or $E_\gamma = (2.0 \times 10^{-14}\text{ J})/(1.60 \times 10^{-16}\text{ J/keV}) = 1.3 \times 10^{2}$ keV.

27.44 $(\Delta x)(\Delta p) \geq \frac{h}{4\pi}$. We have: v = 30.0 m/s, and Δv = 0.10%(v) = 3.00×10^{-2} m/s.

Thus, $\Delta p = (50.0 \times 10^{-3}\text{ kg})(3.00 \times 10^{-2}\text{ m/s}) = 1.50 \times 10^{-3}$ kg m/s, and

$$\Delta x \geq \frac{h}{4\pi(\Delta p)} = \frac{6.63 \times 10^{-34}\text{ J s}}{4\pi(1.50 \times 10^{-3}\text{ kg m/s})} = 3.5 \times 10^{-32}\text{ m}$$

27.45 We have: $\Delta x = 0.50\text{ cm} = 5.0 \times 10^{-3}$ m.

Thus, $\Delta p \geq \frac{h}{4\pi(\Delta x)} = \frac{6.63 \times 10^{-34}\text{ J s}}{4\pi(5.0 \times 10^{-3}\text{ m})} = 1.1 \times 10^{-32}$ kg m/s, and

$\Delta p = m(\Delta v)$, so $\Delta v = \frac{\Delta p}{m} \geq \frac{1.1 \times 10^{-32}\text{ kg m/s}}{0.50\text{ kg}} = 2.2 \times 10^{-32}$ m/s.

Thus, v is of the order of the uncertainty, and equal to:

$v = 2.2 \times 10^{-32}$ m/s

27.46 $\Delta p = \frac{h}{4\pi(\Delta x)} = \frac{6.63 \times 10^{-34}\text{ J s}}{4\pi(1.0 \times 10^{-10}\text{ m})} = 5.3 \times 10^{-25}$ kg m/s.

$\Delta v = \frac{\Delta p}{m} = \frac{5.3 \times 10^{-25}\text{ kg m/s}}{9.11 \times 10^{-31}\text{ kg}} = 5.8 \times 10^{5}$ m/s.

Thus, v is of the order of 10^5 m/s.

27.47 Using $(\Delta x)(\Delta p) \geq \frac{h}{4\pi}$, we get: $(\Delta x)(m\Delta v) \geq \frac{h}{4\pi}$, so

$$\Delta v \geq \frac{h}{4\pi m(\Delta x)} = \frac{(6.63 \times 10^{-34}\text{ J s})}{4\pi(9.11 \times 10^{-31}\text{ kg})(500 \times 10^{-9}\text{ m})} = 116\text{ m/s}.$$

27.48 (a) The kinetic energy of a classical particle is:

$$KE = \frac{1}{2}mv^2 = \frac{(mv)^2}{2m} = \frac{p^2}{2m}.$$

(b) From the uncertainty principle:

$$\Delta p \geq \frac{h}{4\pi(\Delta x)} = \frac{(6.63 \times 10^{-34}\text{ J s})}{4\pi(1.0 \times 10^{-15}\text{ kg})} = 5.3 \times 10^{-20}\text{ kg m/s}.$$

The smallest momentum is also of the order of Δp.

Thus, $p_{min} \approx 5.3 \times 10^{-20}$ kg m/s and

$$KE_{min} = \frac{(p_{min})^2}{2(1.67 \times 10^{-27}\text{ kg})} = 8.4 \times 10^{-13}\text{ J} = 5.3\text{ MeV}.$$

27.49 From Wien's displacement law, $\lambda_{max} T = 0.2898 \times 10^{-2}$ mK, we find:

$T = \frac{0.2898 \times 10^{-2}\text{ mK}}{560 \times 10^{-9}\text{ m}} = 5.18 \times 10^{3}$ K. Clearly, a firefly is not near this temperature, and hence, this is not blackbody radiation.

27.50 The energy of one photon is:

$$E_\gamma = \frac{(6.63 \times 10^{-34}\ \text{J s})(3.00 \times 10^{8}\ \text{m/s})}{589.3 \times 10^{-9}\ \text{m}} = 3.38 \times 10^{-19}\ \text{J}$$

The energy emitted per second is: $E =$ (power) $t = (100\ \text{J/s})(10.0\ \text{s}) = 100\ \text{J}$
Thus, the number of photons emitted is:

$$N = \frac{E}{E_\gamma} = \frac{100\ \text{J}}{3.38 \times 10^{-19}\ \text{J}} = 2.96 \times 10^{20}$$

27.51 $E = (KE)_{max} = \frac{1}{2}mv^2 = \frac{1}{2}(70.0\ \text{kg})(2.0\ \text{m/s})^2 = 1.4 \times 10^2\ \text{J}.$

(a) If $E = nhf$, then $n = \frac{E}{hf} = \frac{1.4 \times 10^2\ \text{J}}{(6.63 \times 10^{-34}\ \text{J s})(0.50\ \text{Hz})} = 4.2 \times 10^{35}.$

(b) If $\Delta n = 1$, then $\Delta E = hf = (6.63 \times 10^{-34}\ \text{J s})(0.50\ \text{Hz}) = 3.3 \times 10^{-34}\ \text{J}$

27.52 (a) $\lambda = \frac{hc}{eV} = \frac{1243\ \text{nm eV}}{e(5.00 \times 10^4\ \text{V})} = 2.49 \times 10^{-2}\ \text{nm}.$

(b) From $n\lambda = 2d\sin\theta$, $d = \frac{n\lambda}{2\sin\theta} = \frac{(1)(2.49 \times 10^{-2}\ \text{nm})}{2\sin 2.5^\circ} = 0.285\ \text{nm}.$

27.53 From Bragg's law, $\sin\theta = \frac{m\lambda}{2d}$, and $m = 1$ for the smallest angle. Thus,

$\sin\theta = \frac{1(0.070\ \text{nm})}{2(0.30\ \text{nm})} = 0.12$, and $\theta = 6.9^\circ$

27.54 We recall that the radius of the path of a charged particle in a magnetic field is given by: $r = \frac{mv}{qB}$, or $p = mv = qrB$. Thus, the momentum is:

$$p_{max} = (1.60 \times 10^{-19}\ \text{C})(0.200\ \text{m})(2.00 \times 10^{-5}\ \text{T}) = 6.40 \times 10^{-25}\ \text{kg m/s},$$

so $KE_{max} = \frac{(p_{max})^2}{2m} = \frac{(6.40 \times 10^{-25}\ \text{kg m/s})^2}{2(9.11 \times 10^{-31}\ \text{kg})} = 2.25 \times 10^{-19}\ \text{J} = 1.41\ \text{eV}.$

The photon energy is: $E_\gamma = \frac{hc}{\lambda} = \frac{(6.63 \times 10^{-34}\ \text{J·s})(3.00 \times 10^{8}\ \text{m/s})}{450 \times 10^{-9}}$, or

$E_\gamma = 2.76$ eV. Therefore, $\phi = E_\gamma - KE_{max} = 2.76\ \text{eV} - 1.41\ \text{eV} = 1.35\ \text{eV}.$

27.55 We use the Photoelectric equation: $KE_{max} = E_\gamma - \phi.$ (1)

The energy per photon of the first source is: $E_\gamma = \frac{hc}{\lambda}.$

The photon energy for the second source is: $E'_\gamma = \frac{hc}{\lambda'} = \frac{hc}{\frac{\lambda}{2}} = 2\frac{hc}{\lambda} = 2E.$

Thus, for case 1, (1) becomes: $1.00\ \text{eV} = E - \phi.$ (2)
For case 2, (1) becomes: $4.00\ \text{eV} = 2E - \phi.$ (3)
Solving (2) and (3) simultaneously, we find: $\phi = 2.00\ \text{eV}.$

27.56 $KE_{max} = E - \phi = hf - \phi = \frac{hc}{\lambda} - \phi.$

For wavelength λ_1: $KE_1 = \frac{hc}{\lambda_1} - \phi,$

For wavelength λ_2: $KE_2 = \frac{hc}{\lambda_2} - \phi.$ Thus, if $KE_2 = 1.5 KE_1$, we have

$$\frac{hc}{\lambda_2} - \phi = (1.5)\left(\frac{hc}{\lambda_1} - \phi\right), \quad \text{or} \quad \phi = 2hc\left(\frac{1.5}{\lambda_1} - \frac{1}{\lambda_2}\right).$$

$$\phi = 2(6.63 \times 10^{-34} \text{ J s})(3 \times 10^8 \text{ m/s})\left(\frac{1.5}{670 \times 10^{-9} \text{ m}} - \frac{1}{520 \times 10^{-9} \text{ m}}\right), \text{ or}$$

$$\phi = 1.26 \times 10^{-19} \text{ J} = 0.784 \text{ eV}.$$

27.57 (a) For $\lambda = 10.0$ nm, $E = \frac{hc}{\lambda}$ becomes: $E = 124$ eV which is very small compared to the electron's rest mass of 0.511 MeV. Therefore nonrelativistic equations can be used. Thus,

$$\frac{1}{2}mv^2 = 124 \text{ eV} = 2.00 \times 10^{-17} \text{ J, giving } v = 6.61 \times 10^6 \text{ m/s} = 0.0220c.$$

(b) For $\lambda = 10^{-4}$ nm, $E = \frac{hc}{\lambda}$ becomes: $E = 12.4$ MeV and relativistic equations must be used. Therefore,

$$E = (\gamma - 1)E_0 \text{ gives: } \gamma = 1 + \left(\frac{E}{E_0}\right), \text{ or } \gamma = 1 + \frac{12.4 \text{ MeV}}{0.511 \text{ MeV}} = 25.3.$$

From this, $v = 0.9992c$.

27.58 (a) The wavelength of the student is $\lambda = \frac{h}{p} = \frac{h}{mv}$. If w is the width of the diffraction aperture, then we need $w \leq 10\lambda = 10\left(\frac{h}{mv}\right)$, so that

$$v \leq 10\frac{h}{mw} = 10\left(\frac{(6.626 \times 10^{-34} \text{ J s})}{(80 \text{ kg})(0.75 \text{ m})}\right) = 1.1 \times 10^{-34} \text{ m/s}.$$

(b) Using $t = \frac{d}{v}$, we get: $t \geq \frac{0.15 \text{ m}}{1.1 \times 10^{-34} \text{ m/s}} = 1.4 \times 10^{33}$ s.

(c) No, the minimum time to pass through the door is over 10^{15} times the age of the Universe.

27.59 The de Broglie wavelength is $\lambda = \frac{h}{p} = \frac{h}{\gamma m_0 v} = \left(\frac{h}{m_0 c}\right)\frac{c}{\gamma v}$. Recognizing that the Compton wavelength is, $\lambda_c = \frac{h}{m_0 c}$, the wavelength may be written as: $\lambda = \frac{\lambda_c c}{\gamma v}$, or $\gamma\left(\frac{v}{c}\right) = \frac{\lambda_c}{\lambda}$, and $\dfrac{v/c}{\sqrt{1 - \left(\frac{v}{c}\right)^2}} = \frac{\lambda_c}{\lambda}$.

Therefore, if $\lambda = 10^{-3}$ nm: $\dfrac{v/c}{\sqrt{1 - \left(\frac{v}{c}\right)^2}} = \frac{2.43 \times 10^{-3} \text{ nm}}{1.0 \times 10^{-3} \text{ nm}} = 2.43$

From which: $\left(\frac{v}{c}\right)^2 = 0.8552$, and $\gamma = 2.63$. The kinetic energy is then given by: $KE = (\gamma - 1)E_0 = (1.63)(0.511 \text{ MeV}) = 0.83$ MeV.

27.60 Using $(\Delta x)(\Delta p) \geq \frac{h}{4\pi}$, we see:

$$\Delta p \geq \frac{h}{4\pi \Delta x} = \frac{(6.63 \times 10^{-34}\ \text{J s})}{4\pi(2.0 \times 10^{-15}\ \text{m})} = 2.63 \times 10^{-20}\ \text{kg m/s}.$$

The total energy of the particle is then: $E^2 = (pc)^2 + E^2{}_0$, or

$$\left(\frac{E}{E_0}\right)^2 = \left(\frac{pc}{E_0}\right)^2 + 1 = \frac{(2.63 \times 10^{-20}\ \text{kg m/s})(3.00 \times 10^8\ \text{m/s})}{E_0} + 1,$$

$$\left(\frac{E}{E_0}\right)^2 = \left(\frac{49.5\ \text{MeV}}{E_0}\right)^2 + 1.$$

For an electron: $E_0 = 0.511$ MeV, and $\left(\frac{E}{E_0}\right)^2 = 9370$, or $E = 96.8E_0$, which is highly relativistic. For a proton: $E_0 = 939.4$ MeV, and $\left(\frac{E}{E_0}\right)^2 = 1.001$, which is quite classical.

27.61 (a) We are given that $\lambda_{photon} = \lambda_{de\ Broglie}$, or $\lambda = \frac{h}{p} = \frac{hc}{pc}$.

Thus, $pc = \frac{hc}{\lambda} = E_\gamma$. Using $E_e{}^2 = (pc)^2 + E_0{}^2$ for the electron, we find: $E_e{}^2 = E_\gamma{}^2 + E_0{}^2$. (1)

From conservation of energy, we also obtain: $E_\gamma + E_0 = E_e + \phi$.

Thus, $E_e = E_\gamma + (E_0 - \phi)$ and $E_e{}^2 = E_\gamma{}^2 + 2E_\gamma(E_0 - \phi) + (E_0 - \phi)^2$. (2)

Equating equations (1) and (2) gives:

$E_\gamma{}^2 + E_0{}^2 = E_\gamma{}^2 + 2E_\gamma(E_0 - \phi) + (E_0 - \phi)^2$

which reduces to: $E_\gamma = \frac{E_0{}^2 - (E_0 - \phi)^2}{2(E_0 - \phi)}$. This easily reduces to the desired result: $E_\gamma = \frac{\phi(E_0 - \frac{\phi}{2})}{(E_0 - \phi)}$, where $E_0 = m_0c^2$.

(b) From the photoelectric equation $E_\gamma = KE_{max} + \phi$, and using the result above, we get:

$$\frac{\phi(E_0 - \frac{\phi}{2})}{E_0 - \phi} = KE_{max} + \phi, \text{ or } \quad KE_{max} = \frac{\phi(E_0 - \frac{\phi}{2})}{E_0 - \phi} - \phi = \frac{\phi^2}{2(E_0 - \phi)}.$$

With $\phi = 6.2$ eV, and $E_0 = 0.511$ MeV, this becomes:

$$KE_{max} = \frac{(6.3\ \text{eV})^2}{2(0.511 \times 10^6\ \text{eV} - 6.3\ \text{eV})} = 3.88 \times 10^{-5}\ \text{eV} = 6.21 \times 10^{-24}\ \text{J},$$

so $v = \sqrt{\frac{2KE}{m}} = \sqrt{\frac{2(6.21 \times 10^{-24}\ \text{J})}{9.11 \times 10^{-31}\ \text{m/s}}} = 3.69 \times 10^3$ m/s.

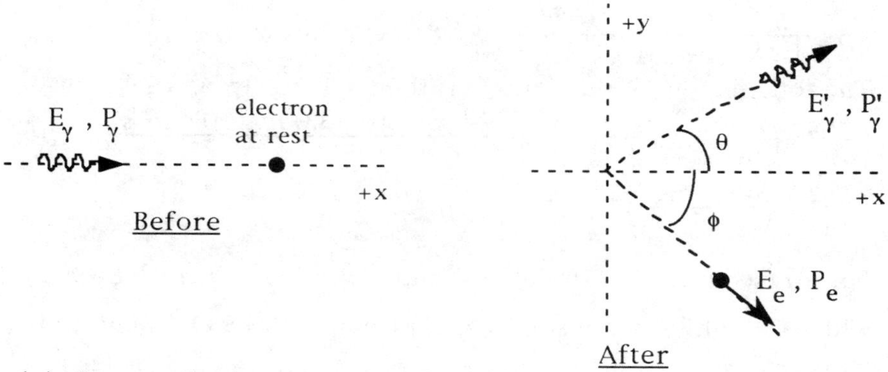

27.62 (a) Conserving mass-energy:
$E_\gamma + E_0 = E'_\gamma + (E_0 + KE)$ where E'_γ = the energy of the scattered photon, E_γ is the energy of the incident photon, and $(E_0 + KE)$ is the energy of the scattered electron.

Thus, $E_\gamma = 120\text{ keV} + 40.0\text{ keV} = 160\text{ keV}$, and $\lambda = \frac{hc}{E_\gamma}$ becomes:

$$\lambda = \frac{(6.63 \times 10^{-34}\text{ J s})(3.00 \times 10^{8}\text{ m/s})}{(160\text{ keV})1.60 \times 10^{-16}\text{ J/keV}} = 7.77 \times 10^{-12}\text{ m}.$$

(b) $$\lambda' = \frac{hc}{E'_\gamma} = \frac{(6.63 \times 10^{-34}\text{ J s})(3.00 \times 10^{8}\text{ m/s})}{(120\text{ keV})1.60 \times 10^{-16}\text{ J/keV}} = 1.04 \times 10^{-11}\text{ m}.$$

Therefore, $\Delta\lambda = \lambda' - \lambda = \lambda_c(1 - \cos\theta)$, or

$$\Delta\lambda = 1.04 \times 10^{-11}\text{ m} - 7.77 \times 10^{-12}\text{ m} = (2.43 \times 10^{-12}\text{ m})(1 - \cos\theta).$$

From which $\theta = 94.9°$.

(c) $p_\gamma = \frac{E_\gamma}{c} = 160\frac{\text{keV}}{c}$, and $p'_\gamma = \frac{E'_\gamma}{c} = 120\frac{\text{keV}}{c}$, so

Applying conservation of momentum in the x direction, we have:
$p_x)_{before} = p_x)_{after}$, or $p_\gamma = p_e\cos\phi + p'_\gamma\cos\theta$, which gives:
$p_e\cos\phi = p_\gamma - p'_\gamma\cos\theta = 160\text{ keV/c} - (120\text{ keV/c})\cos(94.9°)$, or

$$p_e\cos\phi = 170.2\text{ keV/c}. \qquad (1)$$

Applying conservation of momentum in the y direction:
$p_y)_{before} = p_y)_{after}$, or $0 = p'_\gamma\sin\theta - p_e\sin\phi$, which gives

$$p_e\sin\phi = (120\text{ keV/c})\sin 94.9° = 120\text{ keV/c}. \qquad (2)$$

Solving (1) and (2) simultaneously gives: $\phi = 35.2°$.

27.63 The woman tries tohold the pellets just above the spot on the floor, with the same *x*-coordinate. In so doing she gives them some *x*-velocity, at least as large as in

$\Delta x m \Delta v_x = \frac{h}{4\pi}$ In falling they will then scatter to fill an angle θ

around the vertical, with $m\Delta v_x = p\sin\theta = mv\frac{\Delta x}{H}$ where

v is the final speed.
So, eliminating Δv_x,

$$\Delta x m v\frac{\Delta x}{H} = \frac{h}{4\pi} \text{ or } (\Delta x)^2 = \frac{\frac{h}{4\pi}H}{mv}$$

We also have $H = \frac{1}{2}gt^2$ and $v = gt$, so

$$v = \sqrt{2gH}$$

and $$(\Delta x)^2 = \frac{h}{4\pi\mu}\left(\frac{H}{2g}\right) \qquad \Delta x = \left(\frac{\frac{h}{4\pi}}{m}\right)^{1/2}\left(\frac{H}{2g}\right)^{1/4}$$

(b) $$\Delta x = \left(\frac{6.63 \times 10^{-34}\ \text{J s}}{4\pi(5.00 \times 10^{-4}\ \text{kg})}\right)^{1/2}\left(\frac{2.00\ \text{m s}^2}{2\ (9.80\ \text{m})}\right)^{1/4} = 1.84 \times 10^{-16}\ \text{m}$$

ANSWERS TO CONCEPTUAL QUESTIONS

2. A microscope can see details no smaller than the wavelength of the waves it uses to produce images. Electrons with kinetic energies of several electron volts have wavelengths of less than a nanometer, which is much smaller than the wavelength of visible light (having wavelengths ranging from about 400 to 700 nm). Therefore, an electron microscope can resolve details of much smaller sizes as compared to an optical microscope.

4. Measuring the position of a particle implies bouncing a photon off it. However, this will change the velocity of the particle.

6. Light has both wave and particle characteristics. In Young's double-slit experiment, light behaves as a wave. In the photoelectric effect, it behaves like a particle. Light can be characterized as an electromagnetic wave with a particular wavelength or frequency, yet at the same time, light can be characterized as a stream of photons, each carrying a discrete energy, hf.

8. The principle of conservation of mass must be broadened as a law of conservation of mass-energy. When this occurs, the appearance of the mass of the pair is accompanied by the disappearance of an equal amount of pure energy.

10. Ultraviolet light has a shorter wavelength and higher photon energy than visible light.

12. Increasing the temperature of the substance increases the average kinetic energy of the electrons inside the material. This makes it slightly easier for an electron to escape from the material when it absorbs a photon.

14. Most stars radiate nearly as blackbodies. Vega has a higher surface temperature than Arcturus. Vega radiates more intensely at shorter wavelengths.

CHAPTER TWENTY-EIGHT SOLUTIONS

Chapter Twenty-Eight Readings

Andrade, E.N., Rutherford and the Nature of the Atom, New York, Doubleday Anchor, 1964

Berns, M.W., "Laser Surgery," *Scientific American*, June 1991, p. 84

Curl, R.F. and Smalley, R.E., "Fullerenes," Scientific American, October 1991, p. 54.

Gamow, G. *Mr. Tomkins Explores the Atom*, New York, Cambridge University Press, 1945.

Gunshor, R.L. and Normikko, A.V., "Blue-Laser CD Technology," *Scientific American*, July 1996, p. 48.

Koppel, T., "Lightning Lure," *Scientific American*, February 1993, p. 105.

Krim, J., "Friction at the Atomic Scale," *Scientific American*, October 1996, p. 74.

La Rocca, A.V., "Laser Applications in Manufacturing," *Scientific American*, March 1982, p. 94.

Lasers and Light, San Francisco, Freeman, 1969 (readings from *Scientific American*).

Latham, R.E., "Holography in the Science Classroom," *The Physics Teacher*, October 1986, p. 395.

Leith, E.N., "White-Light Holograms," *Scientific American*, October 1976, p.80.

Moore, R., *Niels Bohr, The Man, His Science, and the World They Changed*, New York, Knopf, 1966.

Morrison, P., "1997:Subatomic Centenary: Discovery of Electrons," *Scientific American*, August 1997, p. 93.

Schewe, P., "Lasers," *The Physics Teacher*, November 1981, p. 534.

Strong, C.L., "How to Make Holograms," *Scientific American*, February 1967, p. 122.

Wheeler, J.A., "Niels Bohr, the Man," *Physics Today*, October 1985, p. 66.

Zorpette, G., "Technology and Business: "X"(rays) Mark the Tumor," *Scientific American*, October 1996 p. 44.

Review (a) The energy levels for hydrogen are at:
-13.6 eV, - 3.4 eV, -1.51 eV, -0.85 eV, -0.544 eV, ...

If the photon emitted from the atom needs at least 4.58 eV of energy to overcome the tungsten work function, the final Bohr orbit must be the ground state, since transitions to any higher state will involve energies less than 4.58 eV. Therefore, $n_f = 1$.

(b) Using $V_o = 7.51$ V, the electron kinetic energy must have been $KE = (7.51\text{ V})(1\text{ e}) = 7.51$ eV. Therefore, the total energy supplied by the photon is: 7.51 eV + 4.58 eV = 12.09 eV. Since $E_\gamma = E_i - E_f$ and $E_f = -13.6$ eV, we find $E_i = E_\gamma + E_f = 12.09\text{ eV} - 13.6\text{ eV} = -1.51$ eV. Thus, we observe that $n_i = 3$.

28.1 The Balmer equation is: $\frac{1}{\lambda} = R_H\left(\frac{1}{2^2} - \frac{1}{n^2}\right)$.

When $n = 3$, $\frac{1}{\lambda} = (1.0974 \times 10^7\text{ m}^{-1})\left(\frac{1}{4} - \frac{1}{9}\right) = 1.524 \times 10^6\text{ m}^{-1}$, or

$\lambda = 6.56 \times 10^{-7}\text{ m} = 656\text{ nm}$.

When $n = 4$, $\frac{1}{\lambda} = (1.0974 \times 10^7\text{ m}^{-1})\left(\frac{1}{4} - \frac{1}{16}\right) = 2.058 \times 10^6\text{ m}^{-1}$, or

$\lambda = 4.86 \times 10^{-7}\text{ m} = 486\text{ nm}$.

When $n = 5$, $\frac{1}{\lambda} = (1.0974 \times 10^7\text{ m}^{-1})\left(\frac{1}{4} - \frac{1}{25}\right) = 2.304 \times 10^6\text{ m}^{-1}$, or

$\lambda = 4.34 \times 10^{-7}\text{ m} = 434\text{ nm}$.

28.2 The Balmer equation is:

$$\frac{1}{\lambda} = R_H\left(\frac{1}{2^2} - \frac{1}{n^2}\right)$$

(a) With $R_H = 2.00 \times 10^7\text{ m}^{-1}$ and $n \geq 3$, we get:
$200\text{ nm} \leq \lambda \leq 360\text{ nm}$, which is in the ultraviolet region.

(b) With $R_H = 0.500 \times 10^7\text{ m}^{-1}$ and $n \geq 3$, we get:
$800\text{ nm} \leq \lambda \leq 1440\text{ nm}$, which is in the infrared region.

28.3 (a) From Coulomb's law:

$$F = k\frac{q_1q_2}{r^2} = (8.99 \times 10^9\text{ Nm}^2/\text{C})\frac{(1.6 \times 10^{-19}\text{ C})^2}{(1.0 \times 10^{-10}\text{ m})^2} = 2.3 \times 10^{-8}\text{ N}$$

(b) The electrostatic potential energy is:

$$V = k\frac{q_1q_2}{r} = (8.99 \times 10^9\text{ Nm}^2/\text{C})\frac{(1.6 \times 10^{-19}\text{ C})^2}{(1.0 \times 10^{-10}\text{ m})} = 2.3 \times 10^{-18}\text{ J} = 14\text{ eV}$$

28.4 (a) From Coulomb's law:

$$F = k\frac{q_1q_2}{r^2} = 9 \times 10^9\text{ Nm}^2/\text{C})\frac{(1.6 \times 10^{-19}\text{ C})^2}{(1.0 \times 10^{-15}\text{ m})^2} = 230\text{ N}$$

(b) The electrostatic potential energy is:

$$V = k\frac{q_1q_2}{r} = (9 \times 10^9\text{ Nm}^2/\text{C})\frac{(1.6 \times 10^{-19}\text{ C})^2}{(1.0 \times 10^{-15}\text{ m})} = 2.3 \times 10^{-13}\text{ J} = 1.4\text{ MeV}$$

28.5 (a) The attractive electrical force between the electron and proton produces the centripetal acceleration as: $F = k\frac{q_1q_2}{r^2} = \frac{mv^2}{r}$, giving

$$v = \sqrt{\frac{kq_1q_2}{mr}} = \sqrt{\frac{(8.99 \times 10^9\ N\ m^2/C^2)(1.6 \times 10^{-19}\ C)^2}{(9.11 \times 10^{-31}\ kg)(1.0 \times 10^{-10}\ m)}},\ \text{or}$$

$v = 1.6 \times 10^6$ m/s.

(b) No, since $v << c$.

(c) The de Broglie wavelength is $\lambda = \frac{h}{p} = \frac{h}{mv}$, or

$$\lambda = \frac{(6.63 \times 10^{-34}\ J\ s)}{(9.11 \times 10^{-31}\ kg)(1.6 \times 10^6\ m/s)} = 4.5 \times 10^{-10}\ m = 0.45\ nm.$$

(d) Yes, the wavelength and the atom are the same order of magnitude.

28.6 Apply the conservation of energy $KE_f + PE_f = KE_i + PE_i$ with $PE = k\frac{q_1q_2}{r}$. The initial potential energy is zero because $r_i = \infty$ and the final kinetic energy is zero because the α particle comes to rest momentarily. Thus, we have: $PE_f = KE_i$, or $k\frac{q_1q_2}{r} = KE_i$ which gives

$$r_f = k\frac{q_1q_2}{KE_i} = (8.99 \times 10^9\ Nm^2/C)\frac{(79)(2)(1.6 \times 10^{-19}\ C)^2}{(5.0\ MeV)(1.6 \times 10^{-13}\ J/MeV)} = \text{or}$$

$r_f = 4.6 \times 10^{-14}$ m $= 46 \times 10^{-15}$ m $= 46$ fm

---

28.7 (a) $r_f = n^2 a_o = (2)^2(0.0529\ nm) = 0.212\ nm.$

(b) The Coulomb is the force that causes the centripetal acceleration,

so $m\frac{v^2}{r} = \frac{ke^2}{r^2}$, or $v^2 = \frac{ke^2}{mr}$ and $p = \sqrt{m^2v^2} = \sqrt{\frac{mke^2}{r}}$

$$\text{Thus, } p = \sqrt{\frac{(9.11 \times 10^{-31}\ kg)(8.99 \times 10^9\ N\ m^2/C^2)(1.60 \times 10^{-19}\ C)^2}{0.212 \times 10^{-9}\ m}}$$

or $p = 9.95 \times 10^{-25}$ kg m/s

(c) $L = n\hbar = 2(1.05 \times 10^{-34}\ J\ s) = 2.10 \times 10^{-34}\ J\ s$

(d) $KE = \frac{p^2}{2m} = \frac{(9.95 \times 10^{-25}\ kg\ m/s)^2}{2(9.11 \times 10^{-31}\ kg)} = 5.43 \times 10^{-19}\ J = 3.40\ eV$

(e) $PE = -\frac{ke^2}{r} = -\frac{(8.99 \times 10^9\ N\ m^2C^2)(1.60 \times 10^{-19}\ C)^2}{0.212 \times 10^{-9}\ m}$, or

$PE = -1.09 \times 10^{-18}\ J = -6.80\ eV$

(f) $E = KE + PE = 3.40\ eV - 6.80\ eV = -3.40\ eV$

28.8 By Bohr's quantization rule, $L = n\hbar = \frac{nh}{2\pi} = mv_nr_n$. Thus, $v_n = \frac{nh}{2\pi mr_n}$ and

$$KE = \frac{1}{2}mv_n^2 = \frac{n^2h^2}{8\pi^2mr_n^2} = \frac{n^2h^2}{8\pi^2m(a_on^2)^2} = \frac{h^2}{8\pi^2m(a^2_on^2)}.$$

Also $PE = -\frac{ke^2}{r_n} = -\frac{ke^2}{a_on^2}$

For the ground state, $n = 1$ and we obtain:

$$KE = \frac{(6.63 \times 10^{-34}\ J\ s)^2}{8\pi^2(9.11 \times 10^{-31}\ kg)(5.29 \times 10^{-11}\ m)^2} = 2.18 \times 10^{-18}\ J = 13.6\ eV,$$

and

$$PE = \frac{(8.99 \times 10^9 \text{ N m}^2/\text{C}^2)(1.60 \times 10^{-19} \text{ C})^2}{5.29 \times 10^{-11} \text{ m}} = -4.35 \times 10^{-18} \text{ J} = -27.2 \text{ eV}$$

28.9 Starting with the knowledge that the force supplying the centripetal acceleration is the Coulomb force, $\frac{mv^2}{r} = k\frac{q_1q_2}{r^2}$, $v^2 = \frac{ke^2}{mr}$.

Using $r_n = \frac{n^2\hbar^2}{mke^2}$, gives: $v_n^2 = \frac{ke^2}{m\left(\frac{n^2\hbar^2}{mke^2}\right)}$, or $v_n = \frac{ke^2}{n\hbar}$.

28.10 Start with the knowledge that the centripetal acceleration is supplied by the Coulomb force, $\frac{mv^2}{r} = k\frac{q_1q_2}{r^2}$, or $v^2 = \frac{ke^2}{mr}$. Using $r_1 = a_0$ gives

$$\frac{v_1}{c} = \sqrt{\frac{ke^2}{ma_0c^2}} \sqrt{\frac{(8.99 \times 10^9 \text{ N m}^2/\text{C}^2)(1.60 \times 10^{-19} \text{ C})^2}{(9.11 \times 10^{-31} \text{ kg})(5.29 \times 10^{-11} \text{ m})(3.00 \times 10^8 \text{ m/s})^2}},$$

or $\frac{v_1}{c} = 7.285 \times 10^{-3}$ J or $v_1 = \frac{c}{137.3} \approx \frac{c}{137}$

28.11 In the ground state, $r = a_0 = 5.29 \times 10^{-11}$ m. Thus,

$$F = k\frac{q_1q_2}{r^2} = 8.99 \times 10^9 \text{ Nm}^2/\text{C} \frac{(1.60 \times 10^{-19} \text{ C})^2}{(5.29 \times 10^{-11} \text{ m})^2} = 8.22 \times 10^{-8} \text{ N}$$

28.12 $\Delta E = E_f - E_i = \left(-\frac{13.6}{n_f^2}\right) - \left(-\frac{13.6}{n_i^2}\right) = (13.6 \text{ eV})\left(\frac{1}{n_i^2} - \frac{1}{n_f^2}\right)$

For $\Delta E > 0$, we have absorption, and for $\Delta E < 0$, we have emission.

(A) for $n_i = 2$ and $n_f = 5$ $\quad \Delta E = 2.86$ eV (absorption)
(B) for $n_i = 5$ and $n_f = 3$ $\quad \Delta E = -0.967$ eV (emission)
(C) for $n_i = 7$ and $n_f = 4$ $\quad \Delta E = -0.572$ eV (emission)
(D) for $n_i = 4$ and $n_f = 7$ $\quad \Delta E = 0.572$ eV (absorption)

(a) $\lambda = \frac{hc}{\Delta E}$ so the shortest wavelength is *emitted* in transition B.
(b) atom *gains* the most energy in transition A.
(c) atom loses energy in transitions B and C.

28.13 For absorption:

$$E_\gamma = E_f - E_i = \left(-\frac{13.6}{n_f^2}\right) - \left(-\frac{13.6}{n_i^2}\right) = (13.6 \text{ eV})\left(\frac{1}{n_i^2} - \frac{1}{n_f^2}\right)$$

(a) $E_\gamma = (13.6 \text{ eV})\left(\frac{1}{3^2} - \frac{1}{5^2}\right) = 0.967$ eV, and

(b) $E_\gamma = (13.6 \text{ eV})\left(\frac{1}{5^2} - \frac{1}{7^2}\right) = 0.266$ eV.

28.14 (a) From the energy level sketch shown, we find the energy of the absorbed photon, $E_\gamma = E_3 - E_1$ is:

$$E_\gamma = -1.51\,\text{eV} - (-13.6\,\text{eV}) = 12.09\,\text{eV}$$

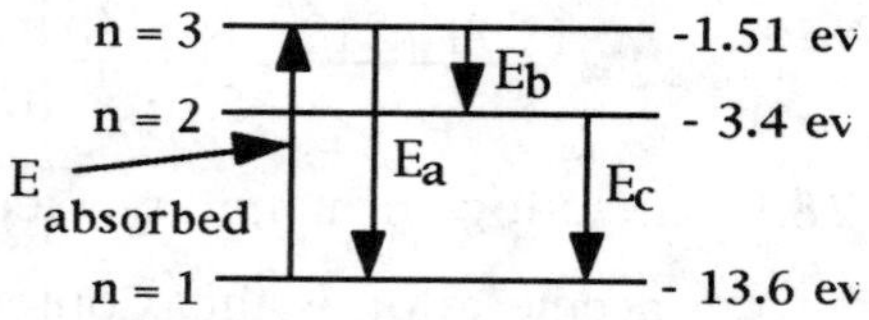

(b) The three possible transitions are shown in the energy level diagram. The energies are:

$E_a = E_i - E_f = -1.51\text{ eV} - (-13.6\text{ eV}) = 12.09\text{ eV}$

$E_b = E_i - E_f = -1.51\text{ eV} - (-3.40\text{ eV}) = 1.89\text{ eV}$

$E_c = E_i - E_f = -3.40\text{ eV} - (-13.6\text{ eV}) = 10.2\text{ eV}$

28.15 The energy of this photon is: $E_\gamma = \dfrac{hc}{\lambda} = \dfrac{1243\text{ nm eV}}{657.7\text{ nm}} = 1.89\,\text{eV}.$

Since the energy levels for the hydrogen atom are:
-13.6 eV, -3.40 eV, - 1.51 eV, -0.850 eV, ..., we see that
1.89 eV = (-1.51 eV) - (-3.40 eV) , so that the transition was from the $n = 3$ orbit to the $n = 2$ orbit.

28.16 To ionize the atom when the electron is in the nth level, it is necessary to add an amount of energy given by: $\Delta E = E_f - E_i = 0 - E_n = \dfrac{13.6\text{ eV}}{n^2}$.

(a) Thus, in the ground state where $n = 1$, we have $\Delta E = 13.6\,\text{eV}$.

(b) In the $n = 3$ level, $\Delta E = \dfrac{13.6\text{ eV}}{9} = 1.51\text{ eV}.$

28.17 The energy of an emitted photon is $E_\gamma = E_f - E_i = \dfrac{hc}{\lambda}$,

so $\lambda = \dfrac{hc}{\Delta E} = \dfrac{1243\text{ nm eV}}{E_f - E_i}$.

For the longest wavelength in a series, we need the minimum ΔE. The maximum possible ΔE will lead to the shortest wavelength in the series.
(a) Lyman series lines occur when a transition terminates on the $n = 1$ levels, so $E_f = E_1 = -13.6$ eV.

$\Delta E_{min} = E_2 - E_1 = -3.40\text{ eV} - (-13.6\text{ eV}) = 10.2\text{ eV}$, and

$\lambda_{max} = \dfrac{hc}{\Delta E_{min}} = \dfrac{1243\text{ nm eV}}{10.2\text{ eV}} = 122$ nm (longest wavelength in Lyman series).

$\Delta E_{max} = E_\infty - E_1 = 0 - (-13.6\text{ eV}) = 13.6$ eV, and the shortest wavelength in the Lyman series is $\lambda_{min} = \dfrac{hc}{\Delta E_{max}} = \dfrac{1243\text{ nm eV}}{13.6\text{ eV}} = 91.4\text{ nm}$

(b) Paschen series lines arise when the transition terminates on the $n = 3$ level and $E_f = E_3 = -1.51$ eV.

$\Delta E_{min} = E_4 - E_3 = -0.850\text{ eV} - (-1.51\text{ eV}) = 0.660\text{ eV}$, and

$\lambda_{max} = \dfrac{hc}{\Delta E_{min}} = \dfrac{1243\text{ nm eV}}{0.660\text{ eV}} = 1.88 \times 10^3\text{ nm}$ (longest wavelength in Paschen series).

$\Delta E_{max} = E_\infty - E_3 = 0 - (-1.51\text{ eV}) = 1.51$ eV, and the shortest wavelength in the Paschen series is $\lambda_{min} = \dfrac{hc}{\Delta E_{max}} = \dfrac{1243\text{ nm eV}}{1.51\text{ eV}} = 823\text{ nm}.$

28.18 (a) Six different transitions, and hence wavelengths, are possible. The transitions are: $n = 4$ to $n = 1$, $n = 4$ to $n = 2$, $n = 4$ to $n = 3$,

$n = 3$ to $n = 1$, $n = 3$ to $n = 2$, $n = 2$ to $n = 1$.

(b) Transition $n = 4$ to $n = 3$ yields the smallest energy photon and hence the longest wavelength:

$$\lambda = \frac{hc}{\Delta E} = \frac{1243 \text{ nm eV}}{-0.850 \text{ eV} - (-1.51 \text{ eV})} = 1.88 \times 10^3 \text{ nm (in Paschen series).}$$

28.19 (a) $E_\gamma = E_4 - E_2$, or $\frac{hc}{\lambda} = (-0.85 \text{ eV}) - (-3.40 \text{ eV}) = 2.55 \text{ eV}$, giving

$$\lambda = \frac{1243 \text{ eV nm}}{2.55 \text{ eV}} = 487 \text{ nm}.$$

(b) Since the total momentum was originally zero, we must have:

$p_{atom} - p_\gamma = 0$, or $p_{atom} = p_\gamma$. This becomes: $mv = \frac{E_\gamma}{c}$, or $v = \frac{E_\gamma}{mc}$.

Thus, $$v = \frac{(2.55 \text{ eV})(1.60 \times 10^{-19} \text{ J/eV})}{(1.67 \times 10^{-27})(3.00 \times 10^8 \text{ m/s})} = 0.814 \text{ m/s}.$$

28.20 (a) In the first Bohr orbit, we have $n = 1$ and $r = a_0 = 0.529 \times 10^{-10}$ m.

From the quantization of angular momentum, we have: $v_n = \frac{n\hbar}{mr_n}$

or $$v_1 = \frac{\hbar}{ma_0} = \frac{1.05 \times 10^{-34} \text{ J s}}{(9.11 \times 10^{-31} \text{ kg})(0.529 \times 10^{-10})} = 2.18 \times 10^6 \text{ m/s}.$$

(b) $$t = \frac{2\pi r_1}{v_1} = \frac{2\pi(0.529 \times 10^{-10} \text{ m})}{2.18 \times 10^6 \text{ m/s}} = 1.52 \times 10^{-16} \text{ s}.$$

(c) $$I = \frac{\Delta Q}{\Delta t} = \frac{e}{t} = \frac{1.60 \times 10^{-19} \text{ C}}{1.52 \times 10^{-16} \text{ s}} = 1.05 \times 10^{-3} \text{ A}.$$

28.21 The magnetic force produces the centripetal acceleration. Thus, $qvB = \frac{mv^2}{r}$, or $mv = qrB$. Since $L_n = mv_n r_n = qBr_n^2 = nh/2\pi$, we find: $r_n = \sqrt{\frac{n\hbar}{qB}}$.

28.22 To have minimum kinetic energy, $KE_{total} = 0$ after collision, the two atoms must have equal and opposite momenta before impact.. Thus, $(KE_1)_i = (KE_2)_i = KE$ and the total energy converted in excitation energy during the collision is $2KE = 2E_{excitation} = 2(E_2 - E_1) = 20.4$ eV. We then have: $KE = \frac{1}{2}mv^2 = 10.2 \text{ eV} = 1.63 \times 10^{-18}$ J,

or $$v = \sqrt{\frac{2\,KE}{m}} = \sqrt{\frac{2(1.63 \times 10^{-18} \text{ J})}{1.67 \times 10^{-27} \text{ kg}}} = 4.42 \times 10^4 \text{ m/s}.$$

28.23 (a) We begin with $G\frac{Mm}{r^2} = \frac{mv^2}{r}$, so $KE = \frac{1}{2}mv^2 = G\frac{Mm}{2r}$.

Then, the total energy is: $E = KE + PE = G\frac{Mm}{2r} - G\frac{Mm}{r} = -G\frac{Mm}{2r}$.

(b) According to the Bohr quantization rule, $mvr = n\hbar$, so $v_n = \dfrac{n\hbar}{mr}$.

Substituting this into: $G\dfrac{Mm}{r^2} = \dfrac{mv^2}{r}$, gives $v^2 = \dfrac{GM}{r}$, or

$r_n = \dfrac{(n\hbar)^2}{(GM(m^2))} = n^2 r_0$, where $r_0 = \dfrac{(\hbar)^2}{GM(m)^2} = 2.32 \times 10^{-138}$ m.

(c) Using the results of (a) and (b), the total energy is:

$E = -\dfrac{GMm}{2r} = -\dfrac{E_0}{n^2}$, where $E_0 = \dfrac{GMm}{2r_0} = \dfrac{G^2M^2m^3}{2\hbar^2} = 1.71 \times 10^{182}$ J

(d) We have $r_n = n^2 r_0$ where $r_0 = 2.32 \times 10^{-138}$ m.
Thus, if $r_n = 1.49 \times 10^{11}$ m, we find:

$n^2 = \dfrac{r_n}{r_0} = \dfrac{1.49 \times 10^{11}\text{ m}}{2.32 \times 10^{-138}\text{ m}} = 6.42 \times 10^{148}$, or $n = 2.53 \times 10^{74}$.

(e) No, the quantum numbers are too large and the allowed energies are practically continuous in this region.

28.24 (a) The velocity of the moon in its orbit is

$v = \dfrac{2\pi r}{T} = \dfrac{2\pi(3.84 \times 10^8\text{ m})}{2.36 \times 10^6\text{ s}} = 1.02 \times 10^3$ m/s, so $L = mvr$, or

$L = (7.36 \times 10^{22}\text{ kg})\left(1.02 \times 10^3 \dfrac{\text{m}}{\text{s}}\right)(3.84 \times 10^8\text{ m}) = 2.89 \times 10^{34}\text{ kg}\dfrac{\text{m}^2}{\text{s}}$.

(b) We have: $L = n\hbar$, or $n = \dfrac{L}{\hbar} = \dfrac{2.89 \times 10^{34}\text{ kg m}^2/\text{s}}{1.055 \times 10^{-34}\text{ J s}} = 2.74 \times 10^{68}$.

(c) We have: $\dfrac{\Delta r}{r} = \dfrac{(n+1)^2 R - n^2 R}{n^2 R} = \dfrac{2n+1}{n^2}$,

which is approximately equal to $\dfrac{2}{n} = 7.30 \times 10^{-69}$.

28.25 The energy and frequency of the emitted photon is given by:

$E_\gamma = E_f - E_i = \left(-\dfrac{13.6}{n_i^2}\right) - \left(-\dfrac{13.6}{n_f^2}\right) = (13.6\text{ eV})\left(\dfrac{1}{n_f^2} - \dfrac{1}{n_i^2}\right)$

and $f_\gamma = \dfrac{E_\gamma}{h}$. $f_{orb} = \dfrac{1}{T} = \dfrac{v_n}{2\pi r_n}$. But $L_n = m v_n r_n = \dfrac{nh}{2\pi}$, so $v_n = \dfrac{nh}{2\pi m r_n}$

For the orbital motion:

Therefore, $f_{orb} = \dfrac{nh}{(2\pi)^2 m r^2{}_n}$ with $r_n = a_0 n^2$, we have

$$f_{orb} = \frac{h}{(2\pi)^2 m a_0^2 n^3}.$$

$$f_{orb} = \frac{(6.63 \times 10^{-34}\text{ J s})}{(2\pi)^2(9.11 \times 10^{-31}\text{ kg})(5.29 \times 10^{-11}\text{ m})^2 n^3} = \frac{6.56 \times 10^{15}\text{ Hz}}{n^3}$$

(a) For the $n = 2$ to $n = 1$ transition $E_\gamma = (13.6\text{ eV})\left(\dfrac{1}{1} - \dfrac{1}{4}\right) = 10.2$ eV

and $f_\gamma = \dfrac{E_\gamma}{h} = \dfrac{(10.2\text{ eV})(1.60 \times 10^{-19}\text{ J/eV})}{6.63 \times 10^{-34}\text{ J s}} = 2.46 \times 10^{15}$ Hz.

For $n = 2$ $\quad f_{orb} = \dfrac{6.56 \text{ x } 10^{15} \text{ H}}{n^3} = \dfrac{6.56 \text{ x } 10^{15} \text{ H}}{2^3} = 8.19 \text{ x } 10^{14} \text{ Hz}$

(b) For the $n = 10000$ to $n = 9999$ transition

$$E_\gamma = (13.6 \text{ eV})\left(\frac{1}{(9999)^2} - \frac{1}{10^8}\right) = 2.72 \text{ x } 10^{-11} \text{ eV. and}$$

$$f_\gamma = \frac{E_\gamma}{h} = \frac{(2.72 \text{ x } 10^{-11} \text{ eV})(1.60 \text{ x } 10^{-19} \text{ J/eV})}{6.63 \text{ x } 10^{-34} \text{ J s}} = 6.57 \text{ x } 10^{3} \text{ Hz.}$$

For $n = 10000$, $f_{orb} = \dfrac{6.56 \text{ x } 10^{15} \text{ Hz}}{n^3} = \dfrac{6.56 \text{ x } 10^{15} \text{ H}}{(10^4)^3} = 6.56 \text{ x } 10^{3} \text{ Hz}$

For small n, significant differences between classical and quantum results appear. However, as n becomes large, classical theory and quantum theory approach one another in their results. (correspondence principle)

28.26 (a) From $E_n = -\dfrac{Z^2(13.6 \text{ eV})}{n^2}$, we have (with $Z = 3$ and $n = 1$),

$E_1 = -9(13.6 \text{ eV}) = -122 \text{ eV}.$

(b) From $r_n = \dfrac{n^2 a_0}{Z}$, with $n = 1$ and $Z = 3$,

$$r_1 = \frac{5.29 \text{ x } 10^{-11} \text{ m}}{3} = 1.76 \text{ x } 10^{-11} \text{ m.}$$

28.27 The plot originates from the equation $E_n = -\dfrac{Z^2(13.6 \text{ eV})}{n^2}$, with $Z = 2$.

$E_n = -\dfrac{4(13.6 \text{ eV})}{n^2} = -\dfrac{54.4 \text{ eV}}{n^2}$, and the diagram should look somewhat like that sketched below:

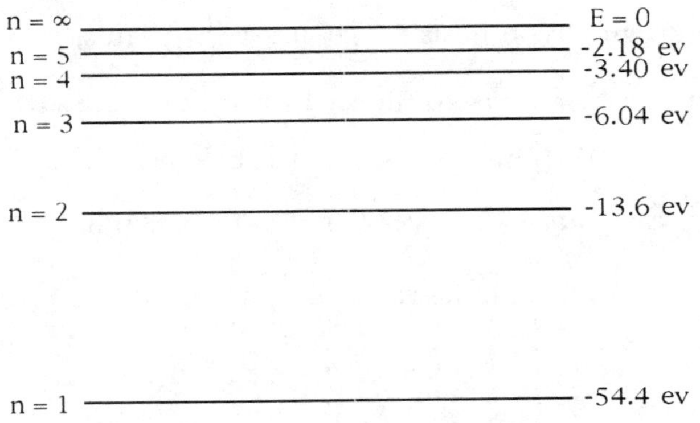

28.28 (a) We have: $\quad R = \dfrac{Z^2 m k^2 e^4}{4\pi c \hbar^2} = Z^2 R_{hydrogen}.$

For singly ionized helium $Z = 2$, so

$R_{He} = 4R_{hydrogen} = 4(1.0974 \text{ x } 10^7 \text{ m}^{-1}) = 4.39 \text{ x } 10^7 \text{ m}^{-1}.$

(b) $\dfrac{1}{\lambda} = R_{He}\left(\dfrac{1}{n_f^2} - \dfrac{1}{n_i^2}\right) = 4.39 \text{ x } 10^7 \text{ m}^{-1}\left(\dfrac{1}{1} - \dfrac{1}{4}\right) = 3.29 \text{ x } 10^7 \text{ m}^{-1}$, or

$\lambda = 3.04 \text{ x } 10^{-8} \text{ m} = 30.4 \text{ nm}.$

(c) This wavelength is in the deep ultraviolet region.

28.29 We use $E = -\dfrac{Z^2(13.6\ \text{eV})}{n^2}$, with $Z = 3$ to give: $E = -\dfrac{122.4\ \text{eV}}{n^2}$.

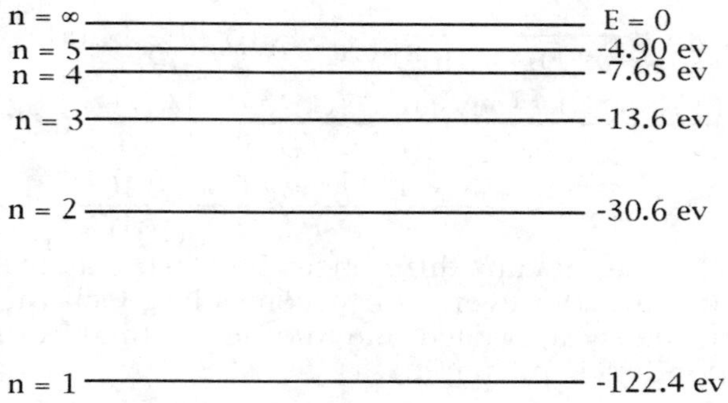

28.30 (a) For standing waves in a string fixed at both ends, $L = \dfrac{n\lambda}{2}$, or $\lambda = \dfrac{2L}{n}$.

According to the de Broglie hypothesis, $p = \dfrac{h}{\lambda}$. Combining these expressions gives $p = mv = \dfrac{nh}{2L}$.

(b) Using $E = \dfrac{1}{2}mv^2 = \dfrac{p^2}{2m}$, with p as found in (a) above:

$$E_n = \frac{n^2h^2}{4L^2(2m)} = n^2E_o, \quad \text{where } E_o = \frac{h^2}{8mL^2}.$$

28.31 From Bohr's quantization rule: $L = mvr = n\hbar$, or $mv = \dfrac{n\hbar}{r_n}$. According to the de Broglie hypothesis: $p = mv = \dfrac{h}{\lambda}$. Thus,

$\lambda = \dfrac{h}{p} = \dfrac{h}{mv} = \dfrac{h r_n}{n\hbar} = \dfrac{2\pi r_n}{n}$. In the hydrogen atom, $r_n = n^2 a_o$,

where $a_o = 0.0529$ nm. Thus, for the third excited state ($n = 4$), we have

$$\lambda = \frac{2\pi a_o n^2}{n} = 2\pi a_o n = 2\pi(0.0529\ \text{nm})(4) = 1.33\ \text{nm}.$$

28.32 We list the quantum numbers as:

$n = 4$ $\quad l = 3 \quad m_l = \pm 3, \pm 2, \pm 1, 0$

$l = 2 \quad m_l = \pm 2, \pm 1, 0$

$l = 1 \quad m_l = \pm 1, 0$

$l = 0 \quad m_l = 0$

There are (a) 4 different values for l, and (b) there are 16 different combinations, but only 7 different (or distinct) values for m_l.

28.33 In the 3p subshell, $n = 3$ and $l = 1$. The 6 possible quantum states are:

n	l	m_l	m_s
3	1	+1	+1/2
3	1	+1	-1/2
3	1	0	+1/2
3	1	0	-1/2
3	1	-1	+1/2
3	1	-1	-1/2

28.34 The 3d subshell has $l = 2$, and $n = 3$. Also, we have $s = 1$. Therefore, we can have $n = 3$, $l = 2$, $m_l = -2, -1, 0, 1, 2$, $s = 1$, and $m_s = -1, 0, 1$, leading to the following table:

n	l	m_l	s	m_s
3	2	-2	1	-1
3	2	-2	1	0
3	2	-2	1	+1
3	2	-1	1	-1
3	2	-1	1	0
3	2	-1	1	+1
3	2	0	1	-1
3	2	0	1	0
3	2	0	1	+1
3	2	+1	1	-1
3	2	+1	1	0
3	2	+1	1	+1
3	2	+2	1	-1
3	2	+2	1	0
3	2	+2	1	+1

28.35 (a) For $n = 1$, $l = 0$, and there are $2(2l + 1)$ states $= 2(1) = 2$ sets of quantum numbers

(b) For $n = 2$, $l = 0$ for $2(2l + 1)$ states $= 2(1) = 2$ sets
and $l = 1$ for $2(2l + 1)$ states $= 2(3) = 6$ sets
total number of sets = 8

(c) For $n = 3$, $l = 0$ for $2(2l + 1)$ states $= 2(1) = 2$ sets
and $l = 1$ for $2(2l + 1)$ states $= 2(3) = 6$ sets
and $l = 2$ for $2(2l + 1)$ states $= 2(5) = 10$ sets
total number of sets = 18

(d) For $n = 4$ $l = 0$ for $2(2l + 1)$ states $= 2(1) = 2$ sets
and $l = 1$ for $2(2l + 1)$ states $= 2(3) = 6$ sets
and $l = 2$ for $2(2l + 1)$ states $= 2(5) = 10$ sets
and $l = 3$ for $2(2l + 1)$ states $= 2(7) = 14$ sets
total number of sets = 32

(e) For $n = 5$ $l = 0$ for $2(2l + 1)$ states $= 2(1) = 2$ sets
and $l = 1$ for $2(2l + 1)$ states $= 2(3) = 6$ sets
and $l = 2$ for $2(2l + 1)$ states $= 2(5) = 10$ sets
and $l = 3$ for $2(2l + 1)$ states $= 2(7) = 14$ sets
and $l = 4$ for $2(2l + 1)$ states $= 2(9) = 18$ sets
total number of sets = 50

For $n = 1$: $2n^2 = 2$. For $n = 2$: $2n^2 = 8$.
For $n = 3$: $2n^2 = 18$. For $n = 4$: $2n^2 = 32$.

For $n = 5$: $2n^2 = 50$.
Thus, the number of sets of quantum states agrees with the $2n^2$ rule.

28.36 (a) The electronic configuration for oxygen ($Z = 8$) is: $1s^2 2s^2 2p^4$
(b) The quantum numbers are:

$1s^2$ states	$n = 1$	$l = 0$	$m_l = 0$	$m_s = \pm 1/2$
$2s^2$ states	$n = 2$	$l = 0$	$m_l = 0$	$m_s = \pm 1/2$
$2p^4$ states	$n = 2$	$l = 1$	$m_l = -1$	$m_s = \pm 1/2$
			$m_l = 0$	$m_s = \pm 1/2$

28.37 (a) Zirconium, with 40 electrons, has 4 electrons outside a closed Krypton core. The Krypton core, with 36 electrons, has all states up through the $4p$ subshell filled. Normally, one would expect the next 4 electrons to go into the $4d$ subshell. However, an exception to the rule occurs at this point, and the $5s$ subshell fills (with 2 electrons) before the $4d$ subshell starts filling. The two remaining electrons in Zirconium are in an incomplete $4d$ subshell. Thus, $n = 4$, $l = 2$, and $s = 1/2$ for each of these electrons.
(b) For electrons in the .$4d$ subshell, with $l = 2$, the possible values of m_l are $(m_l = 0, \pm 1, \pm 2)$ and those for m_s are $(m_s = \pm 1/2)$.
(c) We have 40 electrons, so the electron configuration is:
$1s^2 2s^2 2p^6 3s^2 3p^6 3d^{10} 4s^2 4p^6 4d^2 5s^2 = [Kr]4d^2 5s^2$.

28.38 $n = 3$, $l = 0$, $m_l = 0$, and $m_s = \pm 1/2$
(a) If the exclusion principle were inoperative, so electrons could be in identical states, there would be 4 possible states for the system as shown:

state	electron 1 (n,l,m_l,m_s)	electron 2 (n,l,m_l,m_s)
1	3,0,0,+1/2	3,0,0,+1/2
2	3,0,0,+1/2	3,0,0,-1/2
3	3,0,0,-1/2	3,0,0,+1/2
4	3,0,0,-1/2	3,0,0,-1/2

(b) Taking the exclusion principle into account, it is seen that states 1 and 4 above are not allowed, leaving only the remaining two states.

28.39 The energy of an electron in the K shell of Nickel should be:
$$E_K = -(Z - 1)^2(13.6 \text{ eV}) = -(27)^2(13.6 \text{ eV}) = -9.91 \times 10^3 \text{ eV}.$$
The energy of an electron in the L shell of nickel is given by:
$$E_L = -(Z - 3)^2(13.6 \text{ eV}/4) = -(25)^2(13.6 \text{ eV}/4) = -2.13 \times 10^3 \text{ eV}.$$
Thus, the energy of the emitted photon is $E_\gamma = E_L - E_K = 7.78 \times 10^3$ eV and the wavelength of the K_α x-ray is $\lambda = \dfrac{hc}{E_\gamma} = \dfrac{1243 \text{ nm eV}}{7.78 \times 10^3 \text{ eV}} = 0.160$ nm.

28.40 $E_\gamma = E_L - E_K = -951 \text{ eV} - (-8979 \text{ eV}) = 8028 \text{ eV}$, and
$$\lambda = \frac{(6.63 \times 10^{-34} \text{ J s})(3.00 \times 10^8 \text{ m/s})}{(8028 \text{ eV})(1.60 \times 10^{-19} \text{ J/eV})} = 0.155 \text{ nm}.$$

To produce a K_α line, an electron must be excited from the K shell to the L shell and must give 8028 eV to the atom. Thus, the target must be bombarded with 8028 eV electrons, so an accelerating voltage of **8.03 kV** is needed.

28.41

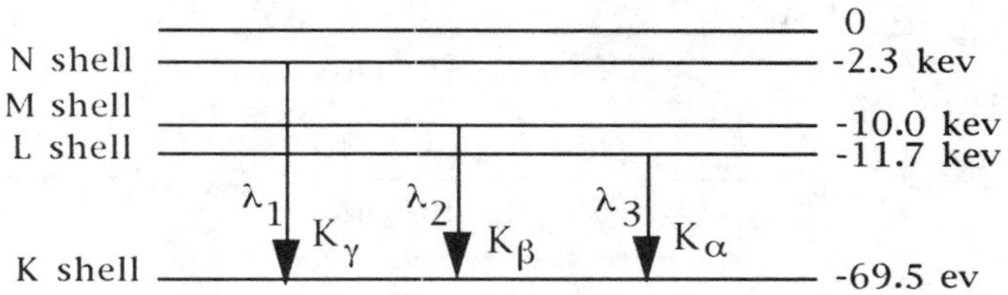

$$E_\gamma = \frac{hc}{\lambda} = \frac{1243 \text{ eV nm}}{\lambda} = \frac{1.243 \text{ keV nm}}{\lambda}.$$

For: $\lambda_1 = 0.0185$ nm, $E_\gamma = 67.2$ keV,

$\lambda_2 = 0.0209$ nm, $E_\gamma = 59.5$ keV,

$\lambda_3 = 0.0215$ nm, $E_\gamma = 57.8$ keV.

The ionization energy for the K shell = 69.5 keV, so the ionization energies for the other shells are:

L shell = 69.5 keV - 57.8 keV = 11.7 keV,

M shell = 69.5 keV - 59.5 keV = 10.0 keV,

N shell = 69.5 keV - 67.2 keV = 2.3 keV.

28.42 The energies of an electron in the K and M shells are:

$$E_K = -(Z-1)^2(13.6 \text{ eV}), \text{ and } \quad E_M = -\frac{(Z-9)^2(13.6 \text{ eV})}{3^2}.$$

Therefore, when an electron makes a transition from the M to the K shell, the radiated energy is:

$$E_\gamma = E_M - E_K = (13.6 \text{ eV})[-\frac{(Z-9)^2}{9} + (Z-1)^2]. \quad (1)$$

The energy of the observed x-ray photon is:

$$E_\gamma = \frac{hc}{\lambda} = \frac{1243 \text{ eV nm}}{0.101 \text{ nm}} = 12307 \text{ eV}. \quad (2)$$

Equating equations (1) and (2) gives: $\quad (Z-1)^2 - \frac{(Z-9)^2}{9} = 905$, or

$9(Z-1)^2 - (Z-9)^2 = 8145$, which reduces to: $\quad 8Z^2 = 8217$.

Therefore, $Z^2 = 1027$, and $Z = 32$. **The element is germanium.**

28.43 (a) The energy absorbed will equal the energy difference between these two states.

Thus, $\quad E = E_2 - E_1 = \frac{-13.6 \text{ eV}}{4} - \frac{(-13.6 \text{ eV})}{1} = 10.2 \text{ eV} = 1.63 \times 10^{-18}$ **J.**

(b) The kinetic energy of the atoms must equal the needed exitation energy. $\frac{3}{2} k_B T = E$, so $T = \frac{2E}{3k_B} = \frac{2(1.63 \times 10^{-18} \text{ J})}{3(1.38 \times 10^{-23} \text{ J/K})} = 7.88 \times 10^4$ **K.**

28.44 According to the Bohr model, the radius of the electron orbits in hydrogen are given by $r_n = a_0 n^2$ with $a_0 = 5.29 \times 10^{-11}$ m.

Then, for $r_n = 1.00 \times 10^{-6}$ m, we must have

$$n^2 = \frac{r_n}{a_o} = \frac{1.00 \times 10^{-6}\ \text{m}}{5.29 \times 10^{-11}\ \text{m}} = 1.89 \times 10^4, \text{ or } n = 137.$$

28.45 (a) The energy is found as,

$$E = (\text{power})t = (5.0 \times 10^{-3}\ \text{J/s})(25 \times 10^{-3}\ \text{s}) = 1.3 \times 10^{-4}\ \text{J}.$$

(b) The energy of a single photon is:

$$E_\gamma = \frac{hc}{\lambda} = \frac{(6.63 \times 10^{-34}\ \text{J s})(3.00 \times 10^8\ \text{m/s})}{632.8 \times 10^{-9}\ \text{m}} = 3.14 \times 10^{-19}\ \textbf{J/photon.}$$

Thus, the number of photons per pulse is:

$$N = \frac{E}{E_\gamma} = \frac{1.3 \times 10^{-4}\ \text{J/pulse}}{3.14 \times 10^{-19}\ \text{J/photon}} = 4.1 \times 10^{14}\ \textbf{photons/pulse.}$$

28.46 (a) Using $a_o = \frac{h^2}{mke^2}$, with $m = 207\, m_e = 1.89 \times 10^{-28}$ kg, **gives:**

$$a_o = \frac{(1.05 \times 10^{-34})^2}{(1.89 \times 10^{-28}\ \text{kg})(9 \times 10^9\ \text{N m}^2/\text{C}^2)(1.6 \times 10^{-19}\ \text{C})^2}, \text{ or}$$

$$a_o = 2.53 \times 10^{-4}\ \text{nm}.$$

(b) The allowed energies are: $E_n = -\frac{ke^2}{2r_n} = -\frac{ke^2}{2n^2 a_o}$,

or

$$E_n = -\frac{(8.99 \times 10^9\ \text{N m}^2/\text{C}^2)(1.60 \times 10^{-19}\ \text{C})^2}{2n^2(2.53 \times 10^{-13}\ \text{m})} = \frac{4.55 \times 10^{-16}\ \text{J}}{n^2},$$

and $E_n = -\frac{2.84\ \text{keV}}{n^2}$. The three lowest energy **levels are:**

$E_1 = -2.84$ keV, $E_2 = -0.710$ keV, $E_3 = -0.316$ keV,

28.47 (a) The energy of the ground state is:

$$E = E_1 = -\frac{hc}{\lambda_{\text{series limit}}} = -\frac{1243\ \text{eV nm}}{152.0\ \text{nm}} = -8.178\ \text{eV}.$$

From the wavelength of the L_α line, we see:

$$E_\gamma = E_2 - E_1 = \frac{hc}{\lambda_\alpha} = \frac{1243\ \text{nm eV}}{202.6\ \text{nm}} = 6.135\ \text{eV, so}$$

$$E_2 = E_1 + 6.135\ \text{eV} = -2.043\ \text{eV}.$$

Using the wavelength of the L_β line gives:

$$E_\gamma = E_3 - E_1 = \frac{1243\ \text{nm eV}}{170.9\ \text{nm}} = 7.273\ \text{eV, so}$$

$$E_3 = E_1 + 7.273\ \text{eV} = -0.905\ \text{eV}.$$

Next, using the L_γ line gives:

$$E_\gamma = E_4 - E_1 = \frac{1243\ \text{nm eV}}{162.1\ \text{nm}} = 7.668\ \text{eV, so}$$

$$E_4 = E_1 + 7.668\ \text{eV} = -0.510\ \text{eV}.$$

Finally, using the L_δ line gives:

$$E_\gamma = E_5 - E_1 = \frac{1243\ \text{nm eV}}{158.3\ \text{nm}} = 7.852\ \text{eV, so}$$

$$E_5 = E_1 + 7.852\ \text{eV} = -0.326\ \text{eV}.$$

(b) For the Balmer series, $E_\gamma = E_i - E_2 = \frac{hc}{\lambda}$ or $\lambda = \frac{1243\ \text{nm eV}}{E_i - E_2}$.

For the α line: $E_i = E_3$, and we obtain:

$$\lambda_\alpha = \frac{1243 \text{ nm eV}}{-0.905 \text{ eV} - (-2.043 \text{ eV})} = 1092 \text{ nm.}$$

For the series limit, $E_i = 0$ and

$$\lambda_{\text{series limit}} = \frac{1243 \text{ nm eV}}{0 - (-2.043 \text{ eV})} = 608.4 \text{ nm.}$$

28.48

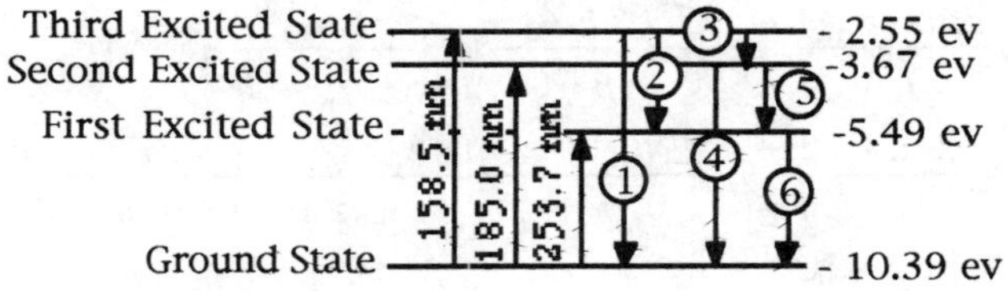

(a) $E = \frac{hc}{\lambda} = \frac{1243 \text{ eV nm}}{\lambda}$, so

For: $\lambda = 253.7$ nm, $E_\gamma = 4.899$ eV,

$\lambda = 185.0$ nm, $E_\gamma = 6.719$ eV,

$\lambda = 158.5$ nm, $E_\gamma = 7.842$ eV.

Thus, the energies of the first three excited states are:

$E_1 = -10.39 \text{ eV} + 4.899 \text{ eV} = -5.49$ ev

$E_2 = -10.39 \text{ eV} + 6.719 \text{ eV} = -3.67$ ev

$E_1 = -10.39 \text{ eV} + 7.842 \text{ eV} = -2.55$ ev

(b) The wavelengths of the emission lines shown are:

$\lambda_1 = 158.5$ nm, $\lambda_2 = 422.8$ nm, $\lambda_3 = 1110$ nm, $\lambda_4 = 185.0$ nm,

$\lambda_5 = 683.0$ nm, and $\lambda_6 = 253.7$ nm.

(c) To have an inelastic collision, we must excite the atom from ground state to the first excited state, and electron must have a minimum kinetic energy of 10.39 eV - 5.49 eV = 4.90 eV, so

$$v = \sqrt{\frac{2KE}{m}} = \sqrt{\frac{2(4.90 \text{ eV})(1.60 \times 10^{-19} \text{ J/eV})}{9.11 \times 10^{-31} \text{ kg}}} = 1.31 \times 10^6 \text{ m/s.}$$

28.49

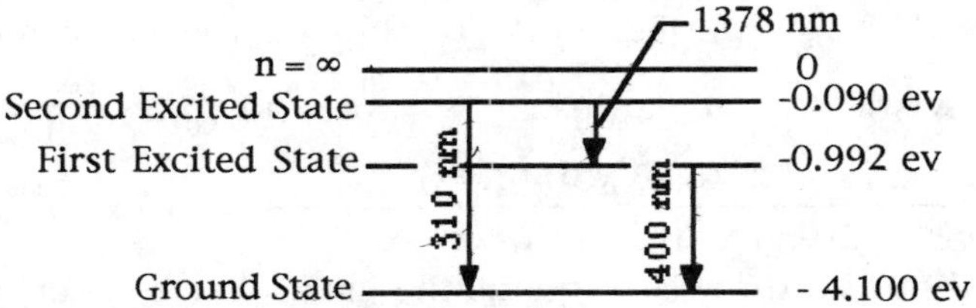

$$E_\gamma = \frac{hc}{\lambda} = \frac{1243 \text{ eV nm}}{\lambda} = \Delta E.$$

For: $\lambda_1 = 310$ nm, $\Delta E_1 = 4.010$ eV,

$\lambda_2 = 400$ nm, $\Delta E_2 = 3.108$ eV,

$\lambda_3 = 1378$ nm, $\Delta E_3 = 0.9020$ eV,

and the ionization energy = 4.100 eV

The energy level diagram having the fewest number of levels and consistent with these energy differences is shown above.

28.50 (a) The time for one complete orbit is: $T = \frac{2\pi r_n}{v_n}$. From Bohr's quantization postulate, $L = mvr = n\hbar$, we see that $v_n = \frac{n\hbar}{mr_n}$. Thus, the orbital period becomes:

$$T = \frac{2\pi m(r_n)^2}{n\hbar} = \frac{2\pi m(a_0 n^2)^2}{n\hbar} = \left(\frac{2\pi m a_0^2}{\hbar}\right) n^3, \text{ or } \quad T = \tau_0 n^3, \text{ where}$$

$$\tau_0 = \frac{2\pi m(a_0)^2}{\hbar} = \frac{2\pi(9.11 \times 10^{-31}\text{ kg})(0.0529 \times 10^{-9}\text{ m})^2}{(1.05 \times 10^{-34}\text{ J s})},$$

$\tau_0 = 1.53 \times 10^{-16}$ s.

(b) With $n = 2$, we have $T = 8\tau_0 = 8(1.53 \times 10^{-16}\text{ s}) = 1.22 \times 10^{-15}$ s. Thus, if the electrons stay in the $n = 2$ state for 10^{-8} s, it will make

$$\frac{10^{-8}\text{ s}}{1.22 \times 10^{-15}\text{ s/rev}} = 8.2 \times 10^6 \text{ revolutions of the nucleus.}$$

(c) Yes, for 8.2×10^6 "electron years".

(d) With that many revolutions in such a short time, it appears like the electron (or at least some part of it) is present everywhere in the $n = 2$ orbit at any instant.

28.51 (a) In this problem, the electron must be treated relativistically. The momentum of the electron is:

$$p = \frac{h}{\lambda} = \frac{6.63 \times 10^{-34}\text{ J s}}{1.0 \times 10^{-14}\text{ m}} = 6.6 \times 10^{-20}\text{ kg m/s.}$$

The energy of the electron is: $E = \sqrt{p^2 c^2 + m^2 c^4}$, or

$$E = \sqrt{(6.6 \times 10^{-20})^2(3.0 \times 10^8)^2 + (9.11 \times 10^{-31})^2(3.0 \times 10^8)^4}\text{ J}$$

$E = 1.98 \times 10^{-11}\text{ J} = 1.24 \times 10^8$ eV, so $\quad K = E - m_0 c^2 \approx 120$ MeV.

(b) The kinetic energy is too large to expect that the electron could be confined to a region the size of the nucleus.

28.52 Since $\lambda = d = 2a_0 = 2(0.0529\text{ nm}) = 0.1058$ nm, the electron is nonrelativistic and we can use: $\quad p = \frac{h}{\lambda}$, and $\quad KE = \frac{p^2}{2m}$.

$$KE = \frac{h^2}{2m\lambda^2} = \frac{(6.63 \times 10^{-34}\text{ J}\cdot\text{s})^2}{2(9.11 \times 10^{-31}\text{ kg})(0.1058 \times 10^{-9})^2} = 2.16 \times 10^{-17}\text{J} = 135\text{eV}.$$

This is about 10 times as large as the ground-state energy of hydrogen, which is 13.6 eV.

28.53 (a) $I = \frac{3.00 \times 10^{-3}\text{ J}}{(10^{-9}\text{ s})\pi(15.0 \times 10^{-6}\text{ m})^2} = 4.24 \times 10^{-15}\text{ W/m}^2$

(b) $(3.00 \times 10^{-3}\text{ J})\frac{(0.60 \times 10^{-9}\text{ m})^2}{(30.0 \times 10^{-6}\text{ m})^2} = 1.20 \times 10^{-12}$ J

28.54 (a) The length of the pulse is $\Delta L = c\Delta\tau$.

(b) The energy of each photon is

$$E_\gamma = \frac{hc}{\lambda} \qquad N = \frac{E}{E_\gamma} = \frac{E\lambda}{hc}$$

(c) $V = \Delta L\pi\frac{d^2}{4}$ $\qquad n = \frac{N}{V} = \left(\frac{4}{\Delta L\pi d^2}\right)\left(\frac{E\lambda}{hc}\right)$

28.55 (a) The intensity of the beam is $I = \frac{P}{A} = \frac{1.00 \times 10^{-3}\ \text{W}}{10.0 \times 10^{-6}\ \text{m}^2} = 100\,\text{W/m}^2$.

The power incident on our one atom is

$$P_a = IA = (100\,\text{W/m}^2)(1.00 \times 10^{-20}\ \text{m}^2) = 1.00 \times 10^{-18}\ \text{W}$$

To absorb $1.50\ \text{eV} = 2.40 \times 10^{-19}$ J, the atom must be in the beam for time

$$t = \frac{E}{P} = \frac{2.40 \times 10^{-19}\ \text{J}}{1.00 \times 10^{-18}\ \text{J/s}} = 0.240\ \text{s}$$

(b) The classical answer is too large by a factor of about a billion because the beam does not carry smeared-out energy but energy in photon lumps. The atoms do not have to wait together for energy to accumulate. In the first nanosecond of absorption, some atom will get hit with a photon and release an electron. the photocurrent begins right away.

28.56 (a) Since $Z = 2$, and $m = 273m_e$, we see:

$E_0 = 2^2(-13.6\ \text{eV})(273) = -14{,}851.2$ eV. The energy levels are then:

$E_n = -\frac{14851.2\ \text{eV}}{n^2}$, which give (for the lowest six levels):

-14,851.2 eV, -3,712.8 eV, -1,650.1 eV,
-928.2 eV, -594.05 eV, -412.55 eV.

(b) Using Compton's equation:

$\lambda' = \lambda + \lambda_c(1 - \cos\theta)$

so $\lambda = 0.0899293\ \text{nm} - (0.00243\ \text{nm})(1 - \cos 50.00°)$, or

$\lambda = 0.08906127$ nm, so the energy of the incident photon is:

$E_\gamma = \frac{1243\ \text{nm eV}}{0.08906127} = 13{,}923$ eV. Since 13,923 eV > 3,712.8 eV, the final Bohr orbit must have been $n_f = 1$.

Then 13,923 eV - 14,851.2 eV = -928.3 eV is the energy of the initial orbit, which corresponds to $n_i = 4$.

28.57 In the Bohr model: $hf = \Delta E = \frac{4\pi^2 mk^2e^4}{2h^2}\left(\frac{1}{(n - 1)^2} - \frac{1}{n^2}\right)$, which reduces

to $f = \frac{2\pi^2 mk^2e^4}{h^3}\left(\frac{2n - 1}{(n - 1)^2 n^2}\right)$.

28.58 As n approaches infinity, $n - 1 \approx n$, so the frequency given by the result of problem 28.57 approaches: $f \approx \frac{2\pi^2 mk^2e^4}{h^3}\frac{2}{n^3}$.

The classical frequency is: $f = \frac{v}{2\pi r} = \frac{1}{2\pi}\sqrt{\frac{ke^2}{m}}\frac{1}{r^{3/2}}$, where $r = \frac{n^2h^2}{4\pi^2 mke^2}$

.

Using this equation to eliminate r from the expression for f, we find:

$$f = \left(\frac{2\pi^2 mk^2e^4}{h^3}\right)\frac{2}{n^3}.$$

28.59 (a) $\frac{1}{\alpha}=\frac{\hbar c}{ke^2}=\frac{(6.63 \times 10^{-34})(3.00 \times 10^8)}{2\pi(9 \times 10^9)(1.60 \times 10^{-19})^2}=137.395.$

(b) $\frac{r_0}{\lambda}=\frac{\hbar^2}{mke^2}/\frac{h}{mc}=\frac{1}{2\pi}\left(\frac{hc}{ke^2}\right)=\frac{1}{2\pi\alpha}.$

(c) $\frac{1}{Rr_0}=\frac{mke^2}{\hbar^2}\frac{4\pi c\hbar^3}{mk^2e^4}=\frac{4\pi}{\alpha}.$

28.60 (a) Using $F=k\frac{q_1q_2}{r^2}=ma$, we obtain:

$$a=9 \times 10^9 \frac{\text{N m}^2}{\text{C}^2}\left(\frac{(1.6 \times 10^{-19}\ \text{C})^2}{(0.0529 \times 10^{-9}\ \text{m})^2(9.11 \times 10^{-31}\ \text{kg})}\right),\ \text{or}$$

$a=9.04 \times 10^{22}\ \text{m/s}^2$.

(b) The rate of energy loss is: $P=-\frac{2kq^2a^2}{3c^3}$, or

$$P=\frac{-2(9 \times 10^9\ \text{N m}^2/\text{C}^2)(1.6 \times 10^{-19}\ \text{C})^2(9.04 \times 10^{22}\ \text{m/s}^2)^2}{3(3 \times 10^8\ \text{m/s})^3},$$

$P=-4.647 \times 10^{-8}\ \text{W}=-2.90 \times 10^{11}\ \text{eV/s}$.

(c) In the $n = 1$ orbit of hydrogen, the electron's energy is - 13.6 eV. Radiating 13.6 eV of energy at the rate computed in (b) would require a time of: $t=\frac{|E|}{P}=\frac{13.6\ \text{eV}}{2.90 \times 10^{11}\text{eV/s}}=4.69 \times 10^{-11}$ s.

ANSWERS TO CONCEPTUAL QUESTIONS

2. Neon signs do not emit a continuous spectrum. They emit many discrete wavelengths as could be determined by observing the light from the sign through a spectrometer. However, they do not emit all wavelengths. The specific wavelengths and intensities account for the color of the sign.

4. An atom does not have to be ionized to emit light. For example, hydrogen emits light when a transition carries an electron from a higher state to the n = 2 state.

6. Classically, the electron can occupy any energy state. That is, all energies would be allowed. Therefore, if the electron obeyed classical mechanics, its spectrum, which originates from transitions between states would be continuous rather than discrete.

8. The de Broglie wavelength of macroscopic objects such as a baseball moving with a typical speed such as 30 m/s is very small and impossible to measure. That is, $\lambda = h/mv$, is a very small number for macroscopic objects. We are not able to observe diffraction effects because the wavelength is much smaller than any aperture through which the object could pass.

10. In both cases the answer is yes. Recall that the ionization energy of hydrogen is 13.6 eV. The electron can absorb a photon of energy less than 13.6 eV by making a transition to some intermediate state such as one with n = 2. It can also absorb a photon of energy greater than 13.6 eV, but in doing so, the electron would be separated from the proton and have some residual kinetic energy.

12. It replaced the simple circular orbits in the Bohr theory with electron clouds. More important, quantum mechanics is consistent with Heisenberg's uncertainty principle, which tells us about the limits of accuracy in making measurements. In quantum mechanics, we talk about the probabilistic nature of the outcome of a measurement of a system, a concept which is incompatible with the Bohr theory. Finally, the Bohr theory of the atom contains only one quantum number n, while quantum mechanics provides the basis for additional quantum numbers to explain the finer details of atomic structure.

14. In quantum mechanics, an electron in a state for which L = 0 simply means that the electron is in an orbital which has spherical symmetry. That is, the electron cloud has the same density at all points at a given distance r from the nucleus. It is incorrect to view an L = 0 electron as one which travels in a straight line through the nucleus.

CHAPTER TWENTY-NINE SOLUTIONS

Chapter Twenty-Nine Readings

Bertsch, G.F., "Vibrations of the Atomic Nucleus," *Scientific American*, May 1983, p. 62.

Bethe, H., "What Holds the Nucleus Together?" *Scientific American*, September 1953, p. 201.

Bromley, D.A., "Nuclear Models," *Scientific American*, December 1978, p. 58.

Fetter, S.A. and Tsipis, K., "Catastrophic Releases of Radioactivity," *Scientific American*, April 1981, p. 41.

Fishman, G.J., Hartmann, D.H., "Gamma-Ray Bursts," *Scientific American*, January 1998, p. 80.

Greiner, W. and Sandulescu, A., "New Radioactivities," *Scientific American*, March 1990, p. 58.

Hahn, O., "The Discovery of Fission," *Scientific American*, February 1958, p. 76.

Hedges, R.E. and Gowlett, J., "Radiocarbon Dating by Accelerator Mass Spectrometry," *Scientific American*, January 1986, p. 100.

Hedges, R.E., "Radioisotope Clocks in Archaeology," *Nature*, Vol. 281, No. 5725, 1979, p. 19.

Jacob, M. and Landshoff, P., "The Inner Structure of the Proton," *Scientific American*, March 1980, p. 66.

Learned, J.G. and Eichler, D., "A Deep-Sea Neutrino Telescope," *Scientific American*, February 1981, p. 138.

Marshak, R.B., "The Nuclear Force," *Scientific American*, March 1960, p 98.

Moran, P.R. Nickles, R.J. and Zagzebski, J.A., "The Physics of Medical Imaging," *Physics Today*, July 1983, p. 36.

Pykett, I.L., "NMR Imaging in Medicine," *Scientific American*, May 1982, p. 78.

Sime, R.L., "Lise Meitner and the Discovery of Nuclear Fission," *Scientific American*, January 1998, p. 80.

Ter-Pogossian, M.M. Raichle, M.E. and Sobol, B.E., "Positron-Emission Tomography," *Scientific American*, October 1980, p. 170.

Upton, A.C., "The Biological Effects of Low-Level Ionizing Radiation," *Scientific American*, February 1982, p. 41.

Weinberg, S., "The Decay of the Proton," *Scientific American*, June 1981, p.64.

Weisskipf, V.F. and Rosenbaum, E.P., "A Model of the Nucleus," *Scientific American,* December 1955, p. 261.

Witten, E., "New Ideas About Neutrino Masses," *The Physics Teacher,* February 1983, p. 78.

Zorpette, G., "Hanford's Nuclear Wasteland," *Scientific American,* May 1996, p. 88.

29.1 $r = r_o A^{1/3}$

For $A = 2$, $r = (1.2 \times 10^{-15}\text{ m})(2)^{1/3} = 1.5 \times 10^{-15}$ m.

For $A = 60$, $r = (1.2 \times 10^{-15}\text{ m})(60)^{1/3} = 4.7 \times 10^{-15}$ m.

For $A = 197$, $r = (1.2 \times 10^{-15}\text{ m})(197)^{1/3} = 7.0 \times 10^{-15}$ m.

For $A = 239$, $r = (1.2 \times 10^{-15}\text{ m})(239)^{1/3} = 7.4 \times 10^{-15}$ m.

29.2 (a) $r = r_o A^{1/3} = (1.2 \times 10^{-15}\text{ m})(4)^{1/3} = 1.9 \times 10^{-15}$ m.

(b) $r = r_o A^{1/3} = (1.2 \times 10^{-15}\text{ m})(238)^{1/3} = 7.4 \times 10^{-15}$ m.

29.3 We have: mass of sphere = mass of earth, or

(Volume x density)$_{sphere}$ = mass of earth, or $\frac{4}{3}\pi R^3(\rho_n) = 5.98 \times 10^{24}$ kg

Thus, $R = \left(\frac{(5.98 \times 10^{24}\text{ kg})}{4\pi(2.3 \times 10^{17}\text{ kg/m}^3)}\right)^{1/3} = 1.8 \times 10^2$ m

---

29.4 The mass of the hydrogen atom is approximately equal to the mass of the proton which is 1.67×10^{-27} kg. If the radius of the atom is

0.53×10^{-10} m, the volume is $V = \frac{4}{3}\pi r^3 = 6.2 \times 10^{-31}\text{ m}^3$.

Therefore, the density of the atom is:

$$\rho_a = \frac{m}{V} = \frac{1.67 \times 10^{-27}\text{ kg}}{6.2 \times 10^{-31}\text{ kg/m}^3} = 2.7 \times 10^3\text{ kg/m}^3,\text{ and}$$

the ratio of the nuclear density to the atomic density is:

$$\frac{\rho_n}{\rho_a} = \frac{2.3 \times 10^{17}\text{ kg/m}^3}{2.7 \times 10^3\text{ kg/m}^3} = 8.5 \times 10^{13}.$$

29.5 Assuming a head-on collision, the potential energy of the alpha particle at the point of closest approach equals the kinetic energy at a great distance from the nucleus.

(a) The potential energy of an alpha particle at a distance of $r_{min} = 3.2 \times 10^{-14}$ m from a gold nucleus is:

$$PE = \frac{kQ_1Q_2}{r_{min}} = \frac{(8.99 \times 10^9\text{ N m}^2/\text{C}^2)(2e)(79e)}{3.2 \times 10^{-14}\text{ m}} = 1.13 \times 10^{-12}\text{ J. Thus,}$$

$\frac{1}{2}m_\alpha v^2 = 1.1 \times 10^{-12}$ J, and $m_\alpha \approx 4(1.66 \times 10^{-27}\text{ kg}) = 6.64 \times 10^{-27}$ kg.

Therefore, $\frac{1}{2}(6.64 \times 10^{-27}\text{ kg})v^2 = 1.1 \times 10^{-12}$ J, from which,

$v = 1.9 \times 10^7$ m/s.

(b) $KE = 1.13 \times 10^{-12}\text{ J}\left(\frac{1\text{ MeV}}{1.6 \times 10^{-13}\text{ J}}\right) = 7.1$ MeV.

29.6 Assuming a head-on collision, the potential energy of the alpha particle at the point of closest approach equals the kinetic energy at a great distance from the nucleus. Thus, $PE)_f = KE)_i$, or $\frac{kQ_1Q_2}{r_{min}} = 0.50$ MeV.
For an alpha particle, $Q = 2e$, and for gold, $Q = 79e$.
Thus, $\frac{k(2e)(79e)}{r_{min}} = (0.50 \text{ MeV})(1.6 \times 10^{-13} \text{ J/MeV})$, or

$$r_{min} = \frac{(8.99 \times 10^9 \text{ N m}^2/\text{C}^2)(158)(1.60 \times 10^{-19} \text{ C})^2}{(0.50)(1.6 \times 10^{-13} \text{ J})} = 4.6 \times 10^{-13} \text{ m}.$$

29.7 (a) $F = k\frac{Q_1Q_2}{r^2} = (8.99 \times 10^9 \text{ N m}^2/\text{C}^2)\frac{(2)(6)(1.60 \times 10^{-19} \text{ C})^2}{(1.00 \times 10^{-14} \text{ m})^2} = 27.6$ N.

(b) $a = \frac{F}{m} = \frac{27.6 \text{ N}}{6.64 \times 10^{-27} \text{ kg}} = 4.16 \times 10^{27} \text{ m/s}^2$.

(c) $PE = k\frac{Q_1Q_2}{r} = (8.99 \times 10^9 \text{ N m}^2/\text{C}^2)\frac{(2)(6)(1.6 \times 10^{-19} \text{ C})^2}{(1.00 \times 10^{-14} \text{ m})}$, or
$PE = 2.76 \times 10^{-13} \text{ J} = 1.73$ MeV.

29.8 For $^{24}_{12}$Mg:
$\Delta m = 12m_H + 12m_n - m_{mg} = 12(1.007825\,\mu) + 12(1.008665\,\mu) - 23.985042\,\mu$,
$\Delta m = 0.212838\,\mu$, and $E_b = (\Delta m)c^2 = 198.26$ MeV, so
$\frac{E_b}{A} = \frac{198.26 \text{ MeV}}{24} = 8.26$ MeV/nucleon.

For $^{85}_{37}$Rb:
$\Delta m = 37m_H + 48m_n - m_{Rb} = 37(1.007825\,\mu) + 48(1.008665\,\mu) - 84.911793\,\mu$,
$\Delta m = 0.793652\,\mu$, and $E_b = (\Delta m)c^2 = 739.3$ MeV, so
$\frac{E_b}{A} = \frac{739.3 \text{ MeV}}{85} = 8.70$ MeV/nucleon.

29.9 For $^{93}_{41}$Nb:
$\Delta m = 41m_H + 52m_n - m_{Nb} = 41(1.007825\,\mu) + 52(1.008665\,\mu) - 92.906376\,\mu$,
or $\Delta m = 0.865029\,\mu$.
Therefore, $E_b = (\Delta m)c^2 = (0.865029\,\mu)(931.5 \text{ MeV}/\mu) = 805.8$ MeV, and
$\frac{E_b}{A} = \frac{805.8 \text{ MeV}}{93} = 8.66$ MeV/nucleon.

For $^{197}_{79}$Au:
$\Delta m = 79m_H + 118m_n - m_{Au} = 79(1.007825\,\mu) + 118(1.008665\,\mu) - 196.966543\,\mu$, or $\Delta m = 1.674102\,\mu$.
Therefore, $E_b = (\Delta m)c^2 = (1.674102\,\mu)(931.5 \text{ MeV}/\mu) = 1559.4$ MeV, and
$\frac{E_b}{A} = \frac{1559.4 \text{ MeV}}{197} = 7.92$ MeV/nucleon.

29.10 For $^{23}_{11}$Na: $Z = 11$, and $A - Z = 12$. Thus,
$E_b = (11m_H + 12m_n - 22.989770\,\mu)(931.5 \text{ MeV}/\mu)$,

$E_b = (0.200285\,\mu)(931.5\text{ MeV}/\mu) = 186.6\text{ MeV}$, and

$$\frac{E_b}{A} = 8.112\text{ MeV/nucleon.}$$

For ${}^{23}_{12}\text{Mg}$: $Z = 12$, and $A - Z = 11$. Thus,

$E_b = (12m_H + 11m_n - 22.994127\,\mu)(931.5\text{ MeV}/\mu)$,

$E_b = (0.195088\,\mu)(931.5\text{ MeV}/\mu) = 181.7\text{ MeV}$, and

$$\frac{E_b}{A} = 7.901\text{ MeV/nucleon.}$$

Thus, $\Delta\left(\frac{E_b}{A}\right) = 0.211$ MeV/nucleon. The difference is mostly due to increased Coulomb repulsion, due to the extra proton in ${}^{23}_{12}\text{Mg}$.

29.11 For ${}^{15}_{8}\text{O}$: $Z = 8$, and $A - Z = 7$. Thus,

$E_b = (8m_H + 7m_n - 15.003065\,\mu)(931.5\text{ MeV}/\mu) = (0.12019\,\mu)(931.5\text{ MeV}/\mu)$,

$E_b = 111.96$ MeV.

For ${}^{15}_{7}\text{N}$: $Z = 7$, and $A - Z = 8$. Thus,

$E_b = (7m_H + 8mn - 15.000108\,\mu)(931.5\text{ MeV}/\mu) = (0.123987\,\mu)(931.5\text{ MeV}/\mu)$,

$E_b = 115.49$ MeV.

Therefore: $\Delta E_b = 3.53$ MeV.

29.12 The energy to remove the last neutron in ${}^{43}_{20}\text{Ca}$ is:

$E = [(M_{42Ca} + m_n) - M_{43Ca}]\,(931.5\text{ MeV}/\mu)$

$= [41.95863\,\mu + 1.008665\,\mu - 42.958770\,\mu]\,(931.5\text{ MeV/nucleon})$

$= (0.008525\,\mu)(931.5\text{ MeV}/\mu) = 7.94\text{ MeV}$

29.13 $T_{1/2} = 14\text{ days} = 1.21 \times 10^6$ s, and $\lambda = \dfrac{\ln(2)}{T_{1/2}} = \dfrac{\ln(2)}{1.21 \times 10^6\text{ s}} = 5.73 \times 10^{-7}\text{ s}^{-1}$.

The activity is: $R = \lambda N = (5.73 \times 10^{-7}\text{ s}^{-1})(3.0 \times 10^{16}) = 1.72 \times 10^{10}$ Bq.

But using the conversion 1 curie = 3.7×10^{10} decays/s, we find:

$R = 0.47$ curies.

29.14 $R = \lambda N = \lambda(N_0 e^{-\lambda t}) = R_0 e^{-\lambda t}$, and $\lambda = \dfrac{\ln(2)}{T_{1/2}} = \dfrac{\ln(2)}{6.05\text{ h}} = 0.115\text{ /h}$.

Thus, if $R_0 = 1.1 \times 10^4$ Bq, and $t = 2.0$ h;

$R = (1.1 \times 10^4\text{ Bq})e^{-(0.115/\text{h})(2.0\text{ h})} = 8.7 \times 10^3\text{ Bq} = 8.7 \times 10^3$ decays/s.

29.15 (a) $\lambda = \dfrac{\ln(2)}{T_{1/2}} = \dfrac{\ln(2)}{8.04\text{ days}} = 8.62 \times 10^{-2}\text{ days}^{-1} = 9.98 \times 10^{-7}\text{ s}^{-1}$.

(b) $N = \dfrac{R}{\lambda}$ Thus, if $R = 0.50\,\mu\text{Ci} = (0.50 \times 10^{-6})(3.7 \times 10^{10}\text{ 1/s})$, or

$R = 1.9 \times 10^4$ decays/s, then

$$N = \frac{1.9 \times 10^4\text{ decays/s}}{9.98 \times 10^{-7}\text{ s}^{-1}} = 1.9 \times 10^{10}\text{ nuclei.}$$

29.16 (a) One mole of ^{11}C has a mass of 11.0 g. The number of moles contained in 3.50 μg is: $\frac{(3.50 \times 10^{-6}\ g)}{11.0\ g/mol} = 3.18 \times 10^{-7}$ mol.

(b) Since 1 mole contains Avogadro's number of atoms (and hence nuclei), the number of nuclei initially present is:

$$N_0 = (3.18 \times 10^{-7}\ mol)(6.02 \times 10^{23}\ nuclei/mol) = 1.91 \times 10^{17}\ nuclei$$

(c) The half-life is $T_{1/2} = 20.4$ min $= 1224$ s, and the decay constant is:

$\lambda = \frac{\ln(2)}{1224\ s} = 5.66 \times 10^{-4}\ s^{-1}$. The initial activity is therefore:

$$R_0 = (5.66 \times 10^{-4}\ s^{-1})(1.91 \times 10^{17}\ nuclei)$$
$$= 1.08 \times 10^{14}\ decays/s = 1.08 \times 10^{14}\ Bq.$$

(d) After 8.00 h, the activity is:

$$R = R_0 e^{-\lambda t}$$
$$= (1.08 \times 10^{14}\ Bq)e^{-(5.66 \times 10^{-4}\ s^{-1})(8.00\ h)(3600\ s/h)} = 9.00 \times 10^{6}\ Bq$$

29.17 (a) Using $R = R_0 e^{-\lambda t}$, with $R = 0.842R_0$ when $t = 2.00$ days gives:

$0.842 = e^{-\lambda(2.00\ d)}$, so $\lambda = -\frac{\ln(0.842)}{2.00\ d} = 8.60 \times 10^{-2}\ d^{-1}$.

The measured half-life is, $T_{1/2} = \frac{\ln(2)}{\lambda} = \frac{\ln(2)}{8.60 \times 10^{-2}\ d^{-1}} = 8.06$ d.

(b) Yes, the material could be ^{131}I which has a half-life of 8.04 d.

29.18 Start with $N = N_0 e^{-\lambda t}$ and multiply by sides by m, the mass of a nucleus. Thus, $mN = mN_0 e^{-\lambda t}$. But, $mN = M$ = the current mass of the sample, and $mN_0 = M_0$ (the original mass of the sample).

Using $M = M_0 e^{-\lambda t}$ we have: $\frac{M}{M_0} = \frac{0.25 \times 10^{-3}\ g}{1.00 \times 10^{-3}\ g} = 0.25 = e^{-\lambda(2.0\ h)}$.

From which, $\lambda = 0.693\ h^{-1}$.and $T_{1/2} = \frac{\ln(2)}{\lambda} = \frac{0.693}{0.693\ h^{-1}} = 1.0$ h.

29.19 Start with $N = N_0 e^{-\lambda t}$ and multiply by sides by m, the mass of a nucleus. Thus, $mN = mN_0 e^{-\lambda t}$. But, $mN = M$ = the current mass of the sample, and $mN_0 = M_0$ (the original mass of the sample).

Thus, using $M = M_0 e^{-\lambda t}$, with $\lambda = \frac{\ln(2)}{3.83\ d} = 0.181\ d^{-1}$, we have:

$$M = (3.00\ g)e^{-(0.181\ d^{-1})(1.50\ d)} = 2.29\ g$$

29.20 Here we have: $\frac{R}{R_0} = e^{-\lambda t} = 0.125$, so $\lambda t = 2.08$.

But, $\lambda = \frac{\ln(2)}{5730\ y} = 1.21 \times 10^{-4}\ y^{-1}$, giving $t = 1.72 \times 10^{4}$ y.

29.21 If the sample has activity R_0 at time $t = 0$, the activity at time t later is $R = R_0 e^{-\lambda t}$ Thus, when $R = 0.001R_0$, we have $e^{-\lambda t} = 0.001$ or $-\lambda t = \ln(0.001)$. This gives

$$t = \frac{6.91}{\lambda} = \frac{6.91}{(\ln 2)/T_{1/2}}) = T_{1/2}\left(\frac{6.91}{\ln 2}\right) = 432\ y\left(\frac{6.91}{\ln 2}\right) = 4.31 \times 10^{3}\ y.$$

29.22 $N_o = \frac{\text{mass present}}{\text{mass of nucleus}}$

$= \frac{5.0 \text{ kg}}{(89.9077 \ \mu)(1.66 \times 10^{-27} \text{ kg}/\mu)} = 3.35 \times 10^{25}$ nuclei, and

$\lambda = \frac{\ln(2)}{T_{1/2}} = \frac{0.693}{(28.8 \text{ y})} = 2.41 \times 10^{-2} \text{ y}^{-1} = 4.58 \times 10^{-8} \text{ min}^{-1}$ (half-life is taken from appendix B). Therefore,

$R_o = \lambda N_o = (4.58 \times 10^{-8} \text{ min}^{-1})(3.35 \times 10^{25}) = 1.53 \times 10^{18}$ counts/min, so

$\frac{R}{R_o} = e^{-\lambda t} = \frac{10}{1.53 \times 10^{18} \text{ counts/min}} = 6.54 \times 10^{-18}$, and

$\lambda t = -\ln(6.54 \times 10^{-18}) = 39.6$, giving $t = 1.64 \times 10^{3}$ y.

29.23 (a) $R_o = 10.0$ mCi $= 3.7 \times 10^{8}$ decays/s. We have: $R = \lambda N$, and $R_o = \lambda N_o$.

Thus, $\frac{R}{R_o} = \frac{\lambda N}{\lambda N_o} = \frac{N}{N_o} = e^{-\lambda t}$.

If $R_o = 10.0$ mCi initially, and $R = 8.00$ mCi after 4.00 hours, we have:

$\frac{8.00}{10.0} = e^{-\lambda(4.00 \text{ h})}$, and from this, $\lambda = 5.58 \times 10^{-2} \text{ h}^{-1}$.

Now, $T_{1/2} = \frac{\ln(2)}{\lambda} = \frac{\ln(2)}{5.58 \times 10^{-2} \text{ h}^{-1}} = 12.4$ h.

(b $N_o = \frac{R_o}{\lambda} = \frac{3.7 \times 10^{8} \text{ decays/s}}{(5.58 \times 10^{-2} \text{ h}^{-1})(1 \text{ h}/3600 \text{ s})} = 2.4 \times 10^{13}$ nuclei.

(c) $R = R_o e^{-\lambda t} = (10.0 \text{ mCi})e^{-(5.58 \times 10^{-2} \text{ h}^{-1})(30 \text{ h})} = 1.9$ mCi.

29.24 ${}^{12}_{5}\text{B} \rightarrow {}^{12}_{6}\text{C} + {}^{0}_{-1}\text{e}$

${}^{234}_{90}\text{Th} \rightarrow {}^{230}_{88}\text{Ra} + {}^{4}_{2}\text{He}$

${}^{14}_{6}\text{C} \rightarrow {}^{14}_{7}\text{N} + {}^{0}_{-1}\text{e}$

29.25 ${}^{212}_{83}\text{Bi} \rightarrow {}^{208}_{81}\text{Tl} + {}^{4}_{2}\text{He}$

${}^{95}_{36}\text{Kr} \rightarrow {}^{95}_{37}\text{Rb} + {}^{0}_{-1}\text{e}$

${}^{144}_{60}\text{Nd} \rightarrow {}^{4}_{2}\text{He} + {}^{140}_{58}\text{Ce}$

29.26

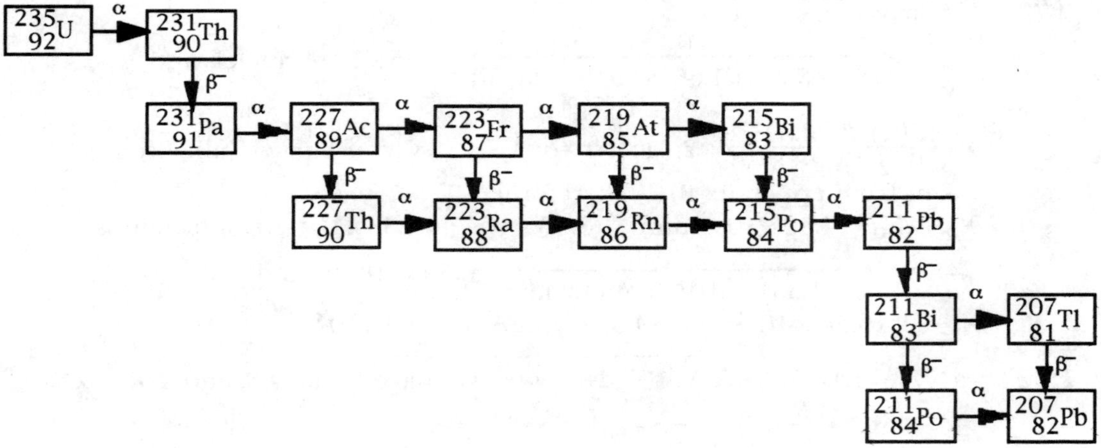

29.27 The heavier one $^{56}_{27}Co$ decays into the lighter one $^{56}_{26}Fe$. To conserve charge, the charge of the emitted particle must be +1e. Since both parent and daughter have the same mass number, the emitted particle must have essentially zero mass. This must be β^+ decay:

$$^{56}_{27}Co \rightarrow {}^{56}_{26}Fe + {}^{0}_{+1}e + \nu.$$

29.28 $^{238}_{92}U \rightarrow {}^{4}_{2}He + {}^{234}_{90}Th$

$E = (\Delta m)c^2 = [(M_{238U}) - (M_{4He} + M_{234Th})]$ (931.5 Mev/μ), or

$E =$[238.050784 μ- (4.002602 μ+ 234.043583 μ)] (931.5 Mev/μ), giving

$E =$ (0.0046 μ)(931.5 Mev/μ) = 4.28 MeV.

29.29 The mass number of the recoiling daughter nucleus will be 224. The total momentum of the system is zero. Thus, the magnitude of the momentum of the recoiling nucleus must equal the magnitude of the momentum of the α particle, or $p_\alpha = p_{nucleus}$. The kinetic energy of the recoiling nucleus is therefore:

$$KE_{nucleus} = \frac{p^2_{nucleus}}{2m_{nucleus}} = \frac{p_\alpha{}^2}{2m_{nucleus}} = \frac{m_\alpha}{m_{nucleus}}\frac{p_\alpha{}^2}{2m_\alpha},$$

or $KE_{nucleus} = \frac{m_\alpha}{m_{nucleus}} KE_\alpha = \frac{4}{224}$ (4 MeV) = 0.0714 MeV= 71.4 keV.

29.30 (a) $^{40}_{20}Ca \rightarrow {}^{0}_{+1}e + {}^{40}_{19}K$

For positron decay: $\Delta m = M_C - M_K - 2m_e$.

Δm = 39.962591 μ - 39.96400 μ - 2(0.000549 μ) < 0. Since $\Delta m < 0$, energy must be added and the decay cannot occur spontaneously.

(b) $^{144}_{60}Nd \rightarrow {}^{4}_{2}He + {}^{140}_{58}Ce$

For alpha decay:

$\Delta m = M_{Nd} - (M_{Ce} + m_\alpha)$ = 143.910082 μ - (139.905434 μ + 4.002602 μ), or

$\Delta m = 2.046 \times 10^{-3}\ \mu$. The mass difference is greater than zero, energy is released and the decay can occur spontaneously.

29.31 In the decay ${}_{1}^{3}H \rightarrow {}_{2}^{3}He + {}_{-1}^{0}e + \bar{\nu}$ the energy released is:
$E = (\Delta m)c^2 = [M_{3H} - M_{3He}]\ c^2$ since the antineutrino is massless and the mass of the electron is accounted for in the atomic masses of ${}_{1}^{3}H$ and ${}_{2}^{3}He$. Thus, $E = (3.016049\ \mu - 3.016029\ \mu)(931.5) = 0.0186\ MeV = 18.6\ keV$.

29.32 (a) ${}_{28}^{66}Ni \rightarrow {}_{29}^{66}Cu + {}_{-1}^{0}e + \bar{\nu}$

(b) $KE_{max} = (M_{ni} - M_{cu})c^2$,
$KE_{max} = (65.9291\ \mu - 65.9289\ \mu)(931.5\ MeV/\mu) = 0.186\ MeV = 186\ keV$.

29.33 We are given that $R = 0.600 R_0$, or $\frac{R}{R_0} = e^{-\lambda t} = 0.600$.
Thus, $\lambda t = -\ln(0.600) = 0.511$, and for carbon-14,

$$\lambda = \frac{\ln(2)}{T_{1/2}} = \frac{\ln(2)}{5730\ y} = 1.21 \times 10^{-4}\ y^{-1}.\ \text{Thus,}$$

$$t = \frac{0.511}{\lambda} = \frac{0.511}{1.21 \times 10^{-4}\ y^{-1}} = 4.22 \times 10^{3}\ y.$$

29.34 The original activity of this 1000 g sample of carbon was:
$R_0 = m(15\ \text{decays/min g}) = 1000\ g(15\ \text{decays/min g}) = 15000\ \text{decays/min}$.
The current activity = 2000 decays/min.
The halflife of ${}_{6}^{14}C$ is 5730 y, and the decay constant is:

$$\lambda = \frac{\ln(2)}{T_{1/2}} = \frac{\ln(2)}{5730\ y} = 1.21 \times 10^{-4}\ y^{-1}.\ \text{Therefore, } R = R_0 e^{-\lambda t} \text{ becomes:}$$

$$2000\ \text{decays/min} = (15000\ \text{decays/min})e^{-(1.21 \times 10^{-4} y^{-1})t},$$

yielding $t = 1.67 \times 10^{4}$ y.

29.35 (a) ${}_{5}^{10}B + {}_{2}^{4}He \rightarrow {}_{6}^{13}C + {}_{1}^{1}H$. The product nucleus is ${}_{6}^{13}C$.

(b) ${}_{6}^{13}C + {}_{1}^{1}H \rightarrow {}_{5}^{10}B + {}_{2}^{4}He$. The product nucleus is ${}_{5}^{10}B$.

29.36 ${}_{2}^{4}He + {}_{7}^{14}N \rightarrow {}_{1}^{1}H + {}_{8}^{17}O$

${}_{3}^{7}Li + {}_{1}^{1}H \rightarrow {}_{2}^{4}He + {}_{2}^{4}He$

29.37 (a) Using conservation of charge and mass number, we get:
${}_{79}^{197}Au + {}_{0}^{1}n \rightarrow {}_{80}^{198}Hg + {}_{-1}^{0}e + \bar{\nu}$.

(b) The Qvalue for the reaction is:
$Q = (196.966543\ \mu + 1.008665\ \mu - 197.96675\ \mu)(931.5\ MeV/\mu) = 7.88\ MeV$.
This released energy is shared (as kinetic energy) by the electron and the antineutrino. The maximum energy of the electron is:
$E = 7.88$ MeV.

29.38 $Q = [(M_{7Li} + M_H) - (M_{He} + M_{He})]$ (931.5 Mev/μ),
$Q = [(7.016003\,\mu + 1.007825\,\mu) - (4.002602\,\mu + 4.002602\,\mu)]$ (931.5 MeV/μ),
$Q = (0.018624\mu)(931.5 \text{ MeV}/\mu) = 17.3$ MeV.

29.39 (a) ${}^{27}_{13}Al + {}^{4}_{2}He \rightarrow {}^{30}_{15}P + {}^{1}_{0}n$. The product nucleus is ${}^{30}_{15}P$.
(b) $Q = [(M_{Al} + M_{He}) - (M_P + M_n)]$ (931.5 Mev/μ), or
$$Q = [(26.981538\mu + 4.002602\mu) - (29.978310\mu + 1.008665\mu)]\left(931.5\ \frac{\text{MeV}}{\mu}\right)$$
Thus, $Q = (-2.835 \times 10^{-3}\ \mu)(931.5 \text{ MeV}/\mu) = -2.64$ MeV.

29.40 (a) ${}^{7}_{3}Li + {}^{4}_{2}He \rightarrow {}^{10}_{5}B + {}^{1}_{0}n$. The product nucleus is ${}^{10}_{5}B$.
(b) $\Delta m = (M_{Li} + m_\alpha) - (M_B + m_n)$, or
$\Delta m = (7.016003\,\mu + 4.002602\,\mu) - (10.012936\,\mu + 1.008665\,\mu)$, giving
$\Delta m = -0.002996\,\mu = -4.97 \times 10^{-30}$ kg, and
$Q = \Delta mc^2 = (-0.002996\,\mu)(931.5 \text{ MeV}/\mu) = -2.79$ MeV.

29.41 Neglect recoil of product nucleus. (i.e. do not require momentum conservation). Then energy balance gives: $KE_{emerging} = KE_{incident} + Q$
To find Q: $\Delta m = (m_p + M_{Al}) - (M_{Si} + m_n)$ gives
$\Delta m = (1.007825\,\mu + 26.981538\,\mu) - (26.986721\,\mu + 1.008665\,\mu)$
$= -6.02 \times 10^{-3}\ \mu$,
and $Q = \Delta mc^2 = (-6.02 \times 10^{-3}\ \mu)(931.5 \text{ MeV}/\mu) = -5.61$ MeV.
Thus, $KE_{emerging} = 6.61 \text{ MeV} - 5.61 \text{ MeV} = 1.00$ MeV.

29.42 ${}^{1}_{0}n + {}^{4}_{2}He \rightarrow {}^{2}_{1}H + {}^{3}_{1}H$. The Q value is:
$Q = [(M_n + M_{He}) - (M_{2H} + M_{3H})]$ (931.5 Mev/μ), or
$Q = [(1.008665\,\mu + 4.002602\,\mu) - (2.014102\,\mu + 3.016049\,\mu)]$ (931.5 MeV/μ),
$Q = (-0.018884\mu)(931.5 \text{ MeV}/\mu) = -17.6$ MeV.
$$\text{Thus,}\quad KE_{min} = \left(1 + \frac{m_{\text{incident projectile}}}{m_{\text{target nucleus}}}\right)|Q| = \left(1 + \frac{1.008665}{4.002602}\right)(17.6 \text{ MeV}),$$
or $KE_{min} = 22.0$ MeV.

29.43 (a) ${}^{18}_{8}O + {}^{1}_{1}H \rightarrow {}^{18}_{9}F + {}^{1}_{0}n$. The other particle is a neutron.
(b) $Q = [(M_O + M_H) - (M_F + M_n)]$ (931.5 Mev/μ), which gives:
$Q = [(17.999160\mu + 1.007825\,\mu) - (M_F + 1.008665\,\mu)]$ (931.5 MeV/μ).
Since we are given: $Q = -2.453$ MeV, we find $M_F = 18.000953\,\mu$.

29.44 To have equivalent doses of heavy ions and x-rays, we must have:
(Heavy ion dose in rad) x $(\text{RBE})_{\text{Heavy ions}}$
= (x-ray dose in rad) x $(\text{RBE})_{\text{x-rays}}$
The RBE factors involved are: $(\text{RBE})_{\text{x-rays}} = 1.0$, and $(\text{RBE})_{\text{Heavy ions}} = 20$
Thus, the heavy ion dose equivalent to a 100 rad x-ray dose is given by:
$$\text{Heavy ion dose in rad} = \frac{(100 \text{ rad}) \times 1.0}{20} = 5.0 \text{ rad}.$$

29.45 One rad is that amount of radiation that deposits 10^{-2} J of energy per kilogram of absorbing material. Thus, if 75.0 kg of absorbing material receives 25.0 rad of radiation, the total energy deposited is:

$E_{total} = (1.0 \times 10^{-2}\ \text{J/kg/rad})(75\ \text{kg})(25\ \text{rad}) = 18.8\ \text{J}.$

29.46 (a) One rad is that amount of radiation that deposits 10^{-2} J of energy per kilogram of absorbing material. Thus, in a 200 rad dose, the energy delivered per unit of mass is:

$$E = (1.0 \times 10^{-2}\ \text{J/kg/rad})(200\ \text{rad}) = 2.0\ \text{J/kg}.$$

(b) The energy absorbed by 0.25 kg is $Q = (2.0\ \text{J/kg})(0.25\ \text{kg}) = 0.50\ \text{J}$. Assuming a specific heat equal to that of water, the expected temperature rise is:

$$Q = mc(\Delta T),\ \text{or}\ \Delta T = \frac{Q}{mc} = \frac{0.50\ \text{J}}{(0.25\ \text{kg})(4186\ \text{J/kg°C})} = 4.8 \times 10^{-4}\ \text{°C}$$

29.47 The rate at which energy is being deposited in each kg of water is:

$$\frac{\Delta Q}{\Delta t} = (1.0 \times 10^{-2}\ \text{J/kg/rad})(10\ \text{rad/s}) = 1.0 \times 10^{-1}\ \text{J/kg/s}.$$

To raise the temperature by 50° C, the energy needed per unit mass is:

$$\frac{Q}{m} = c(\Delta T) = (4.186\ \text{J/kg °C})(50\ \text{°C}) = 2.1 \times 10^{5}\ \text{J/kg}.$$

The time required is then:

$$t = \frac{\text{energy needed}}{\text{rate of delivery}} = \frac{2.1 \times 10^{5}\ \text{J/kg}}{1.0 \times 10^{-1}\ \text{J/kg/s}} = 2.1 \times 10^{6}\ \text{s (about 24.3 days)}.$$

29.48 (a) The number of x-rays taken per year is:

$$n = (8/\text{day})(5\ \text{days/week})(50\ \text{weeks/y}) = 2.0 \times 10^{3}\ \text{x-rayS}.$$

Then, $$\text{dose per x-ray} = \frac{\text{dose per year}}{\#\ \text{x-rays per year}}$$

$$= \frac{5\ \text{rem}}{2.0 \times 10^{3}\ \text{x-rays}} = 2.5 \times 10^{-3}\ \text{rem/x-ray}.$$

(b) The technician receives low-level background radiation at a rate of 0.13 rem/y. The average dose rate received as a result of the job is

$$5.0\ \text{rem/y, or}\ \frac{5.0\ \text{rem/y}}{0.13\ \text{rem/y}} \approx 38\ \text{background levels}.$$

29.49 The initial activity is $1.31\ \text{MBq} = 1.31 \times 10^{6}$ decays/s and the decay constant is $\lambda = \frac{\ln 2}{14.3\ \text{d}} = 4.85 \times 10^{-2}\ \text{d}^{-1}$. Thus, the original number of 32P nuclei present was

$$N_0 = \frac{R_0}{\lambda} = \frac{(1.31 \times 10^{6}\ \text{decays/s})(86\ 400\ \text{s/d})}{4.85 \times 10^{-2}\ \text{d}^{-1}} = 2.33 \times 10^{12}.$$

The number of 32P nuclei remaining after 10 days is:

$$N = N_0 e^{-\lambda t} = (2.33 \times 10^{12})e^{-(4.85 \times 10^{-2}\ \text{d}^{-1})(10\ \text{d})} = 1.43 \times 10^{12}.$$

(a) The number that have decayed (and hence the number of electrons emitted) in the 10 day interval is

$$n = N_0 - N = 2.33 \times 10^{12} - 1.43 \times 10^{12} = 9.00 \times 10^{11}$$

(b) At 700 keV per electron, the total energy deposited in 10 days is:

$$E = (700\ \text{keV/electron})(1.6 \times 10^{-16}\ \text{J/keV})(9.00 \times 10^{11}\ \text{electrons})$$
$$= 1.01 \times 10^{-1}\ \text{J}.$$

(c) If all this energy is deposited into 100 g = 0.100 kg of absorbing material, the absorbed dose is:

$$\text{dose in rad} = \frac{E}{m(10^{-2}\ \text{J/kg/rad})} = \frac{0.101\ \text{J}}{(0.100\ \text{kg})(10^{-2}\ \text{J/kg/rad})} = 101\ \text{rad}.$$

29.50 (a) The dose rate is: dose rate in rad/h = 100 mrad/h = 0.10 rad/h.
The dose rate in rem/h is:
dose rate in rem/h = (dose rate in rad/h)(RBE)
and the RBE for gamma rays is 1.0. Thus, dose rate in rem/h = 0.10 rem/h and the time required to receive a 1.0 rem dose is:

$$t = \frac{\text{dose}}{\text{rate}} = \frac{1.0\ \text{rem}}{0.10\ \text{rem/h}} = 10\ \text{h}.$$

(b) If the radiation is emitted uniformly in all directions, the intensity (and hence the dose rate) is inversely proportional to the square of the distance from the source. That is:

$$\frac{\text{dose rate at distance r}}{\text{dose rate at 1 meter}} = \frac{(1\ \text{m})^2}{r^2}.$$ Therefore,

$$r^2 = \frac{\text{dose rate at 1 meter}}{\text{dose rate at distance r}}(1\ \text{m})^2 = \frac{100\ \text{mrad/h}}{10\ \text{mrad/h}}(1\ \text{m})^2 = 10\,\text{m}^2$$

or $R = 3.16\,\text{m}$.

29.51 The decay constant is: $\lambda = \frac{\ln(2)}{T_{1/2}} = \frac{\ln(2)}{14\ \text{days}} = 4.95 \times 10^{-2}\ \text{day}^{-1}$.

Therefore, from: $R = R_0 e^{-\lambda t}$, we have: $\frac{R}{R_0} = e^{-\lambda t}$.

Thus, $\frac{20.0\ \text{mCi}}{200\ \text{mCi}} = e^{-(4.95\ \times\ 10^{-2}\ \text{day}^{-1})t}$, which gives: $t = 46.5$ days.

29.52 (a) For $t = T_{1/2}$:

$N = N_0 e^{-\lambda t} = N_0 e^{-(\ln 2)t/T_{1/2}} = N_0 e^{-(\ln 2)} = 0.500 N_0$, and

$N = N_0 (1/2)^{t/T_{1/2}} = N_0 (1/2)^1 = 0.500 N_0$.

(b) For $t = 0.318\,T_{1/2}$:

$N = N_0 e^{-\lambda t} = N_0 e^{-(\ln 2)0.318} = 0.802 N_0$,

and $N = N_0 (1/2)^{t/T_{1/2}} = \frac{N_0}{2^{0.318}} = 0.802 N_0$.

(c) For $t = 4.72\,T_{1/2}$:

$N = N_0 e^{-\lambda t} = N_0 e^{-(\ln 2)4.72} = 0.038 N_0$,

and $N = N_0 (1/2)^{t/T_{1/2}} = \frac{N_0}{2^{4.72}} = 0.038 N_0$.

In general: $e^{-\lambda t} = e^{-(t/T_{1/2})\ln 2} = e^{(t/T_{1/2})\ln(2^{-1})} = e^{(t/T_{1/2})\ln(1/2)}$

$$= \left(\frac{1}{2}\right)^{t/T_{1/2}}.$$

The last step is based on the fact that $e^{\ln x} = x$. Thus, we see that

$$N_0 e^{-\lambda t} = N_0\left(\frac{1}{2}\right)^{t/T_{1/2}}$$ or the two expressions are completely equivalent.

29.53 The original activity of the sample was:

$R_0 = 18$ g(15 decays/min g) = 2.7×10^2 decays/min.

The decay constant for $^{14}_{6}C$ is: $\lambda = \frac{\ln 2}{T_{1/2}} = \frac{\ln 2}{5730\ \text{y}} = 1.21 \times 10^{-4}\ \text{y}^{-1}$, and

$$R = R_0 e^{-\lambda t} = (2.7 \times 10^2\ \text{decays/min})e^{-(1.21\ \times\ 10^{-4}\ \text{y}^{-1})(2.00\ \times\ 10^4\ \text{y})}.$$

From which, $R = 24$ decays/min.

29.54 $^{1}_{1}H + ^{7}_{3}Li \rightarrow ^{7}_{4}Be + ^{1}_{0}n$. Thus, $Q = [(M_H + M_{Li}) - (M_{Be} + M_n)]$ (931.5 Mev/μ).
$Q = [(1.007825\mu + 7.016003\mu) - (7.016928\mu + 1.008665\,\mu)]$ (931.5 MeV/μ), or
$Q = (-1.765 \times 10^{-3}\ \mu)(931.5\ \text{MeV}/\mu) = -1.644$ MeV. Thus,

$$KE_{min} = (1 + \frac{m_{\text{incident projectile}}}{m_{\text{target nucleus}}})|Q|$$

$$= (1 + \frac{1.007825}{7.016003})(1.644\ \text{MeV}) = 1.88\ \text{MeV}$$

29.55 The Q value is: $Q = [(2M_{2H}) - (M_{3He} + M_n)]$ (931.5 Mev/μ), which gives
$Q = [2(2.014102\,\mu) - (3.016029\,\mu + 1.008665\,\mu)]$ (931.5 MeV/μ), or
$Q = (3.51 \times 10^{-3}\ \mu)(931.5\ \text{MeV}/\mu) = 3.27$ MeV.
Because the $Q > 0$, no threshold energy is required.

29.56 $R = 10\,\text{Ci} = 10(3.7 \times 10^{10}\ \text{decays/s}) = 3.7 \times 10^{11}$ decays/s. The decay constant is: $\lambda = \frac{\ln(2)}{T_{1/2}} = \frac{\ln(2)}{5.2\ \text{y}} = 0.13\ \text{y}^{-1} = 4.1 \times 10^{-9}\ \text{s}^{-1}$.
Also, $R = R_0 e^{-\lambda t}$, becomes $R_0 = Re^{+\lambda t}$, which with $t = 2.5$ y gives:

$$R_0 = (3.7 \times 10^{11}\ \text{decays/s})e^{+(0.13\ \text{y}^{-1})(2.5\ \text{y})} = 5.1 \times 10^{11}\ \frac{\text{decays}}{\text{s}}.$$

The number of original nuclei needed is: $N_0 = R_0/\lambda$, or

$$N_0 = (5.1 \times 10^{11}\ \text{decays/s})/(4.1 \times 10^{-9}\ \text{s}^{-1}) = 1.2 \times 10^{20}.$$

The initial mass of ^{60}Co needed is then: $M = m_{\text{nucleus}} N_0$, or

$$M = (60\ \mu)(1.66 \times 10^{-27}\ \text{kg}/\mu)(1.2 \times 10^{20}) = 1.2 \times 10^{-5}\ \text{kg} = 12\ \text{mg}.$$

29.57 The kinetic energy of the neutrons is: $\frac{1}{2}mv^2 = 0.040\ \text{eV} = 6.40 \times 10^{-21}$ J, and from this, the velocity of the neutrons (mass = 1.675×10^{-27} kg) is: $v = 2.76 \times 10^{3}$ m/s. The time for these neutrons to move 10.0 km is:
$t = \frac{L}{v} = \frac{10.0 \times 10^3\ \text{m}}{2.76 \times 10^3\ \text{m/s}} = 3.62$ s. The decay constant for the neutron is: $\lambda = \frac{\ln(2)}{T_{1/2}} = \frac{\ln(2)}{12\ \text{min}(60\ \text{s/min})} = 9.63 \times 10^{-4}\ \text{s}^{-1}$, and
from $N = N_0 e^{-\lambda t}$ we have the fraction of the neutrons remaining at the end of the 10.0 km as: $\frac{N}{N_0} = e^{-\lambda t} = e^{-(9.63 \times 10^{-4}\ \text{s}^{-1})(3.62\ \text{s})} = 0.997$.
The fraction having decayed is then: $1 - \frac{N}{N_0} = 0.003$, or 0.3 %.

29.58 Let R_0 equal the total activity withdrawn from the stock solution.
$R_0 = (2.5\ \text{mCi/ml})(10\ \text{ml}) = 25$ mCi.
Let R'_0 equal the initial activity of the working solution. Then, we have
$R'_0 = \frac{25\ \text{mCi}}{250\ \text{ml}} = 0.10$ mCi/ml. The half-life of $^{24}_{11}Na$ is 15.0 h.
After 48 hours the activity of the working solution will be:

$$R' = R'_0 e^{-\lambda t} = (0.10\ \text{mCi/ml})e^{-(0.693/15.0\ \text{h})(48\ \text{h})} = 1.1 \times 10^{-2}\ \text{mCi/ml},$$

and the activity in the sample will be:

$$R'_{\text{sample}} = (1.1 \times 10^{-2}\ \text{mCi/ml})(5.0\ \text{ml}) = 5.5 \times 10^{-2}\ \text{mCi}.$$

29.59 Let isotope #1 be ^{235}U and isotope #2 be ^{238}U. Assuming there were N_0, of each type nuclei present initially, the number of each type nuclei still remaining should be: $N_1 = N_0 e^{-\lambda_1 t}$, and $N_2 = N_0 e^{-\lambda_2 t}$
Thus, with the current ratio of 0.007 as given:

$$\frac{\#235U}{\#238U} = \frac{N_1}{N_2} = e^{-(\lambda_1 - \lambda_2)t} = 0.007.$$

We then have: $e^{-(\lambda_1 - \lambda_2)t} = 0.007$, or $t = -\frac{\ln(0.007)}{\lambda_1 - \lambda_2}$.

Then, using $\lambda = \frac{\ln 2}{T_{1/2}}$,

(for ^{235}U) $\lambda_1 = \frac{\ln 2}{0.70 \times 10^9 \text{ y}} = 9.9 \times 10^{-10} \text{ y}^{-1}$.

and

(for ^{238}U) $\lambda_2 = \frac{\ln 2}{4.47 \times 10^9 \text{ y}} = 1.55 \times 10^{-10} \text{ y}^{-1}$.

Therefore, our estimate of the age of the Earth is:

$$t = -\frac{\ln(0.007)}{(9.9 \times 10^{-10} \text{ y}^{-1} - 1.55 \times 10^{-10} \text{ y}^{-1})}$$

$$= 5.9 \times 10^9 \text{ y} = 5.9 \text{ billion years.}$$

29.60 The decay constant for $^{59}_{26}Fe$ is:

$$\lambda = \frac{\ln 2}{T_{1/2}} = \frac{\ln 2}{(45.1 \text{ d})(24 \text{ h/d})} = 6.40 \times 10^{-4} \text{ h}^{-1}.$$

The intial specific activity of ^{59}Fe in the steel is,

$$\left(\frac{R}{m}\right)_0 = \left(\frac{20 \ \mu\text{Ci}}{0.2 \text{ kg}}\right)\left(\frac{3.7 \times 10^4 \text{ Bq}}{1.0 \ \mu\text{Ci}}\right) = 3.7 \times 10^6 \text{ Bq/kg}.$$

After 1000 h,

$$\frac{R}{m} = \left(\frac{R}{m}\right)_0 e^{-\lambda t} = (3.7 \times 10^6 \text{ Bq/kg}) e^{-(6.40 \times 10^{-4} \text{ h}^{-1})(1000 \text{ h})}$$

$$= 2.0 \times 10^6 \text{ Bq/kg}.$$

The total activity in the oil is:

$$R_{oil} = (800 \text{ decay/min/liter})(1.0 \text{ min/60 s})(6.5 \text{ liter}) = 87 \text{ Bq}.$$

Therefore, the mass of $^{59}_{26}Fe$ in the oil is:

$$m = \frac{R_{oil}}{R/m} = \frac{87 \text{ Bq}}{2.0 \times 10^6 \text{ Bq/kg}} = 4.4 \times 10^{-5} \text{ kg}$$

and the wear rate is given by:

$$\text{Wear rate} = \frac{\text{mass worn away}}{\text{elapsed time}} = \frac{4.4 \times 10^{-5} \text{ kg}}{1000 \text{ h}} = 4.4 \times 10^{-8} \text{ kg/h}.$$

29.61 $N_{Rb} = 1.82 \times 10^{10}$ (^{87}Rb atoms/g)
$N_{Sr} = 1.07 \times 10^9$ (^{87}Sr atoms/g)

(a) If we assume that all the ^{87}Sr came from ^{87}Rb, then $N_{Rb} = N_0 e^{-\lambda t}$

$$1.82 \times 10^{10} = (1.82 \times 10^{10} + 1.07 \times 10^9) e^{-(\ln 2/4.8 \times 10^{10})t}$$

$$-\ln(0.94447) = \frac{\ln 2}{4.8 \times 10^{10}}\, t$$

gives $t = 3.96 \times 10^9$ y

(b) It could be no older. The rock could be younger if some ^{87}Sr were initially present.

29.62 (a) The energy released in the reaction $4(^1_1\text{H}) \rightarrow {}^4_2\text{He} + 2(^0_1\text{e}) + 2\nu + \gamma$ is:

$$Q = [4M_{1\text{H}} - M_{4\text{He}} - 2(2m_e)](931.5\ \text{MeV}/\mu).$$

There are two positron decays as intermediate steps in the overall reaction. Each positron decay requires a factor of $2m_e$ to balance electron masses when neutral atomic masses are used in the calculation as is done here. Thus, we find:

$Q = [4(1.007825\,\mu) - 4.002603\,\mu - 2(2 \times 0.000549\,\mu)](931.5\ \text{MeV}/\mu)$, or

$Q = 24.7\ \text{MeV} = 3.95 \times 10^{-12}$ J.

(b) If the entire mass (of 1.99×10^{30} kg) consisted of hydrogen, there would be 1.99×10^{33} moles, each containing Avogadro's number of nuclei, or $N = (1.99 \times 10^{33}\ \text{mol})(6.02 \times 10^{23}\ \text{nuclei/mol})$,

$N = 1.198 \times 10^{57}$ nuclei available to enter into the fusion reactions.

(c) Since 4 hydrogen nuclei are consumed per event, the number of events that could occur is: $N/4 = 2.995 \times 10^{56}$ reactions.

The total energy that could be released is, therefore:

$E = (2.995 \times 10^{56}\ \text{reactions})(3.95 \times 10^{-12}\ \text{J/reaction}) = 1.183 \times 10^{45}$ J.

At an output rate of 3.9×10^{26} J/s, the lifetime of the Sun should be

$$t = \frac{1.183 \times 10^{45}\ \text{J}}{3.9 \times 10^{26}\ \text{J/s}} = 3.03 \times 10^{18}\ \text{s} = 9.6 \times 10^{10}\ \text{y} = 96 \text{ billion years.}$$

(d) This calculation grossly overestimates the lifetime of the Sun because (1): the Sun is only about 75% hydrogen, not 100% as assumed, and (2): the density of remaining hydrogen atoms will become too low to sustain the chain reaction long before the hydrogen is totally consumed.

29.63 (a) The radius of the ^{40}Ca nucleus is given as: $r = r_o A^{1/3}$, with $A = 40$.

$r = (1.2 \times 10^{-15}\ \text{m})(40)^{1/3} = 4.10 \times 10^{-15}$ m.

The energy required to overcome electrostatic repulsion is:

$$E = \frac{3kQ^2}{5r} = \frac{(3)(9 \times 10^9\ \text{N m}^2/\text{C}^2)(20 \times 1.6 \times 10^{-19})^2}{(5)(4.1 \times 10^{-15})}, \text{ or}$$

$E = 1.35 \times 10^{-11}\ \text{J} = 84.2$ MeV.

(b) $E_b = 342$ MeV

(c) In order for the nucleus to be stable, the total binding energy must exceed the minimum energy needed to overcome electrostatic repulsion.

29.64 (a) $\#\ \text{nuclei} = \dfrac{\text{mass parent}}{\text{mass of 1 nucleus}}$, or

$$\#\ \text{nuclei} = \frac{1\ \text{kg}}{239\ \mu(1.66 \times 10^{-27}\ \text{kg}/\mu)} = 2.52 \times 10^{24}.$$

(b) $$\lambda = \frac{0.693}{T_{1/2}} = \frac{0.693}{(2.4 \times 10^4\ \text{y})(3.156 \times 10^7\ \text{s/yr})} = 9.149 \times 10^{-13}\ \text{s}^{-1}.$$

$R_o = \lambda N_o = (9.149 \times 10^{-13}\ \text{s}^{-1})(2.52 \times 10^{24}) = 2.306 \times 10^{12}$ decays/s, or

$R_0 = 2.306 \times 10^{12}$ Bq.

(c) $R = R_0 e^{-\lambda t}$, or $e^{-\lambda t} = \dfrac{R}{R_0} = \dfrac{0.1 \text{ Bq}}{2.306 \times 10^{12} \text{ Bq}} = 4.336 \times 10^{-14}$ Bq,

giving: $\lambda t = -\ln(4.336 \times 10^{-14}) = 30.77$, and

$$t = \frac{30.77}{\lambda} = \frac{30.77}{9.149 \times 10^{-13} \text{ s}^{-1}} = 3.363 \times 10^{13} \text{ s} = 1.07 \times 10^{6} \text{ years.}$$

29.65 The original activity per unit area is:

$R_0 = \dfrac{5 \times 10^{6} \text{ Ci}}{10^{10} \text{ m}^2} = 5 \times 10^{-4}$ Ci/m^2, and the final desired activity is

$R = 2 \times 10^{-6}$ Ci/m^2.

The decay constant is: $\lambda = \dfrac{0.693}{T_{1/2}} = \dfrac{0.693}{28.7 \text{ y}} = 2.414 \times 10^{-2} \text{ y}^{-1}$.

From $R = R_0 e^{-\lambda t}$, we have:

$$\frac{R}{R_0} = \frac{2 \times 10^{-6} \text{ Ci/m}^2}{5 \times 10^{-4} \text{ Ci/m}^2} = .004 = e^{-(2.414 \times 10^{-2} \text{ y}^{-1})t}, \text{ and } \quad t = 230 \text{ y.}$$

29.66 (a) $R = R_0 e^{-\lambda t}$, and $R_0 = N_0\lambda = 1.3 \times 10^{-12} N_0(^{12}C)\lambda$, or

$R_0 = (1.3 \times 10^{-12} \text{ X } 25 \text{ X } \dfrac{6.02 \times 10^{23}}{12})\ \lambda$, where

$\lambda = \dfrac{0.693}{5730 \text{ X } 3.15 \times 10^{7}} = 3.84 \times 10^{-12}$ decays/s, so $R_0 = 376 \dfrac{\text{decays}}{\text{min}}$.

Thus, at t = $(2.5 \times 10^4 \text{ y})(3.15 \times 10^7 \text{ s/y}) = 7.875 \times 10^{11}$ s, we find:

$R = (376/\text{min})e^{(-3.84 \times 10^{-12} \text{ s}^{-1})(7.875 \times 10^{11} \text{ s})} = 18.3$ counts/min.

(b) The observed count rate is slightly less than the average background and would be difficult to measure accurately within reasonable counting times.

ANSWERS TO CONCEPTUAL QUESTIONS

2. All isotopes contain the same number of protons, but have differing numbers of neutrons.

4. An alpha particle is a doubly positive charged helium nucleus, is very massive and does not penetrate very well. A beta particle is a singly negative charged electron, and is very light and only slightly more difficult to shield from. A gamma ray is a high energy photon or high frequency electromagnetic wave, and has high penetrating ability.

6. Beta particles have greater penetrating ability than do alpha particles.

8. The much larger mass of the alpha particle as compared to that of the beta particle ensures that it will not deflect as much as does the beta, which has a mass about 7000 times smaller.

10. Consider the reaction ${}^{14}_{6}C \rightarrow {}^{14}_{7}N + {}^{0}_{-1}e + \bar{\nu}$. We have six positive charges before the event on the carbon-14 nucleus. After the decay, we still have a net of six positive charges, as + 7 from the nitrogen and -1 from the electron. Thus, in order to have conservation of charge, the neutrino must be uncharged.

12. We would have to revise our age values upward for ancient materials. That is, we would conclude that the materials were older than we had thought, because the greater cosmic ray intensity would have left the samples with a larger percentage of carbon-14 when they died, and a longer time would have been necessary for it to decay to the percentage found at present.

14. The amount of carbon-14 left in very old materials is extremely small, and detection cannot be accomplished with a high degree of accuracy.

16. The alpha particle and the daughter nucleus must carry equal and opposite momenta because momentum is conserved. Since kinetic energy can be expressed as $p^2/2m$, the smaller-mass alpha particle carries more energy than the recoiling nucleus.

CHAPTER THIRTY SOLUTIONS

Chapter Thirty Readings

Aftergood, S. Hafemeister, D.W. Prilutsky, O.F. Primack, J.R. and Rodionov, S.N., "Nuclear Power in Space," *Scientific American*, June 1991, p. 42.

Bloom, E.D. and Feldmann, G.J., "Quarkonium," *Scientific American*, May, 1982.

Chandler, D., "An Expanding Universe in the Classroom," *The Physics Teacher*, 29,103,1991.

Close, F., *The Cosmic Onion: Quarks and the Nature of the Universe*, The American Institute of Physics, 1986. A timely monograph on particle physics, including lively discussion of the Big Bang Theory.

Cohen, B.L., "The Discovery of Radioactive Wastes from Fission Reactors," *Scientific American*, June 1977, p. 21.

Conn, R.W., "The Magnetic Fusion Reactors," *Scientific American*, October 1983, p. 176.

Fermi, L., *Atoms in the Family: My Life with Enrico Fermi*, Chicago, University of Chicago Press, 1954.

Furth, H.P., "Progress Toward a Tokamak Fusion Reactor," *Scientific American*, August 1979, p. 50.

Golay, M.W. and Todreas, N.E., "Advanced Light-Water Reactors," *Scientific American*, April 1990, p. 82.

Hafele, W., "Energy from Nuclear Power," *Scientific American*, September 1990, p. 136.

Harari, H., "The Structure of Quarks and Leptons," *Scientific American*, April, 1983.

Lederman, L.M., "The Value of Fundamental Science," *Scientific American*, November 1984.

Lester, R.K., "Rethinking Nuclear Power," *Scientific American*, March 1986, p. 31.

Lewis, H.W., "The Safety of Fission Reactors," *Scientific American*, March 1980, p. 3.

Liss, T.M. and Tipton, P.L., "The Discovery of the Top Quark," *Scientific American*, September 1997, p. 54.

Mistry, N. B. Poling, R.A. and Thorndike, E.H., "Particles with Naked Beauty," *Scientific American*, July 1983.

Osterbrock, D.E., Gwinn, J.A. and Brashear, R.S., "Edwin Hubble and the Expanding Universe," *Scientific American*, July 1993, p. 84.

Quigg, C., "Elementary Particles and Forces," *Scientific American*, April, 1985.

Weinberg, S., "The Decay of the Proton," *Scientific American*, June, 1981.

Review (a) Using Wien's displacement law (Chapter 27):

$\lambda_{max}T = 0.2898 \times 10^{-2}$ mK, or $\lambda_{max} = \dfrac{0.2898 \times 10^{-2} \text{ mK}}{3.0 \text{ K}}$

$= 9.66 \times 10^{-4}$ m $= 0.97$ mm.

(b) This lies in the microwave region of the electromagnetic spectrum.

30.1 ${}^{1}_{0}n + {}^{235}_{92}U \rightarrow {}^{141}_{56}Ba + {}^{92}_{36}Kr + 3{}^{1}_{0}n$. (3 neutrons are produced)

30.2 ${}^{1}_{0}n + {}^{235}_{92}U \rightarrow {}^{144}_{56}Ba + {}^{89}_{36}Kr + 3{}^{1}_{0}n$

$Q = (\Delta m)c^2 = [(M_n + M_U) - (M_{Ba} + M_{Kr} + 3m_n)]$ (931.5 MeV/μ),

$Q = [235.043925\mu - 143.922673\mu - 88.917563\mu - 2(1.008665\mu)]$(931.5 MeV/c),

$Q = (0.186359\mu)$(931.5 MeV/c) = 174 MeV.

30.3 ${}^{1}_{0}n + {}^{235}_{92}U \rightarrow {}^{88}_{38}Sr + {}^{136}_{54}Xe + 12{}^{1}_{0}n$

$Q = (\Delta m)c^2 = [(M_n + M_U) - (M_{Sr} + M_{Xe} + 12m_n)]$ (931.5 MeV/μ),

$Q = [1.008665 + 235.043924\mu - 87.905618\mu - 135.907215\mu$
$- 12(1.008665\mu)]$(931.5 MeV/μ)

$Q = (0.135776\mu)$(931.5 MeV/μ) = 126.5 MeV.

30.4 The energy needed by the bulb in one hour is:

$E = (\text{power})t = (100 \text{ J/s})(3600 \text{ s}) = 3.60 \times 10^5 \text{ J} = 2.25 \times 10^{18}$ MeV.

Thus, the number of fission events required is:

$N = \dfrac{\text{total energy needed}}{\text{energy per event}} = \dfrac{2.25 \times 10^{18} \text{ MeV}}{208 \text{ MeV/fission}} = 1.1 \times 10^{16}$ fissions.

30.5 (a) The mass of soil in the top 1 meter on this 1 acre plot is:

$M = \rho V = \rho[(\text{area})(\text{thickness})]$

$= (4000 \text{ kg/m}^3)(1 \text{ m}/3.281 \text{ ft})^2(43560 \text{ ft}^2)(1.00 \text{ m}) = 1.62 \times 10^7$ kg.

If 1 part per million (by mass) of this soil is uranium, the mass of uranium present is: $M_U = M/(1.00 \times 10^6) = 1.62 \times 10^1$ kg = 16.2 kg.

(b) The isotope U-235 makes up 0.72% of naturally occuring uranium (see Appendix B). The mass of U-235 in this soil is therefore:

$M_{U\text{-}235} = (0.0072)M_U = (0.0072)(16.2 \text{ kg}) = 0.117 \text{ kg} = 117$ g.

30.6 The weight of ${}^{235}_{92}U$ present is:

$w = (1.0 \times 10^9 \text{ tons})(7.2 \times 10^{-3}) = 7.2 \times 10^6$ tons, equivalent to a mass of 6.5×10^9 kg. The number of moles of U-235 included in this is:

$n = (6.5 \times 10^{12} \text{ g})\left(\dfrac{1 \text{ mol}}{235 \text{ g}}\right) = 2.8 \times 10^{10}$ mol,

And the total number of U-235 nuclei is:

$N = (2.8 \times 10^{10} \text{ mol})(6.02 \times 10^{23} \text{ nuclei/mol}) = 1.7 \times 10^{34}$ nuclei.

Assuming 208 MeV released per fission, the energy available is:
$E = (208\ \text{MeV/fission})(1.7 \times 10^{34}\ \text{nuclei}) = 3.5 \times 10^{36}\ \text{MeV} = 5.6 \times 10^{23}\ \text{J}$
(The calculation of E assumes that all the nuclei fission and there is 100% conversion efficiency in the production of power.)
The length of time is:

$$t = \frac{E}{\text{rate}} = \frac{5.6 \times 10^{23}\ \text{J}}{7.0 \times 10^{12}\ \text{J/s}} = 8.0 \times 10^{10}\ \text{s} = 2.5 \times 10^{3}\ \text{y}.$$

30.7 The energy used in one year = (2000 kWh/mo)(12 mo/y), or
$E_{year} = 2.4 \times 10^{4}\ \text{kWh/y} = 8.64 \times 10^{10}\ \text{J/y}.$
Assuming 208 MeV of energy released per fission event, the number of nuclei which must fission to yield this energy is:

$$N = \frac{8.64 \times 10^{10}\ \text{J}}{(208\ \text{MeV/fission})(1.6 \times 10^{-13}\ \text{J/MeV})} = 2.60 \times 10^{21}\ \text{nuclei}$$

This represents a mass of:
$M = Nm_{nucleus} = (2.60 \times 10^{21}\ \text{nuclei})(235\ \mu/\text{nucleus})(1.66 \times 10^{-27}\ \text{kg}/\mu),$
or $M = 1.01 \times 10^{-3}\ \text{kg} = 1.01\ \text{g}.$

30.8 The total energy output of the plant in one day is:
$E = (\text{power})t = (1000 \times 10^{6}\ \text{J/s})(86{,}400\ \text{s}) = 8.64 \times 10^{13}\ \text{J}.$
And the total energy which must be released is:

$$E_r = \frac{\text{energy required}}{\text{efficiency}} = \frac{8.64 \times 10^{13}\ \text{J}}{0.300} = 2.88 \times 10^{14}\ \text{J}.$$

The number of events required is:

$$N = \frac{E_r}{Q} = \frac{2.88 \times 10^{14}\ \text{J}}{(208\ \text{MeV/fission})(1.60 \times 10^{-13}\ \text{J/MeV})} = 8.65 \times 10^{24}\ \text{events}.$$

The number of moles of uranium required is:

$$\left(8.65 \times 10^{24}\ \text{nuclei}\right)\left(\frac{1\ \text{mol}}{6.02 \times 10^{23}\ \text{atoms}}\right) = 14.4\ \text{mol},$$ and the mass

required is: $m = (14.4\ \text{mol})\left(\frac{235\ \text{g}}{\text{mol}}\right) = 3.38 \times 10^{3}\ \text{g} = 3.38\ \text{kg}.$

30.9 The mass of U-235 present in 1 kg of fuel is:
$M_{U235} = 0.017(1\ \text{kg}) = 1.7 \times 10^{-2}\ \text{kg} = 17.0\ \text{g}.$
The number of U-235 atoms (and nuclei) present is:

$$N = 17\ \text{g}\left(\frac{6.02 \times 10^{23}\ \text{atoms/mol}}{235\ \text{g/mol}}\right) = 4.4 \times 10^{22}\ \text{nuclei}.$$

Thus, in using 1 kg of fuel, 4.4×10^{22} fissions occur with the release of 208 MeV per fission. The energy released is:
$E = 4.4 \times 10^{22}\ (208\ \text{MeV})(1.6 \times 10^{-13}\ \text{J/MeV}) = 1.5 \times 10^{12}\ \text{J}$
Energy used effectively = (energy released)(efficiency)
$E_{used} = (1.5 \times 10^{12}\ \text{J})(0.20) = 3.0 \times 10^{11}\ \text{J}.$
Thus, the work done is: $W = (1.0 \times 10^{5}\ \text{N})S = 3.0 \times 10^{11}\ \text{J}$, and
$S = 3.0 \times 10^{6}\ \text{m} = 3.0 \times 10^{3}\ \text{km} \approx 1.9 \times 10^{3}\ \text{miles}.$

30.10 In the fusion reaction ${}^{1}_{1}\text{H} + {}^{2}_{1}\text{H} \rightarrow {}^{3}_{2}\text{He} + \gamma$, the energy released is

$$Q = [(M_{1H} + M_{2H}) - M_{3He}]\, c^2$$
$$= (1.007825\,\mu + 2.014102\,\mu - 3.016029\,\mu)(931.5\ \text{MeV}/\mu),$$

or $Q = 5.49$ MeV.

30.11 (a) ${}^{4}_{2}He + {}^{4}_{2}He \rightarrow {}^{8}_{4}Be + \gamma$ $\quad (A = {}^{8}_{4}Be)$

(b) ${}^{8}_{4}Be + {}^{4}_{2}He \rightarrow {}^{12}_{6}C + \gamma$ $\quad (B = {}^{12}_{6}C)$

(c) Consider the first reaction:

$Q_1 = [2(4.002602\,\mu) - 8.005305\,\mu](931.5\text{ MeV}/\mu) = -0.094$ MeV.

The second reaction yields:

$Q_2 = (\Delta m)c^2 = [8.005305\,\mu + 4.002602\,\mu - 12.00000\,\mu]\,(931.5\text{ MeV}/\mu)$, or

$Q_2 = 7.37$ MeV.

The total energy released = -0.094 MeV + 7.37 MeV = 7.28 MeV.

30.12 (a) ${}^{1}_{1}H + {}^{12}_{6}C \rightarrow {}^{13}_{7}N + \gamma$ $\quad (A = {}^{13}_{7}N)$

(b) ${}^{13}_{7}N \rightarrow {}^{0}_{+1}e + {}^{13}_{6}C$ $\quad (B = {}^{13}_{6}C)$

(c) ${}^{1}_{1}H + {}^{13}_{6}C \rightarrow {}^{14}_{7}N + \gamma$ $\quad (C = {}^{14}_{7}N)$

(d) ${}^{1}_{1}H + {}^{14}_{7}N \rightarrow {}^{15}_{8}O + \gamma$ $\quad (D = {}^{15}_{8}O)$

(e) ${}^{15}_{8}O \rightarrow {}^{0}_{+1}e + {}^{15}_{7}N$ $\quad (E = {}^{15}_{7}N)$

(f) ${}^{15}_{7}N + {}^{1}_{1}H \rightarrow {}^{4}_{2}He + {}^{12}_{6}C$ $\quad (F = {}^{12}_{6}C)$

30.13 The total energy required per year is:

$E = (2000\text{ kWh/mo})(12\text{ mo/y})(3.60 \times 10^{6}\text{ J/kWh}) = 8.64 \times 10^{10}$ J/y.

The energy released per occurence of the reaction

${}^{2}_{1}H + {}^{3}_{1}H \rightarrow {}^{4}_{2}He + {}^{1}_{0}n$ is:

$Q = [(M_{2H} + M_{3H}) - (M_{4He} + M_{n})]\,c^2$, or

$Q = (2.014102\,\mu + 3.016049\,\mu - 4.002602\,\mu - 1.008665\,\mu)(931.5\text{ MeV}/\mu)$

$= 17.59$ MeV.

The number of fusion events per year is therefore:

$$N = \frac{E}{Q} = \frac{8.64 \times 10^{10}\text{ J/y}}{(17.59\text{ MeV/event})(1.60 \times 10^{-13}\text{ J/MeV})}$$

$= 3.07 \times 10^{22}$ events/y.

30.14 (a) 1.0 gallon = 3786 cm^3 = 3786 g of water, and the number of moles of water present is: $\quad n = \dfrac{3786\text{ g}}{18\text{ g/mol}} = 2.1 \times 10^{2}$ mol.

The number of water molecules present is:

$N = (2.1 \times 10^{2}\text{ mol})(6.02 \times 10^{23}\text{ molecules/mol})$

$= 1.3 \times 10^{26}$ molecules

The number of hydrogen atoms is (diatomic molecule):

$N_{atoms} = 2(1.3 \times 10^{26}) = 2.6 \times 10^{26}$ hydrogen atoms.

The number of deuterium nuclei in this many hydrogen atoms is:

$N_{deut} = (1.56 \times 10^{-4})(2.6 \times 10^{26}$ hydrogen atoms), or

$N_{deut} = 4.1 \times 10^{22}$ deuterium nuclei.

(b) The reaction: $\quad {}^{2}_{1}H + {}^{2}_{1}H \rightarrow {}^{3}_{2}He + {}^{1}_{0}n \quad$ has a Q value of 3.27 MeV.

The number of reactions which can occur = $\frac{1}{2}$ (number of deuterium nuclei) = 2.1×10^{22} reactions.
Thus, the total energy released is:
$E = (3.27 \text{ MeV/reaction})(2.1 \times 10^{22} \text{ reactions})(1.6 \times 10^{-13} \text{ J/MeV})$,
or $E = 1.1 \times 10^{10}$ J.

(c) Number of gallons of gasoline required is:

$$N_{gal} = \frac{1.1 \times 10^{10} \text{ J}}{2.0 \times 10^{8} \text{ J/gal}} = 55 \text{ gallons}$$

30.15 The number of water molecules present is:

$$N_{molecules} = \left(1.32 \times 10^{21} \text{ kg}\right)\left(\frac{6.02 \times 10^{26} \text{ molecules/kg mol}}{18.0 \text{ kg/kg mol}}\right), \text{ or}$$

$N_{molecules} = 4.41 \times 10^{46}$ molecules.
The number of hydrogen nuclei (diatomic ⇒ 2 per molecule) is:
$N_{nuclei} = 2(4.41 \times 10^{46}) = 8.82 \times 10^{46}$ nuclei.
The number of deuterons = 1.56×10^{-4}(number of hydrogen nuclei), or
$N_{deut} = 1.38 \times 10^{43}$ deuterons.

The number of fusions possible = $\frac{\text{number of deuterons}}{2 \text{ deuterons/fusion}}$, or
$N_{fusions} = 6.90 \times 10^{42}$ fusions.

(a) Energy released = $N_{fusions}(3.27 \text{ MeV/event})(1.60 \times 10^{-13} \text{ J/MeV})$, or
$E_{released} = 3.61 \times 10^{30}$ J.

(b) If rate of consumption = 100(present rate) = 7.00×10^{14} J/s, the time this will last is: $t = \frac{\text{total energy available}}{\text{rate of use}}$, or

$$t = \frac{3.61 \times 10^{30} \text{ J}}{7.00 \times 10^{14} \text{ J/s}} = 5.16 \times 10^{15} \text{ s} = 1.63 \times 10^{8} \text{ yr} = 163 \text{ million years.}$$

30.16 The minimum energy is released, and hence the minimum frequency photons are produced, when the proton and antiproton are at rest when they annihilate. That is, $E = 2E_0$, and $KE = 0$. To conserve momentum, each photon must carry away one-half the energy. Thus,

$$E_{min} = hf_{min} = \frac{1}{2}(2E_0) = E_0 = 938 \text{ MeV.}$$

Thus, $f_{min} = \frac{(938 \text{ MeV})(1.60 \times 10^{-13} \text{ J/MeV})}{6.63 \times 10^{-34} \text{ J s}} = 2.26 \times 10^{23}$ Hz, and

$$\lambda = \frac{c}{f_{min}} = \frac{3.00 \times 10^{8} \text{ m/s}}{2.26 \times 10^{23} \text{ Hz}} = 1.33 \times 10^{-15} \text{ m.}$$

30.17 From conservation of mass-energy, we may write:
$(m_0c^2 + KE_{proton}) + (m_0c^2 + KE_{antiproton}) = E_\gamma$, or
$E_0 + 95 \text{ MeV} + E_0 + KE = 2.09 \text{ GeV} = 2090$ Mev.
Thus, $KE = 1995 \text{ MeV} - 2E_0 = 1995 - 2(938.3 \text{ MeV})$, giving $KE = 118$ MeV.

30.18 The time for a particle traveling at (almost) the speed of light to travel a distance of 3.0×10^{-15} m is: $\Delta t = \frac{d}{v} = \frac{3.0 \times 10^{-15} \text{ m}}{3.0 \times 10^{8} \text{ m/s}} = 1.0 \times 10^{-23}$ s.

30.19 The rest energy of the Z^0 boson is $E_0 = 96$ GeV.

The maximum time a virtual Z^0 boson can exist is found from $\Delta E \Delta t = \hbar$

or $\Delta t \approx \dfrac{\hbar}{\Delta E} = \dfrac{1.05 \times 10^{-34}\ \text{J s}}{(96\ \text{GeV})(1.6 \times 10^{-10}\ \text{J/GeV})} = 6.8 \times 10^{-27}$ s.

The maximum distance it can travel in this time is:

$$d \approx c(\Delta t) = (3.0 \times 10^8\ \text{m/s})(6.8 \times 10^{-27}\ \text{s}) = 2.0 \times 10^{-18}\ \text{m}$$

The distance d is an approximate value for the range of the weak interaction.

30.20 Total momentum after = total momentum before = 0. Thus, the photons must go in opposite directions and have equal momenta, and hence equal energies since $E_\gamma = p_\gamma c$. From mass energy conservation:

$E_0 = 2E_\gamma$ (where E_0 is the rest energy of the π^0), or

$E_\gamma = \frac{1}{2} E_0 = \frac{1}{2}(135\ \text{MeV}) = 67.5$ MeV for each gamma ray

---

30.21

	Reaction	Conservation Law Violated
(a)	$p + \bar{p} \rightarrow \mu^+ + e$	L_e (0 + 0 → 0 + 1) and L_μ (0 + 0 → -1 + 0)
(b)	$\pi^- + p \rightarrow p + \pi^+$	charge (-1 + 1 → +1 + 1)
(c)	$p + p \rightarrow p + \pi^+$	baryon number: (1 + 1→ 1 + 0)
(d)	$p + p \rightarrow p + p + n$	baryon number: (1 + 1 → 1 + 1 + 1)
(e)	$\gamma + p \rightarrow n + \pi^0$	charge: (0 + 1→ 0 + 0)

30.22 $K^0 \rightarrow \pi^+ + \pi^-$

Strangeness, +1→ 0 + 0   Baryon number, 0 → 0 + 0

Lepton number, 0 → 0   charge, 0 → +1 - 1

Does not violate any absolute conservation law, and violates strangeness by only 1 unit. Thus, it can occur via the weak interaction.

$\Lambda^0 \rightarrow \pi^+ + \pi^-$

Baryon number, 1 → 0 + 0. Since all interactions conserve Baryon number, this process cannot occur.

30.23 $? + p \rightarrow n + \mu^+$

Conservation of charge yields $Q + e = 0 + e$, so $Q = 0$

Conservation of Baryon number yields, B + 1 = 1 + 0, so B = 0

Conservation of Lepton number yields, $L_e + 0 = 0 + 0$, so $L_e = 0$

and: $L_\mu + 0 = 0 - 1$, gives $L_\mu = -1$

$L_\tau + 0 = 0 + 0$, so $L_\tau = 0$

Thus, the particle must be an anti muon-lepton with zero charge. The particle on the left must be the $\bar{\nu}_\mu$.

30.24 The relevant conservation laws are: $\Delta L_e = 0$, $\Delta L_\mu = 0$, and $\Delta L_\tau = 0$.

(a) $\pi^+ \rightarrow \pi^0 + e^+ + ?$ L_e: 0 → 0 - 1 + L_e, so $L_e = 1$, and we have a ν_e.

(b) $? + p \rightarrow \mu^- + p + \pi^+$ L_μ: L_μ + 0 → +1 + 0 + 0, so $L_\mu = 1$, ⇒ we have a ν_μ.

(c) $\Lambda^0 \rightarrow p + \mu^- + ?$ L_μ: 0 → 0 + 1 + L_μ, so $L_\mu = -1$, and we have a $\bar{\nu}_\mu$.

(d) $\tau^+ \to \mu^+ + ? + ?$ L_μ: $0 \to -1 + L_\mu$, so $L_\mu = 1$, and we have a ν_μ.
L_τ: $+1 \to 0 + L_\tau$, so $L_\tau = 1$, and we have a $\bar{\nu}_\tau$.

Conclusion for (d): $L_\mu = 1$ for one particle, and $L_\tau = 1$ for the other particle. We have ν_μ, and $\bar{\nu}_\tau$.

30.25 The relevant conservation laws are: $\Delta L_e = 0$, $\Delta L_\mu = 0$, and $\Delta L_\tau = 0$.

(a) $\pi^- \to \mu^- + \bar{\nu}_\mu$: L_μ: $0 \to 1 - 1$, or $\Delta L_\mu = 0$.
(b) $K^+ \to \mu^+ + \nu_\mu$: L_μ: $0 \to -1 + 1$, or $\Delta L_\mu = 0$.
(c) $\bar{\nu}_e + p \to n + e^+$: L_e: $-1 + 0 \to 0 - 1$, or $\Delta L_e = 0$.
(d) $\nu_e + n \to p + e$: L_e: $1 + 0 \to 0 + 1$, or $\Delta L_e = 0$.
(e) $\nu_\mu + n \to p + \mu^-$: L_μ: $1 + 0 \to 0 + 1$, or $\Delta L_\mu = 0$.
(f) $\mu^- \to e + \bar{\nu}_e + \nu_\mu$: L_μ: $1 \to 0 + 0 + 1$, or $\Delta L_\mu = 0$, and
L_e: $0 \to 1 - 1 + 0$, or $\Delta L_e = 0$.

30.26 (a) $p \to \pi^+ + \pi^0$: baryon number is violated; $1 \to 0 + 0$.
(b) $p + p \to p + p + \pi^0$: This reaction can occur.
(c) $p + p \to p + \pi^+$: baryon number is violated: $1 + 1 \to 1 + 0$.
(d) $\pi^+ \to \mu^+ + \nu_\mu$: This reaction can occur.
(e) $n \to p + e + \bar{\nu}_e$: This reaction can occur.
(f) $\pi^+ \to \mu^+ + n$: violates baryon number: $0 \to 0 + 1$, and violates muon-lepton number: $0 \to -1 + 0$.

30.27 (a) $\pi^- + p \to 2\eta^0$
violates conservation of Baryon number as $0 + 1 \to 0$. (not allowed)

(b) $K^- + n \to \Lambda^0 + \pi^-$
Baryon number $= 0 + 1 \to 1 + 0$ charge $= -1 + 0 \to 0 - 1$
Strangeness, $-1 + 0 \to -1 + 0$ Lepton number, $0 \to 0$
All are conserved and the interaction may occur via the strong interaction

(c) $K^- \to \pi^- + \pi^0$
Strangeness, $-1 \to 0 + 0$ Baryon number, $0 \to 0$
Lepton number, $0 \to 0$ charge, $-1 \to -1 + 0$
Strangeness is violated by one unit, but everything else is conserved. Thus, the reaction can occur via the weak interaction, but not the strong or electromagnetic interaction.

(d) $\Omega^- \to \Xi^- + \pi^0$
Baryon number, $1 \to 1 + 0$ Lepton number, $0 \to 0$
Charge, $-1 \to -1 + 0$ Strangeness, $-3 \to -2 + 0$
May occur by weak interaction, but not by strong or electromagnetic

(e) $\eta^0 \to 2\gamma$
Baryon number, $0 \to 0$ Lepton number, $0 \to 0$
Charge, $0 \to 0$ Strangeness, $0 \to 0$
No conservation laws are violated, but photons are the mediators of the electromagnetic interaction. Also, the lifetime of the η^0 is consistent with the electromagnetic interaction.

30.28 The $\rho^0 \rightarrow \pi^+ + \pi^-$ The half-life is characteristic of the strong interaction. Thus, the ρ^0 must have S = 0 so strangeness is conserved.
For $K^0 \rightarrow \pi^+ + \pi^-$ $\Delta S = -1$ and the decay must occur via the weak interaction.
The half-life is consistent with this conclusion.

30.29 (a) $\Lambda^0 \rightarrow p + \pi^-$
Strangeness: $-1 \rightarrow 0 + 0$ ($-1 \neq 0$ so strangeness is not conserved)
(b) $\pi^- + p \rightarrow \Lambda^0 + K^0$
Strangeness: $0 + 0 \rightarrow -1 + 1$ ($0 = 0$ and strangeness is conserved)
(c) $\bar{p} + p \rightarrow \bar{\Lambda}^0 + \Lambda^0$
Strangeness: $0 + 0 \rightarrow +1 - 1$ ($0 = 0$ and strangeness is conserved)
(d) $\pi^- + p \rightarrow \pi^- + \Sigma^+$
Strangeness: $0 + 0 \rightarrow 0 - 1$ ($0 \neq -1$ so strangeness is not conserved)
(e) $\Xi^- \rightarrow \Lambda^0 + \pi^-$
Strangeness: $-2 \rightarrow -1 + 0$ ($-2 \neq -1$ so strangeness not conserved)
(f) $\Xi^0 \rightarrow p + \pi^-$
Strangeness: $-2 \rightarrow 0 + 0$ ($-2 \neq 0$ so strangeness is not conserved)

30.30 (a) $\pi^+ + p \rightarrow K^+ + \Sigma^+$: Baryon number: $0 + 1 \rightarrow 0 + 1$, $\Delta B = 0$.
Charge: $1 + 1 \rightarrow 1 + 1$, $\Delta Q = 0$.
$\pi^+ + p \rightarrow \pi^+ + \Sigma^+$: Baryon number: $0 + 1 \rightarrow 0 + 1$, $\Delta B = 0$.
Charge: $1 + 1 \rightarrow 1 + 1$, $\Delta Q = 0$.
(b) Strangeness is conserved in the first reaction: $0 + 0 \rightarrow 1 - 1$, $\Delta S = 0$. The second reaction violates strangness: $0 + 0 \rightarrow 0 - 1$, $\Delta S = -1$. It cannot occur via the strong or electromagnetic interaction.

30.31 (a) $\Xi^- \rightarrow \Lambda^0 + \mu^- + \nu_u$
Baryon number: $+1 \rightarrow +1 + 0 + 0$ Charge: $-1 \rightarrow 0 - 1 + 0$
L_e: $0 \rightarrow 0 + 0 + 0$ L_μ: $0 \rightarrow 0 + 1 + 1$
L_τ: $0 \rightarrow 0 + 0 + 0$ Strangeness: $-2 \rightarrow -1 + 0 + 0$
Conserved quantities are: B, charge, L_e, L_τ.
(b) $K^0 \rightarrow 2\pi^0$
Baryon number: $0 \rightarrow 0$ charge: $0 \rightarrow 0$
L_e: $0 \rightarrow 0$ L_μ : $0 \rightarrow 0$
L_τ : $0 \rightarrow 0$ Strangeness: $+1 \rightarrow 0$
Conserved quantities are: B, charge, L_e, L_μ, L_τ.
(c) $K^- + p \rightarrow \Sigma^0 + n$
Baryon number: $0 + 1 \rightarrow 1 + 1$ charge: $-1 + 1 \rightarrow 0 + 0$
L_e: $0 + 0 \rightarrow 0 + 0$ L_μ : $0 + 0 \rightarrow 0 + 0$
L_τ : $0 + 0 \rightarrow 0 + 0$ Strangeness: $-1 + 0 \rightarrow -1 + 0$
Conserved quantities are: S, charge, L_e, L_μ, L_τ.

(d) $\Sigma^0 \to \Lambda^0 + \gamma$
Baryon number: $+1 \to 1 + 0$ charge: $0 \to 0$
L_e: $0 \to 0 + 0$ L_μ: $0 \to 0 + 0$
L_τ: $0 \to 0 + 0$ Strangeness: $-1 \to -1 + 0$
Conserved quantities are: B, S, charge, L_e, L_μ, L_τ.

(e) $e^+ + e^- \to \mu^+ + \mu^-$
Baryon number: $0 + 0 \to 0 + 0$ charge: $+1 - 1 \to +1 - 1$
L_e: $-1 + 1 \to 0 + 0$ L_μ: $0 + 0 \to +1 - 1$
L_τ: $0 + 0 \to 0 + 0$ Strangeness: $0 + 0 \to 0 + 0$
Conserved quantities are: B, S, charge, L_e, L_μ, L_τ.

(f) $\bar{p} + n \to \bar{\Lambda}^0 + \Sigma^-$
Baryon number: $-1 + 1 \to -1 + 1$ charge: $-1 + 0 \to 0 - 1$
L_e: $0 + 0 \to 0 + 0$ L_μ: $0 + 0 \to 0 + 0$
L_τ: $0 + 0 \to 0 + 0$ Strangeness: $0 + 0 \to +1 - 1$
Conserved quantities are: B, S, charge, L_e, L_μ, L_τ.

30.32 (a) $K^+ + p \to \underline{\ ?\ } + p$
The strong interaction conserves everything.
Baryon number, $0 + 1 \to B + 1$, so $B = 0$
charge, $+1 + 1 \to Q + 1$, so $Q = +1$
Lepton numbers, $0 + 0 \to L + 0$, so $L_e = L_\mu = L_\tau = 0$
Strangeness, $+1 + 0 \to S + 0$, so $S = 1$
The conclusion is that the particle must be positively charged, a non-Baryon, with strangeness of +1. Of particles in Table 30.2, it can only be the K^+. Thus, this is an elastic scattering process.

The weak interaction conserves all but strangeness, and $\Delta S = \pm 1$.

(b) $\Omega^- \to \underline{\ ?\ } + \pi^-$
Baryon number, $+1 \to B + 0$, so $B = 1$ charge, $-1 \to Q - 1$, so $Q = 0$
Lepton numbers, $0 \to L + 0$, so $L_e = L_\mu = L_\tau = 0$
Strangeness, $-3 \to S + 0$, so $\Delta S = 1$, and $S = -2$
The particle must be a neutral baryon with strangeness of -2. Thus, it is the Ξ^0.

(c) $K^+ \to \underline{\ ?\ } + \mu^+ + \nu_\mu$: Baryon number, $0 \to B + 0 + 0$, so $B = 0$
charge, $+1 \to Q + 1 + 0$, so $Q = 0$ L_e, $0 \to L_e + 0 + 0$, so $L_e = 0$
L_μ, $0 \to L_\mu - 1 + 1$, so $L_\mu = 0$ L_τ, $0 \to L_\tau + 0 + 0$, so $L_\tau = 0$
Strangeness: $1 \to S + 0 + 0$, so $\Delta S = \pm 1$ (for weak interaction), so $S = 0$
The particle must be a neutral meson with strangeness = 0 $\Rightarrow$ π^0.

30.33

	proton	u	u	d	total
strangeness	0	0	0	0	0
baryon number	1	$\frac{1}{3}$	$\frac{1}{3}$	$\frac{1}{3}$	1
charge	e	$2e/3$	$2e/3$	$-e/3$	e

	neutron	u	d	d	total
strangeness	0	0	0	0	0
baryon number	1	$\frac{1}{3}$	$\frac{1}{3}$	$\frac{1}{3}$	1
charge	0	$2e/3$	$-e/3$	$-e/3$	0

30.34

(a) K^0 Particle	K^0	d	$\bar{s}$	total
strangeness	1	0	1	1
baryon number	0	1/3	−1/3	0
charge	0	$-e/3$	$e/3$	0

(b) Λ^0 Particle	Λ^0	u	d	s	total
strangeness	-1	0	0	-1	-1
baryon number	1	1/3	1/3	1/3	1
charge	0	$2e/3$	$-e/3$	$-e/3$	0

30.35 Compare the given quark states to the entries in Table 30.4

(a) suu = Σ^+ (b) $\bar{u}$ d = π^-

(c) $\bar{s}$ d = K^0 (d) ssd = Ξ^-

30.36 (a) $\bar{u}\,\bar{u}\,\bar{d}$: charge $= \left(-\frac{2}{3}e\right) + \left(-\frac{2}{3}e\right) + \left(\frac{1}{3}e\right) = -e$. This is the antiproton.

(b) $\bar{u}\,\bar{d}\,\bar{d}$: charge $= \left(-\frac{2}{3}e\right) + \left(\frac{1}{3}e\right) + \left(\frac{1}{3}e\right) = 0$. This is the antineutron.

30.37 (a) $\pi^- + p \rightarrow K^0 + \Lambda^0$

In terms of constituent quarks: $\bar{u}$ d + uud → d$\bar{s}$ + uds.
up quarks: - 1 + 2 → 0 + 1, or 1 → 1
down quarks: 1 + 1 → 1 + 1, or 2 → 2
strange quarks: 0 + 0 → -1 + 1, or 0 → 0

(b) $\pi^+ + p \rightarrow K^+ + \Sigma^+$:⇒ u$\bar{d}$ + uud → u$\bar{s}$ + uus
up quarks: 1 + 2 → 1 + 2, or 3 → 3
down quarks: -1 + 1 → 0 + 0, or 0 → 0
strange quarks: 0 + 0 → -1 + 1, or 0 → 0

(c) $K^- + p \rightarrow K^+ + K^0 + \Omega^-$ ⇒ $\bar{u}$s + uud → u$\bar{s}$ + d$\bar{s}$ + sss
up quarks: -1 + 2 → 1 + 0 + 0, or 1 → 1
down quarks: 0 + 1 → 0 + 1 + 0, or 1 → 1
strange quarks: 1 + 0 → -1 - 1 + 3, or 1 → 1

(d) $p + p \rightarrow K^0 + p + \pi^+ + ?$: uud + uud → d$\bar{s}$ + uud + u$\bar{d}$ + ?
The quark combination of ? must be such as to balance the last equation for up, down, and strange quarks.
up quarks: 2 + 2 = 0 + 2 + 1 +? (has 1 u quark)
down quarks: 1 + 1 = 1 + 1 - 1 + ? (has 1 d quark)
strange quarks: 0 + 0 = -1 + 0 + 0 + ? (has 1 s quark)
quark composite = uds = Λ^0

30.38 Quark composition of proton = uud, and of neutron = udd.
Thus, if we neglect binding energies, we may write:

$$m_p = 2m_u + m_d, \qquad (1)$$

and

$$m_n = m_u + 2m_d. \qquad (2)$$

Solving simultaneously, we find:

$$m_u = \frac{1}{3}(2m_p - m_n) = \frac{1}{3}\left(2(938.3\ \text{MeV}/c^2) - 939.6\ \text{MeV}/c^2\right)$$

$$= 312.3\ \text{MeV}/c^2,$$

and from either (1) or (2), $m_d = 313.7\ \text{MeV}/c^2$.

30.39 In the second reaction, $\pi^- + p^+ \rightarrow K^0 + n$, the quarks in the particles are:

$\bar{u}d + uud \rightarrow d\bar{s} + udd$. In this case, there is a net of 1 up and 2 down quarks before the reaction but a net of 1 up, 3 down, and 1 anti-strange quark after the reaction. Thus, the reaction does not conserve the net number of each type of quark.

30.40 Total momentum before the reaction = 0. Thus, the total momentum must be zero afterwards. Since the π^+ is at rest, the p and n must go in opposite directions with equal magnitude momenta. For minimum energy of the incident protons, the p and n will be at rest afterward. Mass-energy conservation then gives:

Total mass-energy before = total mass-energy after, or

$2E_p = E_{op} + E_{on} + E_{o\pi} = 938.3 \text{ MeV} + 939.6 \text{ MeV} + 139.6 \text{ MeV}$.

This gives: $E_p = 1008.8$ MeV. But, $E_p = KE + E_{op}$, and

$KE = E_p - E_{op} = 1008.8 - 938.3 \text{ MeV} = 70.5 \text{ MeV}$.

30.41 $K^0 \rightarrow \pi^+ + \pi^-$

From conservation of energy,

$E_{oK0} = E_{\pi+} + E_{\pi-}$ .Since the two pions have equal rest mass and equal momenta (the total momentum is zero before and after the decay), they must leave the event with equal speeds and energies.

Thus, $E_{\pi+} = E_{\pi-} = E$ and $2E = E_{oK0} = 497.7$ MeV, giving $E = 248.9$ MeV as the total energy of each pion. But $E = E_0 + KE = mc^2 = \gamma m_0 c^2 = \gamma E_0$,

so $\gamma = \dfrac{E}{E_0} = \dfrac{248.9 \text{ MeV}}{139.6 \text{ MeV}} = 1.783$.

Therefore, $\dfrac{1}{\sqrt{1 - (v/c)^2}} = 1.783$, yielding $v = 0.8279c$.

30.42 The uncertainty principle limits the time the virtual proton can exist as:

$$(\Delta E)(\Delta t) = \hbar, \text{ or } \Delta t = \frac{\hbar}{\Delta E} = \frac{\hbar}{m_p c^2} = \frac{1.05 \times 10^{-34} \text{ J s}}{(938 \text{ MeV})(1.60 \times 10^{-13} \text{ J/MeV})}$$
$$= 7.00 \times 10^{-25} \text{ s}$$

The maximum distance the virtual proton could travel in this time is:

$d = c(\Delta t) = (3.00 \times 10^8 \text{ m/s})(7.00 \times 10^{-25} \text{ s}) = 2.10 \times 10^{-16} \text{ m} = 0.210 \text{ fm}$.

30.43 In the fusion reaction ${}^1_1H + {}^3_2H \rightarrow {}^4_2He + {}^0_1e + \nu$

the energy released is $Q = [(M_{1H} + M_{3H}) - M_{4He}]\,c^2$

$= (1.007825\,\mu + 3.016029\,\mu - 4.002602\,\mu)(931.5 \text{ MeV}/\mu) = 19.8 \text{ MeV}$

30.44 For the partial reaction, $\mu^+ + e \rightarrow 2\nu$, we know that:

muon-lepton number before = (-1) + (0) = -1

electron-lepton number before = (0) + (1) = 1

Therefore, after the reaction, the muon-lepton number must be -1. Thus, one of the neutrinos must be the anti-neutrino associated with muons, or $\bar{\nu}_\mu$.

Also, after the reaction, the electron-lepton number must be 1. Thus, one of the neutrinos must be the neutrino associated with electrons, or ν_e.
The complete reaction is therefore: $\mu^+ + e \rightarrow \bar{\nu}_\mu + \nu_e$.

30.45 (a) $\mu^- \rightarrow e + \gamma$: L_e goes $0 \rightarrow 1+0$ so $\Delta L_e \neq 0$, and L_μ goes $1 \rightarrow 0+0$ so $\Delta L_\mu \neq 0$.
(b) $n \rightarrow p + e + \nu_e$: L_e goes $0 \rightarrow 0+1+1$ so $\Delta L_e \neq 0$
(c) $\Lambda^0 \rightarrow p + \pi^0$: Charge goes $0 \rightarrow +1+0$ so $\Delta Q \neq 0$.
(d) $p \rightarrow e^+ + \pi^0$: Baryon number goes $+1 \rightarrow 0+0$ so $\Delta B \neq 0$
(e) $\Xi^0 \rightarrow n + \pi^0$: Strangeness goes $-2 \rightarrow 0+0$ (2 unit violation)

30.46 We must conserve both mass-energy and momentum.

$p_{after} = p_\Lambda + p_\gamma = p_{before} = 0$. Thus $|p_\Lambda| = |p_\gamma|$ or $\dfrac{E_\Lambda^2 - E_{0\Lambda}^2}{c^2} = \dfrac{E_\gamma^2}{c^2}$.

This gives: $E_\Lambda^2 - (1115.6 \text{ MeV})^2 = E_\gamma^2$ (1)
From mass-energy conservation, $E_{0\Sigma} = E_\Lambda + E_\gamma$
$E_\gamma = (1192.5 \text{ MeV}) - E_\Lambda$ (2)
Solving (1) and (2) simultaneously gives:
$E_\Lambda = 1118.1$ MeV, and $E_\gamma = 74.4$ MeV.

30.47 KE after a collision $= \dfrac{1}{2}$(KE before collision)

Thus, after N collisions: $KE = \dfrac{1}{2^N}$ (original KE), or

$$2^N = \frac{KE_{original}}{KE_{final}} = \frac{2.00 \times 10^6 \text{ eV}}{0.039 \text{ eV}} = 5.13 \times 10^7.$$ Therefore,

$N(\ln 2) = \ln(5.13 \times 10^7) = 17.8$, from which: $N = 25.6$.
Thus, it requires 26 collisions

30.48 The energy output required = (power)t, or
$E_{output} = (10^8 \text{ J/s})(100 \text{ days})(86{,}400 \text{ s/day}) = 8.64 \times 10^{14}$ J. The total energy input required is:

$$E_{in} = \frac{E_{output}}{\text{efficiency}} = \frac{8.64 \times 10^{14} \text{ J}}{0.300} = 2.88 \times 10^{15} \text{ J}.$$

Assuming an average of 208 MeV per fission of U-235, the number of fission events, or nuclei required, is:

$$N = \frac{2.88 \times 10^{15} \text{ J}}{(208 \text{ MeV/fission})(1.60 \times 10^{-13} \text{ J/MeV})} = 8.65 \times 10^{25} \text{ nuclei}.$$

The number of moles used $= \dfrac{8.65 \times 10^{25} \text{ atoms}}{6.02 \times 10^{23} \text{ atoms/mol}} = 143.7$ mol, and the mass of this much uranium is:
$M = (143.7 \text{ mol})(0.235 \text{ kg/mol}) = 34$ kg.

30.49 (a) $p \rightarrow e^+ + \gamma$
Baryon number: $+1 \rightarrow 0 + 0$ Thus, ΔB does not equal zero, so baryon number is not conserved.
(b) From conservation of momentum, we obtain (since the proton is initially at rest): $p_{before} = p_{after}$ or $= p_e + p_\gamma$ (1)

Using the relativistic equation, $E^2 = (pc)^2 + E_0^2$ for the positron, we have: $E_e^2 = (p_e c)^2 + E_{oe}^2$, and using (1) above this becomes:

$E_e^2 = (p_\gamma c)^2 + E_{oe}^2$ or since $E_\gamma = p_\gamma c$, $E_e^2 = E_\gamma^2 + E_{oe}^2$ (2)

From conservation of mass-energy; $E_{op} = E_e + E_\gamma$, or

$E_e = E_{op} - E_\gamma$, and $E_e^2 = E^2_{op} - 2E_{op}E_\gamma + E_\gamma^2$, (3)

Equating (2) and (3) from above gives:

$E_{op}^2 - 2E_{op}E_\gamma = E_{oe}^2$

or

$$E_\gamma = \frac{E_{op}^2 - E_{oe}^2}{2E_{op}} = \frac{(938\ \text{MeV})^2 - (0.511\ \text{MeV})^2}{2(938.3\ \text{MeV})} = 469\ \text{MeV and}$$

$$p_\gamma = \frac{E_\gamma}{c} = 469\ \text{MeV/c}.$$

(c) From mass-energy conservation, $E_e = E_0 - E_\gamma$.

Thus, the total energy of the positron is:

$E_e = 938.3\ \text{MeV} - 469\ \text{MeV} = 469\ \text{MeV}$.

But, $E_e = \gamma E_{oe} = \dfrac{E_{oe}}{\sqrt{1 - (v/c)^2}}$

so $\sqrt{1 - (v/c)^2} = \dfrac{E_{oe}}{E_e} = \dfrac{0.511\ \text{MeV}}{469\ \text{MeV}} = 1.09 \times 10^{-3}$,

which yields: $v = 0.9999994c$.

30.50 (a) 1 gallon = 3786 cm^3 which is equivalent to a mass of 3786 g.

The number of moles present is: $n = \dfrac{3786\ \text{g}}{18\ \text{g/mol}} = 210\ \text{mol}$.

The number of water molecules present is:

$N_m = (210\ \text{mol})(6.02 \times 10^{23}\ \text{molecules/mol}) = 1.26 \times 10^{26}$ molecules.

Since the water molecule is diatomic, the number of hydrogen atoms present $= 2(1.26 \times 10^{26}) = 2.52 \times 10^{26}$, and

the number of deuterons present $= \dfrac{2.52 \times 10^{26}\ \text{atoms}}{6500\ \text{atoms/deuteron}}$

$= 3.88 \times 10^{22}$.

Thus, the energy available, assuming Q= 3.27 MeV per fusion event (which consumes 2 deuterons) is:

$E = (3.88 \times 10^{22}\ \text{deuterons})(1.64\ \text{MeV/deuteron})$, or

$E = 6.36 \times 10^{22}\ \text{MeV} = 1.02 \times 10^{10}\ \text{J}$.

(b) $t = \dfrac{\text{energy available}}{\text{rate of consumption}} = \dfrac{1.02 \times 10^{10}\ \text{J}}{1.0 \times 10^4\ \text{J/s}} = 1.0 \times 10^6\ \text{s} = 12\ \text{days}$.

30.51 (a) $\langle KE \rangle = \frac{1}{2} m v_{av}^2 = \frac{3}{2} kT$, or

$$\bar{v} = \sqrt{\frac{3kT}{m}} = \sqrt{\frac{3(1.38 \times 10^{-23}\ \text{J/K})(10^8\ \text{K})}{(2.014\ \mu)(1.66 \times 10^{-27}\ \text{kg}/\mu)}} = 1.1 \times 10^6\ \text{m/s}.$$

(b) The average time for one of these deuterons to cross a 10 cm cube is

$t = \dfrac{d}{v} = \dfrac{10^{-1}\ \text{m}}{1.11 \times 10^6\ \text{m/s}} = 9 \times 10^{-8}\ \text{s}$. (about 10^{-7} s)

30.52 (a) $L=\sqrt{\dfrac{(1.055 \times 10^{-34}\ \text{J s})(6.67 \times 10^{-11}\ \text{Nm}^2/\text{kg}^2)}{(3.00 \times 10^8\ \text{m/s})^3}} = 1.61 \times 10^{-35}$ m.

(b) This time is given as $T=\dfrac{L}{c}=\dfrac{1.61 \times 10^{-35}\ \text{m}}{3.00 \times 10^8\ \text{m/s}}= 5.38 \times 10^{-44}$ s, which is approximately equal to the ultra-hot epoch.

SOLUTIONS TO CONCEPTUAL QUESTIONS

2. The two factors presenting the most technical difficulties are the requirements of a high plasma density and a high plasma temperature. These two conditions must occur simultaneously.

4. Notice in the fusion reactions discussed in the text that the most commonly formed by-product of the reactions is helium, inert and nonradioactive.

6. They are hadrons. Such particles decay into other strongly interacting particles such as p, n, and π with very short lifetimes. In fact, they decay so quickly that they cannot be detected directly. Decays which occur via the weak force have lifetimes of 10^{-13} s or longer; particles that decay via the electromagnetic force have times in the range of 10^{-16} s to 10^{-19} s.

8. Each flavor of quark can have three colors, designated as red, green, and blue. Antiquarks are colored antired, antigreen, and antiblue. Baryons consist of three quarks, each having a different color. Mesons consist of a quark of one color and an antiquark with a corresponding anticolor. Thus, baryons and mesons are colorless or white.

10. The decays of the neutral pion, eta, and neutral sigma occur by the electromagnetic interaction. These are the three shortest lifetimes in the table. All produce photons, which are the quanta of the electromagnetic force, and all conserve strangeness.

12. Baryons and antibaryons contain three quarks while mesons and antimesons contain two quarks. Quarks have a spin of 1/2, thus three quarks in a baryon can only combine to form a net spin that is half-integral. Likewise two quarks in a meson can only combine to form a net spin of 0 or 1.

14. A neutron inside a nucleus is stable because it is in a lower energy state than a free neutron and lower in energy than it would be if it decayed into a proton (plus electron and antineutrino). The nuclear force gives it this lower energy by binding it inside the nucleus and by favoring pairing between neutrons and protons.

ANSWERS TO EVEN-NUMBERED PROBLEMS

CHAPTER ONE

2. Based on units alone, the equation might be valid.

4. (a) MLT^{-2}, (b) $kg{\cdot}m/s^2$

6. (a) 3.00×10^8 m/s, (b) 2.9979×10^8 m/s (c) $2.997\,925 \times 10^8$ m/s

8. (a) 797, (b) 11, (c) 17.8

10. (a) 22 cm, (b) 67.9 cm^2

12. 228.8 cm

14. 3.16×10^9 y

16. (a) 1 mi/h = 1.609 km/h, (b) 88.5 km/h, (c) 16.1 km/h

18. 2.95×10^2 m^3, 2.95×10^8 cm^3

20. It will require about 47.5 years to count the money.

22. 2.57×10^6 m^3

24. 2.9 cm

26. 1.25×10^{10} lb, 4.17×10^7 head, assuming 0.25 lb per burger and 300 lb net of meat per head of cattle)

28. 750 tuners, (assumes 1 tuner per 10,000 residents and a population of 7.5 million)

30. 2.2 m

32. 8.1 cm

34. (a) 1.5 m, (b) 2.6 m

36. 8.60 m

38. 2×10^5 tons/yr, (assumes an average of 1 can per person each week, a population of 250 million, and 0.5 oz of aluminum per can)

40. $V = \left(0.579\,\frac{ft^3}{s}\right) t + \left(1.19 \times 10^{-9}\,\frac{ft^3}{s^2}\right) t^2$

42. (a) 4, (b) 8

44. 1.51×10^{-4} m

46. $\frac{m^3}{kg\ s^2}$

48. 1.78×10^{-9} m

CHAPTER TWO

2. (a) 2.50 m/s, (b) -2.27 m/s, (c) 0

4. 2.4×10^4 s = 6.67 h

6. (a) 4.00 m/s, (b) -0.50 m/s, (c) -1.00 m/s, (d) 0

8. 1.32 h (79.2 min)

10. (a) 126 s, (b) 12.6 m

12. 0.18 mi west of the flagpole

14. (b) 41.03 m/s, 41.008 m/s, 41.002 m/s, (c) $\bar{v} = 17.1$ m / s , much less than v at t = 4.0 s

16. 8.60 m/s

18. -1.5×10^3 m/s^2

20. (a) 0, 1.6 m/s^2, 0.80 m/s^2, (b) 0, 1.6 m/s^2 , 0

22. 2.74×10^5 m/s^2 = 2.79×10^4 g

24. (a) 20 s, (b) No, the minimum distance to stop = 1.0 km.

26. (a) 2.32 m/s^2, (b) 14.4 s

28. -3.60 m/s^2

30. (a) 12.5 s, (b) -2.30 m/s^2, (c) 13.1 s

32. 200 m

34. 1.50 m/s, 32.3 m

36. (a) 8.20 s, (b) 134 m

38. 3.94 s

40. 941 m

42. (a) 308 m, (b) 8.52 s, (c) 16.5 s

44. See solution in this manual.

46. 0.60 s

48. (a) 3.00 s, (b) both are - 24.5 m/s, (c) 23.5 m

50. (a) 5.45 s, (b) 73.0 m (c) 26.7 m/s, 22.6 m/s

52. Her acceleration of 0.15 m/s^2 is sufficient.

54. 4.16 m/s

56. (a) 3.75 m/s, (b) 0

58. 1.79 s.

60. (a) 7.82 m, (b) 0.782 s.

CHAPTER THREE

2. 421 ft, 3.0° below horizontal

4. (a) 5.00 units, at 53° below the x axis. (b) 5.00 units, 53° above x axis

6. 83 m, 33° north of west

8. 1.31 km north and 2.81 km east

10. 42.7 yd

12. 788 miles at 48.1° north of east

14. (a) 185 N at 77.8° from x axis (b) 185 N at 257.8° from x axis

16. 2.65 ft (0.807 m)

18. (a) 3.19 s, (b) 36.1 m/s at 60.1°below horizontal

20. (a) clears by 0.85 m (b) v_y = -13.4 m/s falling

22. 18.6 m above ground level

24. 390 mph at 7.4° north of east

26. 10.1 m/s at 8.53° east of north, (b) 45.0 m

28. (a) 14.5° north of west, (b) 194 m/s

30. 15.3 m

32. 196 cm at 14.7° below positive x axis

34. (a) 2.66 m/s, (b) 0.64 m

36. 68.6 km/h

38. (a) 0.85 m/s, (b) 2.1 m/s

40. 14 m/s

42. (a) 284 s (4.73 min), (b) 277 km

44. 29.4 m/s

46. 10.4 m/s

48. (a) 132 cm at 69.6° (male), 111 cm at 70° (female), (b) 146 cm at 69.6° (male), 132.0 cm at 70° (female), Δd = 2.24 cm at 65.9°

50. Answer given with problem.

52. (a) 1.2 m/s and 0, (b) 0.96 m, (c) 0.5 m/s.

54. 4.12 m.

56. 5.83 m at 59.0° to the right from original dir.

58. 390 mph at 7.37° N of E.

60. (a) 26.6° , (b) 0.949.

CHAPTER FOUR

2. 25 N

4. 7.4 min

6. 310 N

8. (a) 798 N at 8.8° to right of forward direction, (b) 0.266 m/s^2 in direction of resultant force

10. 1.1 x 10^4 N upward

12. 77.8 N in each wire

14. 171 N, 60.6°

16. 1040 N rearward

18. (a) 1.5 m, (b) 1.4 m

20. 4.43 m/s^2 up the incline, 53.7 N

22. (a) 51.3 km/h, (b) 0.589 km

24. 7.90 m/s

26. 236 N (upper rope), 118 N (lower rope)

28. (a) 36.8 N, (b) 2.45 m/s^2, (c) 1.23 m

30. (a) 0, (b) 0.70 m/s^2

32. (a) -1.20 m/s^2, (b) 0.122, (c) 45.0 m

34. 3.16 s

36. (a) 0.366 m/s^2, (b) 1.29 m/s^2 down the incline

38. (a) 98.6 m, (b) 16.4 m

40. (a) 0.125 m/s^2, (b) 39.7 N, (c) 0.235

42. (a) 18.5 N, (b) 25.8 N

44. (a) 2.13 s, (b) 1.67 m

46. 21.5 N

48. (a) 50.0 N, (b) 0.500, (c) 25.0 N

50. 0.814

52. (a) 1.63 m/s^2, (b) 57.2 N for the string connecting the 5-kg and 4-kg block. T = 24.5 N for the string connecting the 4-kg and 3-kg block.

54. (b) 9.8 N, (c) 0.58 m/s^2

56. (b) 2-kg block: 5.8 m/s^2 to left
3-kg block: 5.8 m/s^2 to right
10-kg block: 5.8 m/s^2 downward
(c) T_1 = 17 N, T_2 = 41 N

58. 0.69 m/s^2

60. 104 N

62. 550 N

64. (a) 30.7°, (b) 0.843 N

66. (a) 710 N, 0, (b) 820 N, 1.5 m/s^2, (c)710 N, 0, (d) 650 N, -0.8 m/s^2

68. (a) Answer given, (b) 514 N, 558 N, 325 N.

70. 5100 N

CHAPTER FIVE

2. 30.6 m

4. 1.6 KJ

6. (a) 31.9 J, (b) 0, (c) 0, (d) 31.9 J

8. 160 m/s

10. (a) 1.2 J, (b) 5.0 m/s, (c) 6.3 J

12. 90.0 J

14. (a) -168 J, (b) 500 J, (c) 148 J, (d) 5.64 m/s

16. 2.0 m

18. (a) -19.6 J, (b) 39.2 J, (c) 0

20. 26.5 m/s

22. 5.1 m

24. (a) 9.90 m/s, (b) 7.67 m/s

26. (a) 10.9 m/s, (b) 11.6 m/s

28. (a) 544 N/m, (b) 19.7 m/s

30. 10.2 m

32. 900 J

34. 77 m/s

36. (a) 2.29 m/s, (b) 15.6 J

38. 4.26 m/s

40. 1.5 m (measured along incline)

42. 0.408 m/s, (b) 2.45 x 10^3 J

44. (a) 7.50 x 10^4 J, (b) 33.5 hp, (c) 44.7 hp

46. (a) 7.92 hp, (b) 14.9 hp is cruise power

48. 140 m, The kinetic energy is changed into internal energy associated with the tires, brake pads, and road as they heat up.

50. (a) 4.4 m/s, (b) 1.5 x 10^5 N

52. (a) 3.13 m/s, (b) 4.43 m/s, (c) 1.00 m higher

54. μ = 0.102

56. (a) 42 hp, (b) 85 hp

58. (a) 98 N/m, (b) 1.2 m from base of incline

60. (a) 0.15 m, (b) 0.57 m

62. (a) 0.113 m, (b) 0.074 m.

64. 1.68 m/s

66. (a) 24.5 m/s, (b) Yes, (c) 206 m, (d) Air drag depends on diver's speed.

68. $\mu = 0.115$

70. (a) given in statement of problem.
(b) 2.06 m/s m/s

CHAPTER SIX

2. (a) 8.35×10^{-21} kg·m/s, (b) 4.50 kg·m/s, (c) 750 kg·m/s, (d) 1.78×10^{29} kg·m/s

4. (a) 31.0 m/s,
(b) the bullet, 3375 J versus 69.7 J

6. 364 kg·m/s, 438 N

8. (a) 8.0 N·s, (b) 5.3 m/s, (c) 3.3 m/s

10. (a) 12 N s, (b) 8.0 N s, (c) 8.0 m/s, 5.3 m/s

12. (a) 9.0 m/s, (b) -15 m/s

14. 260 N in -x direction

16. 65 m/s

18. (a) 1.15 m/s, (b) 0.346 m/s in the direction opposite to the girl's velocity

20. (a) 9.0×10^{-24} m/s, (b) The recoil velocity of the Earth is essentially zero in comparison to the velocity of terrestrial objects.

22. 6.00 kg

24. 528 m/s

26. 143 m/s

28. (a) 2.2 m/s toward the right, (b) no

30. -40.0 cm/s (5-g object), 10.0 cm/s (10-g object)

32. (a) 0, 1.50 m/s, (b) -1.00 m/s, 1.50 m/s, (c) 1.00 m/s, 1.50 m/s

34. 12.4 m/s at 14.9° north of east, (b) 7.2%

36. (a) 1.1 m/s at 29.7° from +*x* direction
(b) 0.32 or 32%

38. 2.67 N

40. 240 s (4 min)

42. 0.398%

44. 1.1×10^{3} N

46. (a) 9.90 m/s, -9.90 m/s
(b) -16.5 m/s, +3.3 m/s
(c) 13.9 m, 0.56 m

48. 3.4×10^{2} m/s

50. (a) 0, 3.0 m/s; (b) 0.21 m

52. 23 N

54. 0.410

56. (a) m has speed of $\sqrt{2}\, v_o$, mass 3m moves at $\sqrt{\frac{2}{3}}v_o$, (b) 35.3°

58. (a) the fraction KE(carbon) to KE(neutron) is 0.28, (b) The kinetic energy of the carbon = 4.54 10^{-14} J, KE(neutron) = 1.2 10^{-13} J

60. $\frac{2v_0^2}{9\mu g} - \frac{4d}{9}$

CHAPTER SEVEN

2. 2.2 m, 120 m, 770 m

4. 1.99×10^{-7} rad/s, 0.986 deg/day

6. 41 rad/s^2

8. (a) 8.22×10^{2} rad/s^2, (b) 4.21×10^{3} rad

10. 50.0 rev

12. (a) 0.14 rad/s^2, (b) 8.4 rad/s

14. 36.5 rev

16. (a) 3.37×10^{-2} m/s^2, (b) 0

18. 7.8×10^{3} ft/s^2 toward center of the tire

20. (a) 14.1 m/s, (b) 200 m, (c) 28.3 s

22. 12 m/s

24. (a) 1.46×10^{2} m, (b) 5490 N

26. (a) 9.8 N, (b) 9.8 N, (c) 6.3 m/s^2

28. (a) 1.58 m/s^2, (b) 455 N, (c) 329 N,
(d) 397 N at 9.16° from the vertical

30. 3.13 m/s

32. (a) 4.39×10^{20} N, (b) 1.99×10^{20} N, (c) 3.55×10^{22} N

34. 1.50×10^{11} m (from the Sun)

36. (a) 9.58×10^6 m, (b) 5.56 h

38. (a) 1.62 m/s^2, (b) 1.68×10^3 m/s, (c) 108 min

40. (a) 2.38×10^3 m/s, (b) 4.18×10^3 m/s, (c) 6.02×10^4 m/s

42. (a) 156°, (b) 6.00 rad/s

44. (a) 2.51 m/s, (b) 7.90 m/s^2, (c) 4.00 m/s

46. (a) 126 rad/s, (b) 2.51 m/s, (c) 947 m/s^2, (d) 15.1 m

48. (a) 4.23×10^7 m, (b) 3.59×10^7 m (22,300 miles)

50. (a) 8.42 N, (b) 64.8°, (c) 1.67 N

52. (a) $w_{apparent} = w_{true} - \frac{mv^2}{r}$, so $w_{apparent} < w_{true}$
(b) 733 N (equator), 735 N (poles)

54. (a) 0, (b) 1.3×10^3 N, (c) 2.1×10^3 N

56. Answer is given in the problem.

58. It has turned through 1.30 revolutions.

60. 11.8 km/s

62. 0.75 m.

64. (a) $v_0 = \sqrt{g(R - \frac{2h}{3})}$, (b) $h' = \frac{R}{2} + \frac{2h}{3}$.

CHAPTER EIGHT

2. 0.642 N·m counterclockwise

4. 168 N·m clockwise

6. $x_{cg} = 0$, $y_{cg} = +1.00$ m

8. (-1.5 m, -1.5 m)

10. 139 g

12. 567 N (left end), 333 N (right end)

14. (b) T = 343 N, H = 171 N, V = 683 N
(c) 5.14 m

16. (a) 400 N, (b) H = 346 N (to right), V = 0

18. $F_{deltoid} = 724$ N,
$F_{shoulder} = 716$ N at 8.75° below line OA

20. (a) 267 N (to right), 1300 N (upward),
(b) $\mu_s = 0.324$

22. T = 1465 N, H = 1328 N (to right),
V = 2581 N (upward)

24. 2.8 m

26. $\tau_x = 149$ N·m, $\tau_y = 66.0$ N·m, $\tau_o = 215$ N·m

28. (a) 34 N, (b) 33 cm

30. 24 rad/s^2

32. $\mu_k = 0.524$

34. (a) $mg - T = ma$, (b)
$\tau_{center} = Tr = \left(\frac{1}{2}mr^2\right)\alpha$

36. 0.150 kg·m^2

38. (a) 1.37×10^8 J, (b) 5.11 h

40. 36 rad/s

42. (a) 7.08×10^{33} J·s, (b) 2.66×10^{40} J·s

44. 0.91 km/s

46. 6.73 rad/s

48. 5.99×10^{-2} J

50. (a) $\omega = \left(\frac{I_1}{I_1 + I_2}\right)\omega_o$, (b)
$\frac{KE_f}{KE_i} = \frac{I_1}{I_1 + I_2} < 1$

52. Answer is given in the problem.

54. (a) 46.8 N, (b) 0.234 kg·m^2, (c) 40.0 rad/s

56. $T_1 = 11.2$ N, $T_2 = 1.39$ N, F = 7.23 N

58. (a) Since no external, horizontal forces act on the system, the center of mass of the child-boat system remains stationary as the child moves toward the right end of the boat.
(b) 5.55 m, (c) No, his maximum reach is 6.55 m from the pier.

60. (a) 3.12 m/s^2, (b) $T_1 = 26.7$ N,

(c) $T_2 = 9.36$ N

62. (a) 7.20×10^{-3} kg m^2/s, (b) 9.47 rad/s

64. (a) dMv, (b) Mv^2, (c) dMv, (d) $v_2 = 2v$, (e) $4Mv^2$, (f) $3Mv^2$

66. 1.41 m/s^2.

68. 7.5×10^{-11} s.

70. (a) $T = \frac{Mmg}{M + 4m}$, (b) $a = \frac{4mg}{(M + 4m)}$.

72. Answer given in statement of problem.

CHAPTER NINE

2. 6.89 mm

4. 1.3 mm

6. 7.5×10^6 Pa

8. (a) 2.5 mm, (b) 0.75 mm, (c) 6.9×10^3 kg

10. 1.9×10^4 N

12. 340 m

14. 1.33 m

16. Answer given in problem.

18. 2.31 lb

20. 0.611 kg

22. 11 % of the volume is exposed

24. 16.5 cm

26. (a) 8.57×10^3 kg/m^3, (b) 714 kg/m^3

28. 15.9 cm

30. 17.3 N (upper scale), 31.7 N (lower scale)

32. 13 min

34. 1.5×10^5 N upward

36. 12.6 m/s

38. 9.00 cm

40. 1.5 cm

42. (b) $y_{max} = \frac{P_{atm}}{\rho g}$

44. 8.3×10^{-2} N/m

46. 5.6×10^{-2} N/m

48. 8.6 N

50. 2.1×10^6 Pa

52. 1.5×10^5 Pa

54. $RN = 4.3 \times 10^3$, turblent flow

56. 1.8×10^{-3} kg/m^3

58. 1.4×10^{-5} Pa·s

60. 2.82 μm

62. (a) 16.0 m/s, (b) 1.73×10^5 Pa

64. 4.14×10^3 m^3

66. 22 (down the page in the Figure)

68. 1.3 cm

70. (a) Answer given, (b) 616 MW

72. 2.3 m

74. 6.3 m

76. 17.0 cm

78. 532 cc.

CHAPTER TEN

2. 57.8° C, -88.3° C

4. Answer is given in the problem.

6. (a) -251° C, (b) 1.358 atm

8. 31 cm

10. (a) 1.2995 m, (b) fast

12. 1.39° C

14. Answer is given in the problem.

16. 18.702 m

18. 1.1 L (0.29 gal)

20. 0.08208 (L·atm)/(mol·K)

22. (a) 3.0 mol, (b) 1.8×10^{24} molecules

24. $V_f/V_i = 3/2$

26. 5.87 atm

28. 7.1 m

30. 16.0 cm^3

32. 3.65×10^4 N

34. (a) 3.74×10^3 J, (b) 1.93×10^3 m/s

36. 3.34×10^5 Pa

38. (a) 8.76×10^{-21} J/molecule,

(b) $v_{He} = 1.62 \times 10^3 \ \frac{m}{s}$,

$v_{Ar} = 5.14 \times 10^2 \ \frac{m}{s}$

40. 1.8×10^4 Pa

42. (a) 1.4×10^{-2} cm (b) 6.8×10^{-4} cm
(c) 3.2×10^{-2} cm^3

44. 0.53 kg

46. Answer is given in the problem.

48. 0.060 mm too short

50. 1.15 atm = 1.17×10^5 Pa

52. 15.9 atm

54. (a) 0.60 m, (b) answer given in text, (c) The bridge will not crumble.

56. $\rho = \frac{PM}{RT}$

58. (a) $\theta = L_0(\alpha_2 - \alpha_1)\frac{\Delta T}{r_2 - r_1}$ (b) θ approaches zero as either ΔT or $(\alpha_2 - \alpha_1)$ approaches zero.,

(c) It bends the other way.

CHAPTER ELEVEN

2. 2.84×10^3 m

4. 87 °C

6. 166 °C

8. (a) 9.9×10^{-3} °C, (b) The remaining energy is absorbed by the surface on which the block slides.

10. 1055 J

12. 23 °C

14. 80 g

16. 1.8×10^3 J/kg·°C (0.44 cal/g·°C)

18. 23.6 °C

20. 4.9×10^4 J

22. 1.2×10^5 J

24. 10 g

26. 11 °C

28. (a) 0 °C with 24 g of ice left over,

(b) 8.2 °C

30. (a) 220 J/s, (b)1.3×10^{-2} J/s,
(c) 5.6×10^{-2} J/s

32. 14 ft^2 F° h/Btu

34. 39 m^3/day

36. 7.2×10^{-2} J/s·m·°C

38. $\frac{P_h}{P_c} = 1.4$

40. $\frac{P_Y}{P_X} = 16$

42. 2.44 min

44. 3.80×10^5 J (9.08×10^4 cal)

46. 1.83 h

48. 29.4 °C

50. 45 °C

52. 109 °C

54. (b) 0.65 cal/g·°C

56. (a) 1.68×10^{18} J, (b) 53.1 y

58. 0.294 g

60. 2.22×10^{-2} W/m C°

62. 2.0×10^3 W, (b) 4.5 °C

64. 27 liters

EVEN-NUMBERED ANSWERS

CHAPTER TWELVE

2. 804 J

4. (a) 610 J, (b) 0, (c) -410 J, (d) 0, (e) 200 J

6. (c) More work is done in process (a) because of the higher pressure during the expansion part of the process.

8. 465 J

10. (a) $Q < 0$, $W = 0$, $\Delta U < 0$, (b) $Q > 0$, $W = 0$, $\Delta U > 0$

12. $\Delta U = 0$, $Q < 0$, and $W < 0$

14. (a) -89.0 J, (b) 721 J

16. (a) 338 J, (b) 4.52 x 10^3 J,(c) 4.18 x 10^3 J

18. $Q_{AB} > 0$, $Q_{BC} < 0$, $Q_{CA} < 0$
$W_{AB} > 0$, $W_{BC} = 0$, $W_{CA} < 0$
$\Delta U_{AB} > 0$, $\Delta U_{BC} < 0$, $\Delta U_{CA} < 0$

20. (a) 0.95 J, (b) 3.2 x 10^5 J, (c) 3.2 x 10^5 J

22. Eff = 48.8%

24. 546°C

26. (a) 667 J, (b) 467 J

28. (a) 1.07 x. 10^4 J, (b) 0.53 s

30. (a) 9.1 kW, (b) 1.2 x 10^4 J

32. (a) -1.22 x 10^3 J/K, (b) 1.22 x 10^3 J/K

34. 57.2 J/K

36. (a)

Result	Possible Combinations	Total
all red	RRR	1
2R,1G	RRG,RGR,GRR	3
1R,2G	RGG,GRG,GGR	3
all green	GGG	1

(b)

Result	Possible Combinations	Total
all red	RRRRR	1
4R,1G	RRRRG,RRRGR,RRGRR, RGRRR,GRRRR	5
3R,2G	RRRGG,RRGRG,RGRRG, GRRRG,RRGGR,RGRGR, GRRGR,RGGRR,GRGRR, GGRRR	10
2R,3G	GGGRR,GGRGR,GRGGR, RGGGR,GGRRG,GRGRG, RGGRG,GRRGG,RGRGG, RRGGG	10
1R,4G	RGGGG,GRGGG,GGRGG, GGGRG,GGGGR	5
all green	GGGGG	1

38. (a) 1/52, (b) 1/13, (c) 1/4

40. (a) Eff_{max} = 5.1%, (b) 5.3 x 10^{12} J/h

42. (a) ΔS_h = -16.0 J/K, (b) ΔS_c =26.7 J/K, (c) ΔS_{system} = 10.7 J/K

44. 8.4 x 10^6 J/K·s

46. (a) 251 J, (b) 314 J, (c) 104 J, (d) -104 J, (e) 0 in both cases

48. (a) 26 J, (b) 9.0 x 10^5 J, (c) 9.0 x 10^5 J

50. (a) $W = 4P_OV_O$, (b) $Q = 4P_OV_O$, (c) 9.07 x 10^3 J

52. 453 K

54. Answer given in statement of problem.

56. (a) 55.4%, (b) Carnot efficiency = 74.9%

58. (a) $\frac{21}{2}RT_0$, (b) $\frac{17}{2}RT_0$, (c) 19%, (d) 83.3%

CHAPTER THIRTEEN

2. (a) 110 N, (b) The graph will be a straight line passing through the origin and with a slope of 1.0×10^3 N/m

4. (a) 8.0 s, (b) No, the force is not of Hooke's law form.

6. (a) 575 N/m, (b) 46 J

8. (a) 101 J, (b) 41.2 cm, (c) 90.2 m/s^2

10. 47.8 cm

12. (a) $PE = \frac{E}{4}$, $KE = \frac{3}{4}E$, (b) $x = \frac{A}{\sqrt{2}}$

14. (a) 0.15 J, (b) 0.78 m/s, (c) 18 m/s^2

16. 3.06 m/s

18. The displacement of the piston is $x = A\cos\omega t$, where A = the radius of the circle.

20. 3.95 N/m

22. 2.2 Hz

24. (a) 11.0 N toward left, (b) 0.88 oscillations

26. $v = \pm A\omega \sin(\omega t)$, $a = -A\omega^2 \cos(\omega t)$

28. 21.9 m

30. (a) slow, (b) 9:47:17 A.M.

32. (a) 9.0 cm, (b) 20 cm, (c) 0.04 s, (d) 500 cm/s

34. (a) 1.14×10^{-8} s, (b) 3.41 m

36. 0.08 m to 12 m

38. (a) 0.20 Hz, (b) 0.25 Hz

40. (a) 30.0 N, (b) 25.8 m/s

42. (a) 5.1×10^{-2} kg/m, (b) 20 m/s

44. (a) 0, (b) 0.30 m

46. (a) 0.25 m, (b) 0.47 N/m, (c) 0.23 m, (d) -0.12 m/s

48. 0.990 m

50. (a) 100 m/s, (b) 374 J

52. (a) 19.8 m/s, (b) 8.94 m

54. (a) 6.93 m/s, (b) 1.14 m

56. 1.64 m/s^2

58. Answer given

60. (a) the longitudinal wave, (b) 11.1 min

62. 1.3 cm/s

64. (a) -28 J, (b) 0.446 m

CHAPTER FOURTEEN

2. 32.2 °C

4. 516 m

6. 18.5 m

8. 20 km

10. 10 machines

12. (a) 7.96×10^{-2} W/m^2, (b) 109 dB, (c) 2.82 m

14. 3.1×10^{-3} W

16. 913 Hz

18. 32.1 m/s (72 mph), the cyclist is behind the car

20. 41 kHz

22. (a) 58.0 s, (b) 60.0 km (about 37 miles) away and 20.0 km high

24. (a) 0.431 m, (b) 0.863 m

26. (a) 34.5 cm, (b) constructive

28. 824 N

30. 2550 Hz

32. (a) 79 N, (b) 2.1×10^2 Hz

34. 120 Hz

36. 0.352 Hz, 0.176 Hz, 0.117 Hz, etc.

38. $L_{open} = 65.9$ cm, $L_{closed} = 98.9$ cm

40. (a) 0.555 m, (b) 620 Hz

42. 328 m/s

44. 29.7 cm

46. 4 Hz

48. 1.76 cm

50. (a) 362 Hz, (b) 287 Hz, (c) 0.953 m and 1.20 m

52. 2.0×10^2 m/s

54. 32.9 m/s

56. 0.100 m/s

58. (a) 153 m/s, (b) 614 m

60. 439 Hz to 441 Hz

62. (a) The path difference is half wavelength.

(b) Along a hyperbola given by

$$\frac{x^2}{16} - \frac{y^2}{9} = 1$$

64. 1.93 m/s

66. (a) Answer given in text. (b) Varies from 539 Hz to 466 Hz.

CHAPTER FIFTEEN

2. 1.1×10^{-8} N (attraction)

4. 91 N

6. 5.12×10^5 N

8. -1.2×10^{-8} N (negative x direction)

10. $F_6 = 46.87$ N (left),

$F_{1.5} = 157.3$ N (right),
$F_{-2} = 110.6$ N (left)

12. 3.90×10^{-7} N at 11.3° CCW from +x axis

14. at x = 0.621 m

16. (a) 2.00×10^7 N/C to right, (b) 40.0 N to left

18. (a) 5.27×10^{13} m/s^2, (b) 5.27×10^5 m/s

20. 4.3×10^3 N/C at 91° CCW from +x axis

22. 1.63×10^4 N/C directed opposite to the motion

24. zero

26. 1875 N/C at 4.4° below +x axis

28. (a) $|q_2| = 3|q_1|$, (b) $q_2 > 0$, $q_1 < 0$

30. See solution section of this manual.

32. See solution section of this manual.

34. (a) 0, (b) 1.8×10^6 N/C, (c) 1.1×10^5 N/C

36. (a) 5.3×10^{17} m/s^2, (b) 0.85 mm

38. (a) 2.0×10^6 N·m^2/C, (b) zero

40. 5.65×10^5 N·m^2/C

42. Answer is given in problem.

44. Answer is given in problem.

46. at y = +0.85 m

48. (a)

$E = k(2q)b \,/\, (a^2 + b^2)^{3/2}$ in +x direction,

(b) $E = kQb \,/\, (a^2 + b^2)^{3/2}$ in +x direction

50. 4.4×10^5 N/C

52. 2.51 charges per ten billion

54. 2.25×10^{-9} N/m

56. (a) -4.4×10^{15} m/s^2, (b) 9.1×10^{-10} s, (c) 1.8×10^{-3} m.

58. Answer given in statement of problem.

60. (a) 1.09×10^{-8} C, (b) 5.43×10^{-3} N

CHAPTER SIXTEEN

2. (a) -6.0×10^{-4} J, (b) -50 V

4. 3.2×10^{-19} C

6. 4.3×10^6 J

8. (a) 1.52×10^5 m/s, (b) 6.49×10^6 m/s

10. (a) 9.22×10^4 V, (b) 1.69×10^8 V

12. 230 V

14. -9.1 J

16. (a) 5.93×10^5 m/s, (b) 1.38×10^4 m/s

18. 7.25×10^6 m/s

20. Answer is given in problem.

22. (a) 110 μF, (b) 26 C

24. 5.3×10^{-12} C

26. (a) 90.3 V, (b) 9.03×10^4 V/m

28. (a) 18.0 μF, (b) 1.78 μF

30. See solution section of this manual.

32.

$$Q_1 = 16\ \mu C,\ Q_5 = 80\ \mu C,$$
$$Q_4 = 32\ \mu C,\ Q_8 = 64\ \mu C$$

34. (a) Yes. Connect a parallel combination of two capacitors in series with another parallel combination of two capacitors.

(b) 50 V

36. 30.0 μF

38. 2.55×10^{-11} J

40. 3.2×10^{10} J

42. (a) 3.00×10^3 V/m, (b) 42.5 nC, (c) 5.31×10^{-12} C (or 5.31 pC)

44. 3.8×10^4 V

46. Answer is given in problem.

48. 4.22×10^5 V

50. 6.25 μF

52. 4.29 μF

54. 7.5×10^2 μC on C_1, 2.5×10^2 μC on C_2

56. 40.2 kV

58. $C_1 = \frac{1}{2}C_p + \sqrt{\frac{1}{4}C_p^2 - C_pC_s}$

$C_2 = \frac{1}{2}C_p - \sqrt{\frac{1}{4}C_p^2 - C_pC_s}$

60. (a) and (b) answers given in statement of problem

62. 50 N

CHAPTER SEVENTEEN

2. 45 C

4. 3.75×10^{14} electrons/s

6. 0.159 A

8. 5.90×10^{28} electrons/m^3

10. 32 V, 0.16 V

12. 0.17 mm

14. (a) 30 Ω, (b) 4.7×10^{-4} Ω·m

16. $\rho = \rho_{silver} = 1.59 \times 10^{-8}$ Ω·m

18. (a) 3.0 A, (b) 2.9 A

20. (a) 1.8 m, (b) 0.14 mm

22. 10.8 Ω

24. 30.6°C

26. 1.08×10^{-3} °C^{-1}

28. (a) 1.1968 Ω, (b) 8.00×10^{-4} (0.08%)

30. 36.1% increase

32. (a) 50 MW, (b) 7.1%

34. 1.75×10^{-8} m^2

36. 1.56 cm

38. 13 cents

40. (a) 18.8 A, (b) 7.45×10^6 J (2.07 kWh), (c) 17 cents

42. 16 A. Thus, use a 20 A fuse.

44. 1.1×10^3 m

46. 3.24×10^5 C

48. 0.400 μA

50. (a) 9.48×10^{-7} Ω, (b) (a) 8.07×10^{-7} Ω

52. (a) 9.3 m, (b) 0.93 mm

54. See solution section of this manual.

56. Not adequately protected; should melt at 3.87 A or less.

58. 256 Ω

60. (a) 2.6×10^{-5} Ω. (b) 76 kg

CHAPTER EIGHTEEN

2. (a) 24 Ω, (b) 1.0 A

4. (a) $\frac{24}{11}$ Ω, (b) $I_4 = 6$ A, $I_8 = 3$ A, $I_{12} = 2$ A

6. 15 Ω

8. 9.83 Ω

10. There are 7 distinct values possible: (1) Use one alone, value = R; (2) Use two in series, value = $2R$; (3) three in series, value = $3R$; (4) two in parallel, value = $\frac{R}{2}$; (5) three in parallel, value = $\frac{R}{3}$; (6) two in series with one in parallel, value = $\frac{2R}{3}$; (7) two in parallel with one in series, value = $\frac{3R}{2}$.

12. (a) Connect two 50-Ω resistors in parallel, and then connect this combination in series with a 20-Ω resistor. (b) Connect two 50-Ω resistors in parallel; connect two 20-Ω resistors in parallel, and then connect these two combinations in series with each other.

14. 0.429 A

16. (a) 3.00 mA, (b) -19.0 V, (c) 4.50 V

18. 10.7 V

20. (a) $I_3 = 1.82$ A, $I_6 = 1.09$ A, $I_9 = 0.727$ A, (b) Same as (a).

22. 0.52 W

24. 2.40 V, 320 Ω

26. (a) 9.0 V with b at higher potential than a, (b) 0.42 A flowing b to a

28. (a) 12 s, (b) 120 μC

30. (a) 2.00×10^{-3} s, (b) 180 μC, (c) 113 μC

32. 46.5 μF

34. (a) Toaster, 8.33 A; heater, 10.8 A; grill, 12.5 A
(b) $I_{total} = 31.6$ A, a 30-A circuit is insufficient.

36. (a) 6.25 A, (b) 750 W

38. $Q = 0.865Q_f$ or 86.5%

40. (a) 14 Ω, (b) 56 W, (c) 2.0 A

42. (a) $I_1 = 1.00$ A, $I_2 = I_3 = 0.500$ A, $I_4 = 0.300$ A, $I_5 = 0.200$ A.
(b) $V_{ac} = 6.00$ V, $V_{ce} = 1.20$ V, $V_{ed} = 1.80$ V, $V_{db} = 6.00$ V, $V_{fd} = 1.80$ V, $V_{cd} = 3.00$ V.
(c) $P_{ac} = 6.00$ W, $P_{ce} = 0.600$ W, $P_{ed} = 0.540$ W, $P_{db} = 6.00$ W, $P_{fd} = 0.360$ W, $V_{cd} = 1.50$ W.

44. See solution section of this manual.

46. $I_1 = 0$, $I_2 = I_3 = 0.500$ A

48. (a) R = 0.0999 Ω, current in $R_1 = 50$ A; current in 100 Ω, R_2 and $R_3 = 0.045$ A.
(b) R = 1.09 Ω, current in R_1 and R_2 = 4.55 A; current in 100 Ω and $R_3 = 0.045$ A.
(c) R = 9.99 Ω, current in 100 Ω = 0.050 A; current in R_1, R_2, and $R_3 = 0.450$ A.

50. 112 V, 0.200 Ω

52. (a) $i = \left(\frac{\varepsilon}{R}\right)e^{-t/RC}$, (b) $i = \left(\frac{Q}{RC}\right)e^{-t/RC}$

54. (a) 0.227 A, (b) 5.68 V

56. 0.385 mA L to R through R_1, 2.692 mA upward through R_2, 3.08 mA L to R through R_3. (b) 69.2 V

58. Answer given in problem.

60. (a) and (b) See solution section of this manual.

CHAPTER NINETEEN

2. **(a)** (a) to left, (b) into page, (c) out of page, (d) toward top of page, (e) into page, (f) out of page

(b) If the charge is negative, the direction of all forces above are reversed 180°

4. 2.6×10^{-11} N westward

6. 2.83×10^{7} m/s

8. 2.1×10^{-2} T in $-y$ direction

10. See solution section of this manual.

12. (a) into page (b) toward right (c) toward bottom of page

14. 7.5 N

16. 0.131 T downward

18. 0.245 A

20. 9.04×10^{-4} N·m

22. 0.192 N·m

24. 0.167 Ω

26. 1.94×10^{3} Ω

28. $R_1 = 3.33 \times 10^{-4}$ Ω,

$R_2 = 2.998 \times 10^{-3}$ Ω,
$R_3 = 2.997 \times 10^{-2}$ Ω

30. See solution section of this manual.

32. 1.49×10^{-4} m

34. 3.00 cm

36. (a) right to left, (b) out of page, (c) lower left to upper right

38. (a) 4.00×10^{-5} T into page,

(b) 5.00×10^{-6} T out of page,
(c) 1.67×10^{-6} T out of page

40. 1.67×10^{-7} T out of page

42. (a) 2.00×10^{-4} N/m (attracted),
(b) 2.00×10^{-4} N/m (repelled)

44. 82 A

46. 0.464 T

48. 1.7 N m

50. 8.5×10^{-5} T

52. (a) 30.0 A, (b) 1.60×10^{-4} T (out of page)

54. 3.82×10^{-25} kg

56. 2.7×10^{-5} N to the left

58. $F_h = 0.990 \times 10^{-6}$ N, $F_v = 1.00 \times 10^{-6}$ N

60. (a) 2.46 N, (b) 107.3 m/s^2

62. (a) 6.2 m/s^2, (b) 0.40 s

64. (a) 5.3×10^{-5} T, (b) 2.0×10^{-5} T downward, (c) 0

66. (a) opposite, (b) 67.8 A

CHAPTER TWENTY

2. 7.71×10^{-1} T·m^2

4. zero

6. 2.96×10^{-5} T·m^2

8. 84 mV

10. 34 mV

12. 5.20×10^{-5} T

14. (a) 1.88×10^{-7} T·m^2 , (b) 6.28×10^{-8} V

16. 8.8 A

18. 2.00 mV, (the western end is positive)

20. 2.87 mV

22. left to right

24. (a) left to right, (b) right to left

26. (a) right to left, (b) right to left, (c) left to right, (d) left to right

28. 13 mV

30. (a) 11 Ω, (b) 76 V

32. (a) 60 V, (b) 57 V, (c) 0.12 s

34. Answer is given in statement of problem.

36. (a) 1.97 mH, (b) 38 A/s

38. See solution section of this manual.

40. 12 mH

42. (a) 4.00 A, (b) 2.53 A

44. 5.55×10^{-4} J

46. 4.7 V

48. 1.9×10^{-3} T

50. 7.4×10^{-4} A

52. (a) Amplitude doubles, period unchanged, (b) Amplitude doubles, period cut in half, (c) Amplitude unchanged, period cut in half

54. 440 μV

56. (a) 0.5 A, (b) 2.00 W, (c) 2.00 W

58. 6.28 V

60. (a) 100 μV, (b) 20 μA, (c) 2 nanowatts, (d) 2 nanowatts, (e) 4 x 10^{-10} N, (f) 2 nanowatts.

62. See solution section of this manual.

64. (a) 0.125 V, (b) 0.02 A.

66. (a) 0.900 A, (b) 0.108 N, (c) b, (d) No.

CHAPTER TWENTY-ONE

2. (a) 106 V, (b) 60.0 Hz, (c) 0, (d) 3.00 A

4. 6.76 W

6. Answer is given in the Problem.

8. 0.360 Ω

10. 0.224 A

12. 2.63 A

14. $L > 7.03$ H

16. (a) 4.67 A, (b) 35.2 V, (c) 93.4 V, (d) 20.7°

18. (a) 0.361 A, (b) 18.1 V, (c) 23.9 V, (d) -53.0°

20. (a) 138 V, (b) 104 V, (c) 729 V, (d) 640 V

22. (a) 652 mA, (b) 1.44 H

24. (a) power factor = 0.492, 48.2 W, (b) power factor = 0.405, 32.6 W

26. (a) 24 Ω, (b) -32 Ω, (c) 8.7 x 10^2 W

28. (a) $P = 100$ W, $\cos\phi = 0.631$, (b) $P = 156$ W, $\cos\phi = 0.791$

30. 2.05 MHz, 146 m

32. (a) 480 W, (b) 0.192 W, (c) 0.03 W, (d) 0.192 W, (e) 0.03 W, maximum power delivered at resonant frequency

34. (a) 1.59 Hz, (b) 15.9 Hz,

36. (a) 1.67 x 10^4 A, (b) 10.0 A, (c) 1.39 x 10^5 W/m, 5.00 x 10^{-2} W/m, (d) 167 lines, 0.100 line (or one line)

38. 0.18%

40. 2.998 x 10^8 m/s

42. 3.74 x 10^{26} W

44. 4.29 x 10^{14} Hz to 7.50 x 10^{14} Hz

46. 11.0 m

48. (a) 18 turns, (b) 3.6 V

50. 5.17 μH

52. 1.8 cents

54. 428 mA

56. (a) 0.63 pF, (b) 8.4 mm, (c) 25 Ω

58. (a) 2.0 x 10^{-8} T, (b) 600 kW

60. (a) 1.76 x 10^{13} m/s^2, (b) 1.75 x 10^{-27} W, (c) reduces to basic units of W.

62. (a) 2.9 x 10^4 W, (b) 0.58%, (c) The maximum power that can be transmitted is far less than the power the customer wants delivered, and all the power is dissipated in the transmission line.

64. 32

CHAPTER TWENTY-TWO

2. (a) 2.1 x 10^4 rev/s, 4.2 x 10^4 rev/s; (b) 2.1 x 10^2 rev/s, 4.2 x 10^2 rev/s

4. (b) 2.999 x 10^8 m/s

6. 2.09 x 10^{-11} s

8. (a) 584 nm, (b) 1.12

10. 26°

12. 25.5°, 442 nm

14. 36.6°

16. First surface: $\theta_i = 30.0°$, $\theta_r = 19.5°$;
Second surface: $\theta_i = 19.5°$, $\theta_r = 30.0°$

18. $\theta = 30.4°$, $\theta' = 22.3°$

20. 6.30 cm

22. (a) First surface: $\theta_i = 30°$, $\theta_r = 20°$;
Second surface: $\theta_i = 41°$, $\theta_r = 77°$
(b) First surface: $\theta_{(reflection)} = 30°$ = angle of incidence; Second surface: $\theta_{(reflection)} = 41°$ = angle of incidence

24. 23.1°

26. 245 nm

28. 0.39°

30. (a) 31.3°, (b) 44.2°, (c) 49.8°

32. 24.4°

34. $n = 1.38$

36. See solution section of this manual

38. $n \geq \sqrt{2}$

40. See solution section of this manual.

42. 22.0°

44. (a) $\theta_2 = 53.1°$, (b) $\theta_1 \geq 38.7°$

46. 40.0°

48. See solution section of this manual.

50. Answer given in statement of problem.

52. 24.7°

54. 62.2%

56. n = 1.93

58. $\theta_1 = \sin^{-1}\left[(n^2 - 1)^{1/2} \sin\phi - \cos\phi\right]$

CHAPTER TWENTY-THREE

2. Answer is given in statement of problem.

4. $M = +0.130$

6. (a) 2.22 cm, (b) $M = 10.0$

8. concave, with $f = 9.52$ cm, $M = -20.0$

10. concave, $R = 40.0$ cm

12. (a) 15.0 cm, (b) 60.0 cm

14. 10.0 cm in front of mirror

16. 30.0 cm in front of mirror

18. 48.0 cm

20. 52.5 cm

22. (a) 1.50 m, (b) 1.75 m

24. (a) 120 cm, (b) -24.0 cm,
(c) -8.00 cm, (d) -3.43 cm

26. 4.80 cm

28. 1.60 cm

30. (a) 40.0 cm past lens, real, inverted,
$M = -1.00$
(b) No image is formed. Rays are parallel.
(c) 20.0 cm in front of lens, erect, virtual, $M = 2.00$

32. (a) 13.3 cm in front of lens, virtual, erect, $M = \frac{1}{3}$
(b) 10.0 cm in front of lens, virtual, erect, $M = \frac{1}{2}$
(c) 6.67 cm in front of lens, virtual, erect, $M = \frac{2}{3}$

34. 7.50 cm in front of lens

36. any distance between 1.10 m and 5.10 m

38. $\frac{f}{9}$ outside the focal point

40. -80.0 cm

42. 30.0 cm in front of second lens, $M = -3.00$

44. 9.3 cm in front of second lens, $M = 0.37$

46. (a) $p = +4.00$ cm or $p = +1.00$ cm,
(b) One image is smaller than the object, $M = -\frac{1}{4}$, while one is larger than the object, $M = -4.00$.

48. (a) 13.3 cm, (b) $M = -5.91$, (c) inverted, virtual

50. Answer is given in statement of problem.

52. 8.0 cm

54. 25.3 cm to right of mirror, virtual, erect, $M = 8.05$

56. (a) 10.0 cm beyond second lens, (b) erect and same size as object, $M = +1.00$ (c) 20.0 beyond the lens combination

58. Final image is at center of upper mirror, real, erect, and same size as object.

60. (a) n = 1.99, (b) 10 cm to left of lens, M = -2.50, (c) inverted.

62. (a) -5.50 m, (b) -8.30 m, (c) -17 m, (d) by surrounding the lens with a higher index of refraction material than the lens.

CHAPTER TWENTY-FOUR

2. (a) 2.62 mm, (b) 2.62 mm

4. 11.3 m

6. 2.61 m

8. (a) 55.7 m, (b) 124 m

10. 75.0 m

12. 148 m

14. 290 nm, 580 nm, 870 nm

16. 233 nm

18. (a) 123 nm, (b) 81.6 nm

20. 290 nm

22. 8 (counting the zeroth order)

24. 6.5×10^2 nm

26. No, the wavelengths intensified are 276 nm, 138 nm, 92 nm, . . .

28. (a) 1.09 m. (b) 1.70 mm

30. Answer is given in problem.

32. 0.227 mm

34. (a) 56.7°, (b) 48.8°

36. 31.2°

38. Answer is given in problem.

40. 6.89 units

42. 432 nm

44. any positive integral multiple of 210 nm

46. 58.2 °

48. (a) 16 m, (b) 8.0 m

50. (a) Answer is given in problem, (b) 99.7 nm

52. 2.5 mm

54. 1.31

56. 126.7 m

58. 313 nm.

60. 0.149 mm

CHAPTER TWENTY-FIVE

2. 177 m

4. 1.09 mm

6. 2.20 mm farther from film

8. 40 cm

10. (a) 33.3 cm, (b) +3.0 diopters

12. 17.0 diopters

14. (a) +50.8 to +60.0 diopters, (b) -0.800 diopters

16. (a) $M = 2.0$, (b) $M = 1.0$

18. (a) $|M| = 1.22$, (b) $\frac{\theta}{\theta_o} = 6.08$

20. 0.810 μm

22. $M = 19$

24. 157 miles

26. (a) $M = 7.50$, (b) 94.4 cm

28. 0.77 m (≈ 30 in)

30. 0.40 μrad

32. (a) 2.29×10^{-4} rad, (b) 43.7 m

34. 38 cm

36. 1.31×10^3 fringe shifts

38. $n_{gas} = 1 + \left(\frac{\lambda_{vac}}{4L}\right)(\#\text{ fringe shifts}) = 1.0005$

40. 40 fringe shifts

42. (a) 479 nm, 647 nm, 698 nm,
(b) 20.5°, 28.3°, 30.7°

44. (a) 13 orders, (b) 1 order

46. 656 lines/mm

48. 44.5 cm

50. No, a resolving power of 2.0×10^5 is needed and that of the grating is only 1.8×10^5.

52. (a) 1.96 cm, (b) $f/3.27$, (c) $f/9.80$

54. 602 lines/mm

56. $n = 1.70$

58. (a) 0.0602 cm, (b) $p = -2.00$ cm,
(c) 6.02 cm, (d) $M = 4.00$

60. 28.5 μrad

62. M = 10.7

64. See solution section of this manual.
Theorder in which these lines are observed is:
$V_1\, G_1\, R_1\, V_2\, G_2\, V_3\, R_2\, V_4\, G_3\, V_5\, G_4\, R_3\, V_6$

CHAPTER TWENTY-SIX

2. (a) 1.9×10^{-15} s, (b) 2.0 fringes

4. (a) 70 beats/min, (b) 30 beats/min

6. (a) 1.38 y, (b) 1.31 lightyear

8. (a) 20 m, (b) 19 m, (c) $0.31c$

10. $0.87c$

12. Yes, with 19 m to spare

14. Ratio = 0.088

16. (a) 2.7×10^{-24} kg·m/s,
(b) 1.6×10^{-22} kg·m/s,
(c) 5.6×10^{-22} kg·m/s,

18. $0.284c$

20. $0.54c$

22. $0.99c$

24. 0.161 pulses/s

26. (a) 939 MeV, (b) 3.00 GeV, (c) 2.06 GeV

28. (a) 4.4×10^9 kg, (b) 1.4×10^{13} y

30. (a) 5.09×10^4 MeV/c, (b) $0.9998c$

32. $0.786c$

34. $0.980c$

36. $0.866c$

38. (a) 2.50 MeV/c, (b) 4.60×10^3 MeV/c

40. 1.2×10^{13} m

42. $0.37c$

44. $0.80c$

46. Answer is given in statement of problem.

48. Answer given in statement of problem.

50. (a) Answer given in problem, (b) 0.942c

52. (a) 7.05 ms, (b) 1.12×10^4 muons

CHAPTER TWENTY-SEVEN

2. 9.66×10^3 K

4. (a) 1000 nm, (b) Peak is in the infrared region.

6. 0.62 nm

8. 5.7×10^3 photons/s

10. 3.7×10^{19} photons

12. (a) 1.4 eV, (b) 3.4×10^{14} Hz

14. (a) lithium and iron,
(b) 1.8 eV and 0.04 eV, respectively

16. 232 nm

18. 8.7×10^{12} electrons/s

20. (a) 0.0828 nm, (b) 0.0124 nm

22. 0.124 nm

24. 18.2°

26. 67.5°

28. 1.8 keV, 1.8 keV/c

30. (a) 2.9 x 10^{-3} nm, (b) 100°

32. 1.98 MeV

34. 2.27 x 10^{23} Hz, 1.32 x 10^{-15} m

36. 1.06 x 10^{-34} m

38. 1.5 x 10^{2} V

40. 545 eV

42. $c/\sqrt{2}$

44. 3.5 x 10^{-32} m

46. $\sim 10^{5}$ m / s

48. (a) Answer is given in statement of problem.
(b) 5.3 MeV

50. 2.96 x 10^{20} photons

52. (a) 2.49 x 10^{-2} nm, (b) 0.285 nm

54. 1.35 eV

56. 0.784 eV

58. (a) 1.1 x 10^{-34} m/s, (b) 1.4 x 10^{33} s, (c) No

60. See solution section of this manual.

62. (a) 7.77 x 10^{-12} m, (b) 94.9°, (c) 35.2°

CHAPTER TWENTY-EIGHT

2. (a) 200 nm $\leq \lambda \leq$ 360 nm (ultraviolet)
(b) 800 nm $\leq \lambda \leq$ 1440 nm (infrared)

4. (a) 230 N, (b) 1.4 MeV

6. 46 fm

8. $KE = 13.6\,\text{eV}$, $PE = -27.2\,\text{eV}$

10. Answer is given in the problem.

12. (a) Transition B, (b) Transition A, (c) Transitions B and C

14. (a) 12.09 eV, (b) 12.09 eV, 1.89 eV, 10.2 eV

16. (a) 13.6 eV, (b) 1.51 eV

18. (a) Six transitions: n = 4 to 1, 4 to 2, 4 to 3, 3 to 1, 3 to 2, and 2 to 1.
(b) 1.88 x 10^{3} nm (in Paschen series)

20. (a) 2.18 x 10^{6} m/s, (b) 1.52 x 10^{-16} s, (c) 1.05 x 10^{-3} A

22. 4.42 x 10^{4} m/s

24. (a) 2.89 x 10^{34} kg m²/s,
(b) n = 2.74 x 10^{68}, $\frac{\Delta r}{r} \approx 7.30 \times 10^{-69}$

26. (a) -122 eV, (b) 1.76 x 10^{-11} m

28. (a) 4.39 x 10^{7} m^{-1}, (b) 30.4 nm
(c) deep ultraviolet region

30. Answers are given in the problem.

32. (a) 4 ($\ell = 3, 2, 1,$ and 0),
(b) 7 ($m_\ell = 0, \pm1, \pm2, \pm3$)

34. For a $s=1$ particle in a 3d subshell, we have $n=3$; $\ell=2$; $m_\ell = 0, \pm1, \pm2$; $s=1$; and $m_s = 0, \pm1$. The possible states are summarized in the following table:

n	ℓ	m_ℓ	s	m_s
3	2	-2	1	-1
3	2	-2	1	0
3	2	-2	1	+1
3	2	-1	1	-1
3	2	-1	1	0
3	2	-1	1	+1
3	2	0	1	-1
3	2	0	1	0
3	2	0	1	+1
3	2	+1	1	-1
3	2	+1	1	0
3	2	+1	1	+1
3	2	+2	1	-1
3	2	+2	1	0
3	2	+2	1	+1

36. (a) $1s^2 2s^2 2p^4$
(b) The quantum numbers are:

$1s^2$ states $n=1, \ell=0, m_\ell=0, m_s=\pm 1/2$

$2s^2$ states $n=2, \ell=0, m_\ell=0, m_s=\pm 1/2$

$2p^4$ states $n=2, \ell=1, \begin{Bmatrix} m_\ell=-1, m_s=\pm 1/2 \\ m_\ell=0 \quad m_s=\pm 1/2 \end{Bmatrix}$

38. (a) 4, (b) 2

40. 0.155 nm, 8.03 kV

42. $Z = 32$, Germanium

44. $n = 137$

46. (a) $a_0 = 2.53 \times 10^{-4}$ nm ;
(b) -2.84 keV, -0.710 keV, -0.316 keV

48. (a) The four lowest energies are:
-10.39 eV, -5.49 eV, -3.67 eV, and
-2.55 eV
(b) The wavelengths of the emission lines are:
158.5 nm, 185.0 nm, 253.7 nm,
422.8 nm, 683.0 nm, and. 1110 nm
(c) 1.31×10^6 m/s

50. (a) $\tau_0 = 1.53 \times 10^{-16}$ s, (b) 8.2×10^6 rev
(c) Yes, for 8.2 million "electron years",
(d) With that many revolutions in such a short time, it appears like the electron (or at least some part of it) is present everywhere in the $n = 2$ orbit at any instant

52. (a) 135 eV, (b) This is about 10 times the ground state energy of hydrogen.

54. (a) $\Delta L = c\Delta\tau$, (b) $\frac{E\lambda}{hc}$,
(c) $\left(\frac{4}{\Delta F L \pi d^2}\right)\left(\frac{E\lambda}{hc}\right)$

56. (a) See solution section of this manual.
(b) $n_i = 4$, $n_f = 1$.

58. See solution section of this manual.

60. (a) 9.04×10^{22} m/s^2,
(b) -2.90×10^{11} eV/s.
(c) 4.69×10^{-11} s

CHAPTER TWENTY-NINE

2. (a) 1.9×10^{-15} m, (b) 7.4×10^{-15} m

4. $\rho_n / \rho_a = 8.5 \times 10^{13}$

6. 4.6×10^{-13} m

8. 8.26 MeV/nucleon for $^{24}_{12}$Mg,
8.70 MeV/nucleon for $^{85}_{37}$Rb

10. 0.211 MeV/nucleon. The difference is largely due to increased coulomb repulsion caused by the extra proton in $^{23}_{12}$Mg.

12. 7.94 MeV

14. 8.7×10^3 Bq

16. (a) 3.18 mol, (b) 1.91×10^{17} nuclei,
(b) 1.08×10^{14} Bq, (c) 9.00×10^6 Bq

18. 1.0 h

20. 1.72×10^4 y

22. 1.64×10^3 y

24. $^{12}_{6}$C, $^{4}_{2}$He, $^{14}_{6}$C

26. See solution section of this manual.

28. 4.28 MeV

30. (a) No, $\Delta m < 0$, (b) Yes, $\Delta m > 0$

32. (a) $^{66}_{28}\text{Ni} \rightarrow ^{66}_{29}\text{Cu} + ^{0}_{-1}e + \bar{\nu}$, (b) 186 keV

34. 1.67×10^4 y

36. $^{4}_{2}$He, $^{4}_{2}$He

38. 17.3 MeV

40. (a) $^{10}_{5}$B, (b) -2.79 MeV

42. 22.0 MeV

44. 5.0 rad

46. (a) 2.0 J/kg, (b) 4.8×10^{-4} °C

48. (a) 2.5×10^{-3} rem/x-ray,
(b) ≈38 times background

50. (a) 10 h, (b) 3.16 m

52. (a) $N = 0.500 N_0$ in both cases,
(b) $N = 0.802 N_0$ in both cases,
(c) $N = 0.038 N_0$ in both cases.

54. 1.88 MeV

56. 12 mg

58. 5.5×10^{-2} mCi

60. 4.4×10^{-8} kg/h

62 (a) 3.95×10^{-12} J, (b) 1.198×10^{57} nuclei,
(c) 96 billion years, (d) The Sun is only 75% hydrogen, and the density of remaining hydrogen atoms will become too low to sustain the chain reaction long before the hydrogen is consumed.

64. (a) 2.52×10^{24} nuclei, (b) 2.306×10^{12} Bq, (c) 1.07×10^6 years

66. (a) 18.3 counts/min, (b) The observed count rate is only slightly less than background.

CHAPTER THIRTY

2. 174 MeV

4. 1.1 x 10^{16} fissions

6. 2.5 x 10^{3} y

8. 3.38 kg

10. 5.49 MeV

12. (a) $^{13}_{7}N$, (b) $^{13}_{6}C$, (c) $^{14}_{7}N$, (d) $^{15}_{8}O$, (e) $^{15}_{7}N$, (f) $^{12}_{6}C$

14. (a) 4.1 x 10^{22} nuclei, (b) 1.1 x 10^{10} J, (c) 55 gallons

16. 2.26 x 10^{23} Hz, 1.33 x 10^{-15} m

18. 1.0 x 10^{-23} s

20. 67.5 MeV

22. First does not violate any absolute conservation law and strangeness is only vilated by one unit Thus, it can occur via the weak interaction. The second violtates conservation of baryon number.

24. (a) ν_e, (b) ν_μ, (c) $\bar{\nu}_\mu$, (d) ν_μ and $\bar{\nu}_\tau$

26. (a) violates conservation of baryon number, (b) can occur, (c) baryon number conservation violated, (d) can occur, (e) can occur, (f) violates conservation of baryon number and muon-lepton number.

28. The first decay is via the strong interaction; the second via the weak interaction.

30. (a) Answer is given in statement of problem.
(b) The second reaction violates strangness. It cannot occur via the strong or electromagnetic interaction.

32. (a) K^+, (b) Ξ^0, (c) π^0

34.

(a) K^0 Particle

	K^0	d	$\bar{s}$	total
strangeness	1	0	1	1
baryon number	0	1/3	−1/3	0
charge	0	$-e/3$	$e/3$	0

(b) Λ^0 Particle

	Λ^0	u	d	s	total
strangeness	-1	0	0	-1	-1
baryon number	1	1/3	1/3	1/3	1
charge	0	$2e/3$	$-e/3$	$-e/3$	0

36. (a) $-e$ (antiproton), (b) 0 (antineutron)

38. $m_u = 312.3$ MeV/c^2, $m_d = 313.7$ MeV/c^2 (neglecting binding energies)

40. 70.5 MeV

42. 0.21 fm

44. $\bar{\nu}_\mu$ and ν_e

46. 74.4 MeV

48. 34 kg

50. (a) Answer is given in statement of problem.
(b) 12 days

52. (a) 1.61 x 10^{-35} m, (b) 5.38 x 10^{-44} s